WITHDRAWN

T3-BNL-207

JOB HUNTER'S
SOURCEBOOK

WITHDRAWN

MONTGOMERY COLLEGE
GERMANTOWN CAMPUS LIBRARY
GERMANTOWN, MARYLAND

ISSN 1053-1874

A   GALE   CAREER   INFORMATION   GUIDE

JOB HUNTER'S SOURCEBOOK

Where to find employment leads and other job search resources

TWELFTH EDITION
Volume 1

Sources of Job Hunting Information by Occupations

Occupations A-K
Entries 1-6741

Joseph Palmisano, Project Editor

GALE
CENGAGE Learning·

Detroit • New York • San Francisco • New Haven, Conn • Waterville, Maine • London

1776280

MAR 0 1 2013

GALE
CENGAGE Learning

Job Hunter's Sourcebook, 12th Edition

Product Management: Jerry Moore

Project Editor: Joseph Palmisano

Editorial Support Services: Scott Flaugher

Composition and Electronic Prepress: Gary Leach

Manufacturing: Rita Wimberley

© 2012 Gale, Cengage Learning

ALL RIGHTS RESERVED. No part of this work covered by the copyright herein may be reproduced, transmitted, stored, or used in any form or by any means graphic, electronic, or mechanical, including but not limited to photocopying, recording, scanning, digitizing, taping, Web distribution, information networks, or information storage and retrieval systems, except as permitted under Section 107 or 108 of the 1976 United States Copyright Act, without the prior written permission of the publisher.

This publication is a creative work fully protected by all applicable copyright laws, as well as by misappropriation, trade secret, unfair competition, and other applicable laws. The authors and editors of this work have added value to the underlying factual material herein through one or more of the following: unique and original selection, coordination, expression, arrangement, and classification of the information.

For product information and technology assistance, contact us at
Gale Customer Support, 1-800-877-4253.
For permission to use material from this text or product,
submit all requests online at **www.cengage.com/permissions.**
Further permissions questions can be emailed to
permissionrequest@cengage.com

While every effort has been made to ensure the reliability of the information presented in this publication, Gale, a part of Cengage Learning, does not guarantee the accuracy of the data contained herein. Gale accepts no payment for listing; and inclusion in the publication of any organization, agency, institution, publication, service, or individual does not imply endorsement of the editors or publisher. Errors brought to the attention of the publisher and verified to the satisfaction of the publisher will be corrected in future editions.

EDITORIAL DATA PRIVACY POLICY: Does this publication contain information about you as an individual? If so, for more information about our editorial data privacy policies, please see our Privacy Statement at www.gale.cengage.com

Gale, Cengage Learning
27500 Drake Rd.
Farmington Hills, MI 48331-3535

ISBN-13: 978-1-4144-9026-7 (set)
ISBN-10: 1-4144-9026-7 (set)
ISBN-13: 978-1-4144-9027-4 (vol. 1)
ISBN-10: 1-4144-9027-5 (vol. 1)
ISBN-13: 978-1-4144-9028-1 (vol. 2)
ISBN-10: 1-4144-9028-3 (vol. 2)
ISBN-13: 978-1-4144-9029-8 (vol. 3)
ISBN-10: 1-4144-9029-1 (vol . 3)

ISSN 1053-1874

Printed in the United States of America
1 2 3 4 5   16 15 14 13 12

FD165

Contents

"The person who gets hired is not necessarily the one who can do that job best; but, the one who knows the most about how to get hired."

Richard Bolles

What Color Is Your Parachute?

Job hunting is often described as a campaign, a system, a strategic process. According to Joan Moore, principal of The Arbor Consulting Group, Inc. in Plymouth, Michigan, "Launching a thorough job search can be a full-time job in itself. It requires as much energy as you would put into any other major project—and it requires a creative mix of approaches to ensure its success."

Job Hunting Is Increasingly Complex

Today's competitive job market has become increasingly complex, requiring new and resourceful approaches to landing a position. The help-wanted ads are no longer the surest route to employment. In fact, most estimates indicate that only a small percentage of all jobs are found through the classified sections of local newspapers.

Although approaches vary among individual job seekers and the levels of jobs sought, a thorough job search today should involve the use of a wide variety of resources. Professional associations, library research, executive search firms, college placement offices, direct application to employers, professional journals, and networking with colleagues and friends are all approaches commonly in use. Job hotlines and resume referral services may be elements of the search as well. High-tech components might include the use of resume databases, and electronic bulletin boards that list job openings.

Job Hunters Are Changing

Just as the methods of job seeking have changed, so have the job hunters themselves. As Joyce Slayton Mitchell notes in College to Career, "Today, the average young person can look forward to six or seven different jobs, six or seven mini-careers, that will make up his or her lifetime of work." Lifelong commitment to one employer is no longer the norm; profes-

sionals seeking to change companies, workers re-entering the job market after a period of absence, and people exploring new career options are also represented in significant numbers in the job seeking pool. And in a time of significant corporate change, restructuring, divestiture, and downsizing, many job seekers are in the market unexpectedly. These include a growing number of white-collar workers who find themselves competing against other professionals in a shrinking market.

Help for Job Hunters

As the job market has become more competitive and complex, job seekers have increasingly looked for job search assistance. The rapid growth in the number of outplacement firms and employment agencies during the last 30 years reflects the perceived need for comprehensive help. Similarly, the library has become an increasingly important and valuable resource in the job hunt. In fact, some librarians report that their most frequently asked reference questions pertain to job seeking. In response to this need, many libraries have developed extensive collections of career and job-hunting publications, periodicals that list job openings, and directories of employers. Some libraries have developed centralized collections of career information, complemented by such offerings as resume preparation software, career planning databases, and interviewing skills videotapes.

Valuable Guide for Job Seekers

Job Hunter's Sourcebook (JHS) was designed to assist those planning job search strategies. Any job hunter—the student looking for an internship, the recent graduate, the executive hoping to relocate—will find *JHS* an important first step in the job search process because it identifies and organizes employment leads quickly and comprehensively. Best of all, *JHS* provides all the information a job hunter needs to turn a local public library into a customized employment agency, available free-of-charge. *Library Journal* and the New York Public Library concurred, and gave the first edition of this work their annual outstanding reference awards.

Job Hunter's Sourcebook (JHS) is a comprehensive guide to sources of information on employment leads and other job search resources. It streamlines the job-seeking process by identifying and organizing the wide array of publications, organizations, audio-visual and electronic resources, and other job hunting tools.

JHS completes much of the research needed to begin a job search, with in-depth coverage of information sources for more than 200 specific professional and vocational occupations. Listings of resources on more than 30 essential topics of interest to job hunters complement the profiles on specific occupations, providing the job seeker with leads to all the information needed to design a complete job search strategy.

Job Hunter's Sourcebook can be used to:

Find a job. JHS is designed for use by job seekers at all levels—from those seeking a first job, to executives on the move, to those in transition. Each individual may select from the wide range of resources presented to develop a customized job campaign.

Use career resources more effectively. As library research becomes an increasingly important component in the job hunting process, librarians are providing more information and support to job seekers. *JHS* helps users go directly to the most appropriate library material by providing comprehensive lists of job hunting resources on high-interest professional and vocational occupations.

Build a better career resources collection. Librarians, career counselors, outplacement firms, spouse relocation services, job referral agencies, and others who advise job seekers can use *JHS* to start or expand their collections of career and job hunting materials.

Comprehensive Coverage and Convenient Arrangement

The job search resources in *JHS* are conveniently arranged into three volumes, which are followed by a master index:

Volumes One and Two: Sources of Job-Hunting Information by Professions and Occupations—identifies information sources on employment opportunities for 249 specific types of jobs. A "List of Profiled Professions and Oc-cupations" lists hundreds of alternate, popular, synonymous, and related job titles and links them to the jobs profiled in *JHS*, providing quick access to information sources on specific occupations or fields of interest by all their variant names—from accountant to aircraft mechanic and sports official to stockbroker. Each profile contains complete contact information and lists a variety of sources of job-opportunity information organized into eight easy-to-use categories:

1. Sources of Help-Wanted Ads
2. Placement and Job Referral Services
3. Employer Directories and Networking Lists
4. Handbooks and Manuals
5. Employment Agencies and Search Firms
6. Online Job Sources and Services
7. Tradeshows
8. Other Sources, including internships and resources such as job hotlines

Volume Three: Sources of Essential Job-Hunting Information—features such employment topics as:

- Interviewing Skills
- Employment Issues for Disabled Workers
- Electronic Job Search Information
- Working at Home
- Opportunities for Freelance Workers and Independent Contractors
- Opportunities for Temporary Workers

Each category includes:

- Reference Works
- Newspapers, Magazines, and Journals
- Audio/Visual Resources
- Online and Database Services
- Software
- Other Sources, such as special associations, job hunting kits, and organizers

The information sources listed under each topic are arranged by type of resource and include complete contact information.

Index to Information Sources—comprehensively lists all of the publications, organizations, electronic resources, and other sources of job hunting information contained in *JHS*.

Please consult the User's Guide for more information about the arrangement, content, and indexing of the information sources cited in *JHS*.

JHS Profiles High-Interest Professions and Occupations

JHS catalogs job hunting resources for more than 200 professional, technical, and trade occupations, carefully selected to provide a broad cross-section of occupations of interest to today's job seekers. The majority are profiled in the Department of Labor's *Occupational Outlook Handbook (OOH)*, a leading career resource containing detailed descriptions of professional and vocational occupations. Most of the professions cited in *OOH* are also included in *JHS*, as are representative vocational occupations selected from those listed in *OOH*. To round out this list, additional occupations were included on the basis of Bureau of Labor Statistics data projecting them as high-growth positions.

Coverage of Employment Alternatives and Trends

In addition to focusing on such "how-to" topics as resume writing and interviewing, the "Sources of Essential Job-Hunting Information" offers resources for non-traditional work options and diverse segments of the work force. Working part-time, at home, and in your own business are featured chapters, as are opportunities for minorities, older workers, women, disabled workers, and gay and lesbian job seekers. A chapter covering sources of electronic job search information is included, as well as a category titled, "Online Job Sources and Services." This category lists Internet websites related to specific job profiles.

New to this Edition

The twelfth edition is a complete revision of the previous *JHS*, incorporating thousands of updates to organization and publication data. This edition also features 5 new career profiles, including environmental scientists and specialists, instructional coordinators, and pharmacy technicians.

Method of Compilation

JHS contains citations compiled from direct contact with a wide range of associations and organizations, from dozens of publisher catalogs and other secondary sources, and from selected information from other Gale databases. While many resources cited in *JHS* contain career planning information, their usefulness in the job hunting process was the primary factor in their selection. Their annotations are tailored to support that function.

Comments and Suggestions Are Welcome

Libraries, associations, employment agencies, executive search firms, referral services, publishers, database producers, and other organizations involved in helping job seekers find opportunities or companies find candidates are encouraged to submit information about their activities and products for use in future editions of *JHS*. Comments and suggestions for improving this guide are also welcome. Please contact:

Project Editor
Job Hunter's Sourcebook
Gale, Cengage Learning
27500 Drake Rd.
Farmington Hills, MI 48331-3535
Phone: (248) 699-4253
Fax: (248) 699-8075
URL: gale.cengage.com

Job Hunter's Sourcebook (JHS) is divided into three volumes:

- Volumes One and Two: Sources of Job-Hunting Information by Professions and Occupations
- Volume Three: Sources of Essential Job-Hunting Information

Access to entries is facilitated by a "List of Profiled Professions and Occupations" and an "Index to Information Sources." Users should consult each section to benefit fully from the information in *JHS*.

Master List of Profiled Professions and Occupations

A "List of Profiled Professions and Occupations" alphabetically lists the job titles used to identify the professions and occupations appearing in Volumes One and Two of *JHS*, as well as alternate, popular, synonymous, and related job titles and names, and occupational specialties contained within job titles. Citations include "See" references to the appropriate occupational profiles and their beginning page numbers.

JHS is designed to meet the needs of job seekers at all levels of experience in a wide range of fields. Managers as well as entry-level job hunters will find information sources that will facilitate their career-specific searches. In addition, information on professions and occupations related to those profiled will be found.

All Career Levels. The title assigned to each profile identifies its occupational field or subject area; these titles are not meant to indicate the level of positions for which information is provided. Information systems managers, for example, will find highly useful information in the "Computer Programmers" and "Computer Systems Analysts" profiles, while financial analysts will benefit from information in the "Financial Managers" profile. The "General Managers and Top Executives" profile, on the other hand, is broad in nature and useful to any management-level search; it does not focus upon a specific profession or occupation.

Other Occupations. Job seekers not finding their specific career fields listed in this guide will discover that related profiles yield valuable sources of information. For example, legal secretaries will find relevant information about employment agencies serving the legal profession and about prospective employers in the "Legal Assistants" and "Law-

yers" profiles. An individual interested in finding a position in radio advertising sales might look to the entries in the broadcasting- and sales-related profiles to find appropriate resources. Career changers, too, can use *JHS* profiles to identify new professions to which their previously acquired skills would be transferable.

Volumes One and Two: Sources of Job-Hunting Information by Professions and Occupations

These volumes feature profiles of job-hunting information for 249 specific careers. Profiles are listed alphabetically by profession or occupation. Each profile contains up to eight categories of information sources, as described below. Within each category, entries are arranged in alphabetical order by name or title. Entries are numbered sequentially, beginning with the first entry in the first profile. All resources listed are included in each relevant profile (and in Volume Three chapters, as appropriate) providing a complete selection of information sources in each occupational profile.

Sources of Help-Wanted Ads. Includes professional journals, industry periodicals, association newsletters, placement bulletins, and online services. In most cases, periodicals that focus on a specific field are cited here; general periodical sources such as the *National Business Employment Weekly* are listed in Volume 3 under "Help-Wanted Ads." Publications specific to an industry will be found in all profiles related to that industry. Candidates in some occupational areas, such as word processing, are usually recruited from the local marketplace and therefore are not as likely to find openings through a professional publication. Profiles for these occupations may contain fewer ad sources as job hunters are better served by local newspapers and periodicals. Entries include: the source's title and the name, address, and phone number of its publisher or producer; publication frequency; subscription rate; description of contents; toll-free or additional phone numbers; and fax numbers, when applicable. Source titles appear in italics.

Placement and Job Referral Services. Various services designed to match job seekers with opportunities are included in this category. Primarily offered by professional associations, these services range from job banks to placement services to employment clearinghouses, operating on the national and local levels. Entries include: the association's or organization's name, address, and phone number; its membership, activities, and services; toll-free or additionall phone numbers; and fax numbers. E-mail and website addresses are provided, when available.

Employer Directories and Networking Lists. Covers directories and rankings of companies, membership rosters from professional associations, and other lists of organizations or groups that can be used to target prospective employers and identify potential contacts for networking purposes. In some cases, Who's Who titles are included where these can provide a source of contact information in a specialized field. General directories of companies such as Standard and Poor's Register of Corporations, Directors, and Executives are cited in Volume Three in the "Identifying Prospective Employers" profile. Entries include: the title and name, address, and phone number of the publisher or distributor; publication date or frequency; price; description of contents; arrangement; indexes; toll-free or additional phone numbers; and fax numbers, when available. Directory titles appear in italics.

Handbooks and Manuals. This category notes books, pamphlets, brochures, and other published materials that provide guidance and insight to the job-hunting process in a particular occupational field. Entries include: the title and name, address, and phone number of its publisher or distributor; editor's or author's name; publication date or frequency; price; number of pages; description of contents; toll-free or additional phone numbers; and fax numbers, when known. Publication titles appear in italics.

Employment Agencies and Search Firms. Features firms used by companies to recruit candidates for positions and, at times, by individuals to pursue openings. The following firms are covered:

1. Employment agencies, which are generally geared toward filling openings at entry- to mid-levels in the local job market. Candidates sometimes pay a fee for using their services. When possible, *JHS* lists agencies where the employer pays the fee.

2. Executive search firms, which are paid by the hiring organization to recruit professional and managerial candidates, usually for higher-level openings and from a regional or national market. Executive search firms are of two types: contingency, where the firm is paid only if it fills the position, and retainer, where the firm is compensated to undertake a recruiting assignment, regardless of whether or not that firm actually fills the opening. The majority of the search firms cited in *JHS* are contingency firms. Although executive search firms work for the hiring organization and contact candidates only when recruiting for a specific position, most will accept unsolicited resumes, and some may accept phone calls.

3. Temporary employment agencies, which also are included in some profiles because they can be a way to identify and obtain regular employment.

For the most part, each profile lists firms that typically service that career. Firms specializing in a particular industry

are included in all profiles relevant to that industry. *JHS* covers a mix of large and small firms. Major national search firms, which are quite broad in scope, are listed only under the "General Managers and Top Executives" profile. Some occupations are not served by employment agencies or search firms (fire fighter, for example); therefore, there are no entries for this category in such profiles. Entries include: the firm's name, address, and phone number; whether it's an employment agency, executive search firm, or temporary agency; descriptive information, as appropriate; toll-free and additional phone numbers; and fax numbers, when applicable.

Online Job Sources and Services. Publicly available electronic databases, including websites that facilitate matching job hunters with openings are cited. Many are tailored to specific occupations. Entries include: the name of the product or service; the name, address, and phone number of the distributor or producer; price; special formats or arrangements; descriptive information; toll-free or additional phone numbers; and fax numbers, when applicable. For websites, URL is included along with descriptive information.

Tradeshows. Covers exhibitions and tradeshows held in the United States. Entries include: the name of the tradeshow; the name of the sponsoring organization; contact information for the sponsoring organization, including address, phone number, toll-free or additional phone numbers, fax number, email address, and URL; types of exhibits; and dates and location, when available.

Other Sources. This category comprises a variety of resources available to the job seeker in a specific field: job hotlines providing 24-hour recordings of openings; lists of internships, fellowships, and apprenticeships; bibliographies of job-hunting materials; video and audio cassettes; and salary surveys to be used as a guide when discussing compensation. Professional associations of significance or those that provide job hunting assistance (but not full placement services) are also included here. Because of the trend toward entrepreneurship, this section offers information sources on being one's own boss in a given field as well. Resources on job and career alternatives are provided for certain professions (such as educators), as is information on working abroad.

Entries for associations and organizations include: name, address, and phone number; the membership, activities, and services of associations; toll-free or additional phone numbers; and fax numbers. E-mail and website addresses are provided, when available. Entries for other resources include: title of the publication or name of the product or service; the name, address, and phone number of its publisher, distributor, or producer; editor's or author's name; pubication date or frequency; price; special formats or arrangements; descriptive information; hotline, toll-free, or additional phone phone numbers; and fax numbers, when available. Publication, videocassette, and audiocassette titles appear in italics.

Volume Three: Sources of Essential Job-Hunting Information

This volume presents 33 profiles on topics of interest to any job hunter, such as resume writing or interviewing, as well as those of specialized interest, such as working at home (see "List of Profiled Professions and Occupations" for the complete list). Profiles are arranged alphabetically by topic and contain up to six categories of information, as listed below. Within each category, citations are organized alphabetically by name or title. Entries are also numbered sequentially, continuing the number sequence from Volumes One and Two. The publications, periodicals, and other sources listed are fully cited in all relevant chapters (and in occupational profiles, as appropriate), providing the reader with a complete selection of resources in single, convenient location.

Reference Works. Includes handbooks and manuals, directories, pamphlets, and other published sources of information. Entries include: the title and name, address, and phone number of its publisher or distributor; editor's or author's name; publication date or frequency; price; number of pages; description of contents; toll-free or additional phone numbers; and fax numbers, when known. Publication titles appear in italics.

Newspapers, Magazines, and Journals. Lists items published on a serial basis. Entries include: the title and name, address, and phone number of its publisher or distributor; frequency; price; description of contents; toll-free or additional phone numbers; and fax numbers, when known. Publication titles appear in italics.

Audio/Visual Resources. Features audiocassettes, videocassettes, and filmstrips. Entries include: the title and name, address, and phone number of its distributor or producer; date; price; special formats; descriptive information; toll-free or additional phone numbers; and fax numbers, when applicable. Videocassette and audiocassette titles appear in italics.

Online and Database Services. Publicly available electronic databases, including websites that facilitate matching job hunters with openings are cited. Entries include: the name of the product or service; the name, address, and phone number of the distributor or producer; price; special formats or arrangements; descriptive information; toll-free or additional phone numbers; and fax numbers, when applicable. For websites: the online address (URL) is included along with descriptive information.

Software. This category notes software programs designed to help with various aspects of job hunting, such as resume preparation. Entries include: the name of the product or service; the name, address, and phone number of the distributor or producer; price; special formats or arrangements; hardware compatibility, if relevant; descriptive information; toll-free or additional phone numbers; and fax numbers, when applicable.

Other Sources. Varied resources such as special associations and organizations and job-hunting bibliographies, kits, and organizers are covered in this section. Citations for journal and newspaper articles are provided if a topic is relatively new. Entries include: the title of the publication or name of the organization, product, or service; the name, address, and phone number of the organization, publisher, distributor, or producer; editor's or author's name; publication date or frequency; price; special formats or arrangements; descriptive information; toll-free or additional phone numbers; and fax numbers, when applicable. Publication titles appear in italics. For article citations: the article title, publication date, and journal or newspaper title, as well as a description of the article.

Index to Information Sources

JHS provides a comprehensive Index to Information Sources that lists all publications, periodicals, associations, organizations, firms, online and database services, and other resources cited in Volumes One, Two, and Three. Entries are arranged alphabetically and are referenced by their entry numbers. Titles of publications, audiocassettes, and videocassettes appear in italics.

List of Profiled Professions and Occupations

This list outlines references to occupations and professions by job titles, alternate names contained within job titles, popular names, and synonymous and related names. Beginning page numbers for each occupation's profile are provided. Titles of profiles appear in boldface.

SOURCES OF HELP-WANTED ADS

1 ■ Accounting for Banks
LexisNexis Group
1275 Broadway
Albany, NY 12204
Ph: (518)487-3000
Fr: 800-227-9597
URL: http://www.lexisnexis.com

Description: $393. Provides analysis and advice to accounting and banking professionals on day to day operations, internal accounting, investments, finances, assets, and more.

2 ■ Accounting and Finance
John Wiley & Sons Inc.
350 Main St., Commerce Pl.
Malden, MA 02148-5089
Ph: (781)388-8200
Fax: (781)388-8210
URL: http://www.wiley.com/bw/journal.asp?ref=0810-5391

Quarterly. $442.00/year for institutions, print + online, Australia/New Zealand; $384.00/year for institutions, print or online, Australia/New Zealand; $597.00/year for institutions, print + online; $519.00/year for institutions, print or online; $416.00/year for institutions, other countries, print + online; $361.00/year for institutions, other countries, print or online. Journal focusing on accounting and finance.

3 ■ Accounting Horizons
American Accounting Association
5717 Bessie Dr.
Sarasota, FL 34233-2399
Ph: (941)921-7747
Fax: (941)923-4093
URL: http://aaahq.org/pubs/horizons.htm

Quarterly. $300.00/year for individuals, print only; $325.00/year for individuals, online, vol. 13 thru current issue; $375.00/year for individuals, online and print. Publication covering the banking, finance, and accounting industries.

4 ■ The Accounting Review
American Accounting Association
5717 Bessie Dr.
Sarasota, FL 34233-2399
Ph: (941)921-7747
Fax: (941)923-4093
E-mail: tar@mccombs.utexas.edu
URL: http://aaahq.org/pubs/acctrev.htm

Quarterly. $395.00/year for institutions, print; $385.00/year for institutions, online from volume 74 through current issue; $445.00/year for institutions, online and print. Accounting education, research, financial reporting, and book reviews.

5 ■ Advances in Accounting
Reed Elsevier
125 Park Ave., 23rd Fl.
New York, NY 10017
Ph: (212)309-8100
Fax: (212)309-8187
URL: http://www.elsevier.com/wps/find/journaldescription.cws_home

Semiannual. $240.00/year for institutions, Europe, Iran; $39,100.00/year for institutions, Japan; $355.00/year for institutions, other countries. Journal covering the field of accounting.

6 ■ Bank Auditing and Accounting Report
Thomson RIA
195 Broadway
New York, NY 10007
Fr: 800-950-1216
URL: http://ria.thomsonreuters.com/EStore/detail.aspx?ID=WBAAR&site=seointaud

Description: Monthly. Provides practical guidance for resolving issues that confront bank professionals every day.

7 ■ CFO Magazine
CFO Publishing Corporation
6 W 48th St., 7th Fl.
New York, NY 10036
Ph: (212)459-3004
Fax: (212)459-3007
URL: http://www3.cfo.com

Monthly. Free for U.S. residents; $120.00/year for subscribers outside U.S. Provides readers with news and trends, analyses of the accomplishments of finance executives facing complex problems, and research about economic issues.

8 ■ The CPA Journal
New York State Society of CPAs
3 Park Ave., 18th Fl.
New York, NY 10016-5991
Ph: (212)719-8300
Fax: (212)719-3364
Fr: 800-537-3635
URL: http://www.cpajournal.com/

Monthly. $42.00/year for individuals; $135.00/year for other countries, 3 years; $98.00/year for other countries, 2 years; $54.00/year for other countries; $74.00/year for two years; $99.00/year for individuals, 3 years. Refereed accounting journal.

9 ■ CPA Magazine
CPA Magazine
1705 W Northwest Hwy., Ste. 170
Grapevine, TX 76051
Ph: (817)421-5340
Fax: (817)756-7252
URL: http://www.cpataxmag.net

Bimonthly. $99.00/year for individuals, elite CPA. Magazine for certified professional accountants.

10 ■ The Edge
American Society of Women Accountants
1760 Old Meadow Rd., Ste. 500
McLean, VA 22102
Ph: (703)506-3265
Fax: (703)506-3266
Fr: 800-326-2163
URL: http://www.aswachicago.org/membership.php

Monthly. free with membership. Magazine containing information on the accounting and financial service professions and its leaders. Provides guidance in maintaining work/life balance.

11 ■ FAO Today
Crossing Media
343 Thornall St., 5th Fl.
Edison, NJ 08837
Ph: (732)476-6160
Fax: (732)476-6155
URL: http://www.faotoday.com

$120.00/year for individuals. Business magazine featuring finance and accounting outsourcing.

12 ■ Foundations and Trends in Accounting
Now Publishers
PO Box 1024
Hanover, MA 02339-1001
Ph: (781)871-0245
URL: http://www.nowpublishers.com/product.aspx?product=ACC

$390.00/year for individuals, online only; $450.00/year for individuals, print and online; $390.00/year for other countries, online only; $450.00/year for other countries, print and online. Academic journal publishing new research in all branches of accounting.

13 ■ Government Financial Management Topics
Association of Government Accountants
2208 Mt. Vernon Ave.
Alexandria, VA 22301
Ph: (703)684-6931
Fax: (703)548-9367
Fr: 800-242-7211
E-mail: mforce@agacgfm.com
URL: http://www.agacgfm.org/publications/topics

Description: Weekly, Monday. Updates the latest developments relating to government financial management, educational registration forms, and general association news. Recurring features include news of research, a calendar of events, reports of meetings, news of educational opportunities, job listings, notices of publications available, and a column titled Presidential Perspective, interviews with leading government financial managers.

14 ■ Internal Auditor
Institute of Internal Auditors Inc.
247 Maitland AVE
Altamonte Springs, FL 32701-4201
Ph: (407)937-1100
Fax: (407)937-1101

Fr: 877-867-4957
E-mail: iaonline@theiia.org
URL: http://www.theiia.org/intAuditor/index.cfm

Bimonthly. $60.00/year for individuals, electronic; $84.00/year for other countries. Internal auditing.

15 ■ International Journal of Accounting Information Systems
Elsevier Science Inc.
360 Park Ave. S
New York, NY 10010-1710
Ph: (212)989-5800
Fax: (212)633-3990
Fr: 888-437-4636
URL: http://www.elsevier.com/wps/find/journaldescription.cws_home

Quarterly. $131.00/year for other countries; $13,000.00/year for individuals, for Japan; $97.00/year for individuals, for European countries and Iran; $553.00/year for institutions, other countries; $65,400.00/year for institutions, for Japan; $495.00/year for institutions, for European countries and Iran. Journal examining the rapidly evolving relationship between accounting and information technology.

16 ■ International Journal of Auditing
John Wiley & Sons Inc.
350 Main St., Commerce Pl.
Malden, MA 02148-5089
Ph: (781)388-8200
Fax: (781)388-8210
URL: http://www.wiley.com/bw/journal.asp?ref=1090-6738

$82.00/year for individuals, print and online; $54.00/year for individuals, BAA, print and online; $947.00/year for institutions, print and online; $823.00/year for institutions, print or online; $564.00/year for institutions, other countries, print and online; $490.00/year for institutions, other countries, print or online; $49.00/year for individuals, print and online; $74.00/year for individuals, print and online. Journal focusing on global auditing perspectives.

17 ■ Journal of Accountancy
The American Institute of Certified Public Accountants
1211 Avenue of the Americas
New York, NY 10036-8775
Ph: (212)596-6200
Fax: (212)596-6213
URL: http://www.journalofaccountancy.com/

Monthly. $75.00/year for individuals; $60.00/year for members. Accounting journal.

18 ■ Journal of Bank Cost & Management Accounting
Association for Management Information in Financial Services
14247 Saffron Cir.
Carmel, IN 46032
Ph: (317)815-5857
Fax: (317)815-5877
URL: http://www.amifs.org/

for Included in membership. Journal covering various areas of management accounting and outstanding presentations from association conferences and workshops.

19 ■ Journal of Business Finance and Accounting
John Wiley & Sons Inc.
350 Main St., Commerce Pl.
Malden, MA 02148-5089
Ph: (781)388-8200
Fax: (781)388-8210
URL: http://www.wiley.com/bw/journal.asp?ref=0306-686X

$247.00/year for individuals, U.S. print + online; $2,237.00/year for institutions, U.S. print + online; $1,945.00/year for institutions, U.S. print or online. Journal focusing on finance and economic aspects of accounting.

20 ■ The Journal of the Society of Depreciation Professionals
Society of Depreciation Professionals
PO Box 651046
Sterling, VA 20163-1046
Ph: (732)737-7376
URL: http://www.depr.org/journal.htm

Annual. Professional journal covering depreciation issues for accountants.

21 ■ The Journal of Taxation
RIA Group
195 Broadway
New York, NY 10007-3100
Fr: 800-431-9025
URL: http://ria.thomson.com/estore/detail.aspx?ID=JTAX

Monthly. $390.00/year for individuals, print; $565.00/year for individuals, online/print bundle; $440.00/year for individuals, online. Journal for sophisticated tax practitioners.

22 ■ Main Street Practitioner
National Society of Accountants
1010 N Fairfax St.
Alexandria, VA 22314-1504
Ph: (703)549-6400
Fax: (703)549-2984
Fr: 800-966-6679
URL: http://www.nsacct.org/MemberBenefits/NSAPublications/tabid/6

Bimonthly. Public accounting magazine.

23 ■ Management Accounting Quarterly
Institute of Management Accountants
10 Paragon Dr., Ste. 1
Montvale, NJ 07645-1718
Ph: (201)573-9000
Fax: (201)474-1600
Fr: 800-638-4427
URL: http://www.imanet.org/resources_and_publications/management_

Quarterly. $60.00/year for nonmembers. Trade publication covering accounting theory and practices for accountants.

24 ■ National Association of Black Accountants-News Plus
National Association of Black Accountants Inc.
7474 Greenway Center Dr., Ste. 1120
Greenbelt, MD 20770
Ph: (301)474-6222
Fax: (301)474-3114
Fr: 888-571-2939
E-mail: customerservice@nabainc.org
URL: http://www.nabainc.org/

Description: Quarterly. Addresses concerns of black business professionals, especially in the accounting profession. Reports on accounting education issues, developments affecting the profession, and the Association's activities on the behalf of minorities in the accounting profession. Recurring features include member profiles, job listings, reports of meetings, news of research, and a calendar of events.

25 ■ NewsAccount
Colorado Society of Certified Public Accountants
7979 E Tufts Ave., Ste. 1000
Denver, CO 80237-2847
Ph: (303)773-2877
Fax: (303)773-6344
Fr: 800-523-9082
URL: http://www.cocpa.org

Description: Monthly. Relays information on issues and trends affecting the Society, its members, and the accounting profession. Recurring features include letters to the editor, job listings, a calendar of events and columns titled Committees in Action, Student Corner, SEC Corner, and Technical Update.

26 ■ Research in Accounting Regulation
Reed Elsevier
125 Park Ave., 23rd Fl.
New York, NY 10017
Ph: (212)309-8100
Fax: (212)309-8187
URL: http://www.elsevier.com/wps/find/journaldescription.cws_home

Semiannual. $241.00/year for institutions, Europe, Iran; $38,500.00/year for institutions, Japan; $353.00/year for institutions, other countries. Journal covering the field of accounting.

27 ■ Strategic Finance
Institute of Management Accountants
10 Paragon Dr., Ste. 1
Montvale, NJ 07645-1718
Ph: (201)573-9000
Fax: (201)474-1600
Fr: 800-638-4427
URL: http://www.imanet.org/publications.asp

Monthly. $210.00/year for nonmembers; $48.00/year for members; $25.00/year for students; $18.00/year for single issue, back issue. Magazine reporting on corporate finance, accounting, cash management, and budgeting.

PLACEMENT AND JOB REFERRAL SERVICES

28 ■ Accounting Principals
Bldg. 200, Ste. 400
10151 Deerwood Park Blvd.
Jacksonville, FL 32256
Fr: 800-981-3849
E-mail: info@accountingprincipals.com
URL: http://www.accountingprincipals.com

Description: Provides workforce solutions in the accounting and financial services industries. Offers a range of services including temporary staffing, temp-to-hire, direct placement, payroll services and contract services.

EMPLOYER DIRECTORIES AND NETWORKING LISTS

29 ■ American Society of Women Accountants—Membership Directory
American Society of Women Accountants
1760 Old Meadow Rd., Ste. 500
McLean, VA 22102
Ph: (703)506-3265
Fax: (703)506-3266
Fr: 800-326-2163
URL: http://www.aswa.org

Annual. Covers: Approximately 5,000 members in accounting and accounting-related fields. Entries include: Name, address, phone, fax, e-mail. Arrangement: Classified by chapter, then alphabetical.

30 ■ American Woman's Society of Certified Public Accountants—Roster
American Woman's Society of Certified Public Accountants
136 S Keowee St.
Dayton, OH 45402
Ph: (937)222-1872
Fax: (937)222-5794
Fr: 800-297-2721
URL: http://www.awscpa.org

Annual, October. Number of listings: 1,400. Entries include: Name, title; company name, address, phone; home address and phone; membership classification. Arrangement: Classified by type of membership, then geographical. Indexes: Alphabetical.

31 ■ Vault Guide to the Top 40 Accounting Firms
Vault.com Inc.
150 W 22nd St., 5th Fl.
New York, NY 10011
Ph: (212)366-4212
Fax: (212)366-6117
Fr: 888-562-8285
URL: http://www.vault.com

Latest edition 2009. $29.95 for individuals. Covers: Accounting firms in United States and 750 accounting professionals. Entries include: Company name, address, phone and fax numbers, zip code, statistics and website address.

HANDBOOKS AND MANUALS

32 ■ Accountants' Handbook
John Wiley & Sons, Inc.
111 River St.
Hoboken, NJ 07030
Ph: (201)748-6000
Fax: (201)748-6088
E-mail: info@wiley.com
URL: http://as.wiley.com/WileyCDA

D.R. Carmichael and Lynford Graham. 2012. $119.95. 1056 pages. Series covering accounting and financial reporting of interest to accountants, auditors, financial analysts, and users of accounting information.

33 ■ Accounting Ethics: Critical Perspectives on Business and Management
Routledge
711 3rd Ave., 8th Fl.
New York, NY 10017
Ph: (212)216-7800
Fax: (212)563-2269
Fr: 800-634-7064
URL: http://www.routledge.com/books/Accounting-Ethics-isbn9780415350785

J. Edward Ketz. $1,665.00. 1600 pages. This research collection includes important papers from key journals and books that reassess theories, research studies, and professional practices in the field of accounting ethics.

34 ■ Accounting Trends & Techniques
American Institute of Certified Public Accountants
Harborside Financial Ctr.
201 Plaza Three
Jersey City, NJ 07311-3881
Ph: (201)938-3000
Fax: (201)938-3329
Fr: 888-777-7077
URL: http://www.aicpa.org

Rick Rikert. 2009. $168.75 (paper).

35 ■ Assistant Accountant-Auditor
National Learning Corporation
212 Michael Dr.
Syosset, NY 11791
Ph: (516)921-8888
Fax: (516)921-8743
Fr: 800-632-8888
URL: http://www.passbooks.com

2009. $34.95 (paper). Serves as an exam preparation guide for assistant accountants and auditors.

36 ■ Careers for Financial Mavens and Other Money Movers
The McGraw-Hill Companies
PO Box 182604
Columbus, OH 43272
Fax: (614)759-3749
Fr: 877-883-5524
E-mail: customer.service@mcgraw-hill.com
URL: http://www.mhprofessional.com/product.php?cat=106&isbn=0071454551

Marjorie Eberts and Margaret Gisler. Second edition, 2004. $19.95 (paper). 153 pages.

37 ■ CIMA Study Systems 2006: Financial Accounting Fundamentals
CIMA Publishing
525 B St., Ste. 1900
San Diego, CA 92101
Ph: (619)231-6616
Fax: (619)699-6422
Fr: 800-545-2522
E-mail: usbkinfo@elsevier.com
URL: http://www.elsevier.com

Henry Lunt and Margaret Weaver. 2005. $61.95. 640 pages. Provides comprehensive study material for the exams; incorporates legislative and syllabus changes.

38 ■ Great Jobs for Accounting Majors
McGraw-Hill Companies
7500 Chavenelle Rd.
Dubuque, IA 52002
Fax: (614)759-3749
Fr: 877-833-5524
E-mail: pbg.ecommerce_custserv@mcgraw-hill.com
URL: http://www.mhprofessional.com/product.php?isbn=0071438548

Jan Goldberg. 2005. $15.95 (paper). 192 pages. Guide covering both the basics of a job search as well as profiles of possible careers in the accounting field. Helps in exploring a variety of job options for accounting majors to determine what will fit for personal, professional, and practical needs.

39 ■ The Inside Track to Careers in Accounting
American Institute of Certified Public Accountants
1211 Avenue of the Americas
New York, NY 10036
Ph: (212)596-6200
Fax: (512)596-6213
URL: http://www.aicpa.org

Stan Ross and James Carberry. 2010. $59.00 for members; $73.75 for non-members. Contains guide to new accounting professionals and students interested in accounting. Includes detailed job descriptions, typical salary ranges and career trajectories, plus invaluable background information, history and personal insights.

40 ■ Opportunities in Financial Careers
The McGraw-Hill Companies
PO Box 182604
Columbus, OH 43272
Fax: (614)759-3749
Fr: 877-883-5524
E-mail: customer.service@mcgraw-hill.com
URL: http://www.mhprofessional.com/product.php?isbn=0071442502

Michael Sumichrast and Martin A. Sumichrast. 2004. $13.95 (paper). 160 pages. A guide to planning for and seeking opportunities in this challenging field.

41 ■ Opportunities in Insurance Careers
The McGraw-Hill Companies
PO Box 182604
Columbus, OH 43272
Fax: (614)759-3749
Fr: 877-883-5524
E-mail: customer.service@mcgraw-hill.com
URL: http://www.mhprofessional.com/product.php?isbn=0071482075

Robert M. Schrayer. Revised, 2007. $14.95 (paper). 160 pages. A guide to planning for and seeking opportunities in the field. Contains bibliography and illustrations.

42 ■ Vault Career Guide to Accounting
Vault, Inc.
132 W 31st St., 15th Fl.
New York, NY 10001
Ph: (212)366-4212
Fax: (212)366-6117
URL: http://www.vault.com/wps/portal/usa/store/bookdetail?item_no=693

Jason Alba et al. 2008. $29.95 (paper). 160 pages.

Features the ins and outs of a career in accounting from the types of accounting, including tax and audit, to the hiring process and workplace culture of major accounting employers.

EMPLOYMENT AGENCIES AND SEARCH FIRMS

43 ■ A-lign Careers
2202 N Westshore Blvd., Ste. 200
Tampa, FL 33607
Ph: (940)648-5045
Fr: 888-702-5446
URL: http://www.aligncareers.com

Specializes in the recruitment of auditing, accounting and finance personnel. Identifies resources that match a client's culture and position requirements.

44 ■ AC Lordi Search
235 Montgomery St., Ste. 630
San Francisco, CA 94104
Ph: (415)781-8644
E-mail: info@aclordi.com
URL: http://www.aclordi.com

Executive search firm for finance and accounting. Uses referral-based outsourcing, affinity networking, and cold-calling to identify talented accounting professionals.

45 ■ Access Staffing
360 Lexington Ave., 8th Fl.
New York, NY 10017
Ph: (212)687-5440
Fax: (212)557-2544
URL: http://www.accessstaffingco.com

Serves as a staffing firm covering accounting/financial, advertising, bilingual Japanese, creative, event planning, fashion/retail, healthcare/ human services, human resources, information technology, insurance, legal, light industrial and office support.

46 ■ Accountemps
1404 I St. NW, Ste. 400
Washington, DC 20005
Ph: (202)626-0120
Fr: 800-803-8367
E-mail: washington.dc@accountemps.com
URL: http://www.accountemps.com

Description: Specializes in staffing for accounting, finance and bookkeeping professionals. Provides staffing support to all fields of an accounting department. Maintains offices all over the United States.

47 ■ Accounting Connections
PO Box 10823
Portland, OR 97296
Ph: (503)228-2335
Fax: (503)534-3535
URL: http://www.accountingconnections.com

Description: Serves as a staffing agency specializing in accounting and finance professionals.

48 ■ Accounting & Finance Personnel
1702 E Highland, Ste. 200
Phoenix, AZ 85016
Ph: (602)277-3700
Fax: (602)926-2629
URL: http://www.afpersonnel.com

Description: Specializes in placing accounting and financial personnel.

49 ■ Accounting Partners
2025 Gateway Pl., Ste. 405
San Jose, CA 95110
Ph: (408)986-1990
Fax: (408)986-1411
URL: http://www.accountingpartners.com

Description: Provides contract, contact-to-hire, and

direct-hire solutions in a wide variety of accounting and finance positions.

50 ■ AccountSource
130 Milestone Way
Greenville, SC 29615
Ph: (864)213-8004
Fax: (864)213-9867
E-mail: recruiters@asijobs.com
URL: http://www.asijobs.com

Description: Acts as a premier placement service for accounting and finance professionals. Offers a wide variety of services including permanent placement, contract and contract to hire staffing solutions.

51 ■ Action Employment Services
121 SW Morrison St., Ste. 425
Portland, OR 97204
Ph: (503)275-9011
Fax: (503)241-8772
Fr: (866)208-1643
E-mail: inquiry@actionemployment.net
URL: http://www.actionemployment.net

Description: Provides administrative, office, accounting, and human resource positions.

52 ■ Advantage Group
350 N Old Woodward Ave., Ste. 218
Birmingham, MI 48009
Ph: (248)540-0400
Fax: (248)540-0401
E-mail: info@advantage-grp.com
URL: http://advantage-grp.com

Specializes in the placement of accounting and financial executives.

53 ■ Ajilon Professional Staffing
521 5th Ave., 4th Fl.
New York, NY 10175
Ph: (212)953-7400
Fax: (212)867-8394
Fr: (866)GOA-JILON
E-mail: staffing@ajilonfinance.com
URL: http://www.ajilonfinance.com

Description: Provides staffing service specializing in the temporary and permanent placement of premier accounting, finance and bookkeeping professionals.

54 ■ Albion Accounting Staffing Solutions
2520 NW 97th Ave., Ste. 110
Miami, FL 33172
Ph: (305)406-1000
Fax: (305)406-1010
E-mail: resumes@albionstaffing.com
URL: http://www.albionaccounting.com

Description: Specializes in the placement of financial, accounting, bookkeeping, mortgage and banking positions on a temporary, temp-to-hire or direct hire basis. Offers full service recruiting and consulting services.

55 ■ Apple and Associates
PO Box 996
Chapin, SC 29036
Ph: (803)932-2000
E-mail: info@appleassoc.com
URL: http://www.appleassoc.com

Provides staffing services to medical device, plastics, pharmaceutical and performance materials industries.

56 ■ Ashton Lane Group
51 John F. Kennedy Pkwy., 1st Fl. W
Short Hills, NJ 07078
Ph: (212)372-9795
Fax: (973)218-2661
E-mail: info@ashtonlanegroup.com
URL: http://www.ashtonlanegroup.com

Specializes in the recruitment of professionals in banking, insurance and alternative investment industries.

57 ■ ATR Finance
1230 Oakmead Pkwy.
Sunnyvale, CA 94085
Ph: (408)328-8000
Fax: (408)328-8001
Fr: 877-412-1100
E-mail: corporate@atr1.com
URL: http://www.atr-finance.com

Description: Serves as an executive placement firm for accounting and finance professionals. Offers career opportunities for finance and accounting professionals interested in either consulting or full-time positions.

58 ■ Aureus Group
C&A Plz., 13609 California St., Ste. 100
Omaha, NE 68154-3503
Ph: (402)891-6900
Fax: (402)891-1290
Fr: 888-239-5993
E-mail: omaha@aureusgroup.com
URL: http://www.aureusgroup.com

Provides human capital management services in a wide variety of industries. Executive search and recruiting consultants specializing in six areas: accounting and finance, data processing, aerospace, engineering, manufacturing and medical professionals. Industries served: hospitals, all mainframe computer shops and all areas of accounting.

59 ■ Bolton Group
3500 Piedmont Rd., Ste. 630
Atlanta, GA 30305
Ph: (404)228-4280
Fax: (404)228-2060
E-mail: info@boltongroup.com
URL: http://www.boltongroup.com

Description: Serves as a specialty niche search firm focusing solely in the areas of accounting and finance. Partners with progressive organizations throughout the country, providing accounting and finance specialists in a variety of areas including accounting, finance, tax, treasury, audit/SOX, and financial systems.

60 ■ Boyce Cunnane Inc.
PO Box 19064
Baltimore, MD 21284-9064
Ph: (410)583-5511
Fax: (410)583-5518
E-mail: bc@cunnane.com
URL: http://www.cunnane.com

Executive search firm.

61 ■ Buxbaum/Rink Consulting L.L.C.
1 Bradley Rd., Ste. 901
Woodbridge, CT 06525-2296
Ph: (203)389-5949
Fax: (203)397-0615

Personnel consulting firms offer contingency search, recruitment and placement of accounting and finance, as well as other business management positions. In addition to serving these two major career areas, also provides similar services to operations, marketing and human resources executives. Industries served: manufacturing, financial services, and service.

62 ■ Capstone Consulting Inc.
723 S Dearborn St.
Chicago, IL 60605
Ph: (312)753-5701
E-mail: mark@capstoneconsulting.com
URL: http://www.capstoneconsulting.com

Executive search firm.

63 ■ Career Advocates International
1539 Ave. A
Katy, TX 77493
Ph: (281)395-9848
Fax: (281)574-3949
URL: http://www.careeradvocates.org

Provides permanent placement and temporary staffing for executive and staff level positions. Specializes in multiple niches including: sales and marketing, accounting and financial services, banking, communications, human resources, chemicals, oil and gas, medical and dental, legal, information technology, energy, technology, engineering, manufacturing, construction, and light industrial.

64 ■ Casey Accounting and Finance Resources
4902 Tollview Dr.
Rolling Meadows, IL 60008
Ph: (224)232-5925
E-mail: info@caseyresources.com
URL: http://www.caseyresources.com

Description: Specializes in the placement of accounting and finance professionals for direct hire, temp-to-hire, project staffing and temporary services.

65 ■ Catalyst Resource Group, LLC
6120 Windward Pkwy., Ste. 170
Alpharetta, GA 30005
Ph: (678)366-3500
Fax: (678)366-9710
Fr: 877-746-3400
E-mail: info@catalystresourcegroup.com
URL: http://www.catalystresourcegroup.com

Description: Serves as an executive search firm specializing in the placement of accounting and finance professionals, and also fills other administrative needs.

66 ■ Centennial, Inc.
8044 Montgomery Rd., Ste. 260
Cincinnati, OH 45236
Ph: (513)366-3760
Fax: (513)366-3761
E-mail: info@centennialinc.com
URL: http://www.centennialinc.com

Serves as an executive search firm specializing in the areas of executive and general management, accounting and finance, human resources, information technology, manufacturing, engineering, marketing and advertising, not-for-profit, sales and business development, and supply chain and logistics. Performs executive coaching as well as career coaching for clients.

67 ■ Chanko-Ward Ltd.
2 W 45th St., Ste. 1201
New York, NY 10036
Ph: (212)869-4040
Fax: (212)869-0281
E-mail: info@chankoward.com
URL: http://www.chankoward.com

Primarily engaged in executive recruiting for individuals and corporations, where disciplines of accounting, planning, mergers and acquisitions, finance, or MIS required. In addition will function as the internal personnel department of a corporation, either to augment present staff or in a situation where there is no formal personnel department. Serves private industries as well as government agencies.

68 ■ Clovis, LLC
10411 Motor City Dr., Ste. 450
Bethesda, MD 20817
Ph: (301)365-8480
Fax: (301)576-3579
Fr: 888-925-6847
E-mail: solutions@clovisgroup.com
URL: http://www.clovisgroup.com

Description: Serves as recruitment outsourcing staffing firm for information technology, accounting and finance professionals.

69 ■ Conselium
14850 Montfort Dr., Ste. 106
Dallas, TX 75254
Ph: (972)934-8444
E-mail: maurice@conselium.com
URL: http://www.conselium.com

Executive search firm with a core expertise in corporate compliance, audit and information technology security.

70 ■ Consultants to Executive Management Company Ltd.
20 S Clark St.
Chicago, IL 60603
Ph: (312)855-1500
Fax: (312)855-1510
Fr: 800-800-2362

National personnel consultancy specializes in executive search with focus on accounting and finance, management information systems, professional medical, and real estate fields. Industries served: All.

71 ■ Cornell Global
PO Box 7113
Wilton, CT 06897
Ph: (203)762-0730
Fax: (203)761-9507
E-mail: info@cornellglobal.com
URL: http://www.cornellglobal.com

Executive search firm.

72 ■ CSI Executive Search LLC
9600 Great Hills Trl., Ste. 150W
Austin, TX 78759
Ph: (512)301-1119
Fax: (512)301-5559
Fr: 877-329-1828
E-mail: info@csi-executivesearch.com
URL: http://www.csi-executivesearch.com

Executive search firm that specializes in the following arenas: accounting, engineering, healthcare, information technology, and legal. Utilizes behavioral, performance, retention variable, social intelligence, and cultural assessments to ensure the best candidate/client fit. Works on a retained, retingency, and contingency search basis.

73 ■ CyberCoders, Inc.
6591 Irvine Center Dr., Ste. 200
Irvine, CA 92618
Ph: (866)421-0200
Fax: (949)885-5150
E-mail: info@cybercoders.com
URL: http://www.cybercoders.com

Description: Recruitment and job search firm specializing in engineering, executive, financial, accounting and sales.

74 ■ DGL Consultants
189 S Main St.
PO Box 450
Richford, VT 05476
Ph: (802)848-7764
Fax: (802)848-3117
E-mail: info@dglconsultants.com
URL: http://www.dglconsultants.com

Executive search firm.

75 ■ Elinvar
1804 Hillsborough St.
Raleigh, NC 27605
Ph: (919)878-4454
E-mail: careers@elinvar.com
URL: http://www.elinvar.com

Executive search firm.

76 ■ Financial Search Group, Ltd.
307 Fourth Ave., Ste. 810
Pittsburgh, PA 15222
Ph: (412)288-0505
Fax: (412)288-0699
E-mail: fsgltd@fsgltd.com
URL: http://www.fsgltd.com

Description: Provides staffing services on a wide variety of companies from contingency or retainer basis. Identifies the candidates that match each employer's needs.

77 ■ Foster McKay Group
30 Vreeland Rd.
Florham Park, NJ 07932
Ph: (973)966-0909
Fax: (973)966-6925
E-mail: careers@fostermckaynj.com
URL: http://www.fostermckay.com

Executive search firm that specializes in accounting and finance. Specializes in placing financial, accounting, and tax professionals.

78 ■ General Ledger Resources
13280 Evening Creek Dr. S, Ste. 225
San Diego, CA 92128
Ph: (858)391-1017
Fax: (858)748-7968
URL: http://www.gl-resources.com

Serves as a finance and accounting professional services firm with practice areas in consulting services and search and placement.

79 ■ GK Finance
7242 Metro Blvd., Ste. 100
Edina, MN 55439
Ph: (952)835-5550
Fax: (952)835-7294
E-mail: info@georgekonik.com
URL: http://www.gkastaffing.com/index_financial.php

Description: Specializes in placing qualified candidates in finance and accounting positions. Offers three staffing options: contract (temporary) staffing, contract-to-direct, and direct hire opportunities from entry to senior or management level candidates.

80 ■ Houser Martin Morris
110th Ave. NE, 110 Atrium Pl., Ste. 580
Bellevue, WA 98004
Ph: (425)453-2700
Fax: (425)453-8726
E-mail: info@houser.com
URL: http://www.houser.com

Focus is in the areas of retained executive search, professional and technical recruiting. Areas of specialization include software engineering, sales and marketing, information technology, legal, human resources, accounting and finance, manufacturing, factory automation, and engineering.

81 ■ Insperity, Inc.
19001 Crescent Springs Dr.
Kingwood, TX 77339-3802
Ph: (281)358-8986
Fr: 800-237-3170
E-mail: douglas.sharp@insperity.com
URL: http://www.insperity.com

Description: Serves as a full-service human resources department for small and medium-sized businesses throughout the United States. Provides client companies with benefits and services such as employment administration, government compliance, recruiting and selection, performance management, benefits management, employer liability management, training and development, and business services.

82 ■ International Search
9717 E 42nd St.
PO Box 470898
Tulsa, OK 74147-0898
Ph: (918)627-9070
Fax: (918)524-8604

Personnel consulting group provides placement expertise in engineering, accounting, and data processing. Industries served: energy, manufacturing, oil and gas, and services.

83 ■ KForce
Fr: 877-4KF-ORCE
URL: http://www.kforce.com

Executive search firm. More than 41 locations throughout the United States and two in the Philippines.

84 ■ Kramer Executive Resources, Inc.
909 3rd Ave., 5th Fl.
New York, NY 10022
Ph: (212)832-1122
Fax: (646)495-3118
E-mail: info@kramerexec.com
URL: http://www.kramerexec.com

Description: Specializes in the recruitment of accounting, tax and financial professionals in the New York metropolitan tri-state region.

85 ■ ManpowerGroup
100 Manpower Pl.
Milwaukee, WI 53212
Ph: (414)961-1000
Fax: (414)906-7822
URL: http://us.manpower.com

Specializes in a wide range of employment services including permanent placement, recruitment process outsourcing, managed service programs, outplacement and human resources consulting. Provides companies with workforce solutions that help them increase productivity and improve efficiency.

86 ■ O'Shea System of Employment Inc.
PO Box 2134
Aston, PA 19014
Ph: (610)364-3964
Fax: (610)364-3962
Fr: 800-220-5203
E-mail: osheasys@aol.com

Offers personnel staff recruiting nationally in the following fields: insurance, health care, financial, information technology, administration, human resource, manufacturing and sales.

87 ■ Pate Resources Group Inc.
505 Orleans St., Ste. 300
Beaumont, TX 77701
Ph: (409)833-4514
Fax: (409)833-4646
Fr: 800-669-4514
E-mail: opportunities@pateresourcesgroup.com
URL: http://www.pateresourcesgroup.com

Offers executive search and recruiting services to professionals who include physicians, healthcare administrators, engineers, accounting and financial disciplines, legal, outplacement, sales and marketing. Industries served: healthcare, petrochemicals, accounting, utility, legal, and municipalities.

88 ■ Penn Search Inc.
1045 1st Ave., Ste. 110
PO Box 688
King of Prussia, PA 19406
Ph: (610)964-8820
Fax: (610)964-8916
E-mail: charlied@pennsearch.com
URL: http://www.pennsearch.com

Assists in recruiting and hiring accounting and financial professionals from staff accountant to chief financial officer. Industries served: all.

89 ■ Phillip's Personnel/Phillip's Temps
1675 Broadway, Ste. 2410
Denver, CO 80204
Ph: (303)893-1850
Fax: (303)893-0639
E-mail: info@phillipspersonnel.com
URL: http://www.phillipspersonnel.com

Personnel recruiting and staffing consultants in: accounting and finance, MIS, sales and marketing, engineering, administration and general and executive management. Industries served: telecommunications, distribution, financial services and general business.

90 ■ Pro Advantage Executive Search
381 Park Ave. S, Ste. 1112
New York, NY 10016
Ph: (212)944-0222

Fax: (212)944-2666
E-mail: info@proadvantagejobs.com
URL: http://www.proadvantagejobs.com

Description: Executive recruiting and research firm specializes in financial services industries. Offers career opportunities in the field of accounting, internal auditing, finance, compliance, tax, operations, and marketing.

91 ■ Pro Staff
14300 Nicollet Ct., Ste. 208
Burnsville, MN 55306
Ph: (952)892-3240
Fax: (952)892-7304
Fr: 800-938-WORK
E-mail: burnsville@prostaff.com
URL: http://www.prostaff.com

Description: Strives to enhance the success and development of client-companies through cost-efficient, comprehensive workforce management solutions. Focuses on the employment market, labor trends, and best practices in administrative, finance and accounting, information technology, technical, and creative services.

92 ■ Q&A Recruiting
J.P. Morgan International Plz., Bldg. III
14241 Dallas Pkwy., Ste. 550
Dallas, TX 75254
Ph: (972)720-1020
Fax: (972)720-1023
E-mail: jobs@qarecruiting.com
URL: http://www.qarecruiting.com

Description: Provides staffing services for accounting, finance, tax, information technology, payroll or accounting support, and human resources. Provides direct hire and contract services divisions.

93 ■ Randstad Finance and Accounting
111 Anza Blvd., No. 202
Burlingame, CA 94010
Ph: (650)343-5111
Fax: (650)343-5485
URL: http://finance.randstadusa.com

Description: Provides staffing solutions for accounting and finance departments in companies large and small, domestic and international, at headquarters and in the field. Pursues quality and excellence in accounting and finance staffing through developing relationships and consistently providing a level of service.

94 ■ Raymond Alexander Associates
97 Lackawanna Ave., Ste. 102
Totowa, NJ 07512-2332
Ph: (973)256-1000
Fax: (973)256-5871
E-mail: raa@raymondalexander.com
URL: http://www.raymondalexander.com

Personnel consulting firm conducts executive search services in the specific areas of accounting, tax and finance. Industries served: manufacturing, financial services, and public accounting.

95 ■ Roberson & Co.
10751 Parfet St.
Broomfield, CO 80021
Ph: (303)410-6510
E-mail: roberson@recruiterpro.com
URL: http://www.recruiterpro.com

Professional and executive recruiting firm working the national and international marketplace. Specializes in accounting, finance, data processing and information services, health care, environmental and mining, engineering, manufacturing, human resources, and sales and marketing.

96 ■ Robert Half Finance & Accounting
2884 Sand Hill Rd.
Menlo Park, CA 94025
Fr: 800-474-4253
URL: http://www.roberthalffinance.com

Description: Provides recruitment services in the areas of accounting and finance.

97 ■ Robert Half Management Resources
2884 Sand Hill Rd.
Menlo Park, CA 94025
Fr: 888-400-7474
URL: http://www.roberthalfmr.com

Description: Serves as a provider of senior-level accounting and finance professionals on a project and interim basis.

98 ■ Rocky Mountain Recruiters, Inc.
1776 S Jackson St., Ste. 320
Denver, CO 80210
Ph: (303)296-2000
E-mail: resumes@rmrecruiters.com
URL: http://www.rmrecruiters.com

Accounting, financial, and executive search firm.

99 ■ Sherpa LLC
1001 Morehead Square Dr., Ste. 600
Charlotte, NC 28203
Ph: (704)374-0001
E-mail: info@sherpallc.com
URL: http://www.sherpallc.com

Specializes in recruiting, staffing and consulting services for accounting/finance, information technology and project management in direct hire, temporary and project-based consulting positions.

100 ■ SHS of Cherry Hill
207 Barclay Pavilion W
Cherry Hill, NJ 08034
Ph: (856)216-9030
Fax: (856)216-7784
E-mail: shs@shsofcherryhill.com
URL: http://www.shsofcherryhill.com

Personnel recruiters operating in the disciplines of accounting, sales, insurance, engineering, and administration. Industries served: insurance, distribution, manufacturing, and service.

101 ■ Spectrum Group, LLC
1919 Gallows Rd., Ste. 600
Vienna, VA 22182
Ph: (703)738-1200
Fax: (703)761-9477
E-mail: web@spectrumcareers.com
URL: http://www.spectrumcareers.com

Description: Serves as executive search firm for accounting and finance, information technology and sales and marketing industries.

102 ■ S.R. Clarke
105 Huntercombe
Williamburg, VA 23188
Ph: (703)934-4200
Fax: (703)344-0259
URL: http://www.srclarke.com/index.html

Serves as an executive search and recruitment firm specializing in commercial construction, commercial real estate development, residential asset management, residential construction and development, subcontractor trades, finance, accounting, administration, heavy construction, architectural design and engineering design.

103 ■ Wendell L. Johnson Associates Inc.
12 Grandview Dr., Ste. 1117
Danbury, CT 06811-4321
Ph: (203)743-4112
Fax: (203)778-5377

Executive search firm specializing in areas of workforce diversity, accounting/finance, human resources, marketing/sales, strategic planning, and MIS.

104 ■ Whitney & Associates Inc.
920 2nd Ave. S, Ste. 625
Minneapolis, MN 55402-4103
Ph: (612)338-5600
Fax: (612)349-6129
E-mail: dwhitney@whitneyinc.com

Accounting and financial personnel recruiting consultants providing full time placement and temporary staffing service with specialized expertise and emphasis in the accounting discipline.

ONLINE JOB SOURCES AND SERVICES

105 ■ Accountantjobs.com
URL: http://www.accountantjobs.com

Description: Serves as a job site network and online portal for accounting careers worldwide. Features job postings, advertisements, resume access and other resources intended to provide both employers and job seekers their online recruitment needs.

106 ■ AccountExecutiveManager.com
URL: http://www.accountexecutivemanager.com

Description: Provides career and employment opportunities for aspiring account executive managers. Offers links, job and resume postings and more.

107 ■ Accounting Technician Jobs
URL: http://www.accountingtechnicianjobs.com

Description: Specializes in accounting technician careers and employment. Offers resume posting and job opening listings.

108 ■ AccountingBoard.com
URL: http://www.accountingboard.com

Description: Features job opportunities in the accounting field.

109 ■ AccountingClassifieds.com
URL: http://www.accountingclassifieds.com

Description: Serves as a specialized career site providing employment opportunities focused on the accounting industry.

110 ■ AccountingCoach.com
URL: http://www.accountingcoach.com

Description: Provides accounting information for business persons or students who are considering a career in accounting. Contains an accounting blog, forums, newsletters, links, advertisements, career resources, and other related information.

111 ■ Accounting.com
E-mail: info@accounting.com
URL: http://www.accounting.com

Description: Job board for those seeking accounting jobs. Employers may also post positions available. Contains directory of CPA firms, discussion forum for job seekers, CPE resources, news bulletins and accounting links.

112 ■ AccountingCrossing.com
URL: http://www.accountingcrossing.com

Description: Offers collection of accounting jobs, including CPA, finance manager, corporate accountant, and forensic accounting positions. Features industry-specific articles relating to job searches and developments in the accounting industry.

113 ■ AccountingEducation.com
E-mail: info@accountingeducation.com
URL: http://www.accountingeducation.com

Description: Offers various advertising services used by schools and professional accounting associations across the world.

114 ■ AccountingJobsite.com
URL: http://www.accountingjobsite.com

Description: Provides listings of accounting jobs, accounting clerk jobs, accounting auditing jobs, and other accounting employment opportunities.

115 ■ AccountingJobsToday.com
URL: http://www.accountingjobstoday.com

Description: Functions as a job resource for accounting and finance professionals worldwide. Offers several career resources including accounting job descriptions, sample accounting resumes, salary tools and education.

116 ■ AccountingProfessional.com
E-mail: info@careermarketplace.com
URL: http://www.accountingprofessional.com

Description: Acts as a job search and recruiting site for accountants, CPAs and related financial jobs. Provides resources for both job seekers and employers.

117 ■ AllAccountantJobs.com
URL: http://allaccountantjobs.com

Description: Provides job seekers access to resources and job opening opportunities in the area of accounting.

118 ■ American Accounting Association Placement Advertising
5717 Bessie Dr.
Sarasota, FL 34233-2399
Ph: (941)921-7747
Fax: (941)923-4093
E-mail: info@aaahq.org
URL: http://careercenter.aaahq.org/home/index.cfm?site_id=7376

Description: Visitors may apply for membership to the Association at this site. Main files include: Placement Postings, Placement Submission Information, Faculty Development, Marketplace, more.

119 ■ American Association of Finance and Accounting
URL: http://www.aafa.com

Description: AAFA is the largest and oldest alliance of executive search firms specializing in the recruitment and placement of finance and accounting professionals. Contains career opportunities site with job board for both job seekers and hiring employers. One does not have to be a member to search for jobs.

120 ■ Association of Certified Fraud Examiners
716 West Ave.
Austin, TX 78701-2727
Ph: (512)478-9000
Fax: (512)478-9297
Fr: 800-245-3321
E-mail: memberservices@acfe.com
URL: http://www.cfenet.com

Description: Association web site contains Career Center with job databank, giving the user the ability to post jobs and career resources and links. Must be a member of organization in order to access databank.

121 ■ AuditorCrossing.com
URL: http://www.auditorcrossing.com

Description: Offers a wide collection of top auditor job openings. Includes listings from Fortune 500 and Fortune 1000 companies.

122 ■ BankingCareers.com
URL: http://www.bankingcareers.com

Description: Provides lists of jobs and products to bankers in the banking and finance community.

123 ■ BookkeeperJobs.com
URL: http://www.bookkeeperjobs.com

Description: Serves as a niche board for bookkeeping jobs and resumes. Allows postings and searching of resumes for first-time and returning job seekers and employers.

124 ■ California Society of Certified Public Accountants Classifieds
1800 Gateway Dr., Ste. 200
San Mateo, CA 94404-4072
Fr: 800-922-5272
E-mail: info@calcpa.org
URL: http://www.calcpa.org/classifieds/public/search.aspx

Description: An accounting job search tool for CPAs in California. Details steps to become a CPA, provides job search posting opportunities for seekers and candidates' pages for employers looking to fill positions.

125 ■ CareerBank
URL: http://www.careerbank.com/home/index.cfm?site_id=8162

Description: Provides jobs in finance, banking, mortgage, insurance, and accounting. Specializes in online job posting and job search, resume upload and resume database search, and career advice services.

126 ■ CareersInAudit.com
URL: http://www.careersinaudit.com

Description: Serves as a career job board for audit, risk, and compliance professionals. Advertises job openings for heads of department, spanning internal audit, external audit, IT audit, risk, and compliance. Conducts research to monitor the latest industry trends.

127 ■ ControllerAccountingManager.com
URL: http://www.controlleraccountingmanager.com

Description: Lists job and career opportunities for aspiring controller accounting managers. Offers links, job listings, resume resources and more.

128 ■ Cost Accountant Jobs
URL: http://www.costaccountantjobs.org

Description: Serves as a job board for candidates seeking employment opportunities in the field of cost accounting.

129 ■ CPA-Resource.com
URL: http://www.cpa-resource.com

Description: Provides access to CPA education, training, forms, tools, CPA articles, white papers, CPA news, jobs, blogs, and more.

130 ■ CPAdirectory.com
CPAdirect Marketing, Inc.
2001 Grove St.
Wantagh, NY 11793
Ph: (516)409-8357
Fax: (516)977-0643
URL: http://www.cpadirectory.com

Description: Nationwide database of Certified Public Accountants and CPA firms searchable by criteria including name, location and industry focus. Taxpayer, small business and investing information is available for the public and professionals, as well as job postings and career information within the accounting profession.

131 ■ CPAjobs.com
URL: http://www.cpajobs.com

Description: Serves as a job site network that lists several accounting and finance jobs for Certified Public Accountants. Features employment listings for CPAs at all levels of their careers.

132 ■ eFinancialCareers.sg
URL: http://www.efinancialcareers.sg

Description: Provides accounting and finance professionals with career opportunities, news and advice, and a variety of tools to market themselves and manage a new job search.

133 ■ Financial Accountant Jobs
URL: http://www.financialaccountantjobs.org

Description: Connects job seekers and employers in the accounting field. Features a searchable database of employment opportunities for financial accountants.

134 ■ Financial Job Network
PO Box 55431
Sherman Oaks, CA 91403
Ph: (818)905-5272
E-mail: info@fjn.com
URL: http://www.fjn.com

Description: Contains information on international and national employment opportunities for those in the financial job market. Job listings may be submitted, as well as resumes. Main files include: Testimonials, Calendar, Corporate Listings, FJN Clients, more. Free to candidates.

135 ■ FinancialJobBank.com
URL: http://www.financialjobbank.com

Description: Works as a job engine that helps individual to find job openings in the areas of accounting, finance, taxation, banking, and mortgage.

136 ■ FinancialJobs.com
URL: http://www.financialjobs.com

Description: Lists accounting and finance jobs for professionals at all levels of their careers. Features resume writing tips, relocation assistance, networking techniques, salary calculator, and other related links.

137 ■ iHireAccounting
URL: http://www.ihireaccounting.com

Description: Serves as a job site network that lists thousands of accounting jobs and includes exclusive job postings, internet job boards, newspapers and classified ads.

138 ■ Illinois Certified Public Accountant Society Career Center
550 W Jackson, Ste. 900
Chicago, IL 60661-5716
Ph: (312)993-0407
Fax: (312)993-9954
Fr: 800-993-0407
URL: http://www.icpas.org/hc-career-center.aspx?id=2178

Description: Offers job hunting aid to members of the Illinois CPA Society only. Opportunity for non-members to join online. Main files include: Overview of Services, Resume Match, Career Seminars, Career Resources, Free Job Listings, Per Diem Pool, and Career Bibliographies.

139 ■ InternalAuditor.net
URL: http://www.internalauditor.net

Description: Provides access to books, magazines, articles, and education programs. Offers job search options, continuing education resources, lists of industry magazines, as well as links to other similar career job sites.

140 ■ Junior Accountant Jobs
URL: http://www.junioraccountantjobs.org

Description: Provides job seekers access to resources and job opening opportunities in the area of accounting.

141 ■ Locate Accounting Jobs
URL: http://www.locateaccountingjobs.com

Description: Serves as a niche job board that connects accounting job seekers and employers. Allows users to customize their search results by using keywords, job title, skills and location.

142 ■ Night Auditor Jobs
URL: http://www.nightauditorjobs.com

Description: Serves as clearinghouse for professionals seeking a position as a night auditor.

143 ■ SeniorAuditor.net
URL: http://www.seniorauditor.net

Description: Provides access to books, magazines, articles, and continuing education to senior finance professionals. Helps individuals find new jobs, post and search resumes, and access career resources for senior auditors.

144 ■ Society of Financial Examiners
12100 Sunset Hills Rd., Ste. 130
Reston, VA 20190-3221
Ph: (703)234-4140
Fax: 888-436-8686
Fr: 800-787-7633
URL: http://www.sofe.org

Description: Association web site contains classified advertisements for financial examiner positions as well as links to resources about the profession and an opportunity to enroll in an annual career development seminar. Visitors do not have to be members of the association to view job postings.

145 ■ Spherion
2050 Spectrum Blvd.
Fort Lauderdale, FL 33309
Ph: (954)308-7600
Fr: 800-774-3746
E-mail: help@spherion.com
URL: http://www.spherion.com

Description: Recruitment firm specializing in accounting and finance, sales and marketing, interim executives, technology, engineering, retail and human resources.

146 ■ Staff Accountant Jobs
URL: http://www.staffaccountantjobs.org

Description: Serves as an online resource for job seekers looking for staff accountant employment opportunities. Allows users to search by job title, skills and location.

147 ■ StaffAccountantJobs.com
URL: http://www.staffaccountantjobs.com

Description: Serves professionals in the accounting industry. Provides resume writing services as well as job posting and job searching.

148 ■ TaxSites.com
URL: http://www.taxsites.com

Description: Provides listings of associations, companies, job opportunities, news, publications, career search and other resources in the fields of tax, accounting and payroll/HR.

149 ■ WebCPA
URL: http://www.accountingtoday.com

Description: Provides online business news for the tax and accounting community. Features breaking news, in-depth features, editorial analysis, and other web-related resources and services.

TRADESHOWS

150 ■ American Accounting Association Annual Meeting
American Accounting Association
5717 Bessie Dr.
Sarasota, FL 34233-2399
Ph: (941)921-7747
Fax: (941)923-4093
E-mail: info@aaahq.org
URL: http://aaahq.org/index.cfm

Annual. Primary Exhibits: Accounting equipment, supplies, and services.

151 ■ American Association of Attorney-Certified Public Accountants Annual Meeting and Educational Conference
American Association of Attorney-Certified Public Accountants
3921 Old Lee Hwy., Ste. No. 71A
Fairfax, VA 22030
Ph: (703)352-8064
Fax: (703)352-8073

Fr: 888-288-9272
URL: http://netforum.avectra.com/eWeb/StartPage.aspx?Site=AAA-CPA

Annual. Primary Exhibits: Exhibits for persons licensed both as attorneys and CPAs.

152 ■ American Society of Women Accountants Conference
American Society of Women Accountants
1760 Old Meadow Rd., Ste. 500
McLean, VA 22102
Ph: (703)506-3265
Fax: (703)506-3266
Fr: 800-326-2163
E-mail: aswa@aswa.org
URL: http://www.aswa.org

Annual. Primary Exhibits: Exhibits relating to accounting.

153 ■ Annual Accounting Show
Florida Institute of Certified Public Accountants
PO Box 5437
Tallahassee, FL 32314
Ph: (850)224-2727
Fr: 800-342-3197
URL: http://www.ficpa.org/content/home.aspx

Primary Exhibits: Accounting information and services.

154 ■ Association for Accounting Administration National Practice Management Conference
Association for Accounting Administration
136 S. Keowee St.
Dayton, OH 45402
Ph: (937)222-0030
Fax: (937)222-5794
E-mail: aaainfo@cpaadmin.org
URL: http://www.cpaadmin.org

Annual. Primary Exhibits: Exhibits relating to accounting. Dates and Locations: 2012 Jun 19-22; Las Vegas, NV.

155 ■ Association of Insolvency and Restructuring Advisors Conference
Association of Insolvency Accountants
132 W. Main, Ste. 200
Medford, OR 97501
Ph: (541)858-1665
Fax: (541)858-9187

Annual. Primary Exhibits: Exhibits for CPAs and licensed public accountants, attorneys, examiners, trustees and receivers involved in insolvency accounting.

156 ■ CICPAC Education Conference and Annual Meeting
Construction Industry CPAs/Consultants Association
15011 E. Twilight View Dr.
Fountain Hills, AZ 85268
Ph: (480)836-0300
Fax: (480)836-0400
Fr: 800-864-0491
E-mail: jcorcoran@cicpac.com
URL: http://www.cicpac.com

Annual. Primary Exhibits: Exhibits relating to accounting and consulting in the construction industry.

157 ■ Florida Accounting and Business Expo
Florida Institute of Certified Public Accountants
PO Box 5437
Tallahassee, FL 32314
Ph: (850)224-2727
Fr: 800-342-3197
URL: http://www.ficpa.org/content/home.aspx

Primary Exhibits: Accounting equipment, supplies, and services.

158 ■ Institute of Internal Auditors - USA International Conference
Institute of Internal Auditors (Altamonte Springs, Florida)
247 Maitland Ave.
Altamonte Springs, FL 32701-4201
Ph: (407)937-1100
Fax: (407)937-1101
URL: http://www.theiia.org

Annual. Primary Exhibits: Internal auditing equipment, supplies, and services, software, computer related equipment.

159 ■ Institute of Management Accountants Conference
Institute of Management Accountants, Inc.
10 Paragon Dr.
Montvale, NJ 07645-1718
Ph: (201)573-9000
Fax: (201)474-1600
Fr: 800-638-4427
E-mail: ima@imanet.org
URL: http://www.imanet.org

Annual. Primary Exhibits: Management accounting equipment, supplies, and services. Review courses, shipping companies, software companies, and risk management consultants.

160 ■ Insurance Accounting and Systems Association Conference
Insurance Accounting and Systems Association
PO Box 51340
Durham, NC 27717-1340
Ph: (919)489-0991
URL: http://www.iasa.org

Annual. Primary Exhibits: Insurance equipment, supplies, and services. Dates and Locations: 2012 Jun 03-06; San Diego, CA; San Diego Convention Center.

161 ■ Interamerican Accounting Association Biennial Conference
Interamerican Accounting Association
275 Fountainebleau Blvd., Ste. 245
Miami, FL 33172
Ph: (305)225-1991
Fax: (305)225-2011
URL: http://www.contadoresaic.org

Biennial. Primary Exhibits: Exhibits relating to accounting.

162 ■ National Association of Black Accountants Annual Convention
National Association of Black Accountants
7474 Greenway Center Dr., Ste. 1120
Greenbelt, MD 20770
Ph: (301)474-6222
Fax: (301)474-3114
Fr: 888-571-2939
E-mail: customerservice@nabainc.org
URL: http://www.nabainc.org

Annual. Primary Exhibits: Exhibits relating to accounting. Dates and Locations: 2012 Jun 13-16; Phoenix, AZ; Sheraton Phoenix Downtown.

163 ■ National Association of Tax Professionals Conference
National Association of Tax Professionals
720 Association Dr.
PO Box 8002
Appleton, WI 54912-8002
Ph: (920)749-1040
Fax: 800-747-0001
Fr: 800-558-3402
E-mail: natp@natptax.com
URL: http://www.natptax.com

Annual. Primary Exhibits: Computer hardware, tax accounting and planning software, tax research information, tax forms, one-write accounting, financial planning information, office products, business equipment, and tax business solutions. Dates and Locations: 2012 Jul 09-12; Baltimore, MD; Baltimore Marriott Waterfront; 2013 Dates not set; Phoenix, AZ; JW Marriott Desert Ridge Resort & Spa.

164 ■ National CPE Expo
National Association of State Boards of Accountancy
150 4th Ave. N, Ste. 700
Nashville, TN 37219-2417
Ph: (615)880-4200
Fax: (615)880-4290
Fr: (866)616-5090
E-mail: cbtcpa@nasba.org
URL: http://www.nasba.org

Annual. Provides multiple platforms through which attendees may learn from top CPE providers and also gain knowledge and awareness of state boards of accountancy, firms, vendors and issues facing the accounting industry.

165 ■ National Society of Accountants for Cooperatives Tax & Accounting Conference for Cooperatives
National Society of Accountants for Cooperatives
136 S. Keowee St.
Dayton, OH 45402
Ph: (937)222-6707
Fax: (937)222-5794
E-mail: info@nsacoop.org
URL: http://www.nsacoop.org

Annual. Primary Exhibits: Exhibits relating to tax and accounting.

166 ■ National Society of Public Accountants Annual Convention
National Society of Public Accountants
1010 N. Fairfax St.
Alexandria, VA 22314-1574
Ph: (703)549-6400
Fax: (703)549-2984
Fr: 800-966-6679
E-mail: NSA@wizard.net
URL: http://www.nsa.org

Annual. Primary Exhibits: Exhibits related to public accounting.

167 ■ New Jersey Accounting, Business & Technology Show & Conference
Flagg Management, Inc.
353 Lexington Ave.
New York, NY 10016
Ph: (212)286-0333
Fax: (212)286-0086
E-mail: flaggmgmt@msn.com
URL: http://www.flaggmgmt.com

Annual. Primary Exhibits: Information and technology, financial and business services, computer accounting systems, software, tax preparation, accounting, audit, practice management software - windows, and computer and business systems. Banking, insurance, financial and business software. Internet, online systems and middle market software and investment services.

OTHER SOURCES

168 ■ Accountants Global Network (AGN)
2851 S Parker Rd., Ste. 850
Aurora, CO 80014
Ph: (303)743-7880
Fax: (303)743-7660
Fr: 800-782-2272
E-mail: rhood@agn.org
URL: http://www.agn-na.org

Description: Represents and promotes the fields of separate and independent accounting and consulting firms serving business organizations.

169 ■ Accountants Motivational Marketing Organization (AMMO)
1 Country Club Exec. Park
Glen Carbon, IL 62034
Ph: (618)288-8795
E-mail: charles@tzinberg.com
URL: http://accountantsadvmarketing.com

Description: Represents professionals and practitio-ners in marketing and accounting. Fosters excellence in accounting practice and services. Promotes the marketing and sales programs of members.

170 ■ Accreditation Council for Accountancy and Taxation (ACAT)
1010 N Fairfax St.
Alexandria, VA 22314-1574
Fax: (703)549-2512
Fr: 888-289-7763
E-mail: info@acatcredentials.org

Description: Strives to raise professional standards and improve the practices of accountancy and taxation. Identifies persons with demonstrated knowledge of the principles and practices of accountancy and taxation. Ensures the continued professional growth of accredited individuals by setting stringent continuing education requirements. Fosters increased recognition for the profession in the public, private, and educational sectors.

171 ■ American Accounting Association (AAA)
5717 Bessie Dr.
Sarasota, FL 34233-2330
Ph: (941)921-7747
Fax: (941)923-4093
E-mail: info@aaahq.org
URL: http://aaahq.org

Description: Professors and practitioners of accounting. Promotes worldwide excellence in accounting education, research and practice.

172 ■ American Accounts Payable Association (AAPA)
660 N Main Ave., Ste. 200
San Antonio, TX 78205-1217
Ph: (210)630-4373
Fax: (210)630-4410
E-mail: info@americanap.org
URL: http://www.americanap.org

Description: Seeks to uphold the standards of practice in the accounts payable profession. Fosters the professional development of members. Offers comprehensive educational programs for accounts payable professionals.

173 ■ American Institute of Certified Public Accountants (AICPA)
1211 Avenue of the Americas
New York, NY 10036-8775
Ph: (212)596-6200
Fax: (212)596-6213
Fr: 888-777-7077
E-mail: service@aicpa.org
URL: http://www.aicpa.org/Pages/Default.aspx

Description: Professional society of accountants certified by the states and territories. Responsibilities include establishing auditing and reporting standards; influencing the development of financial accounting standards underlying the presentation of U.S. corporate financial statements; preparing and grading the national Uniform CPA Examination for the state licensing bodies. Conducts research and continuing education programs and oversight of practice. Maintains over 100 committees including Accounting Standards, Accounting and Review Services, AICPA Effective Legislation Political Action, Auditing Standards, Taxation, Consulting Services, Professional Ethics, Quality Review, Women and Family Issues, and Information Technology.

174 ■ American Society of Women Accountants (ASWA)
1760 Old Meadow Rd., Ste. 500
McLean, VA 22102
Ph: (703)506-3265
Fax: (703)506-3266
Fr: 800-326-2163
E-mail: aswa@aswa.org
URL: http://www.aswa.org

Description: Professional society of women accountants, educators and others in the field of ac-counting dedicated to the achievement of personal, professional and economic potential. Assists women accountants in their careers and promotes development in the profession. Conducts educational and research programs.

175 ■ American Woman's Society of Certified Public Accountants (AWSCPA)
136 S Keowee St.
Dayton, OH 45402
Ph: (937)222-1872
Fax: (937)222-5794
Fr: 800-297-2721
E-mail: info@awscpa.org
URL: http://www.awscpa.org

Description: Citizens who hold Certified Public Accountant certificates as well as those who have passed the CPA examination but do not have certificates. Works to improve the status of professional women and to make the business community aware of the professional capabilities of the woman CPA. Conducts semiannual statistical survey of members; offers specialized education and research programs.

176 ■ Ascend
120 Wall St., 3rd Fl.
New York, NY 10005
Ph: (212)248-4888
E-mail: info@ascendleadership.org
URL: http://www.ascendleadership.org

Description: Enhances the influence and presence of Pan Asian leaders in the finance, accounting and business related professions. Cultivates the growth of finance, accounting and business knowledge. Advances business development opportunities.

177 ■ Association for Accounting Administration (AAA)
136 S Keowee St.
Dayton, OH 45402
Ph: (937)222-0030
Fax: (937)222-5794
E-mail: aaainfo@cpaadmin.org
URL: http://www.cpaadmin.org

Description: Promotes the profession of accounting administration and office management in accounting firms and corporate accounting departments. Sponsors activities, including consulting and placement services, seminars, salary and trends surveys, and speakers' bureau. Provides a forum for representation and exchange. Offers group purchasing opportunities.

178 ■ Association of Chartered Accountants in the United States (ACAUS)
1050 Winter St., Ste. 1000
Waltham, MA 02451
Ph: (508)395-0224
E-mail: admin@acaus.org
URL: http://www.acaus.org

Description: Chartered accountants from England, Wales, Scotland, Ireland, Canada, Australia, New Zealand and South Africa in commerce and public practice. Represents the interests of chartered accountants; promotes career development and international mobility of professionals. Offers educational and research programs. Maintains speakers' bureau and placement service.

179 ■ Association of Government Accountants (AGA)
2208 Mt. Vernon Ave.
Alexandria, VA 22301-1314
Ph: (703)684-6931
Fax: (703)548-9367
Fr: 800-AGA-7211
E-mail: rvandaniker@agacgfm.org
URL: http://www.agacgfm.org

Description: Professional society of financial managers employed by federal, state, county, and city governments in financial management and administrative positions. Conducts research; offers education and professional development programs.

180 ■ Association of Healthcare Internal Auditors (AHIA)
10200 W 44th Ave., Ste. 304
Wheat Ridge, CO 80033
Ph: (303)327-7546
Fax: (303)422-8894
Fr: 888-ASK-AHIA
E-mail: ahia@ahia.org
URL: http://www.ahia.org

Description: Health care internal auditors and other interested individuals. Promotes cost containment and increased productivity in health care institutions through internal auditing. Serves as a forum for the exchange of experience, ideas, and information among members; provides continuing professional education courses and informs members of developments in health care internal auditing. Offers employment clearinghouse services.

181 ■ Association of Insolvency and Restructuring Advisors (AIRA)
221 Stewart Ave., Ste. 207
Medford, OR 97501
Ph: (541)858-1665
Fax: (541)858-9187
E-mail: aira@aira.org
URL: http://www.airacira.org

Description: Certified and licensed public accountants, attorneys, examiners, trustees and receivers. Seeks to define and develop the accountant's role provided by the Bankruptcy Reform Act of 1978 and to improve accounting skills used in insolvency cases. Promotes the primary role of creditors in insolvency situations and the enforcement of ethical standards of practice. Seeks to develop judicial reporting standards for insolvency and provide technical, analytical and accounting skills necessary in insolvent situations. Works to educate others in the field of the role of the accountant in order to foster better working relationships. Provides information about legislative issues that affect members and testifies before legislative bodies. Offers technical referral service. Administers the Certified Insolvency and Restructuring Advisor (CIRA) program.

182 ■ Association of Latino Professionals in Finance and Accounting (ALPFA)
801 S Grand Ave., Ste. 650
Los Angeles, CA 90017
Ph: (213)243-0004
Fax: (213)243-0006
E-mail: ceo@national.alpfa.org
URL: http://www.alpfa.org

Description: Hispanic certified public accountants from the private and public sectors, accounting firms, universities, and banks. Maintains and promotes professional and moral standards of Hispanics in the accounting field. Assists members in practice development and develops business opportunities for members. Sponsors continuing professional education seminars; provides employment services.

183 ■ BKR International (BKR)
19 Fulton St., Ste. 306
New York, NY 10038
Ph: (212)964-2115
Fax: (212)964-2133
Fr: 800-BKR-INTL
E-mail: bkr@bkr.com
URL: http://www.bkr.com

Description: Accounting firms in the U.S. and abroad. Seeks to create an international group of competent professional firms, which will provide full services in major markets of the world and enable member firms to send and receive referrals. Helps reduce operating costs of member firms by: developing consolidated purchasing arrangements for services and supplies at the lowest possible cost; developing recruiting programs, marketing materials, and advertising to reduce the collective recruiting effort of group members; expanding the group to reduce the burden on individual member firms and increase their potential scope of services. Compiles statistics to provide member firms with data helpful to

sound management decisions. Organizes clinical and administrative peer reviews to insure quality and provide management with professional counsel. Develops forms, procedures, and manuals to provide guidance and accommodate the needs of partners. Conducts 12 continuing education programs per year in all areas of expertise.

184 ■ CPA Associates International (CPAAI)
Meadows Office Complex
301 Rte. 17 N
Rutherford, NJ 07070
Ph: (201)804-8686
Fax: (201)804-9222
E-mail: homeoffice@cpaai.com
URL: http://www.cpaai.com

Description: Independent firms of Certified Public Accountants (CPAs) offering professional accounting, auditing, tax, and management advisory services. Fosters exchange of ideas and information among members; works to improve the profitability and practice of the accounting profession.

185 ■ Foundation for Accounting Education (FAE)
PO Box 10490
Uniondale, NY 11555-0490
Ph: (212)719-8383
Fax: (866)495-1354
Fr: 800-537-3635
E-mail: wruppel@markspaneth.com
URL: http://www.nysscpa.org/page/continuing-education

Description: Purpose: Conducts educational and technical programs, seminars, workshops, and conferences for CPAs in private practice and industry.

186 ■ Hospitality Financial and Technology Professionals (HFTP)
11709 Boulder Ln., Ste. 110
Austin, TX 78726
Ph: (512)249-5333
Fax: (512)249-1533
Fr: 800-646-4387
E-mail: membership@hftp.org
URL: http://www.hftp.org

Description: Accountants, financial officers and MIS managers in 50 countries working in hotels, resorts, casinos, restaurants, and clubs. Develops uniform system of accounts. Conducts education, training, and certification programs; offers placement service; maintains hall of fame.

187 ■ Information Systems Audit and Control Association and Foundation (ISACA)
3701 Algonquin Rd., Ste. 1010
Rolling Meadows, IL 60008
Ph: (847)253-1545
Fax: (847)253-1443
E-mail: membership@isaca.org
URL: http://www.isaca.org/Pages/default.aspx

Description: Acts as a harmonizing source for IT control practices and standards all over the world. Serves its members and other constituencies by providing education, research (through its affiliated Foundation), a professional certification, conferences and publications.

188 ■ Institute of Internal Auditors (IIA)
247 Maitland Ave.
Altamonte Springs, FL 32701-4907
Ph: (407)937-1100
Fax: (407)937-1101
E-mail: custserv@theiia.org
URL: http://www.theiia.org

Description: Members in internal auditing, governance, internal control, IT audit, education and security. Provides comprehensive professional, educational and development opportunities; standards and other professional practice guidance; and certification programs.

189 ■ Institute of Management Accountants (IMA)
10 Paragon Dr., Ste. 1
Montvale, NJ 07645-1774
Ph: (201)573-9000
Fax: (201)474-1600
Fr: 800-638-4427
E-mail: ima@imanet.org
URL: http://www.imanet.org

Description: Management accountants in industry, public accounting, government, and academia; other persons interested in internal and management uses of accounting. Conducts research on accounting methods and procedures and the management purposes served. Established Institute of Certified Management Accountants to implement and administer examinations for the Certified Management Accountant (CMA) program and the Certified in Financial Management (CFM) program. Annually presents chapter medals for competition, manuscripts and for the highest scores on the CMA Examination. Offers continuing education programs comprising courses, conferences, and a self-study program in management accounting areas. Offers ethics counseling services for members by telephone. Sponsors the Foundation for Applied Research.

190 ■ Interamerican Accounting Association (IAA)
275 Fountainebleau Blvd., Ste. 245
Miami, FL 33172
Ph: (305)225-1991
Fax: (305)225-2011
E-mail: oficina@contadoresaic.org
URL: http://www.contadores-aic.org

Description: National associations representing 1,100,000 accountants in the Americas. Objectives are to maintain high technical and ethical standards for the accounting profession; further accounting as a scientific discipline by fostering contacts between members and institutions of higher learning; provide members with information on current accounting practices and concepts; encourage members to establish ties with accounting groups worldwide; assure that professional services rendered by members contribute to the social and economic development of their community. Operates speakers' bureau.

191 ■ International Accounts Payable Professionals (IAPP)
PO Box 590373
Orlando, FL 32859-0373
Ph: (407)351-3322
Fax: (407)895-5031
Fr: 877-885-IAPP
E-mail: services@iappnet.org
URL: http://www.iappnet.org

Description: Promotes accounts payable as a professional discipline. Provides education on procedures and technologies that impact the accounts payable profession. Supports local, regional, national, and global networking among members.

192 ■ International Federation of Accountants (IFAC)
545 5th Ave., 14th Fl.
New York, NY 10017
Ph: (212)286-9344
Fax: (212)286-9570
E-mail: communications@ifac.org
URL: http://www.ifac.org

Description: Accounting bodies recognized by law or general consensus representing over 1,000,000 individuals in 78 countries. Seeks to achieve international technical, ethical and educational guidelines and standards for the accountancy profession. Fosters cooperation among members and encourages development of regional groups with similar goals.

193 ■ International Society of Filipinos in Finance and Accounting (ISFFA)
801 S Grand Ave., Ste. 400
Los Angeles, CA 90017

Fr: 800-375-2689
E-mail: csoneil@gmail.com
URL: http://www.isyfa.org

Description: Aims to assist, educate, train and mentor emerging professionals, both domestically as well as globally. Promotes a socially friendly and responsive environment among Filipinos, minority groups and Americans in their respective communities. Assists in providing professional continuing education and mentoring when needed, not only to the professional, but also to the community at large.

194 ■ Leading Edge Alliance (LEA)
621 Cedar St.
St. Charles, IL 60174
Ph: (630)513-9814
Fax: (630)524-9014
URL: http://www.leadingedgealliance.com

Description: Represents independently owned accounting and consulting firms. Provides business development, professional training and education, and peer-to-peer networking opportunities. Offers business advisory expertise and experience and conducts accounting, tax and consulting services.

195 ■ Media Financial Management Association (MFM)
550 W Frontage Rd., Ste. 3600
Northfield, IL 60093
Ph: (847)716-7000
Fax: (847)716-7004
E-mail: info@mediafinance.org
URL: http://www.mediafinance.org

Description: Controllers, chief accountants, auditors, business managers, treasurers, secretaries and related newspaper executives, educators, and public accountants. Conducts research projects on accounting methods and procedures for newspapers. Offers placement service; maintains speakers' bureau. Produces conferences and seminars.

196 ■ Moore Stephens North America (MSNA)
Park 80 West
Plaza II, Ste. 200
Saddle Brook, NJ 07663
Ph: (201)291-2660
Fax: (201)368-1944
E-mail: theteam@msnainc.org
URL: http://www.msnainc.com

Description: North American public accounting and consulting firms. Aids certified public accounting firms in increasing, expanding, and diversifying their practices. Capitalizes on diversity of resources resident throughout the network to build a stronger revenue base for all members. Sponsors training programs in areas such as industry niche development, service niche development tax, staff, and computer auditing; conducts tax and management seminars. Compiles statistics. Offers networking forums, marketing assistance, and technology consulting to member firms.

197 ■ National Association of Black Accountants (NABA)
7474 Greenway Center Dr., Ste. 1120
Greenbelt, MD 20770
Ph: (301)474-6222
Fax: (301)474-3114
Fr: 888-571-2939
E-mail: customerservice@nabainc.org
URL: http://www.nabainc.org

Description: Minority students and professionals currently working, or interested in the fields of accounting, finance, technology, consulting or general business. Seeks, promotes, develops, and represents the interests of current and future minority business professionals.

198 ■ National Association of Certified Public Bookkeepers (NACPB)
162 W Baer Creek Dr.
Kaysville, UT 84037
Fr: (866)444-9989
E-mail: info@nacpb.org
URL: http://www.nacpb.org

Description: Aims to protect the public interest by ensuring that only qualified individuals provide public bookkeeping services. Fosters the professional development of public bookkeepers. Offers certification programs in bookkeeping.

199 ■ National Association of Tax Professionals (NATP)
PO Box 8002
Appleton, WI 54914-8002
Fr: 800-558-3402
E-mail: natp@natptax.com
URL: http://www.natptax.com

Description: Serves professionals who work in all areas of tax practice, including individual practitioners, enrolled agents, certified public accountants, accountants, attorneys and certified financial planners.

200 ■ National Society of Accountants (NSA)
1010 N Fairfax St.
Alexandria, VA 22314
Ph: (703)549-6400
Fax: (703)549-2984
Fr: 800-966-6679
E-mail: members@nsacct.org
URL: http://www.nsacct.org

Description: Professional organization and its affiliates represent 30,000 members who provide auditing, accounting, tax preparation, financial and estate planning, and management services to approximately 19 million individuals and business clients. Most members are sole practitioners or partners in small to mid-size accounting firms.

201 ■ National Society of Accountants for Cooperatives (NSAC)
136 S Keowee St.
Dayton, OH 45402
Ph: (937)222-6707

Fax: (937)222-5794
E-mail: info@nsacoop.org
URL: http://www.nsacoop.org

Description: Employees of cooperatives, certified public accountants, auditors, chief financial officers, attorneys and bankers. Unites persons performing accounting, auditing, financial and legal services for cooperative and non-profit associations. Holds technical sessions annually. Compiles statistics.

202 ■ PKF North American Network (PFK NA)
1745 N Brown Rd., Ste. 350
Lawrenceville, GA 30043
Ph: (770)279-4560
Fax: (770)279-4566
E-mail: tsnyder@pkfnan.org
URL: http://www.pkfna.org

Description: Independent certified public accounting firms practicing on a regional or local basis. Objectives are to: strengthen accounting practices; increase competency and quality of service; provide a practice management program; maintain technical competence in accounting principles and auditing standards; make available a reservoir of specialists who are immediately accessible to members; provide for the sharing of skills, knowledge and experience. Offers technical, marketing, and public relations support; promotes continuing professional education; facilitates networking. Conducts 4 staff development, 2 tax training, and 3 manager/partner training courses per year; operates committees and task forces.

203 ■ Professional Accounting Society of America (PASA)
986 Colina Vista
Ventura, CA 93003
E-mail: info@thepasa.org
URL: http://www.thepasa.org

Description: Represents entry-level and mid-level associates working at accounting firms across America. Addresses the issues that affect entry-level and mid-level accounting professionals. Serves as a voice for everyone in the public accounting industry.

204 ■ Professional Association of Small Business Accountants (PASBA)
6405 Metcalf Ave., Ste. 503
Shawnee Mission, KS 66202
Fax: (913)432-1812
Fr: (866)296-0001
E-mail: director@pasba.org
URL: http://www.smallbizaccountants.com

Description: Represents certified public accountants, public accountants, and enrolled agents who provide accounting services to small businesses throughout the United States. Aims to improve the business management and marketing skills of its members. Strives to uphold and maintain high standards of good accounting practices.

Actors, Directors, and Producers

Sources of Help-Wanted Ads

205 ■ *ArtSEARCH*
Theatre Communications Group
520 8th Ave., 24th Fl.
New York, NY 10018-4156
Ph: (212)609-5900
Fax: (212)609-5901
E-mail: tcg@tcg.org
URL: http://www.tcg.org
Description: Biweekly. Publishes classified listings for job opportunities in the arts, especially theatre, dance, music, and educational institutions. Listings include opportunities in administration, artistic, education, production, and career development.

206 ■ *AV Video & Multimedia Producer*
Access Intelligence L.L.C.
4 Choke Cherry Rd., 2nd Fl.
Rockville, MD 20850-4024
Ph: (301)354-2000
Fax: (301)309-3847
Fr: 800-777-5006
URL: http://www.accessintel.com/

Monthly. Magazine covering audio-visual, video and multimedia production, presentation, people, technology and techniques.

207 ■ *Back Stage West*
Nielsen Business Media
770 Broadway
New York, NY 10003-9595
URL: http://www.backstage.com/bso/index.jsp

Weekly. $195.00/year for individuals; $99.00/year for individuals, 6 months; $12.95/year for individuals, monthly. Trade publication covering the entertainment industry.

208 ■ *Broadcasting & Cable*
Reed Business Information (New York, New York)
360 Park Ave. S
New York, NY 10010
Ph: (646)746-6400
Fax: (646)746-7431
Fr: 800-446-6551
URL: http://www.reedbusiness.com

$199.00/year for individuals; $249.99/year for Canada; $360.99/year for other countries. News magazine covering The Fifth Estate (radio, TV, cable, and satellite), and the regulatory commissions involved.

209 ■ *Contemporary Theatre Review*
Routledge Journals
270 Madison Ave.
New York, NY 10016-0601
Ph: (212)216-7800
Fax: (212)563-2269
URL: http://www.tandf.co.uk/journals/titles/
10486801.asp

Quarterly. $563.00/year for institutions, print + online; $507.00/year for institutions, online only; $63.00/year for individuals, print only; $773.00/year for institutions, print and online; $696.00/year for institutions, online only; $103.00/year for individuals, print only. Journal focusing on wide variety of playwrights to theatres.

210 ■ *Daily Variety*
Reed Business Information
360 Park Ave. S
New York, NY 10010-1710
Ph: (646)746-7764
Fax: (646)746-7583
URL: http://www.reedbusiness.com/
index.asp?layout=theListProfile&

Daily. $329.99/year for individuals. Global entertainment newspaper (tabloid).

211 ■ *Entertainment Employment Journal*
Studiolot Publishing
5632 Van Nuys Blvd., Ste. 320
Van Nuys, CA 91401-4600
Ph: (818)776-2800
Fr: 800-640-4836
E-mail: support@eejonline.com
URL: http://www.eej.com

Semimonthly. $109.00/year for individuals; $67.00/year for individuals, 6 months; $39.00/year for individuals, 3 months. Trade magazine covering business and technical careers in broadcast, electronic media, and motion pictures.

212 ■ *Filmmaker*
IFP
68 Jay St., Rm. 425
Brooklyn, NY 11201
Ph: (212)465-8200
Fax: (212)465-8525
URL: http://www.filmmakermagazine.com/

Quarterly. $18.00/year for individuals; $30.00/year for two years. Magazine covering the craft and business of filmmaking.

213 ■ *Live Design*
Penton Media Inc.
9800 Metcalf Ave.
Overland Park, KS 66212
Ph: (913)341-1300
Fax: (913)967-1898
URL: http://livedesignonline.com

The business of entertainment technology and design.

214 ■ *Millimeter*
NewBay Media, LLC
28 E 28th St., 12th Fl.
New York, NY 10016
Ph: (212)378-0400
Fax: (917)281-4704
URL: http://digitalcontentproducer.com/mil/

Monthly. Magazine focusing on the process of motion picture and television production.

215 ■ *Music and Media*
Nielsen Business Media
770 Broadway
New York, NY 10003-9595
URL: http://www.vnubusinessmedia.com

Weekly. Publication covering the music and entertainment industries.

216 ■ *Post*
Post Pro Publishing Inc.
One Park Ave.
New York, NY 10016
Ph: (212)951-6600
Fax: (212)951-6793
URL: http://www.postmagazine.com/

Monthly. Magazine serving the field of television, film, video production and post-production.

217 ■ *Producers Masterguide*
Producers Masterguide
60 E 8th St., 34th Fl.
New York, NY 10003-6514
Ph: (212)777-4002
Fax: (212)777-4101
URL: http://www.producers.masterguide.com/
cover.html

Annual. $185.00/year for U.S.; $175.00/year for Canada; $205.00/year for other countries. An international film and TV production directory and guide for the professional motion picture, broadcast television, feature film, TV commercial, cable/satellite, digital and videotape industries in the U.S., Canada, the UK, the Caribbean Islands, Mexico, Australia, New Zealand, Europe, Israel, Morocco, the Far East, and South America.

218 ■ *Ross Reports Television and Film*
Nielsen Business Media
770 Broadway
New York, NY 10003-9595
URL: http://www.backstage.com

Bimonthly. $65.00/year for individuals; $10.00/year for individuals. Trade publication covering talent agents and casting directors in New York and Los Angeles, as well as television and film production. Special national issue of agents and casting directors is published annually. Sister publication to Back Stage, Back Stage West.

219 ■ *SMPTE Motion Imaging Journal*
Society of Motion Picture and Television Engineers
3 Barker Ave., 5th Fl.
White Plains, NY 10601
Ph: (914)761-1100
Fax: (914)761-3115
URL: http://www.smpte.org

Monthly. $130.00/year for individuals. Peer-reviewed journal containing articles pertaining to new developments in motion picture and television technology;

standards and recommended practices; general news of the industry.

220 ■ TelevisionWeek
Crain Communications Inc. (Detroit, Michigan)
1155 Gratiot Ave.
Detroit, MI 48207-2997
Ph: (313)446-6000
Fax: (313)567-7681
URL: http://www.tvweek.com/

Weekly. $119.00/year for individuals; $171.00/year for Canada, incl. GST; $309.00/year for other countries, airmail. Newspaper covering management, programming, cable and trends in the television and the media industry.

221 ■ Variety
Reed Business Information
360 Park Ave. S
New York, NY 10010-1710
Ph: (646)746-7764
Fax: (646)746-7583
URL: http://www.reedbusiness.com/us.html

Weekly. $259.00/year for individuals; $25.00/year for individuals, monthly. Newspaper (tabloid) reporting on theatre, television, radio, music, records, and movies.

Employer Directories and Networking Lists

222 ■ 501 Movie Directors
Barron's Educational Series Inc.
250 Wireless Blvd.
Hauppauge, NY 11788-3924
Ph: (631)434-3311
Fax: (631)434-3723
Fr: 800-645-3476
URL: http://barronseduc.com/0764160222.html

Latest edition 2008. $29.99 for individuals; $26.99 for individuals. Covers: 501 film directors.

223 ■ Academy Players Directory
Academy of Motion Picture Arts & Sciences
8949 Wilshire Blvd.
Beverly Hills, CA 90211
Ph: (310)247-3000
Fax: (310)859-9619
URL: http://www.playersdirectory.com

Semiannual, January and July. $95.33 for individuals. Covers: Over 18,000 members of Screen Actors Guild (SAG), American Federation of Television and Radio Artists (AFTRA), and Actors Equity Association (AEA). All listings are paid. Entries include: Name of actor, name of agency and/or personal manager with phone; photograph, contact number. Arrangement: Classified by role type in 4 sections: Part I, Academy Award Nominee and Winners, Leading women/ Ingenues; Part II, Academy Award Nominees and Winners, Leading men/Younger male leads; Part III, Characters/Comedy actors and actresses; Part IV, Children/Master index. Indexes: General, ethnic/ disabled.

224 ■ Billboard's International Talent and Touring Guide
Crown Publishing Group
1745 Broadway
New York, NY 10019
Ph: (212)782-9000
URL: http://www.billboard.biz/bbbiz/directories/ index.jsp

Annual, Latest edition 2010. $149.00 for individuals. Covers: Over 30,000 artists, managers and agents from 69 countries worldwide, including the USA. and Canada; tour facilities and services; venues; entertainers, booking agents, hotels, and others in the entertainment industry; international coverage. Entries include: Company name, address, phone, fax, names and titles of key personnel. Arrangement:

Classified by line of business; venues are then geographical. Indexes: Product/service.

225 ■ Broadcasting & Cable Yearbook
R.R. Bowker L.L.C.
630 Central Ave.
New Providence, NJ 07974
Ph: (908)286-1090
Fr: 888-269-5372
URL: http://www.bowker.com

Annual, latest edition 2010. $395.00 for individuals. Covers: Over 17,000 television and radio stations in the United States, its territories, and Canada; cable MSOs and their individual systems; television and radio networks, broadcast and cable group owners, station representatives, satellite networks and services, film companies, advertising agencies, government agencies, trade associations, schools, and suppliers of professional and technical services, including books, serials, and videos; communications lawyers. Entries include: Company name, address, phone, fax, names of executives. Station listings include broadcast power, other operating details. Arrangement: Stations and systems are geographical, others are alphabetical. Indexes: Alphabetical.

226 ■ Career Opportunities in the Film Industry
Facts On File Inc.
132 W 31st St., 17th Fl.
New York, NY 10001
Ph: (212)967-8800
Fax: 800-678-3633
Fr: 800-322-8755
URL: http://factsonfile.infobasepublishing.com

Latest edition 2nd, 2009. $49.50 for individuals. Covers: More than 80 jobs in the field, from the high-profile positions of director, producer, screenwriter, and actor to the all-important behind-the-scenes positions such as casting director, gaffer, and production designer.

227 ■ Career Opportunities in Theater and the Performing Arts
Facts On File Inc.
132 W 31st St., 17th Fl.
New York, NY 10001
Ph: (212)967-8800
Fax: 800-678-3633
Fr: 800-322-8755
URL: http://www.infobasepublishing.com

Latest edition 3rd; Published April, 2006. Covers: 80 careers, from acting to designing to dance therapy.

228 ■ Careers in Focus—Performing Arts
Facts On File Inc.
132 W 31st St., 17th Fl.
New York, NY 10001
Ph: (212)967-8800
Fax: 800-678-3633
Fr: 800-322-8755
URL: http://www.infobasepublishing.com

Latest edition 2nd; Published September, 2006. Covers: An overview of performing arts, followed by a selection of jobs profiled in detail, including the nature of the job, earnings, prospects for employment, what kind of training and skills it requires, and sources for further information.

229 ■ Contemporary Theatre, Film, and Television
Gale
PO Box 6904
Florence, KY 41022-6904
Fr: 800-354-9706
URL: http://www.gale.cengage.com

Bimonthly, Latest edition December, 2011. $293.00 for individuals. Covers: 116 volumes, more than 20,000 leading and up-and-coming performers, directors, writers, producers, designers, managers, choreographers, technicians, composers, executives, and dancers in the United States, Canada, Great Britain and the world. Each volume includes updated biographies for people listed in previous volumes and

in "Who's Who in the Theatre," which this series has superseded. Entries include: Name, agent and/or office addresses, personal and career data; stage, film, and television credits; writings, awards, other information. Arrangement: Alphabetical. Indexes: Cumulative name index also covers entries in "Who's Who in the Theatre" editions 1-17 and in "Who Was Who in the Theatre.".

230 ■ Directors Guild of America—Directory of Members
Directors Guild of America Inc.
7920 Sunset Blvd.
Los Angeles, CA 90046
Ph: (310)289-2000
Fax: (310)289-2029
Fr: 800-421-4173
URL: http://www.dga.org

Annual, February; Latest edition 2009. $25.00. Covers: Over 11,000 motion picture and television directors and their assistants providing films and tapes for entertainment, commercial, industrial, and other non-entertainment fields; international coverage. Entries include: DGA member name; contact or representative address, phone; specialty; brief description of experience and credits. Arrangement: Alphabetical. Indexes: Geographical, women and minority members, agents.

231 ■ Discovering Careers for Your Future—Performing Arts
Facts On File Inc.
132 W 31st St., 17th Fl.
New York, NY 10001
Ph: (212)967-8800
Fax: 800-678-3633
Fr: 800-322-8755
URL: http://factsonfile.infobasepublishing.com

Latest edition 2nd, 2005. $21.95 for individuals. Covers: Actors, comedians, disc jockeys, film and television directors, orchestra conductors, songwriters, stage production technicians, and more; links career education to curriculum, helping children investigate the subjects they are interested in, and the careers those subjects might lead to.

232 ■ The Dramatists Guild Resource Directory
The Dramatists Guild of America Inc.
1501 Broadway, Ste. 701
New York, NY 10036-3988
Ph: (212)398-9366
Fax: (212)944-0420
URL: http://www.dramatistsguild.com/pub_ directory.aspx

Annual, Latest edition 2009. Publication includes: Lists of Broadway and off-Broadway producers; theater and producing organizations; agents; regional theaters; sources of grants, fellowships, residencies; conferences and festivals; playwriting contests; and sources of financial assistance. Entries include: For producers—Name, address, credits, types of plays accepted for consideration. For groups—Name, address, contact name, type of material accepted for consideration, future commitment, hiring criteria, response time. For agents—Name, address. For theaters—Theater name, address, contact name, submission procedure, types of plays accepted for consideration, maximum cast, limitations, equity contract, opportunities, response time. For grants, fellowships, residencies, financial assistance, conferences, and festivals—Name, address, contact name, description, eligibility and application requirements, deadline. For play contests—Name, address, prize, deadline, description. Arrangement: Contests are by deadline; others are classified.

233 ■ Fashion & Print Directory
Peter Glenn Publications
235 SE 5th Ave., Ste. R
Delray Beach, FL 33483
Ph: (561)404-4685
Fax: (561)279-4672

Fr: 888-332-6700
URL: http://www.pgdirect.com/fpintro.asp

Annual, November; latest edition 47th. $39.95 for individuals. Covers: Advertising agencies, PR firms, marketing companies, 1,000 client brand companies and related services in the U.S. and Canada. Includes photographers, marketing agency, suppliers, sources of props and rentals, fashion houses, beauty services, locations. Entries include: Company name, address, phone; paid listings numbering 5,000 include description of products or services, key personnel. Arrangement: Classified by line of business.

234 ■ Film Directors

Hollywood Creative Directory and Lone Eagle Publishing
5700 Wilshire Blvd., Ste. 500
Los Angeles, CA 90036-4396
Ph: (323)525-2369
Fax: (323)525-2398
Fr: 800-815-0503
URL: http://www.hcdonline.com

Annual, latest edition 16. Covers: over 5,000 living and primarily active theatrical and television film directors who have made films with running times of one hour or more; over 350 deceased directors; directors of videotaped television dramas are not included. Entries include: Name, date and place of birth, address and phone (or that of agent), and chronological list of films that meet stated criteria. Over 42,000 film credits. Arrangement: Alphabetical. Indexes: Director, agent/manager, film title, foreign director name, academy awards and nominations by year, guilds.

235 ■ The Film & TV Music Guide

The Music Business Registry Inc.
7510 Sunset Blvd., No. 1041
Los Angeles, CA 90046-3400
Ph: (818)781-1974
Fax: (740)587-3916
Fr: 800-377-7411
URL: http://musicregistry.com/frame.html

Latest edition 12th. $99.00 for single issue; $250.00 for individuals. List of all movie studios, TV networks and independent production company music departments, record and publishing film/TV departments, music supervisors in film/TV, film composers, managers and agents, music clearance companies, and music editors.

236 ■ HOLA Pages

The Hispanic Organization of Latin Actors
107 Suffolk St., Ste. 302
New York, NY 10002
Ph: (212)253-1015
Fax: (212)253-9651
URL: http://www.hellohola.org

Biennial, January of odd years. Covers: About 500 Hispanic performing artists from New York, New Jersey, and California; all listings are paid. Entries include: Name, photograph, profession(s), phone number(s). Persons listed are contacted through the publisher. Arrangement: Alphabetical.

237 ■ Hollywood Representation Directory

Nielsen Business Media
770 Broadway
New York, NY 10003-9595
URL: http://www.hcdonline.com

Latest edition 38th. $64.95 for individuals. Covers: Over 2,000 agencies and management companies, and over 10,000 agents and personal managers within those companies. Majority of listings are located in Los Angeles and New York. Entries include: company name, staff names and titles, address, phone, fax, e-mail address, web site address, company type, types of clients, and guild and organization affiliations. Arrangement: Alphabetical by company. Indexes: Client category, affiliation, individual names.

238 ■ International Dictionary of Films and Filmmakers

St. James Press
PO Box 9187
Farmington Hills, MI 48333-9187
Ph: (248)699-4253
Fax: (248)699-8035
Fr: 800-877-4253
URL: http://www.gale.cengage.com

Every five years, Latest edition 2004. $238.00 for individuals. Covers: In an illustrated multi-volume set, approximately 500 directors and filmmakers, 650 actors and actresses, and 520 writers and production artists (in volumes 2, 3, and 4 respectively). Both historical and contemporary artists are listed, chosen on the basis of international importance in film history. Entries include: Name; personal, education and career data; address, when available; filmography; bibliography of monographs and articles on and by the subject, critical essay, illustrations. Volume 1 contains entries describing approximately 680 significant films. Arrangement: Alphabetical in each volume. Indexes: Film title and nationality indexes in volumes 2, 3, and 4; geographic and personal name indexes in volume 1.

239 ■ International Motion Picture Almanac

Quigley Publishing Company Inc.
64 Wintergreen Ln.
Groton, MA 01450
Ph: (860)228-0247
Fax: (860)228-0157
Fr: 800-231-8239
URL: http://quigleypublishing.com/

Annual, Latest edition 2011. $235.00 for individuals; $400.00. Covers: Motion picture producing companies, firms serving the industry, equipment manufacturers, casting agencies, literary agencies, advertising and publicity representatives, motion picture theater circuits, buying and booking agencies, independent theaters, international film festivals, associations, theatre equipment supply companies. Entries include: Generally, company name, address, phone. For manufacturers—Products or service provided, name of contact. For producing companies—Additional details. For theaters—Name of owner, screen size. Companion volume is the "International Television and Video Almanac". Arrangement: Classified by service or activity.

240 ■ International Television and Video Almanac

Quigley Publishing Company Inc.
64 Wintergreen Ln.
Groton, MA 01450-4129
Ph: (978)448-0272
Fax: (978)448-9325
Fr: 800-231-8239
URL: http://quigleypublishing.com/

Annual, January; latest edition 2011. $235.00 for individuals. Covers: "Who's Who in Motion Pictures and Television and Home Video," television networks, major program producers, major group station owners, cable television companies, distributors, firms serving the television and home video industry, equipment manufacturers, casting agencies, literary agencies, advertising and publicity representatives, television stations, associations, list of feature films produced for television; statistics, industry's year in review, award winners, satellite and wireless cable provider, primetime programming, video producers, distributors, wholesalers. Entries include: Generally, company name, address, phone; manufacturer and service listings may include description of products and services and name of contact; producing, distributing, and station listings include additional detail, and contacts for cable and broadcast networks. Arrangement: Classified by service or activity. Indexes: Full.

241 ■ National Directory of Arts Internships

National Network for Artist Placement
935 West Ave. 37
Los Angeles, CA 90065

Ph: (323)222-4035
E-mail: info@artistplacement.com
URL: http://www.artistplacement.com

Biennial, odd years; latest edition 11th. $95.00 for individuals. Covers: Over 5,000 internship opportunities in dance, music, theater, art, design, film, and video & over 1,250 host organizations Entries include: Name of sponsoring organization, address, name of contact; description of positions available, eligibility requirements, stipend or salary (if any), application procedures. Arrangement: Classified by discipline, then geographical.

242 ■ New England Theatre Conference—Resource Directory

New England Theatre Conference Inc.
215 Knob Hill Dr.
Hamden, CT 06518-2431
Ph: (617)851-8535
Fax: (203)288-5938
URL: http://www.netconline.org

Annual, January. Covers: 800 individuals and 100 groups. Entries include: For individuals—Name, address, telephone, e-mail and fax indicating type or level of theater activity, theater and school affiliation. For groups—Name, address; telephone, box office, fax, e-mail, names and addresses of delegates. Arrangement: Alphabetical. Indexes: Members by Division.

243 ■ Regional Theater Directory

American Theatre Works Inc.
2349 West Rd.
PO Box 159
Dorset, VT 05251
Ph: (802)867-9333
Fax: (802)867-2297
URL: http://www.theatredirectories.com

Annual, May. $38.50 for individuals. Covers: Regional theater companies and dinner theatres with employment opportunities in acting, design, production, and management. Entries include: Company name, address, phone, name and title of contact; type of company, activities, and size of house; whether union affiliated, whether nonprofit or commercial; year established; hiring procedure and number of positions hired annually, season; description of stage; internships, description of artistic policy and audience. Arrangement: Geographical. Indexes: Company name, type of plays produced.

244 ■ Summer Theater Directory

American Theatre Works Inc.
2349 West Rd.
PO Box 159
Dorset, VT 05251
Ph: (802)867-9333
Fax: (802)867-2297
URL: http://www.theatredirectories.com

Annual, Latest edition 2009. $38.50 for individuals. Covers: Summer theater companies, theme parks and cruise lines that offer employment opportunities in acting, design, production, and management; summer theater training programs. Entries include: Company name, address, phone, name and title of contact; type of company, activities and size of house; whether union affiliated, whether nonprofit or commercial; year established; hiring procedure and number of positions hired annually, season; description of stage; internships; description of company's artistic goals and audience. Arrangement: Geographical. Indexes: Company name.

245 ■ Vault Guide to the Top Media & Entertainment Employers

Vault.com Inc.
150 W 22nd St., 5th Fl.
New York, NY 10011
Ph: (212)366-4212
Fax: (212)366-6117
Fr: 888-562-8285
URL: http://www.vault.com

Latest edition May, 2008. $19.95 for individuals; $19.95 for members. Covers: Top media and entertainment employers in U.S. Entries include: Company name, contact person, address, location, statistics and email.

246 ■ Writers Guide to Hollywood Producers
Fade in Magazine
PO Box 2699
Beverly Hills, CA 90213
Ph: (310)275-0287
Fr: 800-646-3896
URL: http://fadeinonline.com

$59.95 for individuals. Covers: Hollywood producers. Entries include: Name, contact information, and Web site.

HANDBOOKS AND MANUALS

247 ■ Acting A to Z: The Young Person's Guide to a Stage or Screen Career
Watson-Guptill Publications
1745 Broadway
New York, NY 10019
Ph: (212)782-9000
Fax: (212)572-6066
E-mail: info@watsonguptill.com
URL: http://www.randomhouse.com

Katherine Mayfield. 2nd Revised edition, 2007. $16.95 (paper). Author explains exactly what it's like to be an actor, including what kind of training the young person will need, comparisons of the different types of acting, how to find work, how to prepare for an audition, and what to expect during rehearsal. 192 pages.

248 ■ Acting Professionally: Raw Facts about Careers in Acting
McGraw-Hill Companies
PO Box 182604
Columbus, OH 43272
Fax: (614)759-3749
Fr: 877-883-5524
E-mail: customer.service@mcgraw-hill.com
URL: http://highered.mcgraw-hill.com/sites/00725625/

Robert Cohen. 6th edition, 2007. $31.25 (paper). 224 pages. Includes bibliography.

249 ■ The Actor's Other Career Book: Using Your Chops to Survive and Thrive
Allworth Press
307 W 36th St., 11th Fl.
New York, NY 10018
Ph: (212)643-6816
Fax: (212)643-6819
URL: http://www.allworth.com

Lisa Mulcahy. 2006. $19.95. Fifty various positions for actors that are available in cruise ships, trade shows, retail stores, advertising agencies, corporate settings, education, social outreach, tourist attractions, physical fitness, and other areas are outlined.

250 ■ Careers in Focus: Film
Ferguson Publishing
132 W 31st St., 17th Fl.
New York, NY 10001
Fr: 800-322-8755
E-mail: custserv@factsonfile.com
URL: http://factsonfile.infobasepublishing.com

2006. $32.95. 192 pages. Features 19 jobs in the film industry. Contains photographs, indexes, resources and interviews.

251 ■ Careers for the Stagestruck and Other Dramatic Types
The McGraw-Hill Companies
PO Box 182604
Columbus, OH 43272
Fax: (614)759-3749
Fr: 877-883-5524
E-mail: customer.service@mcgraw-hill.com
URL: http://www.mhprofessional.com/product.php?isbn=007144243X

Lucia Mauro. Second edition, 2004. $13.95 (paper). 160 pages. Includes bibliographical references.

252 ■ Creative Careers: Paths for Aspiring Actors, Artists, Dancers, Musicians and Writers
SuperCollege, LLC
3286 Oak Ct.
Belmont, CA 94002
Ph: (650)618-2221
URL: http://www.supercollege.com

Elaina Loveland. 2009. $17.95. 352 pages. Provides tips and advice for job seekers aiming for a career in the field of arts. Includes details on salaries, job descriptions, job outlook, training and education requirements for each artistic career.

253 ■ The Director's Craft: A Handbook for the Theatre
Routledge
711 3rd Ave., 8th Fl.
New York, NY 10017
Ph: (212)216-7800
Fax: (212)563-2269
Fr: 800-634-7064
URL: http://www.routledge.com

Katie Mitchell. 2008. $19.99 (paperback). $70 (hardback). 246 pages. Step-by-step guide to directing for the stage. Provides assistance with each aspect of the varied challenges facing all theatre directors.

254 ■ Enter the Playmakers: Directors and Choreographers on the New York Stage
Scarecrow Press, Inc.
4501 Forbes Blvd., Ste. 200
Lanham, MD 20706-4310
Ph: (301)459-3366
Fax: (301)429-5748
Fr: 800-462-6420
E-mail: custserv@rowman.com
URL: http://www.scarecrowpress.com

Thomas S. Hischak. 2006. $45.00. 154 pages. Features famous artists such as Elia Kazan and Jerome Robbins as well as lesser known artists of the American theatre. A biography of each director or choreographer is included.

255 ■ FabJob Guide to Become a Television Producer
FabJob Inc.
4616 - 25th Ave. NE, No. 224
Seattle, WA 98105
Ph: (403)949-4980
Fr: 888-322-5621
URL: http://www.fabjob.com/Producer.asp

Gary Reynolds. $14.97(e-books). 157 pages. Contains information on how to start a career in television production. Offers useful resources and career advice.

256 ■ Footlight Dreams: Following Your Passion for a Career in Musical Theatre: A Guide for Performers, Parents and Teachers
Hal Leonard Corporation
PO Box 13819
Milwaukee, WI 53213
URL: http://www.halleonard.com

David Ladd. 2011. $12.99. 104 pages. Serves as practical guide for performers, teachers and parents to help with the decision-making process of aspiring performers seeking a career in musical theatre. Includes a discussion on career options, opportunities and resources in the field.

257 ■ Great Jobs for Theater Majors
The McGraw-Hill Companies
PO Box 182604
Columbus, OH 43272
Fax: (614)759-3749

Fr: 877-883-5524
E-mail: customer.service@mcgraw-hill.com
URL: http://www.mhprofessional.com/product.php?isbn=007143853X

Jan Goldberg and Julie DeGalan. 2005. $15.95 (paper). 192 pages.

258 ■ A Killer Life: How an Independent Film Producer Survives Deals and Disasters in Hollywood and Beyond
Hal Leonard Corporation
PO Box 13819
Milwaukee, WI 53213
URL: http://www.halleonard.com

Christine Vachon, as told to Austin Bunn. $16.95. 320 pages. Christine Vachon chronicles twenty years of working in the film industry.

259 ■ The New Business of Acting: How to Build a Career in a Changing Landscape
Ingenuity Press USA
2275 Huntington Dr., Ste. 552
San Marino, CA 91108
Ph: (626)285-4040
E-mail: inquiries@ingenuitypressusa.com
URL: http://www.ingenuitypressusa.com

Brad Lemack. 2010. $22.95. 225 pages. Offers new and working actors a vital perspective on the changing landscape of the business of acting. Covers chapters on the changing roles of agents and managers; the importance of creating, protecting and honoring an actor's 'brand'; and managing job expectations. Includes tips on creating and launching an action plan for career success.

260 ■ Opportunities in Acting Careers
The McGraw-Hill Companies
PO Box 182604
Columbus, OH 43272
Fax: (614)759-3749
Fr: 877-883-5524
E-mail: customer.service@mcgraw-hill.com
URL: http://www.mhprofessional.com/product.php?isbn=0071466452

Dick Moore. 2005. $13.95 (paper). 160 pages. A guide to planning for and seeking opportunities in acting.

261 ■ Opportunities in Film Careers
The McGraw-Hill Companies
PO Box 182604
Columbus, OH 43272
Fax: (614)759-3749
Fr: 877-883-5524
E-mail: customer.service@mcgraw-hill.com
URL: http://www.mhprofessional.com/product.php?isbn=0071442472

Jan Bone and Ana Fernandez. 2004. $19.95 (paper). 160 pages. Provides advice on obtaining a job in film and in corporate non-broadcast film/video production. Illustrated.

262 ■ Promoting Your Acting Career: Step-by-Step Guide to Opening the Right Doors
Allworth Press
307 W 36th St., 11th Fl.
New York, NY 10018
Ph: (212)643-6816
Fax: (212)643-6819
URL: http://www.allworth.com

Glenn Alterman. 2004. $22.95 (paper). 240 pages.

263 ■ Resumes for Performing Arts Careers
The McGraw-Hill Companies
PO Box 182604
Columbus, OH 43272
Fax: (614)759-3749
Fr: 877-883-5524
E-mail: customer.service@mcgraw-hill.com
URL: http://www.mhprofessional.com/product.php?isbn=0071442464

2004. $10.95 (paper). 160 pages.

264 ■ *The Seven Steps to Stardom: How to Become a Working Actor in Movies, TV, and Commercials*
Applause Theatre & Cinema Books
19 W 21st St., Ste. 201
New York, NY 10010
Ph: (212)575-9265
Fax: (212)575-9270
E-mail: info@applausepub.com
URL: http://www.applausepub.com/
  itemDetail.jsp?itemid=314727&order=0&keywords=stardom

Christina Ferra-Gilmor and Wink Martindale. $19.95. 104 pages. The founder of a leading acting school offers seven steps for becoming an actor.

265 ■ *So You Want to be an Actor?*
Nick Hern Books
1045 Westgate Dr., Ste. 90
St. Paul, MN 55114-1065
Ph: (651)221-9035
Fax: (651)917-6406
Fr: 800-283-3572
URL: http://www.nickhernbooks.co.uk/
  index.cfm?nid=home&isbn=1854598791&sr

Timothy West and Prunella Scales. 2006. $20.95. Advice is given to any individual interested in the field of acting.

EMPLOYMENT AGENCIES AND SEARCH FIRMS

266 ■ Filcro Media Staffing
521 5th Ave., Fl. 18
New York, NY 10175
Ph: (212)599-0909
Fax: (212)599-1023
E-mail: mail@executivesearch.tv
URL: http://www.executivesearch.tv

Executive search firm for the entertainment industry.

267 ■ Howard Fischer Associates International Inc.
1800 Kennedy Blvd., Ste. 700
Philadelphia, PA 19103
Ph: (215)568-8363
Fax: (215)568-4815
E-mail: search@hfischer.com
URL: http://www.hfischer.com

Executive search firm. Branches in Campbell, CA and Boston, MA.

ONLINE JOB SOURCES AND SERVICES

268 ■ Acting-Jobs.com
URL: http://acting-jobs.com

Description: Provides information on all available acting jobs in the United States.

269 ■ Acting-Jobs.net
URL: http://www.acting-jobs.net

Description: Provides a searchable database of acting jobs in the United States.

270 ■ BackstageJobs.com
URL: http://www.backstagejobs.com

Description: Lists behind-the-scenes jobs in the live entertainment industry. Also features backstage related news and information.

271 ■ CasinoGigs.net
URL: http://www.casinogigs.net

Description: Serves as a career community for the gambling industry. Features job openings for casino workers, research into the arts, entertainment & gaming employment market, and a career articles section written and frequented by industry professionals.

272 ■ GetGigs.com
URL: http://www.getgigs.com

Description: Seeks to provide an on-line experience for creative types, performing artists, and musicians around the world by integrating internet technologies into a one-stop information resource. Also functions as a creative directory and talent network.

273 ■ Mandy's International Film and TV Production Directory
E-mail: directory@mandy.com
URL: http://www.mandy.com/1/filmtvjobs.cfm

Description: Employment site intended for film and TV professionals. Employers may post free Jobs Offered listings. Job seekers may post free Jobs Wanted ads.

274 ■ Media-Match.com
URL: http://www.media-match.com/usa

Description: Serves as an online database of TV and film professionals' resumes and availabilities. Provides an up-to-date television production jobs board and film production jobs board for new openings in the film and TV production business across the United States.

275 ■ ProductionHub.com
URL: http://www.productionhub.com

Description: Serves as an online resource and industry directory for film, television, video, live event and digital media production. Features job opportunities, events, directory and other resources for the production industry.

OTHER SOURCES

276 ■ Academy of Motion Picture Arts and Sciences (AMPAS)
8949 Wilshire Blvd.
Beverly Hills, CA 90211
Ph: (310)247-3000
Fax: (310)859-9619
E-mail: contact@oscars.org
URL: http://www.oscars.org

Description: Represents motion picture producers, directors, writers, cinematographer, editors, actors and craftsmen.

277 ■ Academy of Television Arts and Sciences (ATAS)
5220 Lankershim Blvd.
North Hollywood, CA 91601-3109
Ph: (818)754-2800
E-mail: membership@emmys.org
URL: http://www.emmys.org

Description: Professionals in the television and film industry. Aims to advance the arts and sciences of television through services to the industry in education, preservation of television programs, and information and community relations; to foster creative leadership in the television industry. Sponsors Television Academy Hall of Fame. Maintains library on television credits and historical material, the Television Academy Archives, and archives at UCLA of over 35,000 television programs. Offers internships to students. Holds luncheon and speakers series and meetings on problems of the various crafts.

278 ■ Actors' Fund
729 Seventh Ave., 10th Fl.
New York, NY 10019
Ph: (212)221-7300
Fr: 800-221-7303
E-mail: info@actorsfund.org
URL: http://www.actorsfund.org

Description: Helps all professionals - both performers and those behind the scenes - in performing arts and entertainment. Serves those in film, theatre, television, music, opera, and dance with a broad spectrum of programs including comprehensive social services, health services, supportive and affordable housing, emergency financial assistance, employment and training services, and skilled nursing and assisted living care. Administered from offices in New York, Los Angeles, and Chicago, it serves as a safety net, providing programs and services for those who are in need, crisis, or transition.

279 ■ Alliance for Inclusion in the Arts
1560 Broadway, Ste. 709
New York, NY 10036
Ph: (212)730-4750
E-mail: info@inclusioninthearts.org
URL: http://inclusioninthearts.org

Description: Advocates the elimination of discrimination in theatre, film, and television. Works to increase the employment of artists of color and artists with disabilities by encouraging cultural diversity throughout the artistic process and all levels of production and administration, and offering consultative services. Maintains the Artist Files containing pictures and resumes of 3,000 actors, directors, writers, designers, and stage managers of color as well as those with disabilities. Sponsors forums.

280 ■ Alliance of Resident Theatres/New York (ART/NY)
520 8th Ave., Ste. 319
New York, NY 10018
Ph: (212)244-6667
Fax: (212)714-1918
E-mail: tgramps@art-newyork.org
URL: http://www.art-newyork.org

Description: Nonprofit professional theatres in New York City and interested theatre-related associations. Promotes recognition of the nonprofit theatre community. Provides members with administrative services and resources pertinent to their field. Facilitates discussion among the theatres; helps to solve real estate problems; serves as a public information source. Acts as advocate on behalf of members with government, corporate, and foundation funders to encourage greater support for New York's not-for-profit theatres. Sponsors seminars, roundtables, and individual consultations for members in areas such as financial management, board development and marketing. Organizes Passports to Off Broadway, an industry-wide marketing campaign.

281 ■ American Association of Community Theatre (AACT)
1300 Gendy St.
Fort Worth, TX 76107
Ph: (817)732-3177
Fax: (817)732-3178
Fr: (866)687-2228
E-mail: info@aact.org
URL: http://www.aact.org

Description: Community theatre organizations and individuals involved in community theatre. Promotes excellence in community theatre through networking, workshops, publications, and festivals of community theatre productions.

282 ■ American Conservatory Theater Foundation (ACT)
30 Grant Ave., 6th Fl.
San Francisco, CA 94109-5800
Ph: (415)834-3200
Fax: (415)749-2291
E-mail: tickets@act-sf.org
URL: http://www.act-sf.org

Description: Provides resources for the American Conservatory Theater which functions as a repertory theatre and accredited acting school, offering a Master of Fine Arts degree. Holds national auditions for the MFA program in Chicago, IL, New York City, and Los Angeles, CA, usually in February. Holds student matinees, school outreach programs, and in-theatre discussions between artist and audiences. Conducts professional actor-training programs, a summer training congress, and a young conservatory evening academy program for children aged 8-18. Offers children's services. Operates speakers' bureau and placement service.

283 ■ Association for Theatre in Higher Education (ATHE)
PO Box 1290
Boulder, CO 80306-1290
Ph: (303)530-2167
Fax: (303)530-2168
Fr: 888-284-3737
E-mail: info@athe.org
URL: http://www.athe.org

Description: Universities, colleges, and professional education programs; artists, scholars, teachers, and other individuals; students. Promotes the exchange of information among individuals engaged in theatre study and research, performance, and crafts. Provides advocacy and support services. Encourages excellence in postsecondary theatre training, production, and scholarship.

284 ■ Coalition of Asian Pacifics in Entertainment (CAPE)
10 Universal City Plz., 20th Fl.
Universal City, CA 91608
Ph: (818)508-1421
E-mail: info@capeusa.org
URL: http://www.capeusa.org

Description: Supports Asian Pacifics in the arts and entertainment. Increases the social, educational and professional opportunities for Asian Pacifics in the entertainment industry. Serves as a forum for Asian Pacifics in feature film, television, video, publishing, music and other entertainment fields to share common interests and concerns through such programs as screenings, panels, workshops, and hosted conversations with notable executives and artists.

285 ■ Directors Guild of America (DGA)
7920 Sunset Blvd.
Los Angeles, CA 90046
Ph: (310)289-2000
Fax: (310)289-2029
Fr: 800-420-4173
E-mail: darrellh@dga.org
URL: http://www.dga.org

Description: Purpose: Independent. Negotiates agreements for members.

286 ■ Film Independent
9911 W Pico Blvd., 11th Fl.
Los Angeles, CA 90035
Ph: (310)432-1200
Fax: (310)432-1203
URL: http://www.filmindependent.org

Description: Represents directors, writers, and producers. Strives to help independent filmmakers get their films made, build the audience for independent film, and increase diversity in the film industry. Provides cameras and casting rooms to rent, a resource library with computers, sample budget and business plans, and film periodicals. Offers free screenings and educational events every year.

287 ■ Health Science Communications Association (HeSCA)
39 Wedgewood Dr., Ste. A
Jewett City, CT 06351-2420
Ph: (860)376-5915
Fax: (860)376-6621
E-mail: hescaone@sbcglobal.net
URL: http://www.hesca.org

Description: Represents media managers, graphic artists, biomedical librarians, producers, faculty members of health science and veterinary medicine schools, health professional organizations, and industry representatives. Acts as a clearinghouse for information used by professionals engaged in health science communications. Coordinates Media Festivals Program that recognizes outstanding media productions in the health sciences. Offers placement service.

288 ■ Independent Film and Television Alliance (IFTA)
10850 Wilshire Blvd., 9th Fl.
Los Angeles, CA 90024-4321

Ph: (310)446-1000
Fax: (310)446-1600
E-mail: rburt@ifta-online.org
URL: http://www.ifta-online.org

Description: Trade association for the worldwide independent film and television industry. Contributes to negotiations with foreign producer associations; develops standardized theatrical, TV and video contracts for international distribution. Established and maintains the IFTA International Arbitration Tribunal, a system through which prominent entertainment attorneys throughout the world assist members and consenting clients in reaching equitable and binding agreements. Facilitates the formulation of policies, standardized private practices and language contracts and the exchange of information and experience among members. Produces the American Film Market (AFM), the largest international motion picture trade event in the world.

289 ■ International Documentary Association
1201 W 5th St., Ste. M270
Los Angeles, CA 90017
Ph: (213)534-3600
Fax: (213)534-3610
URL: http://www.documentary.org

Description: Represents nonfiction film and video makers. Supports the efforts of nonfiction film and video makers throughout the United States and the world. Promotes the documentary form and expands opportunities for the production, distribution, and exhibition of documentaries. Seeks to increase public appreciation and demand for documentary films, videos, and television programs across all ethnic, political, and socioeconomic boundaries.

290 ■ Media Communications Association International (MCA-I)
PO Box 5135
Madison, WI 53705-0135
Fax: 888-862-8150
Fr: 888-899-6224
E-mail: loiswei@aol.com
URL: http://www.mca-i.org

Description: Individuals engaged in multimedia communications needs analysis, scriptwriting, producing, directing, consulting and operations management in the video, multimedia and film fields. Seeks to advance the benefits and image of media communications professionals.

291 ■ National Association of Broadcasters (NAB)
1771 N St. NW
Washington, DC 20036
Ph: (202)429-5300
Fax: (202)429-4199
E-mail: nab@nab.org
URL: http://www.nab.org

Description: Serves as the voice for the nation's radio and television broadcasters. Advances the interests of members in federal government, industry and public affairs; improves the quality and profitability of broadcasting; encourages content and technology innovation; and spotlights the important and unique ways stations serve their communities. Delivers value to its members through advocacy, education and innovation. Relies on the grassroots strength of its television and radio members and state broadcast associations. Helps broadcasters seize opportunities in the digital age. Offers broadcasters a variety of programs to help them grow in their careers, promote diversity in the workplace and strengthen their businesses.

292 ■ National Association of Television Program Executives
5757 Wilshire Blvd., Penthouse 10
Los Angeles, CA 90036-3681
Ph: (310)453-4440
Fax: (310)453-5258
URL: http://www.natpe.org/natpe

Description: Comprised of television program professionals, exhibitors, buyers and faculty. Focuses

on the creation, development and distribution of televised programming in all forms across all mature and emerging media platforms. Provides members with education, networking, professional enhancement and technological guidance through year-round activities and events, and directories.

293 ■ New England Theatre Conference (NETC)
215 Knob Hill Dr.
Hamden, CT 06518
Ph: (617)851-8535
Fax: (203)288-5938
E-mail: mail@netconline.org
URL: http://netconline.org

Description: Individuals and theatre-producing groups in New England who are actively engaged in or have a particular interest in theatre activity either professionally or as an avocation. Aims to develop, expand, and assist theatre activity on community, educational, and professional levels in New England. Activities include: auditions for jobs in New England summer theatres; workshops on performance, administrative, and technical aspects of production.

294 ■ Screen Actors Guild
5757 Wilshire Blvd., 7th Fl.
Los Angeles, CA 90036-3600
Ph: (323)954-1600
Fr: 800-724-0767
E-mail: saginfo@sag.org
URL: http://www.sag.org

Description: Represents working actors in film, television, industrials, commercials, video games, music videos, and other new media. Aims to enhance actors' working conditions, compensation, and benefits. Serves and protects artists' rights.

295 ■ Southeastern Theatre Conference (SETC)
1175 Revolution Mill Dr., Ste. 14
Greensboro, NC 27405
Ph: (336)272-3645
Fax: (336)272-8810
E-mail: info@setc.org
URL: http://www.setc.org

Description: Serves the needs of individuals and theatre organizations involved in professional, university/college, community, children/youth, and secondary school theatres. Brings together people interested in theatre and theatre artists and craftsmen from 10 southeastern states of the U.S., across the nation and internationally in order to promote high standards and to stimulate creativity in all phases of theatrical endeavor. Services include: job contact service for technical hiring and job listings, resume service, etc.; playwriting projects for new plays; scholarships for a variety of theatre interests; and annual auditions (spring and fall) for professional, dinner, repertory, summer indoor and outdoor theatres, cruise lines and entertainment venues.

296 ■ Texas International Theatrical Arts Society (TITAS)
3625 N Hall St., Ste. 740
Dallas, TX 75219
Ph: (214)528-6112
Fax: (214)528-2617
E-mail: csantos@titas.org
URL: http://www.titas.org

Description: Theatrical agencies working to book entertainers and international acts into all live music venues. Provides placement service; conducts educational seminars.

297 ■ University Film and Video Association (UFVA)
3800 Barham Blvd., Ste. 103
Los Angeles, CA 90068
Fr: (866)647-8382
E-mail: ufvahome@aol.com
URL: http://www.ufva.org

Description: Professors and video/filmmakers concerned with the production and study of film and video in colleges and universities. Conducts research programs; operates placement service; presents annual grants.

298 ■ Women in Film (WIF)
6100 Wilshire Blvd., Ste. 710
Los Angeles, CA 90048

Ph: (323)935-2211
Fax: (323)935-2212
E-mail: info@wif.org
URL: http://www.wif.org

Description: Supports women in the film and television industry and serves as a network for information on qualified women in the entertainment field. Sponsors screenings and discussions of pertinent issues. Provides speakers' bureau. Maintains Women in Film Foundation, which offers financial assistance to women for education, research, and/or completion of film projects.

SOURCES OF HELP-WANTED ADS

299 ■ Actuarial Digest
PO Box 1127
Ponte Vedra Beach, FL 32004
Ph: (904)273-1245
URL: http://www.theactuarialdigest.com

Description: Quarterly. Covers issues of concern to working actuaries. Recurring features include letters to the editor, news of research, news of educational opportunities, job listings, book reviews, notices of publications available, and a column titled What's New.

300 ■ Actuarial Review
Casualty Actuarial Society
4350 N Fairfax Dr., Ste. 250
Arlington, VA 22203
Ph: (703)276-3100
Fax: (703)276-3108
E-mail: office@casact.org
URL: http://www.casact.org

Quarterly. $10/year. Features actuarial articles, information and latest development in CAS.

301 ■ ASCnet Quarterly
Applied Systems Client Network
801 Douglas Ave., Ste. 205
Altamonte Springs, FL 32714
Ph: (407)869-0404
Fax: (407)869-0418
Fr: 800-605-1045
URL: http://www.ascnet.org/AM/
    Template.cfm?Section=About

Quarterly. $24.00/year for individuals. Professional magazine covering technical information, association news, and industry information for insurance professionals.

302 ■ Best's Review
A.M. Best Company, Inc.
Ambest Rd.
Oldwick, NJ 08858
Ph: (908)439-2200
URL: http://www.ambest.com/sales/
    newsoverview.asp#br

Monthly. $50.00/year for individuals. Magazine covering issues and trends for the management personnel of life/health insurers, the agents, and brokers who market their products.

303 ■ Business Insurance
Crain Communications Inc.
1155 Gratiot Ave.
Detroit, MI 48207-2997
Ph: (313)446-6000
URL: http://www.businessinsurance.com

Weekly. $399.00/year for individuals, print; $149.00/year for individuals, print & digital; $69.00/year for individuals, digital edition. International newsweekly reporting on corporate risk and employee benefit management news.

304 ■ Contingencies
American Academy of Actuaries
1850 M St. NW, Ste. 300
Washington, DC 20036
Ph: (202)223-8196
Fax: (202)872-1948
URL: http://www.contingencies.org

Bimonthly. $33.00/year for other countries. Magazine on actuarial science and its relevance to current business problems and social issues.

305 ■ The Future Actuary
Society of Actuaries
475 N Martingale Rd., Ste. 600
Schaumburg, IL 60173-2226
Ph: (847)706-3500
Fax: (847)706-3599
E-mail: customerservice@soa.org
URL: http://www.soa.org

Description: Four issues/year. Provides actuarial students with the latest information on jobs, internships, study techniques, career development, professional conduct, and ethics. Recurring features include a calendar of events, news of educational opportunities, and job listings.

306 ■ National Underwriter Property and
    Casualty/Risk and Benefits Management
National Underwriter Co.
5081 Olympic Blvd.
PO Box 14367
Erlanger, KY 41018
Ph: (859)692-2100
Fax: (859)692-2175
Fr: 800-543-0874
URL: http://www.propertycasualty360.com/National-
    Underwriter-Prop

Weekly. $94.00/year for individuals, 2nd class; $133.00/year for Canada, air mail; $178.00/year for U.S. and Canada, air mail; $211.00/year for other countries, air mail. Newsweekly for agents, brokers, executives, and managers in risk and benefit insurance.

307 ■ Pensions & Investments
Crain Communications Inc.
1155 Gratiot Ave.
Detroit, MI 48207-2997
Ph: (313)446-6000
URL: http://www.pionline.com

Biweekly. $279.00/year for individuals, print; $995.00/year for individuals, daily email; $1,149.00/year for individuals, combo. Magazine containing news and features on investment management, pension management, corporate finance, and cash management.

EMPLOYER DIRECTORIES AND NETWORKING LISTS

308 ■ Best's Insurance Reports
A.M. Best Co.
Ambest Rd.
Oldwick, NJ 08858
Ph: (908)439-2200
URL: http://www.ambest.com

Annual, Latest edition 2011. Published in three editions—Life-health insurance, covering about 1,750 companies, property-casualty insurance, covering over 3,200 companies; and international, covering more than 1,200 insurers. Each edition lists state insurance commissioners and related companies and agencies (mutual funds, worker compensation funds, underwriting agencies, etc.). Entries include: For each company—Company name, address, phone; history; states in which licensed; names of officers and directors; financial data; financial analysis and Best's rating. Arrangement: Alphabetical.

309 ■ Insurance Phone Book
Briefings Media Group
2807 N Parham Rd., Ste. 200
Richmond, VA 23294
Ph: (570)567-1982
Fr: 800-791-8699
URL: http://www.douglaspublications.com

Annual, latest edition 2009-2010. $195.00; $389.00. Covers: About 3,700 life, accident and health, worker's compensation, auto, fire and casualty, marine, surety, and other insurance companies; 2,300 executive contacts from presidents and CEOs to claims and customer service managers. Entries include: Company name, address, phone, fax, toll-free number, type of insurance provided. Arrangement: Alphabetical.

HANDBOOKS AND MANUALS

310 ■ Actuaries' Survival Guide: How to
    Succeed in One of the Most Desirable
    Professions
Elsevier
11830 Westline Industrial Dr.
St. Louis, MO 63146
Ph: (314)453-7010
Fax: (314)453-7095
Fr: 800-545-2522
E-mail: usbkinfo@elsevier.com
URL: http://www.elsevier.com

Fred E. Szabo. 2004. $48.95. 268 pages. Explores the function of actuaries.

311 ■ Introductory Stochastic Analysis for
    Finance and Insurance
John Wiley & Sons, Inc.
111 River St.
Hoboken, NJ 07030
Ph: (201)748-6000
Fax: (201)748-6088
E-mail: info@wiley.com
URL: http://as.wiley.com/WileyCDA/Section/
    index.html

X. Sheldon Lin. 2006. $127.95. 248 pages. Introductory stochastic analysis for finance, written specifically for actuaries.

312 ■ *Making the Grade: The Aspiring Actuary's Guidebook to Consistent Exam Success and Advancement in the Workplace*
ACTEX Publications
PO Box 974
Winsted, CT 06098
Ph: (860)379-5470
Fax: (860)738-3152
Fr: 800-282-2839
E-mail: retail@actexmadriver.com
URL: http://www.actexmadriver.com

Nicholas Mocciolo. 2010. $21.95. Serves as a reference on career development for aspiring actuaries. Focuses on suggested techniques to maximize success on actuarial exams. Includes information on actuarial organizations in the U.S. and introduction to non-technical skills for long-term success in the actuarial profession.

313 ■ *Opportunities in Insurance Careers*
The McGraw-Hill Companies
PO Box 182604
Columbus, OH 43272
Fax: (614)759-3749
Fr: 877-883-5524
E-mail: customer.service@mcgraw-hill.com
URL: http://www.mhprofessional.com/
   product.php?isbn=0071482075

Robert M. Schrayer. Revised, 2007. $14.95 (paper). 160 pages. A guide to planning for and seeking opportunities in the field. Contains bibliography and illustrations.

314 ■ *Probability: An Introductory Guide for Actuaries and Other Business Professionals*
BPP Professional Education
4025 S. Riverpoint Pkwy.
Phoenix, AZ 85040
Fax: (866)365-7657
E-mail: info@bpptraining.com
URL: http://www.bpptraining.com/Html/
   Psolutions.htm

David J. Carr and Michael A. Gauger. 2004.

EMPLOYMENT AGENCIES AND SEARCH FIRMS

315 ■ **Actuarial Careers, Inc.**
11 Martine Ave., 9th Fl.
White Plains, NY 10606
Ph: (914)285-5100
Fax: (914)285-9375
Fr: 800-766-0070
E-mail: jobs@actuarialcareers.com
URL: http://www.actuarialcareers.com

Specializes in the placement of actuaries on a worldwide basis and provides responsive and professional service in the industry. Provides actuarial candidates with opportunities to broaden and enhance their personal careers. Maintains a continually updated database containing new actuarial jobs.

316 ■ **Actuarial Jobs, Inc.**
2222 N Beech Daly Rd., Ste. 20
Dearborn Heights, MI 48127
Ph: (702)845-8631
Fr: 800-395-6458
URL: http://www.actuarialjobsinc.com

Specializes in the recruitment and placement of property and casualty actuaries, product managers and modelers. Provides a comprehensive recruitment service for qualified and studying actuarial professionals on both a permanent and contract/interim basis.

317 ■ **Actuary Resources**
115 N Castle Heights Ave., Ste. 202
Lebanon, TN 37087-2768
Ph: (615)360-5171

Fax: (615)360-5173
E-mail: info@actuaryresources.org
URL: http://www.actuaryresources.org

Provides staffing services to several different types of industries. Offers a free screening service to clients.

318 ■ **The Alexander Group**
2700 Post Oak Blvd., Ste. 2400
Houston, TX 77056
Ph: (713)993-7900
URL: http://www.thealexandergroup.com

Executive search firm. Second location in San Francisco.

319 ■ **Andover Research, Ltd.**
60 E 42nd St.
New York, NY 10165
Ph: (212)986-8484
Fax: (212)983-0952
Fr: 800-AND-OVER
E-mail: actuaries@andoverresearch.com
URL: http://www.andoverresearch.com

Specializes in the recruitment and placement of actuaries and benefit consultants worldwide.

320 ■ **Capstone Insurance Search Group**
2480 Berkshire Pkwy., Ste. A
Clive, IA 50325
Ph: (515)987-0242
Fax: (515)987-0004
E-mail: careers@insurance-csg.com
URL: http://www.csgrecruiting.com

Description: Serves as an executive search firm dedicated to the insurance industry. Provides assistance with a variety of product lines including property and casualty, life, health, disability, annuity and pension.

321 ■ **Darwin Rhodes**
48 Wall St., 11th Fl., Ste. 1100
New York, NY 10005
Ph: (212)918-4754
Fax: (212)918-4801
E-mail: recruit-usa@darwinrhodes.us
URL: http://www.darwinrhodes.us/en/home.asp

Specializes in the placement of actuarial, employee benefits, insurance and financial planning professionals. Provides clients with a local recruitment and executive search service that are tailored to their particular goals and focus.

322 ■ **D.W. Simpson & Company**
1800 W Larchmont Ave.
Chicago, IL 60613
Ph: (312)867-2300
Fax: (312)951-8386
Fr: 800-837-8338
E-mail: actuaries@dwsimpson.com
URL: http://www.dwsimpson.com

Serves the actuarial profession worldwide in all disciplines, recruiting at all levels from entry-level through fellowship, and works with clients on both retained and contingent searches.

323 ■ **DW Simpson Global Actuarial Recruitment**
1800 W Larchmont Ave.
Chicago, IL 60613
Ph: (312)867-2300
Fax: (312)951-8386
Fr: 800-837-8338
E-mail: actuaries@dwsimpson.com
URL: http://www.dwsimpson.com

Description: Serves the actuarial profession worldwide in all disciplines, recruiting at all levels from entry-level through fellowship.

324 ■ **Ezra Penland Actuarial Recruitment**
4256 N Ravenswood Ave., Ste. 200
Chicago, IL 60613
Fax: (773)340-4209

Fr: 800-580-3972
E-mail: actuaries@ezrapenland.com
URL: http://www.ezrapenland.com

Specializes on actuarial recruitment. Works on all levels of actuarial positions, from the actuarial analyst and actuarial assistant levels, up through associateship, fellowship, chief actuaries, consulting partners and executive management.

325 ■ **Health Actuary Search**
PO Box 102
Coeur D Alene, ID 83816
Fax: (208)664-5350
Fr: (866)529-2159
E-mail: leslie@healthactuarysearch.com
URL: http://www.healthactuarysearch.com

Description: Provides targeted and personalized health actuarial recruiting services. Combines in-depth knowledge of the health marketplace with a commitment to individualized service, creating a dynamic nexus between candidate and employer.

326 ■ **International Insurance Personnel, Inc.**
300 W Wieuca Rd., Bldg. 2, Ste. 101
Atlanta, GA 30342
Ph: (404)255-9710
Fax: (404)255-9864
E-mail: iipjulie@bellsouth.net
URL: http://realpages.com/sites/intlinspersonnel/
   index.html

Employment agency specializing in the area of insurance.

327 ■ **J Birch Corporation**
1505 S State Highway 8
New Boston, TX 75570
Fr: 800-899-3064
E-mail: jbirch@thebirchcorp.com
URL: http://jbirchcorporation.com

Description: Specializes in actuarial placements in all areas of the insurance industry: life, health, pension, property and casualty and reinsurance. Works with all levels of actuaries from entry level to fellowship.

328 ■ **J. R. Peterman Associates, Inc.**
PO Box 3083
Stowe, VT 05672
Ph: (802)253-6304
Fax: (802)253-6314
E-mail: peterman@jrpeterman.com
URL: http://www.jrpeterman.com

Description: Recruit professionals in permanent and contract positions for the life and health insurance industry and employee benefits consulting.

329 ■ **Lear & Associates, Inc.**
1235 N Orange Ave.
Orlando, FL 32804
Ph: (407)645-4611
Fax: (407)645-5735
E-mail: info@learsearch.com
URL: http://www.learsearch.com

Serves as recruitment firm specializing in the insurance industry.

330 ■ **Lighthouse Search Group**
16610 W 159th St., Ste. 101
Lockport, IL 60441
Ph: (815)588-3400
Fax: (815)588-3418
E-mail: erek.powell@lhsearch.com
URL: http://www.lhsearch.com

Exists as an executive search firm specializing in the actuarial marketplace. Posts jobs from the largest actuarial consulting and insurance firms.

331 ■ **Mitchell Actuarial Recruiting**
4 Woodhaven Dr.
New City, NY 10956
Ph: (845)638-2700

Fr: 800-648-2435
E-mail: info@mitchellactuarialrecruiting.com
URL: http://www.mitchellactuarialrecruiting.com

Offers executive recruiting for the actuarial and benefits fields.

332 ■ Nationwide Actuarial Search
4680 S Polaris Ave., Ste. 240
Las Vegas, NV 89103
Ph: (702)454-9024
Fax: (702)369-2881
Fr: 800-733-3536
E-mail: nas@actuary-recruiter.com
URL: http://www.actuary-recruiter.com/web/nas/home.asp

Description: Specializes in search and recruitment for property and casualty actuarial professionals at all levels.

333 ■ O'Shea System of Employment Inc.
PO Box 2134
Aston, PA 19014
Ph: (610)364-3964
Fax: (610)364-3962
Fr: 800-220-5203
E-mail: osheasys@aol.com

Offers personnel staff recruiting nationally in the following fields: insurance, health care, financial, information technology, administration, human resource, manufacturing and sales.

334 ■ Pinnacle Group, Inc.
6 Greenleaf Woods, Ste. 201
Portsmouth, NH 03801
Ph: (603)427-1700
Fax: (603)427-0526
Fr: 800-308-7205
E-mail: info@pinnaclejobs.com
URL: http://www.pinnaclejobs.com

Provides recruiting services to insurance, consulting and investment firms. Offers career opportunities from entry-level to senior management.

335 ■ Questor Consultants, Inc.
2515 N Broad St.
Colmar, PA 18915
Ph: (215)997-9262
Fax: (215)997-9226
E-mail: sbevivino@questorconsultants.com
URL: http://www.questorconsultants.com

Executive search firm specializing in the insurance and legal fields.

336 ■ Rollins Search Group, Inc.
849 Morningcreek Dr., Ste. 400
Kennesaw, GA 30152
Ph: (770)425-8230
E-mail: rsgwp@rollinssearch.com
URL: http://www.rollinssearch.com

Specializes in permanent placement within the insurance industry for candidates with experience in actuarial and insurance information systems.

337 ■ S.C. International, Ltd.
1315 Butterfield Rd., Ste. 224
Downers Grove, IL 60515
Ph: (630)963-3033
Fax: (630)963-3170
Fr: 800-543-2553
E-mail: search@scinternational.com
URL: http://www.scinternational.com

Description: Works as an executive search firm for the actuarial industry serving job seekers from entry level to senior officer executive positions.

338 ■ S.K. Associates
5825 Glenridge Dr., Bldg. 3, Ste. 101
Atlanta, GA 30328
Ph: (404)257-9294
Fax: (404)257-9289
Fr: 877-SKA-SSOC
E-mail: actuarial@skassociates.com
URL: http://www.skassociates.com

339 ■ S.K. Associates
5825 Glenridge Dr., Bldg. 3, Ste. 101
Atlanta, GA 30328
Ph: (404)257-9294
Fax: (404)257-9289
Fr: 877-SKA-SSOC
E-mail: actuarial@skassociates.com
URL: http://www.skassociates.com

Description: Exists as a recruiting firm specializing in all actuarial disciplines. Provides opportunities from CFO/chief actuaries, and practice leaders, to actuarial associate jobs and actuarial analyst jobs.

340 ■ Stewart Search Advisors, LLC
875 Greenland Rd., Ste. B8
Portsmouth, NH 03801
Ph: (603)430-2122
Fax: (603)430-7339
Fr: 888-JOB-OPEN
E-mail: online@stewartsearch.com
URL: http://www.stewartsearch.com

Description: Exists as an executive search firm for the actuarial industry.

341 ■ Todd Mitchell Associates
3333 New Hyde Park Rd.
New Hyde Park, NY 11042
Fax: (516)365-2460
Fr: 800-886-1562
E-mail: todd.mitchell@toddmitchell.com
URL: http://www.toddmitchell.com

Executive search firm for the insurance industry. Specializes in the recruitment and placement of executive and technical personnel whose expertise is within the disciplines of underwriting, marketing, claims, and loss control.

ONLINE JOB SOURCES AND SERVICES

342 ■ ActuarialCrossing.com
URL: http://www.actuarialcrossing.com

Description: Offers a collection of research actuarial jobs worldwide. Focuses on the hiring needs of actuarial professionals and actuarial company in the United States.

343 ■ Actuary Jobs
URL: http://www.actuaryjob.net

Description: Features employment opportunities for actuaries.

344 ■ Actuary.com
URL: http://www.actuary.com

Description: Actuarial professionals. Focuses on serving as a major resource center for the actuarial community at large. Provides information regarding exams, seminars, actuarial news, actuarial recruiters, actuary jobs postings, discussion forums, actuarial schools, links to many resources, leading actuarial companies information and more.

345 ■ Financial Job Network
PO Box 55431
Sherman Oaks, CA 91403
Ph: (818)905-5272
E-mail: info@fjn.com
URL: http://www.fjn.com

Description: Contains information on international and national employment opportunities for those in the financial job market. Job listings may be submitted, as well as resumes. Main files include: Testimonials, Calendar, Corporate Listings, FJN Clients, more. Free to candidates.

346 ■ Great Insurance Jobs
URL: http://www.greatinsurancejobs.com

Description: Contains varied insurance positions. Job seekers may browse employee profiles, post resumes, and read descriptions of hundreds of recently-posted insurance jobs.

347 ■ InsuranceIndustryCentral.com
URL: http://www.insuranceindustrycentral.com

Description: Features insurance jobs and products to the insurance community.

348 ■ Jobs4Actuary.com
URL: http://www.jobs4actuary.com

Description: Provides users with advanced job search tools and employment resources for career advancement. Offers actuarial recruiting service and actuarial job database.

349 ■ National Insurance Recruiters Association
URL: http://www.insurancerecruiters.com

Description: Contains lists of recruiters (listed by department and line of business) and available insurance positions.

350 ■ UltimateInsuranceJobs.com
URL: http://www.ultimateinsurancejobs.com/index.asp

Description: Provides insurance job listings, recruiter directory, and resources. Offers job seekers the opportunity to post and edit their resumes, and employers the opportunity to search through insurance resumes.

TRADESHOWS

351 ■ International Association of Black Actuaries Meeting
International Association of Black Actuaries
PO Box 369
Windsor, CT 06095
Ph: (860)219-9534
Fax: (860)219-9546
E-mail: iaba@blackactuaries.org
URL: http://www.blackactuaries.org

Annual. Offers professional development workshops, discussion forums, and guest speakers covering topics in life insurance, pensions, and property/casualty insurance. 2012 August 3-5.

OTHER SOURCES

352 ■ American Academy of Actuaries
1850 M St. NW, Ste. 300
Washington, DC 20036
Ph: (202)223-8196
Fax: (202)872-1948
E-mail: downs@actuary.org
URL: http://www.actuary.org

Description: Ensures that the American public recognizes and benefits from the independent expertise of the actuarial profession in the formulation of public policy and the adherence of actuaries to high professional standards in discharging their responsibilities. Seeks to serve the public by providing leadership, objective expertise, and actuarial advice on risk and financial security issues. Represents the entire profession: Casualty Actuarial Society; Conference of Consulting Actuaries; Society of Actuaries; Fraternal Actuarial Association (now defunct). Maintains speakers' bureau.

353 ■ American Council of Life Insurers (ACLI)
101 Constitution Ave. NW, Ste. 700
Washington, DC 20001-2133
Ph: (202)624-2000
Fr: 877-674-4659
E-mail: webadmin@acli.com
URL: http://www.acli.com

Description: Represents the interests of legal reserve life insurance companies in legislative, regulatory and judicial matters at the federal, state and municipal levels of government and at the NAIC.

Member companies hold majority of the life insurance in force in the United States.

354 ■ American Society of Pension Professionals and Actuaries (ASPPA)

4245 N Fairfax Dr., Ste. 750
Arlington, VA 22203
Ph: (703)516-9300
Fax: (703)516-9308
E-mail: asppa@asppa.org
URL: http://www.asppa.org

Description: Aims to educate pension actuaries, consultants, administrators, and other benefits professionals. Seeks to preserve and enhance the private pension system as part of the development of a cohesive and coherent national retirement income policy.

355 ■ Casualty Actuarial Society (CAS)

4350 N Fairfax Dr., Ste. 250
Arlington, VA 22203
Ph: (703)276-3100
Fax: (703)276-3108
E-mail: office@casact.org
URL: http://www.casact.org

Description: Professional society of property/casualty actuaries. Seeks to advance the body of knowledge of actuarial science applied to property, casualty and similar risk exposures, to maintain qualification standards, promote high standards of conduct and competence, and increase awareness of actuarial science. Examinations required for membership.

356 ■ Conference of Consulting Actuaries (CCA)

3880 Salem Lake Dr., Ste. H
Long Grove, IL 60047-5292
Ph: (847)719-6500
Fax: (847)719-6506
E-mail: conference@ccactuaries.org
URL: http://www.ccactuaries.org

Description: Full-time consulting actuaries or governmental actuaries. Develops and maintains structure and programs to reinforce, enhance, or add to members' knowledge and skills; this includes continuing education, through diverse delivery methods, for all practice areas and for consulting and business skills.

357 ■ Insurance Information Institute (III)

110 William St.
New York, NY 10038
Ph: (212)346-5500
E-mail: members@iii.org
URL: http://www.iii.org

Description: Property and casualty insurance companies. Provides information and educational services to mass media, educational institutions, trade associations, businesses, government agencies, and the public.

358 ■ International Association of Black Actuaries

PO Box 369
Windsor, CT 06095
Ph: (860)219-9534
Fax: (860)219-9546
E-mail: iaba@blackactuaries.org
URL: http://www.blackactuaries.org

Description: Promotes career development, civic growth, and achievement among black actuaries. Offers a network of support to black students and professionals pursuing an actuarial career. Provides mentoring and professional development among members.

359 ■ LOMA

2300 Windy Ridge Pkwy., Ste. 600
Atlanta, GA 30339-8443
Ph: (770)951-1770
Fax: (770)984-0441
Fr: 800-275-5662
E-mail: askloma@loma.org
URL: http://www.loma.org

Description: Life and health insurance companies and financial services in the U.S. and Canada; and overseas in 45 countries; affiliate members are firms that provide professional support to member companies. Provides research, information, training, and educational activities in areas of operations and systems, human resources, financial planning and employee development. Administers FLMI Insurance Education Program, which awards FLMI (Fellow, Life Management Institute) designation to those who complete the ten-examination program.

360 ■ National Association of Insurance Women International (NAIW)

9343 E 95th Ct. S
Tulsa, OK 74133
Ph: (918)294-3700
Fax: (918)294-3711
Fr: 800-766-6249
E-mail: joinnaiw@naiw.org
URL: http://www.naiw.org

Description: Insurance industry professionals. Promotes continuing education and networking for the professional advancement of its members. Offers education programs, meetings, services, and leadership opportunities. Provides a forum to learn about other disciplines in the insurance industry.

361 ■ Society of Actuaries (SOA)

475 N Martingale Rd., Ste. 600
Schaumburg, IL 60173
Ph: (847)706-3500
Fax: (847)706-3599
E-mail: feedback@soa.org
URL: http://www.soa.org

Description: Serves as a professional organization of individuals trained in the application of mathematical probabilities to the design of insurance, pension, and employee benefit programs. Sponsors series of examinations leading to designation of fellow or associate in the society. Maintains speakers' bureau; conducts educational and research programs.

SOURCES OF HELP-WANTED ADS

362 ■ *Acupressure News*
Jin Shin Do Foundation
PO Box 416
Idyllwild, CA 92549
Ph: (951)659-5707
Fax: (951)659-5707
E-mail: jinshindo@earthlink.net
URL: http://www.jinshindo.org/products.htm#newssub

Description: Annual. Provides information on body-mind acupressure, news, and main contacts in the U.S., Canada, and Europe. Features a product catalog, a class catalog and articles.

363 ■ *Chinese Medicine*
Scientific Research Publishing
PO Box 54821
Irvine, CA 92619-4821
E-mail: cm@scirp.org
URL: http://www.scirp.org/journal/cm/

Quarterly. $156.00/year for individuals. Peer-reviewed journal publishing articles on the latest advancements in Chinese medicine.

EMPLOYER DIRECTORIES AND NETWORKING LISTS

364 ■ *Careers in Focus—Alternative Healthcare*
Facts On File Inc.
132 W 31st St., 17th Fl.
New York, NY 10001
Ph: (212)967-8800
Fax: 800-678-3633
Fr: 800-322-8755
URL: http://factsonfile.infobasepublishing.com

Latest edition 3rd; 2009. $32.95 for individuals; $26.95 for libraries. Covers: An overview of alternative healthcare, followed by a selection of jobs profiled in detail, including the nature of the job, earnings, prospects for employment, what kind of training and skills it requires, and sources for further information.

365 ■ *Health & Wellness Resource Center—Alternative Health Module*
Gale
PO Box 6904
Florence, KY 41022-6904
Fr: 800-354-9706
E-mail: gale.galeord@cengage.com
URL: http://www.gale.cengage.com

Database includes: Focused upon alternative medicine topics this information is located in the Health Organization Directory component: listings of agencies, schools and organizations; journals, newsletters, and publishers websites; hospitals, health care facilities, programs and special care. Data is derived from the Medical and Health Information Directory. Entries include: Contact information. Principal content of database is a medical encyclopedia, drug and herb locator, health assessment tools, medical dictionary, links to other sites, and health news and includes references to homeopathic treatments, yoga, massage therapy, etc.

HANDBOOKS AND MANUALS

366 ■ *Opportunities in Health and Medical Careers*
The McGraw-Hill Companies
PO Box 182604
Columbus, OH 43272
Fax: (614)759-3749
Fr: 877-883-5524
E-mail: customer.service@mcgraw-hill.com
URL: http://www.mhprofessional.com/product.php?isbn=0071437274

I. Donald Snook, Jr. and Leo D'Orazio. 2004. $14.95 (paper). 157 pages. Covers the full range of medical and health occupations. Illustrated.

367 ■ *Opportunities in Holistic Health Care Careers*
The McGraw-Hill Companies
PO Box 182604
Columbus, OH 43272
Fax: (614)759-3749
Fr: 877-883-5524
E-mail: customer.service@mcgraw-hill.com
URL: http://www.mhprofessional.com/product.php?isbn=007146767X

Gillian Tierney. 2006. $13.95 (paper). 160 pages.

ONLINE JOB SOURCES AND SERVICES

368 ■ *Acupuncture Today*
E-mail: advertising@acupuncturetoday.com
URL: http://www.acupuncturetoday.com

Description: Provides the latest news, articles and featured items that are of interest to, and can be implemented by, the acupuncture and Oriental medicine profession.

369 ■ *Acupuncture.com*
URL: http://www.acupuncture.com

Description: Serves as a gateway to Chinese medicine, health and wellness by featuring articles and research about acupuncture, resources, vendor opportunities, employment opportunities, strategic partnerships, programs and others services.

370 ■ *acupuncturistjobs.net*
URL: http://www.acupuncturistjobs.net

Description: Helps job seekers find acupuncturist career opportunities with various companies. Assists employers and recruiters in matching qualified candidates with available positions.

371 ■ *HEALTHeCAREERS Network*
Fr: 888-884-8242
E-mail: info@healthecareers.com
URL: http://www.healthecareers.com

Description: Career search site for jobs in all health care specialties; educational resources; visa and licensing information for relocation; interesting articles; relocation tools; links to professional organizations and general resources.

372 ■ *Medzilla.com*
URL: http://www.medzilla.com

Description: General medical website which matches employers and job hunters to their ideal employees and jobs through search capabilities. Main files include: Post Jobs, Search Resumes, Post Resumes, Search Jobs, Head Hunters, Articles, Salary Survey.

373 ■ *ProHealthJobs.com*
Ph: (484)443-8545
Fax: (484)443-8549
E-mail: info@prohealthjobs.com
URL: http://prohealthjobs.com/jobboard

Description: Career resources site for the medical and health care field. Lists professional opportunities, product information, continuing education and open positions.

TRADESHOWS

374 ■ *AAAOM International Conference & Exposition*
American Association of Acupuncture and Oriental Medicine
PO Box 96503
Washington, DC 20090-6503
Fax: (916)443-4766
Fr: (866)455-7999
URL: http://www.aaaomonline.org

Annual. Convenes practitioners and oriental medicine service providers from around the globe.

OTHER SOURCES

375 ■ *Accreditation Commission for Acupuncture and Oriental Medicine (ACAOM)*
14502 Greenview Dr., Ste. 300B
Laurel, MD 20708
Ph: (301)313-0855
Fax: (301)313-0912
E-mail: info@acaom.org
URL: http://www.acaom.org

Description: Acts as an independent body to evaluate first professional master's degree and first professional master's level certificate and diploma programs in acupuncture and in Oriental medicine with concentrations in both acupuncture and herbal therapy for a level of performance, integrity and quality that entitles them to the confidence of the educational community and the public they serve. Evaluates doctoral programs in oriental medicine. Establishes accreditation criteria, arranges site visits, evaluates those programs that desire accredited status and publicly designates those programs that meet the criteria.

376 ■ Acupuncture for Veterans
119-40 Metropolitan Ave.
Concourse 102
Kew Gardens, NY 11415-2642
Ph: (718)847-7278
E-mail: contactus@acupunctureforveterans.com
URL: http://www.acupunctureforveterans.org

Description: Aims to serve United States veterans who have served the country. Offers low-cost group acupuncture treatments for veterans, their families and 9/11 workers. Provides aid in the treatment of post traumatic stress, anxiety, depression and pain.

377 ■ American Abdominal Acupuncture
   Medical Association (AAAMA)
41790 Winchester Rd., Ste. B
Temecula, CA 92590
Ph: (951)296-1688
Fax: (951)296-6662
E-mail: info@aaama.us
URL: http://www.aaama.us

Description: Aims to link together acupuncture professionals interested in or are currently practicing abdominal acupuncture in the United States. Promotes the science of abdominal acupuncture and its benefits across the United States. Seeks to exchange and share knowledge among all acupuncture professionals and academics around the globe.

378 ■ American Academy of Acupuncture
   and Oriental Medicine (AAAOM)
1925 W County Rd. B2
Roseville, MN 55113
Ph: (651)631-0204
Fax: (651)631-0361
E-mail: info@aaaom.edu
URL: http://www.aaaom.edu

Description: Seeks to advance acupuncture and oriental medicine.

379 ■ American Academy of Medical
   Acupuncture (AAMA)
1970 E Grand Ave., Ste. 330
El Segundo, CA 90245
Ph: (310)364-0193
Fax: (310)364-0196
E-mail: administrator@medicalacupuncture.org
URL: http://www.medicalacupuncture.org

Description: Professional society of physicians and osteopaths who utilize acupuncture in their practices. Provides ongoing training and information related to the Chinese practice of puncturing the body at specific points to cure disease or relieve pain. Offers educational and research programs.

380 ■ American Association of Acupuncture
   and Oriental Medicine (AAAOM)
PO Box 96503
Washington, DC 20090-6503
Fax: (916)443-4766
Fr: (866)455-7999
E-mail: jeannie@goodki.com
URL: http://www.aaaomonline.org

Description: Professional acupuncturists and Oriental Medicine Practitioners. Seeks to: elevate the standards of education and practice of acupuncture

and oriental medicine; establish laws governing acupuncture; provide a forum to share information on acupuncture techniques; increase public awareness of acupuncture; support research in the field. Conducts educational programs; compiles statistics. Operates speakers' bureau.

381 ■ American Board of Oriental
   Reproductive Medicine (ABORM)
910 Hampshire Rd., Ste. A
Westlake Village, CA 91361
Ph: (805)497-1335
E-mail: info@aborm.org
URL: http://www.aborm.org

Description: Promotes education and research in integrative reproductive medicine. Advances knowledge of integrated fertility treatment methods including acupuncture, herbal therapy and standardized biomedical research. Offers certification among practitioners in oriental medicine in the field of reproductive health.

382 ■ American Manual Medicine
   Association (AMMA)
2040 Raybrook SE, Ste. 103
Grand Rapids, MI 49546
Fax: (616)575-9066
Fr: 888-375-7245
E-mail: info@americanmanualmedicine.com
URL: http://www.americanmanualmedicine.com

Description: Promotes manual therapy as an allied health care profession. Seeks to advance the practice of manual therapy and manual acupuncture through professional standards, education and testing. Offers training to clinicians in order for them to provide quality medical care to patients. Provides National Board Certification Diplomate status to qualified members.

383 ■ California State Oriental Medical
   Association
703 Market St., Ste. 250
San Francisco, CA 94103-2100
Fax: (415)357-1920
Fr: 800-477-4564
E-mail: info@csomaonline.org
URL: http://www.csomaonline.org

Description: Offers free referrals to over 800 California-based member health professionals who practice Acupuncture and Oriental Medicine.

384 ■ Community Acupuncture Network
   (CAN)
PO Box 55951
Portland, OR 97238-5951
Fr: 800-404-7376
URL: http://www.communityacupuncturenetwork.org

Description: Supports the practice of acupuncture in community settings as a sustainable and practical approach in promoting the health of the public. Strives to make acupuncture more affordable and accessible. Provides support and information on community acupuncture practice.

385 ■ Council for Acupuncture Research and
   Education (CARE)
3448 Horseshoe Bend Rd.
Charlottesville, VA 22901
E-mail: info@councilforacupuncture.org
URL: http://www.councilforacupuncture.com

Description: Promotes comprehensive integration of acupuncture treatment into the American healthcare system. Develops an evidence-based scientific model of the acupuncture system for a Western audience.

386 ■ Council of Chiropractic Acupuncture
510 Baxter Rd., Ste. 8
Chesterfield, MO 63017
Ph: (636)207-6600

Fax: (636)207-6631
URL: http://councilofchiropracticacupuncture.org

Description: Aims to provide excellent educational opportunities to elevate the quality of care, life and practice of chiropractic acupuncture. Serves as a platform for professional communication regarding the practice of acupuncture in the chiropractic profession.

387 ■ Council of Colleges of Acupuncture
   and Oriental Medicine (CCAOM)
600 Wyndhurst Ave.
Baltimore, MD 21210
Ph: (410)464-6040
Fax: (410)464-6042
E-mail: ccaomcnt@comcast.net
URL: http://www.ccaom.org

Description: Represents acupuncture and oriental medicine colleges. Aims to advance the status of acupuncture and oriental medicine through educational programs. Works to provide high-quality classroom and clinical instruction. Promotes the improvement of research and teaching methods.

388 ■ International Veterinary Acupuncture
   Society
1730 S College Ave., Ste. 301
Fort Collins, CO 80525
Ph: (970)266-0666
Fax: (970)266-0777
E-mail: office@ivas.org
URL: http://www.ivas.org

Description: Veterinarians and veterinary students. Encourages knowledge and research of the philosophy, technique, and practice of veterinary acupuncture. Fosters high standards in the field; promotes scientific investigation. Accumulates resources for scientific research and education; collects data concerning clinical and research cases where animals have been treated with acupuncture; disseminates information to veterinary students, practitioners, other scientific groups, and the public. Offers 120-contact hour basic veterinary acupuncture course; administers certification examination; also offers advanced traditional Chinese herbal veterinary medicine.

389 ■ National Certification Commission for
   Acupuncture and Oriental Medicine
   (NCCAOM)
76 S Laura St., Ste. 1290
Jacksonville, FL 32202
Ph: (904)598-1005
Fax: (904)598-5001
E-mail: info@nccaom.org
URL: http://www.nccaom.org

Description: Serves as national certification agency for practitioners of acupuncture, Chinese herbology, and Asian bodywork therapy in the United States. **Purpose:** Establishes and maintains standards of competence for the safe and effective practice of Oriental medicine; to evaluate an applicant's qualifications in relation to these established standards through the administration of national board examinations; to certify practitioners who meet these standards. Acts as a consultant to state agencies in regulation, certification, and licensing of the practice of acupuncture and Oriental medicine.

390 ■ Society for Acupuncture Research
   (SAR)
130 Cloverhurst Ct.
Winston-Salem, NC 27103
E-mail: info@acupunctureresearch.org
URL: http://www.acupunctureresearch.org

Description: Seeks to elevate the standards of education and practice of acupuncture and Oriental medicine. Promotes, advances and disseminates scientific inquiry into Oriental medicine systems, which include acupuncture, herbal therapy and other modalities. Stimulates scholarship in acupuncture and Oriental medicine.

Sources of Help-Wanted Ads

391 ■ Business Performance Management
Penton Media Inc.
249 W 17th St.
New York, NY 10011
Ph: (212)204-4200
URL: http://www.bpmmag.net/

Free to qualified subscribers. Magazine for business managers. Covers organizing, automating, and analyzing of business methodologies and processes.

392 ■ CXO
IDG Communications Inc.
3 Speen St.
Framingham, MA 01701
Ph: (508)875-5000
URL: http://www.idg.com/www/IDGProducts.nsf/0/022796185EED5984852

Monthly. Magazine providing technology information for chief officers and managers.

393 ■ D & O Advisor
American Lawyer Media L.P.
120 Broadway, 5th Fl.
New York, NY 10271
Ph: (212)457-9400
Fax: (646)417-7705
Fr: 800-603-6571
URL: http://www.alm.com

Quarterly. Magazine that offers advice and perspective on corporate oversight responsibilities for directors and officers.

394 ■ E Journal of Organizational Learning and Leadership
WeLEAD Inc.
PO Box 202
Litchfield, OH 44253
Fr: 877-778-5494
URL: http://www.leadingtoday.org/weleadinlearning/

Semiannual. Free. Online academic journal about organizational leadership.

395 ■ Event Management
Cognizant Communications Corp.
3 Hartsdale Rd.
Elmsford, NY 10523-3701
Ph: (914)592-7720
Fax: (914)592-8981
URL: http://www.cognizantcommunication.com/journal-titles/event-

Quarterly. $445.00/year for institutions, online only; $525.00/year for institutions, online & hard copy; $52.00/year for individuals, professional; $50.00/year for members, online & hard copy; $65.00/year for single issue. Peer-reviewed journal covering research and analytic needs of a rapidly growing profession focused on events.

396 ■ Executive Legal Adviser
Incisive Media
120 Broadway, 5th Fl.
New York, NY 10271
Ph: (212)457-9400
Fax: (646)417-7705
URL: http://www.executivelegaladviser.com

Bimonthly. Free to qualified subscribers. Magazine that offers legal advice for corporate executives.

397 ■ Fleet Maintenance
Cygnus Business Media Inc.
3 Huntington Quadrangle, Ste. 301 N
Melville, NY 11747
Ph: (631)845-2700
Fax: (631)845-7109
Fr: 800-308-6397
URL: http://www.fleetmag.com

Business tabloid magazine offering a chapterized curriculum of technical, regulatory and managerial information designed to help maintenance managers, directors and supervisors better perform their jobs and reduce their overall cost-per-mile.

398 ■ Forrester
Forrester Research Inc.
400 Technology Sq.
Cambridge, MA 02139
Ph: (617)613-5730
Fr: (866)367-7378
URL: http://www.forrester.com/mag

Free. Journal that aims to provide ideas and advice that is relevant to today's CEOs.

399 ■ International Journal of Business Research
International Academy of Business and Economics
PO Box 2536
Ceres, CA 95307
Ph: (702)560-0653
Fax: (702)508-9166
URL: http://www.iabe.eu/domains/iabeX/journal.aspx?journalid=12

Peer-reviewed journal publishing theoretical, conceptual, and applied research on topics related to research, practice and teaching in all areas of business, management, and marketing.

400 ■ Journal of Academic Leadership
Academic Leadership
600 Park St.
Rarick Hall 219
Hays, KS 67601-4099
Ph: (785)628-4547
URL: http://www.academicleadership.org/

Journal focusing on the leadership issues in the academic world.

401 ■ Journal of Business and Psychology
Springer-Verlag New York Inc.
233 Spring St.
New York, NY 10013-1578

Ph: (212)460-1500
Fax: (212)460-1575
Fr: 800-777-4643
URL: http://www.springer.com/psychology/community+%26+environment

$904.00/year for institutions, print or online; $1,085.00/year for institutions, print & enchanced access. Journal covering all aspects of psychology that apply to the business segment. Includes topics such as personnel selection and training, organizational assessment and development, risk management and loss control, marketing and consumer behavior research.

402 ■ Journal of International Business Strategy
International Academy of Business and Economics
PO Box 2536
Ceres, CA 95307
Ph: (702)560-0653
Fax: (702)508-9166
URL: http://www.iabe.eu/domains/iabeX/journal.aspx?journalid=7

Peer-reviewed journal publishing theoretical, conceptual, and applied research on topics related to strategy in international business.

403 ■ OfficePRO
Stratton Publishing and Marketing Inc.
5285 Shawnee Rd., Ste. 510
Alexandria, VA 22312-2334
Ph: (703)914-9200
Fax: (703)914-6777
URL: http://www.iaap-hq.org/publications/officepro

$25.00/year for individuals; $40.00/year for individuals, two years; $57.00/year for individuals, three years; $59.00/year for individuals, international; $109.00/year for individuals, international, two years. Magazine for administrative assistants, office managers, and secretaries featuring information on trends in business, technology, career development, and management.

404 ■ Organization Management Journal
Eastern Academy of Management
c/o Vicki Fairbanks Taylor, VP
John I. Grove College of Business
45 Keefer Way
Mechanicsburg, PA 17011
Ph: (518)762-4651
Fax: (518)736-1716
E-mail: omj@palgrave.com
URL: http://www1.wnec.edu/omj

Free to qualified subscribers. Refereed, online journal focusing on organization management issues.

405 ■ Public Performance and Management Review
M.E. Sharpe Inc.
80 Business Pk. Dr.
Armonk, NY 10504
Ph: (914)273-1800

Fax: (914)273-2106
Fr: 800-541-6563
URL: http://www.mesharpe.com/mall/
  results1.asp?ACR=pmr

Quarterly. $95.00/year for individuals; $528.00/year for institutions; $111.00/year for other countries; $560.00/year for institutions, other countries. Journal addressing a broad range of factors influencing the performance of public and nonprofit organizations and agencies. Aims to facilitate the development of innovative techniques and encourage a wider application of those already established; stimulate research and critical thinking about the relationship between public and private management theories; present integrated analyses of theories, concepts, strategies and techniques dealing with productivity, measurement and related questions of performance improvement; and provide a forum for practitioner-academic exchange. Continuing themes include managing for productivity, measuring and evaluating performance, improving budget strategies, managing human resources, building partnerships, and applying new technologies.

406 ■ Supply Chain Management Review
Reed Business Information
360 Park Ave. S
New York, NY 10010-1710
Ph: (646)746-6400
URL: http://www.scmr.com

$199.00/year for individuals; $199.00/year for Canada; $337.00/year for other countries. Publication covering business and management.

EMPLOYER DIRECTORIES AND NETWORKING LISTS

407 ■ Careers in Focus—Clerks & Administrative Workers
Facts On File Inc.
132 W 31st St., 17th Fl.
New York, NY 10001
Ph: (212)967-8800
Fax: 800-678-3633
Fr: 800-322-8755
URL: http://www.infobasepublishing.com

Latest edition 2nd; Published May, 2010. $32.95 for individuals. Covers: An overview of clerks and administrative workers, followed by a selection of jobs profiled in detail, including the nature of the job, earnings, prospects for employment, what kind of training and skills it requires, and sources for further information.

HANDBOOKS AND MANUALS

408 ■ Administrative Assistant's and Secretary's Handbook
AMACOM Publishing
c/o American Management Association
1601 Broadway
New York, NY 10019-7434
Ph: (212)586-8100
Fr: 800-714-6395
E-mail: pubs_cust_serv@amanet.org
URL: http://www.amacombooks.org

James Stroman, Kevin Wilson, and Jennifer Wauson. 2008. $34.95 (hardback). 592 pages. Provides insights and procedures on administrative duties and high-tech office activities from using the phone and making travel arrangements to keyboarding skills and deciphering legal documents.

409 ■ Basic Administrative Law for Paralegals
Aspen Publishers Inc.
76 Ninth Ave., 7th Fl.
New York, NY 10011
Ph: (212)771-0600
Fax: (212)771-0885

Fr: 800-234-1660
URL: http://www.aspenpublishers.com/

Anne Adams. Fourth edition, 2009. $89.95. 384 pages. Explore the basics of Administrative Law.

410 ■ Definitive Personal Assistant and Secretarial Handbook
Kogan Page Publishers
1518 Walnut St., Ste. 1100
Philadelphia, PA 19102
Ph: (215)928-9112
Fax: (215)928-9113
E-mail: info@koganpage.com
URL: http://www.koganpageusa.com

Sue France. 2009. $24.95 (paper). 256 pages. Serves as a guide for management assistants, personal assistants, secretaries, and executive assistants. Discusses the administrative roles and the necessary skills for secretaries and personal assistants including: relationship management, communication, confidence, the secrets of body language, listening and questioning skills, coping with pressure and stress, dealing with difficult people, time management, and personal organization.

411 ■ Great Jobs for History Majors
The McGraw-Hill Companies
PO Box 182604
Columbus, OH 43272
Fax: (614)759-3749
Fr: 877-883-5524
E-mail: customer.service@mcgraw-hill.com
URL: http://www.mhprofessional.com

Julie DeGalan and Stephen Lambert. 2007. $16.95 (paper). 192 pages.

412 ■ Opportunities in Administrative Assistant Careers
McGraw-Hill
PO Box 182604
Columbus, OH 43272
Ph: (609)426-5793
Fax: (609)308-4480
Fr: 800-262-4729
E-mail: customer.service@mcgraw-hill.com
URL: http://www.mhprofessional.com/
  product.php?isbn=0071476091

Blanche Ettinger. 2007. $13.95. 160 pages. Provides a complete overview of the job possibilities, salary figures and experience required to become an administrative assistant.

EMPLOYMENT AGENCIES AND SEARCH FIRMS

413 ■ Action Employment Services
121 SW Morrison St., Ste. 425
Portland, OR 97204
Ph: (503)275-9011
Fax: (503)241-8772
Fr: (866)208-1643
E-mail: inquiry@actionemployment.net
URL: http://www.actionemployment.net

Description: Provides administrative, office, accounting, and human resource positions.

414 ■ Actuary Resources
115 N Castle Heights Ave., Ste. 202
Lebanon, TN 37087-2768
Ph: (615)360-5171
Fax: (615)360-5173
E-mail: info@actuaryresources.org
URL: http://www.actuaryresources.org

Provides staffing services to several different types of industries. Offers a free screening service to clients.

415 ■ Apple One Employment Services
18538 Hawthorne Blvd.
Torrance, CA 90504
Ph: (310)370-0708

Fr: 800-564-5644
E-mail: torrance-ca@appleone.com
URL: http://www.appleone.com
Employment agency. Additional offices in Anaheim, Oakland, Cerritos, San Francisco, Manhattan Beach, and Glendale.

416 ■ ATR Professional
1230 Oakmead Pkwy.
Sunnyvale, CA 94085
Ph: (408)328-8000
Fax: (408)328-8001
Fr: 877-412-1100
E-mail: corporate@atr1.com
URL: http://www.atr-professional.com

Description: Serves as an executive search firm specializing in the placement of administrative, clerical, and customer service, HR, and marketing personnel.

417 ■ Career Center, Inc.
2184 Morris Ave.
Union, NJ 07083
Ph: (908)687-1812
Fr: 800-227-3379
E-mail: career@careercenterinc.com
URL: http://www.careercenterinc.com

Employment agency.

418 ■ CyberCoders, Inc.
6591 Irvine Center Dr., Ste. 200
Irvine, CA 92618
Ph: (866)421-0200
Fax: (949)885-5150
E-mail: info@cybercoders.com
URL: http://www.cybercoders.com

Description: Recruitment and job search firm specializing in engineering, executive, financial, accounting and sales.

419 ■ Express Professional Staffing
8516 NW Expressway
Oklahoma City, OK 73162
Ph: (405)840-5000
Fr: 800-222-4057
E-mail: onlineinfo@expresspros.com
URL: http://www.expresspros.com/us

Temporary help service. Also provides some permanent placements. Several locations across the United States as well as international offices.

420 ■ Insperity, Inc.
19001 Crescent Springs Dr.
Kingwood, TX 77339-3802
Ph: (281)358-8986
Fr: 800-237-3170
E-mail: douglas.sharp@insperity.com
URL: http://www.insperity.com

Description: Serves as a full-service human resources department for small and medium-sized businesses throughout the United States. Provides client companies with benefits and services such as employment administration, government compliance, recruiting and selection, performance management, benefits management, employer liability management, training and development, and business services.

421 ■ The Linde Group, Inc.
301 Sovereign Ct.
Ballwin, MO 63021
Ph: (636)207-1118
Fax: (636)207-1371
E-mail: lincoln@thelindegroup.com
URL: http://www.thelindegroup.com

Permanent placement and temporary help service.

422 ■ ManpowerGroup
100 Manpower Pl.
Milwaukee, WI 53212
Ph: (414)961-1000
Fax: (414)906-7822
URL: http://us.manpower.com

Specializes in a wide range of employment services including permanent placement, recruitment process outsourcing, managed service programs, outplacement and human resources consulting. Provides companies with workforce solutions that help them increase productivity and improve efficiency.

423 ■ OfficeTeam.com
2884 Sand Hill Rd.
Menlo Park, CA 94025
Fr: 800-804-8367
URL: http://www.officeteam.com

Serves as a specialized temporary staffing service for administrative professionals including executive assistant, administrative assistant, office manager, project coordinator, receptionist, human resource assistant, marketing assistant, customer service representative, and data entry specialist.

424 ■ Sullivan and Cogliano
230 2nd Ave.
Waltham, MA 02451
Ph: (781)890-7890
Fax: (781)906-7801
Fr: 888-785-2641
E-mail: jobs@sullivancogliano.com
URL: http://www.sullivancogliano.com

Technical staffing firm.

ONLINE JOB SOURCES AND SERVICES

425 ■ AdminAssistantJobs.com
URL: http://www.adminassistantjobs.com

Description: Features job opportunities and resume searching and posting for administrative assistants.

426 ■ AdminCareers.com
URL: http://www.admincareers.com

Description: Serves as a niche job board for administrative related jobs, including administrative assistants, receptionists, secretaries, office managers, executive assistants and all office professionals.

427 ■ AdminCrossing.com
URL: http://www.admincrossing.com

Description: Offers a wide database of research administrative job openings worldwide. Includes openings from Fortune 500 and Fortune 1000 companies.

428 ■ AdministrativeCareers.com
URL: http://www.administrativecareers.com

Description: Serves as a niche job board for administrative jobs and resumes. Allows postings and searching of resumes for first-time and returning job seekers and employers.

429 ■ Office Worker Jobs
URL: http://www.officeworkerjobs.com

Description: Features office jobs in various industries. Features full-time, casual, and part-time vacancies.

TRADESHOWS

**430 ■ Association of Executive and
Administrative Professionals Conference**
Association of Executive and Administrative Professionals
900 S Washington St., Ste. G-13
Falls Church, VA 22046

Ph: (703)237-8616
Fax: (703)533-1153
E-mail: headquarters@theaeap.com
URL: http://www.theaeap.com

Annual. Features guest speakers and provides networking opportunities among peers to encourage professional development.

**431 ■ Legal Secretaries International Annual
Meeting**
Legal Secretaries International
2302 Fannin St., Ste. 500
Houston, TX 77002-9136
E-mail: info@legalsecretaries.org
URL: http://www.legalsecretaries.org

Annual. Primary Exhibits: Exhibits relating to legal secretaries. Dates and Locations: 2012 Sep 07-09; New Orleans, LA; The Inn on Bourbon.

OTHER SOURCES

**432 ■ Association of Executive and
Administrative Professionals**
900 S Washington St., Ste. G-13
Falls Church, VA 22046
Ph: (703)237-8616
Fax: (703)533-1153
E-mail: headquarters@theaeap.com
URL: http://www.theaeap.com

Description: Provide administrative professionals with opportunities for professional development and personal growth.

433 ■ Adoptalk
North American Council on Adoptable Children
970 Raymond Ave., Ste. 106
St. Paul, MN 55114
Ph: (651)644-3036
Fax: (651)644-9848
E-mail: info@nacac.org
URL: http://www.nacac.org
Description: Quarterly. Provides legal and activity updates concerning adoption.

434 ■ Adoption
National Adoption Center
1500 Walnut St., Ste. 701
Philadelphia, PA 19102
Ph: (215)735-9988
Fax: (215)735-9410
Fr: 800-TO-ADOPT
E-mail: nac@adopt.org
URL: http://www.adopt.org
Description: Semiannual. Informs on activities of the center. Recurring features include interviews, news of research, and a calendar of events.

435 ■ Adoption Advocate
National Council for Adoption
225 N Washington St.
Alexandria, VA 22314-2561
Ph: (703)299-6633
Fax: (703)299-6004
E-mail: ncfa@adoptioncouncil.org
URL: http://www.adoptioncouncil.org
Description: Monthly. Reviews news and developments concerning adoption programs and services. Provides legislative updates, research reports, and Council news.

436 ■ National Adoption Reports
National Council for Adoption
225 N Washington St.
Alexandria, VA 22314-2561
Ph: (703)299-6633
Fax: (703)299-6004
E-mail: ncfa@adoptioncouncil.org
URL: http://www.adoptioncouncil.org
Description: Quarterly. Provides information on current issues, legislation, events, practices, and policies for adoption. Recurring features include news of research, a calendar of events, reports of meetings, book reviews, and notices of publications available.

Employer Directories and Networking Lists

437 ■ Supervised Visitation Network Standards and Guidelines
Supervised Visitation Network
1223 King St.
Jacksonville, FL 32204

Ph: (904)389-7800
Fax: (904)389-1617
E-mail: info@svnetwork.net
URL: http://www.svnetwork.net
Covers: Forums for networking and sharing of information between supervised child access providers and other professionals involved in providing support to children and parents who are not living together.

Online Job Sources and Services

438 ■ Adoption Forums
URL: http://forums.adoption.com
Description: Includes job postings for adoption professionals.

Tradeshows

439 ■ American Adoption Congress Conference
American Adoption Congress
1025 Connecticut Ave.
Ste. 1012
Washington, DC 20036
Ph: (202)483-3399
URL: http://www.americanadoptioncongress.org/
Annual. Primary Exhibits: Adopted persons, birthparents, and adoptive parents; members of related organizations devoted to leadership in adoption reform. Dates and Locations: 2012 Apr 26-29; Denver, CO; Hyatt Regency Denver Tech Center.

440 ■ North American Council on Adoptable Children Conference
North American Council on Adoptable Children
970 Raymond Ave., Ste. 106
St. Paul, MN 55114
Ph: (651)644-3036
Fax: (651)644-9848
E-mail: info@nacac.org
URL: http://www.nacac.org
Annual. Primary Exhibits: Exhibits related to adoption and post-adoption. Dates and Locations: 2012 Jul 26-28; Crystal City, VA.

Other Sources

441 ■ Adoptee-Birthparent Support Network (ABSN)
6439 Woodridge Rd.
Alexandria, VA 22312-1336
Ph: (301)442-9106
E-mail: absnmail@verizon.net
URL: http://adopteebirthparentsupportnetwork.org
Description: Adoptees, adoptive parents, birthparents (biological parents), and siblings; social workers,

and adoption professionals. Seeks to provide support, information, and education to members and help them come to terms with the effects of adoption. Provides search assistance to adoptees and birthparents who wish to locate their biological relatives. Administers public outreach and education programs; conducts legislative efforts.

442 ■ Adoption Information Services (AIS)
1840 Old Nocross Rd., Ste. 400
Lawrenceville, GA 30044
Ph: (770)339-7236
Fax: (770)456-5961
E-mail: aisteam@adoptioninfosvcs.com
URL: http://www.adoptioninfosvcs.com
Description: Adoptive parents, adoptees, birth parents. Dedicated to providing information regarding adoption, long term foster care opportunities and search information. Sponsors adoption information events.

443 ■ American Adoption Congress (AAC)
PO Box 42730
Washington, DC 20015
Ph: (202)483-3399
E-mail: eileen2155@gmail.com
URL: http://www.americanadoptioncongress.org
Description: Adopted persons, birthparents, and adoptive parents; members of related organizations devoted to leadership in adoption reform. Furthers information on adoptions and related social-psychological issues in the U.S. by study, research, teaching, and conferences; collect, publish, and disseminate information; acts as a national clearinghouse and public information center. Develops alternative model plans for adoption; conducts regional educational conferences; provides research referrals to adoption-related services.

444 ■ Association of Administrators of the Interstate Compact on the Placement of Children (AAICPC)
1133 19th St. NW, Ste. 400
Washington, DC 20036
Ph: (202)682-0100
Fax: (202)289-6555
E-mail: icpcinbox@aphsa.org
URL: http://icpc.aphsa.com
Description: State public social service agency personnel who have been appointed compact administrators and who are responsible for the operation of the Interstate Compact on the Placement of Children. (ICPC is a uniform law that has been enacted in 50 states, the District of Columbia, and the Virgin Islands. Governs the placement of children across state lines for foster care and pre-adoptive placement by legally establishing the extension of responsibility and jurisdiction of the sending party, and the concomitant responsibility of the receiving state.) Enhances arrangements for the delivery of protective and supportive services in situations having interjurisdictional considerations. Provides forum for cooperation, consultation, and exchange of information among the

states in relation to the placement of children from one state to another. Compiles statistics.

445 ■ National Adoption Center (NAC)
1500 Walnut St., Ste. 701
Philadelphia, PA 19102
Ph: (215)735-9988
Fr: 800-TO-ADOPT
E-mail: kmullner@nacenter.adopt.org
URL: http://www.adopt.org

Description: Expands adoption opportunities for children throughout the United States, particularly the adoption of children with special needs and children from minority cultures, through public awareness and information and referral with families nationwide. Pictures and descriptions of waiting children are highlighted on Website.

446 ■ National Council for Adoption (NCFA)
225 N Washington St.
Alexandria, VA 22314
Ph: (703)299-6633
Fax: (703)299-6004
E-mail: ncfa@adoptioncouncil.org
URL: http://www.adoptioncouncil.org

Description: Represents voluntary agencies, adoptive parents, adoptees, and birthparents. Works to protect the institution of adoption and ensure the confidentiality of all involved in the adoption process. Promotes appropriate adoption practice with legislators, policymakers, human service agencies and staff, and the public. Strives for the regulation of all adoptions to ensure the protection of birthparents, children,

and adoptive parents. Serves as an information clearinghouse; provides technical assistance. Conducts research programs; monitors state and national legislation affecting adoption and maternity services. Maintains hall of fame. Compiles statistics. Operates speakers' bureau; compiles statistics.

447 ■ North American Council on Adoptable Children (NACAC)
970 Raymond Ave., Ste. 106
St. Paul, MN 55114
Ph: (651)644-3036
Fax: (651)644-9848
E-mail: info@nacac.org
URL: http://www.nacac.org

Description: Members of citizen adoption groups (composed primarily of adoptive parents of "special needs" children) and other individuals from judicial, child welfare, and legislative areas. Advocates the right of every child to a permanent, loving home. Provides direct assistance to local and state advocacy efforts; acts as a clearinghouse for adoption information; liaises with other adoption organizations. Sponsors an annual national training conference. Also sponsors Adoption Awareness Month. Conducts extensive education and outreach through the media and pre- and post-adoptive support programs. Provides resources for local advocacy programs.

448 ■ Orphan Foundation of America (OFA)
21351 Gentry Dr., Ste. 130
Sterling, VA 20166
Ph: (571)203-0270

Fax: (571)203-0273
E-mail: info@orphan.org
URL: http://fc2success.org

Description: Orphaned and abandoned youth; volunteers and contributors. Assists orphaned, abandoned, and foster-care youth by providing guidance, support, friendship, and emergency help that is seldom available to children raised outside of the traditional family setting. Advocates orphaned and abandoned youth rights nationwide; administers project that develops public policy initiatives. Offers independent living support services and volunteer referral services. Sponsors Project Bridge Program, a community-based volunteer support network that assists youth in their transition from the child welfare system to independent young adulthood. Adult volunteers guide and assist orphans in goal planning, independent living and life skills, career development, job search, maintaining employment, and recreation. Provides research services. Maintains speakers' bureau, resource center, and orphan hall of fame.

449 ■ Stars of David International (SDI)
3175 Commercial Ave., Ste. 100
Northbrook, IL 60062-1915
Fr: 800-STAR-349
E-mail: statsofdavid@aol.com
URL: http://www.starsofdavid.org

Description: Works as a Jewish adoption information and support network. Provides a network of support, adoption information and education to prospective parents, adoptive families, adult adoptees, birth families, and the Jewish community.

450 ■ Better
The Johns Hopkins University Press
2715 N Charles St.
Baltimore, MD 21218-4319
Ph: (410)516-6900
Fax: (410)516-6968
URL: http://www.press.jhu.edu/journals/better_
    evidence_based_educ

$29.50/year for individuals, print and electronic;
$80.00/year for institutions, print and electronic.
Magazine for educators and policy makers interested
in evidence-based education reform.

451 ■ Community Colleges Journal
American Association of Community Colleges
1 Dupont Cir. NW, Ste. 410
Washington, DC 20036-1145
Ph: (202)728-0200
Fax: (202)833-2467
URL: http://www.aacc.nche.edu/Publications/CCJ/
    Pages/default.aspx

$34.00/year for nonmembers; $34.00/year for members; $39.00/year for nonmembers, International;
$39.00/year for members, International; $24.00/year
for single issue, non-member; $24.00/year for single
issue, member. Educational magazine.

452 ■ Creative Education
Scientific Research Publishing
PO Box 54821
Irvine, CA 92619-4821
E-mail: ce@scirp.org
URL: http://www.scirp.org/journal/ce/

$195.00/year for individuals. Peer-reviewed journal
publishing articles on the latest advancements in
creative education.

**453 ■ International Journal of Critical
    Pedagogy**
University of North Carolina at Greensboro
1400 Spring Garden St.
Greensboro, NC 27412
Ph: (336)334-5000
URL: http://libjournal.uncg.edu/ojs/index.php/ijcp/
    index

Peer-reviewed journal publishing innovative understandings and applications of critical pedagogy.

454 ■ Tech Directions
Prakken Publications Inc.
832 Phoenix Dr.
Ann Arbor, MI 48108
Ph: (734)975-2800
Fax: (734)975-2787
Fr: 800-530-9673
E-mail: tdedit@techdirections.com
URL: http://www.techdirections.com

Monthly. $30.00/year for individuals, U.S.; $47.00/

year for institutions; $50.00/year for other countries;
$100.00/year for individuals, domestic. Magazine
covering issues, programs, and projects in industrial
education, technology education, trade and industry,
and vocational-technical career education. Articles
are geared for teacher and administrator use and
reference from elementary school through postsecondary levels.

**455 ■ Career College & Technology School
    Databook**
Chronicle Guidance Publications Inc.
66 Aurora St.
Moravia, NY 13118-3569
Ph: (315)497-0330
Fax: (315)497-0339
Fr: 800-622-7284
URL: http://www.chronicleguidance.com

Annual, latest edition 2009-2010. $26.73 for
individuals. Covers: Over 940 programs of study offered by more than 1,580 vocational schools. Entries
include: School name, city and ZIP code, phone,
programs offered, admissions requirements, costs,
enrollment, financial aid programs, year established,
and student services. Arrangement: Geographical.
Indexes: Vocation/course.

456 ■ Chronicle Two-Year College Databook
Chronicle Guidance Publications Inc.
66 Aurora St.
Moravia, NY 13118-3569
Ph: (315)497-0330
Fax: (315)497-0339
Fr: 800-622-7284
URL: http://www.chronicleguidance.com

Annual, latest edition 2009-2010. $26.74 for in-
dividuals. Covers: Over 954 associate, certificate, occupational, and transfer programs offered by more
than 2,509 technical institutes, two-year colleges,
and universities in the United States. Entries include:
College charts section gives college name, address,
phone; accreditation, enrollment, admissions, costs,
financial aid; accrediting associations' names, addresses, and phone numbers. Arrangement: Part I is
classified by college major; part II is geographical.
Indexes: College name.

457 ■ National Faculty Directory
Gale
PO Box 6904
Florence, KY 41022-6904
Fr: 800-354-9706
URL: http://www.gale.cengage.com

Annual, Latest edition 43rd; October, 2011. $1,391.00
for individuals. Covers: More than 900,000 (60,000
more in supplement) teaching faculty members at
over 4,600 junior colleges, colleges, and universities

in the United States and those in Canada that give
instruction in English. Entries include: Name, department name, institution, address, and phone and fax
numbers. Directory combines main edition and
supplement. Arrangement: Alphabetical.

**458 ■ Peterson's Vocational and Technical
    Schools and Programs**
Peterson's
Princeton Pike Corporate Ctr.
2000 Lenox Dr.
PO Box 67005
Lawrenceville, NJ 08648
Ph: (609)896-1800
Fax: (609)896-4531
Fr: 800-338-3282
URL: http://www.petersons.com/

latest edition 2010. $85.90 for individuals; $99.95 for
individuals. Covers: approximately 5,800 accredited
vocational and technical schools that offer training
programs in over 370 career fields. Available in
separate eastern and western U.S. regional editions.
Entries include: Institution name, address, phone,
name and title of contact, type of institution, year
founded, accreditation, enrollment, faculty-to-student
ratio, registration fee, student body profile, programs
offered, student services, financial aid. Arrangement:
Classified by program type.

459 ■ School Guide
School Guide Publications
210 North Ave.
New Rochelle, NY 10801-6402
Ph: (914)632-7771
Fax: (914)632-3412
Fr: 800-433-7771
URL: http://distance.schoolguides.com

Annual, Latest edition 2008. Covers: Over 3,000 colleges, vocational schools, and nursing schools in the
United States. Entries include: Institution name, address, phone, courses offered, degrees awarded. Arrangement: Classified by type of institution, then
geographical. Indexes: Subject.

**460 ■ Building Professional Pride in
    Literacy: A Dialogical Guide to Professional
    Development for Practitioners of Adult
    Literacy and Basic Education**
Krieger Publishing Company
1725 Krieger Dr.
Malabar, FL 32950
Ph: (321)724-9542
Fax: (321)951-3671
Fr: 800-724-0025
E-mail: info@krieger-publishing.com
URL: http://www.krieger-publishing.com/subcats/
    adulteducation/adulteducation.html

B. Allan Quigley. 2006. $38. 244 pages. Professional
development for adult literacy practitioners.

461 ■ *Employment Opportunities in Education*
Delmar Cengage Learning
5 Maxwell Dr.
Clifton Park, NY 12065
Fr: 800-648-7450
URL: http://www.delmarlearning.com/about/
contact.aspx

Jeanne Machado. 2006. $40.95. Provides current information on education-related jobs and opportunities. Includes information on job locations, qualifications, cover letters, resumes, interview tips, checklists and forms that aid in seeking, holding or advancing a career in education.

462 ■ *Ferguson Career Coach: Managing Your Career in Education*
Facts On File
132 W 31st St., 17th Fl.
New York, NY 10001
Fax: 800-678-3633
Fr: 800-322-8755
E-mail: custserv@factsonfile.com
URL: http://factsonfile.infobasepublishing.com

Shelly Field. 2008. $39.95 (hardcover). 272 pages. Contains tips on achieving career success in the field of education. Provides students with advice on making contacts, interviewing, and career strategies.

463 ■ *Opportunities in Adult Education Careers*
McGraw-Hill Professional
PO Box 182604
Columbus, OH 43272
Ph: 877-833-5524
Fax: (614)759-3749
E-mail: pbg.ecommerce_custserv@mcgraw-hill.com
URL: http://www.mhprofessional.com/
product.php?isbn=0071493069

Blythe Camenson. 2008. $14.95 (paperback). 160 pages. Provides a complete overview of the job possibilities, salary figures, and experience required to enter the field of adult education.

OTHER SOURCES

464 ■ **American Association for Adult and Continuing Education (AAACE)**
10111 Martin Luther King, Jr. Hwy., Ste. 200C
Bowie, MD 20720
Ph: (301)459-6261
Fax: (301)459-6241
E-mail: aaace10@aol.com
URL: http://www.aaace.org

Description: Purpose: Provides leadership in advancing adult education as a lifelong learning process. Serves as a central forum for a wide variety of adult and continuing education special interest groups. Works to stimulate local, state, and regional adult continuing education efforts; encourages mutual cooperation and support; monitors proposed legislation and offers testimony to congress.

465 ■ **American Association of Community Colleges (AACC)**
1 Dupont Cir. NW, Ste. 410
Washington, DC 20036-1176
Ph: (202)728-0200
Fax: (202)833-2467
E-mail: wbumphus@aacc.nche.edu
URL: http://www.aacc.nche.edu

Description: Community colleges; individual associates interested in community college development; corporate, educational, foundation, and international associate members. Office of Federal Relations monitors federal educational programming and legislation. Compiles statistics through data collection and policy analysis. Conducts seminars and professional training programs.

466 ■ **American Association for Women in Community Colleges (AAWCC)**
PO Box 30808
Salt Lake City, UT 84130-0808
Ph: (801)975-4225
Fax: (801)957-4440
E-mail: aawccsupport@gmail.com
URL: http://www.aawccnatl.org

Description: Women faculty members, administrators, staff members, students, and trustees of community colleges. Objectives are to: develop communication and disseminate information among women in community, junior, and technical colleges; encourage educational program development; obtain grants for educational projects for community college women. Disseminates information on women's issues and programs. Conducts regional and state professional development workshops and forums. Recognizes model programs that assist women in community colleges. An affiliate council of the American Association of Community Colleges.

467 ■ **American Federation of Teachers (AFT)**
555 New Jersey Ave. NW
Washington, DC 20001
Ph: (202)879-4400
E-mail: online@aft.org
URL: http://www.aft.org

Description: Affiliated with the AFL-CIO. Works with teachers and other educational employees at the state and local level in organizing, collective bargaining, research, educational issues, and public relations. Conducts research in areas such as educational reform, teacher certification, and national assessments and standards. Represents members' concerns through legislative action; offers technical assistance. Serves professionals with concerns similar to those of teachers, including state employees, healthcare workers, and paraprofessionals.

468 ■ **Association for Career and Technical Education (ACTE)**
1410 King St.
Alexandria, VA 22314
Ph: (703)683-3111
Fax: (703)683-7424
Fr: 800-826-9972
E-mail: acte@acteonline.org
URL: http://www.acteonline.org

Description: Represents teachers, supervisors, administrators, and others interested in the development and improvement of vocational, Technical, and practical arts education. Areas of interest include: secondary, postsecondary, and adult vocational education; education for special population groups; cooperative education. Works with such government agencies as: Bureau of Apprenticeship in Department of Labor; Office of Vocational Rehabilitation in Department of Health and Human Services; Veterans Administration; Office of Vocational and Adult Education of the Department of Education. Maintains hall of fame.

469 ■ **College Reading and Learning Association (CRLA)**
2 Caracal St.
Belen, NM 87002
Ph: (505)861-2142
E-mail: annwolf@crla.net
URL: http://www.crla.net

Description: Professionals involved in college/adult reading, learning assistance, developmental education, and tutorial services. Promotes communication for the purpose of professional growth.

470 ■ **Council for Supervision and Leadership (ITEEA-CSL)**
International Technology and Engineering Educators Association
Maryland Dept. of Education
200 W Baltimore St.
Baltimore, MD 21201
Ph: (410)767-0177

Fax: (410)333-2099
E-mail: lrhine@msde.state.md.us
URL: http://itea-cs.org

Description: Technology education supervisors from the U.S. Office of Education; local school department chairpersons; state departments of education, local school districts, territories, provinces, and foreign countries. Improves instruction and supervision of programs in technology education. Conducts research; compiles statistics. Sponsors competitions. Maintains speakers' bureau.

471 ■ **The International Educator (TIE)**
PO Box 513
Cummaquid, MA 02637
Ph: (508)790-1990
Fax: (508)790-1922
Fr: 877-375-6668
E-mail: tie@tieonline.com
URL: http://www.tieonline.com

Description: Facilitates the placement of teachers and administrators in American, British, and international schools. Seeks to create a network that provides for professional development opportunities and improved financial security of members. Offers advice and information on international school news, recent educational developments, job placement, and investment, consumer, and professional development opportunities. Makes available insurance and travel benefits. Operates International Schools Internship Program.

472 ■ **International Reading Association (IRA)**
PO Box 8139
Newark, DE 19714-8139
Ph: (302)731-1600
Fax: (302)731-1057
Fr: 800-336-7323
E-mail: pubinfo@reading.org
URL: http://www.reading.org

Description: Represents teachers, reading specialists, consultants, administrators, supervisors, researchers, psychologists, librarians, and parents interested in promoting literacy. Seeks to improve the quality of reading instruction and promote literacy worldwide. Disseminates information pertaining to research on reading, including information on adult literacy, early childhood and literacy development, international education, literature for children and adolescents, and teacher education and professional development. Maintains over 40 special interest groups and over 70 committees.

473 ■ **National Association of Blind Teachers (NABT)**
2200 Wilson Blvd., Ste. 650
Arlington, VA 22201
Ph: (202)467-5081
Fax: (703)465-5085
Fr: 800-424-8666
E-mail: info@acb.org
URL: http://www.acb.org

Description: Public school teachers, teachers of the visually impaired, college and university professors, and teachers in residential schools for the blind. Promotes employment and professional goals of blind persons entering the teaching profession or those established in their respective teaching fields. Serves as a vehicle for the dissemination of information and the exchange of ideas addressing special problems of members.

474 ■ **National Community Education Association (NCEA)**
3929 Old Lee Hwy., No. 91-A
Fairfax, VA 22030-2401
Ph: (703)359-8973
Fax: (703)359-0972
E-mail: ncea@ncea.com
URL: http://www.ncea.com

Description: Community school directors, principals, superintendents, professors, teachers, students, and laypeople. Promotes and establishes community schools as an integral part of the educational plan of every community. Emphasizes community and parent involvement in the schools, lifelong learning, and enrichment of K-12 and adult education. Serves as a clearinghouse for the exchange of ideas and information, and the sharing of efforts. Offers leadership training.

475 ■ National Council of Teachers of Mathematics (NCTM)
1906 Association Dr.
Reston, VA 20191-1502
Ph: (703)620-9840
Fax: (703)476-2970
Fr: 800-235-7566
E-mail: nctm@nctm.org
URL: http://www.nctm.org

Description: Aims to improve teaching and learning of mathematics.

476 ■ North American Council of Automotive Teachers (NACAT)
PO Box 80010
Charleston, SC 29416
Ph: (843)556-7068
URL: http://www.nacat.com

Description: Provides support for automotive educators, secondary, post-secondary, and industry. Enhances technical training opportunities, peer interaction and resources sharing. Represents automotive teachers on councils and committees where automotive teachers' interests are involved.

477 ■ *Overseas Employment Opportunities for Educators: Department of Defense Dependents Schools*
DIANE Publishing Co.
PO Box 617
Darby, PA 19023-0617
Fr: 800-782-3833
URL: http://www.dianepublishing.net

Barry Leonard, editor. $20.00. 52 pages. An introduction to teachings positions in the Dept. of Defense Dependents Schools (DoDDS), a worldwide school system, operated by the DoD in 14 countries.

Sources of Help-Wanted Ads

478 ■ *Aerospace Engineering & Manufacturing*
Society of Automotive Engineers International
400 Commonwealth Dr.
Warrendale, PA 15096-0001
Ph: (724)776-4841
Fax: (724)776-0790
Fr: 877-606-7323
E-mail: aero@sae.org
URL: http://www.sae.org/magazines/

$65.00/year for U.S., Canada, and Mexico; $100.00/year for other countries; $100.00/year for U.S., Canada, and Mexico, 2 years; $155.00/year for two years, other countries; free to members. Magazine for aerospace manufacturing engineers providing technical and design information.

479 ■ *Aerospace Manufacturing and Design*
GIE Media, Inc.
4020 Kinross Lakes Pky., Ste. 201
Richfield, OH 44286
Fax: (330)659-0823
Fr: 800-456-0707
URL: http://www.onlineamd.com/

$45.00/year for Canada and Mexico; $85.00/year for individuals, UK & Europe; $175.00/year for other countries. Magazine covering aerospace manufacturing and design.

480 ■ *AeroSpaceNews.com*
AeroSpaceNews.com
PO Box 1748
Ojai, CA 93024-1748
Ph: (805)985-2320
URL: http://www.aerospacenews.com/content/view/41/33/

Monthly. $19.95/year for individuals, private. Journal reporting on the insights, impressions and images of tomorrow's technological wonders in the field of aerospace.

481 ■ *AIE Perspectives Newsmagazine*
American Institute of Engineers
4630 Appian Way, Ste. 206
El Sobrante, CA 94803-1875
Ph: (510)758-6240
Fax: (510)758-6240
URL: http://www.members-aie.org

Monthly. Professional magazine covering engineering.

482 ■ *Air Jobs Digest*
World Air Data
PO Box 42724
Washington, DC 20015
Ph: (301)990-6800
Fr: 800-247-5627
URL: http://www.airjobsdigest.com/

Monthly. $96.00/year for individuals. Newspaper covering job listings in aviation and aerospace worldwide.

483 ■ *Aviation Maintenance*
Access Intelligence L.L.C.
4 Choke Cherry Rd., 2nd Fl.
Rockville, MD 20850-4024
Ph: (301)354-2000
Fax: (301)309-3847
Fr: 800-777-5006
URL: http://www.aviationtoday.com/am/

Free. Magazine covering aviation maintenance.

484 ■ *Aviation Week & Space Technology*
McGraw-Hill Inc.
PO Box 182604
Columbus, OH 43218
Ph: (614)430-4000
Fax: (614)759-3749
Fr: 877-833-5524
URL: http://www.aviationweek.com/aw/generic/channel_.jsp?channel=

Weekly. $109.00/year for Canada; $103.00/year for individuals; $160.00/year for other countries. Magazine serving the aviation and aerospace market worldwide.

485 ■ *Engineering*
Scientific Research Publishing
PO Box 54821
Irvine, CA 92619-4821
E-mail: eng@scirp.org
URL: http://www.scirp.org/journal/eng/

Monthly. $708.00/year for individuals. Peer-reviewed journal publishing articles on the latest advancements in engineering.

486 ■ *Engineering Conferences International Symposium Series*
Berkeley Electronic Press
2809 Telegraph Ave., Ste. 202
Berkeley, CA 94705-1167
Ph: (510)665-1200
Fax: (510)665-1201
URL: http://services.bepress.com/eci/

Journal focusing on advance engineering science.

487 ■ *ENR: Engineering News-Record*
McGraw-Hill Inc.
PO Box 182604
Columbus, OH 43218
Ph: (614)430-4000
Fax: (614)759-3749
Fr: 877-833-5524
URL: http://enr.construction.com/Default.asp

Weekly. $49.00/year for individuals, print; $89.00/year for Canada, print; $125.00/year for other countries, print. Magazine focusing on engineering and construction.

488 ■ *Graduating Engineer & Computer Careers*
Career Recruitment Media
2 LAN Dr., Ste. 100
Westford, MA 01886
Ph: (978)692-5092
Fax: (978)692-4174
URL: http://www.graduatingengineer.com

Quarterly. $16.95/year for individuals. Magazine focusing on employment, education, and career development for entry-level engineers and computer scientists.

489 ■ *High Technology Careers Magazine*
HTC
4701 Patrick Henry Dr., No. 1901
Santa Clara, CA 95054
Fax: (408)567-0242
URL: http://www.hightechcareers.com

Bimonthly. $29.00/year; $35.00/year for Canada; $85.00/year for out of country. Magazine (tabloid) containing employment opportunity information for the engineering and technical community.

490 ■ *InterJournal*
New England Complex Systems Institute
283 Main St., Ste. 319
Cambridge, MA 02142
Ph: (617)547-4100
Fax: (617)661-7711
URL: http://www.interjournal.org/

Journal covering the fields of science and engineering.

491 ■ *International Journal of Astronomy and Astrophysics*
Scientific Research Publishing
PO Box 54821
Irvine, CA 92619-4821
E-mail: ijaa@scirp.org
URL: http://www.scirp.org/journal/ijaa/

Quarterly. $156.00/year for individuals. Peer-reviewed journal publishing research on fields of astrophysics and space sciences.

492 ■ *International Journal of Energetic Materials and Chemical Propulsion*
Begell House Inc.
50 Cross Hwy.
Redding, CT 06896
Ph: (203)938-1300
Fax: (203)938-1304
URL: http://www.begellhouse.com/journals/17bbb47e377ce023

$1,240.00/year for institutions. Journal promoting scientific investigation, technical advancements and information exchange on energetic materials and chemical propulsion.

493 ■ Journal of Engineering Education
American Society for Engineering Education
1818 N St. NW, Ste. 600
Washington, DC 20036-2479
Ph: (202)331-3500
Fax: (202)265-8504
URL: http://www.jee.org

Quarterly. $100.00/year for libraries, online; $160.00/year for other countries, library; $150.00/year for U.S., Canada, and Mexico, library; $160.00/year for other countries, library. Peer-reviewed journal covering scholarly research in engineering education.

494 ■ Journal of Women and Minorities in Science and Engineering
Begell House Inc.
50 Cross Hwy.
Redding, CT 06896
Ph: (203)938-1300
Fax: (203)938-1304
URL: http://www.begellhouse.com/journals/00551c876cc2f027

$248.00/year for institutions. Peer-reviewed journal featuring innovative ideas and programs for classroom teachers, scientific studies, and formulation of concepts related to the education, recruitment, and retention of under-represented groups in science and engineering.

495 ■ NASA Tech Briefs
Associated Business Publications Company Ltd.
1466 Broadway, No. 910
New York, NY 10036
Ph: (212)490-3999
Fax: (212)986-7864
URL: http://www.techbriefs.com/

Monthly. Free. Publication covering technology for American industry and government in the fields of electronics, computers, physical sciences, materials, mechanics, machinery, fabrication technology, math and information sciences, and the life sciences.

496 ■ NSBE Magazine
NSBE Publications
205 Daingerfield Rd.
Alexandria, VA 22314
Ph: (703)549-2207
Fax: (703)683-5312
URL: http://www.nsbe.org/News-Media/Magazines/About-NSBE-Magazine

$20.00/year for individuals; $35.00/year for other countries; $15.00/year for students. Journal providing information on engineering careers, self-development, and cultural issues for recent graduates with technical majors.

497 ■ PE
National Society of Professional Engineers
1420 King St.
Alexandria, VA 22314
Ph: (703)684-2800
Fax: (703)684-4875
URL: http://www.nspe.org/PEmagazine/index.html

Monthly. Magazine (tabloid) covering professional, legislative, and techology issues for an engineering audience.

498 ■ SAE International Journal of Aerospace
S.A.E. International
400 Commonwealth Dr.
Warrendale, PA 15096-0001
Ph: (724)776-4841
Fax: (724)776-0790
Fr: 877-606-7323
URL: http://books.sae.org/book-v120-1

$330.00/year for individuals, print; $297.00/year for members, print; $333.00/year for members, online; $370.00/year for individuals, online. Peer-reviewed journal featuring technical papers in aerospace engineering.

499 ■ SWE, Magazine of the Society of Women Engineers
Society of Women Engineers
120 S La Salle St., Ste. 1515
Chicago, IL 60603
Ph: (312)596-5223
Fr: 877-793-4636
URL: http://societyofwomenengineers.swe.org/index.php

Quarterly. $30.00/year for nonmembers. Magazine for engineering students and for women and men working in the engineering and technology fields. Covers career guidance, continuing development and topical issues.

500 ■ TEST Engineering & Management
The Mattingley Publishing Company Inc.
3756 Grand Ave., Ste. 205
Oakland, CA 94610-1545
Ph: (510)839-0909
Fax: (510)839-2950
E-mail: testmag@testmagazine.biz
URL: http://www.testmagazine.biz/

$60.00/year for individuals; $70.00/year for other countries. Trade publication that covers physical and mechanical testing and environmental simulation; edited for test engineering professionals.

501 ■ TsAGI Science Journal
Begell House Inc.
50 Cross Hwy.
Redding, CT 06896
Ph: (203)938-1300
Fax: (203)938-1304
URL: http://www.begellhouse.com/journals/58618e1439159b1f

Bimonthly. $999.00/year for institutions. Journal covering the areas of mechanics, aviation and cosmonautics, industrial aerodynamic and hydrodynamics of rapid motion.

502 ■ WEPANEWS
Women in Engineering Programs & Advocates Network
1901 E Asbury Ave., Ste. 220
Denver, CO 80208
Ph: (303)871-4643
Fax: (303)871-4628
E-mail: dmatt@wepan.org
URL: http://www.wepan.org

Description: 2/year. Seeks to provide greater access for women to careers in engineering. Includes news of graduate, undergraduate, freshmen, pre-college, and re-entry engineering programs for women. Recurring features include job listings, faculty, grant, and conference news, international engineering program news, action group news, notices of publications available, and a column titled Kudos.

503 ■ Woman Engineer
Equal Opportunity Publications, Inc.
445 Broadhollow Rd., Ste. 425
Melville, NY 11747
Ph: (631)421-9421
Fax: (631)421-1352
E-mail: info@eop.com
URL: http://www.eop.com

Annual. Magazine that is offered at no charge to qualified female engineering, computer-science, and information-technology students and professionals seeking to find employment and advancement in their careers.

EMPLOYER DIRECTORIES AND NETWORKING LISTS

504 ■ American Men and Women of Science
Gale
PO Box 6904
Florence, KY 41022-6904

Fr: 800-354-9706
URL: http://www.gale.cengage.com

Biennial, even years; New edition expected 29th, June 2011. $1,368.00 for individuals. Covers: Over 135,000 U.S. and Canadian scientists active in the physical, biological, mathematical, computer science, and engineering fields; includes references to previous edition for deceased scientists and nonrespondents. Entries include: Name, address, education, personal and career data, memberships, honors and awards, research interest. Arrangement: Alphabetical. Indexes: Discipline (in separate volume).

505 ■ Career Opportunities in Aviation and the Aerospace Industry
Facts On File Inc.
132 W 31st St., 17th Fl.
New York, NY 10001
Ph: (212)967-8800
Fax: 800-678-3633
Fr: 800-322-8755
URL: http://www.infobasepublishing.com

Published January, 2005. Covers: Eighty up-to-date job profiles, providing detailed information about the duties, salaries, and prospects of aviation mechanics, designers, technicians, scientists, and administrators.

506 ■ Careers in Focus—Engineering
Facts On File Inc.
132 W 31st St., 17th Fl.
New York, NY 10001
Ph: (212)967-8800
Fax: 800-678-3633
Fr: 800-322-8755
URL: http://www.infobasepublishing.com

Latest edition 3rd; Published July, 2007. $32.95 for individuals. Covers: An overview of engineering, followed by a selection of jobs profiled in detail, including the nature of the job, earnings, prospects for employment, what kind of training and skills it requires, and sources for further information.

507 ■ Directory of Contract Staffing Firms
C.E. Publications Inc.
PO Box 3006
Bothell, WA 98041-3006
Ph: (425)806-5200
Fax: (425)806-5585
URL: http://www.cjhunter.com/dcsf/overview.html

Annual. Covers: Nearly 1,300 contract firms actively engaged in the employment of engineering, IT/IS, and technical personnel for 'temporary' contract assignments throughout the world. Entries include: Company name, address, phone, name of contact, email, web address. Arrangement: Alphabetical. Indexes: Geographical.

508 ■ Indiana Society of Professional Engineers—Directory
Indiana Society of Professional Engineers
PO Box 20806
Indianapolis, IN 46220
Ph: (317)255-2267
Fax: (317)255-2530
URL: http://www.indspe.org

Annual, fall. Covers: Member registered engineers, land surveyors, engineering students, and engineers in training. Entries include: Member name, address, phone, type of membership, business information, specialty. Arrangement: Alpha by chapter area.

HANDBOOKS AND MANUALS

509 ■ Aerospace Engineer
National Learning Corporation
212 Michael Dr.
Syosset, NY 11791
Fr: 800-632-8888
URL: http://www.passbooks.com

2009. $59.95 (paper). Serves as an exam preparation guide for aerospace engineers.

510 ■ *Great Jobs for Engineering Majors*
The McGraw-Hill Companies
PO Box 182604
Columbus, OH 43272
Fax: (614)759-3749
Fr: 877-883-5524
E-mail: customer.service@mcgraw-hill.com
URL: http://www.mhprofessional.com/
product.php?isbn=0071641963

Geraldine O. Garner. Second edition, 2008. $16.95. 192 pages. Covers all the career options open to students majoring in engineering.

511 ■ *Resumes for Scientific and Technical Careers*
The McGraw-Hill Companies
PO Box 182604
Columbus, OH 43272
Fax: (614)759-3749
Fr: 877-883-5524
E-mail: customer.service@mcgraw-hill.com
URL: http://www.mhprofessional.com/
product.php?isbn=0071482199

Third edition, 2007. $12.95 (paper). 144 pages. Provides resume advice for individuals interested in working in scientific and technical careers. Includes sample resumes and cover letters.

EMPLOYMENT AGENCIES AND SEARCH FIRMS

512 ■ Aerospace Solutions
2323 E Magnolia St., Ste. 107
Phoenix, AZ 85034
Ph: (602)354-8180
Fax: (602)354-8589
E-mail: info@aero-us.com
URL: http://aero-us.com

Description: Provides professional staffing, direct placement and outsourcing for firms working exclusively in aerospace and defense-related disciplines.

513 ■ Amtec Human Capital
2749 Saturn St.
Brea, CA 92821
Ph: (714)993-1900
Fax: (714)993-2419
E-mail: info@amtechc.com
URL: http://www.amtechc.com

Employment agency.

514 ■ The Aspire Group
711 Boylston St.
Boston, MA 02116-2616
Fax: (617)500-7284
Fr: 800-487-2967
URL: http://www.bmanet.com/Aspire/index.html

Employment agency.

515 ■ Aureus Group
C&A Plz., 13609 California St., Ste. 100
Omaha, NE 68154-3503
Ph: (402)891-6900
Fax: (402)891-1290
Fr: 888-239-5993
E-mail: omaha@aureusgroup.com
URL: http://www.aureusgroup.com

Provides human capital management services in a wide variety of industries. Executive search and recruiting consultants specializing in six areas: accounting and finance, data processing, aerospace, engineering, manufacturing and medical professionals. Industries served: hospitals, all mainframe computer shops and all areas of accounting.

516 ■ DMR Global Inc.
10230 W Sample Rd.
Coral Springs, FL 33065
Ph: (954)796-5043
Fax: (954)796-5044
Fr: 888-796-0032
E-mail: rdaratany@dmrglobal.com
URL: http://www.dmrglobal.com

Executive search firm.

517 ■ Engineer One, Inc.
PO Box 23037
Knoxville, TN 37933
Fax: (865)691-0110
E-mail: engineerone@engineerone.com
URL: http://www.engineerone.com

Engineering employment service specializing in engineering and management in the chemical process, power utilities, manufacturing, mechanical, electrical, and electronic industries. Maintains an Information Technology Division that works nationwide across all industries. Also provides systems analysis consulting services specializing in VAX based systems.

518 ■ Fisher Personnel Management Services
2351 N Filbert Rd.
Exeter, CA 93221
Ph: (559)594-5774
Fax: (559)594-5777
E-mail: hookme@fisheads.net
URL: http://www.fisheads.net

Executive search firm.

519 ■ Focus Learning Corp.
173 Cross St., Ste. 200
San Luis Obispo, CA 93401
Ph: (805)543-4895
Fax: (805)543-4897
Fr: 800-458-5116
E-mail: info@focuslearning.com
URL: http://www.focuslearning.com

Provides professional services to corporations for the development and implementation of training programs. Assists clients with needs assessment related to training and professional development, goals definition, and development of training materials. Industries served include: government, utility, aerospace, business, and computer.

520 ■ Global Employment Solutions
10375 Park Meadows Dr., Ste. 375
Littleton, CO 80124
Ph: (303)216-9500
Fax: (303)216-9533
URL: http://www.gesnetwork.com

Employment agency.

521 ■ International Staffing Consultants
31655 2nd Ave.
Laguna Beach, CA 92651
Ph: (949)255-5857
Fax: (949)767-5959
E-mail: iscinc@iscworld.com
URL: http://www.iscworld.com

Employment agency. Provides placement on regular or temporary basis. Affiliate office in London.

522 ■ Johnson Personnel Co.
1639 N Alpine Rd.
Rockford, IL 61107
Ph: (815)964-0840
Fax: (815)964-0855
E-mail: darrell@nsonpersonnel.com
URL: http://www.johnsonpersonnel.com

Provide technical and managerial placement in industry. Industries served: aerospace, automotive, machine tool and consumer products.

523 ■ J.R. Bechtle & Company
67 S Bedford St., Ste. 400 W
Burlington, MA 01803-5177

Ph: (781)229-5804
Fax: (781)359-1829
E-mail: jrb.boston@jrbechtle.com
URL: http://www.jrbechtle.com

Executive search firm.

524 ■ Louis Rudzinsky Associates Inc.
394 Lowell St., Ste. 17
PO Box 640
Lexington, MA 02420-2551
Ph: (781)862-6727
Fax: (781)862-6868
E-mail: lra@lra.com
URL: http://www.lra.com

Provides recruitment, placement, and executive search to industry (software, electronics, optics) covering positions in general management, manufacturing, engineering, and marketing. Personnel consulting activities include counsel to small and startup companies. Industries served: electronics, aerospace, optical, laser, computer, software, imaging, electro-optics, biotechnology, advanced materials, and solid-state/semiconductor.

525 ■ ManpowerGroup
100 Manpower Pl.
Milwaukee, WI 53212
Ph: (414)961-1000
Fax: (414)906-7822
URL: http://us.manpower.com

Specializes in a wide range of employment services including permanent placement, recruitment process outsourcing, managed service programs, outplacement and human resources consulting. Provides companies with workforce solutions that help them increase productivity and improve efficiency.

526 ■ Robert Drexler Associates Inc.
PO Box 151
Saddle River, NJ 07458
Ph: (201)760-2300
Fax: (201)760-2301
E-mail: drexler@engineeringemployment.com
URL: http://www.engineeringemployment.com

Executive search firm.

527 ■ S.R. Clarke
105 Huntercombe
Williamburg, VA 23188
Ph: (703)934-4200
Fax: (703)344-0259
URL: http://www.srclarke.com/index.html

Serves as an executive search and recruitment firm specializing in commercial construction, commercial real estate development, residential asset management, residential construction and development, subcontractor trades, finance, accounting, administration, heavy construction, architectural design and engineering design.

528 ■ Strom Aviation
109 S Elm St.
Waconia, MN 55387
Ph: (952)544-3611
Fax: (952)544-3948
Fr: 800-743-8988
E-mail: jobs@stromaviation.com
URL: http://www.stromaviation.com

Serves as a staffing firm specializing in hiring all types of aircraft technicians to provide manpower to service centers, repair stations, and OEMs.

529 ■ Techtronix Technical Search
4805 N 24th Pl.
PO Box 17713
Milwaukee, WI 53217-0173
Ph: (414)466-3100
Fax: (414)466-3598

Firm specializes in recruiting executives for the engineering, information systems, manufacturing, marketing, finance, and human resources industries. Industries include electronic, manufacturing and finance.

ONLINE JOB SOURCES AND SERVICES

530 ■ AeroIndustryJobs.com
URL: http://www.aeroindustryjobs.com
Description: Lists careers in the aerospace, defense and advanced materials industries. Helps industry employers connect with qualified, career-focused job seekers.

531 ■ Aerospace Engineering Jobs
URL: http://www.aerospaceengineeringjobs.us
Description: Provides an online source for aerospace engineering job. Features updated job listings for candidates and job posting for employers.

532 ■ AerospaceCrossing.com
URL: http://www.aerospacecrossing.com
Description: Consolidates jobs from employer websites, job portals, and aerospace websites.

533 ■ AerospaceEngineer.com
URL: http://www.aerospaceengineer.com
Description: Provides job opportunities in the aerospace engineering field.

534 ■ AeroVents.com
E-mail: info@aerovents.com
URL: http://www.aerovents.com/body.shtml
Description: Seeks to spread the word about aviation events. Covers aviation events from conventions, space launches, seminars, model rocketry and aircraft, ballooning, sky diving, plane pulls, open houses, air shows and fly-ins.

535 ■ AircraftEngineers.com
URL: http://www.aircraftengineers.com
Description: Lists aircraft maintenance engineering jobs and aerospace vacancies. Provides career information for individuals who wish to start a career as an aircraft engineer.

536 ■ AirJobsDaily.com
E-mail: staff@airjobsdaily.com
URL: http://www.airjobsdaily.com
Description: Serves as a source of current aviation and aerospace job openings.

537 ■ AirlineCareer.info
URL: http://www.airlinecareer.info
Description: Provides jobs in the airline community covering airport careers, aircraft manufacturing, aerospace careers, and cabin crew careers.

538 ■ American Institute of Aeronautics and Astronautics Career Planning and Placement Services
1801 Alexander Bell Dr., Ste. 500
Reston, VA 20191-4344
Ph: (703)264-7500
Fax: (703)264-7551
Fr: 800-639-2422
E-mail: custserv@aiaa.org
URL: http://www.aiaa.org
Description: Site for AIAA members to place recruitment advertisements, browse career opportunities listings, post resumes, and seek additional employment assistance. Non-members may become members though this site.

539 ■ The Aviation MD
E-mail: adrian@theaviationmd.com
URL: http://www.theaviationmd.com
Description: Serves as international aviation database for employers and jobseekers in the aviation industry.

540 ■ AviationCrossing.com
URL: http://www.aviationcrossing.com
Provides aviation jobs for agents, managers, mechan-

ics, operators, specialists, supervisors, technicians, engineers, maintenance, pilots and other related aviation professionals.

541 ■ AviationEmployment.com
URL: http://www.aviationemployment.com
Description: Serves as an online job search service provider specializing in aviation and aerospace jobs and employment opportunities.

542 ■ AvJobs.com
URL: http://www.avjobs.com
Description: Provides information on a number of different careers in the aviation and aerospace industry. Features aviation schools directory, affiliate programs, research and networking, employment resources, salaries and wages, aviation careers descriptions, aviation guide and other resources.

543 ■ Engineering Classifieds
URL: http://www.engineeringclassifieds.com
Description: Serves as a career site for engineering professionals. Provides services including job search agents, resume creation and posting.

544 ■ EngineerJobs.com
URL: http://www.engineerjobs.com
Description: Provides job opportunities for engineering professionals in the following disciplines: aerospace, agricultural, biomedical, chemical, civil, electrical, environmental, industrial, manufacturing, marine, materials, mechanical, mining, nuclear, petroleum, process, project, quality, sales, software, solar, systems, and structural.

545 ■ Engineer.net
URL: http://www.engineer.net
Description: Provides engineering employment tools such as job search, job posting, and engineering resumes.

546 ■ PlaneJobs.com
E-mail: jobmaster@planejobs.com
URL: http://planejobs.com
Description: Serves as an employment, resume, career, and job search database for the aviation industry.

547 ■ Spherion
2050 Spectrum Blvd.
Fort Lauderdale, FL 33309
Ph: (954)308-7600
Fr: 800-774-3746
E-mail: help@spherion.com
URL: http://www.spherion.com
Description: Recruitment firm specializing in accounting and finance, sales and marketing, interim executives, technology, engineering, retail and human resources.

548 ■ ThinkEnergyGroup.com
E-mail: resumes@thinkjobs.com
URL: http://www.thinkenergygroup.com
Description: Serves as a job board for professionals looking for positions in engineering, power plant, energy, and technical fields. Contains advice and tips on interviews, job searching, resume writing, hiring, and management. Provides choices of work location, pay rates in the field of expertise and contract, temp-to-hire, and direct hiring options.

TRADESHOWS

549 ■ AeroMat Conference and Exposition
ASM International
9639 Kinsman Rd.
Materials Park, OH 44073-0002
Ph: (440)338-5151
E-mail: customerservice@asminternational.org
URL: http://www.asminternational.org

Annual. Primary Exhibits: Providing information covering materials, material applications and processes for designing the next generation of aviation and space vehicles and systems.

550 ■ Aerospace Manufacturing and Automated Fastening Conference & Exhibition
Society of Automotive Engineers, International SAE
400 Commonwealth Dr.
Warrendale, PA 15096-0001
Ph: (724)772-4841
Fax: (724)776-0790
E-mail: exhibitions@sae.org
URL: http://www.sae.org

Annual. Primary Exhibits: Aerospace parts, materials, components, systems, and techniques. Dates and Locations: 2012 Sep 18-20; Fort Worth, TX.

551 ■ Aerospace Medical Association Annual Scientific Meeting
Aerospace Medical Association
320 S. Henry St.
Alexandria, VA 22314-3579
Ph: (703)739-2240
Fax: (703)739-9652
E-mail: gcarter@asma.org
URL: http://www.asma.org

Annual. Primary Exhibits: Products related to aerospace medicine; safety products; diagnostic and research instrumentation for the field of human factors. Dates and Locations: 2012 May 13-17; Atlanta, GA; Atlanta Hilton; 2013 May 12-16; Chicago, IL; 2014 May 11-15; San Diego, CA; 2015 May 10-14; Orlando, FL.

552 ■ AIAA Aerospace Sciences Meeting and Exhibition
American Institute of Aeronautics and Astronautics AIAA
1801 Alexander Bell Dr., Ste. 500
Reston, VA 20191-4344
Ph: (703)264-7500
Fax: (703)264-7551
Fr: 800-639-AIAA
URL: http://www.aiaa.org

Annual. Primary Exhibits: Computer and software technologies for the aerospace industry. Dates and Locations: 2013 Jan 07-10; Grapevine, TX; Gaylord Texan Resort and Convention Center; 2014 Jan 13-16; National Harbor, MD; Gaylord Texan Resort and Convention Center; 2015 Jan 05-08; Orlando, FL; Gaylord Palms; 2016 Jan 04-07; San Diego, CA; Manchester Grand Hyatt.

553 ■ AIAA Applied Aerodynamics Conference
American Institute of Aeronautics and Astronautics AIAA
1801 Alexander Bell Dr., Ste. 500
Reston, VA 20191-4344
Ph: (703)264-7500
Fax: (703)264-7551
Fr: 800-639-AIAA
URL: http://www.aiaa.org

Annual. Primary Exhibits: Technologies related to aerospace guidance, navigation, and control; atmospheric flight; modeling and simulation; and astrodynamics. Dates and Locations: 2012 Jun 25-28; New Orleans, LA; Sheraton New Orleans; 2013 Jun 24-27; San Diego, CA; Sheraton San Diego Hotel & Marina.

554 ■ AIAA/ASME/SAE/ASEE Joint Propulsion Conference and Exhibit
American Institute of Aeronautics and Astronautics AIAA
1801 Alexander Bell Dr., Ste. 500
Reston, VA 20191-4344
Ph: (703)264-7500
Fax: (703)264-7551
Fr: 800-639-AIAA
URL: http://www.aiaa.org

Annual. Primary Exhibits: Aerospace propulsion related exhibits. Dates and Locations: 2012 Jul 30 - Aug 01; Atlanta, GA; Hyatt Regency Atlanta; 2013 Jul 15-17; San Jose, CA; San Jose Convention Center.

555 ■ Air & Space Conference and Technology Exposition

J. Spargo & Associates, Inc.
11208 Waples Mill Rd., Ste. 112
Fairfax, VA 22030
Ph: (703)631-6200
Fax: (703)818-9177
Fr: 800-564-4220
E-mail: info@jspargo.com
URL: http://www.jspargo.com

Annual. Primary Exhibits: Aerospace technology, airplanes, rockets, helicopters, radar, computers, software, and communications systems. Dates and Locations: 2012 Sep 17-19; National Harbor, MD; Gaylord National Resort & Convention Center.

OTHER SOURCES

556 ■ Acoustical Society of America
2 Huntington Quadrangle, Ste. 1NO1
Melville, NY 11747-4502
Ph: (516)576-2360
Fax: (516)576-2377
E-mail: asa@aip.org
URL: http://acousticalsociety.org

Description: Represents members from various fields related to sound including physics, electrical, mechanical and aeronautical engineering, oceanography, biology, physiology, psychology, architecture, speech, noise and noise control, and music. Aims to increase and diffuse the knowledge of acoustics and its practical applications. Organizes meetings, provides reprints of out-of-print classic texts in acoustics, and translation books.

557 ■ Aeronautical Repair Station Association
121 N Henry St.
Alexandria, VA 22314-2903
Ph: (703)739-9543
Fax: (703)739-9488
E-mail: arsa@arsa.org
URL: http://www.arsa.org

Description: Works with legislators to advance an agenda that benefits the membership and aviation safety in general. Helps develop guidance, policy and interpretations that are clear, concise, consistent and applied uniformly to all similarly situated companies and individuals.

558 ■ Aerospace Industries Association
1000 Wilson Blvd., Ste. 1700
Arlington, VA 22209-3928
Ph: (703)358-1000
URL: http://www.aia-aerospace.org

Description: Manufacturers and suppliers of civil, military, and business aircraft, helicopters, unmanned aerial vehicles, space systems, aircraft engines, missiles, and related components, equipment, services, and information technology. Aims to ensure the United States aerospace, defense, and homeland security industry remains preeminent and its members are successful and profitable in a changing global market. Establishes industry goals and strategies, achieving consensus among members and national and global stakeholders and implementing solutions to industry issues related to national and homeland security, civil aviation, and space.

559 ■ American Association of Engineering Societies (AAES)
1801 Alexander Bell Dr.
Reston, VA 20191
Ph: (202)296-2237
Fax: (202)296-1151

Fr: 888-400-2237
E-mail: dbateson@aaes.org
URL: http://www.aaes.org

Description: Coordinates the efforts of the member societies in the provision of reliable and objective information to the general public concerning issues which affect the engineering profession and the field of engineering as a whole; collects, analyzes, documents, and disseminates data which will inform the general public of the relationship between engineering and the national welfare; provides a forum for the engineering societies to exchange and discuss their views on matters of common interest; and represents the U.S. engineering community abroad through representation in WFEO and UPADI.

560 ■ American Engineering Association (AEA)
533 Waterside Blvd.
Monroe Township, NJ 08831
Ph: (201)664-6954
E-mail: aea@aea.org
URL: http://www.aea.org

Description: Members consist of Engineers and engineering professionals. Purpose to advance the engineering profession and U.S. engineering capabilities. Issues of concern include age discrimination, immigration laws, displacement of U.S. Engineers by foreign workers, trade agreements, off shoring of U.S. Engineering and manufacturing jobs, loss of U.S. manufacturing and engineering capability, and recruitment of foreign students. Testifies before Congress. Holds local Chapter meetings.

561 ■ American Indian Science and Engineering Society (AISES)
PO Box 9828
Albuquerque, NM 87119-9828
Ph: (505)765-1052
Fax: (505)765-5608
E-mail: info@aises.org
URL: http://www.aises.org

Description: Represents American Indian and non-Indian students and professionals in science, technology, and engineering fields; corporations representing energy, mining, aerospace, electronic, and computer fields. Seeks to motivate and encourage students to pursue undergraduate and graduate studies in science, engineering, and technology. Sponsors science fairs in grade schools, teacher training workshops, summer math/science sessions for 8th-12th graders, professional chapters, and student chapters in colleges. Offers scholarships. Adult members serve as role models, advisers, and mentors for students. Operates placement service.

562 ■ American Institute of Aeronautics and Astronautics (AIAA)
1801 Alexander Bell Dr., Ste. 500
Reston, VA 20191-4344
Ph: (703)264-7500
Fax: (703)264-7551
Fr: 800-639-AIAA
E-mail: custserv@aiaa.org
URL: http://www.aiaa.org

Description: Represents scientists and engineers in the field of aeronautics and astronautics. Facilitates interchange of technological information through publications and technical meetings in order to foster overall technical progress in the field and increase the professional competence of members. Operates Public Policy program to provide federal decision-makers with the technical information and policy guidance needed to make effective policy on aerospace issues. Public Policy program activities include congressional testimony, position papers, section public policy activities, and workshops. Offers placement assistance; compiles statistics; offers educational programs. Provides abstracting services through its AIAA Access.

563 ■ Association for International Practical Training (AIPT)
10400 Little Patuxent Pkwy., Ste. 250
Columbia, MD 21044-3519

Ph: (410)997-2200
Fax: (410)992-3924
E-mail: aipt@aipt.org
URL: http://www.aipt.org

Description: Providers worldwide of on-the-job training programs for students and professionals seeking international career development and life-changing experiences. Arranges workplace exchanges in hundreds of professional fields, bringing employers and trainees together from around the world. Client list ranges from small farming communities to Fortune 500 companies.

564 ■ Engineering Society of Detroit (ESD)
20700 Civic Center Dr., Ste. 450
Southfield, MI 48076
Ph: (248)353-0735
Fax: (248)353-0736
E-mail: esd@esd.org
URL: http://ww2.esd.org/home.htm

Description: Engineers from all disciplines; scientists and technologists. Conducts technical programs and engineering refresher courses; sponsors conferences and expositions. Maintains speakers' bureau; offers placement services; although based in Detroit, MI, society membership is international.

565 ■ High Frontier (HF)
2800 Shirlington Rd., Ste. 405
Arlington, VA 22206
Ph: (703)671-4111
Fax: (703)931-6432
E-mail: high.frontier@verizon.net
URL: http://users.erols.com/hifront

Description: Represents scientists, space engineers, strategists and economists. Advocates the use of outer space for non-nuclear commercial and military purposes. Seeks to open space for both economic and defensive military uses by the U.S. and its allies. Aims to provide protection for Americans and their property. The group advocates use of equipment currently in development. Maintains speakers' bureau; sponsors educational programs.

566 ■ International Black Aerospace Council
7120 Sugar Maple Dr.
Irving, TX 75063
Ph: (972)373-9551
Fax: (972)373-9551
URL: http://www.blackaerospace.com

Description: Coordinates and develops activities of the world aerospace community to enhance outreach efforts pertaining to minorities in aerospace career fields. Serves as a clearing house for the exchange of information, ideas and prospects for scholastic and employment opportunities for minorities in aerospace careers.

567 ■ International Experimental Aerospace Society (IEAS)
14870 Granada Ave., No. 316
Apple Valley, MN 55124
Ph: (952)583-2587
E-mail: cab@ieas.org
URL: http://www.ieas.org

Description: Represents education and research societies of rocketry and space technology experimenters from around the world. Promotes experimental aerospace. Provides opportunities for exchange of information and coordination of services that will enable private individuals to safely engage in experimental aerospace activities. Assists and encourages regulatory authorities to permit safe experimental activities.

568 ■ International Society of Automation (ISA)
67 Alexander Dr.
PO Box 12277
Research Triangle Park, NC 27709
Ph: (919)549-8411
Fax: (919)549-8288
E-mail: info@isa.org
URL: http://www.isa.org

Description: Sets the standard for automation by helping over 30,000 worldwide members and other professionals solve difficult technical problems, while enhancing their leadership and personal career capabilities. Develops standards; certifies industry professionals; provides education and training; publishes books and technical articles; and hosts the largest conference and exhibition for automation professionals in the Western Hemisphere. Is the founding sponsor of The Automation Federation.

569 ■ Korean-American Scientists and Engineers Association (KSEA)
1952 Gallows Rd., Ste. 300
Vienna, VA 22182
Ph: (703)748-1221
Fax: (703)748-1331
E-mail: sejong@ksea.org
URL: http://www.ksea.org

Description: Represents scientists and engineers holding single or advanced degrees. Promotes friendship and mutuality among Korean and American scientists and engineers; contributes to Korea's scientific, technological, industrial, and economic developments; strengthens the scientific, technological, and cultural bonds between Korea and the U.S. Sponsors symposium. Maintains speakers' bureau, placement service, and biographical archives. Compiles statistics.

570 ■ National Action Council for Minorities in Engineering (NACME)
440 Hamilton Ave., Ste. 302
White Plains, NY 10601-1813
Ph: (914)539-4010
Fax: (914)539-4032
E-mail: info@nacme.org
URL: http://www.nacme.org

Description: Leads the national effort to increase access to careers in engineering and other science-based disciplines. Conducts research and public policy analysis, develops and operates national demonstration programs at precollege and university levels, and disseminates information through publications, conferences and electronic media. Serves as a privately funded source of scholarships for minority students in engineering.

571 ■ National Society of Professional Engineers (NSPE)
1420 King St.
Alexandria, VA 22314-2794
Ph: (703)684-2800
Fax: (703)836-4875
Fr: 888-285-6773
E-mail: memserv@nspe.org
URL: http://www.nspe.org

Description: Represents professional engineers and engineers-in-training in all fields registered in accordance with the laws of states or territories of the U.S. or provinces of Canada; qualified graduate engineers, student members, and registered land surveyors. Is concerned with social, professional, ethical, and economic considerations of engineering as a profession; encompasses programs in public relations, employment practices, ethical considerations, education, and career guidance. Monitors legislative and regulatory actions of interest to the engineering profession.

572 ■ Society of Hispanic Professional Engineers (SHPE)
13181 Crossroads Pkwy. N, Ste. 450
City of Industry, CA 91746-3496
Ph: (323)725-3970
Fax: (323)725-0316
E-mail: shpenational@shpe.org
URL: http://oneshpe.shpe.org/wps/portal/national

Description: Represents engineers, student engineers, and scientists. Aims to increase the number of Hispanic engineers by providing motivation and support to students. Sponsors competitions and educational programs. Maintains placement service and speakers' bureau; compiles statistics.

573 ■ Society of Women Engineers (SWE)
203 N La Salle St., Ste. 1675
Chicago, IL 60601
Ph: (312)596-5223
Fax: (312)596-5252
Fr: 877-SWE-INFO
E-mail: hq@swe.org
URL: http://societyofwomenengineers.swe.org

Description: Educational and service organization representing both students and professional women in engineering and technical fields.

574 ■ Women in Aerospace
204 E St. NE
Washington, DC 20002
Ph: (202)547-0229
Fax: (202)547-6348
E-mail: info@womeninaerospace.org
URL: http://www.womeninaerospace.org

Description: Women and men working in aerospace and related fields, allied organizations and businesses. Aims to expand women's opportunities for leadership and to increase their visibility in the aerospace community. Facilitates discussion of issues facing women, as well as the aerospace industry. Organizes monthly programs geared towards a broad spectrum of aerospace issues, including human space flight, aviation, remote sensing, satellite communications, robotic space exploration, and the policy issues surrounding these fields.

SOURCES OF HELP-WANTED ADS

575 ■ AIE Perspectives Newsmagazine
American Institute of Engineers
4630 Appian Way, Ste. 206
El Sobrante, CA 94803-1875
Ph: (510)758-6240
Fax: (510)758-6240
URL: http://www.members-aie.org

Monthly. Professional magazine covering engineering.

576 ■ Engineering
Scientific Research Publishing
PO Box 54821
Irvine, CA 92619-4821
E-mail: eng@scirp.org
URL: http://www.scirp.org/journal/eng/

Monthly. $708.00/year for individuals. Peer-reviewed journal publishing articles on the latest advancements in engineering.

577 ■ Engineering Conferences International Symposium Series
Berkeley Electronic Press
2809 Telegraph Ave., Ste. 202
Berkeley, CA 94705-1167
Ph: (510)665-1200
Fax: (510)665-1201
URL: http://services.bepress.com/eci/

Journal focusing on advance engineering science.

578 ■ Farmland News
Farmland News
104 Depot St.
PO Box 240
Archbold, OH 43502-0240
Ph: (419)445-9456
Fax: (419)445-4444
URL: http://www.farmlandnews.com

Weekly (Tues.). $42.00/year for individuals; $78.00/year for two years. Rural human-interest newspaper (tabloid).

579 ■ InterJournal
New England Complex Systems Institute
283 Main St., Ste. 319
Cambridge, MA 02142
Ph: (617)547-4100
Fax: (617)661-7711
URL: http://www.interjournal.org/

Journal covering the fields of science and engineering.

580 ■ ISRN Ecology
Hindawi Publishing Corporation
410 Park Ave., 15th Fl.
287 PMB
New York, NY 10022
E-mail: ecology@isrn.com
URL: http://www.isrn.com/journals/ecology

Peer-reviewed journal publishing research articles in all areas of ecology.

581 ■ Journal of Crop Improvement
Taylor & Francis Group Ltd.
270 Madison Ave.
New York, NY 10016-0601
Ph: (212)216-7800
Fax: (212)563-2269
Fr: 800-634-7064
URL: http://www.tandfonline.com/toc/wcim20/current

$323.00/year for individuals, online; $407.00/year for individuals, print & online. Journal focusing on improvements in crop production productivity, quality, and safety to meet the food, feed, and fiber needs of an ever-growing world population.

582 ■ Journal of Engineering Education
American Society for Engineering Education
1818 N St. NW, Ste. 600
Washington, DC 20036-2479
Ph: (202)331-3500
Fax: (202)265-8504
URL: http://www.jee.org

Quarterly. $100.00/year for libraries, online; $160.00/year for other countries, library; $150.00/year for U.S., Canada, and Mexico, library; $160.00/year for other countries, library. Peer-reviewed journal covering scholarly research in engineering education.

583 ■ Journal of Engineering for Sustainable Development
College Publishing
12309 Lynwood Dr.
Glen Allen, VA 23059
Ph: (804)364-8410
Fax: (804)364-8408
Fr: 800-827-0723
URL: http://www.collegepublishing.us/jesdsubs.htm

Annual. $29.00/year for individuals, online only; $69.00/year for institutions, online only. Peer-reviewed journal focusing on sustainable engineering.

584 ■ Journal of Freshwater Ecology
Taylor & Francis Group Journals
325 Chestnut St., Ste. 800
Philadelphia, PA 19106-2608
Ph: (215)625-8900
Fax: (215)625-2940
Fr: 800-354-1420
URL: http://www.tandf.co.uk/journals/TJFE

Quarterly. $117.00/year for institutions, print and online; $193.00/year for institutions, print and online; $154.00/year for institutions, print and online; $42.00/year for individuals, print only; $69.00/year for individuals, print only; $55.00/year for individuals, print only. Peer-reviewed journal publishing a wide variety of original ecological studies, observations and techniques.

585 ■ The Journal of Southern Agricultural Education Research
American Association for Agricultural Education
c/o Robert A. Martin
Dept. of Agricultural Education & Studies
Iowa State University
201 Curtiss Hall
Ames, IA 50011-1050
Ph: (515)294-0896
Fax: (515)294-0530
URL: http://www.jsaer.org

Journal covering agricultural education.

586 ■ Journal of Women and Minorities in Science and Engineering
Begell House Inc.
50 Cross Hwy.
Redding, CT 06896
Ph: (203)938-1300
Fax: (203)938-1304
URL: http://www.begellhouse.com/journals/
00551c876cc2f027

$248.00/year for institutions. Peer-reviewed journal featuring innovative ideas and programs for classroom teachers, scientific studies, and formulation of concepts related to the education, recruitment, and retention of under-represented groups in science and engineering.

587 ■ NSBE Magazine
NSBE Publications
205 Daingerfield Rd.
Alexandria, VA 22314
Ph: (703)549-2207
Fax: (703)683-5312
URL: http://www.nsbe.org/News-Media/Magazines/
About-NSBE-Magazine

$20.00/year for individuals; $35.00/year for other countries; $15.00/year for students. Journal providing information on engineering careers, self-development, and cultural issues for recent graduates with technical majors.

588 ■ PE
National Society of Professional Engineers
1420 King St.
Alexandria, VA 22314
Ph: (703)684-2800
Fax: (703)684-4875
URL: http://www.nspe.org/PEmagazine/index.html

Monthly. Magazine (tabloid) covering professional, legislative, and techology issues for an engineering audience.

589 ■ Resource: Engineering and Technology for Sustainable World
American Society of Agricultural and Biological Engineers
2950 Niles Rd.
St. Joseph, MI 49085-8607
Ph: (269)429-0300

Fax: (269)429-3852
E-mail: hq@asabe.org
URL: http://www.asabe.org

$10.75/single issue for nonmembers; $5.50/single issues for members. Facilitates the exchange of technical information and promoting the science and art of engineering in agricultural, food, and biological systems. Includes a reader opinion page, research on recent developments and trends, an employment section for both job seekers and employers, and agricultural or biological engineering consultant advertisements.

590 ■ Scaffolds Fruit Journal
Cornell University New York State Agricultural Experiment Station
630 W North St.
Geneva, NY 14456
Ph: (315)787-2011
URL: http://www.nysaes.cornell.edu/ent/scaffolds/
   2005/050912.html

Weekly. Magazine focusing on pest management and crop development.

591 ■ SWE, Magazine of the Society of Women Engineers
Society of Women Engineers
120 S La Salle St., Ste. 1515
Chicago, IL 60603
Ph: (312)596-5223
Fr: 877-793-4636
URL: http://societyofwomenengineers.swe.org/
   index.php

Quarterly. $30.00/year for nonmembers. Magazine for engineering students and for women and men working in the engineering and technology fields. Covers career guidance, continuing development and topical issues.

592 ■ Woman Engineer
Equal Opportunity Publications, Inc.
445 Broadhollow Rd., Ste. 425
Melville, NY 11747
Ph: (631)421-9421
Fax: (631)421-1352
E-mail: info@eop.com
URL: http://www.eop.com

Annual. Magazine that is offered at no charge to qualified female engineering, computer-science, and information-technology students and professionals seeking to find employment and advancement in their careers.

PLACEMENT AND JOB REFERRAL SERVICES

593 ■ ASA-CSSA-SSSA Career Placement Center
5585 Guilford Rd.
Madison, WI 53711
Ph: (608)273-8080
Fax: (608)273-2021
URL: http://www.careerplacement.org

Serves as a clearinghouse for resumes and personnel listings. Promotes and encourages career opportunities in the agronomic, crop, soil, and environmental sciences.

EMPLOYER DIRECTORIES AND NETWORKING LISTS

594 ■ Careers in Focus—Engineering
Facts On File Inc.
132 W 31st St., 17th Fl.
New York, NY 10001
Ph: (212)967-8800
Fax: 800-678-3633
Fr: 800-322-8755
URL: http://www.infobasepublishing.com

Latest edition 3rd; Published July, 2007. $32.95 for individuals. Covers: An overview of engineering, followed by a selection of jobs profiled in detail, including the nature of the job, earnings, prospects for employment, what kind of training and skills it requires, and sources for further information.

595 ■ Equipment Marketing and Distribution Association—Membership Directory
Equipment Marketing & Distribution Association
PO Box 1347
Iowa City, IA 52244
Ph: (319)354-5156
Fax: (319)354-5157
URL: http://www.emda.net/directory.htm

Annual. Covers: 120 members; coverage includes Canada. Entries include: Company name, address, phone, name of principal executive, territory covered. Arrangement: Alphabetical.

596 ■ Indiana Society of Professional Engineers—Directory
Indiana Society of Professional Engineers
PO Box 20806
Indianapolis, IN 46220
Ph: (317)255-2267
Fax: (317)255-2530
URL: http://www.indspe.org

Annual, fall. Covers: Member registered engineers, land surveyors, engineering students, and engineers in training. Entries include: Member name, address, phone, type of membership, business information, specialty. Arrangement: Alpha by chapter area.

HANDBOOKS AND MANUALS

597 ■ Great Jobs for Engineering Majors
The McGraw-Hill Companies
PO Box 182604
Columbus, OH 43272
Fax: (614)759-3749
Fr: 877-883-5524
E-mail: customer.service@mcgraw-hill.com
URL: http://www.mhprofessional.com/
   product.php?isbn=0071641963

Geraldine O. Garner. Second edition, 2008. $16.95. 192 pages. Covers all the career options open to students majoring in engineering.

598 ■ Growing Opportunities: Careers in Agriculture
JIST Publishing
875 Montreal Way
St. Paul, MN 55102
Fax: 800-547-8329
Fr: 800-648-5478
E-mail: info@jist.com
URL: http://www.jist.com

2004. $99 for DVD; $109 for VHS. 23 minutes. Video includes thumbnail descriptions of 23 careers that exist in the agricultural industry.

EMPLOYMENT AGENCIES AND SEARCH FIRMS

599 ■ AGRI-Associates
116 W 47th St.
Kansas City, MO 64112
Ph: (816)531-7980
Fax: (816)531-7982
Fr: 800-550-7980
E-mail: gip@agriassociates.com
URL: http://www.agriassociates.com

Agribusiness executive search firm.

600 ■ Agri-Personnel
5120 Old Bill Cook Rd.
Atlanta, GA 30349-0319
Ph: (404)768-5701

Fax: (404)768-5705

Agribusiness consultants active in executive/professional/technical recruitment and placement, and in mergers, acquisitions, and divestitures in various industries including dairy, feed, food, fertilizer, farm chemicals, poultry and egg, animal health, and pulp and paper.

601 ■ Boyle & Associates Retained Search Group
PO Box 16658
St. Paul, MN 55116
Ph: (651)223-5050
Fax: (651)699-5378
E-mail: paul@talenthunt.com
URL: http://www.talenthunt.com

Executive search firm.

602 ■ First Search America Inc.
26746 Main St.
Ardmore, AL 35739
Fr: 800-468-9214
E-mail: firstsearch@ardmore.net
URL: http://www.firstsearchamerica.com

Executive search firm.

603 ■ Florasearch, Inc.
1740 Lake Markham Rd.
Sanford, FL 32771
Ph: (407)320-8177
Fax: (407)320-8083
E-mail: search@florasearch.com
URL: http://www.florasearch.com

Employment agency for the horticulture industry.

604 ■ The Jack De Jong Group
3301 S Goldfield Rd.
Apache Junction, AZ 85119
Fax: (520)579-5293
Fr: 800-266-0515
E-mail: jack@jackdejonggroup.com
URL: http://www.jackdejonggroup.com

Agribusiness executive search firm.

605 ■ Miller & Associates Inc.
9036 NW 36th St.
Polk City, IA 50226
Ph: (515)965-5727
Fax: (515)965-5794
Fr: 888-965-2727
E-mail: millagsrch@aol.com
URL: http://www.ag-careers.com

Agricultural personnel agency.

606 ■ The Montgomery Group Inc.
PO Box 30791
Knoxville, TN 37930-0791
Ph: (865)693-0325
Fax: (865)691-1900
E-mail: tmg@tmgincknox.com
URL: http://www.tmgincknox.com

Executive search firm for the food and agribusiness industries.

607 ■ Robert Drexler Associates Inc.
PO Box 151
Saddle River, NJ 07458
Ph: (201)760-2300
Fax: (201)760-2301
E-mail: drexler@engineeringemployment.com
URL: http://www.engineeringemployment.com

Executive search firm.

608 ■ Search North America Inc.
PO Box 3577
Sunriver, OR 97707-0577
Ph: (503)222-6461
Fax: (503)227-2804
E-mail: mylinda@searchna.com
URL: http://www.searchna.com

An executive search and recruiting firm whose focus is placing engineers, operations and maintenance managers, sales and marketing management, financial and general management executives (both domestic and international). Industries served: forest products, pulp and paper, waste to energy, environmental services, consulting and equipment suppliers for above related industries.

609 ■ Sherwood Lehman Massucco Inc.
3455 W Shaw Ave., Ste. 110
Fresno, CA 93711-3201
Ph: (559)276-8572
Fax: (559)276-2351
Fr: 800-277-8572
E-mail: slinc@employmentexpert.com
URL: http://www.employmentexpert.com
Executive search firm.

610 ■ Smith, Brown & Jones
5817 W 163rd Terr.
Stilwell, KS 66085
Ph: (913)814-8177
E-mail: jrich@smithbrownjones.com
URL: http://www.smithbrownjones.com
Executive search firm.

611 ■ Spencer Stuart
353 N Clark, Ste. 2400
Chicago, IL 60654
Ph: (312)822-0088
Fax: (312)822-0116
URL: http://www.spencerstuart.com
Executive search firm.

612 ■ Trambley The Recruiter
5325 Wyoming Blvd. NE, Ste. 200
Albuquerque, NM 87109-3132
Ph: (505)821-5440
Fax: (505)821-8509

Personnel consultancy firm recruits and places engineering professionals in specific areas of off-road equipment design and manufacturing. Industries served: construction, agricultural, lawn and garden, oil exploration and mining equipment manufacturing.

Online Job Sources and Services

613 ■ Agricultural Engineering Jobs
URL: http://www.agriculturalengineeringjobs.org

Description: Provides an online source for agricultural engineering job. Features updated job listings for candidates and job posting for employers.

614 ■ AgriculturalCrossing.com
URL: http://www.agriculturalcrossing.com

Description: Provides a database of agricultural job openings worldwide. Includes openings in Fortune 500 and Fortune 1000 companies.

615 ■ EngineerJobs.com
URL: http://www.engineerjobs.com

Description: Provides job opportunities for engineering professionals in the following disciplines: aerospace, agricultural, biomedical, chemical, civil, electrical, environmental, industrial, manufacturing, marine, materials, mechanical, mining, nuclear, petroleum,

process, project, quality, sales, software, solar, systems, and structural.

616 ■ Justmeans - CSR JOBS
URL: http://www.justmeans.com

Description: Serves as online resource that provides available career opportunities for the sustainable business industry.

Tradeshows

617 ■ Agricultural Equipment Technology Conference
American Society of Agricultural and Biological Engineers
2950 Niles Rd.
St. Joseph, MI 49085
Ph: (269)429-0300
Fax: (269)429-3852
E-mail: hq@asabe.org
URL: http://www.asabe.org

Annual. Brings together engineers, managers, researchers and other professionals in the agricultural equipment industry to exchange information, discuss opportunities and address challenges for production agriculture in the 21st century.

Other Sources

618 ■ American Engineering Association (AEA)
533 Waterside Blvd.
Monroe Township, NJ 08831
Ph: (201)664-6954
E-mail: aea@aea.org
URL: http://www.aea.org

Description: Members consist of Engineers and engineering professionals. Purpose to advance the engineering profession and U.S. engineering capabilities. Issues of concern include age discrimination, immigration laws, displacement of U.S. Engineers by foreign workers, trade agreements, off shoring of U.S. Engineering and manufacturing jobs, loss of U.S. manufacturing and engineering capability, and recruitment of foreign students. Testifies before Congress. Holds local Chapter meetings.

619 ■ American Farmers for the Advancement and Conservation of Technology (AFACT)
4255 S Buckley Rd., No. 178
Aurora, CO 80013
Fax: 888-356-5023
Fr: 800-340-0737
E-mail: information@itisafact.org
URL: http://itisafact.org

Description: Promotes the use of technology in farming to produce safe, nutritious and affordable food. Encourages consumers to demand access to high-quality, affordable food with minimal impact on the environment. Supports advancements in modern agriculture that would benefit food production both domestically and internationally.

620 ■ American Society of Agricultural and Biological Engineers (ASABE)
2950 Niles Rd.
St. Joseph, MI 49085-8607
Ph: (269)429-0300
Fax: (269)429-3852
Fr: 800-371-2723
E-mail: hq@asabe.org
URL: http://www.asabe.org

Description: International professional and technical organization of individuals interested in engineering and technology for agriculture, food and biological systems. Publishes textbooks and journals. Develops engineering standards used in agriculture, food and biological systems. Sponsors technical meetings and continuing education programs. Maintains biographical archives and placement services. Sponsors competitions and special in-depth conferences. Maintains over 200 committees.

621 ■ Council for Agricultural Science and Technology (CAST)
4420 Lincoln Way
Ames, IA 50014-3447
Ph: (515)292-2125
Fax: (515)292-4512
E-mail: cast@cast-science.org
URL: http://www.cast-science.org

Description: Scientific societies, associate societies, individuals, corporations, foundations, and trade associations. Promotes science-based information on food, fiber, agricultural, natural resource, and related societal and environmental issues.

622 ■ Farm and Ranch Freedom Alliance (FARFA)
PO Box 809
Cameron, TX 76520
Ph: (254)697-2661
Fr: (866)687-6452
E-mail: info@farmandranchfreedom.org
URL: http://farmandranchfreedom.org

Description: Strives to save family farms and individuals from expensive and unnecessary government regulation. Works to assure the independence of farmers, ranchers, livestock owners and homesteaders in the management, control, identification and marketing of their products. Supports and enhances sustainable agriculture, family farms and domestic agricultural products.

623 ■ National Coalition for Food and Agricultural Research (NCFAR)
2441 Village Green Pl.
Champaign, IL 61822
Ph: (217)356-3182
Fax: (217)398-4119
E-mail: ncfar@assochq.org
URL: http://www.ncfar.org

Description: Represents food, agriculture, nutrition, conservation and natural resource stakeholders. Aims to support the sustaining and increasing public investment at the national level in food and agricultural research, extension and education. Seeks to sustain and enhance federal funding for food and agricultural research, extension and education. Strives to help bring about research outcomes that provide a range of major public benefits.

SOURCES OF HELP-WANTED ADS

624 ■ *Agriculture & Food*
National Technical Information Service
5301 Shawnee Rd.
Alexandria, VA 22312
Ph: (703)605-6585
Fax: (703)605-6900
Fr: 888-584-8332
E-mail: info@ntis.gov
URL: http://www.ntis.gov/products/alerts.aspx

Description: Biweekly. $235/year. Publishes abstracts of reports on agricultural chemistry, agricultural equipment, facilities, and operations. Also covers agronomy, horticulture, and plant pathology; fisheries and aquaculture; animal husbandry and veterinary medicine; and food technology. Also available via e-mail.

625 ■ *American Journal of Alternative Agriculture*
Henry A. Wallace Institute for Alternative Agriculture
9200 Edmonston Rd., Ste. 117
Greenbelt, MD 20770-4575
Ph: (301)441-8777
Fax: (301)220-0164
URL: http://eap.mcgill.ca/MagRack/AJAA/ajaa_ ind.htm

Quarterly. $24.00/year for individuals, U.S.; $26.00/ year for Canada and Mexico; $28.00/year for other countries; $44.00/year for institutions, U.S.; $46.00/ year for institutions, Canada & Mexico; $48.00/year for institutions, other countries; $12.00/year for students, U.S.; $14.00/year for students, Canada & Mexico; $16.00/year for students, other countries. Journal covering agricultural science.

626 ■ *Cell*
Cell Press
600 Technology Sq.
Cambridge, MA 02139
Ph: (617)661-7057
Fax: (617)661-7061
Fr: (866)314-2355
E-mail: celleditor@cell.com
URL: http://www.cell.com

$212.00/year for U.S. and Canada, individual, print and online; $320.00/year for other countries, individual, print and online; $212.00/year for U.S. and Canada, online only, individual; $212.00/year for other countries, online only, individual; $1,425.00/ year for U.S. and Canada, institution, print only; $1,605.00/year for institutions, other countries, print only. Peer-reviewed journal on molecular and cell biology.

627 ■ *CSANews*
American Society of Agronomy
5585 Guilford Rd.
Madison, WI 53711
Ph: (608)273-8080
Fax: (608)273-2021
E-mail: news@agronomy.org
URL: http://www.agronomy.org

Description: Monthly. $36/volume for non-members; $54 for international postage. Publishes information on agronomy, crop science, soil science, and related topics. Provides news of the societies and members; reports of annual meetings; listings of publications; announcements of awards, retirements, and deaths; job listings; and a calendar of events.

628 ■ *Culture and Agriculture*
American Anthropological Association
2200 Wilson Blvd., Ste. 600
Arlington, VA 22201
Ph: (703)528-1902
Fax: (703)528-3546
URL: http://www.aaanet.org

Description: Quarterly. Provides information on agriculture and related policies and practices and the consequences they have on the environment and human life.

629 ■ *Farmland News*
Farmland News
104 Depot St.
PO Box 240
Archbold, OH 43502-0240
Ph: (419)445-9456
Fax: (419)445-4444
URL: http://www.farmlandnews.com

Weekly (Tues.). $42.00/year for individuals; $78.00/ year for two years. Rural human-interest newspaper (tabloid).

630 ■ *Feedstuffs*
Miller Publishing Co.
12400 Whitewater Dr., Ste. 160
Minnetonka, MN 55343
Ph: (952)931-0211
Fax: (952)938-1832
Fr: 800-441-1410
URL: http://www.feedstuffs.com/ME2/Default.asp

Weekly. $144.00/year for individuals; $230.00/year for two years; $150.00/year for Canada; $235.00/ year for individuals, Europe and Mid East; airmail; $280.00/year for other countries, Japan, Far E./Aus. airmail; $210.00/year for individuals, Mexico/Central/ South America; $196.00/year for individuals, print & internet version; $334.00/year for two years, print & internet version; $202.00/year for Canada, print & internet version; $404.00/year for Canada, print & internet version, 2 years. Magazine serving the grain and feed industries and animal agriculture.

631 ■ *ICASA News*
International Consortium for Agricultural Systems Applications
2440 Campus Rd.
PO Box 527
Honolulu, HI 96822
Ph: (808)956-2713
Fax: (808)956-2711
E-mail: icasa@icasa.net
URL: http://www.icasa.net

Description: 2/year. Reports on the development and application of system simulation products and tools for agricultural production. Recurring features include news of research and a calendar of events.

632 ■ *International Journal of Vegetable Science*
Taylor & Francis Group Ltd.
270 Madison Ave.
New York, NY 10016-0601
Ph: (212)216-7800
Fax: (212)563-2269
Fr: 800-634-7064
URL: http://www.tandfonline.com/toc/wijv20/current

Quarterly. $93.00/year for individuals, online; $102.00/year for individuals, print & online. Journal focusing on all aspects of vegetable science from land preparation to consumption.

633 ■ *ISRN Ecology*
Hindawi Publishing Corporation
410 Park Ave., 15th Fl.
287 PMB
New York, NY 10022
E-mail: ecology@isrn.com
URL: http://www.isrn.com/journals/ecology

Peer-reviewed journal publishing research articles in all areas of ecology.

634 ■ *Journal of Agricultural & Food Industrial Organization*
Berkeley Electronic Press
2809 Telegraph Ave., Ste. 202
Berkeley, CA 94705-1167
Ph: (510)665-1200
Fax: (510)665-1201
E-mail: info@bepress.com
URL: http://www.bepress.com/jafio/

Annual. $250.00/year academic; $750.00/year corporate. Journal dealing with the research in industrial organization mainly focusing on the agricultural and food industry worldwide.

635 ■ *Journal of Crop Improvement*
Taylor & Francis Group Ltd.
270 Madison Ave.
New York, NY 10016-0601
Ph: (212)216-7800
Fax: (212)563-2269
Fr: 800-634-7064
URL: http://www.tandfonline.com/toc/wcim20/current

$323.00/year for individuals, online; $407.00/year for individuals, print & online. Journal focusing on improvements in crop production productivity, quality, and safety to meet the food, feed, and fiber needs of an ever-growing world population.

636 ■ Journal of Engineering for Sustainable Development
College Publishing
12309 Lynwood Dr.
Glen Allen, VA 23059
Ph: (804)364-8410
Fax: (804)364-8408
Fr: 800-827-0723
URL: http://www.collegepublishing.us/jesdsubs.htm

Annual. $29.00/year for individuals, online only; $69.00/year for institutions, online only. Peer-reviewed journal focusing on sustainable engineering.

637 ■ Journal of Freshwater Ecology
Taylor & Francis Group Journals
325 Chestnut St., Ste. 800
Philadelphia, PA 19106-2608
Ph: (215)625-8900
Fax: (215)625-2940
Fr: 800-354-1420
URL: http://www.tandf.co.uk/journals/TJFE

Quarterly. $117.00/year for institutions, print and online; $193.00/year for institutions, print and online; $154.00/year for institutions, print and online; $42.00/year for individuals, print only; $69.00/year for individuals, print only; $55.00/year for individuals, print only. Peer-reviewed journal publishing a wide variety of original ecological studies, observations and techniques.

638 ■ The Journal of Southern Agricultural Education Research
American Association for Agricultural Education
c/o Robert A. Martin
Dept. of Agricultural Education & Studies
Iowa State University
201 Curtiss Hall
Ames, IA 50011-1050
Ph: (515)294-0896
Fax: (515)294-0530
URL: http://www.jsaer.org

Journal covering agricultural education.

639 ■ Journal of Women and Minorities in Science and Engineering
Begell House Inc.
50 Cross Hwy.
Redding, CT 06896
Ph: (203)938-1300
Fax: (203)938-1304
URL: http://www.begellhouse.com/journals/00551c876cc2f027

$248.00/year for institutions. Peer-reviewed journal featuring innovative ideas and programs for classroom teachers, scientific studies, and formulation of concepts related to the education, recruitment, and retention of under-represented groups in science and engineering.

640 ■ Nature International Weekly Journal of Science
Nature Publishing Group
75 Varick St., 9th Fl.
New York, NY 10013-1917
Ph: (212)726-9200
Fax: (212)696-9006
Fr: 888-331-6288
E-mail: nature@natureny.com
URL: http://www.nature.com/nature/index.html

Weekly. $199.00/year for individuals, print and online; $338.00/year for two years, print and online. Magazine covering science and technology, including the fields of biology, biochemistry, genetics, medicine, earth sciences, physics, pharmacology, and behavioral sciences.

641 ■ NewsCAST
Council for Agricultural Science & Technology
4420 W Lincoln Way
Ames, IA 50014-3447
Ph: (515)292-2125

Fax: (515)292-4512
E-mail: cast@cast-science.org
URL: http://www.cast-science.org
Description: Semiannual. Serves a consortium of food and agricultural science societies, which promotes understanding by providing a background in agricultural science and technology. Carries features of interest to food and agricultural scientists and news of the organization's activities and programs. Recurring features include announcements of available publications and honors awarded; and a progress report on the work of authorized task forces.

642 ■ Pesticides, People and Nature
Begell House Inc.
50 Cross Hwy.
Redding, CT 06896
Ph: (203)938-1300
Fax: (203)938-1304
URL: http://www.begellhouse.com/journals/33b67499180f0876

$180.00/year for institutions. Journal covering the impact of pesticides on people and the environment.

643 ■ Scaffolds Fruit Journal
Cornell University New York State Agricultural Experiment Station
630 W North St.
Geneva, NY 14456
Ph: (315)787-2011
URL: http://www.nysaes.cornell.edu/ent/scaffolds/2005/050912.html

Weekly. Magazine focusing on pest management and crop development.

644 ■ The Scientist
The Scientist Inc.
121 W 27th St., Ste. 604
New York, NY 10001
Ph: (212)461-4470
Fax: (347)626-2385
URL: http://www.the-scientist.com

Monthly. $39.95/year for individuals, print only; $49.95/year for individuals, print & online; $64.95/year for other countries, print only; $74.95/year for other countries, print & online. News journal (tabloid) for life scientists featuring news, opinions, research, and professional section.

PLACEMENT AND JOB REFERRAL SERVICES

645 ■ ASA-CSSA-SSSA Career Placement Center
5585 Guilford Rd.
Madison, WI 53711
Ph: (608)273-8080
Fax: (608)273-2021
URL: http://www.careerplacement.org

Serves as a clearinghouse for resumes and personnel listings. Promotes and encourages career opportunities in the agronomic, crop, soil, and environmental sciences.

EMPLOYER DIRECTORIES AND NETWORKING LISTS

646 ■ American Men and Women of Science
Gale
PO Box 6904
Florence, KY 41022-6904
Fr: 800-354-9706
URL: http://www.gale.cengage.com

Biennial, even years; New edition expected 29th, June 2011. $1,368.00 for individuals. Covers: Over 135,000 U.S. and Canadian scientists active in the physical, biological, mathematical, computer science, and engineering fields; includes references to previous edition for deceased scientists and

nonrespondents. Entries include: Name, address, education, personal and career data, memberships, honors and awards, research interest. Arrangement: Alphabetical. Indexes: Discipline (in separate volume).

647 ■ Career Opportunities in Science
Facts On File Inc.
132 W 31st St., 17th Fl.
New York, NY 10001
Ph: (212)967-8800
Fax: 800-678-3633
Fr: 800-322-8755
URL: http://factsonfile.infobasepublishing.com

Latest edition 2008. $49.50 for individuals. Covers: More than 80 jobs, such as biochemist, molecular biologist, bioinformatic specialist, pharmacologist, computer engineer, geographic information systems specialist, science teacher, forensic scientist, patent agent, as well as physicist, astronomer, chemist, zoologist, oceanographer, and geologist.

648 ■ Directory of State Departments of Agriculture
U.S. Department of Agriculture
1400 Independence Ave. SW, Rm. 2503-S
PO Box 0201
Washington, DC 20250-0254
Ph: (202)690-4944
Fax: (202)720-0016
URL: http://www.ams.usda.gov

Biennial, late summer of odd years. Free. Covers: State departments of agriculture and their officials. Entries include: Department name, address, phone, names and titles of key personnel, department branches. Arrangement: Geographical.

649 ■ Equipment Marketing and Distribution Association—Membership Directory
Equipment Marketing & Distribution Association
PO Box 1347
Iowa City, IA 52244
Ph: (319)354-5156
Fax: (319)354-5157
URL: http://www.emda.net/directory.htm

Annual. Covers: 120 members; coverage includes Canada. Entries include: Company name, address, phone, name of principal executive, territory covered. Arrangement: Alphabetical.

HANDBOOKS AND MANUALS

650 ■ Careers in Focus: Agriculture
Ferguson Publishing
132 W 31st St., 17th Fl.
New York, NY 10001
Fr: 800-322-8755
E-mail: custserv@factsonfile.com
URL: http://factsonfile.infobasepublishing.com

2006. $32.95. 192 pages. Covers an overview of agricultural jobs, followed by a selection of jobs profiled in detail, including the nature of the job, earnings, prospects for employment, what kind of training and skills it requires, and sources for further information.

651 ■ Careers in Health Care
The McGraw-Hill Companies
PO Box 182604
Columbus, OH 43272
Fax: (614)759-3749
Fr: 877-883-5524
E-mail: customer.service@mcgraw-hill.com
URL: http://www.mhprofessional.com/product.php?isbn=0071466533

Barbara M. Swanson. Fifth edition, 2005. $19.95 (paper). 192 pages. Describes job duties, work settings, salaries, licensing and certification requirements, educational preparation, and future outlook. Gives ideas on how to secure a job.

652 ■ Careers for Plant Lovers and Other Green Thumb Types
The McGraw-Hill Companies
PO Box 182604
Columbus, OH 43272
Fax: (614)759-3749
Fr: 877-883-5524
E-mail: customer.service@mcgraw-hill.com
URL: http://www.mhprofessional.com/product.php?isbn=0071442413

Blythe Camenson. Second edition, 2004. $13.95. 160 pages. Describes careers for people who love working with plants and flowers.

653 ■ Math for Soil Scientists
Cengage Learning
PO Box 6904
Florence, KY 41022
Fax: 800-487-8488
Fr: 800-354-9706
E-mail: esales@cengage.com
URL: http://www.cengage.com

Mark S. Coyne and James A. Thompson. 2006. $39.95. 288 pages. Soil science students and practitioners are offered a review of basic mathematical operations in the field.

654 ■ Resumes for Scientific and Technical Careers
The McGraw-Hill Companies
PO Box 182604
Columbus, OH 43272
Fax: (614)759-3749
Fr: 877-883-5524
E-mail: customer.service@mcgraw-hill.com
URL: http://www.mhprofessional.com/product.php?isbn=0071482199

Third edition, 2007. $12.95 (paper). 144 pages. Provides resume advice for individuals interested in working in scientific and technical careers. Includes sample resumes and cover letters.

EMPLOYMENT AGENCIES AND SEARCH FIRMS

655 ■ Agra Placements, Ltd.
8435 University Ave., Ste. 6
Des Moines, IA 50325
Ph: (515)225-6563
Fax: (515)225-7733
Fr: 888-696-5624
E-mail: careers@agrapl.com
URL: http://www.agraplacements.com

Executive search firm. Branch offices in Peru, IN, Lincoln, IL, and Andover, KS.

656 ■ Wellington Executive Search
3162 Johnson Ferry Rd., Ste. 260
Marietta, GA 30062
Ph: (770)645-5799
Fax: (678)278-0928
E-mail: jobs@wellingtonsearch.com
URL: http://www.wellingtonsearch.com

Serves as an executive search firm covering sales representative, research and development, food scientists, and purchasing managers.

ONLINE JOB SOURCES AND SERVICES

657 ■ AgCareers.com
URL: http://www.agcareers.com

Description: Serves as an agriculture employment search engine. Supplies human resource services to the agriculture, food, natural resources and biotechnology industry.

658 ■ AgricultureJobs.com
URL: http://www.agriculturejobs.com

Description: Provides new job openings for Agricul-

turists in addition to research into the farming, fishing and forestry employment markets. Maintains a career articles section written and frequented by industry professionals.

TRADESHOWS

659 ■ Agri News Farm Show
Agri News Farm Show
PO Box 6118
18 1st Ave., S.E.
Rochester, MN 55903-6118
Ph: (507)285-7600
Fax: (507)281-7436
Fr: 800-533-1727
URL: http://www.agrinews.com

Annual. Primary Exhibits: Agricultural equipment, supplies, and services.

660 ■ American Seed Trade Association Convention
American Seed Trade Association
1701 Duke St., Ste. 275
Alexandria, VA 22314-3415
Ph: (703)837-8140
Fax: (703)837-9365
E-mail: info@amseed.org
URL: http://www.amseed.com

Annual. Brings together seed industry professionals across all divisions of the association. Prepares attendees for the trends and issues facing the seed industry. Features special events and networking opportunities with colleagues across all commodities, both seed companies and suppliers alike.

661 ■ Empire Farm Days
Empire State Potato Growers, Inc.
PO Box 566
Stanley, NY 14561
Ph: (585)526-5356
Fax: (585)526-6576
Fr: 877-697-7837
E-mail: mwickham@nypotatoes.org
URL: http://www.empirepotatogrowers.com

Annual. Primary Exhibits: Agricultural equipment, supplies, and services. Dates and Locations: 2012 Aug 07-09.

662 ■ Farm Progress Show
Farm Progress Companies, Inc.
255 38th Ave.
St. Charles, IL 60174
Ph: (630)462-2900
Fr: 800-441-1410
URL: http://www.farmprogress.com

Annual. Primary Exhibits: Farm machinery and equipment, trucks, livestock equipment, buildings, seed, chemicals, computers, and other agricultural products and services. Dates and Locations: 2012 Aug 28-30; Boone, IA; 2013 Aug 27-29; Decatur, IL; 2014 Aug 26-28; Boone, IA.

663 ■ International Feed Expo
American Feed Industry Association
2101 Wilson Blvd., Ste. 916
Arlington, VA 22201
Ph: (703)524-0810
Fax: (703)524-1921
E-mail: afia@afia.org
URL: http://www.afia.org

Annual. Primary Exhibits: Feed equipment, services, and ingredients. Dates and Locations: 2012 Jan 24-26; Atlanta, GA; Georgia World Congress Center.

664 ■ Mid-America Farm Exposition
Salina Area Chamber of Commerce
120 W. Ash
PO Box 586
Salina, KS 67402-0586
Ph: (785)827-9301
Fax: (785)827-9758
URL: http://www.salinakansas.org

Annual. Primary Exhibits: Agricultural equipment, supplies, and services, including irrigation equipment, fertilizer, farm implements, hybrid seed, agricultural chemicals, tractors, feed, farrowing crates and equipment, silos and bins, storage equipment, and farm buildings. Dates and Locations: 2012 Mar 27-29; Salina, KS; Salina Bicentennial Center and the Saline Country Livestock.

665 ■ Mid-South Farm and Gin Supply Exhibit
Southern Cotton Ginners Association
874 Cotton Gin Pl.
Memphis, TN 38106
Ph: (901)947-3104
Fax: (901)947-3103
E-mail: mary.stice@southerncottonginners.org
URL: http://www.southerncottonginners.org

Annual. Primary Exhibits: Agricultural equipment, supplies and services.

666 ■ Midwest Farm Show
North Country Enterprises LLC
5322 250th St.
Cadott, WI 54727
Ph: (715)289-4632
Fax: (715)289-4632
E-mail: nceinfo@yahoo.com
URL: http://www.northcountryenterprises.com

Annual. Primary Exhibits: Farm materials handling equipment, supplies, and services.

667 ■ National Western Stock Show
The Western Stock Show Association
4655 Humboldt St.
Denver, CO 80216
Ph: (303)297-1166
Fax: (303)292-1708
Fr: 800-336-6977
URL: http://www.nationalwestern.com

Annual. Primary Exhibits: Jewelry, apparel, household goods, agricultural products, and service groups. A blend of agriculture, western and urban products including agriculture equipment, supplies and services, horse items, household products, apparel, jewelry, buildings, children's items, art, food and tools. Dates and Locations: 2013 Jan 12-27; Denver, CO.

668 ■ Northwest Agricultural Show
Northwest Horticultural Congress
4672 Drift Creek Rd., S.E.
Sublimity, OR 97385
Ph: (503)769-7120
Fax: (503)769-3549
E-mail: info@nwagshow.com
URL: http://www.nwagshow.com

Annual. Primary Exhibits: Agricultural equipment and services. Dates and Locations: 2012 Jan 24-26; Portland, OR; Portland Expo Center.

669 ■ Triumph of Agriculture Exposition - Farm and Ranch Machinery Show
Mid-America Expositions, Inc.
7015 Spring St.
Omaha, NE 68106-3518
Ph: (402)346-8003
Fax: (402)346-5412
Fr: 800-475-SHOW
E-mail: info@showofficeonline.com
URL: http://www.showofficeonline.com

Annual. Primary Exhibits: Farm equipment and supplies. Dates and Locations: 2012 Feb 29 - Mar 01; Omaha, NE; QWEST CENTER OMAHA.

670 ■ Western Farm Show
SouthWestern Association
PO Box 419264
Kansas City, MO 64141-6264
Ph: (816)561-5323
Fax: (816)561-1249
Fr: 800-762-5616
E-mail: oholcombe@swassn.com
URL: http://www.southwesternassn.com

Annual. Primary Exhibits: equipment, supplies, and services relating to the agricultural industry. Dates and Locations: 2012 Feb 24-26; Kansas City, MO; American Royal Complex.

OTHER SOURCES

671 ■ American Farmers for the Advancement and Conservation of Technology (AFACT)
4255 S Buckley Rd., No. 178
Aurora, CO 80013
Fax: 888-356-5023
Fr: 800-340-0737
E-mail: information@itisafact.org
URL: http://itisafact.org

Description: Promotes the use of technology in farming to produce safe, nutritious and affordable food. Encourages consumers to demand access to high-quality, affordable food with minimal impact on the environment. Supports advancements in modern agriculture that would benefit food production both domestically and internationally.

672 ■ American Institute of Biological Sciences (AIBS)
1313 Dolley Madison Blvd.
McLean, VA 22101
Ph: (703)790-1745
Fax: (703)790-2672
E-mail: adm@aibs.org
URL: http://www.aibs.org

Description: Professional member organization and federation of biological associations, laboratories, and museums whose members have an interest in the life sciences. Promotes unity and effectiveness of effort among persons engaged in biological research, education, and application of biological sciences, including agriculture, environment, and medicine. Seeks to further the relationships of biological sciences to other sciences and industries. Conducts roundtable series; provides names of prominent biologists who are willing to serve as speakers and curriculum consultants; provides advisory committees and other services to the Department of Energy, Environmental Protection Agency, National Science Foundation, Department of Defense, and National Aeronautics and Space Administration. Maintains educational consultant panel.

673 ■ American Seed Trade Association
1701 Duke St., Ste. 275
Alexandria, VA 22314
Ph: (703)837-8140
Fax: (703)837-9365
URL: http://www.amseed.com

Description: Represents companies involved in seed production and distribution, plant breeding and related industries in North America. Promotes the development of better seed to produce better crops for a better quality of life. Informs members about environmental and conservation issues and new developments in plant breeding such as the use of modern biotechnology.

674 ■ American Society of Agronomy (ASA)
5585 Guilford Rd.
Madison, WI 53711
Ph: (608)273-8080
Fax: (608)273-2021
E-mail: headquarters@agronomy.org
URL: http://www.agronomy.org

Description: Professional society of agronomists, plant breeders, physiologists, soil scientists, chemists, educators, technicians, and others concerned with crop production and soil management, and conditions affecting them. Sponsors fellowship program and student essay and speech contests. Provides placement service.

675 ■ American Society for Horticultural Science (ASHS)
1018 Duke St.
Alexandria, VA 22314
Ph: (703)836-4606
Fax: (703)836-2024
URL: http://www.ashs.org

Description: Promotes and encourages scientific research and education in horticulture throughout the world. Members represent all areas of horticulture science.

676 ■ Association of Applied IPM Ecologists (AAIE)
PO Box 1119
Coarsegold, CA 93614
Ph: (559)761-1064
E-mail: director@aaie.net
URL: http://www.aaie.net

Description: Professional agricultural pest management consultants, entomologists, and field personnel. Promotes the implementation of integrated pest management in agricultural and urban environments. Provides a forum for the exchange of technical information on pest control. Offers placement service.

677 ■ Association for International Practical Training (AIPT)
10400 Little Patuxent Pkwy., Ste. 250
Columbia, MD 21044-3519
Ph: (410)997-2200
Fax: (410)992-3924
E-mail: aipt@aipt.org
URL: http://www.aipt.org

Description: Providers worldwide of on-the-job training programs for students and professionals seeking international career development and life-changing experiences. Arranges workplace exchanges in hundreds of professional fields, bringing employers and trainees together from around the world. Client list ranges from small farming communities to Fortune 500 companies.

678 ■ Council for Agricultural Science and Technology (CAST)
4420 Lincoln Way
Ames, IA 50014-3447
Ph: (515)292-2125
Fax: (515)292-4512
E-mail: cast@cast-science.org
URL: http://www.cast-science.org

Description: Scientific societies, associate societies, individuals, corporations, foundations, and trade associations. Promotes science-based information on food, fiber, agricultural, natural resource, and related societal and environmental issues.

679 ■ Crop Science Society of America
5585 Guilford Rd.
Madison, WI 53711
Ph: (608)273-8080
Fax: (608)273-2021
E-mail: cca@agronomy.org
URL: http://www.crops.org

Description: Commits to the conservation and wise use of natural resources to produce food, feed and fiber crops while maintaining and improving the environment. Supports its members through publications, recognition and awards, placement service, certification programs, meetings and student activities.

680 ■ Farm and Ranch Freedom Alliance (FARFA)
PO Box 809
Cameron, TX 76520
Ph: (254)697-2661
Fr: (866)687-6452
E-mail: info@farmandranchfreedom.org
URL: http://farmandranchfreedom.org

Description: Strives to save family farms and individuals from expensive and unnecessary government regulation. Works to assure the independence of farmers, ranchers, livestock owners and homesteaders in the management, control, identification and marketing of their products. Supports and enhances sustainable agriculture, family farms and domestic agricultural products.

681 ■ Federation of American Societies for Experimental Biology (FASEB)
9650 Rockville Pike
Bethesda, MD 20814
Ph: (301)634-7000
Fax: (301)634-7001
E-mail: info@faseb.org
URL: http://www.faseb.org

Description: Federation of scientific societies with a total of 40,000 members: the American Physiological Society; American Society for Biochemistry and Molecular Biology; American Society for Pharmacology and Experimental Therapeutics; American Society for Investigative Pathology; American Society for Nutritional Sciences; the American Association of Immunologists; the American Society for Bone and Mineral Research; American Society for Clinical Investigation; the Indocrine Society; the American Society of Human Genetics; Society for Developmental Biology; Biophysical Society; American Association of Anatomists; and the Protein Society. Maintains placement service.

682 ■ *Growing Opportunities: Careers in Agriculture*
JIST Publishing
875 Montreal Way
St. Paul, MN 55102
Fax: 800-547-8329
Fr: 800-648-5478
E-mail: info@jist.com
URL: http://www.jist.com

2004. $99 for DVD; $109 for VHS. 23 minutes. Video includes thumbnail descriptions of 23 careers that exist in the agricultural industry.

683 ■ Korean-American Scientists and Engineers Association (KSEA)
1952 Gallows Rd., Ste. 300
Vienna, VA 22182
Ph: (703)748-1221
Fax: (703)748-1331
E-mail: sejong@ksea.org
URL: http://www.ksea.org

Description: Represents scientists and engineers holding single or advanced degrees. Promotes friendship and mutuality among Korean and American scientists and engineers; contributes to Korea's scientific, technological, industrial, and economic developments; strengthens the scientific, technological, and cultural bonds between Korea and the U.S. Sponsors symposium. Maintains speakers' bureau, placement service, and biographical archives. Compiles statistics.

684 ■ Minorities in Agriculture, Natural Resources and Related Sciences (MANRRS)
PO Box 79506
Atlanta, GA 30357
Ph: (404)347-2975
Fax: (404)892-9405
E-mail: exec.office@manrrs.org
URL: http://www.manrrs.org

Description: Promotes natural and agricultural sciences and other related fields among ethnic minorities in all phases of career preparation and participation. Provides a network to support the professional development of minorities.

685 ■ National Coalition for Food and Agricultural Research (NCFAR)
2441 Village Green Pl.
Champaign, IL 61822
Ph: (217)356-3182
Fax: (217)398-4119
E-mail: ncfar@assochq.org
URL: http://www.ncfar.org

Description: Represents food, agriculture, nutrition, conservation and natural resource stakeholders. Aims to support the sustaining and increasing public investment at the national level in food and agricultural research, extension and education. Seeks to sustain and enhance federal funding for food and agricultural research, extension and education. Strives to help bring about research outcomes that provide a range of major public benefits.

686 ■ National Postsecondary Agricultural Student Organization (PAS)
AgrowKnowledge Ctr.
PO Box 2068
Cedar Rapids, IA 52406
Ph: (208)670-3704
E-mail: info@nationalpas.org
URL: http://www.nationalpas.org

Description: Agriculturally-related student organization; provides opportunity for individual growth, leadership and career preparation. Promotes development of leadership abilities through employment programs, course work, and organization activities.

687 ■ National Society of Consulting Soil Scientists
PO Box 1219
Sandpoint, ID 83864
Ph: (208)263-9391
Fax: (208)263-7013
Fr: 800-535-7148
URL: http://www.nscss.org

Description: Represents the consulting, service, and business interests of professional soil scientists. Advances the discipline and practice of soil science and promotes interaction between professional soil scientists and their communities. Facilitates the exchange of business and soil science experiences within the society.

688 ■ Soil Science Society of America (SSSA)
677 S Segoe Rd.
Madison, WI 53711
Ph: (608)273-8080
Fax: (608)273-2021
E-mail: headquarters@soils.org
URL: http://www.soils.org

Description: Professional soil scientists, including soil physicists, soil classifiers, land use and management specialists, chemists, microbiologists, soil fertility specialists, soil cartographers, conservationists, mineralogists, engineers, and others interested in fundamental and applied soil science.

SOURCES OF HELP-WANTED ADS

689 ■ AI Magazine
American Association for Artificial Intelligence
445 Burgess Dr., Ste. 100
Menlo Park, CA 94025-3442
Ph: (650)328-3123
Fax: (650)321-4457
URL: http://www.aaai.org/Magazine/magazine.php

Quarterly. Magazine about artificial intelligence.

690 ■ Biomedical Technology & Human Factors Engineering
National Technical Information Service
5301 Shawnee Rd.
Alexandria, VA 22312
Ph: (703)605-6585
Fax: (703)605-6900
Fr: 800-553-6847
E-mail: info@ntis.gov
URL: http://www.ntis.gov/products/alerts.aspx#EA95BTHF

Description: Biweekly. $255/year. Carries abstracts of reports on biomedical facilities, instrumentation, and supplies. Also covers human factors engineering and man-machine relations; bionics and artificial intelligence; prosthetics and mechanical organs; life-support systems; space biology; and tissue preservation and storage. Recurring features include a form for ordering reports from NTIS. Also available via e-mail.

691 ■ Cybernetics and Systems
Taylor & Francis Group Journals
325 Chestnut St., Ste. 800
Philadelphia, PA 19106-2608
Ph: (215)625-8900
Fax: (215)625-2940
Fr: 800-354-1420
URL: http://www.tandf.co.uk/journals/titles/01969722.asp

$2,486.00/year for institutions, print & online; $2,237.00/year for individuals, online only. International forum for developments in cybernetics with applications spanning artificial intelligence to economics.

692 ■ eIntelligence
Edward Rosenfeld
PO Box 20008
New York, NY 10025-1510
Ph: (212)222-1123
Fax: (212)222-1123
E-mail: subs@eintelligence.com
URL: http://eintelligence.com

Description: Monthly. $395/year; $450/year outside the United States. Covers technologies that affect the future of computing and offers viewpoints. Concentrates on business, research and government activities in neural networks, parallel processing, pattern recognition, natural language interfaces, voice and speech technologies, and art and graphics. Recur-

ring features include editorials and news of research, and columns on the Net, Nanotechnologies, and Quantum computing.

693 ■ Intelligent Control and Automation
Scientific Research Publishing
PO Box 54821
Irvine, CA 92619-4821
E-mail: ica@scirp.org
URL: http://www.scirp.org/journal/ica/

$156.00/year for individuals. Peer-reviewed journal publishing articles on theories, methods and applications in intelligent control and automation.

694 ■ International Journal on Artificial Intelligence Tools
World Scientific Publishing
27 Warren St., Ste. 401-402
Hackensack, NJ 07601
Ph: (201)487-9655
Fax: (201)487-9656
Fr: 800-227-7562
URL: http://www.worldscinet.com/ijait/ijait.shtml

Bimonthly. $898.00/year for institutions, electronic + print; $862.00/year for institutions, electronic only; $36.00/year for individuals, postage; $47.00/year for individuals, postage; $719.00/year for institutions, electronic + print; $690.00/year for institutions, electronic only. Journal covering design, development, and testing of AI tools.

695 ■ Journal of Artificial Intelligence Research (JAIR)
American Association for Artificial Intelligence Press
2275 E Bayshore Rd., Ste. 160
Palo Alto, CA 94303
Ph: (650)328-3123
Fax: (650)321-4457
URL: http://www.jair.org

$425. Covers all areas of artificial intelligence.

696 ■ PC AI Online
Knowledge Technology Inc.
PO Box 30130
Phoenix, AZ 85046-0130
Ph: (602)971-1869
Fax: (602)971-2321
E-mail: info@pcai.com
URL: http://www.pcai.com

Bimonthly. Geared toward practical application of intelligent technology, covers developments in robotics, expert systems, neural networks, fuzzy logic, object-oriented development, languages and all other areas of artificial intelligence.

697 ■ Presence
MIT Press
55 Hayward St.
Cambridge, MA 02142-1315
Ph: (617)253-5646

Fax: (617)258-6779
E-mail: presence@mit.edu
URL: http://www.mitpressjournals.org/loi/pres

Bimonthly. $98.00/year for individuals, print & online; $91.00/year for individuals, online only; $710.00/year for institutions, print & online; $629.00/year for institutions, online only; $51.00/year for students, print and online; $47.00/year for students, online only, retired. Peer-reviewed journal on teleoperators and virtual environments.

698 ■ Robotica
Cambridge University Press
32 Avenue of the Americas
New York, NY 10013-2473
Ph: (212)924-3900
Fax: (212)691-3239
E-mail: ad_sales@cambridge.org
URL: http://journals.cambridge.org/action/displayJournal?jid=ROB

Bimonthly. $700.00/year for institutions, online & print; $615.00/year for institutions, online; $175.00/year for individuals, online & print; $1,250.00/year for institutions, online & print; $1,100.00/year for institutions, online; $300.00/year for individuals, online & print; $45.00/year for individuals, article. Peer-reviewed journal on robotics studies.

699 ■ Robotics World
Briefings Media Group
2807 N Parham Rd., Ste. 200
Richmond, VA 23294
Ph: (570)567-1982
Fr: 800-791-8699
URL: http://www.roboticsworld.com

$72.00/year; free in U.S.; $99.00/year for Canada and Mexico; $112.00/year for other countries; $162.00/year for Canada and Mexico, 2 years; $162.00/year for other countries, 2 years. Professional magazine covering flexible automation and intelligent machines.

EMPLOYER DIRECTORIES AND NETWORKING LISTS

700 ■ Advanced Manufacturing Technology
Wiley-Blackwell
111 River St.
Hoboken, NJ 07030-5774
Ph: (201)748-6000
Fax: (201)748-6088
E-mail: amtinfo@insights.com
URL: http://www.apnf.org/frostbody.htm

Monthly. Publication includes: List of companies involved in developing advanced manufacturing technologies such as robotics, artificial intelligence in computers, ultrasonics, lasers, and waterjet cutters; also lists sources of information and education on high-technology. Entries include: Company or organization name, address, phone, name of contact;

description of process, product, or service. Principal content is articles and analysis of advanced manufacturing technology. Arrangement: Classified by subject.

HANDBOOKS AND MANUALS

701 ■ AI Application Programming
Charles River Media
20 Channel Center St.
Boston, MA 02210
Ph: (617)289-7700
Fax: (617)289-7844
Fr: 800-354-9706
E-mail: info@charlesriver.com
URL: http://www.courseptr.com

M. Tim Jones. 2005. Second Edition. $59.95. 500 pages. Software engineer Jones demystifies techniques associated with artificial intelligence and shows how they can be useful in everyday applications.

702 ■ Artificial Intelligence: A Modern Approach
Prentice Hall/Pearson Education
1 Lake St.
Upper Saddle River, NJ 07458
Ph: (201)236-7000
Fr: 800-922-0579
E-mail: communications@pearsoned.com
URL: http://www.pearsonhighered.com

Stuart J. Russell and Peter Norvig. Third edition. 2010. $128.00. 1152 pages. Provides an introduction to the theory and practice of artificial intelligence.

703 ■ Careers for Computer Buffs and Other Technological Types
The McGraw-Hill Companies
PO Box 182604
Columbus, OH 43272
Fax: (614)759-3749
Fr: 877-883-5524
E-mail: customer.service@mcgraw-hill.com
URL: http://www.mhprofessional.com/
    product.php?isbn=0071458778

Marjorie Eberts and Margaret Gisler. Third edition, 2006. $13.95 (paper). 160 pages. Suggested jobs in a wide range of settings, from the office to the outdoors.

704 ■ Expert Resumes for Computer and Web Jobs
Jist Publishing
875 Montreal Way
St. Paul, MN 55102
Fr: 800-648-5478
E-mail: info@jist.com
URL: http://www.jist.com

Wendy Enelow and Louise Kursmark. Third edition, 2011. $17.95 (paper). 304 pages.

ONLINE JOB SOURCES AND SERVICES

705 ■ AIJobs.net
URL: http://www.aijobs.net

Description: Features artificial intelligence jobs and careers, resumes search and postings.

706 ■ ComputerJobs.com
URL: http://www.computerjobs.com

Description: Provides listings of computer-related job opportunities.

707 ■ Guru.com
5001 Baum Blvd., Ste. 760
Pittsburgh, PA 15213
Fax: (412)687-4466
Fr: 888-687-1316
URL: http://www.guru.com

Description: Job board specializing in contract jobs for creative and information technology professionals. Also provides online incorporation and educational opportunities for independent contractors along with articles and advice.

708 ■ ZDNet Tech Jobs
URL: http://www.zdnet.com

Description: Site houses a listing of national employment opportunities for professionals in high tech fields. Also contains resume building tips and relocation resources.

TRADESHOWS

709 ■ International Joint Conference on Artificial Intelligence
International Joint Conferences on Artificial Intelligence
PO Box 5490
Somerset, NJ 08875
Ph: (313)667-4669
Fax: (313)667-4966
E-mail: info@ijcai.org
URL: http://www.ijcai.org/

Biennial. Primary Exhibits: Artificial intelligence systems, projects, and services.

OTHER SOURCES

710 ■ Association for the Advancement of Artificial Intelligence (AAAI)
445 Burgess Dr., Ste. 100
Menlo Park, CA 94025
Ph: (650)328-3123
Fax: (650)321-4457
E-mail: info08@aaai.org
URL: http://www.aaai.org

Description: Artificial Intelligence researchers; students, libraries, corporations, and others interested in the subject. (Artificial Intelligence is a discipline in which an attempt is made to approximate the human thinking process through computers.) Seeks to unite researchers and developers of Artificial Intelligence in order to provide an element of cohesion in the field. Serves as focal point and organizer for conferences; areas of interest include interpretation of visual data, robotics, expert systems, natural language processing, knowledge representation, and Artificial Intelligence programming technologies. Holds tutorials.

711 ■ Cognitive Science Society (CSS)
University of Texas
Department of Psychology
1 University Sta. A8000
Austin, TX 78712-0187
Ph: (512)471-2030
Fax: (512)471-3053
E-mail: cogsci@psy.utexas.edu
URL: http://www.cognitivesciencesociety.org

Description: Represents published PhD's; students and PhD's not actively publishing in the fields of psychology, artificial intelligence, and cognitive science. Promotes the dissemination of research in cognitive science and allied sciences. (Cognitive science is a branch of artificial intelligence that seeks to simulate human reasoning and associative powers on a computer, using specialized software).

712 ■ Computer Society (CS)
IEEE
2001 L St. NW, Ste. 700
Washington, DC 20036-4910
Ph: (202)371-0101
Fax: (202)728-9614
Fr: 800-272-6657
E-mail: help@computer.org
URL: http://www.computer.org

Description: Computer professionals. Promotes the development of computer and information sciences and fosters communication within the information processing community. Sponsors conferences, symposia, workshops, tutorials, technical meetings, and seminars. Operates Computer Society Press. Presents scholarships; bestows technical achievement and service awards and certificates.

713 ■ Computing Research Association (CRA)
1828 L St. NW, Ste. 800
Washington, DC 20036-4632
Ph: (202)234-2111
Fax: (202)667-1066
E-mail: info@cra.org
URL: http://www.cra.org

Description: An association of more than 200 North American academic departments of computer science, computer engineering, and related fields; laboratories and centers in industry government, and academia engaging in basic computing research; and affiliated professional societies.

714 ■ IMAGE Society
PO Box 6221
Chandler, AZ 85246-6221
E-mail: image@image-society.org
URL: http://image-society.org

Description: Individuals and organizations interested in the technological advancement and application of real-time visual simulation (medical, virtual reality, telepresence, aeronautical, and automotive) and other related virtual reality technologies.

715 ■ International Association for Artificial Intelligence and Law (IAAIL)
286 Selby Ln.
Atherton, CA 94027
Ph: (650)368-1297
E-mail: info@iaail.org
URL: http://www.iaail.org

Description: Computer science and law academics and professionals. Promotes research and development in the field of artificial intelligence and law.

716 ■ International Society of Applied Intelligence (ISAI)
Texas State University, San Marcos
Dept. of Computer Science
601 University Dr.
San Marcos, TX 78666-4616
Ph: (512)245-8050
Fax: (512)245-8750
E-mail: ma04@txstate.edu
URL: http://isai.cs.txstate.edu

Description: Researchers, academicians, computer scientists, industry, and government. Promotes dissemination of Research in the area of intelligent systems' technology and improves scientific literacy. Sponsors an International conference on Industrial, Engineering, and other Applications of Applied Intelligent Systems.

717 ■ MIT Computer Science and Artificial Intelligence Laboratory
32 Vassar St.
Cambridge, MA 02139
Ph: (617)253-5851
Fax: (617)258-8682
URL: http://www.csail.mit.edu

Description: Active since 1959. Interdisciplinary laboratory of over 200 people that spans several academic departments and has active projects ongoing with members of every academic school at MIT. Offers research, current job listings, and educational outreach.

718 ■ Society for Modeling and Simulation International (SCS)
2598 Fortune Way, Ste. I
Vista, CA 92081
Ph: (858)277-3888
Fax: (858)277-3930
E-mail: scs@scs.org
URL: http://www.scs.org

Description: Persons professionally engaged in simulation, particularly through the use of computers and similar devices that employ mathematical or physical analogies. Maintains speakers' bureau.

719 ■ Special Interest Group on Artificial Intelligence (SIGART)
Association for Computing Machinery
2 Penn Plz., Ste. 701
New York, NY 10121-0701
Ph: (212)626-0605
Fax: (212)302-5826
E-mail: frawley@acm.org
URL: http://www.sigart.org

Description: A special interest group of the Association for Computing Machinery. Individuals interested in the application of computers to tasks normally requiring human intelligence. Enhances the capabilities of computers in this area.

720 ■ Special Interest Group on Simulation (SIGSIM)
PO Box 3082
Auburn, AL 36831
Ph: (334)844-6360
E-mail: drew@drew-hamilton.com
URL: http://www.sigsim.org

Description: A special interest group of Association for Computing Machinery. Researchers and practitioners in computer simulation including professionals in business and industry. Holds technical meetings at annual conference of ACM. Promotes research and conducts surveys on topics such as the type of computer simulation courses being offered at colleges and universities. Researches the application of simulation principles and theory to sub disciplines of computer science.

721 ■ SRI International Artificial Intelligence Center
333 Ravenswood Ave.
Menlo Park, CA 94025-3493

Ph: (650)859-2641
Fax: (650)859-3735
E-mail: action@ai.sri.com
URL: http://www.ai.sri.com

Description: Seeks to develop methods for building computer-based systems to solve problems.

722 ■ Systems, Man, and Cybernetics Society (SMCS)
IEEE
3 Park Ave., 17th Fl.
New York, NY 10016-5997
Ph: (212)419-7900
Fax: (212)752-4929
E-mail: michael.berthold@uni-konstanz.de
URL: http://www.ieeesmc.org

Description: A society of the Institute of Electrical and Electronics Engineers. Serves as a forum on the theoretical and practical considerations of systems engineering, human machine systems, and cybernetics—with a particular focus on synthetic and natural systems involving humans and machines.

723 ■ AeroSpaceNews.com
AeroSpaceNews.com
PO Box 1748
Ojai, CA 93024-1748
Ph: (805)985-2320
URL: http://www.aerospacenews.com/content/view/41/33/

Monthly. $19.95/year for individuals, private. Journal reporting on the insights, impressions and images of tomorrow's technological wonders in the field of aerospace.

724 ■ Air Jobs Digest
World Air Data
PO Box 42724
Washington, DC 20015
Ph: (301)990-6800
Fr: 800-247-5627
URL: http://www.airjobsdigest.com/

Monthly. $96.00/year for individuals. Newspaper covering job listings in aviation and aerospace worldwide.

725 ■ Air Safety Week
Access Intelligence L.L.C.
4 Choke Cherry Rd.
Rockville, MD 20850
Ph: (301)354-2000
Fax: (301)309-3847
Fr: 800-777-5006
E-mail: info@accessintel.com
URL: http://www.accessintel.com/products/defense

Description: Weekly. $1,319/year. Covers air safety issues, crashes, regulations, legal cases, air traffic control technology, maintenance, engineering, and aviation and airport security. Also available online and via e-mail.

726 ■ ATCA Bulletin
Air Traffic Control Association
1101 King St., Ste. 300
Alexandria, VA 22314
Ph: (703)299-2430
Fax: (703)299-2437
E-mail: info@atca.org
URL: http://www.atca.org

Description: Monthly. Features news of the Association, which is interested in the establishment and maintenance of a safe and efficient air traffic control system.

727 ■ Aviation Today
Access Intelligence L.L.C.
4 Choke Cherry Rd., 2nd Fl.
Rockville, MD 20850
Ph: (301)354-2000
Fax: (301)309-3847

Fr: 800-777-5006
E-mail: info@accessintel.com
URL: http://www.accessintel.com

Description: Covers the commuter/regional airline industry, including airline management, marketing, labor, personnel changes, aircraft acquisitions, new products, and the financial and operational environment. Recurring features include interviews, news of research, a calendar of events, reports of meetings, job listings, and notices of publications available.

728 ■ Aviation Week & Space Technology
McGraw-Hill Inc.
PO Box 182604
Columbus, OH 43218
Ph: (614)430-4000
Fax: (614)759-3749
Fr: 877-833-5524
URL: http://www.aviationweek.com/aw/generic/channel_.jsp?channel=

Weekly. $109.00/year for Canada; $103.00/year for individuals; $160.00/year for other countries. Magazine serving the aviation and aerospace market worldwide.

729 ■ Avion Magazine
Airline Passenger Experience Association
355 Lexington Ave., 15th Fl.
New York, NY 10017
Ph: (212)297-2177
Fax: (212)370-9047
URL: http://meetings.apex.aero/member_center/benefits-of-membersh

Quarterly. Magazine covering aviation.

730 ■ Flying
Hachette Filipacchi Media U.S. Inc.
1633 Broadway
New York, NY 10019-6708
Ph: (212)767-6000
URL: http://www.flyingmag.com

Monthly. $14.00/year for individuals, print; $22.00/year for two years, print; $33.00/year for Canada, print; $33.00/year for other countries, print. General aviation magazine.

731 ■ In Flight USA
In Flight USA
PO Box 5402
San Mateo, CA 94402
Ph: (650)358-9908
Fax: (650)358-9254
URL: http://www.inflightusa.com/index.html

Monthly. $24.95/year for individuals; $44.95/year for two years. Magazine on Aviation.

732 ■ Journal of Transportation Technologies
Scientific Research Publishing
PO Box 54821
Irvine, CA 92619-4821
E-mail: jtts@scirp.org
URL: http://www.scirp.org/journal/jtts/

Quarterly. $156.00/year for individuals. Peer-reviewed journal publishing articles on the latest advancement of transportation technologies.

733 ■ AOPA's Airport Directory
Aircraft Owners and Pilots Association
421 Aviation Way
Frederick, MD 21701
Ph: (301)695-2000
Fax: (301)695-2375
Fr: 800-872-2672
E-mail: airportdirectory@aopa.org
URL: http://www.aopa.org

Biennial, January; Latest edition 2009-2010. $3995.00 for individuals. Covers: 5,300 U.S. public-use landing facilities, including airports, heliports, seaplane bases, and approximately 1,800 private-use landing facilities; 5,000 aviation service companies. Entries include: For landing facilities—Airport type and name, city, phone, runway dimensions, types of instrument approaches, hours operated, communications frequencies, runway light system, local attractions, ground transportation, restaurants, hotels. For aviation service companies—Company name, phone, airport affiliation, operating hours, fuel type, Unicom frequency. Arrangement: Geographical. Indexes: Cross-Reference index of U.S. landing facilities.

734 ■ National Air Transportation Association—Aviation Resource and Membership Directory
National Air Transportation Association
4226 King St.
Alexandria, VA 22302
Ph: (703)845-9000
Fax: (703)845-8176
Fr: 800-808-6282
URL: http://www.nata.aero

Annual, Latest edition 2008. $50.00 for nonmembers; $25.00 for members. Covers: More than 1,000 regular, associate, and affiliate members; regular members include airport service organizations, air taxi operators, and commuter airlines. Entries include: Company name, address, phone, fax number, name and title of contact. Arrangement: Regular members are classified by service; associate and affiliate members are alphabetical in separate sections. Indexes: Geographical.

735 ■ World Aviation Directory & Aerospace Database (WAD&AD)
McGraw-Hill, Inc.
1200 G St. NW, Ste. 200
Washington, DC 20005
Ph: (515)237-3682
Fax: 888-385-1428

Fr: 800-525-5003
E-mail: wad@mcgraw-hill.com
URL: http://a1.ecom01.com/aw_marketdatacenter?s_
    id=7

Semiannual, Latest edition 2010. $269.00 for U.S.;
$1,295.00 for U.S.; $595.00 for U.S.; $495.00 for
U.S.; $149.00 for U.S. Database covers: 22,000
airlines, manufacturers, MRO stations, airports
military/government and distributors/suppliers; 6,000
product/service categories and 166,000 listings;
69,000 aviation/aerospace professionals; 500,000
users across all 3 platforms/formats and, Commercial, Military & Business Aviation Fleet Data. Arrangement: Classified by major activity
(manufacturers, airlines, etc.). Indexes: Company
and organization, personnel, product, trade name.

HANDBOOKS AND MANUALS

736 ■ Air Traffic Control Career Prep
Aviation Supplies & Academics, Inc.
7005 132nd Place SE
Newcastle, WA 98059-3153
Ph: (425)235-1500
Fr: 800-272-2359
URL: http://www.asa2fly.com/
    product1.aspx?SID=1&Product_ID=714&

Patrick Mattson. 2006. $49.95 (paper). 240 pages.
Provides introduction on air traffic controller career
and helps readers improve chances of earning a high
score on the FAA's air traffic selection and training
aptitude test. Features general information on opportunities, working conditions, training and qualification requirements, available roles and positions, pay
and benefits, and contact phone numbers.

737 ■ Master the Air Traffic Controller Test
Peterson's
Princeton Pike Corporate Center
2000 Lenox Dr.
Lawrenceville, NJ 08648
Ph: (609)896-1800
Fax: (609)896-4531
Fr: 800-338-3282
E-mail: custsvc@petersons.com
URL: http://www.petersons.com

Michael S. Nolan. 2007. 360 pages. Gives readers
the information needed to score high on the FAA
entrance exams and launch a career in air traffic
control. Contains a thorough explanation of the U.S.

air traffic control system, 700 sample knowledge
questions and answers and navigation charts.

ONLINE JOB SOURCES AND SERVICES

738 ■ AirJobsDaily.com
E-mail: staff@airjobsdaily.com
URL: http://www.airjobsdaily.com

Description: Serves as a source of current aviation
and aerospace job openings.

739 ■ AirlineCareer.info
URL: http://www.airlinecareer.info

Description: Provides jobs in the airline community
covering airport careers, aircraft manufacturing,
aerospace careers, and cabin crew careers.

740 ■ The Aviation MD
E-mail: adrian@theaviationmd.com
URL: http://www.theaviationmd.com

Description: Serves as international aviation database for employers and jobseekers in the aviation
industry.

741 ■ AviationCrossing.com
URL: http://www.aviationcrossing.com

Provides aviation jobs for agents, managers, mechanics, operators, specialists, supervisors, technicians,
engineers, maintenance, pilots and other related aviation professionals.

TRADESHOWS

**742 ■ Air Traffic Control Association
Convention ATCA Annual Conference and
Exposition**
Air Traffic Control Association
1101 King St., Ste. 300
Alexandria, VA 22314-2944
Ph: (703)299-2430
Fax: (703)299-2437
E-mail: info@atca.org
URL: http://www.atca.org

Annual. Primary Exhibits: ATC/aviation equipment,
supplies, and services. Dates and Locations: 2012
Sep 30 - Oct 03; National Harbor, MD.

**743 ■ Airports Council International - North
America Convention**
Airports Council International - North America
1775 K St. N.W., Ste. 500
Washington, DC 20006
Ph: (202)293-8500
Fax: (202)331-1362
Fr: 888-424-7767
E-mail: memberservices@aci-na.org
URL: http://www.aci-na.org

Annual. Primary Exhibits: Air Aviation industry equipment, products and services.

OTHER SOURCES

744 ■ Air Traffic Control Association (ATCA)
1101 King St., Ste. 300
Alexandria, VA 22314
Ph: (703)299-2430
Fax: (703)299-2437
E-mail: info@atca.org
URL: http://www.atca.org

Description: Air traffic controllers; private, commercial, and military pilots; private and business
aircraft owners and operators; aircraft and electronics
engineers; airlines, aircraft manufacturers, and
electronic and human engineering firms. Promotes
the establishment and maintenance of a safe and efficient air traffic control system. Conducts special
surveys and studies on air traffic control problems.
Participates in aviation community conferences.

**745 ■ National Black Coalition of Federal
Aviation Employees (NBCFAE)**
PO Box 845
Hampton, GA 30228
Fr: 888-311-1622
E-mail: info@nbcfae.org
URL: http://nbcfae.org

Description: Federal Aviation Administration
employees. Purposes are to: promote professionalism and equal opportunity in the workplace; locate
and train qualified minorities for FAA positions; help
the FAA meet its affirmative action goals; monitor
black, female, and minority trainees; educate members and the public about their rights and FAA personnel and promotion qualifications; develop a voice for
black, female, and minority FAA employees. Recruits
minorities from community and schools who qualify
for employment; sponsors seminars for members and
for those who wish to be employed by the FAA.
Maintains speaker's bureau; sponsors competitions.

Aircraft Mechanics and Engine Specialists

746 ■ *AeroSpaceNews.com*
AeroSpaceNews.com
PO Box 1748
Ojai, CA 93024-1748
Ph: (805)985-2320
URL: http://www.aerospacenews.com/content/view/
41/33/

Monthly. $19.95/year for individuals, private. Journal reporting on the insights, impressions and images of tomorrow's technological wonders in the field of aerospace.

747 ■ *Air Jobs Digest*
World Air Data
PO Box 42724
Washington, DC 20015
Ph: (301)990-6800
Fr: 800-247-5627
URL: http://www.airjobsdigest.com/

Monthly. $96.00/year for individuals. Newspaper covering job listings in aviation and aerospace worldwide.

748 ■ *Aviation Maintenance*
Access Intelligence L.L.C.
4 Choke Cherry Rd., 2nd Fl.
Rockville, MD 20850-4024
Ph: (301)354-2000
Fax: (301)309-3847
Fr: 800-777-5006
URL: http://www.aviationtoday.com/am/

Free. Magazine covering aviation maintenance.

749 ■ *Aviation Week & Space Technology*
McGraw-Hill Inc.
PO Box 182604
Columbus, OH 43218
Ph: (614)430-4000
Fax: (614)759-3749
Fr: 877-833-5524
URL: http://www.aviationweek.com/aw/generic/
channel_.jsp?channel=

Weekly. $109.00/year for Canada; $103.00/year for individuals; $160.00/year for other countries. Magazine serving the aviation and aerospace market worldwide.

750 ■ *Avion Magazine*
Airline Passenger Experience Association
355 Lexington Ave., 15th Fl.
New York, NY 10017
Ph: (212)297-2177
Fax: (212)370-9047
URL: http://meetings.apex.aero/member_center/
benefits-of-membersh

Quarterly. Magazine covering aviation.

751 ■ *Flying*
Hachette Filipacchi Media U.S. Inc.
1633 Broadway
New York, NY 10019-6708
Ph: (212)767-6000
URL: http://www.flyingmag.com

Monthly. $14.00/year for individuals, print; $22.00/year for two years, print; $33.00/year for Canada, print; $33.00/year for other countries, print. General aviation magazine.

752 ■ *In Flight USA*
In Flight USA
PO Box 5402
San Mateo, CA 94402
Ph: (650)358-9908
Fax: (650)358-9254
URL: http://www.inflightusa.com/index.html

Monthly. $24.95/year for individuals; $44.95/year for two years. Magazine on Aviation.

753 ■ *Rotor & Wing*
Access Intelligence L.L.C.
4 Choke Cherry Rd., 2nd Fl.
Rockville, MD 20850-4024
Ph: (301)354-2000
Fax: (301)309-3847
Fr: 800-777-5006
URL: http://www.aviationtoday.com/rw/

Monthly. Free. Magazine covering helicopters.

754 ■ *World Journal of Mechanics*
Scientific Research Publishing
PO Box 54821
Irvine, CA 92619-4821
E-mail: wjm@scirp.org
URL: http://www.scirp.org/journal/wjm/

Quarterly. $156.00/year for individuals. Peer-reviewed journal publishing articles in the general field of mechanics.

755 ■ *AOPA's Airport Directory*
Aircraft Owners and Pilots Association
421 Aviation Way
Frederick, MD 21701
Ph: (301)695-2000
Fax: (301)695-2375
Fr: 800-872-2672
E-mail: airportdirectory@aopa.org
URL: http://www.aopa.org

Biennial, January; Latest edition 2009-2010. $3995.00 for individuals. Covers: 5,300 U.S. public-use landing facilities, including airports, heliports, seaplane bases, and approximately 1,800 private-use landing facilities; 5,000 aviation service companies. Entries include: For landing facilities—Airport type and name, city, phone, runway dimensions, types of instrument approaches, hours operated, communications frequencies, runway light system, local attractions, ground transportation, restaurants, hotels. For aviation service companies—Company name, phone, airport affiliation, operating hours, fuel type, Unicom frequency. Arrangement: Geographical. Indexes: Cross-Reference index of U.S. landing facilities.

756 ■ *National Air Transportation Association—Aviation Resource and Membership Directory*
National Air Transportation Association
4226 King St.
Alexandria, VA 22302
Ph: (703)845-9000
Fax: (703)845-8176
Fr: 800-808-6282
URL: http://www.nata.aero

Annual, Latest edition 2008. $50.00 for nonmembers; $25.00 for members. Covers: More than 1,000 regular, associate, and affiliate members; regular members include airport service organizations, air taxi operators, and commuter airlines. Entries include: Company name, address, phone, fax number, name and title of contact. Arrangement: Regular members are classified by service; associate and affiliate members are alphabetical in separate sections. Indexes: Geographical.

757 ■ *World Aviation Directory & Aerospace Database (WAD&AD)*
McGraw-Hill, Inc.
1200 G St. NW, Ste. 200
Washington, DC 20005
Ph: (515)237-3682
Fax: 888-385-1428
Fr: 800-525-5003
E-mail: wad@mcgraw-hill.com
URL: http://a1.ecom01.com/aw_marketdatacenter?s_
id=7

Semiannual, Latest edition 2010. $269.00 for U.S.; $1,295.00 for U.S.; $595.00 for U.S.; $495.00 for U.S.; $149.00 for U.S. Database covers: 22,000 airlines, manufacturers, MRO stations, airports military/government and distributors/suppliers; 6,000 product/service categories and 166,000 listings; 69,000 aviation/aerospace professionals; 500,000 users across all 3 platforms/formats and, Commercial, Military & Business Aviation Fleet Data. Arrangement: Classified by major activity (manufacturers, airlines, etc.). Indexes: Company and organization, personnel, product, trade name.

758 ■ *Careers in Travel, Tourism, and Hospitality*
The McGraw-Hill Companies
PO Box 182604
Columbus, OH 43272

Fax: (614)759-3749
Fr: 877-883-5524
E-mail: customer.service@mcgraw-hill.com
URL: http://www.mhprofessional.com

Marjorie Eberts, Linda Brothers, and Ann Gisler. Second edition, 2005. $15.95 (paper). 224 pages.

759 ■ Engineering, Mechanics, and Architecture
Ferguson Publishing
132 W 31st St., 17th Fl.
New York, NY 10001
Fax: 800-678-3633
Fr: 800-322-8755
E-mail: custserv@factsonfile.com
URL: http://www.infobasepublishing.com

Kelly Wiles. 2010. $39.95. 160 pages (hardcover). Serves as a guide for readers interested in switching jobs. Contains useful advice, career tips, interviews and self-asessment questions.

EMPLOYMENT AGENCIES AND SEARCH FIRMS

760 ■ Amtec Human Capital
2749 Saturn St.
Brea, CA 92821
Ph: (714)993-1900
Fax: (714)993-2419
E-mail: info@amtechc.com
URL: http://www.amtechc.com

Employment agency.

761 ■ Jet Professionals
114 Charles A. Lindbergh Dr.
Teterboro, NJ 07608
Ph: (201)393-6900
Fax: (201)462-4081
Fr: 800-441-6016
E-mail: jobs@jet-professionals.com
URL: http://www.jet-professionals.com

Provides staffing services to the aviation industry. Offers jobs for corporate aviation executives, chief pilots, flight attendants, maintenance professionals, dispatchers, schedulers and more.

762 ■ Strom Aviation
109 S Elm St.
Waconia, MN 55387
Ph: (952)544-3611
Fax: (952)544-3948
Fr: 800-743-8988
E-mail: jobs@stromaviation.com
URL: http://www.stromaviation.com

Serves as a staffing firm specializing in hiring all types of aircraft technicians to provide manpower to service centers, repair stations, and OEMs.

ONLINE JOB SOURCES AND SERVICES

763 ■ AeroIndustryJobs.com
URL: http://www.aeroindustryjobs.com

Description: Lists careers in the aerospace, defense and advanced materials industries. Helps industry employers connect with qualified, career-focused job seekers.

764 ■ AeroVents.com
E-mail: info@aerovents.com
URL: http://www.aerovents.com/body.shtml

Description: Seeks to spread the word about aviation events. Covers aviation events from conventions, space launches, seminars, model rocketry and aircraft, ballooning, sky diving, plane pulls, open houses, air shows and fly-ins.

765 ■ AircraftEngineers.com
URL: http://www.aircraftengineers.com

Description: Lists aircraft maintenance engineering jobs and aerospace vacancies. Provides career information for individuals who wish to start a career as an aircraft engineer.

766 ■ AircraftMechanicJobs.org
URL: http://aircraftmechanicjobs.org

Description: Lists aircraft mechanic jobs from different companies throughout the country.

767 ■ AirJobsDaily.com
E-mail: staff@airjobsdaily.com
URL: http://www.airjobsdaily.com

Description: Serves as a source of current aviation and aerospace job openings.

768 ■ AirlineCareer.com
Ph: (978)615-3190
E-mail: jbelotti@airlinecareer.com
URL: http://www.airlinecareer.com

Web-based training center. Provides flight attendant job placement services.

769 ■ AirlineCareer.info
URL: http://www.airlinecareer.info

Description: Provides jobs in the airline community covering airport careers, aircraft manufacturing, aerospace careers, and cabin crew careers.

770 ■ AvCrew.com
URL: http://www.avcrew.com

Description: Provides service designed exclusively for career employment in the business aviation sector. Features flight crew jobs, conducts applicant screening, and assists selected flight departments with candidate searches.

771 ■ AviaNation
URL: http://www.avianation.com

Description: Features aviation jobs, pilot jobs, flight attendant jobs, jobs for A&P mechanics, and other aviation job openings around the world.

772 ■ AviationCrossing.com
URL: http://www.aviationcrossing.com

Provides aviation jobs for agents, managers, mechanics, operators, specialists, supervisors, technicians, engineers, maintenance, pilots and other related aviation professionals.

773 ■ AvJobs.com
URL: http://www.avjobs.com

Description: Provides information on a number of different careers in the aviation and aerospace industry. Features aviation schools directory, affiliate programs, research and networking, employment resources, salaries and wages, aviation careers descriptions, aviation guide and other resources.

774 ■ BestAviation.net
URL: http://www.bestaviation.net

Description: Provides source for information on flight school training, helicopter schools, aviation college programs, flight attendant careers, aircraft maintenance and pilot jobs.

775 ■ FlightLevelJobs.com
URL: http://www.flightleveljobs.com

Description: Serves as a source of aviation employment information. Features aviation and aerospace jobs and employment opportunities.

776 ■ JetEmployment.com
URL: http://jetemployment.com

Description: Features employment opportunities for pilots and other workers in the airline, airport, and business aviation industry.

777 ■ PlaneJobs.com
E-mail: jobmaster@planejobs.com
URL: http://planejobs.com

Description: Serves as an employment, resume, career, and job search database for the aviation industry.

OTHER SOURCES

778 ■ Aircraft Electronics Association (AEA)
3570 NE Ralph Powell Rd.
Lee's Summit, MO 64064
Ph: (816)347-8400
Fax: (816)347-8405
E-mail: info@aea.net
URL: http://www.aea.net

Description: Companies engaged in the sales, engineering, installation, and service of electronic aviation equipment and systems. Seeks to: advance the science of aircraft electronics; promote uniform and stable regulations and uniform standards of performance; establish and maintain a code of ethics; gather and disseminate technical data; advance the education of members and the public in the science of aircraft electronics. Offers supplement type certificates, test equipment licensing, temporary FCC licensing for new installations, spare parts availability and pricing, audiovisual technician training, equipment and spare parts loan, profitable installation, and service facility operation. Provides employment information, equipment exchange information and service assistance on member installations anywhere in the world.

779 ■ Professional Aviation Maintenance Association (PAMA)
400 N Washington St., Ste. 300
Alexandria, VA 22314
Ph: (703)778-4647
Fax: (703)683-5480
E-mail: hq@pama.org
URL: http://www.pama.org

Description: Airframe and powerplant (A&P) technicians and aviation industry-related companies. Strives to increase the professionalism of the individual aviation technician through greater technical knowledge and better understanding of safety requirements. Establishes communication among technicians throughout the country. Fosters and improves methods, skills, learning and achievement in the aviation maintenance field.

SOURCES OF HELP-WANTED ADS

780 ■ AeroSpaceNews.com
AeroSpaceNews.com
PO Box 1748
Ojai, CA 93024-1748
Ph: (805)985-2320
URL: http://www.aerospacenews.com/content/view/
41/33/

Monthly. $19.95/year for individuals, private. Journal reporting on the insights, impressions and images of tomorrow's technological wonders in the field of aerospace.

781 ■ Air Jobs Digest
World Air Data
PO Box 42724
Washington, DC 20015
Ph: (301)990-6800
Fr: 800-247-5627
URL: http://www.airjobsdigest.com/

Monthly. $96.00/year for individuals. Newspaper covering job listings in aviation and aerospace worldwide.

782 ■ Air Safety Week
Access Intelligence L.L.C.
4 Choke Cherry Rd.
Rockville, MD 20850
Ph: (301)354-2000
Fax: (301)309-3847
Fr: 800-777-5006
E-mail: info@accessintel.com
URL: http://www.accessintel.com/products/defense

Description: Weekly. $1,319/year. Covers air safety issues, crashes, regulations, legal cases, air traffic control technology, maintenance, engineering, and aviation and airport security. Also available online and via e-mail.

783 ■ AOPA Pilot
Aircraft Owners and Pilots Association
421 Aviation Way
Frederick, MD 21701
Ph: (301)695-2000
Fax: (301)695-2375
Fr: 800-872-2672
URL: http://www.aopa.org/pilot/

Monthly. $8.00/year for members; $5.00/year for nonmembers. Magazine for general aviation pilots and aircraft owners who are members of the Aircraft Owners and Pilots Assn. Articles are tailored to address the special informational requirements of both recreational and business pilots.

784 ■ Aviation Today
Access Intelligence L.L.C.
4 Choke Cherry Rd., 2nd Fl.
Rockville, MD 20850
Ph: (301)354-2000
Fax: (301)309-3847

Fr: 800-777-5006
E-mail: info@accessintel.com
URL: http://www.accessintel.com

Description: Covers the commuter/regional airline industry, including airline management, marketing, labor, personnel changes, aircraft acquisitions, new products, and the financial and operational environment. Recurring features include interviews, news of research, a calendar of events, reports of meetings, job listings, and notices of publications available.

785 ■ Aviation Week & Space Technology
McGraw-Hill Inc.
PO Box 182604
Columbus, OH 43218
Ph: (614)430-4000
Fax: (614)759-3749
Fr: 877-833-5524
URL: http://www.aviationweek.com/aw/generic/
channel_.jsp?channel=

Weekly. $109.00/year for Canada; $103.00/year for individuals; $160.00/year for other countries. Magazine serving the aviation and aerospace market worldwide.

786 ■ Avion Magazine
Airline Passenger Experience Association
355 Lexington Ave., 15th Fl.
New York, NY 10017
Ph: (212)297-2177
Fax: (212)370-9047
URL: http://meetings.apex.aero/member_center/
benefits-of-membersh

Quarterly. Magazine covering aviation.

787 ■ Collegiate Aviation News Newsletter
University Aviation Association
3410 Skyway Dr.
Auburn, AL 36830-6444
Ph: (334)844-2434
Fax: (334)844-2432
E-mail: uaamail@uaa.aero
URL: http://www.uaa.aero/

Description: Quarterly. $42/yr. for non-members. Provides information on Association activities and projects, events of other aviation organizations that bear on higher education, and the future impact of collegiate aviation education. Recurring features include feature articles on outstanding individual and institutional members, statistics, a calendar of events, news of members, news of research, an editorial, letters to the editor, book reviews, employment information, and the president's report.

788 ■ Flying
Hachette Filipacchi Media U.S. Inc.
1633 Broadway
New York, NY 10019-6708
Ph: (212)767-6000
URL: http://www.flyingmag.com

Monthly. $14.00/year for individuals, print; $22.00/

year for two years, print; $33.00/year for Canada, print; $33.00/year for other countries, print. General aviation magazine.

789 ■ In Flight USA
In Flight USA
PO Box 5402
San Mateo, CA 94402
Ph: (650)358-9908
Fax: (650)358-9254
URL: http://www.inflightusa.com/index.html

Monthly. $24.95/year for individuals; $44.95/year for two years. Magazine on Aviation.

790 ■ International Journal of Energetic Materials and Chemical Propulsion
Begell House Inc.
50 Cross Hwy.
Redding, CT 06896
Ph: (203)938-1300
Fax: (203)938-1304
URL: http://www.begellhouse.com/journals/
17bbb47e377ce023

$1,240.00/year for institutions. Journal promoting scientific investigation, technical advancements and information exchange on energetic materials and chemical propulsion.

791 ■ International Women Pilots
The Ninety-Nines Inc.
4300 Amelia Earhart Rd.
Oklahoma City, OK 73159
Ph: (405)685-7969
Fax: (405)685-7985
Fr: 800-994-1929
E-mail: 99s@ninety-nines.org
URL: http://www.ninety-nines.org/index.cfm/99_
news_magazine.htm

Description: Bimonthly. $20 for non-members. Includes material of interest to the members of The Ninety-Nines, Inc., an international organization of women pilots. Recurring features include interviews, news of research, letters to the editor, news of educational opportunities, a calendar of events, and columns titled President's and Careers.

792 ■ NAFI Mentor
National Association of Flight Instructors
730 Grand St.
Allegan, MI 49010
Fr: (866)806-6156
E-mail: nafi@nafinet.org
URL: http://www.nafinet.org

Description: Monthly. Supports NAFI in its efforts to serve as a central point for dissemination of knowledge, methodology, and new information relative to flight instruction. Recurring features include letters to the editor, news of research, reports of meetings, and notices of publications available. Also includes news of relevant legislative and regulatory activity.

793 ■ Rotor & Wing
Access Intelligence L.L.C.
4 Choke Cherry Rd., 2nd Fl.
Rockville, MD 20850-4024
Ph: (301)354-2000
Fax: (301)309-3847
Fr: 800-777-5006
URL: http://www.aviationtoday.com/rw/

Monthly. Free. Magazine covering helicopters.

794 ■ TsAGI Science Journal
Begell House Inc.
50 Cross Hwy.
Redding, CT 06896
Ph: (203)938-1300
Fax: (203)938-1304
URL: http://www.begellhouse.com/journals/
    58618e1439159b1f

Bimonthly. $999.00/year for institutions. Journal covering the areas of mechanics, aviation and cosmonautics, industrial aerodynamic and hydrodynamics of rapid motion.

795 ■ Woman Engineer
Equal Opportunity Publications, Inc.
445 Broadhollow Rd., Ste. 425
Melville, NY 11747
Ph: (631)421-9421
Fax: (631)421-1352
E-mail: info@eop.com
URL: http://www.eop.com

Annual. Magazine that is offered at no charge to qualified female engineering, computer-science, and information-technology students and professionals seeking to find employment and advancement in their careers.

EMPLOYER DIRECTORIES AND NETWORKING LISTS

796 ■ AOPA's Airport Directory
Aircraft Owners and Pilots Association
421 Aviation Way
Frederick, MD 21701
Ph: (301)695-2000
Fax: (301)695-2375
Fr: 800-872-2672
E-mail: airportdirectory@aopa.org
URL: http://www.aopa.org

Biennial, January; Latest edition 2009-2010. $3995.00 for individuals. Covers: 5,300 U.S. public-use landing facilities, including airports, heliports, seaplane bases, and approximately 1,800 private-use landing facilities; 5,000 aviation service companies. Entries include: For landing facilities—Airport type and name, city, phone, runway dimensions, types of instrument approaches, hours operated, communications frequencies, runway light system, local attractions, ground transportation, restaurants, hotels. For aviation service companies—Company name, phone, airport affiliation, operating hours, fuel type, Unicom frequency. Arrangement: Geographical. Indexes: Cross-Reference index of U.S. landing facilities.

797 ■ Career Opportunities in Aviation and the Aerospace Industry
Facts On File Inc.
132 W 31st St., 17th Fl.
New York, NY 10001
Ph: (212)967-8800
Fax: 800-678-3633
Fr: 800-322-8755
URL: http://www.infobasepublishing.com

Published January, 2005. Covers: Eighty up-to-date job profiles, providing detailed information about the duties, salaries, and prospects of aviation mechanics, designers, technicians, scientists, and administrators.

798 ■ Careers in Focus—Aviation
Facts On File Inc.
132 W 31st St., 17th Fl.
New York, NY 10001
Ph: (212)967-8800
Fax: 800-678-3633
Fr: 800-322-8755
URL: http://www.infobasepublishing.com

Published October, 2010. $32.95 for individuals. Covers: An overview of aviation, followed by a selection of jobs profiled in detail, including the nature of the job, earnings, prospects for employment, what kind of training and skills it requires, and sources for further information.

799 ■ National Air Transportation Association—Aviation Resource and Membership Directory
National Air Transportation Association
4226 King St.
Alexandria, VA 22302
Ph: (703)845-9000
Fax: (703)845-8176
Fr: 800-808-6282
URL: http://www.nata.aero

Annual, Latest edition 2008. $50.00 for nonmembers; $25.00 for members. Covers: More than 1,000 regular, associate, and affiliate members; regular members include airport service organizations, air taxi operators, and commuter airlines. Entries include: Company name, address, phone, fax number, name and title of contact. Arrangement: Regular members are classified by service; associate and affiliate members are alphabetical in separate sections. Indexes: Geographical.

800 ■ World Aviation Directory & Aerospace Database (WAD&AD)
McGraw-Hill, Inc.
1200 G St. NW, Ste. 200
Washington, DC 20005
Ph: (515)237-3682
Fax: 888-385-1428
Fr: 800-525-5003
E-mail: wad@mcgraw-hill.com
URL: http://a1.ecom01.com/aw_marketdatacenter?s_
    id=7

Semiannual, Latest edition 2010. $269.00 for U.S.; $1,295.00 for U.S.; $595.00 for U.S.; $495.00 for U.S.; $149.00 for U.S. Database covers: 22,000 airlines, manufacturers, MRO stations, airports military/government and distributors/suppliers; 6,000 product/service categories and 166,000 listings; 69,000 aviation/aerospace professionals; 500,000 users across all 3 platforms/formats and, Commercial, Military & Business Aviation Fleet Data. Arrangement: Classified by major activity (manufacturers, airlines, etc.). Indexes: Company and organization, personnel, product, trade name.

HANDBOOKS AND MANUALS

801 ■ Airline Pilot Technical Interviews
Aviation Supplies & Academics, Inc.
7005 132nd Place SE
Newcastle, WA 98059-3153
Ph: (425)235-1500
Fax: (425)235-0128
Fr: 800-272-2359
URL: http://www.asa2fly.com/Airline-Pilot-Technical-
    Interviews--P596_product1.aspx

Ronald D. McElroy. 2005. $29.95 (paper). 144 pages. Provides guidelines for a successful airline checkride and technical interview.

802 ■ Careers in Travel, Tourism, and Hospitality
The McGraw-Hill Companies
PO Box 182604
Columbus, OH 43272
Fax: (614)759-3749

Fr: 877-883-5524
E-mail: customer.service@mcgraw-hill.com
URL: http://www.mhprofessional.com

Marjorie Eberts, Linda Brothers, and Ann Gisler. Second edition, 2005. $15.95 (paper). 224 pages.

803 ■ Professional Pilot Career Guide
McGraw-Hill Companies
PO Box 182604
Columbus, OH 43272
Fax: (614)759-3479
Fr: 877-833-5524
E-mail: customer.service@mcgraw-hill.com
URL: http://mcgraw-hill.co.uk/html/0071485538.html

Robert Mark. 2007. $14.99 (paper). 455 pages. Provides sources for professional flying opportunities. Contains detailed coverage of pilot ratings and practical test standards, plus goal-achieving tips on job hunting, networking, regional airlines, the majors, and more.

804 ■ Reporting Clear?: A Pilot's Interview Guide to Background Checks & Presentation of Personal History
Aviation Supplies & Academics, Inc.
7005 132nd Place SE
Newcastle, WA 98059-3153
Ph: (425)235-1500
Fr: 800-272-2359
URL: http://www.asa2fly.com/Reporting-Clear--P705_
    product1.aspx

Cheryl A. Cage. 2006. $19.95 (paper). 94 pages. Provides pilots with interview guides to background checks and the proper presentation of personal history.

EMPLOYMENT AGENCIES AND SEARCH FIRMS

805 ■ Aviation Recruiting
420 College Dr., Ste. 207
Middleburg, FL 32068
Ph: (904)264-0097
Fax: (904)264-0230
E-mail: staffing@aviationrecruiting.net
URL: http://www.aviationrecruiting.net

Specializes in recruitment for the aviation industry. Offers aviation employment services to companies that specialize in commercial/cargo airlines, MRO facilities, military aircraft, manufacturing and completion centers, rotary wing aircraft and corporate aircraft.

806 ■ Jet Professionals
114 Charles A. Lindbergh Dr.
Teterboro, NJ 07608
Ph: (201)393-6900
Fax: (201)462-4081
Fr: 800-441-6016
E-mail: jobs@jet-professionals.com
URL: http://www.jet-professionals.com

Provides staffing services to the aviation industry. Offers jobs for corporate aviation executives, chief pilots, flight attendants, maintenance professionals, dispatchers, schedulers and more.

ONLINE JOB SOURCES AND SERVICES

807 ■ AeroVents.com
E-mail: info@aerovents.com
URL: http://www.aerovents.com/body.shtml

Description: Seeks to spread the word about aviation events. Covers aviation events from conventions, space launches, seminars, model rocketry and aircraft, ballooning, sky diving, plane pulls, open houses, air shows and fly-ins.

808 ■ AirJobsDaily.com
E-mail: staff@airjobsdaily.com
URL: http://www.airjobsdaily.com

Description: Serves as a source of current aviation and aerospace job openings.

809 ■ AirlineCareer.com
Ph: (978)615-3190
E-mail: jbelotti@airlinecareer.com
URL: http://www.airlinecareer.com

Web-based training center. Provides flight attendant job placement services.

810 ■ AirlineCareer.info
URL: http://www.airlinecareer.info

Description: Provides jobs in the airline community covering airport careers, aircraft manufacturing, aerospace careers, and cabin crew careers.

811 ■ AvCrew.com
URL: http://www.avcrew.com

Description: Provides service designed exclusively for career employment in the business aviation sector. Features flight crew jobs, conducts applicant screening, and assists selected flight departments with candidate searches.

812 ■ AviaNation
URL: http://www.avianation.com

Description: Features aviation jobs, pilot jobs, flight attendant jobs, jobs for A&P mechanics, and other aviation job openings around the world.

813 ■ Aviation Jobs Online
URL: http://www.aviationjobsonline.com

Description: Provides list of various jobs within the aviation industry.

814 ■ The Aviation MD
E-mail: adrian@theaviationmd.com
URL: http://www.theaviationmd.com

Description: Serves as international aviation database for employers and jobseekers in the aviation industry.

815 ■ AviationCrossing.com
URL: http://www.aviationcrossing.com

Provides aviation jobs for agents, managers, mechanics, operators, specialists, supervisors, technicians, engineers, maintenance, pilots and other related aviation professionals.

816 ■ AviationEmployment.com
URL: http://www.aviationemployment.com

Description: Serves as an online job search service provider specializing in aviation and aerospace jobs and employment opportunities.

817 ■ AvJobs.com
URL: http://www.avjobs.com

Description: Provides information on a number of different careers in the aviation and aerospace industry. Features aviation schools directory, affiliate programs, research and networking, employment resources, salaries and wages, aviation careers descriptions, aviation guide and other resources.

818 ■ BestAviation.net
URL: http://www.bestaviation.net

Description: Provides source for information on flight school training, helicopter schools, aviation college programs, flight attendant careers, aircraft maintenance and pilot jobs.

819 ■ Engineering Classifieds
URL: http://www.engineeringclassifieds.com

Description: Serves as a career site for engineering professionals. Provides services including job search agents, resume creation and posting.

820 ■ FindaPilot.com
URL: http://www.findapilot.com

Description: Exists as a niche pilot jobs website. Provides a database of pilot jobs, allows posting of employments ads, and features a pilot directory.

821 ■ FlightLevelJobs.com
URL: http://www.flightleveljobs.com

Description: Serves as a source of aviation employment information. Features aviation and aerospace jobs and employment opportunities.

822 ■ FlyContract.com
URL: http://www.flycontract.com

Description: Provides a directory to help corporate pilots and corporate flight attendants obtain jobs.

823 ■ JetEmployment.com
URL: http://jetemployment.com

Description: Features employment opportunities for pilots and other workers in the airline, airport, and business aviation industry.

824 ■ PlaneJobs.com
E-mail: jobmaster@planejobs.com
URL: http://planejobs.com

Description: Serves as an employment, resume, career, and job search database for the aviation industry.

825 ■ USPilot.com
URL: http://www.uspilot.com

Description: Provides information on pilot job openings, interview gouge, forums, and evaluation of pilot resumes.

Tradeshows

826 ■ AOPA Aviation Summit - Aircraft Owners and Pilots Association
Aircraft Owners and Pilots Association
421 Aviation Way
Frederick, MD 21701
Ph: (301)695-2000
Fax: (301)695-2375
URL: http://www.aopa.org

Annual. Primary Exhibits: Single-engine and multi-engine aircraft, avionics, airframes, power plant and equipment, financing information, and related equipment, supplies, and services. Dates and Locations: 2012 Nov 11-13; Palm Springs, CA.

827 ■ Organization of Black Airline Professionals Annual Convention
Organization of Black Airline Pilots
1 Westbrook Corporate Ctr., Ste. 300
Westchester, IL 60154
Ph: (703)753-2047
Fax: (703)753-1251
Fr: 800-JET-OBAP
E-mail: nationaloffice@obap.org
URL: http://www.obap.org

Annual. Primary Exhibits: Exhibits relating to black airline pilots.

Other Sources

828 ■ National Black Coalition of Federal Aviation Employees (NBCFAE)
PO Box 845
Hampton, GA 30228
Fr: 888-311-1622
E-mail: info@nbcfae.org
URL: http://nbcfae.org

Description: Federal Aviation Administration employees. Purposes are to: promote professionalism and equal opportunity in the workplace; locate and train qualified minorities for FAA positions; help the FAA meet its affirmative action goals; monitor black, female, and minority trainees; educate members and the public about their rights and FAA personnel and promotion qualifications; develop a voice for black, female, and minority FAA employees. Recruits minorities from community and schools who qualify for employment; sponsors seminars for members and for those who wish to be employed by the FAA. Maintains speaker's bureau; sponsors competitions.

829 ■ Ninety-Nines, International Organization of Women Pilots
4300 Amelia Earhart Rd.
Oklahoma City, OK 73159
Ph: (405)685-7969
Fax: (405)685-7985
Fr: 800-994-1929
E-mail: 99s@ninety-nines.org
URL: http://www.ninety-nines.org

Description: Represents women pilots. Fosters a better understanding of aviation. Encourages cross-country flying; provides consulting service and gives indoctrination flights; flies missions for charitable assistance programs; endorses air races. Develops programs and courses for schools and youth organizations and teaches ground school subjects. Participates in flying competitions. Maintains resource center and women's aviation museum. Conducts lecture on personal aviation experience, and charitable event. Compiles statistics.

830 ■ Organization of Black Airline Pilots (OBAP)
1 Westbrook Corporate Center
Westchester, IL 60154
Ph: (703)753-2047
Fax: (703)753-1251
Fr: 800-JET-OBAP
E-mail: nationaloffice@obap.org
URL: http://www.obap.org

Description: Cockpit crew members of commercial air carriers, corporate pilots and other interested individuals. Seeks to enhance minority participation in the aerospace industry. Maintains liaison with airline presidents and minority and pilot associations. Conducts lobbying efforts, including congressional examinations into airline recruitment practices. Provides scholarships; cosponsors Summer Flight Academy for Youth. Offers job placement service and charitable program; operates speakers' bureau; compiles statistics on airline hiring practices.

SOURCES OF HELP-WANTED ADS

831 ■ AAAP News
American Academy of Addiction Psychiatry
400 Massasoit Ave., Ste. 307, 2nd Fl.
East Providence, RI 02914
Ph: (401)524-3076
Fax: (401)272-0922
URL: http://www2.aaap.org/advertising/newsletter-
advertising

$45.00/year for individuals, per year; $15.00/year for
individuals, per issue; $50.00/year for individuals,
international; $20.00/year for individuals, per issue.
Professional journal covering addiction psychiatry.

832 ■ Alcoholism
John Wiley & Sons Inc.
350 Main St., Commerce Pl.
Malden, MA 02148-5089
Ph: (781)388-8200
Fax: (781)388-8210
E-mail: mnewcomb-acer@earthlink.net
URL: http://www.wiley.com/bw/journal.asp?ref=0145-
6008&site=1

Monthly. $506.00/year for individuals, print & online;
$1,341.00/year for institutions, print & online;
$1,166.00/year for institutions, print or online;
$327.00/year for individuals, UK, print & online;
$819.00/year for institutions, UK, print & online;
$327.00/year for other countries, print & online;
$1,041.00/year for institutions, Europe, print & online;
$905.00/year for institutions, Europe, print or online;
$712.00/year for institutions, UK, print or online.
Publishing original clinical and research studies on
alcoholism and alcohol-induced organ damage.

**833 ■ The American Journal of Drug and
Alcohol Abuse**
Informa Healthcare
52 Vanderbilt Ave., 7th Fl.
New York, NY 10017-3846
Ph: (212)520-2777
E-mail: custserv@dekker.com
URL: http://informahealthcare.com/ada

$1,260.00/year for institutions; $2,070.00/year for
institutions; $1,660.00/year for institutions. Medical
Journal focusing on the preclinical, clinical, pharmacological, administrative, and social aspects of substance misuse.

834 ■ AMHCA Advocate
American Mental Health Counselors Association
801 N Fairfax St., Ste. 304
Alexandria, VA 22314
Ph: (703)548-6002
Fax: (703)548-4775
Fr: 800-326-2642
E-mail: lmorano@amhca.org
URL: http://www.amhca.org

Description: Monthly. Publishes news of the programs, members, and activities of AMHCA. Provides

updates regarding credentialing of counselors, mental
health-related legislation, and insurance coverage of
the expenses of mental health counseling. Recurring
features include news of meetings and conferences
and articles on topics of interest to clinical mental
health counselors.

835 ■ Counseling Today
American Counseling Association
5999 Stevenson Ave.
Alexandria, VA 22304
Ph: (703)823-6862
Fax: (703)823-0252
Fr: 800-347-6647
URL: http://www.counseling.org

Description: Monthly. Covers news and issues
relevant to the counseling profession.

836 ■ Counselor Education and Supervision
American Counseling Association
5999 Stevenson Ave.
Alexandria, VA 22304
Ph: (703)823-6862
Fax: (703)823-0252
Fr: 800-347-6647
E-mail: ces@unco.edu
URL: http://www.counseling.org/Publications/
Journals.aspx

Quarterly. $53.00/year for nonmembers; $84.00/year
for institutions, non-member; print only. Journal covering research in counselor teaching, training, and
trends.

837 ■ Journal of Addictions Nursing
Informa Healthcare
52 Vanderbilt Ave., 7th Fl.
New York, NY 10017-3846
Ph: (212)520-2777
URL: http://informahealthcare.com/journal/jan

$342.00/year for institutions; $556.00/year for institutions; $444.00/year for institutions. Journal for nurs-
ing addiction professionals.

**838 ■ Journal of Child and Adolescent
Substance Abuse**
Routledge Journals
270 Madison Ave.
New York, NY 10016-0601
Ph: (212)216-7800
Fax: (212)563-2269
URL: http://www.informaworld.com/smpp/
title~content=t792303974

$133.00/year for individuals, online only; $141.00/
year for individuals, print + online; $572.00/year for
institutions, online only; $636.00/year for institutions,
print + online. Journal covering strategies for chemi-
cally dependent adolescents and their families.

839 ■ Journal of Counseling Psychology
American Psychological Association
750 1st St. NE
Washington, DC 20002-4242

Ph: (202)336-5500
Fax: (202)336-5549
Fr: 800-374-2721
E-mail: journals@apa.org
URL: http://www.apa.org/pubs/journals/cou/
index.aspx

Quarterly. $55.00/year for members, domestic;
$77.00/year for members, foreign, surface; $89.00/
year for members, foreign, air mail; $44.00/year for
students, domestic; $66.00/year for students, foreign,
surface; $78.00/year for students, foreign, air mail;
$145.00/year for nonmembers, domestic; $172.00/
year for nonmembers, foreign, surface; $183.00/year
for nonmembers, foreign, air mail; $415.00/year for
institutions, domestic. Journal presenting empirical
studies about counseling processes and interventions, theoretical articles about counseling, and studies dealing with evaluation of counseling applications
and programs.

**840 ■ Journal of Studies on Alcohol and
Drugs**
Rutgers University
607 Allison Rd.
Piscataway, NJ 08854-8001
Ph: (732)445-3510
Fax: (732)445-3500
URL: http://www.jsad.com/

Bimonthly. $140.00/year for individuals; $29.00/year
for single issue. Peer-reviewed journal containing
original research reports about alcohol and other
drugs, their use and misuse, and their biomedical,
behavioral, and sociocultural effects.

841 ■ Monitor on Psychology
American Psychological Association
750 1st St. NE
Washington, DC 20002-4242
Ph: (202)336-5500
Fax: (202)336-5549
Fr: 800-374-2721
E-mail: journals@apa.org
URL: http://www.apa.org/monitor/

$50.00/year for nonmembers; $99.00/year for individuals, foreign, surface freight; $126.00/year for
individuals, foreign, air mail; $93.00/year for institu-
tions; $190.00/year for institutions, surface freight;
$217.00/year for institutions, air freight; $20.00/year
for single issue. Magazine of the APA. Reports on
the science, profession, and social responsibility of
psychology, including latest legislative developments
affecting mental health, education, and research
support.

842 ■ Spectrum
Association for Counselor Education and Supervi-
sion (ACES)
5999 Stevenson Ave.
Alexandria, VA 22304
Ph: (703)212-2237
Fr: (866)815-2237
E-mail: aces@counseling.org
URL: http://www.acesonline.net

Description: Quarterly. Focuses on "the need for quality education and supervision of counselors in all work settings," the accreditation process, and professional development activities for counselors. Recurring features include news of the activities, programs, and members of ACES and related organizations.

843 ■ Substance Use & Misuse
Informa Healthcare
52 Vanderbilt Ave., 7th Fl.
New York, NY 10017-3846
Ph: (212)520-2777
URL: http://informahealthcare.com/sum
$2,700.00/year for institutions; $4,455.00/year for institutions; $3,565.00/year for institutions. Medical Journal reporting individual and community problems brought on by drug, alcohol, and tobacco use, abuse, and dependency. Also considers legal and social aspects of addiction.

EMPLOYER DIRECTORIES AND NETWORKING LISTS

844 ■ Directory of Alcoholism Resources and Services
Alcoholism Council of New York
2 Washington St., 7th Fl.
New York, NY 10004
Ph: (212)252-7001
Fax: (212)252-7021
Fr: 800-56S-OBER
URL: http://www.alcoholism.org
Biennial, Latest edition 2005. $40.00 for individuals. Covers: Over 100 detoxification facilities, sobering-up stations, inpatient rehabilitation agencies, residences, halfway houses, outpatient alcohol abuse services, and related agencies and organizations in New York City. Entries include: Organization or facility name, address, phone, services offered, and other data. Arrangement: Classified by type of treatment or service offered.

845 ■ Drug Information for Teens
Omnigraphics Inc.
PO Box 31-1640
Detroit, MI 48231
Fr: 800-234-1340
URL: http://www.omnigraphics.com
latest edition 3rd; February 2011. $62.00 for individuals. Publication includes: List of state and national organizations with additional information and assistance regarding substance abuse. Principal content of publication is information about various aspects of drug and alcohol abuse. Indexes: Alphabetical.

846 ■ Iowa Substance Abuse & Gambling Service Directory
Iowa Substance Abuse Information Center
2600 Edgewood Rd. SW, Ste. 866
Cedar Rapids, IA 52404
Ph: (319)398-5133
Fax: (319)398-0476
Fr: (866)242-4111
URL: http://www.drugfreeinfo.org
Annual, Fall. Free. Covers: about 190 alcohol and drug abuse treatment and prevention programs. Entries include: For treatment and prevention programs—Name, organization name, address, phone, services; names, addresses, and phone numbers of branch offices, counties covered; code indicates whether a recipient of state or federal substance abuse funds. For others—Name, name and title of contact, address, phone. Arrangement: Classified by activity; treatment programs, gambling treatment programs and prevention programs are geographical. Indexes: Program name, program county.

847 ■ National Directory of Drug and Alcohol Abuse Treatment Programs
Substance Abuse and Mental Health Services Administration
1 Choke Cherry Rd.
Rockville, MD 20857

Ph: (240)276-1212
URL: http://www.findtreatment.samhsa.gov
Annual, Latest edition 2011. Covers: About 11,000 federal, state, local, and privately funded facilities providing drug abuse and alcoholism treatment services. Entries include: Facility name, address, phone, and selected services provided; based on the National Survey of Substance Abuse Treatment Services. Arrangement: State, city, alphabetical by facility.

HANDBOOKS AND MANUALS

848 ■ 101 Careers in Counseling
Springer Publishing Company
11 W 42nd St., 15th Fl.
New York, NY 10036
Ph: (212)431-4370
Fax: (212)941-7842
Fr: 877-687-7476
URL: http://www.springerpub.com
Shannon Hodges. 2012. $25.00 (paper). 332 pages. Describes the many benefits of a counseling career and explores a wealth of opportunities in both traditional and non-traditional settings. Includes an overview, salary range, employment prospects, best and most challenging aspects of the job, and educational and licensing requirements.

849 ■ Careers in Social and Rehabilitation Services
The McGraw-Hill Companies
PO Box 182604
Columbus, OH 43272
Fax: (614)759-3749
Fr: 877-883-5524
E-mail: customer.service@mcgraw-hill.com
URL: http://www.mhprofessional.com/
    product.php?isbn=0071641955
Geraldine O. Garner. 2008. $16.95. 192 pages.

850 ■ Clinical Supervision in Alcohol and Drug Abuse Counseling: Principles, Models, Methods
Jossey-Bass
989 Market St.
San Francisco, CA 94103
Ph: (415)433-1740
Fax: (415)433-0499
Fr: 800-255-5945
E-mail: custserv@wiley.com
URL: http://www.josseybass.com/WileyCDA/
David J. Powell, Archie Brodsky. 2004. $51.50. 448 pages.

851 ■ Great Jobs for Liberal Arts Majors
The McGraw-Hill Companies
PO Box 182604
Columbus, OH 43272
Fax: (614)759-3749
Fr: 877-883-5524
E-mail: customer.service@mcgraw-hill.com
URL: http://www.mhprofessional.com/
    product.php?isbn=0071482148
Blythe Camenson. Second edition, 2007. $16.95 (paper). 192 pages.

EMPLOYMENT AGENCIES AND SEARCH FIRMS

852 ■ Foundation Rehab Staffing
416 W 15th St., Bldg. 600
Edmond, OK 73013
Fax: 800-774-9252
Fr: (866)337-6113
URL: http://www.foundationrehabstaffing.com
Provides staffing services; specializes in rehabilitation therapy.

ONLINE JOB SOURCES AND SERVICES

853 ■ Recovery Today Online
URL: http://www.recoverytoday.net
Description: Provides resources for the recovery field. Features research, treatment, professional interests, training, and job openings in the drug and alcohol counseling field.

TRADESHOWS

854 ■ American Counseling Association Conference and Exposition
American Counseling Association
5999 Stevenson Ave.
Alexandria, VA 22304-3300
Fax: 800-473-2329
Fr: 800-347-6647
E-mail: membership@counseling.org
URL: http://www.counseling.org
Annual. Primary Exhibits: Books, career development information, college selection, student financial aid, testing and measurement techniques, practice management companies, software, rehabilitation aids, and community agencies and private clinics specializing in substance abuse and mental health. Dates and Locations: 2012 Mar 21-25; San Francisco, CA.

855 ■ Association for Counselor Education and Supervision National Conference
Association for Counselor Education and Supervision
5999 Stevenson Ave.
Alexandria, VA 22304
Ph: (703)212-2237
Fr: (866)815-2237
URL: http://www.acesonline.net
Annual. Primary Exhibits: Exhibits relating to the professional preparation of counselors.

OTHER SOURCES

856 ■ Alcoholics Anonymous World Services (AA)
PO Box 459
New York, NY 10163
Ph: (212)870-3400
URL: http://www.aa.org
Description: Individuals recovering from alcoholism. Maintains that members can solve their common problem and help others achieve sobriety through a twelve step program that includes sharing their experience, strength, and hope with each other. Self-supported through members' contributions, not allied with any sect, denomination, political organization, or institution and does not endorse nor oppose any cause.

857 ■ American Academy of Addiction Psychiatry (AAAP)
400 Massasoit Ave., Ste. 307
East Providence, RI 02914
Ph: (401)524-3076
Fax: (401)272-0922
E-mail: information@aaap.org
URL: http://www.aaap.org
Description: Psychiatrists and other health care and mental health professionals treating people with addictive behaviors. Promotes accessibility to highest quality treatment for all who need it; promotes excellence in clinical practice in addiction psychiatry; educates the public to influence public policy regarding addictive illness; provides continuing education for addiction professionals; disseminates new information in the field of addiction psychiatry; and encourages research on the etiology, prevention, identification, and treatment of the addictions.

858 ■ American Society of Addiction Medicine (ASAM)
4601 N Park Ave., Upper Arcade No. 101
Chevy Chase, MD 20815
Ph: (301)656-3920
Fax: (301)656-3815
E-mail: email@asam.org
URL: http://www.asam.org

Description: Physicians with special interest and experience in the field of alcoholism and other drug dependencies and who wish to share this experience with other professionals in order to extend their knowledge of addictive diseases; promote dissemination of that knowledge; enlighten the public regarding these problems; advance education and research in the field of addiction. Holds annual Ruth Fox Course for Physicians, annual Medical-Scientific Conference and five other conferences/courses.

859 ■ Christian Addiction Rehabilitation Association (CARA)
Whosoever Gospel Mission
101 E Chelten Ave.
Philadelphia, PA 19144
Ph: (215)438-3094
Fr: 800-624-5156
E-mail: agrm@agrm.org
URL: http://www.iugm.org/cara.html

Description: Provides support and serves as a clearinghouse of information for individuals involved in ministry to addicts. Conducts two conferences per year.

860 ■ Do It Now Foundation (DINF)
PO Box 27568
Tempe, AZ 85285-7568
Ph: (480)736-0599
Fax: (480)736-0771
E-mail: email@doitnow.org
URL: http://www.doitnow.org

Description: Works to provide factual information to students and adults about prescription drugs, over-the-counter drugs, street drugs, alcohol, eating disorders, AIDS, and related health issues. Assists

organizations engaged in alcohol and drug abuse education.

861 ■ Hazelden Foundation (HF)
PO Box 11
Center City, MN 55012-0011
Ph: (651)213-4200
Fr: 800-257-7810
E-mail: info@hazelden.org
URL: http://www.hazelden.org

Description: Provides treatment, recovery, education, and professional services for chemical dependency and other addictive behaviors. Operates: Hazelden Foundation Center, a treatment center; Fellowship Club in New York, St. Paul and West Palm Beach, Florida, an intermediate care facility; Hazelden Center for Youth and Families for adolescents and young adults; Hazelden Renewal Center for individuals recovering from addictive behaviors and their families; Hanley-Hazelden Center in West Palm Beach, Florida, for inpatient and outpatient treatment; Provides: aftercare therapy; counselor training; 5-7 day, live-in family program that acquaints relatives and other associates of chemically-dependent individuals with problems of chemical dependency; continuing education programs for professionals; and communities.

862 ■ NAADAC: The Association for Addiction Professionals (NAADAC)
1001 N Fairfax St., Ste. 201
Alexandria, VA 22314
Ph: (703)741-7686
Fax: (703)741-7698
Fr: 800-548-0497
E-mail: naadac@naadac.org
URL: http://www.naadac.org

Description: Promotes excellence in care by promoting up-to-date and science-based services to clients, families, and communities. Provides education, clinical training and certification. Among the organization's national certification programs are the National Certified Addiction Counselor, Tobacco Addiction Credential and the Masters Addiction Counselor designations.

863 ■ Narcotic Educational Foundation of America (NEFA)
28245 Ave. Crocker, Ste. 230
Santa Clarita, CA 91355-1201
Ph: (661)775-6960
Fax: (661)775-1648
Fr: 877-775-6272
E-mail: info@cnoa.org
URL: http://www.cnoa.org/nefa/nefa.php

Description: Conducts an education program revealing the dangers that result from the illicit and abusive use of narcotics and dangerous drugs, so that youth and adults will be protected from both mental and physical drug dependency and harm.

864 ■ National Association on Drug Abuse Problems (NADAP)
355 Lexington Ave.
New York, NY 10017
Ph: (212)986-1170
Fax: (212)697-2939
E-mail: info@nadap.org
URL: http://www.nadap.org

Description: Serves as an information clearinghouse and referral bureau for corporations and local communities interested in prevention of substance abuse and treatment of substance abusers. Provides: resources to local communities seeking to combat drug and alcohol abuse; corporate services for employers interested in creating a drug-free workplace. Makes available vocational education services including training in job hunting, job interview workshops, training programs for substance abuse treatment professionals, and individual consultations for recovering substance abusers seeking to return to the job market. Provides placement services; has conducted surveys on the employability of rehabilitated drug users and found that former addicts perform comparably with others hired for similar jobs. Operates Neighborhood Prevention Network, through which local communities develop parent support groups and youth peer leadership groups dedicated to combating drug and alcohol abuse. Maintains speakers' bureau.

SOURCES OF HELP-WANTED ADS

865 ■ *ISRN Allergy*
Hindawi Publishing Corporation
410 Park Ave., 15th Fl.
287 PMB
New York, NY 10022
E-mail: allergy@isrn.com
URL: http://www.isrn.com/journals/allergy

Peer-reviewed journal publishing research in all areas of allergy.

866 ■ *World Journal of AIDS*
Scientific Research Publishing
PO Box 54821
Irvine, CA 92619-4821
E-mail: wja@scirp.org
URL: http://www.scirp.org/journal/wja/

Quarterly. $156.00/year for individuals. Peer-reviewed journal publishing articles on research data and education in all aspects of HIV and AIDS.

867 ■ *World Journal of Vaccines*
Scientific Research Publishing
PO Box 54821
Irvine, CA 92619-4821
E-mail: wjv@scirp.org
URL: http://www.scirp.org/journal/wjv/

Quarterly. $156.00/year for individuals. Peer-reviewed journal publishing articles on the latest advancements in vaccine.

Animal Caretakers, Technicians, and Trainers

SOURCES OF HELP-WANTED ADS

868 ■ American Bee Journal
Dadant & Sons Inc.
51 S 2nd St.
Hamilton, IL 62341
Ph: (217)847-3324
Fax: (217)847-3660
Fr: 888-922-1293
E-mail: info@americanbeejournal.com
URL: http://www.americanbeejournal.com

Monthly. $75.00/year for other countries, airmail; $48.00/year for individuals, foreign , surface mail; $26.00/year for U.S., U.S. standard mail; $59.95/year for Canada, airmail; $49.30/year for individuals, two years; $77.30/year for Canada, two years; $93.30/year for other countries, two years. Magazine for hobbyist and professional beekeepers. Covers hive management, honey handling, disease control, honey markets, foreign beekeeping, beekeeping history, bee laws, honey plants, marketing, and government beekeeping research.

869 ■ American Journal of Veterinary Research
American Veterinary Medical Association
1931 N Meacham Rd., Ste. 100
Schaumburg, IL 60173-4360
Ph: (847)925-8070
Fax: (847)925-1329
Fr: 800-248-2862
URL: http://www.avma.org/journals/ajvr/ajvr_about.asp

Monthly. $245.00/year for individuals; $255.00/year for other countries; $35.00/year for single issue; $40.00/year for single issue, other Country. Veterinary research on nutrition and diseases of domestic, wild, and furbearing animals.

870 ■ American Mustang and Burro Association Journal
American Mustang and Burro Association
PO Box 608
Greenwood, DE 19950
URL: http://www.ambainc.net/

Quarterly. Journal covering horses and burros.

871 ■ Animal Keepers' Forum
American Association of Zoo Keepers Inc.
3601 SW 29th St., Ste. 133
Topeka, KS 66614-2054
Ph: (785)273-9149
Fax: (785)273-1980
URL: http://aazk.org/category/akf/toc/

Monthly. $10.00/year for members; $20.00/year for Canada, members. Professional journal of the American Association of Zoo Keepers, Inc.

872 ■ ASA Bulletin
Avicultural Society of America
c/o Helen Hanson
PO Box 5516
Riverside, CA 92517-5516
Ph: (951)780-4102
Fax: (951)789-9366
URL: http://www.asabirds.org/publication.htm

Bimonthly. $12.00/year for students; $25.00/year for individuals; $33.00/year for other countries. Covers the care, feeding, and breeding of birds in captivity. Contains membership roster and listings of bird specialty organizations and new members.

873 ■ California Thoroughbred
California Thoroughbred Breeders Association
PO Box 60018
Arcadia, CA 91066-6018
Ph: (626)445-7800
Fax: (626)574-0852
Fr: 800-573-2822
URL: http://www.ctba.com/

Monthly. $55.00/year for individuals; $85.00/year for other countries; $100.00/year for two years; $170.00/year for other countries, two years. Magazine about horse breeding and racing.

874 ■ Cats & Kittens
Pet Publishing
7-L Dundas Cir.
Greensboro, NC 27407
Ph: (336)292-4047
Fax: (336)292-4272
URL: http://www.petpublishing.com/catkit/

$14.97/year for individuals; $20.97/year for Canada. Magazine dedicated to cats. Covering feline stories, reports on feline medicine, breed profiles, and training advice.

875 ■ The Chronicle of the Horse
The Chronicle of the Horse Inc.
PO Box 46
108 De Plains
Middleburg, VA 20118
Ph: (540)687-6341
Fax: (540)687-3937
E-mail: staff@chronofhorse.com
URL: http://www.chronofhorse.com/index.php?cat=40311032977488

Weekly. $2.95/year; $2.95/year for single issue; $159.00/year for other countries, print only; $60.00/year for individuals, print & digital; $160.00/year for other countries, print & digital; $109.00/year for two years, print & digital; $35.00/year for individuals, digital only; $59.00/year for individuals, print only; $108.00/year for two years, print only. Magazine covering English riding and horse sports.

876 ■ CME Supplement to Veterinary Clinics of North America
Elsevier Science Inc.
360 Park Ave. S
New York, NY 10010-1710
Ph: (212)989-5800
Fax: (212)633-3990
Fr: 888-437-4636
URL: http://www.elsevier.com/wps/find/journaldescription.cws_home

$55.00/year for individuals. Journal covering veterinary medicine, surgical treatment of animals.

877 ■ Dog World
Bowtie, Inc.
PO Box 6050
Mission Viejo, CA 92690-6040
Ph: (949)855-8822
Fax: (949)855-3045
E-mail: letters@dogworld.com
URL: http://www.dogchannel.com/dog-magazines/dogworld/default.asp

Monthly. $15.00/year for individuals; $27.00/year for other countries. Magazine serving breeders, exhibitors, hobbyists and professionals in kennel operations, groomers, veterinarians, animal hospitals/clinics and pet suppliers.

878 ■ DVM Newsmagazine
Advanstar Communications
Veterinary Group
8033 Flint
Lenexa, KS 66214
Fr: 800-255-6864

Monthly. Magazine for veterinarians in private practices in the U.S.

879 ■ Equus
Primedia Equine Network
656 Quince Orchard Rd., Ste. 600
Gaithersburg, MD 20878
Ph: (301)977-3900
Fax: (301)990-9015
E-mail: eqletters@equinetwork.com
URL: http://www.equisearch.com/equus

Monthly. $29.95/year for two years; $14.97/year for individuals; $26.97/year for Canada; $53.95/year for Canada, two years. Magazine featuring health, care, and understanding of horses.

880 ■ Journal of Animal Science
American Society of Animal Science
2441 Village Green Pl.
Champaign, IL 61822
Ph: (217)356-9050
Fax: (217)398-4119
URL: http://jas.fass.org/

Monthly. $135.00/year for members, U.S. online; $135.00/year for Canada and Mexico, members online; $135.00/year for other countries, members online; $210.00/year for members, U.S. print + online; $210.00/year for Canada and Mexico, members print + online; $235.00/year for other countries, members print + online; $575.00/year for institutions, U.S. print + online; $575.00/year for Canada and Mexico, print + online; $600.00/year for other countries, print + online. Professional journal covering animal science.

881 ■ *The Morgan Horse*
American Morgan Horse Association
4066 Shelburne Rd., Ste. 5
Shelburne, VT 05482
Ph: (802)985-4944
Fax: (802)985-8897
URL: http://www.morganhorse.com/

Monthly. $31.50/year for individuals, 2nd class; $70.50/year for individuals, 1st class; $53.50/year for Canada and Mexico; $61.50/year for other countries, surface; $130.50/year for other countries, mail. Magazine for Morgan horse enthusiasts.

882 ■ *Mushing*
Mushing Magazine
Box 1195
Willow, AK 99688
Ph: (907)495-2468
URL: http://www.mushing.com/

Bimonthly. $26.00/year for individuals; $48.00/year for two years; $35.00/year for Canada; $63.00/year for Canada, two years; $47.00/year for other countries; $84.00/year for other countries, two years. Magazine dealing with all aspects of dog-powered sports.

883 ■ *Newsletter-Animal Behavior Society*
Animal Behavior Society
ABS Central Office
402 N Park St.
Bloomington, IN 47408
Ph: (812)856-5541
Fax: (812)856-5542
E-mail: aboffice@indiana.edu
URL: http://animalbehaviorsociety.org/central-office/
   abs-newsletters

Description: Quarterly. Informs members of the Society of activities, events, meetings, announcements and opportunities in the field of animal behavior. Recurring features include news of educational opportunities, job listings, and notices of publications available.

884 ■ *The Pointing Dog Journal*
Village Press Publications
2779 Aero Park Dr.
PO Box 968
Traverse City, MI 49685
Ph: (231)946-3712
Fax: (231)946-3289
Fr: 800-327-7377
URL: http://www.pointingdogjournal.com

$26.95/year for individuals; $49.95/year for two years. Magazine covering tips on nutrition, healthcare, and first-aid for sporting dogs.

885 ■ *Saddle Horse Report*
Saddle Horse Report
730 Madison St.
PO Box 1007
Shelbyville, TN 37162-1007
Ph: (931)684-8123
Fax: (931)684-8196
E-mail: info@saddlehorsereport.com
URL: http://www.saddlehorsereport.com

Weekly. $60.00/year for individuals; $95.00/year for two years; $135.00/year for individuals, 3 years. Newspaper containing national coverage of horse shows and sales.

886 ■ *TRENDS Magazine*
American Animal Hospital Association
12575 W Bayaud Ave.
Lakewood, CO 80228
Ph: (303)986-2800
Fax: (303)986-1700
Fr: 800-883-6301
URL: http://www.aahanet.org/publications/
   trendsmagazine.aspx

$60.00/year for U.S. and Canada; $70.00/year for other countries; $20.00/year for single issue. Professional magazine covering the management of small animal veterinary practices.

887 ■ *Veterinary Practice News*
Bowtie Inc.
477 Butterfield, Ste. 200
Lombard, IL 60148
Ph: (630)515-9493
Fax: (630)515-9784
URL: http://www.veterinarypracticenews.com/

Monthly. $42.00/year for U.S. and Canada, digital; $48.00/year for individuals, print. Magazine covering veterinary practice in the United States featuring developments and trends affecting companion animals and livestock.

888 ■ *Western Horseman*
Western Horseman
2112 Montgomery St.
Fort Worth, TX 76107
Ph: (817)737-6397
Fax: (817)737-9266
E-mail: edit@westernhorseman.com
URL: http://www.westernhorseman.com/

Monthly. $18.00/year for individuals; $58.00/year for other countries; $38.00/year for Canada; $1.50/year for single issue. Magazine covering forms of horsemanship and all breeds of horses; emphasizing western stock horses and western lifestyle.

EMPLOYER DIRECTORIES AND NETWORKING LISTS

889 ■ *Breeders & Trainers Directory*
American Paint Horse Association
PO Box 961023
Fort Worth, TX 76161-0023
Ph: (817)834-2742
Fax: (817)834-3152
URL: http://www.apha.com/publications/index.shtml

Latest edition 2006-2007. Covers: 400 ALPHA regional clubs in North America. Entries include: Company name, address, phone, fax, contact person and e-mail. Arrangement: Alphabetical by state.

HANDBOOKS AND MANUALS

890 ■ *Career Choices for Veterinary Technicians: Opportunities for Animal Lovers*
American Animal Hospital Association
12575 W Bayaud Ave.
Lakewood, CO 80228
Ph: (303)986-2800
Fax: (303)986-1700
Fr: 800-883-6301
E-mail: info@aahanet.org
URL: http://www.aahanet.org

Rebecca Rose, Carina A. Smith. 2009. $24.95 for member; $29.95 for non-member (paper). 144 pages. Covers multiple career options within the field of veterinary technology, including careers within general practice, specialty practice, industry, higher education, government and more.

891 ■ *Career Opportunities Working with Animals*
Ferguson Publishing
132 W 31st St., 17th Fl.
New York, NY 10001
Fax: 800-678-3633
Fr: 800-322-8755
URL: http://www.infobasepublishing.com

Shelly Field. 2011. $49.50 (hardcover). 308 pages. Describes more than 80 occupations in animal-related fields such as veterinary medicine; shelters, sanctuaries, and refuges; veterinary offices/hospitals/clinics; animal advocacy organizations; care and conservation of wildlife; zoos and aquariums; creative careers; pet care, training, and grooming; pet food, pet supply, and pet merchandise stores; and horses.

892 ■ *Equine Science*
Cengage Learning
PO Box 6904
Florence, KY 41022
Fax: 800-487-8488
Fr: 800-354-9706
URL: http://www.cengage.com

R.O. Parker. 2013. $149.95 (hardcover). 608 pages. 4th edition. Provides equine professionals and horse enthusiasts with information and tips for success in equine care and management. Includes website references, end-of-chapter activities, glossary and appendix of terms, conversion factors and worksheets, and contact information for professional organizations.

893 ■ *Kicked, Bitten, and Scratched: Life and Lessons at the World's Premier School for Exotic Animal Trainers*
Penguin Group (USA)
375 Hudson St.
New York, NY 10014
Ph: (212)366-2372
Fax: (212)366-2933
URL: http://us.penguingroup.com

Amy Sutherland. 2007. $15.00. 336 pages.

894 ■ *Large Animal Clinical Procedures for Veterinary Technicians*
Elsevier
1600 John F. Kennedy Blvd., Ste. 1800
Philadelphia, PA 19103
Ph: (215)239-3900
Fax: (215)239-3990
Fr: 800-523-1649
URL: http://us.elsevierhealth.com

Kristin J. Holtgrew-Bohling. 2012. $43.46. 584 pages. Large animal medical and surgical techniques are described. The book is divided into four parts: equine, bovine, small ruminant (sheep and goats), and swine.

895 ■ *Senior Laboratory Animal Caretaker*
National Learning Corporation
212 Michael Dr.
Syosset, NY 11791
Fr: 800-632-8888
URL: http://www.passbooks.com

2009. $34.95 (paper). Serves as an exam preparation guide for senior laboratory animal caretakers.

ONLINE JOB SOURCES AND SERVICES

896 ■ *AnimalJobs.com*
URL: http://www.animaljobs.com

Description: Functions as a niche job board for people who work with animals including veterinarians, pet stores, groomers, farmers, horse breeders, rescuers, and shelters.

897 ■ *Go Pets America*
URL: http://www.gopetsamerica.com

Description: Provides information and resources for dog, cat, bird, small pet, and horse owners. Features available jobs in animal care.

TRADESHOWS

898 ■ *Association of Pet Dog Trainers Annual Conference*
Association of Pet Dog Trainers
101 N. Main St., Ste. 610
Greenville, SC 29601
Fax: (864)331-0767
Fr: 800-PET-DOGS
E-mail: information@apdt.com
URL: http://www.apdt.com

Annual. Primary Exhibits: Exhibits relating to dog training.

OTHER SOURCES

899 ■ American Association for Laboratory Animal Science (AALAS)
9190 Crestwyn Hills Dr.
Memphis, TN 38125-8538
Ph: (901)754-8620
Fax: (901)753-0046
E-mail: info@aalas.org
URL: http://www.aalas.org

Description: Persons and institutions professionally concerned with the production, use, care, and study of laboratory animals. Serves as clearinghouse for collection and exchange of information on all phases of laboratory animal care and management and on the care, use, and procurement of laboratory animals used in biomedical research. Conducts examinations and certification through its Animal Technician Certification Program.

900 ■ American Association of Wildlife Veterinarians
c/o Dr. Mark Drew, Treas.
Idaho Department of Fish and Game
16569 S 10th Ave.
Caldwell, ID 83607
E-mail: mdrew@idfg.idaho.gov
URL: http://www.aawv.net

Description: Consists of veterinary practitioners, pathologists, researchers and policy makers. Seeks to enhance the contribution of veterinary medicine to the welfare of wildlife resources. Promotes and encourages the utilization of veterinarians in the fields of wildlife management, conservation and research.

901 ■ American Border Leicester Association (ABLA)
PO Box 500
Cuba, IL 61427
Ph: (309)785-5058
E-mail: ads.banner@sybertech.net
URL: http://www.ablasheep.org

Description: Owners and admirers of Border Leicester sheep. Promotes Border Leicesters as a source of wool and meat. Sets breed standards and confers certification; maintains breed registry. Sponsors competitions; conducts educational programs.

902 ■ American Veterinary Medical Association (AVMA)
1931 N Meacham Rd., Ste. 100
Schaumburg, IL 60173-4340
Fax: (847)925-1329
Fr: 800-248-2862
E-mail: avmainfo@avma.org
URL: http://www.avma.org

Description: Professional society of veterinarians. Conducts educational and research programs. Provides placement service. Sponsors American Veterinary Medical Association Foundation and Educational Commission for Foreign Veterinary Graduates. Compiles statistics. Accredits veterinary medical education programs and veterinary technician education programs.

903 ■ American Water Spaniel Club (AWSC)
6 Golfview Ln.
Lake Barrington, IL 60010-1941
Ph: (847)277-7948
E-mail: kevinsmg@sbcglobal.net
URL: http://www.americanwaterspanielclub.org

Description: Owners, breeders, and admirers of water spaniels. Promotes quality breeding and acceptance of breed standards as approved by the American Kennel Club. Represents the interests of breeders; provides shelter and care to abandoned and abused water spaniels; conducts educational programs; sponsors competitions; compiles statistics.

904 ■ Association of Zoos and Aquariums
8403 Colesville Rd., Ste. 710
Silver Spring, MD 20910
Ph: (301)562-0777
Fax: (301)562-0888
URL: http://www.aza.org

Description: 218 accredited members. Promotes the welfare of animals and encourages the advancement of education, animal care, conservation and sciences.

905 ■ International Forensic Entomology Detection Canine Association (IFEDCA)
1913 Hooper Ave.
Toms River, NJ 08753
Ph: (732)255-1649
Fax: (732)255-1539
E-mail: info@actionpestcontrol.com
URL: http://www.ifedca.com

Description: Represents the interests of trained canines, teams and facilities within the forensic entomology detection canine industry. Promotes quality and fair business practices within the canine detection industry. Provides training, education and certification to members.

906 ■ International Marine Animal Trainers' Association
1200 S Lake Shore Dr.
Chicago, IL 60605
Ph: (312)692-3193
Fax: (312)939-2216
E-mail: info@imata.org
URL: http://www.imata.org

Description: Advances the humane care and handling of marine animals by fostering communication among professionals that serve marine animal science. Provides opportunities for marine animal trainers to exchange and disseminate knowledge, research, and training information.

907 ■ International Police Work Dog Association (IPWDA)
PO Box 7455
Greenwood, IN 46142
Ph: (317)882-9191
E-mail: ipwda1@yahoo.com
URL: http://www.ipwda.org

Description: Aims to unite and assist all law enforcement agencies in the training and continued progress of all police work dogs. Seeks to establish a working standard for all police work dogs, handlers, and train- ers through an accreditation program. Promotes the image of the police work dog.

908 ■ National Animal Control Association (NACA)
PO Box 480851
Kansas City, MO 64148-0851
Ph: (913)768-1319
Fax: (913)768-1378
E-mail: naca@nacanet.org
URL: http://www.nacanet.org

Description: Animal control agencies, humane societies, public health and safety agencies, corporations, and individuals. Works to educate and train personnel in the animal care and control professions. Seeks to teach the public responsible pet ownership; operates the NACA Network to provide animal control information; evaluates animal control programs. Provides training guides for animal control officers; makes available audiovisual materials. Conducts research. Operates placement service and speakers' bureau.

909 ■ National Dog Groomers Association of America (NDGAA)
PO Box 101
Clark, PA 16113-0101
Ph: (724)962-2711
Fax: (724)962-1919
E-mail: ndga@nationaldoggroomers.com
URL: http://www.nationaldoggroomers.com

Description: Dog groomers and supply distributors organized to upgrade the profession. Conducts state and local workshops; sponsors competitions and certification testing. Makes groomer referrals.

910 ■ National Entomology Scent Detection Canine Association (NESDCA)
PO Box 3840
Seminole, FL 33775
E-mail: nesdca@nesdca.com
URL: http://www.nesdca.com

Description: Unites and assists entomology scent detection canine teams in the training and continued improvement. Strives to improve the image of the entomology scent-detecting canine teams. Educates consumers about the benefits of using trained entomology scent detecting dog teams in the process of locating and eradicating pest problems.

911 ■ Pet Care Services Association
2670 Academy Blvd.
Colorado Springs, CO 80917
Ph: (719)667-1600
Fax: (719)667-0116
Fr: 877-570-7788
E-mail: membership@petcareservices.org
URL: http://www.petcareservices.org

Description: Persons or firms that board pets; kennel suppliers; others interested in the facility boarding kennel industry. Seeks to upgrade the industry through accreditation educational programs, seminars and conventions. Provides insurance resources for members and supplies pet care information to the public. Promotes code of ethics and accreditation program for recognition and training of superior kennel operators. Compiles boarding facility statistics.

Sources of Help-Wanted Ads

912 ■ *Anthropology in Action*
Berghahn Journals
c/o Turpin North America
143 West St.
New Milford, CT 06776
Ph: (860)350-0041
Fax: (860)350-0039
URL: http://journals.berghahnbooks.com/aia/

$161.00/year for institutions, print & online; $60.00/year for individuals, print & online; $25.00/year for students, print only; $90.00/year for institutions, print & online; $33.00/year for individuals, print & online; $15.00/year for students, print only; $115.00/year for institutions, print & online; $43.00/year for individuals, print & online; $20.00/year for students, print only; $114.00/year for institutions, online only. Peer-reviewed journal featuring the use of anthropology in all areas of policy and practice.

913 ■ *Anthropology of Consciousness*
American Anthropological Association
2200 Wilson Blvd., Ste. 600
Arlington, VA 22201
Ph: (703)528-1902
Fax: (703)528-3546
E-mail: bdavis@aaanet.org
URL: http://www.aaanet.org

Description: 2/year. Serves as an information exchange for researchers investigating the effect of culture on man's psychological and supernatural behavior patterns. Examines the topics of dreaming, altered states of consciousness, spirit possession, healing, divination, extrasensory perception, mysticism, myth, shamanism, and psychic archeology. Recurring features include book reviews, queries, notices of publications and symposia, news of members, and obituaries.

914 ■ *Anthropology News*
American Anthropological Association
2200 Wilson Blvd., Ste. 600
Arlington, VA 22201-3357
Ph: (703)528-1902
Fax: (703)528-3546
Fr: 800-545-4703
URL: http://www.aaanet.org/issues/anthronews

Free to qualified subscribers, members of AAA. Periodical covering anthropology, including archaeological, biological, ethnological, and linguistic research.

915 ■ *Anthropology of Work Review*
American Anthropological Association
2200 Wilson Blvd., Ste. 600
Arlington, VA 22201
Ph: (703)528-1902
Fax: (703)528-3546
URL: http://www.aaanet.org

Description: Quarterly. Promotes the development of ideas, data, and methods concerning all aspects of the study of anthropology of work.

916 ■ *AnthroSource*
John Wiley & Sons Inc.
350 Main St., Commerce Pl.
Malden, MA 02148-5089
Ph: (781)388-8200
Fax: (781)388-8210
URL: http://www.anthrosource.net

Irregular. Journal serving the research, teaching, and professional needs of anthropologists.

917 ■ *The Asia Pacific Journal of Anthropology*
Routledge Journals
270 Madison Ave.
New York, NY 10016-0601
Ph: (212)216-7800
Fax: (212)563-2269
URL: http://www.tandf.co.uk/journals/titles/14442213.asp

$542.00/year for institutions, print + online; $328.00/year for institutions, print + online; $488.00/year for institutions, online only; $122.00/year for individuals, print only; $72.00/year for individuals, print only; $155.00/year for individuals, print only; $383.00/year for institutions, print and online; $295.00/year for institutions, online only; $345.00/year for institutions, online only. Journal focusing on anthropological study.

918 ■ *Classical Antiquity*
University of California Press/Journals
2120 Berkeley Way
Berkeley, CA 94704-1012
Ph: (510)642-4247
Fax: (510)643-7127
URL: http://www.ucpressjournals.com/journal.asp?j=ca

Semiannual. $52.00/year for individuals, print only; $201.00/year for institutions, print & electronic; $28.00/year for students, print only; $161.00/year for institutions, electronic only; $27.00/year for single issue, individual/student/retired; $109.00/year for single issue, institutions. Peer-reviewed scholarly journal covering interdisciplinary research and issues in Classics-Greek and Roman literature, history, art, philosophy, archaeology, and philology.

919 ■ *Collaborative Anthropologies*
University of Nebraska Press
1111 Lincoln Mall
Lincoln, NE 68588-0630
Ph: (402)472-3581
Fax: (402)472-6214
Fr: 800-848-6224
URL: http://www.marshall.edu/coll-anth/

Annual. $38.00/year for individuals; $54.00/year for other countries; $66.00/year for institutions; $82.00/year for institutions, other countries. Peer-reviewed journal featuring collaborative research and practice in anthropology and closely related fields.

920 ■ *General Anthropology*
John Wiley & Sons Inc.
111 River St.
Hoboken, NJ 07030-5773
Ph: (201)748-6000
Fax: (201)748-6088
Fr: 800-825-7550
URL: http://www.wiley.com/bw/journal.asp?ref=1537-1727

$15.00/year for institutions, Americas (print and online); $7.00/year for institutions, UK (print and online); $9.00/year for institutions, Europe (print and online); $13.00/year for institutions, other countries, print and online; $13.00/year for institutions, Americas (online only); $6.00/year for institutions, UK (online only); $7.00/year for institutions, Europe (online only); $11.00/year for institutions, other countries, online only. Journal covering the fields of anthropology and applied anthropology.

921 ■ *Histories of Anthropology Annual*
University of Nebraska Press
1111 Lincoln Mall
Lincoln, NE 68588-0630
Ph: (402)472-3581
Fax: (402)472-6214
Fr: 800-848-6224
URL: http://www.nebraskapress.unl.edu/product/Histories-of-Anthro

$38.00/year for individuals; $66.00/year for institutions; $54.00/year for other countries; $82.00/year for institutions, other countries. Journal covering historical approaches in teaching, learning, and applying anthropology.

922 ■ *International Journal of Paleopathology*
Elsevier Science Inc.
360 Park Ave. S
New York, NY 10010-1710
Ph: (212)989-5800
Fax: (212)633-3990
Fr: 888-437-4636
URL: http://www.elsevier.com/wps/find/journaldescription.cws_home

Journal publishing research studies on paleopathology.

923 ■ *ISEM Newsletter*
Institute for the Study of Earth and Man
N.L. Heroy Hall
PO Box 0274
Dallas, TX 75275-0274
Ph: (214)768-2425
E-mail: isem@mail.smu.edu
URL: http://www.smu.edu/isem

Description: Semiannual. Reports on research in the anthropological, geological, and statistical sciences. Includes notices of research funds, grants, and contracts awarded. Provides biographical sketches of new faculty members in the anthropological, geological, and statistical sciences departments at Southern Methodist University. Recurring features include news of research and news of members.

924 ■ *Journal of Folklore Research*

Indiana University Press
601 N Morton St.
Bloomington, IN 47404-3778
Ph: (812)855-8817
Fax: (812)855-8507
Fr: 800-842-6796
E-mail: jofr@indiana.edu
URL: http://inscribe.iupress.org/loi/jfr

$38.50/year for individuals, print and online; $35.00/year for individuals, print only; $31.50/year for individuals, online only; $90.75/year for institutions, print and online; $65.50/year for institutions, print only; $58.95/year for institutions, online only. Peer-reviewed journal covering anthropology and folklore.

925 ■ *Journal of the Society for the Anthropology of Europe*

John Wiley & Sons Inc.
350 Main St., Commerce Pl.
Malden, MA 02148-5089
Ph: (781)388-8200
Fax: (781)388-8210
URL: http://www.wiley.com/bw/journal.asp?ref=1535-5632&site=1

Semiannual. $53.00/year for institutions, print & online; $48.00/year for institutions, online only. Journal containing articles and book reviews related to European anthropology.

926 ■ *Kansas Anthropological Association Newsletter*

Kansas Anthropological Association
PO Box 750962
Topeka, KS 66675-0962
Ph: (785)272-8681
Fax: (785)272-8682
URL: http://www.kshs.org/p/kansas-anthropological-association-kaa/14619

Description: Four issues/year. Covers Association field projects, conferences, and fundraising activities. Contains reports from local chapters. Recurring features include news of research, a calendar of events, and news of educational opportunities.

927 ■ *Magic, Ritual, and Witchcraft*

University of Pennsylvania Press
3905 Spruce St.
Philadelphia, PA 19104-4112
Ph: (215)898-6261
Fax: (215)898-0404
URL: http://magic.pennpress.org/strands/magic/home.htm;jsessionid

Semiannual. Peer-reviewed journal covering magic, ritual and witchcraft on a wide geographical scope and chronological range, from prehistory to modern era and from the Old World to the New.

928 ■ *NAPA Bulletin*

John Wiley & Sons Inc.
350 Main St., Commerce Pl.
Malden, MA 02148-5089
Ph: (781)388-8200
Fax: (781)388-8210
URL: http://onlinelibrary.wiley.com/journal/10.1111/(ISSN)1556-47

Annual. $58.00/year for institutions, print & online; $52.00/year for institutions, online. Journal focusing on information relevant to the advancement of professionals in the field from the National Association for the Practice of Anthropology (NAPA).

929 ■ *North American Dialogue*

American Anthropological Association
2200 Wilson Blvd., Ste. 600
Arlington, VA 22201-3357
Ph: (703)528-1902
Fax: (703)528-3546

Fr: 800-545-4703
URL: http://www.blackwellpublishing.com/journal.asp?ref=1539-2546

Semiannual. $13.00/year for institutions, online only; $11.00/year for institutions, other countries, online only. Journal of the Society for the Anthropology of North America.

930 ■ *SFAA Newsletter*

Society for Applied Anthropology
PO Box 2436
Oklahoma City, OK 73101
Ph: (405)843-5113
Fax: (405)843-8553
E-mail: info@sfaa.net
URL: http://www.sfaa.net

Quarterly. $10.00 for U.S. residents; $15.00 for non-U.S. residents. Features issues of interest and latest information about the society and its members.

931 ■ *Society for Historical Archaeology Newsletter*

Society for Historical Archaeology
9707 Key West Ave., Ste. 100
Rockville, MD 20850
Ph: (301)990-2454
Fax: (301)990-9771
E-mail: hq@sha.org
URL: http://www.sha.org

Description: Quarterly. Supports the aims of the Society, which "promotes scholarly research and the dissemination of knowledge concerning historical archeology." Presents information on current research, legislative developments, and Society meetings and activities. Recurring features include editorials, letters to the editor, news of members, and a calendar of events.

932 ■ *Voices*

American Anthropological Association
2200 Wilson Blvd., Ste. 600
Arlington, VA 22201-3357
Ph: (703)528-1902
Fax: (703)528-3546
Fr: 800-545-4703
URL: http://www.aaanet.org/sections/afa/Voices/voices.html

Annual. Periodical covering activities in feminist anthropology.

933 ■ *WAS Newsletter*

World Archaeological Society
120 Lakewood Dr.
Hollister, MO 65672
Ph: (417)334-2377
E-mail: ronwriterartist@aol.com
URL: http://www.worldarchaeologicalsociety.com

Description: Periodic. Promotes the scientific and constructive study of antiquity within the international fields of archaeology, anthropology, and art history. Recurring features include announcements of recommended books; items on people, museums, and societies; news of research; letters to the editor; obituaries; verses; and columns titled Career Notes and Democracy Club.

EMPLOYER DIRECTORIES AND NETWORKING LISTS

934 ■ *American Journal of Physical Anthropology—American Association of Physical Anthropologists Membership Directory Issue*

American Association of Physical Anthropologists
246 Lord Hall
Columbus, OH 43210-1364
Ph: (614)292-9766
Fax: (614)292-4155
URL: http://www.physanth.org/publications

Annual, December. Publication includes: 1,500 physical anthropologists and scientists in closely related

fields interested in the advancement of the science of physical anthropology through research and teaching of human variation, primate paleoanthropology, and primate evolution. Entries include: Name, affiliation, address. Arrangement: Alphabetical.

935 ■ *Newsletter—Society for Historical Archaeology Membership Directory Issue*

Society for Historical Archaeology
9707 Key West Ave., Ste. 100
Rockville, MD 20850
Ph: (301)990-2454
Fax: (301)990-9771
URL: http://www.sha.org

Quarterly, Latest edition 2011. Publication includes: List of about 2,100 member archaeologists, historians, anthropologists, and ethnohistorians, and other individuals and institutions having an interest in historical archeology or allied fields. Entries include: Name, address. Arrangement: Alphabetical.

HANDBOOKS AND MANUALS

936 ■ *The Anthropology Graduate's Guide: From Student to a Career*

Left Coast Press, Inc.
1630 N Main St., No. 400
Walnut Creek, CA 94596
Ph: (925)935-3380
Fax: (925)935-2916
E-mail: explore@lcoastpress.com
URL: http://www.lcoastpress.com

Carol J. Ellick and Joe E. Watkins. 2011. $24.95 (paper). 160 pages. Contains a set of practical steps that will guide an individual through the transition from the life of being a student into a career within a wide range of professions involving an anthropology degree. Includes stories, scenarios, and activities pertinent to building a career in anthropology.

937 ■ *Opportunities in Social Science Careers*

The McGraw-Hill Companies
PO Box 182604
Columbus, OH 43272
Fax: (614)759-3749
Fr: 877-883-5524
E-mail: customer.service@mcgraw-hill.com
URL: http://www.mcgraw-hill.com

Rosanne J. Marek. 2004. $13.95. 160 Pages. VGM Opportunities Series.

938 ■ *Visions of Culture: An Introduction to Anthropological Theories and Theorists*

AltaMira Press
4501 Forbes Blvd., Ste. 200
Lanham, MD 20706
Ph: (301)459-3366
Fax: (301)429-5748
URL: http://www.altamirapress.com/

Jerry D. Moore. Third edition, 2008. $39.95 (paper). 416 pages. Focused on college students interested in Anthropology.

TRADESHOWS

939 ■ *American Association of Physical Anthropologists Scientific/Professional Meeting*

American Association of Physical Anthropologists
PO Box 1897
Lawrence, KS 66044-8897
URL: http://www.physanth.org

Annual. Primary Exhibits: Exhibits for the advancement of the science of physical anthropology through research and teaching of human variation, primate paleoanthropology, and primate evolution.

940 ■ American Society for Ethnohistory Conference
American Society for Ethnohistory
c/o R. David Edmunds, Pres.
University of Texas at Dallas
2601 N Floyd Rd.
Richardson, TX 75080
URL: http://ethnohistory.org

Annual. Primary Exhibits: Exhibits relating to the cultural history of ethnic groups worldwide.

941 ■ Congress of the International Society for Human Ethology
International Society for Human Ethology
PO Box 418
Nyack, NY 10960
Ph: (207)581-2044
Fax: (207)581-6128
URL: http://www.ishe.org

Biennial. Primary Exhibits: Books, journals, and equipment for observational research. Dates and Locations: 2012 Aug 13-17; Vienna, Austria; University of Vienna.

942 ■ Organization of American Historians Annual Meeting
Organization of American Historians
112 N. Bryan Ave.
PO Box 5457
Bloomington, IN 47408-5457
Ph: (812)855-7311
Fax: (812)855-0696
E-mail: help@oah.org
URL: http://www.oah.org

Annual. Primary Exhibits: Equipment, supplies, and services of interest to historians, including textbooks and computer software. Dates and Locations: 2012 Apr 19-22; Milwaukee, WI.

OTHER SOURCES

943 ■ African Studies Association (ASA)
Rutgers University, Livingston Campus
54 Joyce Kilmer Ave.
Piscataway, NJ 08854-8045
Ph: (848)445-8173
Fax: (732)445-1366
E-mail: karen.jenkins@africanstudies.org
URL: http://www.africanstudies.org

Description: Persons specializing in teaching, writing, or research on Africa including political scientists, historians, geographers, anthropologists, economists, librarians, linguists, and government officials; persons who are studying African subjects; institutional members are universities, libraries, government agencies, and others interested in receiving information about Africa. Seeks to foster communication and to stimulate research among scholars on Africa. Sponsors placement service; conducts panels and discussion groups; presents exhibits and films.

944 ■ American Academy of Forensic Sciences (AAFS)
410 N 21st St.
Colorado Springs, CO 80904
Ph: (719)636-1100
Fax: (719)636-1993
E-mail: awarren@aafs.org
URL: http://www.aafs.org

Description: Represents criminalists, scientists, members of the bench and bar, pathologists, biologists, psychiatrists, examiners of questioned documents, toxicologists, odontologists, anthropologists, and engineers. Works to: encourage the study, improve the practice, elevate the standards, and advance the cause of the forensic sciences; improve the quality of scientific techniques, tests, and criteria; plan, organize, and administer meetings, reports, and other projects for the stimulation and advancement of these and related purposes. Maintains Forensic Sciences Job Listing; conducts selected research for the government; offers forensic expert referral service.

945 ■ American Anthropological Association (AAA)
2200 Wilson Blvd., Ste. 600
Arlington, VA 22201-3357
Ph: (703)528-1902
Fax: (703)528-3546
E-mail: bdavis@aaanet.org
URL: http://www.aaanet.org

Description: Aims to further the professional interests of anthropologists; to disseminate anthropological knowledge and its use to address human problems; to promote the entire field of anthropology in all its diversity; to represent the discipline nationally and internationally, in the public and private sectors; to bring together anthropologists from all subfields and specializations, providing networking opportunities across the broad range of the discipline.

946 ■ American Association of Physical Anthropologists (AAPA)
University of South Florida
Dept. of Anthropology
Tampa, FL 33620-8100
Fr: 800-627-0326
E-mail: madrigal@cas.usf.edu
URL: http://www.physanth.org

Description: Professional society of physical anthropologists and scientists in closely related fields interested in the advancement of the science of physical anthropology through research and teaching of human variation, paleoanthropology and primatology.

947 ■ American Society for Eighteenth-Century Studies (ASECS)
Wake Forest University
PO Box 7867
Winston-Salem, NC 27109
Ph: (336)727-4694
Fax: (336)727-4697
E-mail: asecs@wfu.edu
URL: http://asecs.press.jhu.edu

Description: Scholars and others interested in the cultural history of the 18th century. Encourages and advances study and research in this area; promotes the interchange of information and ideas among scholars from different disciplines (such as librarianship and bibliography) who are interested in the 18th century. Co-sponsors seven fellowship programs; sponsors Graduate Student Caucus.

948 ■ American Society of Primatologists (ASP)
Trinity University
Department of Psychology
One Trinity Pl.
San Antonio, TX 78212
Ph: (210)999-7102
Fax: (210)999-8323
E-mail: kimberley.phillips@trinity.edu
URL: http://www.asp.org

Description: Promotes the discovery and exchange of information regarding nonhuman primates, including all aspects of their anatomy, behavior, development, ecology, evolution, genetics, nutrition, physiology, reproduction, systematics, conservation, husbandry and use in biomedical research.

949 ■ American Studies Association (ASA)
1120 19th St. NW, Ste. 301
Washington, DC 20036
Ph: (202)467-4783
Fax: (202)467-4786
Fr: 800-548-1784
E-mail: asastaff@theasa.net
URL: http://www.theasa.net

Description: Serves as professional society of persons interested in American literature, American history, sociology, anthropology, political science, philosophy, fine arts, and other disciplines; librarians, museum directors, and government officials. Concerned with any field of study relating to American life and culture, past and present. Members are interested in research and teaching that crosses traditional departmental lines.

950 ■ Amerind Foundation (AF)
PO Box 400
Dragoon, AZ 85609
Ph: (520)586-3666
Fax: (520)586-4679
E-mail: amerind@amerind.org
URL: http://www.amerind.org

Description: Conducts research in anthropology and archaeology of the greater American southwest and northern Mexico and ethnology in the Western Hemisphere. Offers artist shows; volunteer opportunities, public programs, and visiting scholar program. Operates museum.

951 ■ Association of Black Anthropologists (ABA)
AAA Member Services
2200 Wilson Blvd., Ste. 600
Arlington, VA 22201-3357
Ph: (703)528-1902
E-mail: abawebinfo@gmail.com
URL: http://www.aaanet.org/sections/aba/htdocs

Description: A section of the American Anthropological Association. Anthropologists and others interested in the study of blacks and other people subjected to exploitation and oppression. Works to: formulate conceptual and methodological frameworks to advance understanding of all forms of human diversity and commonality; advance theoretical efforts to explain the conditions that produce social inequalities based on race, ethnicity, class, or gender; develop research methods that involve the people studied and local scholars in all stages of investigation and dissemination of findings.

952 ■ Biological Anthropology Section (BAS)
University of Delaware
Dept. of Anthropology
John Munroe Hall
Newark, DE 19716
Ph: (302)831-1855
E-mail: krr@udel.edu
URL: http://www.aaanet.org/sections/bas

Description: A unit of American Anthropological Association. International group of anthropologists concerned with the biological aspects of anthropology. Aims to maintain communication among biological anthropologists. Promotes scientific and public understanding of human origins and the interaction between biological and cultural dimensions that underlie the evolution of humans.

953 ■ Institute for the Study of Man (ISM)
1133 13th St. NW, Ste. C-2
Washington, DC 20005
Ph: (202)371-2700
Fax: (202)371-1523
E-mail: iejournal@aol.com
URL: http://www.jies.org

Description: Aims to publish books and journals in areas related to anthropology, historical linguistics, and the human sciences.

954 ■ International Studies Association (ISA)
University of Arizona
324 Social Sciences Bldg.
Tucson, AZ 85721
Ph: (520)621-7715
Fax: (520)621-5780
E-mail: isa@isanet.org
URL: http://www.isanet.org

Description: Social scientists and other scholars from a wide variety of disciplines who are specialists in international affairs and cross-cultural studies; academicians; government officials; officials in international organizations; business executives; students. Promotes research, improved teaching, and the orderly growth of knowledge in the field of international studies; emphasizes a multidisciplinary approach to problems. Conducts conventions, workshops and discussion groups.

955 ■ **International Women's Anthropology Conference (IWAC)**
New York University
Anthropology Department
25 Waverly Pl.
New York, NY 10003
Ph: (212)998-8550
Fax: (212)995-4014
E-mail: constance.sutton@nyu.edu
URL: http://homepages.nyu.edu/~crs2/index.html

Description: Women anthropologists and sociologists who are researching and teaching topics such as women's role in development, feminism, and the international women's movement. Encourages the exchange of information on research, projects, and funding; addresses policies concerning women from an anthropological perspective. Conducts periodic educational meetings with panel discussions.

956 ■ **Kroeber Anthropological Society (KAS)**
University of California, Berkeley
Dept. of Anthropology
232 Kroeber Hall
Berkeley, CA 94720-3710
Ph: (510)642-6932
Fax: (510)643-8557
E-mail: kas@berkeley.edu
URL: http://anthropology.berkeley.edu/kas.html

Description: Represents anthropologists, students, interested laypersons and institutional members (300 major universities and anthropological institutions).

957 ■ **National Association for the Practice of Anthropology (NAPA)**
2200 Wilson Blvd., Ste. 600
Arlington, VA 22201
Ph: (703)528-1902
Fax: (703)528-3546
E-mail: tmwallace@mindspring.com
URL: http://www.practicinganthropology.org

Description: A section of the American Anthropological Association. Professional anthropologists serving social service organizations, government agencies, and business and industrial firms. Works to help anthropologists develop and market their expertise in areas such as social and political analysis, and program design, evaluation, and management. Compiles statistics.

958 ■ **Program for the Advancement of Research on Conflict and Collaboration (PARCC)**
Syracuse University
400 Eggers Hall
Syracuse, NY 13244-1020
Ph: (315)443-2367
Fax: (315)443-3818
E-mail: parcc@maxwell.syr.edu
URL: http://sites.maxwell.syr.edu/parc

Description: Anthropologists. Fosters research on the social and cultural dynamics of peace and war. Provides curricular services; operates speakers' bureau and placement service; compiles statistics. Sponsors seminars and professional workshops.

959 ■ **Society for Applied Anthropology (SfAA)**
PO Box 2436
Oklahoma City, OK 73101-2436
Ph: (405)843-5113
Fax: (405)843-8553
E-mail: info@sfaa.net
URL: http://www.sfaa.net

Description: Professional society of anthropologists, sociologists, psychologists, health professionals, industrial researchers, and educators. Promotes scientific investigation of the principles controlling relations between human beings, and encourages wide application of these principles to practical problems.

960 ■ **Society for Cultural Anthropology (SCA)**
University of California, Santa Cruz
Dept. of Anthropology
1156 High St.
Santa Cruz, CA 95064
Ph: (831)459-5717
E-mail: druther1@ucsc.edu
URL: http://sca.culanth.org

Description: A section of the American Anthropological Association, dedicated to the study of culture. Compiles statistics.

961 ■ **Society for Linguistic Anthropology (SLA)**
UCSD
Dept. of Anthropology, 0532
9500 Gilman Dr.
La Jolla, CA 92093-5004
Ph: (858)534-4639
Fax: (858)534-5946
E-mail: kwoolard@ucsd.edu
URL: http://www.linguisticanthropology.org

Description: Serves as section of the American Anthropological Association. Represents University faculty; students. Promotes the anthropological study of language.

962 ■ **Society for Urban, National and Transnational/Global Anthropology (SUNTA)**
University of North Carolina
Department of Anthropology
301 Alumni Bldg., CB No. 3115
Chapel Hill, NC 27599-3115
E-mail: dnonini@email.unc.edu
URL: http://www.sunta.org

Description: Seeks to advance the science and profession of urban, national and transnational/global anthropology. Promotes the advancement of research and the professional interests of urban national and transnational/global anthropologists. Encourages the distribution and application of knowledge acquired in the study of urban, national and transnational/global anthropology.

963 ■ **World Archaeological Society (WAS)**
120 Lakewood Dr.
Hollister, MO 65672
Ph: (417)334-2377
E-mail: ronwriterartist@aol.com
URL: http://www.worldarchaeologicalsociety.com

Description: Professional and amateur archaeologists, anthropologists, and art historians in 32 countries. Promotes the scientific and constructive study of antiquity within the fields of archaeology, anthropology, and art history. Conducts research on biblical archaeology, democracy, and the anthropology of drug addiction. Projects include the "Living" Museum of Democracy and the restoration of old Bibles. Conducts special research projects upon request. Supplies tape lectures for special programs. Provides ink and color illustrations for researchers.

Sources of Help-Wanted Ads

964 ■ American Archaeology
Archaeological Conservancy
5301 Central Ave. NE, Ste. 902
Albuquerque, NM 87108-1517
Ph: (505)266-1540
URL: http://www.americanarchaeology.com/
 aamagazine.html

Quarterly. $25.00/year for individuals. Magazine covering archaeology in the Americas.

965 ■ American Journal of Archaeology
Archaeological Institute of America
656 Beacon St., 6th Fl.
Boston, MA 02215-2006
Ph: (617)353-9361
Fax: (617)353-6550
URL: http://www.archaeological.org/
 webinfo.php?page=10041

Quarterly. $80.00/year for individuals, print; $50.00/year for students, print; $280.00/year for institutions, print; $50.00/year for students, print; $90.00/year for individuals, print & electronic; $60.00/year for students, print & electronic; $310.00/year for institutions, print & electronic; $120.00/year for other countries, print & electronic. Professional journal covering archaeological subjects.

966 ■ ASOR Newsletter
American Schools of Oriental Research
656 Beacon St., 5th Fl.
Boston, MA 02215
Ph: (617)353-6570
Fax: (617)353-6575
E-mail: asor@bu.edu
URL: http://www.asor.org

Description: Quarterly. Carries news and reports from archaeological institutes in Amman, Jerusalem, and Cyprus. Recurring features include news of research, a calendar of events, reports of meetings, news of educational opportunities, job listings, and notices of publications available.

967 ■ Classical Antiquity
University of California Press/Journals
2120 Berkeley Way
Berkeley, CA 94704-1012
Ph: (510)642-4247
Fax: (510)643-7127
URL: http://www.ucpressjournals.com/
 journal.asp?j=ca

Semiannual. $52.00/year for individuals, print only; $201.00/year for institutions, print & electronic; $28.00/year for students, print only; $161.00/year for institutions, electronic only; $27.00/year for single issue, individual/student/retired; $109.00/year for single issue, institutions. Peer-reviewed scholarly journal covering interdisciplinary research and issues in Classics-Greek and Roman literature, history, art, philosophy, archaeology, and philology.

968 ■ Geoarchaeology
John Wiley & Sons Inc.
111 River St.
Hoboken, NJ 07030-5773
Ph: (201)748-6000
Fax: (201)748-6088
Fr: 800-825-7550
URL: http://onlinelibrary.wiley.com/journal/10.1002/
 (ISSN)1520-65

Bimonthly. $279.00/year for U.S., Canada, and Mexico, individual (print only); $335.00/year for other countries, individual (print only); $2,326.00/year for institutions, print and online; $2,438.00/year for institutions, Canada and Mexico, print and online; $2,494.00/year for institutions, other countries, print and online; $2,022.00/year for institutions, print only; $2,134.00/year for institutions, Canada and Mexico, print only; $2,190.00/year for institutions, other countries, print only. Journal covering the methodological and theoretical interface between archaeology and the geosciences.

969 ■ International Journal of Paleopathology
Elsevier Science Inc.
360 Park Ave. S
New York, NY 10010-1710
Ph: (212)989-5800
Fax: (212)633-3990
Fr: 888-437-4636
URL: http://www.elsevier.com/wps/find/
 journaldescription.cws_home

Journal publishing research studies on paleopathology.

970 ■ Magic, Ritual, and Witchcraft
University of Pennsylvania Press
3905 Spruce St.
Philadelphia, PA 19104-4112
Ph: (215)898-6261
Fax: (215)898-0404
URL: http://magic.pennpress.org/strands/magic/
 home.htm;jsessionid

Semiannual. Peer-reviewed journal covering magic, ritual and witchcraft on a wide geographical scope and chronological range, from prehistory to modern era and from the Old World to the New.

971 ■ PE & RS Photogrammetric Engineering & Remote Sensing
The Imaging and Geospatial Information Society
5410 Grosvenor Ln., Ste. 210
Bethesda, MD 20814-2160
Ph: (301)493-0290
Fax: (301)493-0208
URL: http://www.asprs.org/PE-RS-Journal/

Monthly. $410.00/year for individuals, first class mail; $426.00/year for Canada, airmail; $420.00/year for other countries, air standard. Peer-reviewed journal covering photogrammetry, remote sensing, geographic information systems, cartography, and surveying, global positioning systems, digital photogrammetry.

972 ■ SAA Bulletin
Society for American Archaeology
1111 14th St. NW, Ste. 800
Washington, DC 20005-5615
Ph: (202)789-8200
Fax: (202)789-0284
E-mail: headquarters@saa.org
URL: http://www.saa.org

Description: 5/yr. Publishes informative articles about archaeology. Recurring features include letters to the editor, job listings, a calendar of events, notices of publications available, and columns titled Obituaries and News and Notes.

973 ■ Stanford Journal of Archaeology
Stanford University
Bldg. 120, Rm. 160
Stanford, CA 94305-2047
Ph: (650)723-3956
Fax: (650)725-6471
URL: http://www.stanford.edu/dept/archaeology/
 journal/

Irregular. Free, online. Online scholarly journal publishing research in archaeology.

Employer Directories and Networking Lists

974 ■ Andean Explorers Foundation & Ocean Sailing Club—Membership Roster
Andean Explorers Foundation & Ocean Sailing Club
PO Box 3279
Reno, NV 89505
Ph: (775)348-1818
Fax: (775)332-3086
URL: http://www.aefosc.org

Covers: Non-profit group of archeological enthusiasts and explorers conducting research on archeological remains and making documented works available to scientific institutions, museums, and specialists in Peru and other countries.

975 ■ Newsletter—Society for Historical Archaeology Membership Directory Issue
Society for Historical Archaeology
9707 Key West Ave., Ste. 100
Rockville, MD 20850
Ph: (301)990-2454
Fax: (301)990-9771
URL: http://www.sha.org

Quarterly, Latest edition 2011. Publication includes: List of about 2,100 member archaeologists, historians, anthropologists, and ethnohistorians, and other individuals and institutions having an interest in historical archeology or allied fields. Entries include: Name, address. Arrangement: Alphabetical.

HANDBOOKS AND MANUALS

976 ■ Careers for Mystery Buffs and Other Snoops and Sleuths
The McGraw-Hill Companies
PO Box 182604
Columbus, OH 43272
Fax: (614)759-3749
Fr: 877-883-5524
E-mail: customer.service@mcgraw-hill.com
URL: http://www.mhprofessional.com

Blythe Camenson. Second edition. $14.95 (hardback). 160 pages.

977 ■ FabJob Guide to Become an Archaeologist
FabJob Inc.
4616 - 25th Ave. NE, No. 224
Seattle, WA 98105
Ph: (403)949-4980
Fr: 888-322-5621
URL: http://www.fabjob.com/Archaeology.asp

Robert Larkin. $14.97(e-book). 112 pages. Offers valuable advice about where to look for jobs, how to approach employers, and what markets may be best for employment. Highlights the qualities employers are looking for, how to ace the interview, and how to advance through networking and professional development.

978 ■ Opportunities in Social Science Careers
The McGraw-Hill Companies
PO Box 182604
Columbus, OH 43272
Fax: (614)759-3749
Fr: 877-883-5524
E-mail: customer.service@mcgraw-hill.com
URL: http://www.mcgraw-hill.com

Rosanne J. Marek. 2004. $13.95. 160 Pages. VGM Opportunities Series.

ONLINE JOB SOURCES AND SERVICES

979 ■ ArchaeologyFieldwork.com
URL: http://www.archaeologyfieldwork.com/AFW

Description: Provides an archaeology resource database that includes employment listings, resume and CV postings, job hunt, archaeology announcements, and archaeology volunteer opportunities. Features other resources such as a forum for discussions on wages and per diem in CRM, working conditions, professional organizations and unions, and other issues of interest for field archaeologists.

980 ■ eCulturalResources
URL: http://www.eculturalresources.com

Description: Provides sources of news, jobs, announcements, consultant listings, and resources for the cultural resource industry.

981 ■ ScientistCrossing.com
URL: http://www.scientistcrossing.com

Description: Provides job listings and other resources related to scientist employment opportunities.

TRADESHOWS

982 ■ American Society for Ethnohistory Conference
American Society for Ethnohistory
c/o R. David Edmunds, Pres.
University of Texas at Dallas
2601 N Floyd Rd.
Richardson, TX 75080
URL: http://ethnohistory.org

Annual. Primary Exhibits: Exhibits relating to the cultural history of ethnic groups worldwide.

983 ■ Conference on Historical and Underwater Archaeology
Society for Historical Archaeology
9707 Key West Ave., Ste. 100
Rockville, MD 20850
Ph: (301)990-2454
Fax: (301)990-9771
E-mail: hq@sha.org
URL: http://www.sha.org

Annual. Primary Exhibits: Archaeologists, historians, anthropologists, and ethnohistorians; other individuals and institutions with an interest in historical archaeology or allied fields.

984 ■ Society for American Archaeology Conference
Society for American Archaeology
1111 14th St., N.W., Ste. 800
Washington, DC 20005-5622
Ph: (202)789-8200
Fax: (202)789-0284
E-mail: headquarters@saa.org
URL: http://www.saa.org

Annual. Primary Exhibits: Archaeological equipment, supplies, and services academic books, GPS, GIS, software.

OTHER SOURCES

985 ■ American Philological Association (APA)
University of Pennsylvania
220 S 40th St., Ste. 201E
Philadelphia, PA 19104-3543
Ph: (215)898-4975
Fax: (215)573-7874
Fr: 800-548-1784
E-mail: apaclassics@sas.upenn.edu
URL: http://www.apaclassics.org

Description: Teachers of Latin and Greek, classical archaeologists with literary interests, and comparative linguists. Works for the advancement and diffusion of philological information. Sponsors placement service and campus advisory service to provide advice on instructional programs in classical studies.

986 ■ Amerind Foundation (AF)
PO Box 400
Dragoon, AZ 85609
Ph: (520)586-3666
Fax: (520)586-4679
E-mail: amerind@amerind.org
URL: http://www.amerind.org

Description: Conducts research in anthropology and archaeology of the greater American southwest and northern Mexico and ethnology in the Western Hemisphere. Offers artist shows; volunteer opportunities, public programs, and visiting scholar program. Operates museum.

987 ■ Archaeological Conservancy (AC)
5301 Central Ave. NE, Ste. 902
Albuquerque, NM 87108
Ph: (505)266-1540
E-mail: tacinfo@nm.net
URL: http://www.americanarchaeology.com

Description: People interested in preserving prehistoric and historic sites for interpretive or research purposes (most members are not professional archaeologists). Seeks to acquire for permanent preservation, through donation or purchase, the ruins of past American cultures, primarily those of American Indians. Works throughout the U.S. to preserve cultural resources presently on private lands and protect them from the destruction of looters, modern agricultural practices, and urban sprawl. Operates with government agencies, universities, and museums to permanently preserve acquired sites.

988 ■ Archaeological Institute of America (AIA)
656 Beacon St., 6th Fl.
Boston, MA 02215-2006
Ph: (617)353-9361
Fax: (617)353-6550
Fr: 877-524-6300
E-mail: aia@aia.bu.edu
URL: http://www.archaeological.org

Description: Educational and scientific society of archaeologists and others interested in archaeological study and research. Founded five schools of archaeology: American School of Classical Studies (Athens, 1881); School of Classical Studies of the American Academy (Rome, 1895); American Schools of Oriental Research (Jerusalem, 1900 and Baghdad, 1921); School of American Research (1907, with headquarters at Santa Fe, NM). Is allied with three research institutes: American Research Institute in Turkey; American Institute of Iranian Studies; American Research Center in Egypt. Maintains annual lecture programs for all branch societies. Operates placement service for archeology educators. Sponsors educational programs for middle school children.

989 ■ ASPRS - The Imaging and Geospatial Information Society
5410 Grosvenor Ln., Ste. 210
Bethesda, MD 20814-2160
Ph: (301)493-0290
Fax: (301)493-0208
E-mail: asprs@asprs.org
URL: http://www.asprs.org

Description: Firms, individuals, government employees and academicians engaged in photogrammetry, photointerpretation, remote sensing, and geographic information systems and their application to such fields as archaeology, geographic information systems, military reconnaissance, urban planning, engineering, traffic surveys, meteorological observations, medicine, geology, forestry, agriculture, construction and topographic mapping. Seeks to advance knowledge and improve understanding of these sciences and promote responsible applications. Offers voluntary certification program open to persons associated with one or more functional area of photogrammetry, remote sensing and GIS. Surveys the profession of private firms in photogrammetry and remote sensing in the areas of products and services.

990 ■ Center for American Archeology (CAA)
PO Box 366
Kampsville, IL 62053
Ph: (618)653-4316
E-mail: caa@caa-archeology.org
URL: http://www.caa-archeology.org

Description: Philanthropic organizations, foundations, corporations, professional and amateur archaeologists, students, and others interested in archaeology in the U.S. Conducts archaeological research and disseminates the results. Excavates, analyzes, and conserves archaeological sites and artifacts. Sponsors tours, lectures, and educational and outreach programs, including university, middle school and junior high, and high school field schools; offers professional training at levels of detail ranging from secondary to postgraduate. Maintains speakers' bureau. Operates Visitors Center.

991 ■ Epigraphic Society (ES)
97 Village Post Rd.
Danvers, MA 01923
Ph: (978)774-1275
E-mail: donalbb@epigraphy.org
URL: http://www.epigraphy.org

Description: Launches expeditions to North America and overseas. Reports discoveries and decipherments and assesses their historical implications. Participates in group lecture and teaching programs with other archaeological societies and university departments of archaeology and history.

992 ■ Exploring Solutions Past: The Maya Forest Alliance
PO Box 3962
Santa Barbara, CA 93130
Ph: (805)893-8191
Fax: (805)893-7995
E-mail: ford@marc.ucsb.edu
URL: http://www.espmaya.org

Description: Strives to come up with solutions to today's environmental crisis through archaeology. Supports exploration of the archaeological and contemporary Maya traditions. Works to preserve endangered resources through local and international education.

993 ■ Register of Professional Archaeologists (RPA)
5024-R Campbell Blvd.
Baltimore, MD 21236
Ph: (410)933-3486
Fax: (410)931-8111
E-mail: info@rpanet.org
URL: http://www.rpanet.org

Description: Represents archaeologists satisfying basic requirements in training and experience, including private consultants, individuals working with large firms, and academic personnel. Seeks to define professionalism in archaeology; provide a measure against which to evaluate archaeological actions and research; establish certification standards; provide for grievance procedures; demonstrate to other archaeologists and the public the nature of professional archaeology. Monitors related legislative activities; maintains register archives. Is developing educational programs and drafting standards and guidelines for field schools.

994 ■ Society for American Archaeology (SAA)
1111 14th St. NW, Ste. 800
Washington, DC 20005
Ph: (202)789-8200
Fax: (202)789-0284
E-mail: headquarters@saa.org
URL: http://www.saa.org

Description: Professionals, vocationals, students, and others interested in American archaeology. Stimulates scientific research in the archaeology of the New World by: creating closer professional relations among archaeologists, and between them and others interested in American archaeology; advocating the conservation of archaeological data and furthering the control or elimination of commercialization of archaeological objects; promoting a more rational public appreciation of the aims and limitations of archaeological research. Maintains placement service and educational programs.

995 ■ Society for Historical Archaeology (SHA)
9707 Key West Ave., Ste. 100
Rockville, MD 20850
Ph: (301)990-2454
Fax: (301)990-9771
E-mail: hq@sha.org
URL: http://www.sha.org

Description: Represents archaeologists, historians, anthropologists, and ethnohistorians; other individuals and institutions with an interest in historical archaeology or allied fields. Aims to bring together persons interested in studying specific historic sites, manuscripts, and published sources, and to develop generalizations concerning historical periods and cultural dynamics as these emerge through the techniques of archaeological excavation and analysis. Main focus is the era beginning with the exploration of the non-European world by Europeans, and geographical areas in the Western Hemisphere, but also considers Oceanian, African, and Asian archaeology during the relatively late periods.

SOURCES OF HELP-WANTED ADS

996 ■ American Institute of Architects-AIArchitect
American Institute of Architects Press
1735 New York Ave., NW
Washington, DC 20006-5292
Ph: (202)626-7300
Fax: (202)626-7547
Fr: 800-242-3837
E-mail: infocentral@aia.org
URL: http://www.aia.org

Description: Monthly. Concerned with the architectural profession. Discusses business and legislative trends, practice and design information, and AIA activities. Recurring features include news of members and a calendar of events.

997 ■ Architect Magazine
Russell S. Ellis
One Thomas Cir. NW, Ste. 600
Washington, DC 20005
Ph: (202)452-0800
Fax: (202)785-1974
E-mail: rellis@hanleywood.com
URL: http://www.architectmagazine.com

Monthly. Free of charge to those who qualify. Online edition is also available. Provides the practicing architect with vital business tips, design inspiration, plus ideas for skill development and practice management.

998 ■ Architectural Products
Construction Business Media L.L.C.
579 First Bank Dr., Ste. 220
Palatine, IL 60067
Ph: (847)359-6493
Fax: (847)359-6754
URL: http://www.arch-products.com/

Free to qualified subscribers; $55.00/year for other countries. Magazine provides product and product application information to architects, designers, and product specifiers.

999 ■ Architectural Record
McGraw-Hill Inc.
PO Box 182604
Columbus, OH 43218
Ph: (614)430-4000
Fax: (614)759-3749
Fr: 877-833-5524
URL: http://archrecord.construction.com

Monthly. $49.00/year for individuals; $59.00/year for Canada; $109.00/year for other countries. Magazine focusing on architecture.

1000 ■ ArchitectureWeek
Artifice, Inc.
PO Box 1588
Eugene, OR 97440-1588

Ph: (541)345-7421
Fax: (541)345-7438
Fr: 800-203-8324
E-mail: artifice@artifice.com
URL: http://www.architectureweek.com

Weekly. Provides information and images for architects, builders, designers, planners and other AEC industry professionals. Also caters to home makers, students and teachers of design. Covers buildings as they open worldwide.

1001 ■ Axis Journal
American Institute of Architects, Golden Empire Chapter
1201 24th St., Ste. B110-164
Bakersfield, CA 93301
E-mail: info@aiage.org
URL: http://www.aiage.org

Description: Monthly. Covers activities of American Institute of Architects, Golden Empire Chapter. Provides information to clients and public leaders on architects' concerns and activities.

1002 ■ Builder
Hanley-Wood L.L.C.
1 Thomas Cir. NW, Ste. 600
Washington, DC 20005-5803
Ph: (202)452-0800
Fax: (202)785-1974
E-mail: builder@omeda.com
URL: http://www.hanleywood.com/
    default.aspx?page=magazines

$29.95/year for U.S. and Canada; $54.95/year for U.S. and Canada, 2 years; $192.00/year for other countries. Magazine covering housing and construction industry.

1003 ■ Builder and Developer
Peninsula Publishing Inc.
1602 Monrovia Ave.
Newport Beach, CA 92663
Ph: (949)631-0308
Fax: (949)631-2475
URL: http://www.bdmag.com

Magazine for homebuilders.

1004 ■ Building Industry Technology
National Technical Information Service
5301 Shawnee Rd.
Alexandria, VA 22312
Ph: (703)605-6585
Fax: (703)605-6900
Fr: 800-553-6847
E-mail: info@ntis.gov
URL: http://www.ntis.gov/products/alerts.aspx

Description: Biweekly. $255. Consists of abstracts of reports on architectural and environmental design, building standards, construction materials and equipment, and structural analyses. Recurring features include a form for ordering reports from NTIS. Also available via e-mail.

1005 ■ Civil Engineering-ASCE
American Society of Civil Engineers (ASCE)
1801 Alexander Bell Dr.
Reston, VA 20191
Fr: 800-548-2723

Monthly. $230.00/year for institutions; $275.00/year for institutions, other countries; $230.00/year for individuals; $275.00/year for other countries; $30.00/year for members, domestic; $69.00/year for other countries, member; $30.00/year for students, member; domestic; $69.00/year for students, member; international. Professional magazine.

1006 ■ Design Cost Data
DC & D Technologies Inc.
PO Box 948
Valrico, FL 33595-0948
Ph: (813)662-6830
Fax: (813)662-6793
Fr: 800-533-5680
URL: http://www.dcd.com

Bimonthly. $94.00/year for individuals, silver; $157.00/year for two years, silver; $149.00/year for individuals, gold; $239.00/year for two years, gold. Publication providing real cost data case studies of various types completed around the country for design and building professionals.

1007 ■ Design Line
American Institute of Building Design
7059 Blair Rd. NW, Ste. 201
Washington, DC 20012
Fax: (866)204-0293
Fr: 800-366-2423
E-mail: info@aibd.org
URL: http://www.aibd.org

Description: Quarterly. Focuses on all aspects of building design. Recurring features include letters to the editor, interviews, a collection, reports of meetings, news of educational opportunities, and notices of publications available.

1008 ■ Design Lines Magazine
American Institute of Building Design
7059 Blair Rd. NW, Ste. 201
Washington, DC 20012
Fax: (202)249-2473
Fr: 800-366-2423
URL: http://www.aibd.org/publications/design_lines_
    magazine.php

Quarterly. Magazine focusing on issues, education, and events in the building design industry.

1009 ■ Environmental & Architectural Phenomenology Newsletter
Dr. David Seamon
211 Seaton Hall
Architecture Dept.
Kansas State University
Manhattan, KS 66506-2901
Ph: (785)532-5953

Fax: (785)532-6722
E-mail: triad@ksu.edu
URL: http://www.arch.ksu.edu/seamon/EAP.html

Description: Three/year. Focuses on the nature of environmental and architectural experience.

1010 ■ Fabric Architecture
Industrial Fabrics Association International
1801 County Rd. B W
Roseville, MN 55113
Ph: (651)222-2508
Fax: (651)631-9334
Fr: 800-225-4324
URL: http://fabricarchitecturemag.com/

Bimonthly. $39.00/year for two years; $49.00/year for two years, Canada and Mexico; $69.00/year for two years, international. Magazine specializing in interior and exterior design ideas and technical information for architectural fabric applications in architecture and the landscape.

1011 ■ Green Home Builder
Peninsula Publishing Inc.
1602 Monrovia Ave.
Newport Beach, CA 92663
Ph: (949)631-0308
Fax: (949)631-2475
URL: http://www.greenhomebuildermag.com/

Quarterly. Magazine for home builders and home building industry.

1012 ■ Grey Room
MIT Press
55 Hayward St.
Cambridge, MA 02142-1315
Ph: (617)253-5646
Fax: (617)258-6779
E-mail: editors@greyroom.org
URL: http://www.mitpressjournals.org/loi/grey

Quarterly. $63.00/year for individuals, online only; $70.00/year for individuals, print & online; $41.00/year for students, print and online, retired; $37.00/year for students, online only, retired; $242.00/year for institutions, online only; $277.00/year for institutions, print and online. Scholarly journal devoted to the theorization of modern and contemporary architecture, art, media, and politics. Dedicated to the task of promoting and sustaining critical investigation into each of these fields separately and into their mutual interactions. Develops a rigorous, cross-disciplinary dialogue among the fields of architecture, art, and media to forge and promote a politically-informed, critical discourse uniquely relevant to the current historical situation.

1013 ■ Kitchen and Bath Design News
Cygnus Business Media Inc.
3 Huntington Quadrangle, Ste. 301 N
Melville, NY 11747
Ph: (631)845-2700
Fax: (631)845-7109
Fr: 800-308-6397
URL: http://www.cygnusb2b.com/
    PropertyPub.cfm?PropertyID=78

Monthly. Trade journal.

1014 ■ Marine Technology and SNAME News
Society of Naval Architects and Marine Engineers
601 Pavonia Ave.
Jersey City, NJ 07306
Ph: (201)798-4800
Fax: (201)798-4975
Fr: 800-798-2188
URL: http://www.sname.org/SNAME/SNAME/Home

Quarterly. $320.00 for U.S. list; $350.00 for international list; complimentary for members. Covers research on technological breakthroughs, trends, concepts and discoveries in the marine industry. Features society news and information on national, section and local levels as well as updates on committee activities, meetings, seminars, professional conferences and employment opportunities.

1015 ■ Masonry Magazine
Mason Contractors Association of America
1481 Merchant Dr.
Algonquin, IL 60102
Ph: (224)678-9709
Fax: (224)678-9714
Fr: 800-536-2225
URL: http://www.masoncontractors.org

Monthly. $43.00/2 years; $29.00/year. Covers every aspect of the mason contractor profession, from equipment and techniques to building codes and standards, training the future masonry labor force, business planning, promoting business, job interviewing, negotiation and legal issues.

1016 ■ Metal Architecture
Modern Trade Communications Inc.
7450 Skokie Blvd.
Skokie, IL 60077
Ph: (847)674-2200
Fax: (847)674-3676
URL: http://www.moderntrade.com/
    Default.aspx?PublicationID=3

Monthly. $75.00/year for Canada and Mexico; $150.00/year for other countries; $45.00/year for individuals. Trade journal serving architectural, engineering, and construction firms.

1017 ■ The Military Engineer
The Society of American Military Engineers
607 Prince St.
Alexandria, VA 22314-3117
Ph: (703)549-3800
Fax: (703)684-0231
URL: http://www.same.org/i4a/pages/
    index.cfm?pageid=4273

Bimonthly. $88.00/year for U.S. and Canada, individuals, second class mail; $168.00/year for U.S. and Canada, two years; $222.00/year for U.S. and Canada, three years; $188.00/year for other countries, air mail, individuals; $358.00/year for other countries, two years, air mail; $458.00/year for other countries, three years, air mail; $22.00/year for students, U.S., Canada, and foreign (regular mail). Journal on military and civil engineering.

1018 ■ Municipal Art Society Newsletter
Municipal Art Society
111 W 57th St.
New York, NY 10019
Ph: (212)935-3960
Fax: (212)753-1816
E-mail: info@mas.org
URL: http://mas.org

Description: Six issues/year. Provides updates on advocacy efforts, exhibitions, and programming on urban issues. Recurring features include a calendar of events and tour schedule.

1019 ■ Professional Builder
SGC Horizon LLC
3030 W Salt Creek Ln., Ste. 201
Arlington Heights, IL 60005
Ph: (847)391-1000
Fax: (847)390-0408
URL: http://www.housingzone.com/pb/pubhome/

Monthly. Free. The integrated engineering magazine of the building construction industry.

1020 ■ Residential Architect
Hanley-Wood L.L.C.
1 Thomas Cir. NW, Ste. 600
Washington, DC 20005-5803
Ph: (202)452-0800
Fax: (202)785-1974
E-mail: res@omeda.com
URL: http://www.residentialarchitectmediakit.com/r5/
    home.asp

$39.95/year for individuals; $66.00/year for Canada; $132.50/year for other countries. Magazine for architects, designers, and building professionals.

1021 ■ Residential Contractor
Peninsula Publishing Inc.
1602 Monrovia Ave.
Newport Beach, CA 92663
Ph: (949)631-0308
Fax: (949)631-2475
URL: http://www.residentialcontractormag.com/

Quarterly. Magazine for small volume residential builders, contractors, and specialty trades.

1022 ■ SARAScope
Society of American Registered Architects
14 E 38th St., 11th Fl.
New York, NY 10016
Fax: 888-985-7272
Fr: 888-985-7272
URL: http://www.sara-national.org

Description: Bimonthly. Tracks Society activities at national and local levels.

1023 ■ Texas Architect
Texas Society of Architects
500 Chicon St.
Austin, TX 78702
Ph: (512)478-7386
Fax: (512)478-0528
E-mail: coti@texasarchitect.org
URL: http://texasarchitect.org/publications.php?sess_
    id=66b886ac9

Bimonthly. $30.00/year for individuals; $53.00/year for two years; $25.00/year for students. Magazine for design professionals and their clients.

1024 ■ The Times
Council on Tall Buildings & Urban Habitat
Illinois Institute of Technology
S.R. Crown Hall
3360 S State St.
Chicago, IL 60616-3796
Ph: (312)567-3487
Fax: (312)567-3820
E-mail: info@ctbuh.org
URL: http://www.ctbuh.org

Description: 3-4 issues/year. Concerned with all aspects of the planning, design, construction, and operation of tall buildings. Examines the role of tall buildings in the urban environment and acts as a forum for exchange of information among engineering, architectural, and planning professionals. Recurring features include news of research, book reviews, notices of publications available, reports on the committees of the Council, a calendar of events, and a column titled On My Mind.

EMPLOYER DIRECTORIES AND NETWORKING LISTS

1025 ■ Almanac of Architecture and Design
Greenway Consulting
25 Technology Pkwy. S, Ste. 101
Norcross, GA 30092-2952
Ph: (678)879-0929
Fax: (678)879-0930
URL: http://www.greenway.us

Annual, Latest edition 9th, 2008. $49.50 for individuals. Publication includes: Lists of professional organizations, degree programs, and leading firms in architecture and design. Principal content of publication is a collection of information regarding architecture and design.

1026 ■ Athletic Business—Professional Directory Section
Athletic Business Publications Inc.
4130 Lien Rd.
Madison, WI 53704
Ph: (608)249-0186
Fax: (608)249-1153
Fr: 800-722-8764
URL: http://www.athleticbusiness.com

Monthly, Latest edition 2010. $8.00. Publication

includes: List of architects, engineers, contractors, and consultants in athletic facility planning and construction; all listings are paid. Entries include: Company name, address, phone, fax and short description of company. Arrangement: Alphabetical.

1027 ■ Career Ideas for Teens in Architecture and Construction
Facts On File Inc.
132 W 31st St., 17th Fl.
New York, NY 10001
Ph: (212)967-8800
Fax: 800-678-3633
Fr: 800-322-8755
URL: http://www.infobasepublishing.com
Published August, 2005. Covers: A multitude of career possibilities based on a teenager's specific interests and skills and links his/her talents to a wide variety of actual professions.

1028 ■ ENR—Top 500 Design Firms Issue
McGraw-Hill Inc.
PO Box 182604
Columbus, OH 43218
Ph: (614)430-4000
Fax: (614)759-3749
Fr: 877-833-5524
URL: http://enr.construction.com/toplists/ sourcebooks/2010/design
Annual, latest edition 2010. $82.00 for individuals. Publication includes: List of 500 leading architectural, engineering, and specialty design firms selected on basis of annual billings. Entries include: Company name, headquarters location, type of firm, current and prior year rank in billings, types of services, countries in which operated in preceding year. Arrangement: Ranked by billings.

1029 ■ The Military Engineer—Directory
The Society of American Military Engineers
607 Prince St.
Alexandria, VA 22314-3117
Ph: (703)549-3800
Fax: (703)684-0231
URL: http://www.same.org
updated daily. Database covers: About 2,800 member architect, engineer, engineering-related firms and government agencies and equipment manufacturers, suppliers and contractors who provide products and services to government and private sector entities; also lists firms with experience and equipment useable in event of disasters/emergencies. Database includes: Firm name, address, phone, E-mail, home page, names of principals, business class, type of ownership, number of employees, and the engineering specialties of the firm. Arrangement: Alphabetical. Indexes: Alphabetical by state and country; alphabetical by business class.

1030 ■ ProFile—The Architects Sourcebook
Reed Construction Data
30 Technology Pkwy. S, Ste. 100
Norcross, GA 30092
Ph: (770)417-4000
Fax: (770)417-4002
Fr: 800-424-3996
E-mail: profile@reedbusiness.com
URL: http://www.reedfirstsource.com
Annual. Covers: more than 27,000 architectural firms. Entries include: For firms—Firm name, address, phone, fax, year established, key staff and their primary responsibilities (for design, specification, etc.), number of staff personnel by discipline, types of work, geographical area served, projects. "ProFile" is an expanded version of, and replaces, the "Firm Directory." Arrangement: Firms are geographical. Indexes: Firm name, key individuals, specialization by category, consultants. Firm name, key individuals, specialization by category, consultants.

HANDBOOKS AND MANUALS

1031 ■ Architecture Student's Handbook of Professional Practice
John Wiley & Sons Inc.
1 Wiley Dr.
Somerset, NJ 08873

Ph: (732)469-4400
Fax: (732)302-2300
Fr: 800-225-5945
E-mail: custserv@wiley.com
URL: http://as.wiley.com/WileyCDA/WileyTitle/ productCd-0470088699.html
The American Institute of Architects. Fourteenth edition, 2008. $100.00. 720 pages.

1032 ■ Information Technologies for Construction Managers, Architects, and Engineers
Cengage Learning
PO Box 6904
Florence, KY 41022
Fax: 800-487-8488
Fr: 800-354-9706
E-mail: esales@cengage.com
URL: http://www.cengage.com
Trefor Williams. 2007. $102.95. 256 pages. Profiles information technology applications in construction trades, from traditional computer applications to emerging Web-based and mobile technologies.

1033 ■ Opportunities in Architecture Careers
The McGraw-Hill Companies
PO Box 182604
Columbus, OH 43272
Fax: (614)759-3749
Fr: 877-883-5524
E-mail: customer.service@mcgraw-hill.com
URL: http://www.mhprofessional.com/ product.php?isbn=0071458689
Robert J. Piper. 2006. $13.95 (paper). 160 pages. Guide to planning for and seeking opportunities in the field. Illustrated. Includes training and education requirements, salary statistics, and professional and Internet resources.

EMPLOYMENT AGENCIES AND SEARCH FIRMS

1034 ■ Agra Placements, Ltd.
8435 University Ave., Ste. 6
Des Moines, IA 50325
Ph: (515)225-6563
Fax: (515)225-7733
Fr: 888-696-5624
E-mail: careers@agrapl.com
URL: http://www.agraplacements.com
Executive search firm. Branch offices in Peru, IN, Lincoln, IL, and Andover, KS.

1035 ■ Claremont-Branan, Inc.
1298 Rockbridge Rd., Ste. B
Stone Mountain, GA 30087
Fr: 800-875-1292
URL: http://cbisearch.com
Employment agency. Executive search firm.

1036 ■ The Coxe Group Inc.
1904 Third Ave., Ste. 229
Seattle, WA 98101-1194
Ph: (206)467-4040
Fax: (206)467-4038
E-mail: info@coxegroup.com
URL: http://www.coxegroup.com
Executive search firm.

1037 ■ ENTEGEE
70 Blanchard Rd., Ste. 102
Burlington, MA 01803
Fr: 800-368-3433
E-mail: corporate@entegee.com
URL: http://www.entegee.com
Specializes in recruiting experienced professionals in the engineering and technical industries. Features a searchable database of employment opportunities in the engineering and technical fields.

1038 ■ Insperity, Inc.
19001 Crescent Springs Dr.
Kingwood, TX 77339-3802
Ph: (281)358-8986
Fr: 800-237-3170
E-mail: douglas.sharp@insperity.com
URL: http://www.insperity.com
Description: Serves as a full-service human resources department for small and medium-sized businesses throughout the United States. Provides client companies with benefits and services such as employment administration, government compliance, recruiting and selection, performance management, benefits management, employer liability management, training and development, and business services.

1039 ■ Interior Talent
1430 Lake Baldwin Ln., Ste. A
Orlando, FL 32814
Ph: (407)228-1938
Fax: (407)228-1935
Fr: 800-915-3012
URL: http://www.interiortalent.com
Description: Recruiters for architecture and design professionals worldwide.

1040 ■ Metzner Group
10130 Harmony Rd.
Myersville, MD 21773
Ph: (301)293-4206
URL: http://www.themetznergroup.com
Specializes in the recruitment of architects, civil engineers, environmental engineers and planners for the A/E/P communities.

1041 ■ RitaSue Siegel Resources, Inc.
PO Box 845
New York, NY 10150
Ph: (917)725-1603
E-mail: contact@ritasue.com
URL: http://www.ritasue.com
Executive search firm specializing in industrial and product design.

ONLINE JOB SOURCES AND SERVICES

1042 ■ AECWorkForce.com
E-mail: jclarke@zweigwhite.com
URL: http://aecworkforce.com
Description: Serves as job board for professionals and employers in architecture, engineering and construction.

1043 ■ AEJob.com
E-mail: customerservice@aejob.com
URL: http://aejob.com
Description: Provides lists of architectural jobs, engineering jobs and environmental consulting jobs nationwide.

1044 ■ Archinect.com
E-mail: jobs@archinect.com
URL: http://archinect.com
Description: Functions as an online destination for progressive-design oriented students, architects, educators and fans. Brings together designers from around the world to introduce new ideas from all disciplines.

1045 ■ Architect Jobs
URL: http://www.jobsarchitect.org
Description: Provides architect jobs and employment opportunities. Offers updated job listings for candidates and job posting for employers.

1046 ■ Architect Jobs.com
E-mail: jobs@architectjobs.com
URL: http://www.architectjobs.com
Description: Features architect jobs, resumes,

interview tips, degree programs, recruiters lists, salary information, and other career resources.

1047 ■ ArchitectureCrossing.com
URL: http://www.architecturecrossing.com

Description: Offers a comprehensive collection of architectural job openings worldwide. Includes job listings from top companies and from virtually every employer career webpage and job board in America.

1048 ■ Bright Green Talent - Green Jobs
URL: http://www.brightgreentalent.com/green-jobs

Description: Serves as online tool that offers green jobs listing and career advice to candidates interested and engaged in environmental career.

1049 ■ Builder Jobs
URL: http://www.builderjobs.com

Description: Serves as an online career resource for home building professionals. Features career development articles, salary tools, home building and construction job listings, resume postings, and job alerts.

1050 ■ Construction Executive Online
URL: http://www.constructionexecutive.com

Description: Serves as a career management center for construction executives. Provides members access to a job board of executive construction jobs and to career counseling from top executive coaches.

1051 ■ ConstructionJobs.com
URL: http://www.constructionjobs.com/index_eng.cfm

Description: Serves as an employment job board and resume database built exclusively for the construction, design, and building industries. Provides targeted candidate searches by geographic region, specific industries, job titles, education, and experience.

1052 ■ Interior Architect Jobs
URL: http://www.interiorarchitectjobs.com

Description: Serves as a niche job board for employment opportunities in the field of interior architecture.

1053 ■ Locate Architecture Jobs
URL: http://www.locatearchitecturejobs.com

Description: Serves as an employment and job posting resource for the architectural field.

1054 ■ New Architecture Jobs
URL: http://www.newarchitecturejobs.com

Description: Provides job seekers the opportunity to easily contact employers with available architecture jobs in all specialties.

TRADESHOWS

1055 ■ American Institute of Architects National Convention
American Institute of Architects
1735 New York Ave., N.W.
Washington, DC 20006-5292
Ph: (202)626-7300
Fax: (202)626-7547
Fr: 800-AIA-3837
E-mail: infocentral@aia.org
URL: http://www.aia.org

Annual. Primary Exhibits: Architects equipment, supplies, and services. Dates and Locations: 2012 May 17-19; Washington, DC.

1056 ■ American Society of Golf Course Architects Annual Meeting
American Society of Golf Course Architects
125 N Executive Dr., Ste. 302
Brookfield, WI 53005
Ph: (262)786-5960
Fax: (262)786-5919
URL: http://www.asgca.org

Annual. Serves as an event for interaction, innovation and education relating to golf course architecture in the United States.

1057 ■ Association of Licensed Architects Conference & Product Show
Association of Licensed Architects
22159 N Pepper Rd., Ste. 2N
Barrington, IL 60010
Ph: (847)382-0630
Fax: (847)382-8380
E-mail: ala@alatoday.org
URL: http://www.alatoday.org/ala/Main.nsf

Annual. Serves as a continuing education event for design professionals and an opportunity for showcasing what architects, contractors, owners and engineers need to know to improve knowledge and compete in their jobs.

1058 ■ National Organization of Minority Architects Conference
National Organization of Minority Architects
Howard University
College of Engineering, Architecture & Computer Sciences
School of Architecture & Design
2366 6th St., NW, Rm. 100
Washington, DC 20059
Ph: (202)686-2780
E-mail: conference@noma.net
URL: http://www.noma.net

Annual. Provides an opportunity to reach design professionals that include architecture, engineering, planning, landscape design, contracting and building, urban design, interior design, building operations and maintenance, green or sustainable design and downtown revitalization and economic development officials.

1059 ■ Society of Architectural Historians Annual Meeting
Society of Architectural Historians
1365 N Astor St.
Chicago, IL 60610-2144
Ph: (312)573-1365
Fax: (312)573-1141
E-mail: info@sah.org
URL: http://sah.org

Annual. Features a preservation colloquium, workshops for historians, roundtable discussions, reunions, evening lectures and receptions, and an extensive array of local and regional tours.

1060 ■ Texas Society of Architects Design Products & Ideas Expo
Texas Society of Architects
500 Chicon St.
Austin, TX 78702
Ph: (512)478-7386
Fax: (512)478-0528
E-mail: info@texasarchitect.org
URL: http://www.texasarchitect.org

Annual. Primary Exhibits: Designing and building materials and systems for both interior/exterior residential and commercial projects.

OTHER SOURCES

1061 ■ American Concrete Institute
PO Box 9094
Farmington Hills, MI 48333-9094
Ph: (248)848-3700
Fax: (248)848-3701
URL: http://www.concrete.org

Description: Comprised of engineers, architects, contractors, educators, and others interested in improving techniques of design construction and maintenance of concrete products and structures. Advances engineering and technical education, scientific investigation and research, and development of standards for design and construction incorporating concrete and related materials. Gath-

ers, correlates, and disseminates information for the improvement of the design, construction, manufacture, use and maintenance of concrete products and structures.

1062 ■ American Institute of Architects (AIA)
1735 New York Ave. NW
Washington, DC 20006-5292
Ph: (202)626-7300
Fax: (202)626-7547
Fr: 800-AIA-3837
E-mail: infocentral@aia.org
URL: http://www.aia.org

Description: Represents architects, licensed architects, graduate architects, not yet licensed and retired architects. Fosters professionalism and accountability among members through continuing education and training. Promotes design excellence by influencing change in the industry. Sponsors educational programs with schools of architecture, graduate students, and elementary and secondary schools. Advises on professional competitions. Supplies construction documents. Established the American Architectural Foundation. Sponsors Octagon Museum; operates bookstore; stages exhibitions; compiles statistics. Provides monthly news service on design and construction. Conducts professional development programs, research programs, charitable activities, and children's services.

1063 ■ ArchVoices
1014 Curtis St.
Albany, CA 94706
Ph: (510)757-6213
E-mail: editors@archvoices.org
URL: http://www.archvoices.org

Description: Aims to advance the profession of architecture. Fosters a culture of communication through the collection and dissemination of architectural information and research. Compiles data and research on architecture and other licensed professions.

1064 ■ Asian American Architects and Engineers (AAAE)
1167 Mission St., 4th Fl.
San Francisco, CA 94103
Ph: (415)552-1118
E-mail: info@aaaenc.org
URL: http://www.aaaenc.org

Description: Minorities. Provides contracts and job opportunities for minorities in the architectural and engineering fields. Serves as a network for the promotion in professional fields.

1065 ■ Association of Architecture Organizations (AAO)
224 S Michigan Ave., Ste. 116
Chicago, IL 60604
Ph: (312)922-3432
Fax: (312)922-2607
E-mail: aao@architecture.org
URL: http://aaonetwork.org

Description: Fosters the development of an alliance of like-minded organizations that inform and engage the public about architecture and the built environment. Supports the creation of new architecture centers. Facilitates knowledge sharing between members, partner organizations and other similar entities.

1066 ■ Association for International Practical Training (AIPT)
10400 Little Patuxent Pkwy., Ste. 250
Columbia, MD 21044-3519
Ph: (410)997-2200
Fax: (410)992-3924
E-mail: aipt@aipt.org
URL: http://www.aipt.org

Description: Providers worldwide of on-the-job training programs for students and professionals seeking international career development and life-changing experiences. Arranges workplace exchanges in hundreds of professional fields, bringing employers and trainees together from around the world. Client list ranges from small farming communities to Fortune 500 companies.

1067 ■ Association of Licensed Architects
22159 N Pepper Rd., Ste. 2N
Barrington, IL 60010
Ph: (847)382-0630
Fax: (847)382-8380
E-mail: ala@alatoday.org
URL: http://www.alatoday.org/ala/Main.nsf

Description: Represents architects and related professionals who are united to advance the profession of architecture. Works to advance the architectural profession through education and by supporting and improving the profession's role in the built environment. Unites, educates, promotes and advances the architectural profession and addresses critical issues confronting it.

1068 ■ CoreNet Global
260 Peachtree St. NW, Ste. 1500
Atlanta, GA 30303
Ph: (404)589-3200
Fax: (404)589-3201
Fr: 800-726-8111
E-mail: acain@corenetglobal.org
URL: http://www.corenetglobal.org

Description: Executives, attorneys, real estate department heads, architects, engineers, analysts, researchers and anyone responsible for the management, administration and operation of national and regional real estate departments of national and international corporations. Encourages professionalism within corporate real estate through education and communication; protects the interests of corporate realty in dealing with adversaries, public or private; maintains contact with other real estate organizations; publicizes the availability of fully qualified members to the job market. Conducts seminars, including concentrated workshops on the corporate real estate field. Compiles statistics; sponsors competitions; maintains biographical archives and placement service.

1069 ■ Council of Educational Facility Planners International (CEFPI)
9180 E Desert Cove Dr., Ste. 104
Scottsdale, AZ 85260-6231
Ph: (480)391-0840
Fax: (480)391-0940
E-mail: michelle@cefpi.org
URL: http://www.cefpi.org

Description: Individuals and firms who are responsible for planning, designing, creating, maintaining, and equipping the physical environment of education. Sponsors an exchange of information, professional experiences, best practices research results, and other investigative techniques concerning educational facility planning. Activities include publication and review of current and emerging practices in educational facility planning; identification and execution of needed research; development of professional training programs; strengthening of planning services on various levels of government and in institutions of higher learning; leadership in the development of higher standards for facility design and the physical environment of education. Operates speakers' bureau; sponsors placement service; compiles statistics.

1070 ■ Fusion Architecture
PO Box 66853
Phoenix, AZ 85082-6853
E-mail: info@fusionarchitecture.org
URL: http://www.fusionarchitecture.org

Description: Represents the interests of architecture, urban design, graphic design, engineering and cultural practitioners. Encourages young designers to create design solutions to socio-cultural issues. Promotes the use of graphic and information design tools to reach out and produce projects that have influence on the economics, politics, cultural and social structure facing urban communities.

1071 ■ Institute of Destination Architects and Designers
3590 Round Bottom Rd.
PMB F273796
Cincinnati, OH 45244-3026
Ph: (434)334-1909
Fax: (602)865-7771
E-mail: office@idad.org
URL: http://www.idad.org/idadh.htm

Description: Represents the interests of architects from various disciplines, designers in various specialties, managers, scientists, and executives. Focuses on developing and disseminating techniques which can make resort and hydro-scape zones successful. Conducts projects, design developments, and research inquiries dealing with the development of tourism destinations including themed, entertainment, resort, and coastal architecture.

1072 ■ Ministry Architecture
1904 S Union Pl.
Lakewood, CO 80228
Ph: (720)937-9664
Fax: (303)989-0884
E-mail: ministryarchitecture@hotmail.com
URL: http://www.ministryarchitecture.com

Description: Represents design professionals and architecture students. Works primarily on giving architectural, engineering and planning services to evangelical ministries in developing countries.

1073 ■ National Center for Construction Education and Research (NCCER)
3600 NW 43rd St., Bldg. G
Gainesville, FL 32606
Ph: (352)334-0911
Fax: (352)334-0932
Fr: 888-622-3720
E-mail: marketing@nccer.org
URL: http://www.nccer.org

Description: Education foundation committed to the development and publication of Contren(TM) Learning Series, the source of craft training, management education and safety resources for the construction industry.

1074 ■ National Council of Architectural Registration Boards (NCARB)
1801 K St. NW, Ste. 700-K
Washington, DC 20006-1310
Ph: (202)783-6500
Fax: (202)783-0290
E-mail: customerservice@ncarb.org
URL: http://www.ncarb.org

Description: Federation of state boards for the registration of architects in the United States, District of Columbia, Puerto Rico, Virgin Islands, Guam, and the Northern Mariana Islands.

1075 ■ National Organization of Minority Architects
Howard University
College of Engineering, Architecture & Computer Sciences
School of Architecture & Design
2366 6th St. NW, Rm. 100
Washington, DC 20059
Ph: (202)686-2780
URL: http://www.noma.net

Description: Represents minority architects who work together to fight discriminatory policies that limit or bar minority architects from participating in design and constructions programs. Commits to minimizing the effect of racism in the architectural profession. Acts as a clearing house for information and maintain a roster on practitioners.

1076 ■ Organization of Women Architects and Design Professionals
PO Box 10078
Berkeley, CA 94709
E-mail: info@owa-usa.org
URL: http://owa-usa.org

Description: Comprised of architects, interior designers, landscape architects, planners, lighting designers, graphic designers, photographers, artists, writers, educators and students. Strives to improve the professional standing of women in architecture and design-related fields. Advocates young women and students entering design related fields through mentoring, education, and employment opportunities.

1077 ■ Professional Women in Construction (PWC)
315 E 56th St.
New York, NY 10022-3730
Ph: (212)486-4712
Fax: (212)486-0228
E-mail: pwc@pwcusa.org
URL: http://www.pwcusa.org

Description: Management-level women and men in construction and allied industries; owners, suppliers, architects, engineers, field personnel, office personnel and bonding/surety personnel. Provides a forum for exchange of ideas and promotion of political and legislative action, education and job opportunities for women in construction and related fields; forms liaisons with other trade and professional groups; develops research programs. Strives to reform abuses and to assure justice and equity within the construction industry. Sponsors mini-workshops. Maintains Action Line, which provides members with current information on pertinent legislation and on the association's activities and job referrals.

1078 ■ Public Architecture
1211 Folsom St., 4th Fl.
San Francisco, CA 94103
Ph: (415)861-8200
Fax: (415)431-9695
E-mail: info@publicarchitecture.org
URL: http://www.publicarchitecture.org

Description: Works to put the resources of architecture in the service of public interest. Encourages and inspires architecture and design firms to participate in pro bono work. Acts as a catalyst for public discourse through education, advocacy and the design of public spaces and amenities.

1079 ■ Society of American Registered Architects (SARA)
PO Box 280
Newport, TN 37822
Ph: (423)721-0129
Fr: 888-385-7272
E-mail: cmoscato@sara-national.org
URL: http://www.sara-national.org

Description: Architects registered or licensed under the laws of states and territories of the U.S. Sponsors seminars and professional and student design competitions. Offers placement service.

1080 ■ Society of Architectural Historians
1365 N Astor St.
Chicago, IL 60610-2144
Ph: (312)573-1365
Fax: (312)573-1141
E-mail: info@sah.org
URL: http://sah.org

Description: Architectural historians, architects, preservationists, students, professionals in allied fields and the interested public. Advances the knowledge and understanding of the history of architecture, design, landscape and urbanism worldwide. Offers an on-site tours, lectures, discussions, and other events geared toward appreciation and understanding of architectural history.

1081 ■ Society of Iranian Architects and Planners (SIAP)
PO Box 643066
Los Angeles, CA 90064
E-mail: abdiziai@gmail.com
URL: http://siap.org

Description: Represents Iranian graduates in the field of architecture, planning, interior design and landscape architecture. Promotes cultural, scientific and professional aspects in the field architecture and encourages members to develop and advance their skills and abilities in the profession. Provides members with a means of communication for coordination of mutual professional and cultural relationships with similar Iranian organizations around the globe.

Sources of Help-Wanted Ads

1082 ■ AMIA Newsletter
Association of Moving Image Archivists
1313 N Vine St.
Hollywood, CA 90028
Ph: (323)463-1500
Fax: (323)463-1506
E-mail: amia@amianet.org
URL: http://www.amianet.org

Description: Quarterly. $50/year. Presents information on the preservation of film and video materials, and the moving image archival profession. REC news of research, a calendar of events, reports of meetings, job listings, book reviews, and notices of publications available.

1083 ■ Annotation
National Historical Publications and Records Commission
700 Pennsylvania Ave. NW, Rm. 106
Washington, DC 20408-0001
Ph: (202)357-5010
Fax: (202)357-5914
E-mail: nhprc@nara.gov
URL: http://www.archives.gov/nhprc/annotation

Description: Quarterly. Contains information of interest to National Historical Publications and Records Commission members. Recurring features include columns titled From the Editor, and The Executive Director's Column.

1084 ■ Archival Outlook
Society of American Archivists
17 N State St., Ste. 1425
Chicago, IL 60602
Ph: (312)606-0722
Fax: (312)606-0728
Fr: (866)SAA-7858
E-mail: info@archivists.org
URL: http://www.archivists.org/periodicals/

Description: Bimonthly. Publishes news of relevance to the professional archival community. Recurring features include a calendar of events, news from constituent groups, news of educational opportunities, professional resources available, and job listings.

1085 ■ Children and Libraries
American Library Association
50 E Huron St.
Chicago, IL 60611-2729
Ph: (312)280-4223
Fax: (312)280-4380
Fr: 800-545-2433
URL: http://www.ala.org/ala/mgrps/divs/alsc/compubs/childrenlib/i

for Included in membership; $50.00/year for other countries; $40.00/year for nonmembers. Journal that focuses on the continuing education of librarians working with children.

1086 ■ Collections Journal
AltaMira Press
4501 Forbes Blvd., Ste. 200
Lanham, MD 20706
Ph: (301)459-3366
Fax: (301)429-5748
Fr: 800-462-6420
E-mail: info@altamirapress.com
URL: http://www.altamirapress.com/rla/journals/collections/

Quarterly. $43.00/year for individuals; $99.00/year for institutions, museum; $149.00/year for institutions, non-museum; $86.00/year for two years; $198.00/year for institutions, museum, 2 years; $298.00/year for institutions, non-museum, 2 years. Journal that offers information on handling, preserving, researching, and organizing museum and archive collections.

1087 ■ Conference of Inter-Mountain Archivists (CIMA) Newsletter
Conference of Inter-Mountain Archivists
PO Box 2048
Salt Lake City, UT 84110
Ph: (801)581-8863
E-mail: walter.jones@utah.edu
URL: http://cimarchivists.org

Description: Quarterly. $12/year for members; $25/year for institutions. Concerned with the preservation and use of archival and manuscript materials in the Inter-mountain West and adjacent areas. Disseminates information on research materials and archival methodology; provides a forum for the discussion of common concerns; and cooperates with similar cultural and educational organizations. Recurring features include news of research, preservation, members, and job openings.

1088 ■ ConservatioNews
Arizona State University Libraries
Box 871006
Tempe, AZ 85287
Ph: (480)965-6164
Fax: (480)965-9233
URL: http://library.lib.asu.edu/record=b3078319

Description: Quarterly. Concerned with the preservation of paper documents, magnetic media, published materials, photographs, and film. Carries articles on the theory and practice of conservation, questions and answers to specific problems, and product news. Recurring features include news of members, book reviews, and a calendar of events.

1089 ■ Dirty Goat
Host Publications, Inc.
277 Broadway, Ste. 210
New York, NY 10007
Ph: (212)905-2365
Fax: (212)905-2369
URL: http://www.thedirtygoat.com/index.html

Semiannual. $20.00/year for individuals. Journal covering poetry, prose, drama, literature and visual art.

1090 ■ Dispatch
American Association for State & Local History
1717 Church St.
Nashville, TN 37203-2991
Ph: (615)320-3203
Fax: (615)327-9013
E-mail: membership@aaslh.org
URL: http://www.aaslh.org/pdispatch.htm

Description: Monthly. Offers general information about state and local historical societies and the study of state and local history in the U.S. and Canada. Informs members of new training programs, seminars, and exhibits in the field. Recurring features include information on grant opportunities, updates on legislation, Association activities, and historical society personnel, interviews, job listings, and notices of publications available.

1091 ■ Film History
Indiana University Press
601 N Morton St.
Bloomington, IN 47404-3778
Ph: (812)855-8817
Fax: (812)855-8507
Fr: 800-842-6796
E-mail: filmhist@aol.com
URL: http://inscribe.iupress.org/loi/fil

Quarterly. $82.50/year for individuals, print and online; $75.00/year for individuals, print only; $67.50/year for individuals, online only; $273.50/year for institutions, print and online; $199.50/year for institutions, print only; $179.50/year for institutions, online only. Journal tracing the history of the motion picture with reference to social, technological, and economic aspects, covering various aspects of motion pictures such as production, distribution, exhibition, and reception.

1092 ■ History News
American Association for State and Local History
1717 Church St.
Nashville, TN 37203-2991
Ph: (615)320-3203
Fax: (615)327-9013
URL: http://www.aaslh.org/historynews.htm

Quarterly. Magazine for employees of historic sites, museums, and public history agencies. Coverage includes museum education programs and techniques for working with volunteers.

1093 ■ Infinity
Society of American Archivists, Preservation Section
17 N State St., Ste. 1425
Chicago, IL 60602
Ph: (312)606-0722
Fax: (312)606-0728
Fr: (866)SAA-7858
E-mail: info@archivists.org
URL: http://www2.archivists.org

Description: Quarterly. Informs members of the Society of archives news and events. Recurring features include news of research, a calendar of events, reports of meetings, news of educational opportunities, book reviews, notices of publications available, and a column titled From the Chair.

1094 ■ *Journal of Access Services*
Routledge Journals
270 Madison Ave.
New York, NY 10016-0601
Ph: (212)216-7800
Fax: (212)563-2269
URL: http://www.tandf.co.uk/journals/WJAS

Quarterly. $77.00/year for individuals, online only; $82.00/year for individuals, print + online; $210.00/year for institutions, online only; $233.00/year for institutions, print + online. Journal focusing on the basic business of providing library users with access to information, and helping librarians stay up to date on continuing education and professional development in the field of access services.

1095 ■ *Journal of Classification*
Springer-Verlag New York Inc.
233 Spring St.
New York, NY 10013-1578
Ph: (212)460-1500
Fax: (212)460-1575
Fr: 800-777-4643
URL: http://www.springer.com/statistics/
   statistical+theory+and+me

Semiannual. $447.00/year for institutions, print or online; $536.00/year for institutions, print & enchanced access. Journal of the Classification Society of North America.

1096 ■ *Journal of Interlibrary Loan,*
   Document Delivery & Electronic Reserve
Routledge Journals
270 Madison Ave.
New York, NY 10016-0601
Ph: (212)216-7800
Fax: (212)563-2269
URL: http://www.informaworld.com/smpp/
   title~content=t792306877

$100.00/year for individuals, online only; $108.00/year for individuals, print + online; $396.00/year for institutions, online only; $440.00/year for institutions, print + online. Journal focusing on a broad spectrum of library and information center functions that rely heavily on interlibrary loan, document delivery, and electronic reserve.

1097 ■ *MAC Newsletter*
Midwest Archives Conference
4440 PGA Blvd., Ste. 600
Palm Beach Gardens, FL 33410
E-mail: membership@midwestarchives.org
URL: http://www.midwestarchives.org

Description: Quarterly. Covers activities of Midwest Archives Conference. Includes employment opportunities, conference reports, financial statements, meeting minutes, news of members, and listing of publications available.

1098 ■ *MAHD Bulletin*
Museums, Arts, and Humanities Div., Special Libraries Assn.
331 S Patrick St.
Alexandria, VA 22314-3501
Ph: (703)647-4900
Fax: (703)647-4901
E-mail: membership@sla.org
URL: http://units.sla.org/division/dmah

Description: Four issues/year. Discusses pertinent events, issues, and publications concerning special libraries. Recurring features include interviews, news of research, a calendar of events, reports of meetings, news of educational opportunities, book reviews, notices of publications available, and a column titled On My Mind.

1099 ■ *Mid-Atlantic Archivist*
Mid-Atlantic Regional Archives Conference
PO Box 1773
Carlisle, PA 17013
Ph: (717)713-9973
Fax: (717)245-1439
E-mail: administrator@marac.info
URL: http://www.marac.info

Description: Quarterly. $35 per year. Contains news and information for and about members of the Conference. Seeks exchange of information between colleagues, improvement of competence among archivists, and encourages professional involvement of persons actively engaged in the preservation and use of historical research materials. Recurring features include letters to the editor, news of members, book reviews, a calendar of events, and columns titled Preservation News, Reference Shelf, Session Abstracts, Software News, and Employment Opportunities.

1100 ■ *Museum Archivist*
Society of American Archivists, Museum Archives Section
17 N State St., Ste. 1425
Chicago, IL 60602
Ph: (312)606-0722
Fax: (312)606-0728
Fr: (866)SAA-7858
E-mail: info@archivists.org
URL: http://www2.archivists.org

Description: 2/year. Provides news of Society and Section activities, meetings, symposia, educational programs, project research, repository reports, notes, and announcements. Recurring features include letters to the editor, news of research, reports of meetings, and news of educational opportunities.

1101 ■ *New England Archivists Newsletter*
New England Archivists
c/o Juliana Kuipers
Harvard University Archives
Pusey Library
Cambridge, MA 02138
E-mail: neamembership@gmail.com
URL: http://www.newenglandarchivists.org

Description: Quarterly. Contains regional archival news and announcements. Recurring features include a calendar of events, reports of meetings, job listings, book reviews, workshops, reports on repositories, and feature articles on archival subjects.

1102 ■ *Preservation*
National Trust for Historic Preservation
1785 Massachusetts Ave. NW
Washington, DC 20036-2117
Ph: (202)588-6000
Fax: (202)588-6038
Fr: 800-944-6847
URL: http://www.preservationnation.org/

Bimonthly. $20.00/year for members, individual; $30.00/year for members, family; $50.00/year for members, contributing; $100.00/year for members, sustaining; $250.00/year for members, preservation council steward; $1,000.00/year for members, preservation council heritage society. Magazine featuring historic preservation.

1103 ■ *The Primary Source*
Society of Mississippi Archivists
PO Box 4024
Clinton, MS 39058
E-mail: info@msarchivists.org
URL: http://www.msarchivists.org

Description: Annually. Focuses on activities and trends in the archival and library community both regionally and nationally. Includes information on conservation and articles on state repositories and their holdings. Recurring features include news of research, book reviews, and a calendar of events.

1104 ■ *The Rocky Mountain Archivist*
Society of Rocky Mountain Archivists
c/o Beverly Allen, Pres.
University Library, 6th Fl.
2200 Bonforte Blvd.
Colorado State University
Pueblo, CO 81001-4901
Ph: (719)549-2475
E-mail: srmapres@srmarchivists.org
URL: http://www.srmarchivists.org/

Description: Quarterly. Covers activities of Society of Rocky Mountain Archivists. Includes local and national news on archives and special collections.

1105 ■ *The Southwestern Archivist*
Society of Southwest Archivists
PO Box 301311
Austin, TX 78703-0022
URL: http://southwestarchivists.org

Description: Quarterly. Supports the aims of the Society, which include: "to provide a means for effective cooperation among people concerned with the documentation of human experience," and "to promote the adoption of sound principles and standards for the preservation and administration of records." Recurring features include news of research, news of members, and a calendar of events.

1106 ■ *Tennessee Archivist*
Society of Tennessee Archivists
c/o STA Treasurer
1301 East Main St.
MTSU Box 242
Murfreesboro, TN 37132
Ph: (615)898-5884
Fax: (615)898-5829
E-mail: info@tennesseearchivists.org
URL: http://www.tennesseearchivists.org/
   newsletter.html

Description: Quarterly. Provides information on state and national archival activities. Announces professional meetings and workshops, archival job openings, and new collections. Features articles on archives and records repositories in Tennessee. Recurring features include a calendar of events, reports of meetings, news of educational opportunities, job listings, notices of publications available, and columns titled Editorial, Message from the President, and Committee Reports.

EMPLOYER DIRECTORIES AND NETWORKING LISTS

1107 ■ *Directory of Special Libraries and*
   Information Centers
Gale
PO Box 6904
Florence, KY 41022-6904
Fr: 800-354-9706
URL: http://www.gale.cengage.com

Annual, Latest edition 40th; March, 2012. $2576.00. Covers: Over 34,800 special libraries, information centers, documentation centers, etc.; about 500 networks and consortia; major special libraries abroad also included. Volume 1 part 3 contains 6 other appendices (besides networks and consortia): Regional and Subregional Libraries for the Blind & Physically Handicapped, Patent & Trademark Depository Libraries, Regional Government Depository Libraries, United Nations Depository Libraries, World Bank Depository Libraries, and European Community Depository Libraries. Entries include: Library name, address, phone, fax, e-mail address; contact; year founded; sponsoring organization; special collections; subject interests; names and titles of staff; services (copying, online searches); size of collection; subscriptions; computerized services and automated operations; Internet home page address; publications; special catalogs; special indexes. For consortia and networks—Name, address, phone, contact. Other appendices have varying amounts of directory information. Contents of Volume 1 are available in "Subject Directory of Special Libraries and Information Centers". Arrangement: Libraries are alphabetical by name of sponsoring organization or institution; consortia and networks are geographical. Indexes: Subject. Geographic and personnel indexes constitute volume 2.

1108 ■ *Guide to Employment Sources in the Library & Information Professions*
Office for Human Resource Development and Recruitment
50 E Huron St.
Chicago, IL 60611
Ph: (312)280-2428
Fax: (312)280-3256
Fr: 800-545-2433
E-mail: customerservice@ala.org
URL: http://www.ala.org

Annual, Latest edition 2009. Covers: Library job sources, such as specialized and state and regional library associations, state library agencies, federal library agencies, and overseas exchange programs. Entries include: Library, company, or organization name, address, phone; contact name, description of services, publications, etc. This is a reprint of a segment of the "Bowker Annual of Library and Book Trade Information," described separately. Arrangement: Classified by type of source.

1109 ■ *Midwest Archives Conference—Membership Directory*
Midwest Archives Conference
4440 PGA Blvd., Ste. 600
Palm Beach Gardens, FL 33410
URL: http://www.midwestarchives.org

Annual. Covers: More than 1,150 individual and institutional members, largely librarians, archivists, records managers, manuscripts curators, historians, and museum and historical society personnel; about 25 archival associations in the Midwest. Entries include: For institutions—Name of archives, parent organization, address, phone. For individuals—Name, title, business address, phone. Arrangement: Separate alphabetical sections for individuals and institutions.

HANDBOOKS AND MANUALS

1110 ■ *Creative Careers in Museums*
Allworth Press
307 W 36th St., 11th Fl.
New York, NY 10018
Ph: (212)643-6816
Fax: (212)643-6819
URL: http://www.allworth.com/book/
?GCOI=58115100056180

Jan E. Burdick. 2008. $15.95 (paperback). 210 pages. Details how to land a museum job, where to look, how to put together a successful resume and cover letter, and what to expect at interviews. Contains information on professional associations, museum studies programs, and job search resources in the museum field.

1111 ■ *Ferguson Career Coach: Managing Your Career in the Art Industry*
Facts On File
132 W 31st St., 17th Fl.
New York, NY 10001
Fax: 800-678-3633
Fr: 800-322-8755
E-mail: custserv@factsonfile.com
URL: http://factsonfile.infobasepublishing.com

Shelly Field. 2008. $39.95 (hardcover). 304 pages. Contains tips for students who dream of a career as a graphic artist or an art gallery curator.

1112 ■ *Great Jobs for History Majors*
The McGraw-Hill Companies
PO Box 182604
Columbus, OH 43272

Fax: (614)759-3749
Fr: 877-883-5524
E-mail: customer.service@mcgraw-hill.com
URL: http://www.mhprofessional.com

Julie DeGalan and Stephen Lambert. 2007. $16.95 (paper). 192 pages.

1113 ■ *Great Jobs for Liberal Arts Majors*
The McGraw-Hill Companies
PO Box 182604
Columbus, OH 43272
Fax: (614)759-3749
Fr: 877-883-5524
E-mail: customer.service@mcgraw-hill.com
URL: http://www.mhprofessional.com/
product.php?isbn=0071482148

Blythe Camenson. Second edition, 2007. $16.95 (paper). 192 pages.

1114 ■ *Museum Archives: An Introduction*
Society of American Archivists
17 N State St., Ste. 1425
Chicago, IL 60602
Ph: (312)606-0722
Fax: (312)606-0728
Fr: (866)722-7858
E-mail: info@archivists.org
URL: http://www.archivists.org/

Deborah Wythe. Second edition, 2004. $62.00. 256 pages.

1115 ■ *Museum Careers: A Practical Guide for Students and Novices*
Left Coast Press
1630 N Main St., No. 400
Walnut Creek, CA 94596
Ph: (925)935-3380
Fax: (925)935-2916
E-mail: explore@lcoastpress.com
URL: http://www.lcoastpress.com/book.php?id=152

N. Elizabeth Schlatter. 2008. $24.95 (paperback). 184 pages. Outlines the nature of the profession as a whole, the rewards and challenges of museum work, types of museums, and jobs within museums, including salary ranges.

1116 ■ *Opportunities in Museum Careers*
The McGraw-Hill Companies
PO Box 182604
Columbus, OH 43272
Fax: (614)759-3749
Fr: 877-883-5524
E-mail: customer.service@mcgraw-hill.com
URL: http://www.mhprofessional.com/
product.php?isbn=0071467696

Blythe Camenson. 2006. $13.95 (paper). 160 pages.

ONLINE JOB SOURCES AND SERVICES

1117 ■ *Archivist Jobs*
URL: http://www.archivistjobs.us

Description: Serves as an online source for archivist recruiting and job listings.

1118 ■ *eCulturalResources*
URL: http://www.eculturalresources.com

Description: Provides sources of news, jobs, announcements, consultant listings, and resources for the cultural resource industry.

1119 ■ *Get Curator Jobs*
URL: http://www.getcuratorjobs.com

Description: Features a searchable database for curator job listings.

1120 ■ *Museum Employment Resource Center*
E-mail: questions@museum-employment.com
URL: http://www.museum-employment.com

Description: Provides job listings and other informa-

tion related to the museum, heritage management, and cultural resource communities.

TRADESHOWS

1121 ■ *Art Libraries Society of North America Conference*
Art Libraries Society of North America
7044 S 13th St.
Oak Creek, WI 53154
Ph: (414)768-8000
Fax: (414)768-8001
Fr: 800-817-0621
URL: http://www.arlisna.org

Annual. 2013 April 25-29; Pasadena, CA. Provides networking opportunities for attendees.

1122 ■ *Society of American Archivists Meeting*
Society of American Archivists
17 N State St., Ste. 1425
Chicago, IL 60602
Ph: (312)606-0722
Fax: (312)606-0728
Fr: (866)722-7858
E-mail: servicecenter@archivists.org
URL: http://www.archivists.org

Annual. Includes sessions, pre-conference programs, tours of local repositories, special events, exhibits, and networking opportunities. 2012 August 6-12; San Diego, CA; San Diego Hilton Bayfront.

OTHER SOURCES

1123 ■ *American Association of Museums (AAM)*
1575 Eye St. NW, Ste. 400
Washington, DC 20005
Ph: (202)289-1818
Fax: (202)289-6578
Fr: (866)226-2150
E-mail: fbell@aam-us.org
URL: http://www.aam-us.org

Description: Represents directors, curators, registrars, educators, exhibit designers, public relations officers, development officers, security managers, trustees, and volunteers in museums as well as all museums, including art, history, science, military and maritime, and youth, as well as aquariums, zoos, botanical gardens, arboretums, historic sites, and science and technology centers. Dedicated to promoting excellence within the museum community. Assists museum staff, boards, and volunteers through advocacy, professional education, information exchange, accreditation, and guidance.

1124 ■ *American Institute for Conservation of Historic and Artistic Works (AIC)*
1156 15th St., Ste. 320
Washington, DC 20005-1714
Ph: (202)452-9545
Fax: (202)452-9328
E-mail: info@conservation-us.org
URL: http://www.conservation-us.org

Description: Professionals, scientists, administrators, and educators in the field of art conservation; interested individuals. Advances the practice and promotes the importance of the preservation of cultural property. Coordinates the exchange of knowledge, research, and publications. Establishes and upholds professional standards. Publishes conservation literature. Compiles statistics. Represents membership to allied professional associations and advocates on conservation-related issues. Solicits and dispenses money exclusively for charitable, scientific, and educational objectives.

1125 ■ *American Society for Information Science and Technology (ASIS&T)*
1320 Fenwick Ln., Ste. 510
Silver Spring, MD 20910

Ph: (301)495-0900
Fax: (301)495-0810
E-mail: asis@asis.org
URL: http://www.asis.org

Description: Information specialists, scientists, librarians, administrators, social scientists, and others interested in the use, organization, storage, retrieval, evaluation, and dissemination of recorded specialized information. Seeks to improve the information transfer process through research, development, application, and education. Provides a forum for the discussion, publication, and critical analysis of work dealing with the theory, practice, research, and development of elements involved in communication of information. Members are engaged in a variety of activities and specialties including classification and coding systems, automatic and associative indexing, machine translation of languages, special librarianship and library systems analysis, and copyright issues. Sponsors National Auxiliary Publications Service, which provides reproduction services and a central depository for all types of information. Maintains placement service. Sponsors numerous special interest groups. Conducts continuing education programs and professional development workshops.

1126 ■ Art Libraries Society of North America

7044 S 13th St.
Oak Creek, WI 53154
Ph: (414)768-8000
Fax: (414)768-8001
Fr: 800-817-0621
URL: http://www.arlisna.org

Description: Consists of architecture and art librarians, visual resources professionals, artists, curators, educators, publishers, students, and others interested in visual arts information. Promotes the advancement of art library and information professionals. Collaborates with other professional and educational organizations through participation in international forums.

1127 ■ College Art Association (CAA)

275 7th Ave., 18th Fl.
New York, NY 10001
Ph: (212)691-1051
Fax: (212)627-2381
E-mail: nyoffice@collegeart.org
URL: http://www.collegeart.org

Description: Professional organization of artists, art historians and fine art educators, museum directors, and curators. Seeks to raise the standards of scholarship and of the teaching of art and art history throughout the country.

1128 ■ Print Council of America (PCA)

The Art Institute of Chicago
Dept. of Drawings and Prints
111 S Michigan Ave.
Chicago, IL 60603
Ph: (312)857-7162
E-mail: mtedeschi@artic.edu
URL: http://www.printcouncil.org

Description: Museum professionals. Fosters the study and appreciation of new and old prints, drawings, and photographs; stimulates discussion. Sponsors educational programs and research publications; offers placement services.

1129 ■ Society of American Archivists (SAA)

17 N State St., Ste. 1425
Chicago, IL 60602-4061
Ph: (312)606-0722
Fax: (312)606-0728
Fr: (866)722-7858
E-mail: servicecenter@archivists.org
URL: http://www.archivists.org

Description: Individuals and institutions concerned with the identification, preservation, and use of records of historical value.

1130 ■ Special Libraries Association (SLA)

331 S Patrick St.
Alexandria, VA 22314-3501
Ph: (703)647-4900
Fax: (703)647-4901
E-mail: janice@sla.org
URL: http://www.sla.org

Description: International association of information professionals who work in specialized information environments such as business, research, government, universities, newspapers, museums, and institutions. Seeks to advance the leadership role of information professionals through learning, networking and advocacy. Offers consulting services to organizations that wish to establish or expand a library or information services. Conducts strategic learning and development courses, public relations, and government relations programs. Provides employment services. Operates knowledge exchange on topics pertaining to the development and management of special libraries.

1131 ■ Women's Caucus for Art (WCA)

Canal St. Sta.
PO Box 1498
New York, NY 10013
Ph: (212)634-0007
E-mail: president@nationalwca.org
URL: http://www.nationalwca.org

Description: Professional women in visual art fields: artists, critics, art historians, museum and gallery professionals, arts administrators, educators and students, and collectors of art. Aims to increase recognition for contemporary and historical achievements of women in art. Ensures equal opportunity for employment, art commissions, and research grants. Encourages professionalism and shared information among women in art. Stimulates and publicizes research and publications on women in the visual arts. Conducts workshops, periodic affirmative action research, and statistical surveys.

Sources of Help-Wanted Ads

1132 ■ American Art Therapy Association Newsletter
American Art Therapy Association Inc.
225 N Fairfax St.
Alexandria, VA 22314
Ph: (703)548-5860
Fax: (703)783-8468
Fr: 888-290-0878
E-mail: info@arttherapy.org
URL: http://www.arttherapy.org

Description: Quarterly. Publishes news of developments and events in art therapy. Provides information on Association activities, related organizations, and available resources. Recurring features include legislative updates, letters to the editor, news of members, a calendar of events, board and committee reports, conference and symposia information.

1133 ■ Art Therapy
American Art Therapy Association, Inc.
11160-C1 S Lakes Dr., Ste. 813
Reston, VA 20191
Fr: 888-290-0878
E-mail: info@arttherapy.org
URL: http://www.arttherapyjournal.org

Quarterly. $135.00/year for individuals, U.S.; $235.00/year for institutions, U.S.; $200.00/year for individuals, out of the country; $255.00/year for institutions, out of the country. Journal for art therapists.

1134 ■ ArtSEARCH
Theatre Communications Group
520 8th Ave., 24th Fl.
New York, NY 10018-4156
Ph: (212)609-5900
Fax: (212)609-5901
E-mail: tcg@tcg.org
URL: http://www.tcg.org

Description: Biweekly. Publishes classified listings for job opportunities in the arts, especially theatre, dance, music, and educational institutions. Listings include opportunities in administration, artistic, education, production, and career development.

1135 ■ Dirty Goat
Host Publications, Inc.
277 Broadway, Ste. 210
New York, NY 10007
Ph: (212)905-2365
Fax: (212)905-2369
URL: http://www.thedirtygoat.com/index.html

Semiannual. $20.00/year for individuals. Journal covering poetry, prose, drama, literature and visual art.

1136 ■ Film History
Indiana University Press
601 N Morton St.
Bloomington, IN 47404-3778

Ph: (812)855-8817
Fax: (812)855-8507
Fr: 800-842-6796
E-mail: filmhist@aol.com
URL: http://inscribe.iupress.org/loi/fil

Quarterly. $82.50/year for individuals, print and online; $75.00/year for individuals, print only; $67.50/year for individuals, online only; $273.50/year for institutions, print and online; $199.50/year for institutions, print only; $179.50/year for institutions, online only. Journal tracing the history of the motion picture with reference to social, technological, and economic aspects, covering various aspects of motion pictures such as production, distribution, exhibition, and reception.

Handbooks and Manuals

1137 ■ Art Therapy Activities: A Practical Guide for Teachers, Therapists and Parents
Charles C Thomas Publisher, Ltd.
2600 S 1st St.
Springfield, IL 62704
Ph: (217)789-8980
Fax: (217)789-9130
Fr: 800-258-8980
E-mail: books@ccthomas.com
URL: http://www.ccthomas.com

Pamela J. Stack. 2006. $31.95. 154 pages. Profiles activities used for art therapy.

1138 ■ Careers in Social and Rehabilitation Services
The McGraw-Hill Companies
PO Box 182604
Columbus, OH 43272
Fax: (614)759-3749
Fr: 877-883-5524
E-mail: customer.service@mcgraw-hill.com
URL: http://www.mhprofessional.com/product.php?isbn=0071641955

Geraldine O. Garner. 2008. $16.95. 192 pages.

1139 ■ Counseling As an Art: The Creative Arts in Counseling
American Counseling Association
5999 Stevenson Ave.
Alexandria, VA 22304-3300
Ph: (703)823-9800
Fax: 800-473-2329
Fr: 800-347-6647
URL: http://www.counseling.org

Samuel T. Gladding. Third edition, 2004. $42.95 (paper). 237 pages.

1140 ■ Introduction to Art Therapy
Routledge
711 3rd Ave., 8th Fl.
New York, NY 10017
Ph: (212)216-7800

Fax: (212)563-2269
URL: http://www.routledge.com/books/Introduction-to-Art-Therapy-isbn9780415960939

Judith A. Rubin. 2009. $52.95. 356 pages. Part of the Basic Principles Into Practice Series.

1141 ■ A Therapist's Guide to Art Therapy Assessments: Tools of the Trade
Charles C Thomas Publisher, Ltd.
2600 S 1st.
PO Box 19265
Springfield, IL 62794-9265
Ph: (217)789-8980
Fax: (217)789-9130
Fr: 800-258-8980
E-mail: books@ccthomas.com
URL: http://www.ccthomas.com

Stephanie L. Brooke. Second edition, 2004. $53.95. 256 pages.

Online Job Sources and Services

1142 ■ ActivityJobs.com
URL: http://www.activityjobs.com

Description: Provides employment listing for recreation therapists, activity therapists, activity coordinators, creative arts therapists and leisure counselors.

Tradeshows

1143 ■ American Art Therapy Association Conference
Stygar Associates, Inc.
1202 Allanson Rd.
Mundelein, IL 60060-3808
Fax: (847)566-4580
E-mail: estygarIII@aol.com
URL: http://stygar.net

Annual. Primary Exhibits: Art supplies, books, therapeutic materials, and schools. Dates and Locations: 2012 Jul 09-13; Savannah, GA.

Other Sources

1144 ■ American Art Therapy Association (AATA)
225 N Fairfax St.
Alexandria, VA 22314
Ph: (703)548-5860
Fax: (703)783-8468
Fr: 888-290-0878
E-mail: info@arttherapy.org
URL: http://www.arttherapy.org

Description: Art therapists, students, and individuals in related fields. Supports the progressive development of therapeutic uses of art, the advancement of research, and improvements in the standards of practice. Has established specific professional criteria for training art therapists. Facilitates the exchange of information and experience. Compiles statistics.

1145 ■ Art Therapy Connection (ATC)
1800 Ridge Ave., Unit 211
Evanston, IL 60201
E-mail: info@arttherapyconnection.net
URL: http://www.arttherapyconnection.net
Description: Promotes art therapy as a form of psychotherapy. Works with children and teenagers to develop self-awareness and self-management skills by integrating art and creativity with therapy. Increases the concentration levels, self-control and interpersonal skills of youth and children.

1146 ■ International Expressive Arts Therapy Association (IEATA)
PO Box 320399
San Francisco, CA 94132
Ph: (415)522-8959
E-mail: info@ieata.org
URL: http://www.ieata.org

Description: Provides resources about the expressive arts and how they may relate to other disciplines, such as psychology, education and business.

1147 ■ National Art Education Association (NAEA)
1806 Robert Fulton Dr., Ste. 300
Reston, VA 20191
Ph: (703)860-8000
Fax: (703)860-2960
Fr: 800-299-8321
E-mail: info@arteducators.org
URL: http://www.arteducators.org

Description: Teachers of art at elementary, middle, secondary, and college levels; colleges, libraries, museums, and other educational institutions. Studies problems of teaching art; encourages research and experimentation. Serves as a clearinghouse for information on art education programs, materials, and methods of instruction. Sponsors special institutes. Cooperates with other national organiza-

tions for the furtherance of creative art experiences for youth.

1148 ■ National Coalition of Creative Arts Therapies Associations (NCCATA)
8455 Colesville Rd., Ste. 1000
Silver Spring, MD 20910
E-mail: mforinas@lesley.edu
URL: http://www.nccata.org

Description: Creative arts therapists. Promotes therapeutic and rehabilitative uses of the arts in medicine, mental health, special education, and forensic and social services; coordinates member associations' activities and efforts in meeting common objectives while supporting and advancing each group's discipline. Works to: represent members' interests in legislative activities; define joint positions on public policy issues; facilitate communication among members; initiate educational and research programs. Compiles statistics.

HANDBOOKS AND MANUALS

1149 ■ Administrative Topics in Athletic Training: Concepts to Practice

SLACK, Inc.
6900 Grove Rd.
Thorofare, NJ 08086
Ph: (856)848-1000
Fax: (856)848-6091
Fr: 800-257-8290
URL: http://www.slackbooks.com

Gary Harrelson, Greg Gardner, and Andrew P. Winterstein. 2009. $66.95 (hardcover). 320 pages. Addresses essential administrative issues and procedures as well as fundamental concepts, strategies, and techniques related to athletic training management.

1150 ■ Advances in Functional Training

On Target Publications
PO Box 1335
Aptos, CA 95001
Ph: (831)466-9182
Fax: (831)466-9183
URL: http://ontargetpublications.net

Dave Draper. 2010. $34.95 (paper). 315 pages. Presents modern and effective training strategies for coaches, personal trainers, and athletes. Discusses injury prevention, treatment, rehabilitation and training after injury.

1151 ■ AMAA Journal

American Medical Athletic Association
4405 East-West Hwy., Ste. 405
Bethesda, MD 20814
Ph: (301)913-9517
Fax: (301)913-9520
Fr: 800-776-2732
E-mail: amaa@americanrunning.org
URL: http://www.amaasportsmed.org

Three issues/year. Presents essential topics related to the medical aspects of sports, exercise, and fitness that assist physicians and other healthcare professionals in caring for active patients.

1152 ■ Athletic Footwer and Orthoses in Sports Medicine

Springer Science+Business Media LLC
233 Spring St.
New York, NY 10013
Ph: (212)460-1500
Fax: (212)460-1575
URL: http://www.springer.com

Matthew B. Werd and Leslie E. Knight. 2010. $29.95 (softcover). 400 pages. Guides sports medicine physicians, podiatrists, physical therapists, and athletic trainers in prescribing footwear to maximize performance and minimize injury in athletes.

1153 ■ Athletic Taping and Bracing

Human Kinetics
PO Box 5076
Champaign, IL 61825-5076
Fax: (217)351-1549
Fr: 800-747-4457
E-mail: info@hkusa.com
URL: http://www.humankinetics.com

David Perrin. 2012. $54.00 (paper). 152 pages. 3rd edition. Features step-by-step guide on the 46 most frequently used taping and bracing procedures by athletic trainers in clinical practice. Includes basic stretching and strengthening exercises for injury rehabilitation.

1154 ■ The Athletic Trainer's Pocket Guide to Clinical Teaching

SLACK, Inc.
6900 Grove Rd.
Thorofare, NJ 08086
Ph: (856)848-1000
Fax: (856)848-6091
Fr: 800-257-8290
URL: http://www.slackbooks.com

Thomas G. Weidner. 2009. $48.95 (softcover). 208 pages. Provides athletic training clinical instructors with practical information on effective clinical teaching.

1155 ■ Athletic Training Clinical Education Guide

Delmar Cengage Learning
PO Box 6904
Florence, KY 41022-6904
Fax: 800-487-8488
Fr: 800-354-9706
URL: http://www.cengage.com

Tim Laurent. 2010. $61.95 (spiralbound). Serves as activity and reference guide for all levels of athletic training students to maximize learning during clinical education.

1156 ■ Athletic Training Exam Review

Lippincott Williams & Wilkins
2 Commerce Sq.
2001 Market St.
Philadelphia, PA 19103
Ph: (215)521-8300
Fax: (215)521-8902
URL: http://www.lww.com

Barbara Long and Charles Hale. 2009. $51.50. 400 pages. Prepares applicants for the certification exam in athletic training. Includes figures and tables illustrating key concepts and at-a-glance summaries of key facts. Offers test-taking strategies and tips.

1157 ■ Athletic Training Exam Review: A Student Guide to Success

Slack, Inc.
6900 Grove Rd.
Thorofare, NJ 08086
Ph: (856)848-1000

Fax: (856)848-6091
Fr: 800-257-8290
URL: http://www.slackbooks.com

Lynn Van Ost, Karen Manfre and Karen Lew. 2009. $54.95 (softcover). 304 pages. Serves as a guide for athletic training students who are preparing to take the board of certification exam. Provides students with a solid foundation to assist in the studying process. Features new questions, additional sections, and more on-line testing components.

1158 ■ Athletic Training and Sports Medicine: An Integrated Approach

Jones & Bartlett Learning
5 Wall St.
Burlington, MA 01803
Fax: (978)443-8000
Fr: 800-832-0034
E-mail: info@jblearning.com
URL: http://www.jblearning.com

Chad Starkey. 2013. $161.95 (hardcover). 680 pages. 5th edition. Focuses on the post-injury management techniques used by athletic trainers and physicians in orthopaedic management and care.

1159 ■ Athletic Training Student Primer: A Foundation for Success

SLACK, Inc.
6900 Grove Rd.
Thorofare, NJ 08086
Ph: (856)848-1000
Fax: (856)848-6091
Fr: 800-257-8290
E-mail: pslack@slackinc.com
URL: http://www.slackbooks.com

Andrew P. Winterstein. 2009. $54.95 (softcover). 336 pages. Covers topics relevant to the study of athletic training. Prepares students for what they will learn, study, encounter and achieve during their educational and professional career.

1160 ■ Become a Certified Personal Trainer

McGraw-Hill Professional
PO Box 182604
Columbus, OH 43272
Fax: (609)308-4480
Fr: 800-262-4729
E-mail: customer.service@mcgraw-hill.com
URL: http://www.mhprofessional.com

Robert Wolff. 2009. $21.95 (paperback). 288 pages. Serves as a guide through the entire certification process. Provides sample questions and offers advice about the business side of the job.

1161 ■ BOC Exam Candidate Handbook

Board of Certification, Inc.
1415 Harney St., Ste. 200
Omaha, NE 68102
Ph: (402)559-0091
Fax: (402)561-0598

Fr: 877-262-3926
E-mail: staff@bocatc.org
URL: http://www.bocatc.org

2011. Contains information on eligibility requirements, application process, BOC certification, and ongoing responsibilities to maintain certification. Assists candidates for certification or recertification as athletic trainers.

1162 ■ Careers in Sport, Fitness, and Exercise

Human Kinetics
PO Box 5076
Champaign, IL 61825
Fax: (217)351-1549
Fr: 800-747-4457
E-mail: info@hkusa.com
URL: http://www.humankinetics.com

2011. $24.95 (paper). 184 pages. Includes detailed job descriptions, information on working conditions, salary ranges, responsibilities, key skills, and required certifications for 36 careers in sport and fitness.

1163 ■ Clinical Journal of Sport Medicine

Lippincott Williams & Wilkins
2001 Market St.
Philadelphia, PA 19103
Ph: (215)521-8300
Fax: (215)521-8902
URL: http://journals.lww.com/cjsportsmed

Bimonthly. $390.00/year (individuals); $729.00/year (institutions). Journal covering research and review articles on diagnostics, therapeutics, and rehabilitation of healthy and physically-challenged individuals engaged in all levels of sports and exercise activities.

1164 ■ Co-Active Coaching: Changing Business, Transforming Lives

Nicholas Brealey Publishing
20 Park Plz., Ste. 1115A
Boston, MA 02116
Ph: (617)523-3801
Fax: (617)523-3708
E-mail: info@nicholasbrealey.com
URL: http://nicholasbrealey.com

Henry Kimsey-House, Karen Kimsey-House and Phillip Sandahl. 2011. $39.95 (paperback). 3rd edition. Serves as resource in professional coaching. Provides tools and techniques for career success as professional coach. Contains online Coaches' Toolkit, new coaching demonstrations and updated exercises, questionaires, checklists and reproducible forms.

1165 ■ Coaching: A Problem Solving Approach

American Press
60 State St., No. 700
Boston, MA 02109
Ph: (617)247-0022
E-mail: americanpress@flash.net
URL: http://www.americanpresspublishers.com

William F. Stier, Jr. 2009. $43.95 (paperback). 440 pages. 2nd edition. Helps undergraduate students deal with preparation of athletic coaches. Includes problem solving strategies, tactics and techniques within a sport setting.

1166 ■ Coaching for Performance: Growing Human Potential and Purpose: The Principles and Practice of Coaching Leadership

Nicholas Brealey Publishing
20 Park Plz., Ste. 1115A
Boston, MA 02116
Ph: (617)523-3801
Fax: (617)523-3708
E-mail: info@nicholasbrealey.com
URL: http://nicholasbrealey.com

John Whitmore. 2009. $24.95 (paperback). 244 pages. 4th edition. Explains the principles of coaching and illustrates the examples of high performance from business and sport.

1167 ■ Concepts of Athletic Training

Jones & Bartlett Learning
5 Wall St.
Burlington, MA 01803
Fax: (978)443-8000
Fr: 800-832-0034
URL: http://www.jblearning.com

Ronald P. Pfeiffer and Brent C. Mangus. 2012. $104.95 (paperback). 376 pages. 6th edition. Focuses on care and management of sports and other activity-related injuries. Presents key concepts useful to individuals considering careers in athletic training, K-12 physical education, or coaching.

1168 ■ Core Assessment and Training

Human Kinetics
PO Box 5076
Champaign, IL 61825-5076
Fax: (217)351-1549
Fr: 800-747-4457
E-mail: info@hkusa.com
URL: http://www.humankinetics.com

2010. $42.00 (DVD and paper). 160 pages. Serves as reference for coaches, athletic and personal trainers, and physical therapists. Covers all aspects of core training, from basic to advanced core exercises, stretches, and pylometrics. Includes photos, illustrations and instructions for more than 120 exercises. Accompanying DVD features demontrations of proper exercise techniques and protocols for review. Helps professionals in the field assess clients' needs and design customized training programs.

1169 ■ Core Concepts in Athletic Training and Therapy with Web Resource

Human Kinetics
PO Box 5076
Champaign, IL 61825-5076
Fax: (217)351-1549
Fr: 800-747-4457
URL: http://www.humankinetics.com

Susan Kay Hillman. 2012. $94.00 (hardback). 640 pages. Covers breadth and theory and application of athletic training, including evidence-based practice, prevention, and health promotion. Contains case studies and general information on the athletic trainer profession, such as training, education, licensure, certification and employment opportunities.

1170 ■ Developing Clinical Proficiency in Athletic Training

Human Kinetics
PO Box 5076
Champaign, IL 61825-5076
Fax: (217)351-1549
Fr: 800-747-4457
E-mail: info@hkusa.com
URL: http://www.humankinetics.com

Kenneth Knight, Kirk Brumels. 2010. $48.00 (spiral-bound). 352 pages. Guides students and clinical instructors through the educational competencies required for entry-level athletic trainers.

1171 ■ Documentation for Athletic Training, Second Edition

SLACK Incorporated
6900 Grove Rd.
Thorofare, NJ 08086
Ph: (856)848-1000
Fax: (856)848-6091
Fr: 800-257-8290
URL: http://www.slackbooks.com

Jeff G. Konin, John M. Kaltenborn, and Margaret Frederick Thompson. 2011. $49.95. 320 pages (softcover). Presents the different types, methods, and benefits of written/electronic documentation, as well as e-health records, in athletic training. Includes professional advice, practice worksheets, evaluation, study questions, and medical abbreviation list.

1172 ■ Emergencies in Sports Medicine

Oxford University Press (USA)
198 Madison Ave.
New York, NY 10016

Ph: (212)726-6000
Fax: (919)677-1303
Fr: 800-445-9714
E-mail: custserv.us@oup.com
URL: http://www.oup.com/us/

Julian Redhead and Jonathan Gordon. 2012. $47.95 (flexicover). 288 pages. Covers every type of sporting emergency from head injuries to altitude sickness, and all aspects of sports medicine, including event planning and communication, to common sports-related emergency situations.

1173 ■ Emergency Care in Athletic Training

F.A. Davis Company
1915 Arch St.
Philadelphia, PA 19103
Ph: (215)568-2270
Fax: (215)568-5065
Fr: 800-523-4049
E-mail: info@fadavis.com
URL: http://www.fadavis.com

Keith M. Gorse, Francis Feld, Robert Blanc and Matthew Radelet. 2010. $59.95 (hardback). 352 pages. Prepares athletic trainers in providing emergency treatment for acute sports-related injuries and illnesses in children, adolescents, and adults on and off the field.

1174 ■ Emergency Response Management for Athletic Trainers

Lippincott Williams & Wilkins
2001 Market St.
Philadelphia, PA 19103
Ph: (215)521-8300
Fax: (215)521-8902
URL: http://www.lww.com

Michael Miller and David Berry. 2010. $78.50 (softbound). 656 pages. Teaches how to quickly and effectively assess and manage the broad range of medical emergencies that athletes may experience. Contains theoretical and practical guidance helping readers perform essential emergency response management techniques.

1175 ■ Encyclopedia of Sports Medicine

SAGE Publications, Inc.
2455 Teller Rd.
Thousand Oaks, CA 91320
Ph: (805)499-0721
Fax: 800-583-2665
Fr: 800-818-7243
E-mail: info@sagepub.com
URL: http://www.sagepub.com

Lyle J. Micheli. 2011. $1,045.00. 1880 pages (hardcover). Provides relevant information in the field of sports medicine. Includes contributions from preeminent healthcare professionals, tables and images, illustrations of diagnostic and treatment techniques, and details on the various career opportunities in the profession.

1176 ■ Every Trainer's Handbook

SAGE Publications
2455 Teller Rd.
Thousand Oaks, CA 91320
Fax: 800-583-2665
Fr: 800-818-7243
E-mail: journals@sagepub.com
URL: http://www.sagepub.com

Devendra Agochiya. 2009. $34.95 (paperback). 440 pages. Serves as a guide that takes the reader through a step-by-step process of planning, organizing and delivering an effective training program. Offers suggestions and guidelines to trainers for enhancing knowledge and competencies while engaging into a substantive discussion on various concepts, theories and issues related to training.

1177 ■ Fitness Professional's Guide to Strength Training Older Adults

Human Kinetics
PO Box 5076
Champaign, IL 61825-5076
Fax: (217)351-1549

Fr: 800-747-4457
E-mail: info@hkusa.com
URL: http://www.humankinetics.com

Thomas R. Baechle and Wayne Westcott. 2010. $34.00 (paper). 344 pages. 2nd edition. Contains information and tools to educate, motivate and assist older adults in committing to and benefiting from individualized strength training programs. Includes updated information on: sport conditioning programs; program design and performance for special populations; and specific nutrition guidelines.

1178 ■ Functional Testing in Human Performance

Human Kinetics
PO Box 5076
Champaign, IL 61825-5076
Fax: (217)351-1549
Fr: 800-747-4457
E-mail: info@hkusa.com
URL: http://www.humankinetics.com

Michael Reiman and Robert Manske. 2009. $79.00 (DVD and cloth). 328 pages. Serves as resource for the accurate assessment of an individual's functional abilities. Offers clinicians the compilation of information on clinical and data-based functional testing for sport, exercise and occupational settings. Accompanying DVD features live-action demonstrations of 40 of the most advanced tests.

1179 ■ Fundamentals of Athletic Training

Human Kinetics
PO Box 5076
Champaign, IL 61825-5076
Fax: (217)351-1549
Fr: 800-747-4457
E-mail: info@hkusa.com
URL: http://www.humankinetics.com

Lorin A. Cartwright and William A. Pitney. 2011. $69.00 (hardback). 408 pages. Explains the foundational concepts in athletic training. Includes latest developments in athletic training with regard to treatment, care, administration and certification.

1180 ■ Innovative Communication in College Athletics

Human Kinetics
PO Box 5076
Champaign, IL 61825-5076
Fax: (217)351-1549
Fr: 800-747-4457
E-mail: info@hkusa.com
URL: http://www.humankinetics.com

International Journal of Sport Communication. 2012. $25.00 (paper). Covers various sport communication topics that bring a unique perspective to innovative communication issues prevalent in college athletics.

1181 ■ Introduction to Sports Medicine and Athletic Training

Delmar Cengage Learning
PO Box 6904
Florence, KY 41022-6904
Fax: 800-487-8488
Fr: 800-354-9706
URL: http://www.cengage.com

Robert C. France. 2011. $143.95 (hardcover). 720 pages. 2nd edition. Covers sports medicine, athletic training, including anatomy and physiology. Offers discussion and insight on a wide range of careers related to sports medicine.

1182 ■ Leadership and Management in Athletic Training: An Integrated Approach

Lippincott Williams & Wilkins
2 Commerce Sq.
2001 Market St.
Philadelphia, PA 19103
Ph: (215)521-8300
Fax: (215)521-8902
URL: http://www.lww.com

Matthew R. Kutz. 2009. $70.00 (softbound). 352 pages. Helps athletic trainers integrate the art of leadership with the science of management. Covers leadership, management theories and techniques, communication, and conflict resolution; supplies tools for mastering essential skills and behaviors. Explores legal and risk management issues, professional ethics, and globalization as it relates to athletic training.

1183 ■ Management Strategies in Athletic Training

Human Kinetics
PO Box 5076
Champaign, IL 61825-5076
Fax: (217)351-1549
Fr: 800-747-4457
E-mail: info@hkusa.com
URL: http://www.humankinetics.com

Richard Ray and Jeff Konin. 2011. $74.00 (hardback). 360 pages. Helps future and current athletic trainers deal creatively with management challenges on the job. Includes extensive updates and new information emphasizing the practice of evidence-based medicine, with sections on cultural awareness, healthcare financial management and injury surveillance systems.

1184 ■ Managing Intercollegiate Athletics

Holcomb Hathaway Publishers, Inc.
8700 E Via de Ventura Blvd., Ste. 265
Scottsdale, AZ 85258
Ph: (480)991-7881
Fax: (480)991-4770
E-mail: info@hh-pub.com
URL: http://www.hh-pub.com

Daniel Covell and Carol A. Barr. 2010. $47.00 (paperbound). 400 pages. Provides an overview of the management process in athletic departments and explores the conferences and governing organizations that impact them. Contains examples, case studies and theoretical concepts to prepare individuals pursuing a career in collegiate athletics management.

1185 ■ Netter's Sports Medicine

Saunders
c/o Elsevier
1600 John F. Kennedy Blvd., Ste. 1800
Philadelphia, PA 19103-2899
Ph: (215)239-3900
Fax: (215)239-3990
Fr: 800-523-1649
URL: http://www.us.elsevierhealth.com

Christopher Madden, Margot Putukian, Eric McCarty, and Craig Young. 2010. $99.95 (hardcover). 800 pages. Serves as tool for professionals in sports medicine. Covers physical examination techniques and imaging examples, as well as specific types of injuries, and different types of sports. Includes topics on musculoskeletal injuries, sports nutrition, and sports psychology.

1186 ■ NSCA-CPT Practice Exam

Human Kinetics
PO Box 5076
Champaign, IL 61825-5076
Fax: (217)351-1549
Fr: 800-747-4457
E-mail: info@hkusa.com
URL: http://www.humankinetics.com

National Strength and Conditioning Association. 2011. $40.00 (DVD and book). Helps applicants prepare for the NSCA-Certified Personal Trainer examination. Covers the nature and scope of the NSCA-CPT, plus the level of difficulty of typical exam questions. Includes exam booklet and DVD.

1187 ■ NSCA's Essentials of Personal Training

Human Kinetics
PO Box 5076
Champaign, IL 61825-5076
Fax: (217)351-1549
Fr: 800-747-4457
E-mail: info@hkusa.com
URL: http://www.humankinetics.com

National Strength and Conditioning Association. 2012. $295.00. Serves as a tool for personal trainers, health and fitness instructors, and other fitness professionals in taking the NSCA-CPT exam.

1188 ■ NSCA's Guide to Program Design

Human Kinetics
PO Box 5076
Champaign, IL 61825-5076
Fax: (217)351-1549
Fr: 800-747-4457
E-mail: info@hkusa.com
URL: http://www.humankinetics.com

National Strength and Conditioning Association. 2012. $44.00 (hardback). 336 pages. Offers strength and conditioning professionals a scientific basis for developing training programs for specific athletes.

1189 ■ Orthopedic and Athletic Injury Examination Handbook

F.A. Davis Co.
1915 Arch St.
Philadelphia, PA 19103
Ph: (215)568-2270
Fax: (215)569-5065
Fr: 800-523-4049
URL: http://www.fadavis.com

Chad Starkey and Sara D. Brown. 2010. $44.95 (paperback). 614 pages. 2nd edition. Contains step-by-step guide for evaluating specific orthopedic and athletic injuries. Covers procedures of over 185 special, neurological, ligamentous, and range of motion tests; aids for identifying postural disorders; and proper measuring techniques. Serves as a preparation tool for the BOC examination.

1190 ■ Pocket Orthopaedics: Evidence-Based Survival Guide

Jones & Bartlett Learning
5 Wall St.
Burlington, MA 01803
Fax: (978)443-8000
Fr: 800-832-0034
E-mail: info@jblearning.com
URL: http://www.jblearning.com

Michael S. Wong. 2011. $41.95 (spiral/paperback). 412 pages. Serves as learning aide in evidence-based practice for both students and clinicians.

1191 ■ Practical Guide to Athletic Training

Jones and Bartlett Learning
5 Wall St.
Burlington, MA 01803
Fr: 800-832-0034
E-mail: info@jblearning.com
URL: http://www.jblearning.com

Ted Eaves. 2010. $86.95 (paper). 256 pages. Provides an essential guide for students interested in the fields of sports medicine and athletic training. Contains information on how to enter the workforce and succeed as an athletic professional.

1192 ■ Praeger Handbook of Sports Medicine and Athlete Health

ABC-CLIO
PO Box 1911
Santa Barbara, CA 93116-1911
Fax: (866)270-3856
Fr: 800-368-6868
E-mail: customerservice@abc-clio.com
URL: http://www.abc-clio.com

Claude T. Moorman, Donald T. Kirkendall, and Ruben J. Echemendia. 2010. $154.95 (hardcover). 915 pages (3 volumes). Covers all aspects of sports medicine and the career paths available in the field. Includes topics on specific injury and anatomical locations, and treatment. Also includes glossary of sports medicine terms and abbreviations.

1193 ■ Principles of Pharmacology for Athletic Trainers

SLACK, Inc.
6900 Grove Rd.
Thorofare, NJ 08086-9447

Ph: (856)848-1000
Fax: (856)848-6091
Fr: 800-257-8290
E-mail: pslack@slackinc.com
URL: http://www.slackbooks.com/atpharm

Joel E. Houglum and Gary Harrelson. 2011. $42.95 (softcover). 480 pages. Provides information on determining the pharmacological treatment strategy and management by athletic trainers.

1194 ■ Rehabilitation Techniques in Sports Medicine
McGraw-Hill Higher Education
1221 Avenue of the Americas
New York, NY 10020-1095
Ph: (212)904-2000
URL: http://catalogs.mhhe.com

William E. Prentice. 2011. $172.67 (hardcover). 720 pages. Guides athletic trainers and sports therapists in managing sports injuries and rehabilitating programs for injured athletes.

1195 ■ Sports Medicine: Study Guide and Review for Boards
Demos Medical Publishing
11 W 42nd St., 15th Fl.
New York, NY 10036
Ph: (212)683-0072
Fr: 800-532-8663
E-mail: info@demosmedpub.com
URL: http://www.demosmedpub.com

Mark Harrast and Jonathan Finnoff. 2011. $90.00. 552 pages. Covers topics pertinent to the Sports Medicine Board Exam. Serves as study tool for applicants preparing for certification in sports medicine. Includes discussion on basic science and general procedures; health promotion; emergency assessment and care; and diagnosis, management and treatment of sports-related injuries and conditions.

1196 ■ Study Guide for the Board of Certification, Inc., Entry-Level Athletic Trainer Certification Examination
F.A. Davis Company
1915 Arch St.
Philadelphia, PA 19103
Ph: (215)568-2270
Fax: (215)568-5065
Fr: 800-523-4049
E-mail: info@fadavis.com
URL: http://www.fadavis.com

Susan L. Rozzi, Michelle G. Futrell and Douglas M. Kleiner. 2011. $54.95 (paper). 256 pages. Includes exam overview, study tips and test-taking techniques needed to pass the athletic trainer certification exam.

1197 ■ Tarascon Sports Medicine Pocketbook
Tarascon Publishing
c/o Jones & Bartlett Learning
5 Wall St.
Burlington, MA 01803
Fax: (978)443-8000
Fr: 800-832-0034
E-mail: info@tarascon.com
URL: http://www.tarascon.com

Brent S.E. Rich and Mitchell K. Pratte. 2010. $20.95 (paperback). 176 pages. Covers up-to-date information on sports medicine relevant to non-surgical primary care physicians, athletic trainers, and physical therapists in providing primary care medical treatment for the active individual.

1198 ■ Therapeutic Modalities: For Sports Medicine and Training
McGraw-Hill Higher Education
1221 Avenue of the Americas
New York, NY 10020-1095
Ph: (212)904-2000
URL: http://catalogs.mhhe.com

William E. Prentice. 2009. $176.67 (hardcover). 448 pages. 6th edition. Applies for athletic trainers and physical therapists involved in a sports medicine curriculum.

ONLINE JOB SOURCES AND SERVICES

1199 ■ AT Placement
URL: http://www.atplacement.com

Description: Serves as a platform for athletic trainers where they can post resumes, search job boards and contact potential employers. Maintains up-to-date information on placement notices pertinent to the athletic training profession.

1200 ■ AT4HIRE.com
URL: http://www.at4hire.com

Description: Aims to help certified athletic trainers find the most comprehensive database of sport camps, events, full-time and part-time jobs.

1201 ■ Athletic Administration Jobs
URL: http://www.athleticadministrationjobs.com

Description: Serves as a job board for athletic administration professionals. Offers updated job listings for candidates and job posting for employers.

1202 ■ Athletic Jobs
URL: http://www.athleticjobs.org

Description: Serves as niche job board that provides listings on athletic jobs.

1203 ■ Athletic Trainer Jobs
URL: http://www.athletictrainerjobs.org

Description: Features a searchable database of employment opportunities for athletic trainers.

1204 ■ Athletic Training Jobs
URL: http://www.athletictrainingjobs.org

Description: Serves as a niche job board that focuses on athletic training employment opportunities and candidate recruiting. Features athletic training positions posted by top employers in the industry.

1205 ■ Athletictrainer4hire.com
URL: http://www.athletictrainer4hire.com

Description: Serves as a resource for athletic trainers and event coordinators to communicate and match their respective needs.

1206 ■ athletictrainerjobs.us
URL: http://www.athletictrainerjobs.us

Description: Serves as a niche job board that focuses on athletic trainer employment opportunities and candidate recruiting. Assists employers and recruiters by matching qualified candidates with open athletic trainer positions.

1207 ■ Coachjobs.us
URL: http://www.coachjobs.us

Description: Serves as a job board that focuses on coach employment opportunities and candidate recruiting.

1208 ■ Get Athletic Trainer Jobs
URL: http://www.getathletictrainerjobs.com

Description: Serves as an informational resource for athletic trainer job seekers and employers. Offers free athletic trainer job postings and career opportunities.

1209 ■ iHireSportsandRecreation.com
URL: http://www.ihiresportsandrecreation.com

Description: Features sports and recreation jobs from job postings, internet job boards, newspapers and classified ads.

1210 ■ Sports Trainer Jobs
URL: http://www.sportstrainerjobs.com

Description: Serves as a niche job board that features job posting functionality for employers, recruiters and hiring managers as well as job search options for employment candidates in the field of athletic training.

1211 ■ SportsMedicineJobs.org
URL: http://sportsmedicinejobs.org

Description: Provides job search engine that finds job listings from company career pages, other job boards, newspapers and associations.

1212 ■ TrainerJobs.org
URL: http://trainerjobs.org

Description: Features search job boards, company career pages and associations for athletic trainer jobs.

1213 ■ trainerjobs.us
URL: http://www.trainerjobs.us

Description: Serves as a niche job board that focuses on trainer employment opportunities and candidate recruiting. Assists employers and recruiters by matching qualified candidates with open trainer positions.

OTHER SOURCES

1214 ■ American Medical Athletic Association
4405 East-West Hwy., Ste. 405
Bethesda, MD 20814
Ph: (301)913-9517
Fax: (301)913-9520
Fr: 800-776-2732
E-mail: amaa@americanrunning.org
URL: http://www.amaasportsmed.org

Description: Provides information on training, diet, injury prevention, and sports medicine to physicians and other healthcare professionals as leaders of active and healthy lifestyles. Hosts a sports medicine professional referral service made up of doctors, nutritionists, and other sports-oriented professionals.

1215 ■ American Medical Society for Sports Medicine
4000 W 114th St., Ste. 100
Leawood, KS 66211
Ph: (913)327-1415
Fax: (913)327-1491
URL: http://www.amssm.org

Description: Aims to advance the discipline of sports medicine through education, research, advocacy and excellence in patient care. Promotes collegial relationship among sports medicine specialists. Includes an electronic recruitment resource for the sports medicine industry.

1216 ■ Athletic Trainer System
Keffer Development Systems
24 Village Park Dr.
Grove City, PA 16127
Ph: (724)458-5289
Fax: (724)458-0621
URL: http://www.athletictrainersystem.com

Description: Serves as a flexible and customizable software designed to assist athletic trainers in tracking and reporting information relating to athletes, students or employees.

1217 ■ College Athletic Trainer's Society
PO Box 250325
Atlanta, GA 30325
E-mail: jlee@collegeathletictrainer.org
URL: http://www.collegeathletictrainer.org

Description: Consists of athletic trainers, team physicians and allied health care professionals who are interested in supporting the college and university athletic trainer. Provides high quality care to student-athletes and promotes intercollegiate athletics. Addresses the needs and concerns of full-time head and assistant athletic trainers at colleges and universities.

1218 ■ Mental Health Challenges in the Athletic Training Room: A Team Physician's Perspective
American College of Sports Medicine
401 W Michigan St.
Indianapolis, IN 46202-3233
Ph: (317)637-9200
Fax: (317)634-7817
URL: http://www.acsmstore.org
Description: DVD. Focuses on the role of physicians as primary care providers in the field of athletic training. Provides basic overview of the clinical features, diagnostic criteria, and screening tools appropriate for mental health conditions diagnosed in primary care sports medicine clinics.

1219 ■ National Collegiate Athletic Association
PO Box 6222
Indianapolis, IN 46206
Ph: (317)917-6222
Fax: (317)917-6888
URL: http://www.ncaa.org
Description: Consists of universities, colleges, and allied educational athletics associations devoted to the administration of intercollegiate athletics. Aims to govern competition in a fair, safe, equitable and sportsmanlike manner and integrate intercollegiate athletics into higher education.

Auctioneers

SOURCES OF HELP-WANTED ADS

1220 ▪ *The Auctioneer*
National Auctioneers Association
8880 Ballentine St.
Overland Park, KS 66214
Ph: (913)541-8084
Fax: (913)894-5281
URL: http://www.auctioneers.org/advertise
Trade magazine for auctioneers.

PLACEMENT AND JOB REFERRAL SERVICES

1221 ▪ Florida Auctioneer Academy
5029 Edgewater Dr.
Orlando, FL 32810
Ph: (321)229-0722
Fr: 800-422-9155
E-mail: info@f-a-a.com
URL: http://www.f-a-a.com
Purpose: School for the training of auctioneers. **Activities:** Provides students information on career opportunities and licensing, as well as acting as a job placement service upon graduation.

EMPLOYER DIRECTORIES AND NETWORKING LISTS

1222 ▪ *Antique Week*
Mayhill Publications
27 N Jefferson St.
PO Box 90
Knightstown, IN 46148
Ph: (765)345-5133
Fax: (765)345-3398
Fr: 800-876-5133
URL: http://www.antiqueweek.com
Weekly. $41.00 for individuals. Covers: In each issue, 100-150 antiques auctions and antique shows, occurring during the week or two after publication. Each issue also contains separate calendar of about 200-300 antique shows, flea markets, and auctions occurring during the months after publication; separate Central edition (Illinois, Indiana, Iowa, Kentucky, Michigan, Minnesota, Missouri, Ohio, western Pennsylvania, Tennessee, and Wisconsin), and Eastern edition (Connecticut, Delaware, District of Columbia, Maryland, New Jersey, New York, North Carolina, Pennsylvania, Rhode Island, South Carolina, Virginia, and West Virginia). Entries include: Name of event, location, type of event, dates, name of show manager or auctioneer. Arrangement: Geographical.

1223 ▪ *Auctioneer—Directory Issue*
National Auctioneers Association
8880 Ballentine St.
Overland Park, KS 66214

Ph: (913)541-8084
Fax: (913)894-5281
URL: http://www.auctioneers.org
Annual, February. Publication includes: List of about 6,000 auctioneers. Entries include: Name, address, phone, fax, e-mail, website, specialization. Arrangement: Geographical and alphabetical.

1224 ▪ *Directory of Licensed Auctioneers, Apprentice Auctioneers, and Auction Firms Engaged in the Auction Profession*
South Carolina Department of LLR-Auctioneers Commission
Synergy Business Pk., Kingstree Bldg.
110 Centerview Dr.
PO Box 11329
Columbia, SC 29210
Ph: (803)896-4300
Fax: (803)896-4393
URL: http://www.llr.state.sc.us
Annual, December. Free. Covers: Approximately 1,500 auctioneers, apprentices, and firms licensed in South Carolina, including resident and non-resident licensees. Entries include: Company or personal name, address, phone, and license number. Arrangement: Geographical. Indexes: Alphabetical.

1225 ▪ *National Auto Auction Association—Membership Directory*
National Auto Auction Association
5320 Spectrum Dr., Ste. D
Frederick, MD 21703
Ph: (301)696-0400
Fax: (301)631-1359
URL: http://www.naaa.com
Annual, Latest edition 2011. $15.00 for members; $35.00 for nonmembers. Covers: 25,446 automobile auction firms. Entries include: Company name, address, names and phone numbers of auction personnel; pick up, delivery, and reconditioning services available. Arrangement: Geographical.

HANDBOOKS AND MANUALS

1226 ▪ *Auctioneer Exam Secrets Study Guide*
Mometrix Media, LLC
3827 Phelan Blvd., No. 179
Beaumont, TX 77707
Fr: 800-673-8175
E-mail: css@mometrix.com
URL: http://www.mo-media.com
2011. $39.99. Helps test takers ace the Auctioneer exam. Includes specific content areas, study tips and essential skills needed for the exam.

ONLINE JOB SOURCES AND SERVICES

1227 ▪ AuctioneerJobs.com
URL: http://auctioneerjobs.com/a/jobs/find-jobs

Description: Features a searchable database of job listings for auctioneers.

1228 ▪ National Auction List
URL: http://www.nationalauctionlist.com
Description: Provides a list of professional auctioneers, a list of upcoming auctions, and current auction news.

OTHER SOURCES

1229 ▪ AuctionServices.com
PO Box 20038
Roanoke, VA 24018
Ph: (540)206-3311
Fax: 877-644-4571
E-mail: inquiries@auctionservices.com
URL: http://auctionservices.com
Purpose: Develops and creates websites for professional auctioneers. Provides secure hosting for individual websites. **Activities:** Offers the auction industry websites to promote professionalism and connect with other auctioneers worldwide.

1230 ▪ California State Auctioneers Association
520 N 2nd Ave.
Upland, CA 91786
E-mail: info@caauctioneers.org
URL: http://caauctioneers.org
Members: Professional auctioneers. **Purpose:** Promotes professionalism, growth, and competency in the auction profession. **Activities:** Develops ethical standards in the industry, provides members with learning opportunities, reviews and develops information on technology changes in the industry, and provides opportunities to network and exchange ideas with professionals in the industry.

1231 ▪ Industrial Auctioneers Association (IAA)
3213 Ayr Ln.
Dresher, PA 19025
Ph: (215)366-5450
Fax: (215)657-1964
Fr: 800-805-8359
E-mail: info@industrialauctioneers.org
URL: http://www.industrialauctioneers.org
Description: Represents industrial machinery and equipment auctioneers. Promotes the use of auction sales in idle industrial equipment. Maintains ethical and professional standards among member auctioneers.

1232 ▪ Kentucky Auctioneers Association
3200 Goose Creek Rd.
Louisville, KY 40241
Ph: (502)595-8955
E-mail: kaamember@insightbb.com
URL: http://www.kentuckyauctioneers.org

Members: Professional auctioneers. **Purpose:** Promotes and advances the profession and fosters and encourages cooperation and mutual aid among those engaged in the auction profession. **Activities:** Acts as a networking forum for its members, provides information for writing contracts, and publishes a membership directory and quarterly magazine.

1233 ■ Michigan State Auctioneers Association

4529 Gibbs, NW
Grand Rapids, MI 49544
Ph: (616)785-8288
Fax: (616)447-3761
E-mail: info@msaa.org
URL: http://www.msaa.org

Members: Professional auctioneers. **Purpose:** Represents the interests of auctioneers and provides a forum for networking and sharing ideas and experiences. **Activities:** Sponsors educational courses and seminars, publishes an annual directory, and provides networking opportunities with other auctioneers.

1234 ■ National Association of Public Auto Auctions (NAPAA)

PO Box 41368
Raleigh, NC 27629
Ph: (919)876-0687
E-mail: elaine@execman.net
URL: http://www.publicautoauctionassoc.org

Description: Aims to uphold the standards of practices within the automotive auction industry. Strives to protect the general public, dealers, and fleet accounts from unscrupulous practices. Fosters honesty and integrity in all dealings.

1235 ■ National Auctioneers Association (NAA)

8880 Ballentine St.
Overland Park, KS 66214
Ph: (913)541-8084
Fax: (913)894-5281
E-mail: support@auctioneers.org
URL: http://www.auctioneers.org

Description: Professional auctioneers. Provides continuing education classes for auctioneers, promotes use of the auction method of marketing in both the private and public sectors. Encourages the highest ethical standards for the profession.

1236 ■ Virginia Auctioneers Association

PO Box 41368
Raleigh, NC 27629
Ph: (919)878-0601
Fax: (919)878-7413
Fr: 888-878-0601
E-mail: vaauctioneers@vaa.org
URL: http://vaa.org

Members: Professional auctioneers. **Activities:** Provides a membership directory and networking opportunities with other auctioneers.

1237 ■ World Wide College of Auctioneering

PO Box 949
Mason City, IA 50402-0949
Ph: (641)423-5242
Fax: (641)423-3067
Fr: 800-423-5242
E-mail: wwca@netconx.net
URL: http://worldwidecollegeofauctioneering.com

Purpose: Provides instruction and training in professional auctioneering. **Activities:** Offers advice on setting up an auctioneering business upon completion of the course.

SOURCES OF HELP-WANTED ADS

1238 ■ Automotive Fleet
Bobit Business Media
3520 Challenger St.
Torrance, CA 90503
Ph: (310)533-2400
URL: http://www.automotive-fleet.com/

Monthly. Free. Automotive magazine covering the car and light truck fleet market.

1239 ■ Automotive News
Crain Communications Inc. (Detroit, Michigan)
1155 Gratiot Ave.
Detroit, MI 48207-2997
Ph: (313)446-6000
Fax: (313)567-7681
URL: http://www.autonews.com

Weekly. $159.00/year for individuals, print and digital online; $99.00/year for individuals, digital/online; $199.00/year for individuals, data center only; $24.95/year for individuals, 1 month, website access only; $14.95/year for individuals, 1 week, website access only. Tabloid reporting on all facets of the automotive and truck industry, as well as related businesses.

1240 ■ Blue Seal Tech News
National Institute for Automotive Service Excellence
101 Blue Seal Dr. SE, No. 101
Leesburg, VA 20175
Ph: (703)669-6600
Fax: (703)669-6123
Fr: 888-273-8378
URL: http://www.asecert.org

Description: Quarterly. Covers news of the Institute's efforts to certify auto, medium/heavy truck, engine machinists, collision repair technicians, and parts specialists. Discusses industry trends, vehicle repair tips, and training information, and highlights activities of ASE-certified technicians.

1241 ■ BodyShop Business
Babcox
3550 Embassy Pky.
Akron, OH 44333
Ph: (330)670-1234
URL: http://www.bodyshopbusiness.com

Monthly. Free to qualified subscribers. Magazine providing management and technical information that can be applied to running an efficient and profitable collision repair shop.

1242 ■ Bus Ride
Power Trade Media L.L.C.
4742 N 24th St., Ste. 340
Phoenix, AZ 85016
Ph: (602)265-7600
Fax: (602)227-7588
Fr: 800-541-2670
URL: http://busride.com

Monthly. $39.00/year for individuals; $64.00/year for individuals; $42.00/year for Canada; $69.00/year for two years, Canada; $98.00/year for Canada, 3 years; $75.00/year for other countries; $125.00/year for two years, other countries; $175.00/year for two years, 3 years. Magazine for managers of bus, motorcoach and transit operations.

1243 ■ Cooling Journal
NARSA
300 Village Run Rd., Ste. 103, No. 221
Wexford, PA 15090-6315
Ph: (724)799-8415
Fax: (724)799-8416
E-mail: acj@narsa.org
URL: http://narsa.org/publication/cooling-journal/

Monthly. $65.00/year for individuals; $130.00/year for other countries; $97.00/year for Canada. Automotive trade magazine.

1244 ■ Engine Builder
Babcox
3550 Embassy Pky.
Akron, OH 44333
Ph: (330)670-1234
URL: http://www.engine-builder.com

Monthly. Free to qualified subscribers. Magazine covering management topics, technical information, and new product news for owners and managers of leading volume rebuilding businesses.

1245 ■ GEARS Magazine
Automatic Transmission Rebuilders Association
2400 Latigo Ave.
Oxnard, CA 93030
Ph: (805)604-2000
Fax: (805)604-2003
Fr: (866)664-2872
URL: http://www.atra.com

Description: Monthly. Contains news of the Association, its chapters, and Association programs. Lists service contract and insurance information, job listings, and personnel changes in the Association. Recurring features include news of research, notices of publications available, reports of meetings, news of educational opportunities, and a calendar of events.

1246 ■ Import Automotive Parts & Accessories
Meyers Publishing
799 Camarillo Springs Rd.
Camarillo, CA 93012-8111
Ph: (805)445-8881
Fax: (805)445-8882
URL: http://www.meyerspublishing.com/
    IAPA%20Home%20Page_6.h

Monthly. $75.00/year for Canada and Mexico; $105.00/year for other countries; $55.00/year for individuals; $10.00/year for single issue; $25.00/year for individuals, import industry sourcebook; $35.00/year for individuals, import industry sourcebook

outside the U.S.; $20.00/year for single issue, outside the U.S. Trade magazine for the automotive aftermarket.

1247 ■ ImportCar
Babcox
3550 Embassy Pky.
Akron, OH 44333
Ph: (330)670-1234
URL: http://www.import-car.com

Monthly. Free. Magazine focusing on import specialist repair shops that derive more than 50% of revenue from servicing import nameplates.

1248 ■ The Motion Systems Distributor
Penton Media Inc.
249 W 17th St.
New York, NY 10011
Ph: (212)204-4200
URL: http://www.penton.com/

Bimonthly. Completely separate from PT Design, this bi-monthly publication is tailored to the informational needs of the motion systems distributor. Published six times, this sales and management magazine goes to sales and branch management personnel, owners/operators of distributor companies in the U.S. and their technical personnel, and selected suppliers.

1249 ■ Motor Age
Adams Business Media
833 W Jackson, 7th Fl.
Chicago, IL 60607
Ph: (312)846-4600
Fax: (312)977-1042
URL: http://www.motorage.com

Monthly. $49.00/year for individuals; $75.00/year for two years; $90.00/year for other countries. Magazine for auto repair shops.

1250 ■ Popular Mechanics
Hearst Magazines
300 W 57th St.
New York, NY 10019-3741
Ph: (212)649-4115
URL: http://www.popularmechanics.com/

Monthly. $12.00/year for individuals; $20.00/year for two years. Magazine focusing on autos, the home, and leisure. Prints Latin American Edition.

1251 ■ Transmission Digest
MD Publications Inc.
3057 E Cairo St.
PO Box 2210
Springfield, MO 65802
Ph: (417)866-3917
Fax: (417)866-2781
Fr: 800-274-7890
URL: http://www.transmissiondigest.com/

Monthly. Automotive transmission industry news.

1252 ■ *Undercar Digest*
MD Publications Inc.
3057 E Cairo St.
PO Box 2210
Springfield, MO 65802
Ph: (417)866-3917
Fax: (417)866-2781
Fr: 800-274-7890
URL: http://www.undercardigest.com/

Monthly. $49.00/year for individuals. Magazine for the undercar service and supply industry.

1253 ■ *Underhood Service*
Babcox
3550 Embassy Pky.
Akron, OH 44333
Ph: (330)670-1234
URL: http://www.underhoodservice.com

Monthly. Magazine covering service and repair shops doing 50% or more of service underhood.

1254 ■ *World Journal of Mechanics*
Scientific Research Publishing
PO Box 54821
Irvine, CA 92619-4821
E-mail: wjm@scirp.org
URL: http://www.scirp.org/journal/wjm/

Quarterly. $156.00/year for individuals. Peer-reviewed journal publishing articles in the general field of mechanics.

EMPLOYER DIRECTORIES AND NETWORKING LISTS

1255 ■ *Career Opportunities in the Automotive Industry*
Facts On File Inc.
132 W 31st St., 17th Fl.
New York, NY 10001
Ph: (212)967-8800
Fax: 800-678-3633
Fr: 800-322-8755
URL: http://factsonfile.infobasepublishing.com

Published 2005. $49.50 for individuals. Covers: 70 jobs from pit crew mechanic to restoration expert, from mechanical engineer to parts distribution director, from RV specialist to exotic car museum director.

HANDBOOKS AND MANUALS

1256 ■ *Careers in Focus: Automotives*
Ferguson Publishing
132 W 31st St., 17th Fl.
New York, NY 10001
Fr: 800-322-8755
E-mail: custserv@factsonfile.com
URL: http://factsonfile.infobasepublishing.com

2009. $32.95. 192 pages. Covers an overview in automotive industry, followed by a selection of jobs profiled in detail, including the nature of the job, earnings, prospects for employment, what kind of training and skills it requires and sources for further information.

1257 ■ *Denman's Handbook for Auto Mechanics and Technicians*
Xlibris Corporation
1663 Liberty Dr., Ste. 200
Bloomington, IN 47403
Fax: (610)915-0294
Fr: 888-795-4274
URL: http://info@xlibris.com

Ernest Denman. 2011. $24.99 (casebound hardcover). 63 pages. Serves as a quick-reference aid for technicians specializing in auto mechanics, heavy equipment, hydraulics or welding.

ONLINE JOB SOURCES AND SERVICES

1258 ■ AutoJobs.com
E-mail: sales@autojobs.com
URL: http://www.autojobs.com

Description: Provides job lists and career opportunities for the automotive industry including dealerships, manufacturers, automotive aftermarket companies, and independent service and body shops.

1259 ■ AutomotiveCrossing.com
URL: http://www.automotivecrossing.com

Description: Offers a comprehensive collection of researched job openings in the automotive field. Includes free job postings, free job searching, free resuming posting, free resume searching, and job management tools.

1260 ■ AutoPersonnel.com
URL: http://www.autopersonnel.com

Description: Specializes in automotive staffing covering sales, office management, accounting, technicians and other positions.

1261 ■ Diesel Mechanic Jobs
URL: http://www.dieselmechanicjobs.com

Description: Features job opportunities for diesel mechanics.

1262 ■ FindAMechanic.com
URL: http://www.findamechanic.com

Description: Connects employers with mechanics and technicians. Focuses on auto, truck, diesel, equipment and/or marine mechanics and other positions in the industry.

1263 ■ iHireAutomotiveProfessionals
URL: http://www.ihireautomotiveprofessionals.com

Description: Provides job listings for automotive professionals.

1264 ■ NeedTechs.com
E-mail: info@needtechs.com
URL: http://www.needtechs.com

Description: Provides resources for automotive employment and technician jobs. Matches employers who need auto techs with employees who need auto tech jobs.

TRADESHOWS

1265 ■ AERA Expo
Engine Rebuilders Association AERA
500 Coventry Ln.
Crystal Lake, IL 60014-7592
Ph: (815)526-7600
Fax: (815)526-7601
Fr: 888-326-2372
URL: http://www.aera.org

Annual. Primary Exhibits: Automotive services equipment, parts, tools, supplies, and services.

1266 ■ International Autobody Congress and Exposition - NACE
Nielsen Business Media
770 Broadway
New York, NY 10003-9595
Ph: (646)654-4500
E-mail: bmcomm@nielsen.com
URL: http://www.nielsenbusinessmedia.com/

Annual. Primary Exhibits: Auto body repair equipment, supplies, and services. Dates and Locations: 2012 Oct 10-13; New Orleans, LA; Morial Convention Center.

1267 ■ National Automotive Radiator Service Association Annual Trade Show and Convention
National Automotive Radiator Service Association
PO Box 97
East Greenville, PA 18041
Ph: (215)541-4500
Fax: (215)679-4977

Annual. Primary Exhibits: Manufacturers in the automotive cooling industry. Dates and Locations: 2012 Oct 29 - Nov 01; Las Vegas, NV; Harrah's/Sands Expo.

OTHER SOURCES

1268 ■ Association of Diesel Specialists
400 Admiral Blvd.
Kansas City, MO 64106
Ph: (816)285-0810
Fax: (847)770-4952
E-mail: info@diesel.org
URL: http://www.diesel.org

Description: Represents the interests of independent repair shops specializing in diesel fuel injection, governor and turbocharger service, manufacturers and distributors of replacement parts and allied equipment, and post-secondary schools offering programs in diesel mechanic training.

1269 ■ Automotive Service Association (ASA)
PO Box 929
Bedford, TX 76095-0929
Ph: (817)283-6205
Fax: (817)685-0225
Fr: 800-272-7467
E-mail: asainfo@asashop.org
URL: http://www.asashop.org

Description: Automotive service businesses including body, paint, and trim shops, engine rebuilders, radiator shops, brake and wheel alignment services, transmission shops, tune-up services, and air conditioning services; associate members are manufacturers and wholesalers of automotive parts, and the trade press. Represents independent business owners and managers before private agencies and national and state legislative bodies. Promotes confidence between consumer and the automotive service industry, safety inspection of motor vehicles, and better highways.

1270 ■ Gasoline and Automotive Service Dealers Association (GASDA)
372 Doughty Blvd., Ste. 2C
Inwood, NY 11096
Ph: (516)371-6201
Fax: (516)371-1579
E-mail: gasda@nysassrs.com
URL: http://www.nysassrs.com/gasda/gasdamainpage.htm

Description: Owners/operators or dealers of service stations or automotive repair facilities; interested individuals. Aims to educate, inform and help increase professionalism of members and of the industry. Offers periodic technical training clinics and other educational programs including advanced automotive technical training, prepaid group legal services plan and group health insurance and liaison with government agencies. Informs members of political and legislative action or changes affecting their industry.

1271 ■ International Society of Automation
PO Box 12277
Research Triangle Park, NC 27709
Ph: (919)549-8411
Fax: (919)549-8288
E-mail: info@isa.org
URL: http://www.isa.org

Description: Represents the interests of automation professionals. Aims to set the standard for automation by helping members and other professionals solve technical problems while enhancing leadership and personal career capabilities. Develops standards, certifies industry professionals, provides education and training, publishes books and technical articles, and hosts conferences and exhibitions for automation professionals.

1272 ■ National Institute for Automotive Service Excellence (ASE)
101 Blue Seal Dr. SE, Ste. 101
Leesburg, VA 20175
Ph: (703)669-6600
Fax: (703)669-6123
Fr: 888-273-8378
E-mail: tmolla@ase.com
URL: http://www.ase.com

Description: Governed by a 40-member board of directors selected from all sectors of the automotive service industry and from education, government, and consumer groups. Encourages and promotes the highest standards of automotive service in the public interest. Conducts continuing research to determine the best methods for training automotive technicians; encourages the development of effective training programs. Tests and certifies the competence of automobile, medium/heavy truck, collision repair, school bus and engine machinist technicians as well as parts specialists.

1273 ■ Truck-Frame and Axle Repair Association (TARA)
364 W 12th St.
Erie, PA 16501
Fax: 877-735-1688
Fr: 877-735-1687
E-mail: leafspg@aol.com
URL: http://www.taraassociation.com

Description: Owners and operators of heavy-duty truck repair facilities and their mechanics; allied and associate members are manufacturers of heavy-duty trucks and repair equipment, engineers, trade press and insurance firms. Seeks to help members share skills and technical knowledge and keep abreast of new developments and technology to better serve customers in areas of minimum downtime, cost and maximum efficiency. Conducts studies and surveys regarding safety, fuel conservation and heavy-duty truck maintenance and repairs. Has formed TARA's Young Executives to help make young people at members' repair facilities more proficient in normal business functions and to ensure the future of the Association.

Sources of Help-Wanted Ads

1274 ■ Engineering
Scientific Research Publishing
PO Box 54821
Irvine, CA 92619-4821
E-mail: eng@scirp.org
URL: http://www.scirp.org/journal/eng/

Monthly. $708.00/year for individuals. Peer-reviewed journal publishing articles on the latest advancements in engineering.

1275 ■ International Journal of Energetic Materials and Chemical Propulsion
Begell House Inc.
50 Cross Hwy.
Redding, CT 06896
Ph: (203)938-1300

Fax: (203)938-1304
URL: http://www.begellhouse.com/journals/17bbb47e377ce023

$1,240.00/year for institutions. Journal promoting scientific investigation, technical advancements and information exchange on energetic materials and chemical propulsion.

1276 ■ Journal of Women and Minorities in Science and Engineering
Begell House Inc.
50 Cross Hwy.
Redding, CT 06896
Ph: (203)938-1300
Fax: (203)938-1304
URL: http://www.begellhouse.com/journals/00551c876cc2f027

$248.00/year for institutions. Peer-reviewed journal featuring innovative ideas and programs for classroom teachers, scientific studies, and formulation of

concepts related to the education, recruitment, and retention of under-represented groups in science and engineering.

Handbooks and Manuals

1277 ■ Plunkett's Automobile Industry Almanac 2012
Plunkett Research, Ltd.
PO Drawer 541737
Houston, TX 77254-1737
Ph: (713)932-0000
Fax: (713)932-7080
E-mail: customersupport@plunkettresearch.com
URL: http://www.plunkettresearch.com
Jack W. Plunkett. 2011. $299.99. 561 pages. Features in-depth profiles of leading companies, associations and professional societies in the automobile industry. Covers major issues and trends, market forecasts and industry statistics.

Sources of Help-Wanted Ads

1278 ■ Milling & Baking News
Sosland Publishing Co.
4800 Main St., Ste. 100
Kansas City, MO 64112-2504
Ph: (816)756-1000
Fax: (816)756-0494
Fr: 800-338-6201
E-mail: mbncirc@sosland.com?subject=mbn
URL: http://www.bakingbusiness.com

Weekly (Tues.). $135.00/year for U.S. and Canada; $210.00/year for U.S. and Canada, 2 years; $290.00/year for U.S. and Canada, 3 years; $190.00/year for out of country; $320.00/year for out of country, 2 years; $455.00/year for out of country, 3 years. Trade magazine covering the grain-based food industries.

Handbooks and Manuals

1279 ■ Career Opportunities in the Food and Beverage Industry
Facts on File, Inc.
132 W 31st St., 17th Fl.
New York, NY 10001-2006
Ph: (212)967-8800
Fax: 800-678-3633
Fr: 800-322-8755
E-mail: custserv@factsonfile.com
URL: http://www.infobasepublishing.com

Barbara Sims-Bell. 2010. $18.95 (paper). 223 pages. Provides the job seeker with information about locating and landing 80 skilled and unskilled jobs in the industry. Includes detailed job descriptions for many specific positions and lists trade associations, recruiting organizations, and major agencies. Contains index and bibliography.

1280 ■ How to Open a Financially Successful Bakery
Atlantic Publishing Company
1210 SW 23rd Pl.
Ocala, FL 34474-7014
Fax: (352)622-1875
Fr: 800-814-1132
E-mail: sales@atlantic-pub.com
URL: http://www.atlantic-pub.com/

Sharon L. Fullen. 2004. $39.95 (CD-ROM, paper). Success in business for bakers. 288 pages.

1281 ■ Opportunities in Restaurant Careers
The McGraw-Hill Companies
PO Box 182604
Columbus, OH 43272
Fax: (614)759-3749
Fr: 877-883-5524
E-mail: customer.service@mcgraw-hill.com
URL: http://www.mhprofessional.com/
   product.php?isbn=0071442480

Carol Caprione Chmelynski. 2004. $13.95 (paper). 160 pages. Covers opportunities in the food service industry and details salaries, benefits, training opportunities, and professional associations. Special emphasis is put on becoming a successful restaurant manager by working up through the ranks. Illustrated.

Employment Agencies and Search Firms

1282 ■ Chefs' Professional Agency
870 Market St., 863
San Francisco, CA 94102
Ph: (415)392-1563
E-mail: hospitality@chefsprofessional.com
URL: http://chefsprofessional.com
Locates talent for restaurants, hotels, clubs and resorts. Provides resume kits, career tools, and other candidate resources while also providing resources for employers.

Online Job Sources and Services

1283 ■ BakingJobs.org
URL: http://bakingjobs.org
Description: Features job sites, company career pages and associations for baking jobs.

1284 ■ BestfoodJobs.com
URL: http://www.bestfoodjobs.com
Description: Provides information on employment opportunities for the restaurant and food service industry.

1285 ■ Foodservice.com
URL: http://www.foodservice.com
Description: Serves as an online community of foodservice professionals. Provides services such as a virtual foodshow, employment center, market reports, daily industry news and editorials, discussion forums, culinary school connections, and the weekly foodservice.com express e-Newsletter.

1286 ■ New Restaurant and Food Jobs
URL: http://www.newrestaurantandfoodjobs.com
Description: Provides an online listing of companies with available restaurant and food jobs in all specialties.

1287 ■ PastryBakerChef.com
URL: http://www.pastrybakerchef.com
Description: Features employment opportunities for bakers and pastry chefs.

Tradeshows

1288 ■ BEMA, The Baking Industry Suppliers Association Annual Meeting
The Baking Industry Suppliers Association BEMA
10740 Nall Ave., Ste. 230
Overland Park, KS 66211

Ph: (913)338-1300
Fax: (913)338-1327
E-mail: info@bema.org
URL: http://www.bema.org +SLK

Annual. Primary Exhibits: Exhibits relating to baking industry suppliers. Dates and Locations: 2012 Jun 21-26.

1289 ■ Dairy-Deli-Bake Seminar and Expo
International Dairy-Deli-Bakery Association
PO Box 5528
Madison, WI 53705-0528
Ph: (608)310-5000
Fax: (608)238-6330
E-mail: iddba@iddba.org
URL: http://www.iddba.org

Annual. Primary Exhibits: Dairy, deli, and bakery products, packaging, and equipment. Dates and Locations: 2012 Jun 10-12; New Orleans, LA; Ernest N. Morial Convention Center.

1290 ■ Institute of Food Technologists Annual Meeting and Food Expo
Institute of Food Technologists
525 W, Van Buren St., Ste. 1000
Chicago, IL 60607
Ph: (312)782-8424
Fax: (312)782-8348
E-mail: info@ift.org
URL: http://www.ift.org

Annual. Primary Exhibits: Food ingredients, equipment, laboratory equipment and supplies, and other services rendered to the food processing industry. Dates and Locations: 2012 Jun 25-28; Las Vegas, NV.

1291 ■ International Baking Industry Exposition
IBIE Exhibition Management
401 N. Michigan Ave.
Chicago, IL 60611
Ph: (312)644-6610
Fax: (312)644-0575
E-mail: pdwyer@smithbucklin.com
URL: http://www.bakingexpo.com

Primary Exhibits: Baking equipment, supplies, and services.

1292 ■ National Restaurant Association Restaurant and Hotel-Motel Show
National Restaurant Association Convention Office
1200 17th St., N.W.
Washington, DC 20036
Ph: (202)331-5900
Fax: (202)331-2429
Fr: 800-424-5156
URL: http://www.restaurant.org

Annual. Primary Exhibits: Food service equipment, supplies, and services and food and beverage products for the hospitality industry. Includes international cuisine pavilion. Dates and Locations: 2012 May 05-08; Chicago, IL; McCormick Place.

OTHER SOURCES

1293 ■ AIB International
1213 Bakers Way
PO Box 3999
Manhattan, KS 66505-3999
Ph: (785)537-4750
Fax: (785)537-1493
Fr: 800-633-5137
E-mail: aibmarketing@aibonline.org
URL: http://www.aibonline.org

Description: Baking research and educational center. Conducts basic and applied research, educational and hands-on training, and in-plant sanitation and worker safety audits. Maintains museum. Provides bibliographic and reference service. Serves as registrar for ISO-9000 quality certification.

1294 ■ Allied Trades of the Baking Industry (ATBI)
2001 Shawnee Mission Pkwy.
Mission Woods, KS 66205
URL: http://atbi.org

Description: Salespeople from the allied trades servicing the baking industry. Promotes the industry through cooperative service to national, state, and local bakery associations; encourages mutual understanding and goodwill between the baking industry and the allied trades. Carries out promotional and service activities.

1295 ■ American Bakers Association (ABA)
1300 I St. NW, Ste. 700 W
Washington, DC 20005
Ph: (202)789-0300
Fax: (202)898-1164
E-mail: rmackie@americanbakers.org
URL: http://www.americanbakers.org

Description: Manufacturers and wholesale distributors of bread, rolls, and pastry products; suppliers of goods and services to bakers. Conducts seminars and expositions.

1296 ■ American Culinary Federation (ACF)
180 Center Place Way
St. Augustine, FL 32095
Ph: (904)824-4468
Fax: (904)825-4758
Fr: 800-624-9458
E-mail: acf@acfchefs.net
URL: http://www.acfchefs.org

Description: Aims to promote the culinary profession and provide on-going educational training and networking for members. Provides opportunities for competition, professional recognition, and access to educational forums with other culinary experts at local, regional, national, and international events. Operates the National Apprenticeship Program for cooks and pastry cooks. Offers programs that address certification of the individual chef's skills, accreditation of culinary programs, apprenticeship of cooks and pastry cooks, professional development, and the fight against childhood hunger.

1297 ■ American Society of Baking
PO Box 336
Swedesboro, NJ 08085
Fax: 888-315-2612
Fr: 800-713-0462
E-mail: info@asbe.org
URL: http://www.asbe.org

Description: Professional organization of persons engaged in bakery production; chemists, production supervisors, engineers, technicians, and others from allied fields. Maintains information service and library references to baking and related subjects.

1298 ■ Independent Bakers Association (IBA)
PO Box 3731
Washington, DC 20007
Ph: (202)333-8190
Fax: (202)337-3809
E-mail: independentbaker@yahoo.com
URL: http://www.independentbaker.net/independentbakersassociation

Description: Trade association representing small-medium wholesale bakers and allied trade members. Represents independent wholesale bakers on federal legislative and regulatory issues. Offers annual Smith-Schaus-Smith internships.

1299 ■ International Association of Culinary Professionals (IACP)
1100 Johnson Ferry Rd., Ste. 300
Atlanta, GA 30342
Ph: (404)252-3663
Fax: (404)252-0774
Fr: 800-928-4227
E-mail: info@iacp.com
URL: http://www.iacp.com

Description: Represents cooking school owners, food writers, chefs, caterers, culinary specialists, directors, teachers, cookbook authors, food stylists, food photographers, student/apprentices, and individuals in related industries in 20 countries. Promotes the interests of cooking schools, teachers, and culinary professionals. Encourages the exchange of information and education. Promotes professional standards and accreditation procedures. Maintains a Foundation to award culinary scholarships and grants.

1300 ■ International Council on Hotel, Restaurant, and Institutional Education (CHRIE)
2810 N Parham Rd., Ste. 230
Richmond, VA 23294
Ph: (804)346-4800
Fax: (804)346-5009
E-mail: kmccarty@chrie.org
URL: http://www.chrie.org

Description: Schools and colleges offering specialized education and training in hospitals, recreation, tourism and hotel, restaurant, and institutional administration; individuals, executives, and students. Provides networking opportunities and professional development.

1301 ■ Les Amis d'Escoffier Society of New York
787 Ridgewood Rd.
Millburn, NJ 07041
Ph: (212)414-5820
Fax: (973)379-3117
URL: http://www.escoffier-society.com

Description: International organization of professionals in the food and wine industries. Maintains museum, speakers' bureau, hall of fame, and placement service. Sponsors charitable programs.

1302 ■ Quality Bakers of America Cooperative (QBA)
1055 Parsippany Blvd., Ste. 201
Parsippany, NJ 07054
Ph: (973)263-6970
Fax: (973)263-0937
E-mail: info@qba.com
URL: http://www.qba.com

Description: Independent national and international wholesale bakeries; composed of three major consulting divisions: marketing, manufacturing and technical research. Offers expertise in business strategy and management, product development, marketing and consumer research, process development, training and procurement.

1303 ■ Retail Bakers of America (RBA)
202 Village Cir., Ste. 1
Slidell, LA 70458
Ph: (985)643-6504
Fax: (985)643-6929
Fr: 800-638-0924
E-mail: info@rbanet.com
URL: http://www.retailbakersofamerica.org

Description: Independent retail and in-store bakeries, food service, specialty bakeries, suppliers of ingredients, tools and equipment; other. Provides information, management, production, merchandising and small business services.

Bill and Account Collectors

SOURCES OF HELP-WANTED ADS

1304 ■ Accounting and Finance
John Wiley & Sons Inc.
350 Main St., Commerce Pl.
Malden, MA 02148-5089
Ph: (781)388-8200
Fax: (781)388-8210
URL: http://www.wiley.com/bw/journal.asp?ref=0810-5391

Quarterly. $442.00/year for institutions, print + online, Australia/New Zealand; $384.00/year for institutions, print or online, Australia/New Zealand; $597.00/year for institutions, print + online; $519.00/year for institutions, print or online; $416.00/year for institutions, other countries, print + online; $361.00/year for institutions, other countries, print or online. Journal focusing on accounting and finance.

1305 ■ Accounting Horizons
American Accounting Association
5717 Bessie Dr.
Sarasota, FL 34233-2399
Ph: (941)921-7747
Fax: (941)923-4093
URL: http://aaahq.org/pubs/horizons.htm

Quarterly. $300.00/year for individuals, print only; $325.00/year for individuals, online, vol. 13 thru current issue; $375.00/year for individuals, online and print. Publication covering the banking, finance, and accounting industries.

1306 ■ Brookings Papers on Economic Activity
Brookings Institution Press
1775 Massashusetts Ave. NW
Washington, DC 20036
Ph: (202)797-6000
URL: http://www.brookings.edu/press/journals.htm#bpea

Semiannual. $55.00/year for individuals; $90.00/year for institutions; $69.00/year for other countries; $104.00/year for institutions, other countries. Publication covering economics and business.

1307 ■ Business Credit
National Association of Credit Management
8840 Columbia 100 Pkwy.
Columbia, MD 21045-2158
Ph: (410)740-5560
Fax: (410)740-5574
URL: http://www.nacm.org/index.php?option=com_content&view=catego

$60.00/year for Canada; $65.00/year for other countries; $54.00/year for individuals; $48.00/year for libraries; $7.00/year for single issue. Magazine covering finance, business risk management, providing information for the extension of credit, maintenance

of accounts receivable, and cash asset management.

1308 ■ Commercial Lending Review
CCH Inc.
PO Box 4307
Chicago, IL 60680
Fr: 800-248-3248
URL: http://www.commerciallendingreview.com/

Bimonthly. $445.00/year for individuals. Journal covering all aspects of lending for commercial banks, community and regional banks and other financial institutions.

1309 ■ Foundations and Trends in Finance
Now Publishers
PO Box 1024
Hanover, MA 02339-1001
Ph: (781)871-0245
URL: http://www.nowpublishers.com/product.aspx?product=FIN

Irregular. $390.00/year for individuals, online only; $450.00/year for individuals, print and online; $390.00/year for other countries, online only; $450.00/year for other countries, print and online. Academic journal that covers corporate finance, financial markets, asset pricing, and derivatives.

1310 ■ Journal of Applied Finance
INFORMS
7240 Parkway Dr., Ste. 300
Hanover, MD 21076
Ph: (443)757-3500
Fax: (443)757-3515
Fr: 800-446-3676
URL: http://69.175.2.130/~finman/Publications/JAF.htm

Semiannual. Journal for financial practice and education developments.

1311 ■ U.S. Banker
SourceMedia Inc.
1 State St. Plz., 27th Fl.
New York, NY 10004-1561
Ph: (212)803-8200
Fax: (646)264-6828
URL: http://www.americanbanker.com/usb.html

Monthly. $109.00/year for individuals; $139.00/year for individuals, Canada; $139.00/year for individuals, outside North America; $179.00/year for two years; $239.00/year for two years, Canada; $239.00/year for two years, outside North America. Magazine serving the financial services industry.

1312 ■ Wilmott Magazine
John Wiley & Sons Inc.
111 River St.
Hoboken, NJ 07030-5773
Ph: (201)748-6000
Fax: (201)748-6088
Fr: 800-825-7550
URL: http://www.wilmott.com

Bimonthly. $528.00/year for institutions, other coun-

tries, print only; $395.00/year for institutions, print only; $695.00/year for institutions, other countries, print only. Journal focusing on the quantitative finance community and concentrating on practicalities.

EMPLOYER DIRECTORIES AND NETWORKING LISTS

1313 ■ Career Opportunities in Banking, Finance, and Insurance
Facts On File Inc.
132 W 31st St., 17th Fl.
New York, NY 10001
Ph: (212)967-8800
Fax: 800-678-3633
Fr: 800-322-8755
URL: http://factsonfile.infobasepublishing.com

Latest edition 2nd; Published February, 2007. $49.50 for individuals. Publication includes: Lists of colleges with programs supporting banking, finance, and industry; professional associations; professional certifications; regulatory agencies; and Internet resources for career planning. Principal content of publication is job descriptions for professions in the banking, finance, and insurance industries. Indexes: Alphabetical.

EMPLOYMENT AGENCIES AND SEARCH FIRMS

1314 ■ American Human Resources Associates Ltd. (AHRA)
PO Box 18269
Cleveland, OH 44118-0269
Ph: (440)317-0981
E-mail: ahra@ahrasearch.com
URL: http://www.ahrasearch.com

Executive search firm. Focused on real estate, banking and credit & collection.

ONLINE JOB SOURCES AND SERVICES

1315 ■ BillingJobs.com
URL: http://www.billingjobs.com

Description: Features billing jobs, billing resumes, accounts payable jobs, and billing careers.

OTHER SOURCES

1316 ■ Allied Finance Adjusters
PO Box 41368
Raleigh, NC 27629
Fax: (325)949-8520

Fr: 800-843-1232
E-mail: alliedfinanceadjusters@gmail.com
URL: http://www.alliedfinanceadjusters.com

Description: Association of professional repossessors, investigators, and recovery agents.

1317 ■ American Bankers Association (ABA)
1120 Connecticut Ave. NW
Washington, DC 20036
Ph: (202)663-5564
Fax: (202)663-7543
Fr: 800-226-5377
E-mail: custserv@aba.com
URL: http://www.aba.com

Description: Members are principally commercial banks and trust companies; combined assets of members represent approximately 90% of the U.S. banking industry; approximately 94% of members are community banks with less than $500 million in assets. Seeks to enhance the role of commercial bankers as preeminent providers of financial services through communications, research, legal action, lobbying of federal legislative and regulatory bodies, and education and training programs. Serves as spokesperson for the banking industry; facilitates exchange of information among members. Maintains the American Institute of Banking, an industry-sponsored adult education program. Conducts educational and training programs for bank employees and officers through a wide range of banking schools and national conferences. Maintains liaison with federal bank regulators; lobbies Congress on issues affecting commercial banks; testifies before congressional committees; represents members in U.S. postal rate proceedings. Serves as secretariat of the International Monetary Conference and the Financial Institutions Committee for the American National Standards Institute. Files briefs and lawsuits in major court cases affecting the industry. Conducts teleconferences with state banking associations on such issues as regulatory compliance; works to build consensus and coordinate activities of leading bank and financial service trade groups. Provides services to members including: public advocacy; news media contact; insurance program providing directors and officers with liability coverage, financial institution bond, and trust errors and omissions coverage; research service operated through ABA Center for Banking Information; fingerprint set processing in conjunction with the Federal Bureau of Investigation; discounts on operational and income-producing projects through the Corporation for American Banking. Conducts conferences, forums, and workshops covering subjects such as small business, consumer credit, agricultural and community banking, trust management, bank operations, and automation. Sponsors ABA Educational Foundation and the Personal Economics Program, which educates schoolchildren and the community on banking, economics, and personal finance.

1318 ■ American Financial Services Association (AFSA)
919 18th St. NW, Ste. 300
Washington, DC 20006-5526

Ph: (202)296-5544
Fax: (202)223-0321
E-mail: susie@afsamail.org
URL: http://www.afsaonline.org

Description: Represents companies whose business is primarily direct credit lending to consumers and/or the purchase of sales finance paper on consumer goods. Has members that have insurance and retail subsidiaries; some are themselves subsidiaries of highly diversified parent corporations. Encourages the business of financing individuals and families for necessary and useful purposes at reasonable charges, including interest; promotes consumer understanding of basic money management principles as well as constructive uses of consumer credit. Includes educational services such as films, textbooks and study units for the classroom and budgeting guides for individuals and families. Compiles statistical reports; offers seminars.

1319 ■ Association of Credit and Collection Professionals
PO Box 390106
Minneapolis, MN 55439
Ph: (952)926-6547
Fax: (952)926-1624
E-mail: aca@acainternational.org
URL: http://www.acainternational.org

Description: Organization of credit and collection professionals that provides accounts receivable management services.

1320 ■ Association for Financial Professionals (AFP)
4520 E West Hwy., Ste. 750
Bethesda, MD 20814
Ph: (301)907-2862
Fax: (301)907-2864
E-mail: afp@afponline.org
URL: http://www.afponline.org

Description: Seeks to establish a national forum for the exchange of concepts and techniques related to improving the management of treasury and the careers of professionals through research, education, publications and recognition of the treasury management profession through a certification program. Conducts educational programs. Operates career center.

1321 ■ Commercial Finance Association (CFA)
370 7th Ave., Ste. 1801
New York, NY 10001-3979
Ph: (212)792-9390
Fax: (212)564-6053
E-mail: info@cfa.com
URL: http://www.cfa.com

Description: Organizations engaged in asset-based financial services including commercial financing and factoring and lending money on a secured basis to small- and medium-sized business firms. Acts as a forum for information and consideration about ideas, opportunities and legislation concerning asset-based financial services. Seeks to improve the industry's

legal and operational procedures. Offers job placement and reference services for members. Sponsors School for Field Examiners and other educational programs. Compiles statistics; conducts seminars and surveys; maintains speakers' bureau and 21 committees.

1322 ■ Consumer Data Industry Association (CDIA)
1090 Vermont Ave. NW, Ste. 200
Washington, DC 20005-4964
Ph: (202)371-0910
Fax: (202)371-0134
E-mail: cdia@cdiaonline.org
URL: http://www.cdiaonline.org

Description: Serves as international association of credit reporting and collection service offices. Maintains hall of fame and biographical archives; conducts specialized educational programs. Offers computerized services and compiles statistics.

1323 ■ Credit Professionals International (CPI)
10726 Manchester Rd., Ste. 210
St. Louis, MO 63122
Ph: (314)821-9393
Fax: (314)821-7171
E-mail: creditpro@creditprofessionals.org
URL: http://www.creditprofessionals.org

Description: Represents individuals employed in credit or collection departments of business firms or professional offices. Conducts educational program in credit work. Sponsors Career Club composed of members who have been involved in credit work for at least 25 years.

1324 ■ National Association of Credit Management (NACM)
8840 Columbia 100 Pkwy.
Columbia, MD 21045-2158
Ph: (410)740-5560
Fax: (410)740-5574
E-mail: nacm_national@nacm.org
URL: http://www.nacm.org

Description: Provides information, products and services for effective business credit and accounts receivable management.

1325 ■ National Association of Credit Union Services Organizations (NACUSO)
3419 Via Lido
PMB 135
Newport Beach, CA 92663
Ph: (949)645-5296
Fax: (949)645-5297
Fr: 888-462-2870
E-mail: info@nacuso.org
URL: http://www.nacuso.org

Description: Credit union service organizations and their employees. Promotes professional advancement of credit union service organization staff; seeks to insure adherence to high standards of ethics and practice among members. Conducts research and educational programs; formulates and enforces standards of conduct and practice; maintains speakers' bureau; compiles statistics.

SOURCES OF HELP-WANTED ADS

1326 ■ American Journal of Biochemistry and Molecular Biology
Academic Journals Inc.
224, 5th Ave., No. 2218
New York, NY 10001
Fr: 888-777-8532
URL: http://www.academicjournalsinc.com/current.php?jid=2150-4210

Peer-reviewed journal focusing on research in biochemistry, molecular biology, cell, and biotechnology.

1327 ■ American Journal of Drug Discovery and Development
Academic Journals Inc.
224, 5th Ave., No. 2218
New York, NY 10001
Fr: 888-777-8532
URL: http://www.academicjournalsinc.com/current.php?jid=2150-427x

Peer-reviewed journal publishing research articles on drug discovery and development.

1328 ■ ASBMB Today
American Society for Biochemistry and Molecular Biology
11200 Rockvile Pike, Ste. 302
Rockville, MD 20852
Ph: (240)283-6614
E-mail: asbmbtoday@asbmb.org
URL: http://www.asbmb.org/asbmbtoday

Monthly. Features an extensive coverage of awards, meetings, research highlights, job placement advertising and human interest articles. Provides insight and updates on budgetary and legislative issues and their impacts on biological research to members of the biochemical science community. Offers career development resources such as continuing education and discussions on non-traditional careers in science.

1329 ■ Asian Journal of Biochemistry
Academic Journals Inc.
224, 5th Ave., No. 2218
New York, NY 10001
Fr: 888-777-8532
URL: http://www.academicjournalsinc.com/current.php?jid=1815-9923

Peer-reviewed journal covering research on biochemistry, molecular biology, cell, and biotechnology.

1330 ■ Bioengineered Bugs
Landes Bioscience
1806 Rio Grande St.
Austin, TX 78701
Ph: (512)637-6050
Fax: (512)637-6079
URL: http://www.landesbioscience.com/journals/biobugs/

Bimonthly. Peer-reviewed journal focusing on research in genetic engineering.

1331 ■ Biomedical Optics Express
Optical Society of America
2010 Massachusetts Ave. NW
Washington, DC 20036
Ph: (202)223-8130
Fax: (202)223-1096
URL: http://www.opticsinfobase.org/boe/journal/boe/about.cfm

Monthly. Peer-reviewed journal focusing on biomedical optics and biophotonics.

1332 ■ Biotechnology Journal
John Wiley & Sons, Inc.
111 River St.
Hoboken, NJ 07030-5774
Ph: (201)748-6000
Fax: (201)748-6088
E-mail: info@wiley.com
URL: http://www.wiley.com

12 issues. $344.00/year for individuals worldwide. Features peer-reviewed papers covering novel aspects and methods in all areas of biotechnology. Presents papers in areas including DNA/protein engineering, all -omics fields (genomics, proteomics, metabolomics, systems biology and others), bioinformatics (algorithms and modeling), imaging, analytical biotech (sensors/detectors for analytes/macromolecules), plant/agricultural, food or environmental biotechnology, health and therapeutical biotechnology (including antisense/siRNAs, enzymes, peptides), regenerative medicine (stem cells, tissue engineering and biomaterials), translational immunology (antibody engineering, xenotransplantation, T-cell therapies) and, biosafety or biosecurity. Contains display and recruitment advertisements.

1333 ■ Bulletin of Mathematical Biology
Springer
233 Spring St.
New York, NY 10013
Ph: (212)460-1500
Fax: (212)460-1575
URL: http://www.springer.com

Features articles in computational, theoretical, and experimental biology. Articles offer a combination of theory and experiment, documenting theoretical advances with expositions on how they further biological understanding.

1334 ■ Current Bioinformatics
Bentham Science Publishers Ltd.
PO Box 446
Oak Park, IL 60303-0446
Ph: (312)413-5867
Fax: (312)996-7107
E-mail: morrissy@benthamscience.org
URL: http://www.benthamscience.com/cbio/index.htm

$1,210/year for corporate; $690/year for academic; $190/year for individuals. Focuses on reviews of advances in computational molecular or structural biology, encompassing areas such as computing in biomedicine and genomics, computational proteomics and systems biology, and metabolic pathway engineering. Contains advertisements of products, events, and services.

1335 ■ Ethics in Biology, Engineering and Medicine
Begell House Inc.
50 Cross Hwy.
Redding, CT 06896
Ph: (203)938-1300
Fax: (203)938-1304
URL: http://www.begellhouse.com/journals/6ed509641f7324e6

$650.00/year for institutions. Peer-reviewed journal covering ethical issues on biomedical research and the development of new biomaterials, implants, devices and treatments.

1336 ■ Evolutionary Computation
MIT Press
55 Hayward St.
Cambridge, MA 02142-1315
Ph: (617)253-5646
Fax: (617)258-6779
URL: http://www.mitpressjournals.org/loi/evco

Quarterly. $76.00/year for individuals, print & online; $70.00/year for individuals, online; $424.00/year for institutions, print & online; $376.00/year for institutions, online only; $40.00/year for students, print and online, retired; $36.00/year for students, online only, retired. Journal providing an international forum for facilitating and enhancing the exchange of information among researchers involved in both the theoretical and practical aspects of computational systems of an evolutionary nature. Publishes both theoretical and practical developments of computational systems drawing their inspiration from nature, with particular emphasis on evolutionary algorithms (EAs), including, but not limited to, genetic algorithms (GAs), evolution strategies (ESs), evolutionary programming (EP), genetic programming (GP), classifier systems (CSs), and other natural computation techniques.

1337 ■ International Journal of Applied Evolutionary Computation
IGI Global
701 E Chocolate Ave.
Hershey, PA 17033
Ph: (717)533-8845
Fax: (717)533-8661
Fr: (866)342-6657
URL: http://www.igi-global.com/Bookstore/TitleDetails.aspx?TitleI

Quarterly. $595.00/year for institutions, print or online; $210.00/year for individuals, print; $860.00/year for institutions, print and online. Peer-reviewed journal publishing research in intelligent and evolutionary computation.

1338 ■ *International Journal of Chemoinformatics and Chemical Engineering*

IGI Global
701 E Chocolate Ave.
Hershey, PA 17033
Ph: (717)533-8845
Fax: (717)533-8661
Fr: (866)342-6657
URL: http://www.igi-global.com/Bookstore/
TitleDetails.aspx?Titlel

Semiannual. $595.00/year for institutions, print or online; $210.00/year for individuals, print; $860.00/year for institutions, print and online. Peer-reviewed journal covering the latest research in chemical informatics and chemical engineering.

1339 ■ *International Journal of Knowledge Discovery in Bioinformatics*

IGI Global
701 E Chocolate Ave.
Hershey, PA 17033
Ph: (717)533-8845
Fax: (717)533-8661
Fr: (866)342-6657
E-mail: cust@igi-global.com
URL: http://www.igi-global.com

Quarterly. $595.00/year for institutions, print or online; $210.00/year for individuals, print; $860.00/year for institutions, print and online. Peer-reviewed journal featuring articles on bioinformatic topics such as systems biology, protein structure, gene expression, and biological data integration.

1340 ■ *Journal of Biomedical Science and Engineering*

Scientific Research Publishing
PO Box 54821
Irvine, CA 92619-4821
E-mail: jbise@scirp.org
URL: http://www.scirp.org/journal/jbise/

Monthly. Peer-reviewed journal covering all aspects of biomedical science and engineering.

1341 ■ *Journal of Geographic Information System*

Scientific Research Publishing
PO Box 54821
Irvine, CA 92619-4821
URL: http://www.scirp.org/journal/jgis/

Peer-reviewed journal featuring the latest advancements in geographic information system.

1342 ■ *Journal of Molecular Cell Biology*

Oxford University Press
2001 Evans Rd.
Cary, NC 27513
Ph: (919)677-0977
Fax: (919)677-1714
Fr: 800-852-7323
URL: http://jmcb.oxfordjournals.org

Peer-reviewed journal focusing on molecular and cell biology studies.

1343 ■ *Molecular and Cellular Proteomics*

American Society for Biochemistry and Molecular Biology
11200 Rockville Pike, Ste. 302
Rockville, MD 20852-3110
Ph: (240)283-6605
Fax: (301)881-2080
URL: http://www.asbmb.org

Monthly. $890.00/year online only. Online journal that features articles and reviews that advance the understanding of the structural and functional properties of proteins and their expression. Offers specifically targeted placement opportunities, with research focusing on protein effects on biological responses, and protein and cellular interactions. Contains banner advertising and career placement ads.

1344 ■ *Proteins: Structure, Function, and Bioinformatics*

John Wiley & Sons, Inc.
111 River St.
Hoboken, NJ 07030-5774
Ph: (201)748-6000
Fax: (201)748-6088
E-mail: info@wiley.com
URL: http://as.wiley.com/WileyCDA/WileyTitle/
productCd-PROT.html

16 issues. $363.00/year for individuals in USA, Canada & Mexico; $475.00/year for individuals in other countries; $5,464.00/year for institutions in USA; $5,688.00/year for institutions in Canada & Mexico; $5,800.00/year for institutions in other countries. Features original reports of significant experimental and analytic research in all areas of protein research: structure, function, computation, genetics, and design.

HANDBOOKS AND MANUALS

1345 ■ *Career Development in Bioengineering and Biotechnology*

Springer
233 Spring St.
New York, NY 10013
Ph: (212)460-1500
Fax: (212)460-1575
URL: http://www.springer.com

Guruprasad Madhavan, Barbara Oakley, and Luis Kun (Editors.) 2009. $49.95. 485 pages. Provides a roadmap to the broad and varied career development opportunities in bioengineering, biotechnology, and related fields.

1346 ■ *Cool Careers in Biotechnology*

Sally Ride Science
9191 Towne Centre Dr. L101
San Diego, CA 92122
Ph: (858)638-1432
Fr: 800-561-5161
URL: http://www.sallyridestore.com

Catherine Ivey Lee. 2009. $7.00. Features professionals working in biotechnology and the wide variety of careers available in the field.

1347 ■ *Opportunities in Biotechnology Careers*

McGraw-Hill
PO Box 182604
Columbus, OH 43218
Fax: (614)759-3749
Fr: 877-833-5524
E-mail: customer.service@mcgraw-hill.com
URL: http://www.mcgraw-hill.com

Sheldon S. Brown. 2007. $13.95 (paper). 160 pages. Contains information on biotechnology careers, training and educational requirements for each career, salary statistics for different positions within each field, as well as professional and internet resources.

EMPLOYMENT AGENCIES AND SEARCH FIRMS

1348 ■ Executec Search Agency, Inc

3156 E Russell Rd.
Las Vegas, NV 89120
Ph: (702)892-8008
URL: http://www.executecsearch.com

Serves as an executive recruiting firm in the scientific instrument and services marketplace. Provides searches for clients in the industries of biotechnology, molecular biology instruments and reagents, cell biology, genetic identity, genomics, proteomics, bioinformatics, high throughput screening instruments, analytical instrument, process, semiconductor, and health & safety.

1349 ■ Exigent Group

91 Central Ave., Ste. 5
Stirling, NJ 07980
Fax: (866)891-8657
Fr: 800-929-5813
E-mail: jobs@exigrp.com
URL: http://www.exigrp.com

Serves as a professional recruitment/search firm for the pharmaceutical, biotechnology, and medical device industries. Specializes in clinical biostatistics and clinical statistical SAS programming.

1350 ■ Greylock Recruiting

749 Main St.
Williamstown, MA 01267
Ph: (617)680-1952
Fax: (617)716-4444
E-mail: info@greylock-recruiting.com
URL: http://greylock-recruiting.com

Executive search firm that focuses on providing employment services for scientific professionals within the pharmaceutical and biotechnology industries.

1351 ■ JD Strategies

444 Castro St., Ste. 318
Mountain View, CA 94041
Ph: (650)941-2900
Fax: (650)941-2933
E-mail: jobs@jdstrategies.net
URL: http://www.jdstrategies.net

Specializes in providing workforce solutions for the technical and functional staffing needs of technology companies. Focuses on all areas of engineering product development, testing, and quality assurance.

1352 ■ Joseph Associates

229 Main St.
Huntington, NY 11743
Ph: (631)351-5805
Fax: (631)421-4123
E-mail: inquiries@jaexecutivesearch.com
URL: http://www.jaexecutivesearch.com

Description: Serves as a recruitment firm for pharmaceutical, biomedical, biotechnical, healthcare, and medical device industries. Specializes in the following job titles: biostatisticians, computational biologists, epidemiologists, HEOR specialists, medical directors, directors of pharmaco epidemiology and pharmaco vigilance, and statisticians.

1353 ■ Neil Michael Group

9 Park Pl.
Great Neck, NY 11021
Ph: (516)482-8810
Fax: (516)482-3343
E-mail: contactus@nmgsearch.com
URL: http://www.nmgsearch.com

Executive search firm that is dedicated to the life sciences industry. Specializes in the following specific areas: biotechnology, biopharmaceuticals, genomics, proteomics, bioinformatics, big pharma, medical diagnostics, and medical devices.

1354 ■ Powell Search Associates

123 Harbor Dr., Ste. 202
Stamford, CT 06902
Ph: (203)327-7671
E-mail: info@powellsearch.com
URL: http://powellsearch.com

Serves as a pharmaceutical and biotech executive search firm. Conducts retained searches, exclusive contingency searches, and contingency searches.

ONLINE JOB SOURCES AND SERVICES

1355 ■ Biohealthmatics.com

URL: http://www.biohealthmatics.com

Description: Serves as a job search networking site for the biotechnology and healthcare IT fields. Allows users to interact with other professionals in the industry and show the knowledge they have picked up as part of their daily involvement in their particular field.

1356 ■ Bioinformatics, Databases and Software for Medicine
URL: http://www.bio-computing.org

Description: Serves as a bioinformatics portal that compiles information about the latest research in bio-computing, databases, and software for medicine. Features job opportunities in the bioinformatics field.

1357 ■ Bioinformatics Directory
URL: http://bioinformaticsdirectory.com

Description: Features white papers, books, general knowledge, magazines, classes, company listings, and job openings in the field of bioinformatics.

1358 ■ BioJobNet
URL: http://www.biojobnet.com

Description: Features job listings in biotechnology, pharmaceuticals, medical devices, and life sciences.

1359 ■ BioPlanet
URL: http://www.bioplanet.com

Description: Provides information about bioinformatics and the skills needed to start a career in the field. Features job postings and bioinformatics companies. Maintains a forum for professionals who wish to discuss their questions and news about the bioinformatics field.

1360 ■ BiosciRegister.com
URL: http://www.biosciregister.com

Description: Serves as an online directory or reference database of suppliers of products and services used in the biotechnology and life sciences industries. Contains job listings.

1361 ■ BiostatisticianCareers.com
URL: http://www.biostatisticiancareers.com

Description: Serves as a job board for biostatisticians. Offers jobs and resume postings.

1362 ■ BiostatisticianJobs.com
E-mail: jobs@biostatisticianjobs.com
URL: http://www.biostatisticianjobs.com

Description: Provides biostatistician employment opportunities. Features jobs from all over the United States.

1363 ■ Biotech Career Center
E-mail: info@biotechcareercenter.com
URL: http://www.biotechcareercenter.com

Description: Serves as a portal for scientists seeking career advancement and/or job opportunities in biotech companies. Provides links to biology career and information sites.

1364 ■ BiotechEmployment.org
URL: http://biotechemployment.org

Description: Provides listings of biotech jobs and other employment opportunities in the United States.

1365 ■ BiotechGigs.com
URL: http://www.biotechgigs.com

Description: Lists new job openings for biotechnologists. Features research in the science and biotech employment market as well as a career articles section.

1366 ■ CCL.net
URL: http://www.ccl.net

Description: Serves as an independent electronic forum for chemistry researchers and educators to find approaches on solving current problems, share experiences, discuss the latest software, and learn about workshops and conferences. Offers job listings for positions in the field of computer applications in chemistry, materials research, and life sciences.

1367 ■ Discover8.com
E-mail: admin@discover8.com
URL: http://www.discover8.com

Description: Focuses on the dissemination and intelligent discussion of life science news, discoveries, hypotheses, and procedures. Features resume postings and career listings.

1368 ■ FierceBiotech
URL: http://www.fiercebiotech.com

Description: Provides information and news about the biotech industry. Offers job listings for life science professionals.

1369 ■ Genomeweb
URL: http://www.genomeweb.com

Description: Contains news focusing on advanced research tools in genomics, proteomics, and bioinformatics. Serves the global community of scientists, technology professionals, and executives who use and develop the latest advanced tools in molecular biology research. Contains job listings.

1370 ■ HireBio.com
URL: http://www.hirebio.com

Description: Features pharmaceutical and biotech jobs, employment resources, as well as education and career resources in bioinformatics.

1371 ■ Hum-Molgen.org
E-mail: info@hum-molgen.de
URL: http://hum-molgen.org

Description: Provides resources for the latest information in human molecular genetics. Features biotechnical sources, diagnostics, ethical, legal and social implications, meetings and conferences, and positions in bioscience and medicine. Provides the opportunity to communicate with scientists, physicians, and other genetics professionals worldwide.

1372 ■ Naturejobs.com
URL: http://www.nature.com/naturejobs/science/welcome

Description: Lists jobs in the following disciplines of science: cell biology, biochemistry, bioinformatics, materials, and nanotechnology. Features scientific career information as well as news and advice.

TRADESHOWS

1373 ■ Experimental Biology Meeting
Federation of American Societies for Experimental Biology
9650 Rockville Pike
Bethesda, MD 20814
Ph: (301)634-7010
Fax: (301)634-7014
URL: http://www.faseb.org

Annual. Features plenary and award lectures, pre-meeting workshops, oral and poster sessions, on-site career services, and exhibits of equipment, supplies

and publications required for research labs and experimental study.

1374 ■ International Conference on Computational Systems Bioinformatics
Life Sciences Society
160 Redland Rd.
Woodside, CA 94062
Ph: (650)851-4588
Fax: (650)851-8643
E-mail: tplummer@buckinstitute.org
URL: http://www.csb2010.org

Annual. Facilitates the exchange of ideas and collaborations between computer scientists and biologists by presenting cutting-edge computational biology research findings.

OTHER SOURCES

1375 ■ International Society for Computational Biology
9500 Gilman Dr.
MC 0505
La Jolla, CA 92093
Ph: (858)822-0852
Fax: (760)888-0313
E-mail: admin@iscb.org
URL: http://www.iscb.org

Description: Represents researchers in bioinformatics and computational biology. Promotes the application of computational methods to problems of biological significance. Facilitates basic and applied research, scientific communication, education, and international cooperation in computational biology.

1376 ■ National Human Genome Research Institute
National Institutes of Health
Bldg. 31, Rm. 4B09
31 Center Dr., MSC 2152
9000 Rockville Pike
Bethesda, MD 20892
Ph: (301)402-0911
Fax: (301)402-2218
E-mail: egreen@mail.nih.gov
URL: http://www.genome.gov

Description: Aims to apply genome technologies to the study of specific diseases. Provides training, educational programs, health professional education, and online careers and training resources.

1377 ■ RCSB Protein Data Bank
Rutgers, the State University of New Jersey
Department of Chemistry and Chemical Biology
610 Taylor Rd.
Piscataway, NJ 08854-8087
E-mail: info@rcsb.org
URL: http://www.rcsb.org/pdb/home/home.do

Description: Serves an international community of users including biologists and other scientists in fields such as bioinformatics, software developers for data analysis and visualization, students and educators, media writers, illustrators, textbook authors, and the general public. Functions as an information portal to biological macromolecular structures including proteins and nucleic acids. Features job listings for open positions in the molecular biology field.

1378 ■ Society for Mathematical Biology
PO Box 11283
Boulder, CO 80301
Ph: (303)661-9942
Fax: (303)665-8264
URL: http://www.smb.org

Description: Promotes and fosters interactions among mathematical and biological sciences communities through membership, journal publications, travel support, and conferences.

SOURCES OF HELP-WANTED ADS

1379 ■ AAPG Explorer
American Association of Petroleum Geologists
1444 S Boulder
Tulsa, OK 74119
Ph: (918)584-2555
Fax: (918)560-2665
Fr: 800-364-2274
URL: http://www.aapg.org/explorer/

Monthly. $75.00/year for nonmembers; $147.00/year for individuals, airmail service; $55.00/year for members, airmail. Magazine containing articles about energy issues with an emphasis on exploration for hydrocarbons and energy minerals.

1380 ■ Advances in Bioscience and Biotechnology
Scientific Research Publishing
PO Box 54821
Irvine, CA 92619-4821
E-mail: abb@scirp.org
URL: http://www.scirp.org/journal/abb/

Peer-reviewed journal publishing the latest advancements in biosciences.

1381 ■ The American Biology Teacher
National Association of Biology Teachers
1313 Dolley Madison Blvd., Ste. 402
McLean, VA 22101
Ph: (703)264-9696
Fax: (703)264-7778
Fr: 800-406-0775
URL: http://www.nabt.org/websites/institution/ index.php?p=26

$9.00/year for members; $24.00/year for nonmembers; $24.00/year for institutions. Peer-reviewed journal featuring articles on biology, science, and education for elementary, high school and college level biology teachers. Includes audio-visual, book, computer, and research reviews.

1382 ■ American Biotechnology Laboratory
American Laboratory/Labcompare
30 Controls Dr.
Shelton, CT 06484-0870
Ph: (203)926-9300
Fax: (203)926-9310
URL: http:// www.americanbiotechnologylaboratory.com

Biotechnology magazine.

1383 ■ American Journal of Agricultural and Biological Science
Science Publications
Vails Gate Heights Dr.
PO Box 879
Vails Gate, NY 12584-0879
URL: http://thescipub.com/ajabs.toc

Quarterly. $1,100.00/year for individuals; $300.00/

year for single issue. Peer-reviewed scholarly journal covering sciences relevant to biology and agriculture.

1384 ■ American Journal of Molecular Biology
Scientific Research Publishing
PO Box 54821
Irvine, CA 92619-4821
E-mail: ajmb@scirp.org
URL: http://www.scirp.org/Journal/ajmb/

Peer-reviewed journal featuring the latest advancements in molecular biology.

1385 ■ American Journal of Respiratory Cell and Molecular Biology
American Thoracic Society
25 Broadway
New York, NY 10006-2755
Ph: (212)315-8600
Fax: (212)315-6498
E-mail: atsinfo@thoracic.org
URL: http://www.thoracic.org

Monthly. Contains original and basic research in the area of pulmonary biology including cellular, biochemical, molecular, development, genetic, and immunologic studies of lung cells and molecules. Displays professional recruitment and announcement advertising.

1386 ■ American Laboratory News
American Laboratory/Labcompare
30 Controls Dr.
Shelton, CT 06484-0870
Ph: (203)926-9300
Fax: (203)926-9310
URL: http://www.americanlaboratory.com

Monthly. Trade magazine for scientists.

1387 ■ Annual Review of Genetics
Annual Reviews Inc.
4139 El Camino Way
Palo Alto, CA 94306
Ph: (650)493-4400
Fax: (650)424-0910
Fr: 800-523-8635
URL: http://www.annualreviews.org/journal/genet

Annual. $86.00/year for individuals, print & online; $263.00/year for institutions, print & online; $219.00/year for institutions, online; $219.00/year for institutions, print. Periodical covering issues in genetics and the biological sciences.

1388 ■ Annual Review of Microbiology
Annual Reviews Inc.
4139 El Camino Way
Palo Alto, CA 94306
Ph: (650)493-4400
Fax: (650)424-0910
Fr: 800-523-8635
URL: http://www.annualreviews.org/journal/micro

Annual. $86.00/year for individuals, print & online; $263.00/year for institutions, print & online; $219.00/

year for institutions, online; $219.00/year for institutions, print. Periodical covering microbiology and the biological sciences.

1389 ■ ASPB News
American Society of Plant Biologists
15501 Monona Dr.
Rockville, MD 20855-2768
Ph: (301)251-0560
Fax: (301)279-2996
E-mail: info@aspb.org
URL: http://www.aspb.org/newsletter

Description: Bimonthly. $30/year for nonmember. Offers news of interest to plant physiologists, biochemists, horticulturists, and plant molecular and cell biologists engaged in research and teaching. Alerts members to public policy issues, educational opportunities, meetings, seminars, and conventions pertinent to the field. Recurring features include letters to the editor, reports of meetings, job listings, a calendar of events, news from regional sections, and teaching ideas.

1390 ■ Basic and Applied Pathology
John Wiley & Sons Inc.
350 Main St., Commerce Pl.
Malden, MA 02148-5089
Ph: (781)388-8200
Fax: (781)388-8210
URL: http://www.wiley.com/bw/journal.asp?ref=1755-9294

Quarterly. Journal covering the fields of experimental, anatomical, clinical, molecular, forensic and legal, and toxicological pathology in humans and animals.

1391 ■ Biochemistry and Molecular Biology Education
John Wiley & Sons Inc.
111 River St.
Hoboken, NJ 07030-5773
Ph: (201)748-6000
Fax: (201)748-6088
Fr: 800-825-7550
URL: http://onlinelibrary.wiley.com/journal/10.1002/ (ISSN)1539-34

Bimonthly. $583.00/year for institutions, print only; $667.00/year for institutions, Canada and Mexico, print only; $709.00/year for institutions, other countries, print only. Journal covering the field of biochemistry, molecular biology, and related sciences.

1392 ■ CBE—Life Sciences Education
American Society for Cell Biology
8120 Woodmont Ave., Ste. 750
Bethesda, MD 20814-2762
Ph: (301)347-9300
Fax: (301)347-9310
URL: http://www.lifescied.org/

Quarterly. Journal that focuses on life science education at the K-12, undergraduate, and graduate levels.

1393 ■ *Cell*
Cell Press
600 Technology Sq.
Cambridge, MA 02139
Ph: (617)661-7057
Fax: (617)661-7061
Fr: (866)314-2355
E-mail: celleditor@cell.com
URL: http://www.cell.com

$212.00/year for U.S. and Canada, individual, print
and online; $320.00/year for other countries, indi-
vidual, print and online; $212.00/year for U.S. and
Canada, online only, individual; $212.00/year for
other countries, online only, individual; $1,425.00/
year for U.S. and Canada, institution, print only;
$1,605.00/year for institutions, other countries, print
only. Peer-reviewed journal on molecular and cell
biology.

1394 ■ *Chemistry & Biology*
Elsevier Science Inc.
360 Park Ave. S
New York, NY 10010-1710
Ph: (212)989-5800
Fax: (212)633-3990
Fr: 888-437-4636
URL: http://www.elsevier.com/wps/find/
   journaldescription.cws_home

Monthly. $2,137.00/year for institutions, for all
countries except Europe, Japan & Iran; $442.00/year
for U.S. and Canada; $457.00/year for individuals, for
all countries except Europe, Japan and Iran. Journal
focused on genetic, computational, or theoretical
information of chemistry and biology, substantiating
experimental data.

1395 ■ *Current Advances in Cell &*
Developmental Biology
Reed Elsevier
125 Park Ave., 23rd Fl.
New York, NY 10017
Ph: (212)309-8100
Fax: (212)309-8187
URL: http://www.elsevier.com/wps/find/
   journaldescription.cws_home

Monthly. $3,856.00/year for institutions, Europe, Iran;
$507,600.00/year for institutions, Japan; $4,223.00/
year for institutions, other countries; $221.00/year for
individuals, Europe, Iran; $25,500.00/year for indi-
viduals, Japan; $221.00/year for other countries.
Journal covering the field of biology.

1396 ■ *Current Advances in Genetics &*
Molecular Biology
Elsevier Science Inc.
360 Park Ave. S
New York, NY 10010-1710
Ph: (212)989-5800
Fax: (212)633-3990
Fr: 888-437-4636
URL: http://www.elsevier.com/wps/find/
   journaldescription.cws_home

Monthly. $25,500.00/year for individuals, Japan;
$221.00/year for individuals, for all countries except
Europe, Japan and Iran; $221.00/year for individuals,
European countries and Iran; $6,340.00/year for
institutions, other countries; $755,700.00/year for
institutions, Japan; $5,713.00/year for institutions,
European countries and Iran. Journal covering current details of genetics and molecular biology.

1397 ■ *The Electrochemical Society Interface*
Electrochemical Society Inc.
65 S Main St., Bldg. D
Pennington, NJ 08534-2839
Ph: (609)737-1902
Fax: (609)737-2743
E-mail: interface@electrochem.org
URL: http://www.electrochem.org/dl/interface/

Quarterly. $64.00/year for individuals, tier 1, print &
online; $82.00/year for other countries, tier 1, print &
online. Publication featuring news and articles of
interest to members of the Electrochemical Society.

1398 ■ *Engineering in Life Sciences*
John Wiley & Sons Inc.
111 River St.
Hoboken, NJ 07030-5773
Ph: (201)748-6000
Fax: (201)748-6088
Fr: 800-825-7550
URL: http://onlinelibrary.wiley.com/journal/10.1002/
   (ISSN)1618-28

Bimonthly. $989.00/year for institutions, European,
online only; $1,512.00/year for institutions, online
only, Switzerland and Liechtenstein; $1,299.00/year
for institutions, other countries, online only; $663.00/
year for institutions, European, online only; $1,299.00/
year for institutions, online only; $1,299.00/year for
institutions, Canada and Mexico, online only. Journal
focusing on the field of biotechnology and related
topics including microbiology, genetics, biochemistry,
and chemistry.

1399 ■ *Epigenetics*
Landes Bioscience
1806 Rio Grande St.
Austin, TX 78701
Ph: (512)637-6050
Fax: (512)637-6079
URL: http://www.landesbioscience.com/journals/
   epigenetics/

$129.00/year for individuals, online; $350.00/year for
individuals, print and online; $450.00/year for other
countries, print and online; $1,500.00/year for institu-
tions, online; $1,850.00/year for institutions, print and
online; $1,950.00/year for institutions, other countries,
print and online. Journal devoted to practicing physicians, residents and students.

1400 ■ *International Journal on Algae*
Begell House Inc.
50 Cross Hwy.
Redding, CT 06896
Ph: (203)938-1300
Fax: (203)938-1304
URL: http://www.begellhouse.com/journals/
   7dd4467e7de5b7ef

Quarterly. $988.00/year for institutions. Journal cover-
ing fundamental and applied aspects in algology.

1401 ■ *Invertebrate Biology*
John Wiley & Sons Inc.
350 Main St., Commerce Pl.
Malden, MA 02148-5089
Ph: (781)388-8200
Fax: (781)388-8210
URL: http://www.amicros.org/

Quarterly. $268.00/year for institutions, online or print;
$309.00/year for institutions, print & online; $163.00/
year for institutions, print or online; $188.00/year for
institutions, print & online. Scientific journal covering
the biology of invertebrate animals and research in
the fields of cell and molecular biology, ecology,
physiology, systematics, genetics, biogeography and
behavior.

1402 ■ *ISRN Endocrinology*
Hindawi Publishing Corporation
410 Park Ave., 15th Fl.
287 PMB
New York, NY 10022
E-mail: endocrinology@isrn.com
URL: http://www.isrn.com/journals/endocrinology

Peer-reviewed, open access journal publishing
original research articles, review articles, case
reports, and clinical studies in all areas of
endocrinology.

1403 ■ *ISRN Hematology*
Hindawi Publishing Corporation
410 Park Ave., 15th Fl.
287 PMB
New York, NY 10022
E-mail: hematology@isrn.com
URL: http://www.isrn.com/journals/hematology

Peer-reviewed journal covering research in all areas
of hematology.

1404 ■ *ISRN Neurology*
Hindawi Publishing Corporation
410 Park Ave., 15th Fl.
287 PMB
New York, NY 10022
E-mail: neurology@isrn.com
URL: http://www.isrn.com/journals/neurology

Peer-reviewed journal publishing research in all areas
of neurology.

1405 ■ *ISRN Oncology*
Hindawi Publishing Corporation
410 Park Ave., 15th Fl.
287 PMB
New York, NY 10022
E-mail: oncology@isrn.com
URL: http://www.isrn.com/journals/oncology

Peer-reviewed journal publishing research articles in
all areas of oncology.

1406 ■ *ISRN Rheumatology*
Hindawi Publishing Corporation
410 Park Ave., 15th Fl.
287 PMB
New York, NY 10022
E-mail: rheumatology@isrn.com
URL: http://www.isrn.com/journals/rheumatology

Peer-reviewed journal publishing information in all
areas of rheumatology.

1407 ■ *Journal of Adolescent and Young*
Adult Oncology
Mary Ann Liebert Inc., Publishers
140 Huguenot St., 3rd Fl.
New Rochelle, NY 10801-5215
Ph: (914)740-2100
Fax: (914)740-2101
Fr: 800-654-3237
URL: http://www.liebertpub.com/products/
   product.aspx?pid=387

Quarterly. $336.00/year for individuals, print and on-
line; $758.00/year for institutions, print and online.
Peer-reviewed journal focusing on research, education, communication and collaboration between health
professionals in adolescent and young adult oncology.

1408 ■ *Journal of Bacteriology*
ASM Journals
1752 North St. NW
Washington, DC 20036-2904
Ph: (202)737-3600
Fax: (202)942-9335
URL: http://jb.asm.org

Semimonthly. $202.00/year for members, print;
$270.00/year for members, print & online; $315.00/
year for members, Canada, print; $383.00/year for
members, Canada, print & online; $1,714.00/year for
institutions, print & online. Journal publishing articles
about bacteria and other microorganisms, including
fungi and other unicellular, eucaryotic organisms.

1409 ■ *Journal of Biomaterials and*
Nanobiotechnology
Scientific Research Publishing
PO Box 54821
Irvine, CA 92619-4821
URL: http://www.scirp.org/journal/jbnb/

Peer-reviewed journal covering the basic science and
engineering aspects of biomaterials and
nanotechnology.

1410 ■ *Journal of Biomedical Science and*
Engineering
Scientific Research Publishing
PO Box 54821
Irvine, CA 92619-4821
E-mail: jbise@scirp.org
URL: http://www.scirp.org/journal/jbise/

Monthly. Peer-reviewed journal covering all aspects
of biomedical science and engineering.

1411 ■ *Journal of Biophysical Chemistry*
Scientific Research Publishing
PO Box 54821
Irvine, CA 92619-4821
URL: http://www.scirp.org/journal/jbpc/

Peer-reviewed journal publishing the latest advancements in biophysical chemistry.

1412 ■ *Journal of Nanomechanics and Micromechanics*
American Society of Civil Engineers
1801 Alexander Bell Dr.
Reston, VA 20191-4400
Ph: (703)295-6300
Fax: (703)295-6333
Fr: 800-548-2723
URL: http://ascelibrary.org/nmo/

Quarterly. $373.00/year for institutions, print and online; $393.00/year for institutions, other countries, print and online. Peer-reviewed journal featuring articles on nanomechanics and micromechanics.

1413 ■ *Journal of Women and Minorities in Science and Engineering*
Begell House Inc.
50 Cross Hwy.
Redding, CT 06896
Ph: (203)938-1300
Fax: (203)938-1304
URL: http://www.begellhouse.com/journals/
   00551c876cc2f027

$248.00/year for institutions. Peer-reviewed journal featuring innovative ideas and programs for classroom teachers, scientific studies, and formulation of concepts related to the education, recruitment, and retention of under-represented groups in science and engineering.

1414 ■ *Lab Animal*
Nature Publishing Group
75 Varick St., 9th Fl.
New York, NY 10013-1917
Ph: (212)726-9200
Fax: (212)696-6300
Fr: 888-331-6288
E-mail: editors@labanimal.com
URL: http://www.labanimal.com/laban/index.html

Monthly. $250.00/year for individuals; $1,932.00/year for institutions; $139.00/year for individuals; $1,160.00/year for institutions; $270.60/year for individuals; $2,091.19/year for institutions; $215.00/year for individuals; $1,798.00/year for institutions; $20,000.00/year for individuals; $238,280.00/year for institutions. Life science magazine.

1415 ■ *Leukemia Supplements*
Nature Publishing Group
75 Varick St., 9th Fl.
New York, NY 10013-1917
Ph: (212)726-9200
Fax: (212)696-9006
Fr: 888-331-6288
URL: http://www.nature.com/leusup/marketing/
   index.html

Peer-reviewed journal covering all aspects of the research and treatment of leukemia and allied diseases.

1416 ■ *Nanomechanics Science and Technology*
Begell House Inc.
50 Cross Hwy.
Redding, CT 06896
Ph: (203)938-1300
Fax: (203)938-1304
URL: http://www.begellhouse.com/journals/
   11e12455066dab5d

$748.00/year for institutions. Journal covering the areas of nano- and micromechanics.

1417 ■ *Narrative Inquiry in Bioethics*
The Johns Hopkins University Press
2715 N Charles St.
Baltimore, MD 21218-4319
Ph: (410)516-6900
Fax: (410)516-6968
URL: http://www.press.jhu.edu/journals/narrative_
   inquiry_in_bioet

$175.00/year for institutions, print; $50.00/year for individuals, print. Journal publishing information on bioethics.

1418 ■ *Nature Biotechnology*
Nature Publishing Group
75 Varick St., 9th Fl.
New York, NY 10013-1917
Ph: (212)726-9200
Fax: (212)696-9006
Fr: 888-331-6288
E-mail: biotech@natureny.com
URL: http://www.nature.com/nbt/index.html

Monthly. $250.00/year for individuals, print + online; $425.00/year for two years, print + online. Scientific research journal.

1419 ■ *Nature International Weekly Journal of Science*
Nature Publishing Group
75 Varick St., 9th Fl.
New York, NY 10013-1917
Ph: (212)726-9200
Fax: (212)696-9006
Fr: 888-331-6288
E-mail: nature@natureny.com
URL: http://www.nature.com/nature/index.html

Weekly. $199.00/year for individuals, print and online; $338.00/year for two years, print and online. Magazine covering science and technology, including the fields of biology, biochemistry, genetics, medicine, earth sciences, physics, pharmacology, and behavioral sciences.

1420 ■ *OnLine Journal of Biological Sciences*
Science Publications
Vails Gate Heights Dr.
PO Box 879
Vails Gate, NY 12584-0879
URL: http://thescipub.com/ojbs.toc

Quarterly. Peer-reviewd scholarly journal covering all aspects of biological science.

1421 ■ *Ornithological Newsletter*
Ornithological Societies of North America
5400 Bosque Blvd., Ste. 680
Waco, TX 76710
Ph: (254)399-9636
Fax: (254)776-3767
E-mail: business@osnabirds.org
URL: http://www.osnabirds.org

Description: Bimonthly. Provides information of interest to ornithologists. Recurring features include listings of available grants and awards, news of members, a calendar of events, activities of sponsoring societies, and notices of publications available. Notices of employment opportunities are also available on the Web version.

1422 ■ *PALAIOS*
SEPM Publications
4111 S Darlington, Ste. 100
Tulsa, OK 74135-6373
Ph: (918)610-3361
Fax: (918)621-1685
Fr: 800-865-9765
E-mail: palois@ku.edu
URL: http://palaios.ku.edu/

Monthly. $315.00/year for individuals, for U.S.; online version with CD-ROM; $415.00/year for individuals, for U.S.; print and online version with CD-ROM; $315.00/year for other countries, online version with CD-ROM; $425.00/year for other countries, print and online version with CD-ROM. Journal providing

information on the impact of life on Earth history as recorded in the paleontological and sedimentological records. Covers areas such as biogeochemistry, ichnology, sedimentology, stratigraphy, paleoecology, paleoclimatology, and paleoceanography.

1423 ■ *Perspectives in Biology and Medicine*
The Johns Hopkins University Press
2715 N Charles St.
Baltimore, MD 21218-4319
Ph: (410)516-6900
Fax: (410)516-6968
URL: http://www.press.jhu.edu/journals/perspectives_
   in_biology_an

Quarterly. $50.00/year for individuals, print or online; $150.00/year for institutions, print; $100.00/year for individuals, print, 2 years; $45.00/year for students, print; $300.00/year for institutions, print, 2 years. Peer-reviewed journal publishing articles of current interest in medicine and biology in a context with humanistic, social, and scientific concerns. Covers a wide range of biomedical topics such as neurobiology, biomedical ethics and history, genetics and evolution, and ecology.

1424 ■ *Pesticides, People and Nature*
Begell House Inc.
50 Cross Hwy.
Redding, CT 06896
Ph: (203)938-1300
Fax: (203)938-1304
URL: http://www.begellhouse.com/journals/
   33b67499180f0876

$180.00/year for institutions. Journal covering the impact of pesticides on people and the environment.

1425 ■ *Plant Science Bulletin*
Botanical Society of America
PO Box 299
St. Louis, MO 63166
Ph: (314)577-9566
Fax: (314)577-9515
E-mail: bsa-manager@botany.org
URL: http://www.botany.org

Description: Quarterly. Carries news of the Association, with some issues including brief articles of more general interest in the field. Recurring features include notices of awards, meetings, courses, and study and professional opportunities; annotated lists of botanical books; and book reviews.

1426 ■ *PLoS Biology*
Public Library of Science
1160 Battery St.
San Francisco, CA 94111
Ph: (415)624-1200
Fax: (415)546-4090
URL: http://www.plosbiology.org/home.action

Monthly. Free, online; $365.00/year for U.S. and Canada, print only (credit card); $415.00/year for other countries, print only (credit card); $45.00/year for other countries, print only (single copy). Open access, peer-reviewed general biology journal.

1427 ■ *Popular Science*
Time4 Media Inc.
1271 Avenue of the Americas
New York, NY 10020-1300
Ph: (212)522-1212
URL: http://www.popsci.com/popsci

Monthly. $14.00/year for individuals; $24.00/year for two years; $26.00/year for Canada; $45.00/year for other countries, USA. General interest science magazine.

1428 ■ *Science*
American Association for the Advancement of Science
1200 New York Ave., NW
Washington, DC 20005
Ph: (202)326-6550
URL: http://www.scienceonline.org

Weekly (Fri.). $146.00/year for members, professional, print & online; $119.00/year for individuals, NPA postdoctoral, print & online; $99.00/year for individuals, postdoctoral/resident, print & online; $75.00/year for students, print & online; $146.00/year for individuals, k-12 teacher, print & online; $310.00/year for individuals, patron, print & online; $115.00/year for individuals, emeritus, print & online; $211.05/year for Canada, professional members, print & online; $161.00/year for Canada, postdoctoral/resident, print & online; $136.50/year for students, Canada, print & online. Magazine devoted to science, scientific research, and public policy.

1429 ■ The Scientist
The Scientist Inc.
121 W 27th St., Ste. 604
New York, NY 10001
Ph: (212)461-4470
Fax: (347)626-2385
URL: http://www.the-scientist.com

Monthly. $39.95/year for individuals, print only; $49.95/year for individuals, print & online; $64.95/year for other countries, print only; $74.95/year for other countries, print & online. News journal (tabloid) for life scientists featuring news, opinions, research, and professional section.

1430 ■ Seed Technologist Newsletter
Association of Official Seed Analysts Inc.
101 E State St., No. 214
Ithaca, NY 14850
Ph: (607)256-3313
Fax: (607)256-3313
E-mail: aosa.office@twcny.rr.com
URL: http://www.aosaseed.com

Description: Three issues/year. Relates activities of the Society, with reports from various chapters across the U.S. and Canada. Publishes technical information about testing seeds and ensuring seed quality. Recurring features include news of research, a calendar of events, reports of meetings, news of educational opportunities, job listings, book reviews, and notices of publications available.

1431 ■ Soft Nanoscience Letters
Scientific Research Publishing
PO Box 54821
Irvine, CA 92619-4821
E-mail: snl@scirp.org
URL: http://www.scirp.org/journal/snl/

Quarterly. $156.00/year for individuals. Peer-reviewed journal publishing articles in the field of soft nanoscience.

1432 ■ World Journal of Nano Science and Engineering
Scientific Research Publishing
PO Box 54821
Irvine, CA 92619-4821
E-mail: wjnse@scirp.org
URL: http://www.scirp.org/journal/wjnse/

Quarterly. $156.00/year for individuals. Peer-reviewed journal publishing articles on applications of physical, chemical and biological sciences to engineering.

1433 ■ The World Wide Web Journal of Biology
Epress, Inc.
130 Union Terrace Ln.
Plymouth, MN 55441
URL: http://www.epress.com/w3jbio/

Journal on Bio-informatics.

EMPLOYER DIRECTORIES AND NETWORKING LISTS

1434 ■ American Men and Women of Science
Gale
PO Box 6904
Florence, KY 41022-6904

Fr: 800-354-9706
URL: http://www.gale.cengage.com

Biennial, even years; New edition expected 29th, June 2011. $1,368.00 for individuals. Covers: Over 135,000 U.S. and Canadian scientists active in the physical, biological, mathematical, computer science, and engineering fields; includes references to previous edition for deceased scientists and nonrespondents. Entries include: Name, address, education, personal and career data, memberships, honors and awards, research interest. Arrangement: Alphabetical. Indexes: Discipline (in separate volume).

1435 ■ Career Ideas for Teens in Health Science
Facts On File Inc.
132 W 31st St., 17th Fl.
New York, NY 10001
Ph: (212)967-8800
Fax: 800-678-3633
Fr: 800-322-8755
URL: http://www.infobasepublishing.com

Published August, 2005. Covers: A multitude of career possibilities based on a teenager's specific interests and skills and links his/her talents to a wide variety of actual professions.

1436 ■ Career Opportunities in Science
Facts On File Inc.
132 W 31st St., 17th Fl.
New York, NY 10001
Ph: (212)967-8800
Fax: 800-678-3633
Fr: 800-322-8755
URL: http://factsonfile.infobasepublishing.com

Latest edition 2008. $49.50 for individuals. Covers: More than 80 jobs, such as biochemist, molecular biologist, bioinformatic specialist, pharmacologist, computer engineer, geographic information systems specialist, science teacher, forensic scientist, patent agent, as well as physicist, astronomer, chemist, zoologist, oceanographer, and geologist.

1437 ■ Careers in Focus—Earth Science
Facts On File Inc.
132 W 31st St., 17th Fl.
New York, NY 10001
Ph: (212)967-8800
Fax: 800-678-3633
Fr: 800-322-8755
URL: http://www.infobasepublishing.com

Latest edition 2nd; Published February, 2008. $32.95 for individuals. Covers: An overview of earth science, followed by a selection of jobs profiled in detail, including the nature of the job, earnings, prospects for employment, what kind of training and skills it requires, and sources for further information.

1438 ■ Federation of American Societies for Experimental Biology—Directory of Members
Federation of American Societies for Experimental Biology
9650 Rockville Pike
Bethesda, MD 20814-3998
Ph: (301)634-7000
Fax: (301)634-7001
Fr: 800-433-2732
E-mail: directoryinfo@faseb.org
URL: http://www.faseb.org

Annual, Latest edition 2009-2010. $70.00 for individuals; $55.00 for individuals. Covers: About 63,000 members of The American Physiological Society, American Society for Biochemistry and Molecular Biology, American Society for Pharmacology and Experimental Therapeutics, American Society for Investigative Pathology, American Society for Nutritional Sciences, The American Association of Immunologists, Biophysical Society, American Association of Anatomists, The Protein Society, The American Society for Bone and Mineral Research, American Society for Clinical Investigation, The Endocrine Society, The American Society of Human Genetics,

Society for Developmental Biology, American Peptide Society, Society for the Study of Reproduction and Radiation Research Society. Entries include: Name, address, title, affiliation, memberships in federation societies, highest degree, year elected to membership, phone, fax and electronic mail address. Membership directories of the Biophysical Society, The Protein Society, The American Society for Bone and Mineral Research, and American Society for Clinical Investigation are also available separately. Arrangement: Alphabetical. Indexes: Geographical.

HANDBOOKS AND MANUALS

1439 ■ Careers in Horticulture and Botany
The McGraw-Hill Companies
PO Box 182604
Columbus, OH 43272
Fax: (614)759-3749
Fr: 877-883-5524
E-mail: customer.service@mcgraw-hill.com
URL: http://www.mhprofessional.com/
    product.php?isbn=0071467734

Jerry Garner. 2006. 16.95 (paper). 192 pages. Includes bibliographical references.

1440 ■ Opportunities in Biological Science Careers
The McGraw-Hill Companies
PO Box 182604
Columbus, OH 43272
Fax: (614)759-3749
Fr: 877-883-5524
E-mail: customer.service@mcgraw-hill.com
URL: http://www.mhprofessional.com/
    product.php?isbn=007143187X

Charles A. Winter. 2004. $13.95 (paper). 160 pages. Identifies employers and outlines opportunities in plant and animal biology, biological specialties, biomedical sciences, applied biology, and other areas. Illustrated.

1441 ■ Resumes for Scientific and Technical Careers
The McGraw-Hill Companies
PO Box 182604
Columbus, OH 43272
Fax: (614)759-3749
Fr: 877-883-5524
E-mail: customer.service@mcgraw-hill.com
URL: http://www.mhprofessional.com/
    product.php?isbn=0071482199

Third edition, 2007. $12.95 (paper). 144 pages. Provides resume advice for individuals interested in working in scientific and technical careers. Includes sample resumes and cover letters.

EMPLOYMENT AGENCIES AND SEARCH FIRMS

1442 ■ Amtec Human Capital
2749 Saturn St.
Brea, CA 92821
Ph: (714)993-1900
Fax: (714)993-2419
E-mail: info@amtechc.com
URL: http://www.amtechc.com

Employment agency.

1443 ■ Biomedical Search Consultants
275 Wyman St., Ste. 110
Waltham, MA 02451
Ph: (781)890-8824
Fax: (781)998-1266
E-mail: kprovost@biomedicalsearch.com
URL: http://www.biomedicalsearchconsultants.com

Employment agency.

1444 ■ Caliber Associates
6336 Greenwich Dr., Ste. C
San Diego, CA 92122
Ph: (858)551-7880
Fax: (858)551-7887
E-mail: info@caliberassociates.com
URL: http://www.caliberassociates.com

Executive search firm.

1445 ■ CEO Resources Inc.
PO Box 2883
Framingham, MA 01703-2883
Ph: (508)877-2775
Fax: (508)877-8433
E-mail: info@ceoresourcesinc.com
URL: http://ceoresourcesinc.com

Executive search firm.

1446 ■ Clark Executive Search Inc.
135 N Ferry Rd.
PO Box 560
Shelter Island, NY 11964
Ph: (631)749-3540
Fax: (631)749-3539
E-mail: mail@clarksearch.com
URL: http://www.clarksearch.com

Executive search firm.

1447 ■ CTR Group
11843-C Canon Blvd.
Newport News, CA 23606
Ph: (757)462-5900
Fax: (866)597-0055
Fr: 800-945-9095
E-mail: info@ctrc.com
URL: http://www.ctrc.com

Executive search firm.

1448 ■ Daly & Company Inc.
175 Federal St.
Boston, MA 02110-2210
Ph: (617)262-2800
Fax: (617)728-4477
E-mail: info@dalyco.com
URL: http://www.dalyco.com

Executive search firm.

1449 ■ Diversified Search
2005 Market St., Ste. 3300
1 Commerce Sq.
Philadelphia, PA 19103
Ph: (215)732-6666
Fax: (215)568-8399
URL: http://www.diversifiedsearch.com

Executive search firm. Branches in Burlington, MA and New York.

1450 ■ Empire International
1147 Lancaster Ave.
Berwyn, PA 19312
Ph: (610)647-7976
Fax: (610)647-8488
Fr: 800-539-0231
E-mail: info@empire-internl.com
URL: http://www.empire-internl.com

Executive search firm.

1451 ■ Eton Partners
1185 Springdale Rd.
Atlanta, GA 30306
Ph: (404)348-3576
E-mail: ebirchfield@etonpartners.com
URL: http://etonpartners.com

Executive search firm.

1452 ■ JPM International
26034 Acero
Mission Viejo, CA 92691
Ph: (949)699-4300
Fax: (949)699-4333

Fr: 800-685-7856
E-mail: qtek37@yahoo.com
URL: http://www.jpmintl.com/pages/qss.html

Executive search firm and employment agency.

1453 ■ The Katonah Group Inc.
33 Flying Point Rd.
Southampton, NY 11968
Ph: (631)287-9001
Fax: (631)287-9773
E-mail: info@katonahgroup.com
URL: http://www.katonahgroup.com

Company specializes in executive recruiting for companies in the fields of life sciences (genomic and proteomic instrumentation), bio-informatics, chem-informatics, medical devices, clinical diagnostics, and scientific and analytical instrumentation.

1454 ■ K.S. Frary & Associates
16 Schooner Ridge
Marblehead, MA 01945
Ph: (781)631-2464
Fax: (781)631-2465
E-mail: ksfrary@comcast.net
URL: http://www.ksfrary.com

Executive search firm.

1455 ■ Professional Placement Associates, Inc.
287 Bowman Ave.
Purchase, NY 10577-2517
Ph: (914)251-1000
Fax: (914)251-1055
E-mail: careers@ppasearch.com
URL: http://www.ppasearch.com

Executive search firm specializing in the health and medical field.

1456 ■ Team Placement Service, Inc.
1414 Prince St., Ste. 202
Alexandria, VA 22314
Ph: (703)820-8618
Fax: (703)820-3368
Fr: 800-495-6767
E-mail: 4jobs@teamplace.com
URL: http://www.teamplace.com

Full-service personnel consultants provide placement for healthcare staff, physician and dentist, private practice, and hospitals. Conduct interviews, tests, and reference checks to select the top 20% of applicants. Survey applicants' skill levels, provide backup information on each candidate, select compatible candidates for consideration, and insure the hiring process minimizes potential legal liability. Industries served: healthcare and government agencies providing medical, dental, biotech, laboratory, hospitals, and physician search.

ONLINE JOB SOURCES AND SERVICES

1457 ■ American Institute of Biological Sciences Classifieds
1444 I St. NW, Ste. 200
Washington, DC 20005
Ph: (202)628-1500
Fax: (202)628-1509
URL: http://www.aibs.org/classifieds

Description: Section of the American Institute of Biological Sciences website used for posting available positions, research awards and fellowships, and other classified ads.

1458 ■ American Society of Plant Biologists Job Bank
15501 Monona Dr.
Rockville, MD 20855-2768
Ph: (301)251-0560
Fax: (301)279-2996
E-mail: info@aspb.org
URL: http://my.aspb.org/networking

Description: A service of the American Society of

Plant Biologists, intended to aid its members in locating jobs and job resources. Site lists new jobs weekly in its job bank. Fee: A fee of $150 is charged for all academic/government/industry permanent positions and for all positions, regardless of rank, posted by private companies. Postdoctoral positions; research/technical positions (non-Ph.D.); and assistantships, fellowships, and internships at universities and not-for-profit agencies are published for a fee of $25.

1459 ■ BiologyJobs.com
URL: http://www.biologyjobs.com

Description: Provides resource for job seekers and employers who are interested in the life sciences. Includes listings of resumes and job openings.

1460 ■ BiosciRegister.com
URL: http://www.biosciregister.com

Description: Serves as an online directory or reference database of suppliers of products and services used in the biotechnology and life sciences industries. Contains job listings.

1461 ■ BioSpace.com
E-mail: support@biospace.com
URL: http://www.biospace.com

Description: Serves as an online community for industry news and careers for life science professionals. Provides biospace news, career events, recruitment and job seeking opportunities for professionals in the biotechnology and pharmaceutical industries.

1462 ■ Biotech Career Center
E-mail: info@biotechcareercenter.com
URL: http://www.biotechcareercenter.com

Description: Serves as a portal for scientists seeking career advancement and/or job opportunities in biotech companies. Provides links to biology career and information sites.

1463 ■ BiotechCrossing.com
URL: http://www.biotechcrossing.com

Description: Offers a collection of active biotech job listings. Includes the lists of employer career pages, job websites, association websites, newspaper classifieds and recruitment sites.

1464 ■ Discover8.com
E-mail: admin@discover8.com
URL: http://www.discover8.com

Description: Focuses on the dissemination and intelligent discussion of life science news, discoveries, hypotheses, and procedures. Features resume postings and career listings.

1465 ■ FASEB Career Resources
9650 Rockville Pike
Bethesda, MD 20814-3998
Ph: (301)634-7000
Fax: (301)634-7001
E-mail: careers@faseb.org
URL: http://www.faseb.org/MARC-and-Professional-Development/Career-Resources.aspx

Description: A career opportunity site combined with a development service that attempts to pair applicants at all career levels with employers who hire biomedical scientists and technicians. Biomedical career development is highlighted through career resource tools. Main files include: Careers Online DataNet, Career Online Classified.

1466 ■ GrantsNet
E-mail: membership@aaas.org
URL: http://sciencecareers.sciencemag.org/funding

Description: Grant-locating site intended for scientists in training who may become vulnerable in an era of competitive funding. Includes a directory of over 600 programs with contact information within a searchable database.

1467 ■ HireRx.com
URL: http://www.hirerx.com

Description: E-recruiting and training company that is focused on solving workforce issues for biotechnology and pharmaceutical firms. Provides access to job openings, online training courses, and communities in their scientific or functional concentration.

1468 ■ Hum-Molgen.org
E-mail: info@hum-molgen.de
URL: http://hum-molgen.org

Description: Provides resources for the latest information in human molecular genetics. Features biotechnical sources, diagnostics, ethical, legal and social implications, meetings and conferences, and positions in bioscience and medicine. Provides the opportunity to communicate with scientists, physicians, and other genetics professionals worldwide.

1469 ■ Naturejobs.com
URL: http://www.nature.com/naturejobs/science/welcome

Description: Lists jobs in the following disciplines of science: cell biology, biochemistry, bioinformatics, materials, and nanotechnology. Features scientific career information as well as news and advice.

TRADESHOWS

1470 ■ American Society for Biochemistry and Molecular Biology Annual Meeting
American Society for Biochemistry and Molecular Biology
11200 Rockville Pike, Ste. 302
Rockville, MD 20852-3110
Ph: (240)283-6600
Fax: (301)881-2080
E-mail: asbmb@asbmb.org
URL: http://www.asbmb.org

Annual. Primary Exhibits: Biological chemistry and molecular biology equipment, supplies, and services. Dates and Locations: 2012 Apr 21-25; San Diego, CA; San Diego Convention Center; 2013 Apr 20-24; Boston, MA; 2014 Apr 26-30; San Diego, CA.

1471 ■ American Society for Cell Biology Annual Meeting
American Society for Cell Biology ASCB
8120 Woodmont Ave., Ste. 750
Bethesda, MD 20814-2762
Ph: (301)347-9300
Fax: (301)347-9310
E-mail: ascbinfo@ascb.org
URL: http://www.ascb.org

Annual. Primary Exhibits: Equipment, supplies, and services related to doing research in cell and molecular biology. Dates and Locations: 2012 Dec 15-19; San Francisco, CA; 2013 Dec 14-18; New Orleans, LA; 2014 Dec 06-10; Philadelphia, PA; 2015 Dec 12-16; San Diego, CA.

1472 ■ American Society of Cytopathology Annual Scientific Meeting
American Society of Cytopathology
100 W. 10th St., Ste. 605
Wilmington, DE 19801
Ph: (302)543-6583
Fax: (302)543-6597
E-mail: asc@cytopathology.org
URL: http://www.cytopathology.org

Annual. Primary Exhibits: Cytopathology microscopes, analysis equipment and supplies, and publishers. Dates and Locations: 2012 Nov 02-06; Las Vegas, NV; Bally's Las Vegas.

1473 ■ Biophysical Society Annual Meeting
Biophysical Society
11400 Rockville Pike, Ste. 800
Rockville, MD 20852
Ph: (240)290-5600

Fax: (240)290-5555
E-mail: society@biophysics.org
URL: http://www.biophysics.org

Annual. Primary Exhibits: Biomedical research equipment, supplies, and services, including instruments and publications. Dates and Locations: 2012 Feb 25-29; San Diego, CA.

1474 ■ Society for Developmental Biology Annual Meeting
Society for Developmental Biology
9650 Rockville Pike
Bethesda, MD 20814-3998
Ph: (301)634-7815
Fax: (301)634-7825
E-mail: ichow@faseb.org
URL: http://www.sdbonline.org

Annual. Primary Exhibits: Exhibits related to problems of development and growth of organisms, scientific journals and scientific tools and post-doc. openings. Dates and Locations: 2012 Jul 19-12; Montreal, QC, Canada.

OTHER SOURCES

1475 ■ American Academy of Clinical Toxicology (AACT)
110 W Lancaster Ave., Ste. 230
Wayne, PA 19087
Ph: (703)556-9222
Fax: (703)556-8729
E-mail: admin@clintox.org
URL: http://www.clintox.org

Description: Physicians, veterinarians, pharmacists, nurses research scientists, and analytical chemists. Seeks to unite medical scientists and facilitate the exchange of information. Encourages the development of therapeutic methods and technology. Conducts professional training in poison information and emergency service personnel.

1476 ■ American Academy of Forensic Sciences (AAFS)
410 N 21st St.
Colorado Springs, CO 80904
Ph: (719)636-1100
Fax: (719)636-1993
E-mail: awarren@aafs.org
URL: http://www.aafs.org

Description: Represents criminalists, scientists, members of the bench and bar, pathologists, biologists, psychiatrists, examiners of questioned documents, toxicologists, odontologists, anthropologists, and engineers. Works to: encourage the study, improve the practice, elevate the standards, and advance the cause of the forensic sciences; improve the quality of scientific techniques, tests, and criteria; plan, organize, and administer meetings, reports, and other projects for the stimulation and advancement of these and related purposes. Maintains Forensic Sciences Job Listing; conducts selected research for the government; offers forensic expert referral service.

1477 ■ American Association of Anatomists (AAA)
9650 Rockville Pike
Bethesda, MD 20814-3998
Ph: (301)634-7910
Fax: (301)634-7965
E-mail: exec@anatomy.org
URL: http://aaatoday.org

Description: Represents biomedical researchers and educators focusing on anatomical form and function. Focuses on imaging, cell biology, genetics, molecular development, endocrinology, histology, neuroscience, forensics, microscopy, physical anthropology, and other areas. Promotes the three-dimensional understanding of structure as it relates to development and function, from molecule to organism through research and education.

1478 ■ American Institute of Biological Sciences (AIBS)
1313 Dolley Madison Blvd.
McLean, VA 22101
Ph: (703)790-1745
Fax: (703)790-2672
E-mail: adm@aibs.org
URL: http://www.aibs.org

Description: Professional member organization and federation of biological associations, laboratories, and museums whose members have an interest in the life sciences. Promotes unity and effectiveness of effort among persons engaged in biological research, education, and application of biological sciences, including agriculture, environment, and medicine. Seeks to further the relationships of biological sciences to other sciences and industries. Conducts roundtable series; provides names of prominent biologists who are willing to serve as speakers and curriculum consultants; provides advisory committees and other services to the Department of Energy, Environmental Protection Agency, National Science Foundation, Department of Defense, and National Aeronautics and Space Administration. Maintains educational consultant panel.

1479 ■ American Reef Coalition (ARC)
PO Box 844
Kihei, HI 96753
Ph: (808)870-5817
E-mail: info@americanreef.org
URL: http://www.americanreef.org

Description: To protect coral reef ecosystems, ocean resources and wilderness through a variety of proven methods and by providing support to other nonprofit organizations and government agencies engaged in marine, wilderness and natural area research, conservation and education.

1480 ■ American Society for Biochemistry and Molecular Biology (ASBMB)
11200 Rockville Pike, Ste. 302
Rockville, MD 20852-3110
Ph: (240)283-6600
Fax: (301)881-2080
E-mail: asbmb@asbmb.org
URL: http://www.asbmb.org

Description: Biochemists and molecular biologists who have conducted and published original investigations in biological chemistry and/or molecular biology. Operates placement service.

1481 ■ American Society for Cell Biology (ASCB)
8120 Woodmont Ave., Ste. 750
Bethesda, MD 20814-2762
Ph: (301)347-9300
Fax: (301)347-9310
E-mail: ascbinfo@ascb.org
URL: http://www.ascb.org

Description: Represents scientists with educational or research experience in cell biology or an allied field. Offers placement service.

1482 ■ American Society for Histocompatibility and Immunogenetics (ASHI)
15000 Commerce Pkwy., Ste. C
Mount Laurel, NJ 08054-2212
Ph: (856)638-0428
Fax: (856)439-0525
E-mail: info@ashi-hla.org
URL: http://www.ashi-hla.org

Description: Scientists, physicians, and technologists involved in research and clinical activities related to histocompatibility testing (a state of mutual tolerance that allows some tissues to be grafted effectively to others). Conducts proficiency testing and educational programs. Maintains liaison with regulatory agencies; offers placement services and laboratory accreditation. Has co-sponsored development of histocompatibility specialist and laboratory certification program.

1483 ■ American Society for Microbiology (ASM)
1752 N St. NW
Washington, DC 20036
Ph: (202)737-3600
Fax: (202)942-9333
E-mail: oed@asmusa.org
URL: http://www.asm.org

Description: Scientific society of microbiologists. Promotes the advancement of scientific knowledge in order to improve education in microbiology. Encourages the highest professional and ethical standards, and the adoption of sound legislative and regulatory policies affecting the discipline of microbiology at all levels. Communicates microbiological scientific achievements to the public. Maintains numerous committees and 23 divisions, and placement services; compiles statistics.

1484 ■ American Society of Plant Biologists (ASPB)
15501 Monona Dr.
Rockville, MD 20855-2768
Ph: (301)251-0560
Fax: (301)279-2996
E-mail: info@aspb.org
URL: http://www.aspb.org

Description: Professional society of plant biologists, plant biochemists, and other plant scientists engaged in research and teaching. Offers placement service for members; conducts educational and public affairs programs.

1485 ■ American Water Works Association (AWWA)
6666 W Quincy Ave.
Denver, CO 80235-3098
Ph: (303)794-7711
Fax: (303)347-0804
Fr: 800-926-7337
E-mail: custsvc@awwa.org
URL: http://www.awwa.org

Description: Water utility managers, superintendents, engineers, chemists, bacteriologists, and other individuals interested in public water supply; municipal- and investor-owned water departments; boards of health; manufacturers of waterworks equipment; government officials and consultants interested in water supply. Develops standards and supports research programs in waterworks design, construction, operation, and management. Conducts in-service training schools and prepares manuals for waterworks personnel. Maintains hall of fame. Offers placement service via member newsletter; compiles statistics. Offers training; children's services; and information center on the water utilities industry, potable water, and water reuse.

1486 ■ Association of Applied IPM Ecologists (AAIE)
PO Box 1119
Coarsegold, CA 93614
Ph: (559)761-1064
E-mail: director@aaie.net
URL: http://www.aaie.net

Description: Professional agricultural pest management consultants, entomologists, and field personnel. Promotes the implementation of integrated pest management in agricultural and urban environments. Provides a forum for the exchange of technical information on pest control. Offers placement service.

1487 ■ Association for International Practical Training (AIPT)
10400 Little Patuxent Pkwy., Ste. 250
Columbia, MD 21044-3519
Ph: (410)997-2200
Fax: (410)992-3924
E-mail: aipt@aipt.org
URL: http://www.aipt.org

Description: Providers worldwide of on-the-job training programs for students and professionals seeking international career development and life-changing experiences. Arranges workplace exchanges in hundreds of professional fields, bringing employers and trainees together from around the world. Client list ranges from small farming communities to Fortune 500 companies.

1488 ■ Biophysical Society (BPS)
11400 Rockville Pike Rd., Ste. 800
Rockville, MD 20852
Ph: (240)290-5600
Fax: (240)290-5555
E-mail: society@biophysics.org
URL: http://www.biophysics.org

Description: Biophysicists, physical biochemists, and physical and biological scientists interested in the application of physical laws and techniques to the analysis of biological or living phenomena. Maintains placement service.

1489 ■ Black Entomologists (BE)
USDA, ARS
59 Lee Rd.
Stoneville, MS 38776
Ph: (662)686-3646
Fax: (662)686-5281
E-mail: fadamhy@auburn.edu
URL: http://www.blackentomologists.org

Description: Serves the professional, scientific, social and cultural interests and needs of black men and women in entomology and related professions. Promotes the science of entomology and facilitates the advancement of entomology-related careers in the developing world. Fosters communication among black entomologists.

1490 ■ Engineering Society of Detroit (ESD)
20700 Civic Center Dr., Ste. 450
Southfield, MI 48076
Ph: (248)353-0735
Fax: (248)353-0736
E-mail: esd@esd.org
URL: http://ww2.esd.org/home.htm

Description: Engineers from all disciplines; scientists and technologists. Conducts technical programs and engineering refresher courses; sponsors conferences and expositions. Maintains speakers' bureau; offers placement services; although based in Detroit, MI, society membership is international.

1491 ■ Environmental Mutagen Society (EMS)
1821 Michael Faraday Dr., Ste. 300
Reston, VA 20190
Ph: (703)438-8220
Fax: (703)438-3113
E-mail: emshq@ems-us.org
URL: http://www.ems-us.org

Description: Bioscientists in universities, governmental agencies, and industry. Promotes basic and applied studies of mutagenesis (the area of genetics dealing with mutation and molecular biology); disseminates information relating to environmental mutagenesis. Offers placement service.

1492 ■ Federation of American Societies for Experimental Biology (FASEB)
9650 Rockville Pike
Bethesda, MD 20814
Ph: (301)634-7000
Fax: (301)634-7001
E-mail: info@faseb.org
URL: http://www.faseb.org

Description: Federation of scientific societies with a total of 40,000 members: the American Physiological Society; American Society for Biochemistry and Molecular Biology; American Society for Pharmacology and Experimental Therapeutics; American Society for Investigative Pathology; American Society for Nutritional Sciences; the American Association of Immunologists; the American Society for Bone and Mineral Research; American Society for Clinical Investigation; the Indocrine Society; the American Society of Human Genetics; Society for Developmental Biology; Biophysical Society; American Association of Anatomists; and the Protein Society. Maintains placement service.

1493 ■ Forensic Sciences Foundation (FSF)
410 N 21st St.
Colorado Springs, CO 80904
Ph: (719)636-1100
Fax: (719)636-1993
E-mail: awarren@aafs.org
URL: http://www.forensicsciencesfoundation.org

Description: Purposes are to: conduct research in the procedures and standards utilized in the practice of forensic sciences; develop and implement useful educational and training programs and methods of benefit to forensic sciences; conduct programs of public education concerning issues of importance to the forensic sciences; engage in activities which will promote, encourage, and assist the development of the forensic sciences. Provides referral service for forensic scientists. Compiles statistics. Operates the Forensic Sciences Foundation Press.

1494 ■ Korean-American Scientists and Engineers Association (KSEA)
1952 Gallows Rd., Ste. 300
Vienna, VA 22182
Ph: (703)748-1221
Fax: (703)748-1331
E-mail: sejong@ksea.org
URL: http://www.ksea.org

Description: Represents scientists and engineers holding single or advanced degrees. Promotes friendship and mutuality among Korean and American scientists and engineers; contributes to Korea's scientific, technological, industrial, and economic developments; strengthens the scientific, technological, and cultural bonds between Korea and the U.S. Sponsors symposium. Maintains speakers' bureau, placement service, and biographical archives. Compiles statistics.

1495 ■ Moroccan-American Society for Life Sciences
PO Box 324
Dunn Loring, VA 22027-0324
Ph: (202)413-6025
E-mail: board@us.biomatec.org
URL: http://us.biomatec.org

Description: Promotes advances and excellence in the life sciences. Serve as a bridge between scientific communities and organizations in the United States and Morocco. Conducts scientific events and activities.

1496 ■ Overseas Chinese Entomologists Association (OCEA)
4287 Farm Meadows Ct.
Okemos, MI 48864
E-mail: ocea_2010@yahoo.com
URL: http://www.go-to-ocea.org

Description: Aims to advance the study and knowledge of entomology by facilitating communication and collaboration among Chinese entomologists around the world. Provides academic-oriented services for members.

1497 ■ Radiation Research Society (RRS)
PO Box 7050
Lawrence, KS 66044
Fax: (785)843-1274
Fr: 800-627-0326
E-mail: info@radres.org
URL: http://www.radres.org

Description: Professional society of biologists, physicists, chemists, and physicians contributing to knowledge of radiation and its effects. Promotes original research in the natural sciences relating to radiation; facilitates integration of different disciplines in the study of radiation effects.

1498 ■ Save the Frogs!
303 Potrero St., No. 51
Santa Cruz, CA 95060

Ph: (831)621-6215
E-mail: contact@savethefrogs.com
URL: http://www.savethefrogs.com

Description: Seeks to protect amphibian populations and promote a society that respects and appreciates nature and wildlife. Educates the public about the necessity of protecting the world's amphibians and provides them with information and capabilities to protect amphibian populations. Conducts scientific research to stop amphibian extinction.

1499 ■ Society for Biological Engineering (SBE)

American Institute of Chemical Engineers
3 Park Ave., 19th Fl.
New York, NY 10016
Ph: (212)591-8888
E-mail: bio@aiche.org
URL: http://www.aiche.org/SBE

Description: Promotes the integration of biology with engineering and its benefits through bioprocessing, biomedical, and biomolecular applications. Raises interest, understanding, and recognition of engineers' and scientists' roles in biological engineering. Provides opportunities for the successful interaction of engineers and scientists.

1500 ■ Society for Cryobiology (SC)

1 Millennium Way
Branchburg, NJ 08876
Ph: (908)947-1176
Fax: (908)947-1085
E-mail: wsun@lifecell.com
URL: http://www.societyforcryobiology.org

Description: Basic and applied research in the field of low temperature biology and medicine. Promotes interdisciplinary approach to freezing, freeze-drying, hypothermia, hibernation, physiological effects of low environmental temperature on animals and plants, medical applications of reduced temperatures, cryosurgery, hypothermic perfusion and cryopreservation of organs, cryoprotective agents and their pharmacological action, and pertinent methodologies. Operates charitable program and placement service.

1501 ■ Society for In Vitro Biology (SIVB)

514 Daniels St., Ste. 411
Raleigh, NC 27605-1317
Ph: (919)562-0600
Fax: (919)562-0608
E-mail: sivb@sivb.org
URL: http://www.sivb.org

Description: Fosters exchange of knowledge of in vitro biology of cells, tissues and organs from both plant and animals (including humans). Focuses on biological research, development, and applications of significance to science and society. Accomplishes its mission through the society's publications; national and local conferences, meetings and workshops; and through support of teaching initiatives in cooperation with educational institutions. Creates an environment of scientific exchange and interdisciplinary synergy with the goal of advancing current and future systems for in vitro biology.

1502 ■ Society for Industrial Microbiology (SIM)

3929 Old Lee Hwy., Ste. 92A
Fairfax, VA 22030-2421
Ph: (703)691-3357
Fax: (703)691-7991
E-mail: simhq@simhq.org
URL: http://www.simhq.org

Description: Mycologists, bacteriologists, biologists, chemists, engineers, zoologists, and others interested in biological processes as applied to industrial materials and processes concerning microorganisms. Serves as liaison between the specialized fields of microbiology. Maintains placement service; conducts surveys and scientific workshops in industrial microbiology.

1503 ■ Soil Science Society of America (SSSA)

677 S Segoe Rd.
Madison, WI 53711
Ph: (608)273-8080
Fax: (608)273-2021
E-mail: headquarters@soils.org
URL: http://www.soils.org

Description: Professional soil scientists, including soil physicists, soil classifiers, land use and management specialists, chemists, microbiologists, soil fertility specialists, soil cartographers, conservationists, mineralogists, engineers, and others interested in fundamental and applied soil science.

1504 ■ Teratology Society (TS)

1821 Michael Faraday Dr., Ste. 300
Reston, VA 20190
Ph: (703)438-3104
Fax: (703)438-3113
E-mail: tshq@teratology.org
URL: http://www.teratology.org

Description: Individuals from academia, government, private industry, and the professions. Stimulates scientific interest in, and promotes the exchange of ideas and information about, problems of abnormal biological development and malformations at the fundamental or clinical level. Sponsors annual education course, and presentations. Establishes archives of society documents and history.

1505 ■ World Federation for Coral Reef Conservation

PO Box 942
Safety Harbor, FL 34695
E-mail: vic.ferguson@wfcrc.org
URL: http://wfcrc.org/default.aspx

Description: Works to stop the destruction of coral reefs by involving local citizens, scientists and recreational divers. Collaborates with like-minded organizations in implementing programs for coral reef decline management. Supports conservation efforts on coral reefs.

Sources of Help-Wanted Ads

1506 ■ AIE Perspectives Newsmagazine
American Institute of Engineers
4630 Appian Way, Ste. 206
El Sobrante, CA 94803-1875
Ph: (510)758-6240
Fax: (510)758-6240
URL: http://www.members-aie.org

Monthly. Professional magazine covering engineering.

1507 ■ American Biotechnology Laboratory
American Laboratory/Labcompare
30 Controls Dr.
Shelton, CT 06484-0870
Ph: (203)926-9300
Fax: (203)926-9310
URL: http://www.americanbiotechnologylaboratory.com

Biotechnology magazine.

1508 ■ Annual Review of Genetics
Annual Reviews Inc.
4139 El Camino Way
Palo Alto, CA 94306
Ph: (650)493-4400
Fax: (650)424-0910
Fr: 800-523-8635
URL: http://www.annualreviews.org/journal/genet

Annual. $86.00/year for individuals, print & online; $263.00/year for institutions, print & online; $219.00/year for institutions, online; $219.00/year for institutions, print. Periodical covering issues in genetics and the biological sciences.

1509 ■ Annual Review of Microbiology
Annual Reviews Inc.
4139 El Camino Way
Palo Alto, CA 94306
Ph: (650)493-4400
Fax: (650)424-0910
Fr: 800-523-8635
URL: http://www.annualreviews.org/journal/micro

Annual. $86.00/year for individuals, print & online; $263.00/year for institutions, print & online; $219.00/year for institutions, online; $219.00/year for institutions, print. Periodical covering microbiology and the biological sciences.

1510 ■ Biomedical Engineering News
Biomedical Engineering Society
8401 Corporate Dr., Ste. 1125
Landover, MD 20785-2224
Ph: (301)459-1999
Fax: (301)459-2444
Fr: 877-871-BMES
E-mail: info@bmes.org
URL: http://www.bmes.org

Description: Monthly. Provides news and information on the Society; presents articles on bioengineering science. Recurring features include letters to the editor, news of research, a calendar of events, reports of meetings, news of educational opportunities, job listings, and columns titled Public Affairs, Student Chapter News, and Society News.

1511 ■ Biomedical Optics Express
Optical Societyof America
2010 Massachusetts Ave. NW
Washington, DC 20036
Ph: (202)223-8130
Fax: (202)223-1096
URL: http://www.opticsinfobase.org/boe/journal/boe/about.cfm

Monthly. Peer-reviewed journal focusing on biomedical optics and biophotonics.

1512 ■ CBE—Life Sciences Education
American Society for Cell Biology
8120 Woodmont Ave., Ste. 750
Bethesda, MD 20814-2762
Ph: (301)347-9300
Fax: (301)347-9310
URL: http://www.lifescied.org/

Quarterly. Journal that focuses on life science education at the K-12, undergraduate, and graduate levels.

1513 ■ Cell
Cell Press
600 Technology Sq.
Cambridge, MA 02139
Ph: (617)661-7057
Fax: (617)661-7061
Fr: (866)314-2355
E-mail: celleditor@cell.com
URL: http://www.cell.com

$212.00/year for U.S. and Canada, individual, print and online; $320.00/year for other countries, individual, print and online; $212.00/year for U.S. and Canada, online only, individual; $212.00/year for other countries, online only, individual; $1,425.00/year for U.S. and Canada, institution, print only; $1,605.00/year for institutions, other countries, print only. Peer-reviewed journal on molecular and cell biology.

1514 ■ Chemistry & Biology
Elsevier Science Inc.
360 Park Ave. S
New York, NY 10010-1710
Ph: (212)989-5800
Fax: (212)633-3990
Fr: 888-437-4636
URL: http://www.elsevier.com/wps/find/journaldescription.cws_home

Monthly. $2,137.00/year for institutions, for all countries except Europe, Japan & Iran; $442.00/year for U.S. and Canada; $457.00/year for individuals, for all countries except Europe, Japan and Iran. Journal focused on genetic, computational, or theoretical information of chemistry and biology, substantiating experimental data.

1515 ■ Composites
Begell House Inc.
50 Cross Hwy.
Redding, CT 06896
Ph: (203)938-1300
Fax: (203)938-1304
URL: http://www.begellhouse.com/journals/36ff4a142dec9609

$708.00/year for institutions. Journal featuring basic ideas in the mechanics of composite materials and structures between research workers and engineers.

1516 ■ Current Advances in Genetics & Molecular Biology
Elsevier Science Inc.
360 Park Ave. S
New York, NY 10010-1710
Ph: (212)989-5800
Fax: (212)633-3990
Fr: 888-437-4636
URL: http://www.elsevier.com/wps/find/journaldescription.cws_home

Monthly. $25,500.00/year for individuals, Japan; $221.00/year for individuals, for all countries except Europe, Japan and Iran; $221.00/year for individuals, European countries and Iran; $6,340.00/year for institutions, other countries; $755,700.00/year for institutions, Japan; $5,713.00/year for institutions, European countries and Iran. Journal covering current details of genetics and molecular biology.

1517 ■ Engineering
Scientific Research Publishing
PO Box 54821
Irvine, CA 92619-4821
E-mail: eng@scirp.org
URL: http://www.scirp.org/journal/eng/

Monthly. $708.00/year for individuals. Peer-reviewed journal publishing articles on the latest advancements in engineering.

1518 ■ Engineering Conferences International Symposium Series
Berkeley Electronic Press
2809 Telegraph Ave., Ste. 202
Berkeley, CA 94705-1167
Ph: (510)665-1200
Fax: (510)665-1201
URL: http://services.bepress.com/eci/

Journal focusing on advance engineering science.

1519 ■ Engineering in Life Sciences
John Wiley & Sons Inc.
111 River St.
Hoboken, NJ 07030-5773
Ph: (201)748-6000
Fax: (201)748-6088

Fr: 800-825-7550
URL: http://onlinelibrary.wiley.com/journal/10.1002/
   (ISSN)1618-28

Bimonthly. $989.00/year for institutions, European,
online only; $1,512.00/year for institutions, online
only, Switzerland and Liechtenstein; $1,299.00/year
for institutions, other countries, online only; $663.00/
year for institutions, European, online only; $1,299.00/
year for institutions, online only; $1,299.00/year for
institutions, Canada and Mexico, online only. Journal
focusing on the field of biotechnology and related
topics including microbiology, genetics, biochemistry,
and chemistry.

1520 ■ Epigenetics
Landes Bioscience
1806 Rio Grande St.
Austin, TX 78701
Ph: (512)637-6050
Fax: (512)637-6079
URL: http://www.landesbioscience.com/journals/
   epigenetics/

$129.00/year for individuals, online; $350.00/year for
individuals, print and online; $450.00/year for other
countries, print and online; $1,500.00/year for institu-
tions, online; $1,850.00/year for institutions, print and
online; $1,950.00/year for institutions, other countries,
print and online. Journal devoted to practicing physicians, residents and students.

**1521 ■ Ethics in Biology, Engineering and
   Medicine**
Begell House Inc.
50 Cross Hwy.
Redding, CT 06896
Ph: (203)938-1300
Fax: (203)938-1304
URL: http://www.begellhouse.com/journals/
   6ed509641f7324e6

$650.00/year for institutions. Peer-reviewed journal
covering ethical issues on biomedical research and
the development of new biomaterials, implants,
devices and treatments.

**1522 ■ Forum on Immunopathological
   Diseases and Therapeutics**
Begell House Inc.
50 Cross Hwy.
Redding, CT 06896
Ph: (203)938-1300
Fax: (203)938-1304
URL: http://www.begellhouse.com/journals/
   1a654bf03faf67ac.html

$748.00/year for institutions. Journal publishing
articles on immunopathological diseases and
therapeutics.

**1523 ■ Graduating Engineer & Computer
   Careers**
Career Recruitment Media
2 LAN Dr., Ste. 100
Westford, MA 01886
Ph: (978)692-5092
Fax: (978)692-4174
URL: http://www.graduatingengineer.com

Quarterly. $16.95/year for individuals. Magazine
focusing on employment, education, and career
development for entry-level engineers and computer
scientists.

1524 ■ High Technology Careers Magazine
HTC
4701 Patrick Henry Dr., No. 1901
Santa Clara, CA 95054
Fax: (408)567-0242
URL: http://www.hightechcareers.com

Bimonthly. $29.00/year; $35.00/year for Canada;
$85.00/year for out of country. Magazine (tabloid)
containing employment opportunity information for
the engineering and technical community.

1525 ■ InterJournal
New England Complex Systems Institute
283 Main St., Ste. 319
Cambridge, MA 02142
Ph: (617)547-4100
Fax: (617)661-7711
URL: http://www.interjournal.org/

Journal covering the fields of science and
engineering.

1526 ■ Invertebrate Biology
John Wiley & Sons Inc.
350 Main St., Commerce Pl.
Malden, MA 02148-5089
Ph: (781)388-8200
Fax: (781)388-8210
URL: http://www.amicros.org/

Quarterly. $268.00/year for institutions, online or print;
$309.00/year for institutions, print & online; $163.00/
year for institutions, print or online; $188.00/year for
institutions, print & online. Scientific journal covering
the biology of invertebrate animals and research in
the fields of cell and molecular biology, ecology,
physiology, systematics, genetics, biogeography and
behavior.

1527 ■ ISRN Endocrinology
Hindawi Publishing Corporation
410 Park Ave., 15th Fl.
287 PMB
New York, NY 10022
E-mail: endocrinology@isrn.com
URL: http://www.isrn.com/journals/endocrinology

Peer-reviewed, open access journal publishing
original research articles, review articles, case
reports, and clinical studies in all areas of
endocrinology.

1528 ■ ISRN Hematology
Hindawi Publishing Corporation
410 Park Ave., 15th Fl.
287 PMB
New York, NY 10022
E-mail: hematology@isrn.com
URL: http://www.isrn.com/journals/hematology

Peer-reviewed journal covering research in all areas
of hematology.

1529 ■ ISRN Neurology
Hindawi Publishing Corporation
410 Park Ave., 15th Fl.
287 PMB
New York, NY 10022
E-mail: neurology@isrn.com
URL: http://www.isrn.com/journals/neurology

Peer-reviewed journal publishing research in all areas
of neurology.

1530 ■ ISRN Oncology
Hindawi Publishing Corporation
410 Park Ave., 15th Fl.
287 PMB
New York, NY 10022
E-mail: oncology@isrn.com
URL: http://www.isrn.com/journals/oncology

Peer-reviewed journal publishing research articles in
all areas of oncology.

1531 ■ ISRN Pharmacology
Hindawi Publishing Corporation
410 Park Ave., 15th Fl.
287 PMB
New York, NY 10022
E-mail: pharmacology@isrn.com
URL: http://www.isrn.com/journals/pharmacology

Peer-reviewed journal publishing articles in all areas
of pharmacology.

1532 ■ ISRN Rheumatology
Hindawi Publishing Corporation
410 Park Ave., 15th Fl.
287 PMB
New York, NY 10022
E-mail: rheumatology@isrn.com
URL: http://www.isrn.com/journals/rheumatology

Peer-reviewed journal publishing information in all
areas of rheumatology.

1533 ■ ISRN Urology
Hindawi Publishing Corporation
410 Park Ave., 15th Fl.
287 PMB
New York, NY 10022
E-mail: urology@isrn.com
URL: http://www.isrn.com/journals/urology

Peer-reviewed journal publishing research in all areas
of urology.

**1534 ■ Journal of Adolescent and Young
   Adult Oncology**
Mary Ann Liebert Inc., Publishers
140 Huguenot St., 3rd Fl.
New Rochelle, NY 10801-5215
Ph: (914)740-2100
Fax: (914)740-2101
Fr: 800-654-3237
URL: http://www.liebertpub.com/products/
   product.aspx?pid=387

Quarterly. $336.00/year for individuals, print and on-
line; $758.00/year for institutions, print and online.
Peer-reviewed journal focusing on research, education, communication and collaboration between health
professionals in adolescent and young adult oncology.

**1535 ■ Journal of Biomedical Science and
   Engineering**
Scientific Research Publishing
PO Box 54821
Irvine, CA 92619-4821
E-mail: jbise@scirp.org
URL: http://www.scirp.org/journal/jbise/

Monthly. Peer-reviewed journal covering all aspects
of biomedical science and engineering.

1536 ■ Journal of Engineering Education
American Society for Engineering Education
1818 N St. NW, Ste. 600
Washington, DC 20036-2479
Ph: (202)331-3500
Fax: (202)265-8504
URL: http://www.jee.org

Quarterly. $100.00/year for libraries, online; $160.00/
year for other countries, library; $150.00/year for
U.S., Canada, and Mexico, library; $160.00/year for
other countries, library. Peer-reviewed journal covering scholarly research in engineering education.

**1537 ■ Journal of Long-Term Effects of
   Medical Implants**
Begell House Inc.
50 Cross Hwy.
Redding, CT 06896
Ph: (203)938-1300
Fax: (203)938-1304
URL: http://www.begellhouse.com/journals/
   1bef42082d7a0fdf

$1,072.00/year for institutions. Peer-reviewed journal
covering medical implants.

**1538 ■ Journal of Women and Minorities in
   Science and Engineering**
Begell House Inc.
50 Cross Hwy.
Redding, CT 06896
Ph: (203)938-1300
Fax: (203)938-1304
URL: http://www.begellhouse.com/journals/
   00551c876cc2f027

$248.00/year for institutions. Peer-reviewed journal
featuring innovative ideas and programs for classroom teachers, scientific studies, and formulation of

concepts related to the education, recruitment, and retention of under-represented groups in science and engineering.

1539 ■ *Leukemia Supplements*
Nature Publishing Group
75 Varick St., 9th Fl.
New York, NY 10013-1917
Ph: (212)726-9200
Fax: (212)696-9006
Fr: 888-331-6288
URL: http://www.nature.com/leusup/marketing/index.html

Peer-reviewed journal covering all aspects of the research and treatment of leukemia and allied diseases.

1540 ■ *NABR Update*
National Association for Biomedical Research
818 Connecticut Ave. NW, Ste. 900
Washington, DC 20006
Ph: (202)857-0540
Fax: (202)659-1902
E-mail: info@nabr.org
URL: http://www.nabr.org

Description: Periodic. Apprises Association members of government, legal, and media-based activity regarding biomedical research and the animal rights movement. Summarized news items are provided in the Association's sister publication, NABR Alert.

1541 ■ *Narrative Inquiry in Bioethics*
The Johns Hopkins University Press
2715 N Charles St.
Baltimore, MD 21218-4319
Ph: (410)516-6900
Fax: (410)516-6968
URL: http://www.press.jhu.edu/journals/narrative_inquiry_in_bioet

$175.00/year for institutions, print; $50.00/year for individuals, print. Journal publishing information on bioethics.

1542 ■ *NSBE Magazine*
NSBE Publications
205 Daingerfield Rd.
Alexandria, VA 22314
Ph: (703)549-2207
Fax: (703)683-5312
URL: http://www.nsbe.org/News-Media/Magazines/About-NSBE-Magazine

$20.00/year for individuals; $35.00/year for other countries; $15.00/year for students. Journal providing information on engineering careers, self-development, and cultural issues for recent graduates with technical majors.

1543 ■ *PALAIOS*
SEPM Publications
4111 S Darlington, Ste. 100
Tulsa, OK 74135-6373
Ph: (918)610-3361
Fax: (918)621-1685
Fr: 800-865-9765
E-mail: palois@ku.edu
URL: http://palaios.ku.edu/

Monthly. $315.00/year for individuals, for U.S.; online version with CD-ROM; $415.00/year for individuals, for U.S.; print and online version with CD-ROM; $315.00/year for other countries, online version with CD-ROM; $425.00/year for other countries, print and online version with CD-ROM. Journal providing information on the impact of life on Earth history as recorded in the paleontological and sedimentological records. Covers areas such as biogeochemistry, ichnology, sedimentology, stratigraphy, paleoecology, paleoclimatology, and paleoceanography.

1544 ■ *Perspectives in Biology and Medicine*
The Johns Hopkins University Press
2715 N Charles St.
Baltimore, MD 21218-4319
Ph: (410)516-6900

Fax: (410)516-6968
URL: http://www.press.jhu.edu/journals/perspectives_in_biology_an

Quarterly. $50.00/year for individuals, print or online; $150.00/year for institutions, print; $100.00/year for individuals, print, 2 years; $45.00/year for students, print; $300.00/year for institutions, print, 2 years. Peer-reviewed journal publishing articles of current interest in medicine and biology in a context with humanistic, social, and scientific concerns. Covers a wide range of biomedical topics such as neurobiology, biomedical ethics and history, genetics and evolution, and ecology.

1545 ■ *PLoS Biology*
Public Library of Science
1160 Battery St.
San Francisco, CA 94111
Ph: (415)624-1200
Fax: (415)546-4090
URL: http://www.plosbiology.org/home.action

Monthly. Free, online; $365.00/year for U.S. and Canada, print only (credit card); $415.00/year for other countries, print only (credit card); $45.00/year for other countries, print only (single copy). Open access, peer-reviewed general biology journal.

1546 ■ *PLoS Genetics*
Public Library of Science
1160 Battery St.
San Francisco, CA 94111
Ph: (415)624-1200
Fax: (415)546-4090
E-mail: plosgenetics@plos.org
URL: http://www.plosgenetics.org/home.action

Weekly. Free, online. Open access, peer-reviewed journal that publishes research and case studies in the field of genetics.

1547 ■ *Reviews in Biomedical Engineering*
IEEE Inc.
445 Hoes Ln.
Piscataway, NJ 08854-4141
Ph: (732)981-0060
Fax: (732)562-6380
Fr: 800-701-IEEE
URL: http://rbme.embs.org/index.html

Journal focusing on new developments and trends in the field of biomedical engineering.

1548 ■ *SWE, Magazine of the Society of Women Engineers*
Society of Women Engineers
120 S La Salle St., Ste. 1515
Chicago, IL 60603
Ph: (312)596-5223
Fr: 877-793-4636
URL: http://societyofwomenengineers.swe.org/index.php

Quarterly. $30.00/year for nonmembers. Magazine for engineering students and for women and men working in the engineering and technology fields. Covers career guidance, continuing development and topical issues.

1549 ■ *WEPANEWS*
Women in Engineering Programs & Advocates Network
1901 E Asbury Ave., Ste. 220
Denver, CO 80208
Ph: (303)871-4643
Fax: (303)871-4628
E-mail: dmatt@wepan.org
URL: http://www.wepan.org

Description: 2/year. Seeks to provide greater access for women to careers in engineering. Includes news of graduate, undergraduate, freshmen, pre-college, and re-entry engineering programs for women. Recurring features include job listings, faculty, grant, and conference news, international engineering program news, action group news, notices of publications available, and a column titled Kudos.

1550 ■ *Woman Engineer*
Equal Opportunity Publications, Inc.
445 Broadhollow Rd., Ste. 425
Melville, NY 11747
Ph: (631)421-9421
Fax: (631)421-1352
E-mail: info@eop.com
URL: http://www.eop.com

Annual. Magazine that is offered at no charge to qualified female engineering, computer-science, and information-technology students and professionals seeking to find employment and advancement in their careers.

1551 ■ *The World Wide Web Journal of Biology*
Epress, Inc.
130 Union Terrace Ln.
Plymouth, MN 55441
URL: http://www.epress.com/w3jbio/

Journal on Bio-informatics.

EMPLOYER DIRECTORIES AND NETWORKING LISTS

1552 ■ *AGT International Membership Directory*
Association of Genetic Technologists
AGT Executive Office
PO Box 19193
Lenexa, KS 66285
Ph: (913)895-4605
Fax: (913)895-4652
URL: http://www.agt-info.org/IntMembershipDir.aspx

Monthly. Covers: About 520 laboratories studying heritable and acquired chromosomal disorders using cytogenetic, genetics, and cellular biology techniques. Entries include: Laboratory name, address, phone, areas of specialization, techniques, numbers and types of laboratory tests performed, and names of director and cytogenetic technologists. Arrangement: Geographical. Indexes: Director name, ACT member name.

1553 ■ *American Men and Women of Science*
Gale
PO Box 6904
Florence, KY 41022-6904
Fr: 800-354-9706
URL: http://www.gale.cengage.com

Biennial, even years; New edition expected 29th, June 2011. $1,368.00 for individuals. Covers: Over 135,000 U.S. and Canadian scientists active in the physical, biological, mathematical, computer science, and engineering fields; includes references to previous edition for deceased scientists and nonrespondents. Entries include: Name, address, education, personal and career data, memberships, honors and awards, research interest. Arrangement: Alphabetical. Indexes: Discipline (in separate volume).

HANDBOOKS AND MANUALS

1554 ■ *The Biomedical Engineering Handbook*
CRC
6000 Broken Sounds Pkwy. NW, Ste. 300
Boca Raton, FL 33487
Ph: (561)994-0555
Fax: 800-374-3401
Fr: 800-272-7737
E-mail: orders@crcpress.com
URL: http://www.crcpress.com

Joseph D. Bronzino, editor. Third edition, 2006. $229.95. 4,232 pages. Beginning with an overview of physiology and physiological modeling, simulation, and control, the book explores bioelectric phenomena, biomaterials, biomechanics, rehabilitation and human performance engineering, and ethical issues.

1555 ■ *Career Development in Bioengineering and Biotechnology*

Springer
233 Spring St.
New York, NY 10013
Ph: (212)460-1500
Fax: (212)460-1575
URL: http://www.springer.com

Guruprasad Madhavan, Barbara Oakley, and Luis Kun (Editors.) 2009. $49.95. 485 pages. Provides a roadmap to the broad and varied career development opportunities in bioengineering, biotechnology, and related fields.

1556 ■ *Career Opportunities in Biotechnology and Drug Development*

Cold Spring Harbor Laboratory Press
500 Sunnyside Blvd.
Woodbury, NY 11797-2924
Ph: (516)422-4101
Fax: (516)422-4097
Fr: 800-843-4388
E-mail: cshpress@cshl.edu
URL: http://www.cshlpress.com

Toby Freedman. 2009. $59.00 (hardcover). 409 pages. Provides an overview of careers in the life science industry. Features chapters that includes sections on preparing for a prospective career; educational requirements and personality characteristics needed; recommendations of books, magazines, and web site resources; and issues to consider regarding salary and compensation. Includes interviewing and job searching tips, as well as suggestions on writing a resume specifically for the industry.

1557 ■ *Introduction to Biomedical Engineering*

Elsevier
3251 Riverport Ln.
Maryland Heights, MO 63043
Ph: (314)453-7010
Fax: (314)453-7095
Fr: 800-545-2522
E-mail: usbkinfo@elsevier.com
URL: http://www.elsevier.com

Susan M. Blanchard, Joseph D. Bronzino and John Denis Enderle, editors. Second edition. 2005. $108.00. 1144 pages. Provides a historical perspective of the major developments in the biomedical field.

1558 ■ *Opportunities in Biological Science Careers*

The McGraw-Hill Companies
PO Box 182604
Columbus, OH 43272
Fax: (614)759-3749
Fr: 877-883-5524
E-mail: customer.service@mcgraw-hill.com
URL: http://www.mhprofessional.com/
    product.php?isbn=007143187X

Charles A. Winter. 2004. $13.95 (paper). 160 pages. Identifies employers and outlines opportunities in plant and animal biology, biological specialties, biomedical sciences, applied biology, and other areas. Illustrated.

1559 ■ *Resumes for Scientific and Technical Careers*

The McGraw-Hill Companies
PO Box 182604
Columbus, OH 43272
Fax: (614)759-3749
Fr: 877-883-5524
E-mail: customer.service@mcgraw-hill.com
URL: http://www.mhprofessional.com/
    product.php?isbn=0071482199

Third edition, 2007. $12.95 (paper). 144 pages. Provides resume advice for individuals interested in working in scientific and technical careers. Includes sample resumes and cover letters.

EMPLOYMENT AGENCIES AND SEARCH FIRMS

1560 ■ Amtec Human Capital

2749 Saturn St.
Brea, CA 92821
Ph: (714)993-1900
Fax: (714)993-2419
E-mail: info@amtechc.com
URL: http://www.amtechc.com

Employment agency.

1561 ■ Aureus Group

C&A Plz., 13609 California St., Ste. 100
Omaha, NE 68154-3503
Ph: (402)891-6900
Fax: (402)891-1290
Fr: 888-239-5993
E-mail: omaha@aureusgroup.com
URL: http://www.aureusgroup.com

Provides human capital management services in a wide variety of industries. Executive search and recruiting consultants specializing in six areas: accounting and finance, data processing, aerospace, engineering, manufacturing and medical professionals. Industries served: hospitals, all mainframe computer shops and all areas of accounting.

1562 ■ Battalia Winston International

555 Madison Ave.
New York, NY 10022
Ph: (212)308-8080
URL: http://www.battaliawinston.com

Executive search firm. Branches in Los Angeles; Chicago; Wellesley Hills, MA; Edison, NJ.

1563 ■ Biomedical Search Consultants

275 Wyman St., Ste. 110
Waltham, MA 02451
Ph: (781)890-8824
Fax: (781)998-1266
E-mail: kprovost@biomedicalsearch.com
URL: http://www.biomedicalsearchconsultants.com

Employment agency.

1564 ■ BioQuest

100 Spear St., Ste. 1125
San Francisco, CA 94105-1526
Ph: (415)777-2422
E-mail: resumes@bioquestinc.com
URL: http://www.bioquestinc.com

Executive search firm focused in healthcare and life sciences.

1565 ■ The Coelyn Group

1 Park Plaza, Ste. 600
Irvine, CA 92614
Ph: (949)553-8855
Fax: (866)436-2171
E-mail: contact@coelyngroup.com
URL: http://www.coelyngroup.com

Executive search firm.

1566 ■ CSI Executive Search LLC

9600 Great Hills Trl., Ste. 150W
Austin, TX 78759
Ph: (512)301-1119
Fax: (512)301-5559
Fr: 877-329-1828
E-mail: info@csi-executivesearch.com
URL: http://www.csi-executivesearch.com

Executive search firm that specializes in the following arenas: accounting, engineering, healthcare, information technology, and legal. Utilizes behavioral, performance, retention variable, social intelligence, and cultural assessments to ensure the best candidate/client fit. Works on a retained, retingency, and contingency search basis.

1567 ■ D'Antoni Partners Inc.

122 W John Carpenter Fwy., Ste. 525
Irving, TX 75039
Ph: (972)719-4400
Fax: (972)719-4401
E-mail: richard@dantonipartners.com
URL: http://www.dantonipartners.com

Executive search firm.

1568 ■ Day & Associates

577 Airport Blvd., Ste. 130
Burlingame, CA 94010
Ph: (650)343-2660
Fax: (650)344-8460
E-mail: info@dayassociates.net
URL: http://www.dayassociates.net

Executive search firm.

1569 ■ JPM International

26034 Acero
Mission Viejo, CA 92691
Ph: (949)699-4300
Fax: (949)699-4333
Fr: 800-685-7856
E-mail: qtek37@yahoo.com
URL: http://www.jpmintl.com/pages/qss.html

Executive search firm and employment agency.

1570 ■ Lloyd Staffing

445 Broadhollow Rd., Ste. 119
Melville, NY 11747
Ph: (631)777-7600
Fax: (631)777-7626
Fr: 888-292-6678
E-mail: info@lloydstaffing.com
URL: http://www.lloydstaffing.com

Personnel agency and search firm.

1571 ■ O'Keefe and Partners

4 Corporate Dr., Ste 490
Shelton, CT 06484
Ph: (203)929-4222
E-mail: smoore@okeefepartners.com
URL: http://www.okeefepartners.com

Executive search firm.

1572 ■ Techtronix Technical Search

4805 N 24th Pl.
PO Box 17713
Milwaukee, WI 53217-0173
Ph: (414)466-3100
Fax: (414)466-3598

Firm specializes in recruiting executives for the engineering, information systems, manufacturing, marketing, finance, and human resources industries. Industries include electronic, manufacturing and finance.

ONLINE JOB SOURCES AND SERVICES

1573 ■ Biofind

URL: http://www.biofind.com

Description: Provides industry insights for the biotechnology industry. Tracks the latest news from around the biotechnology field. Features job opportunities.

1574 ■ BiomedicalEngineer.com

URL: http://www.biomedicalengineer.com

Description: Features biomedical engineering jobs and products to biomedical engineers.

1575 ■ BiosciRegister.com

URL: http://www.biosciregister.com

Description: Serves as an online directory or reference database of suppliers of products and services used in the biotechnology and life sciences industries. Contains job listings.

1576 ■ Biotech Career Center
E-mail: info@biotechcareercenter.com
URL: http://www.biotechcareercenter.com

Description: Serves as a portal for scientists seeking career advancement and/or job opportunities in biotech companies. Provides links to biology career and information sites.

1577 ■ Discover8.com
E-mail: admin@discover8.com
URL: http://www.discover8.com

Description: Focuses on the dissemination and intelligent discussion of life science news, discoveries, hypotheses, and procedures. Features resume postings and career listings.

1578 ■ EngineerJobs.com
URL: http://www.engineerjobs.com

Description: Provides job opportunities for engineering professionals in the following disciplines: aerospace, agricultural, biomedical, chemical, civil, electrical, environmental, industrial, manufacturing, marine, materials, mechanical, mining, nuclear, petroleum, process, project, quality, sales, software, solar, systems, and structural.

1579 ■ FASEB Career Resources
9650 Rockville Pike
Bethesda, MD 20814-3998
Ph: (301)634-7000
Fax: (301)634-7001
E-mail: careers@faseb.org
URL: http://www.faseb.org/MARC-and-Professional-Development/Career-Resources.aspx

Description: A career opportunity site combined with a development service that attempts to pair applicants at all career levels with employers who hire biomedical scientists and technicians. Biomedical career development is highlighted through career resource tools. Main files include: Careers Online DataNet, Career Online Classified.

1580 ■ Genetics Society of America: Positions Open
URL: http://www.genetics-gsa.org

Description: Listing of position announcements formerly published in Genetics. Members may e-mail job listings to the site to be posted.

1581 ■ Get Biomedical Engineer Jobs
URL: http://www.getbiomedicalengineerjobs.net

Description: Features employment opportunities for biomedical engineers.

1582 ■ GrantsNet
E-mail: membership@aaas.org
URL: http://sciencecareers.sciencemag.org/funding

Description: Grant-locating site intended for scientists in training who may become vulnerable in an era of competitive funding. Includes a directory of over 600 programs with contact information within a searchable database.

1583 ■ HireRx.com
URL: http://www.hirerx.com

Description: E-recruiting and training company that is focused on solving workforce issues for biotechnology and pharmaceutical firms. Provides access to job openings, online training courses, and communities in their scientific or functional concentration.

1584 ■ Hum-Molgen.org
E-mail: info@hum-molgen.de
URL: http://hum-molgen.org

Description: Provides resources for the latest information in human molecular genetics. Features biotechnical sources, diagnostics, ethical, legal and social implications, meetings and conferences, and positions in bioscience and medicine. Provides the opportunity to communicate with scientists, physicians, and other genetics professionals worldwide.

1585 ■ Naturejobs.com
URL: http://www.nature.com/naturejobs/science/welcome

Description: Lists jobs in the following disciplines of science: cell biology, biochemistry, bioinformatics, materials, and nanotechnology. Features scientific career information as well as news and advice.

1586 ■ Spherion
2050 Spectrum Blvd.
Fort Lauderdale, FL 33309
Ph: (954)308-7600
Fr: 800-774-3746
E-mail: help@spherion.com
URL: http://www.spherion.com

Description: Recruitment firm specializing in accounting and finance, sales and marketing, interim executives, technology, engineering, retail and human resources.

TRADESHOWS

1587 ■ American Society for Engineering Education Annual Conference and Exposition
American Society for Engineering Education
1818 N. St. N.W., Ste. 600
Washington, DC 20036-2479
Ph: (202)331-3500
Fax: (202)265-8504
E-mail: conferences@asee.org
URL: http://www.asee.org

Annual. Primary Exhibits: Publications, engineering supplies and equipment, computers, software, and research companies all products and services related to engineering education. Dates and Locations: 2012 Jun 10-13; San Antonio, TX.

1588 ■ Bio-IT World Conference & Expo
Cambridge Healthtech Institute
250 First Ave., Ste. 300
Needham, MA 02494
Ph: (781)972-5400
Fax: (781)972-5425
E-mail: chi@healthtech.com
URL: http://www.bio-itworldexpo.com

Annual. Showcases the myriad applications of IT and informatics to biomedical research and the drug discovery enterprise. Attracts a highly influential audience consisting of senior level scientists, IT professionals and executives from organizations across the life sciences industry including pharmaceutical, biotechnology, health systems, academia, government and national laboratories.

OTHER SOURCES

1589 ■ American Association of Engineering Societies (AAES)
1801 Alexander Bell Dr.
Reston, VA 20191
Ph: (202)296-2237
Fax: (202)296-1151
Fr: 888-400-2237
E-mail: dbateson@aaes.org
URL: http://www.aaes.org

Description: Coordinates the efforts of the member societies in the provision of reliable and objective information to the general public concerning issues which affect the engineering profession and the field of engineering as a whole; collects, analyzes, documents, and disseminates data which will inform the general public of the relationship between engineering and the national welfare; provides a forum for the engineering societies to exchange and discuss their views on matters of common interest; and represents the U.S. engineering community abroad through representation in WFEO and UPADI.

1590 ■ American Indian Science and Engineering Society (AISES)
PO Box 9828
Albuquerque, NM 87119-9828
Ph: (505)765-1052
Fax: (505)765-5608
E-mail: info@aises.org
URL: http://www.aises.org

Description: Represents American Indian and non-Indian students and professionals in science, technology, and engineering fields; corporations representing energy, mining, aerospace, electronic, and computer fields. Seeks to motivate and encourage students to pursue undergraduate and graduate studies in science, engineering, and technology. Sponsors science fairs in grade schools, teacher training workshops, summer math/science sessions for 8th-12th graders, professional chapters, and student chapters in colleges. Offers scholarships. Adult members serve as role models, advisers, and mentors for students. Operates placement service.

1591 ■ Biomedical Engineering Career Alliance
4809 E Thistle Landing Dr., Ste. 100
Phoenix, AZ 85044
Ph: (480)726-7272
Fax: (480)726-7276
E-mail: charla@bmecareer.org
URL: http://www.bmecareer.org

Description: Seeks to facilitate interactions between Biomedical Engineering/Bioengineering Programs and industry. Provides students from universities throughout the country access to industrial experiences and assists these students in achieving their goals of rewarding industrial careers. Enhances knowledge and builds positive perceptions of BME students in the biomedical industry.

1592 ■ Biomedical Engineering Society (BMES)
8201 Corporate Dr., Ste. 1125
Landover, MD 20785-2224
Ph: (301)459-1999
Fax: (301)459-2444
Fr: 877-871-2637
E-mail: info@bmes.org
URL: http://www.bmes.org

Description: Biomedical, chemical, electrical, civil, agricultural and mechanical engineers, physicians, managers, and university professors representing all fields of biomedical engineering; students and corporations. Encourages the development, dissemination, integration, and utilization of knowledge in biomedical engineering.

1593 ■ Engineering Society of Detroit (ESD)
20700 Civic Center Dr., Ste. 450
Southfield, MI 48076
Ph: (248)353-0735
Fax: (248)353-0736
E-mail: esd@esd.org
URL: http://ww2.esd.org/home.htm

Description: Engineers from all disciplines; scientists and technologists. Conducts technical programs and engineering refresher courses; sponsors conferences and expositions. Maintains speakers' bureau; offers placement services; although based in Detroit, MI, society membership is international.

1594 ■ International Functional Electrical Stimulation Society (IFESS)
1854 Los Encinos Ave.
Glendale, CA 91208-2240
E-mail: manfred.bijak@meduniwien.ac.at
URL: http://www.ifess.org

Description: Represents academic leaders in the field of biomedical engineering, physical therapists, medical doctors, members of the electrical stimulation manufacturing community, and students and users of functional electrical stimulation (FES) technology. Promotes the research, application, and understanding of electrical stimulation as it is utilized in the field of medicine. Facilitates cooperation and fellowship among members.

1595 ■ National Action Council for Minorities in Engineering (NACME)

440 Hamilton Ave., Ste. 302
White Plains, NY 10601-1813
Ph: (914)539-4010
Fax: (914)539-4032
E-mail: info@nacme.org
URL: http://www.nacme.org

Description: Leads the national effort to increase access to careers in engineering and other science-based disciplines. Conducts research and public policy analysis, develops and operates national demonstration programs at precollege and university levels, and disseminates information through publications, conferences and electronic media. Serves as a privately funded source of scholarships for minority students in engineering.

1596 ■ National Society of Professional Engineers (NSPE)

1420 King St.
Alexandria, VA 22314-2794
Ph: (703)684-2800
Fax: (703)836-4875
Fr: 888-285-6773
E-mail: memserv@nspe.org
URL: http://www.nspe.org

Description: Represents professional engineers and engineers-in-training in all fields registered in accordance with the laws of states or territories of the U.S. or provinces of Canada; qualified graduate engineers, student members, and registered land surveyors. Is concerned with social, professional, ethical, and economic considerations of engineering as a profession; encompasses programs in public relations, employment practices, ethical considerations, education, and career guidance. Monitors legislative and regulatory actions of interest to the engineering profession.

1597 ■ Society for Biological Engineering (SBE)

American Institute of Chemical Engineers
3 Park Ave., 19th Fl.
New York, NY 10016
Ph: (212)591-8888
E-mail: bio@aiche.org
URL: http://www.aiche.org/SBE

Description: Promotes the integration of biology with engineering and its benefits through bioprocessing, biomedical, and biomolecular applications. Raises interest, understanding, and recognition of engineers' and scientists' roles in biological engineering. Provides opportunities for the successful interaction of engineers and scientists.

1598 ■ Society For Biomaterials (SFB)

15000 Commerce Pkwy., Ste. C
Mount Laurel, NJ 08054
Ph: (856)439-0826
Fax: (856)439-0525
E-mail: info@biomaterials.org
URL: http://www.biomaterials.org

Description: Bioengineers and materials scientists; dental, orthopedic, cardiac, and other surgeons and scientists interested in developing biomaterials as tissue replacements in patients; corporations interested in the research manufacture of biomaterials. Provides an interdisciplinary forum for research in biomaterials. Promotes research, development, and education in the biomaterials sciences.

1599 ■ Society of Hispanic Professional Engineers (SHPE)

13181 Crossroads Pkwy. N, Ste. 450
City of Industry, CA 91746-3496
Ph: (323)725-3970
Fax: (323)725-0316
E-mail: shpenational@shpe.org
URL: http://oneshpe.shpe.org/wps/portal/national

Description: Represents engineers, student engineers, and scientists. Aims to increase the number of Hispanic engineers by providing motivation and support to students. Sponsors competitions and educational programs. Maintains placement service and speakers' bureau; compiles statistics.

1600 ■ Society for Industrial Microbiology (SIM)

3929 Old Lee Hwy., Ste. 92A
Fairfax, VA 22030-2421
Ph: (703)691-3357
Fax: (703)691-7991
E-mail: simhq@simhq.org
URL: http://www.simhq.org

Description: Mycologists, bacteriologists, biologists, chemists, engineers, zoologists, and others interested in biological processes as applied to industrial materials and processes concerning microorganisms. Serves as liaison between the specialized fields of microbiology. Maintains placement service; conducts surveys and scientific workshops in industrial microbiology.

1601 ■ Society of Women Engineers (SWE)

203 N La Salle St., Ste. 1675
Chicago, IL 60601
Ph: (312)596-5223
Fax: (312)596-5252
Fr: 877-SWE-INFO
E-mail: hq@swe.org
URL: http://societyofwomenengineers.swe.org

Description: Educational and service organization representing both students and professional women in engineering and technical fields.

1602 ■ Tissue Engineering International and Regenerative Medicine Society (TERMIS)

223 Park Pl.
San Ramon, CA 94583
Ph: (925)362-0998
Fax: (925)362-0808
E-mail: swilburn@termis.org
URL: http://www.termis.org

Description: Represents professionals in the field of tissue engineering and regenerative medicine. Promotes education and research within the field of tissue engineering and regenerative medicine. Provides a forum for discussion of challenges and therapeutic benefits of the application of tissue engineering and regenerative medicine technologies.

1603 ■ World Association for Chinese Biomedical Engineers (WACBE)

210 Lothrop St., E1641 BST
Pittsburgh, PA 15219
Ph: (412)648-1494
Fax: (412)648-8548
E-mail: info@wacbe.org
URL: http://www.wacbe.org

Description: Networks the worldwide Chinese professionals and students in the field of biomedical engineering. Promotes basic and translational research in the field. Encourages students to become biomedical engineers. Facilitates the professional and career development of members. Promotes cooperation among and between industrialists and academics.

SOURCES OF HELP-WANTED ADS

1604 ■ CopCareer.com
1051 E. Hillsdale Blvd.
Foster City, CA 94404
Fax: (650)350-1423
URL: http://www.copcareer.com

Online job posting site for law enforcement professionals, including border patrol agents.

1605 ■ Homeland Response
Penton Media Inc.
249 W 17th St.
New York, NY 10011
Ph: (212)204-4200
URL: http://www.respondersafetyonline.com/

Bimonthly. Magazine covering homeland security.

1606 ■ HSToday
HSToday
6800 Fleetwood Rd., Ste. 114
McLean, VA 22101
URL: http://www.hstoday.us/

Monthly. Free to qualified subscribers. Magazine covering topics of interest to homeland security professionals.

EMPLOYER DIRECTORIES AND NETWORKING LISTS

1607 ■ What Can I Do Now—Public Safety
Facts On File Inc.
132 W 31st St., 17th Fl.
New York, NY 10001
Ph: (212)967-8800
Fax: 800-678-3633
Fr: 800-322-8755
URL: http://factsonfile.infobasepublishing.com

$22.95 for individuals; $20.65 for libraries. Covers: Border patrol officers, corrections officers, crime analysts, emergency medical technicians, FBI agents, firefighters, and police officers.

HANDBOOKS AND MANUALS

1608 ■ Border Patrol Exam
LearningExpress, LLC
Two Rector St., 26th Fl.
New York, NY 10006
Fax: (212)995-5512
Fr: 888-551-5627
E-mail: customerservice@learningexpressllc.com
URL: http://www.learningexpressllc.com

Shirley Tarbell and Byron Demmer. Fourth edition. $24.95. 179 pages. Contains instruction on all areas covered by the examination, as well as three practice

tests. Includes information on the procedures and requirements for applying for a position as a border patrol agent.

ONLINE JOB SOURCES AND SERVICES

1609 ■ 911hotjobs.com Employment Portal
E-mail: contact@911hotjobs.com
URL: http://www.911hotjobs.com

Description: Online site for those seeking job opportunities in public safety. Testing requirements and job postings are available to those seeking employment in law enforcement, fire careers, and EMS services.

1610 ■ Border Patrol Jobs
URL: http://www.border-patrol-jobs.us

Description: Provides job listings for those seeking employment as border patrol personnel in the federal government.

1611 ■ Honor First
URL: http://www.honorfirst.com

Description: Serves as the unofficial website of the United States Border Patrol. Includes information on how to apply, pay and benefits, hiring process, study guides for the examination, and class schedules. Provides links to other sites with information on becoming a border patrol agent.

OTHER SOURCES

1612 ■ National Border Patrol Council (NBPC)
PO Box 678
Campo, CA 91906
Ph: (619)478-5145
Fr: 888-583-7237
E-mail: nbpc-info@nbpc.net
URL: http://www.nbpc.net

Description: Purpose: Represents employees of the U.S. Border Patrol.

1613 ■ Transportation Security Administration
601 S 12th St.
Arlington, VA 22202
Fr: (866)289-9673
E-mail: tsa-contactcenter@dhs.gov
URL: http://www.tsa.gov

Description: Governmental agency that lists available jobs on its website, including those for border patrol agents.

1614 ■ U.S. Border Patrol Supervisors' Association
591 Telegraph Canyon Rd., Box No. 656
Chula Vista, CA 91910-6497
URL: http://www.bpsups.org

Members: Border patrol supervisors. **Purpose:** Promotes opportunities for training, liaison with other law enforcement associations, and political action efforts for career and retirement goals. **Activities:** Maintains an online chat room and message board to promote networking among its members.

1615 ■ U.S. Customs and Border Protection
1300 Pennsylvania Ave., NW
Washington, DC 20229
Ph: (703)526-4200
Fr: 877-227-5511
URL: http://www.cbp.gov

Activities: Provides news releases and fact sheets on border patrol initiatives.

1616 ■ U.S. Customs and Border Protection - Blaine Sector
2410 Nature's Path Way
Blaine, WA 98230-9114
Ph: (360)332-9200
Fax: (360)332-9263
URL: http://www.cbp.gov/xp/cgov/border_security/ border_patrol/border_patrol_sectors/

Activities: Services the states of Alaska, Oregon, and the western half of the state of Washington. Stations are located in Blaine, Washington; Lynden, Washington; Bellingham, Washington; Port Angeles, Washington; and Roseburg, Oregon. Information about employment opportunities may be obtained by contacting the recruiter at the Sector office.

1617 ■ U.S. Customs and Border Protection - Buffalo Sector
201 Lang Blvd.
Grand Island, NY 14072
Ph: (716)774-7200
URL: http://www.cbp.gov/xp/cgov/border_security/ border_patrol/border_patrol_sectors/

Activities: Covers 450 miles of border with Canada from the Ohio/Pennsylvania state line to Jefferson County, New York. Stations are located in Niagara Falls, New York; Buffalo, New York; Fulton, New York; and Watertown, New York. Information about employment opportunities may be obtained by contacting the recruiter at the Sector office.

1618 ■ U.S. Customs and Border Protection - Del Rio Sector
2401 Dodson Ave.
Del Rio, TX 78840
Ph: (830)778-7000
URL: http://www.cbp.gov/xp/cgov/border_security/ border_patrol/border_patrol_sectors/

Activities: Covers 41 counties in the state of Texas. Stations are located in Abilene, Brackettville, Carrizo Springs, Comstock, Del Rio, Eagle Pass, Llano, Rocksprings, San Angelo, and Uvalde. Information about employment opportunities may be obtained by contacting the recruiter at the Sector office.

1619 ■ **U.S. Customs and Border Protection - Detroit Sector**
26000 South St., Bldg. 1516
Selfridge ANGB, MI 48045-4932
Ph: (586)239-2160
URL: http://www.cbp.gov/xp/cgov/border_security/
   border_patrol/border_patrol_sectors/

Activities: Area of responsibility includes Illinois, Indiana, Michigan, and Ohio. Stations are located in Detroit, Michigan; Port Huron, Michigan; Sault Ste. Marie, Michigan; and Trenton, Michigan. Information about employment opportunities may be obtained by contacting the recruiter at the Sector office.

1620 ■ **U.S. Customs and Border Protection - El Centro Sector**
211 W Aten Rd.
Imperial, CA 92251
Ph: (760)335-5700
URL: http://www.cbp.gov/xp/cgov/border_security/
   border_patrol/border_patrol_sectors/

Activities: Covers the counties of Imperial and Riverside in California. Stations are located in Calexico, California; El Centro, California; Indio, California; and Riverside, California. Information about employment opportunities may be obtained by contacting the recruiter at the Sector office.

1621 ■ **U.S. Customs and Border Protection - El Paso Sector**
8901 Montana Ave.
El Paso, TX 79925-1212
Ph: (915)834-8350
URL: http://www.cbp.gov/xp/cgov/border_security/
   border_patrol/border_patrol_sectors/

Activities: Covers the entire state of New Mexico and Hudspeth and El Paso counties in Texas, totaling 125,500 square miles of territory. Stations are located in El Paso, Texas; Fabens, Texas; Fort Hancock, Texas; Ysleta, Texas; Alamagordo, New Mexico; Albuquerque, New Mexico; Carlsbad, New Mexico; Deming, New Mexico; Las Cruces, New Mexico; Lordsburg, New Mexico; Truth or Consequences, New Mexico; and Santa Teresa, New Mexico. Information about employment opportunities may be obtained by contacting the recruiter at the Sector office.

1622 ■ **U.S. Customs and Border Protection - Grand Forks Sector**
2320 S Washington St.
Grand Forks, ND 58201
Ph: (701)775-6259
URL: http://www.cbp.gov/xp/cgov/border_security/
   border_patrol/border_patrol_sectors/

Activities: Covers the states of North Dakota, Minnesota, Wisconsin, South Dakota, Iowa, Nebraska, Kansas, and Missouri. Stations are located in Grand Forks, North Dakota; Bottineau, North Dakota; Duluth, Minnesota; International Falls, Minnesota; Pembina, North Dakota; Portal, North Dakota; and Warroad, Minnesota. Information about employment opportunities may be obtained by contacting the recruiter at the Sector office.

1623 ■ **U.S. Customs and Border Protection - Havre Sector**
2605 5th Ave., SE
Havre, MT 59501
Ph: (406)262-5600
URL: http://www.cbp.gov/xp/cgov/border_security/
   border_patrol/border_patrol_sectors/

Activities: Patrols 452 miles of border area between Montana and Canada, Wyoming, Colorado, Utah, as well as part of Idaho. Stations are located in Havre, Montana; Plentywood, Montana; Shelby, Montana; and Twin Falls, Idaho. Information about employment opportunities may be obtained by contacting the recruiter at the Sector office.

1624 ■ **U.S. Customs and Border Protection - Houlton Sector**
96 Calais Rd.
Hodgdon, ME 04730

Ph: (207)532-6521
Fr: 800-851-8727
URL: http://www.cbp.gov/xp/cgov/border_security/
   border_patrol/border_patrol_sectors/

Activities: Covers the entire state of Maine. Stations are located in Calais, Fort Fairfield, Houlton, Van Buren, Jackman, and Rangeley. Information about employment opportunities may be obtained by contacting the recruiter at the Sector office.

1625 ■ **U.S. Customs and Border Protection - Laredo Sector**
207 W Del Mar Blvd.
Laredo, TX 78041
Ph: (956)764-3200
URL: http://www.cbp.gov/xp/cgov/border_security/
   border_patrol/border_patrol_sectors/

Activities: Encompasses 116 counties and covers 101,439 square miles of southwest and northeast Texas. Stations are located Zapata, Hebbronville, Cotulla, Dallas, San Antonio, and Laredo. Information about employment opportunities may be obtained by contacting the recruiter at the Sector office.

1626 ■ **U.S. Customs and Border Protection - Marfa Sector**
300 Madrid St.
Marfa, TX 79843
Ph: (432)729-5200
Fr: 888-536-6204
URL: http://www.cbp.gov/xp/cgov/border_security/
   border_patrol/border_patrol_sectors/

Activities: Covers over 135,000 square miles encompassing over 118 counties in Texas and Oklahoma, the largest geographical area of any sector along the southwest border. Stations are located in Sierra Blanca, Van Horn, Marfa, Presidio, Alpine, Sanderson, Pecos, Ft. Stockton, Midland, and Lubbock. Information about employment opportunities may be obtained by contacting the recruiter at the Sector office.

1627 ■ **U.S. Customs and Border Protection - Miami Sector**
15720 Pines Blvd.
Pembroke Pines, FL 33027
Ph: (954)965-6300
URL: http://www.cbp.gov/xp/cgov/border_security/
   border_patrol/border_patrol_sectors/

Activities: Covers the states of Florida, Georgia, North Carolina, and South Carolina. Stations are located in Pembroke Pines, Florida; West Palm Beach, Florida; Orlando, Florida; Jacksonville, Florida; and Tampa, Florida. Information about employment opportunities may be obtained by contacting the recruiter at the Sector office.

1628 ■ **U.S. Customs and Border Protection - New Orleans Sector**
PO Box 6218
New Orleans, LA 70174-6218
Ph: (504)376-2800
URL: http://www.cbp.gov/xp/cgov/border_security/
   border_patrol/border_patrol_sectors/

Activities: Maintains jurisdiction over a seven-state area, which encompasses 592 counties and parishes and approximately 362,310 square miles. Stations are located in New Orleans, Louisiana; Lake Charles, Louisiana; Baton Rouge, Louisiana; Gulfport, Mississippi; Mobile, Alabama; and Little Rock, Arkansas. Information about employment opportunities may be obtained by contacting the recruiter at the Sector office.

1629 ■ **U.S. Customs and Border Protection - Ramey Sector**
PO Box 250467
Ramey, PR 00604
Ph: (787)890-4747
Fr: 800-981-1313
URL: http://www.cbp.gov/xp/cgov/border_security/
   border_patrol/border_patrol_sectors/

Activities: Responsible for Puerto Rico and the U.S.

Virgin Islands. The Sector's only station is located in Ramey. Information about employment opportunities may be obtained by contacting the recruiter at the Sector office.

1630 ■ **U.S. Customs and Border Protection - Rio Grande Valley Sector**
4400 South Expy. 281
Edinburg, TX 78542-2621
Ph: (956)289-4800
URL: http://www.cbp.gov/xp/cgov/border_security/
   border_patrol/border_patrol_sectors/

Activities: Covers over 17,000 square miles in southeast Texas. Stations are located in Brownsville, Fort Brown Station I, Weslaco, Harlingen, McAllen, Rio Grande City, Falfurrias, Kingsville, and Corpus Christi. Information about employment opportunities may be obtained by contacting the recruiter at the Sector office.

1631 ■ **U.S. Customs and Border Protection - San Diego Sector**
2411 Boswell Rd.
Chula Vista, CA 91914-3519
Ph: (619)216-4000
Fr: 800-238-1945
URL: http://www.cbp.gov/xp/cgov/border_security/
   border_patrol/border_patrol_sectors/

Activities: Covers San Diego County in the state of California. Stations are located in Brown Field (the nation's largest Border Patrol station), Boulevard, Campo, Chula Vista, El Cajon, Imperial Beach, San Clemente, and Muriett. Information about employment opportunities may be obtained by contacting the recruiter at the Sector office.

1632 ■ **U.S. Customs and Border Protection - Spokane Sector**
10710 N Newport Hwy.
Spokane, WA 99218
Ph: (509)353-2747
URL: http://www.cbp.gov/xp/cgov/border_security/
   border_patrol/border_patrol_sectors/

Activities: Patrols eastern Washington, Idaho, and western Montana up to the Continental Divide. Stations are located in Spokane, Washington; Colville, Washington; Curlew, Washington; Metaline Falls, Washington; Oroville, Washington; Pasco, Washington; Wenatchee, Washington; Eureka, Montana; Whitefish, Montana; and Bonners Ferry, Idaho. Information about employment opportunities may be obtained by contacting the recruiter at the Sector office.

1633 ■ **U.S. Customs and Border Protection - Swanton Sector**
155 Grand Ave.
Swanton, VT 05488
Ph: (802)868-3361
Fr: 800-247-2434
URL: http://www.cbp.gov/xp/cgov/border_security/
   border_patrol/border_patrol_sectors/

Activities: Encompasses 24,000 square miles and includes the state of Vermont; Clinton, Essex, Franklin, St. Lawrence, and Herkimer counties in New York; and Coos, Grafton, and Carroll counties in New Hampshire. Stations are located in Ogdensburg, New York; Massena, New York; Burke, New York; Champlain, New York; Swanton, Vermont; Richford, Vermont; Newport, Vermont; and Beecher Falls, Vermont. Information about employment opportunities may be obtained by contacting the recruiter at the Sector office.

1634 ■ **U.S. Customs and Border Protection - Tucson Sector**
2430 S Swan Rd.
Tucson, AZ 85711
Ph: (520)748-3000
URL: http://www.cbp.gov/xp/cgov/border_security/
   border_patrol/border_patrol_sectors/

Activities: Covers the state of Arizona. Stations are located in Ajo, Casa Grande, Douglas, Naco,

Nogales, Sonoita, Tucson, and Wilcox. Information about employment opportunities may be obtained by contacting the recruiter at the Sector office.

1635 ■ U.S. Customs and Border Protection - Yuma Sector
4035 South Ave. A
Yuma, AZ 85365
Ph: (928)341-6500
URL: http://www.cbp.gov/xp/cgov/border_security/
border_patrol/border_patrol_sectors/

Activities: Patrols 126 miles of border with Mexico between the Yuma-Pima County line in Arizona and the Imperial Sand Dunes in California. Stations are located in Yuma, Arizona; Wellton, Arizona; and Blythe, California. Information about employment opportunities may be obtained by contacting the recruiter at the Sector office.

1636 ■ U.S. Office of Personnel Management
1900 E St., NW
Washington, DC 20415-1000
Ph: (202)606-1800
E-mail: general@opm.gov
URL: http://www.opm.gov

Purpose: The federal government's human resources agency. **Activities:** Provides information on the specific requirements necessary to qualify as a border patrol agent, including education, experience, testing, language, firearms use, medical, and age.

Bricklayers and Cement Masons

SOURCES OF HELP-WANTED ADS

1637 ■ *BIA News*
Brick Industry Association
1850 Centennial Park Dr., Ste. 301
Reston, VA 20191
Ph: (703)620-0010
Fax: (703)620-3928
URL: http://www.gobrick.com/html/pr.html

Monthly. $30.00/year for individuals. Trade publication covering issues for the brick industry.

1638 ■ *Builder*
Hanley-Wood L.L.C.
1 Thomas Cir. NW, Ste. 600
Washington, DC 20005-5803
Ph: (202)452-0800
Fax: (202)785-1974
E-mail: builder@omeda.com
URL: http://www.hanleywood.com/
   default.aspx?page=magazines

$29.95/year for U.S. and Canada; $54.95/year for U.S. and Canada, 2 years; $192.00/year for other countries. Magazine covering housing and construction industry.

1639 ■ *Building Systems Magazine*
Active Interest Media
300 Continental Blvd., Ste. 650
El Segundo, CA 90245-5067
Ph: (310)356-4100
Fax: (310)356-4110
URL: http://www.buildingsystems.com

Bimonthly. Magazine featuring innovative construction technologies for builders, developers and general contractors.

1640 ■ *Concrete Products*
Mining Media Inc.
8751 E Hampden Ave., Ste. B-1
Denver, CO 80231
Ph: (303)283-0640
Fax: (303)283-0641
E-mail: dmarsh@prismb2b.com
URL: http://concreteproducts.com

Monthly. Free, online; $96.00/year for other countries, print. Magazine on concrete products and ready-mixed concrete.

1641 ■ *Constructor*
Associated General Contractors of America
2300 Wilson Blvd., Ste. 400
Arlington, VA 22201
Ph: (703)548-3118
Fax: (703)548-3119
Fr: 800-242-1767
URL: http://constructor.agc.org/

Bimonthly. $95.00/year for individuals. Management magazine for the Construction Industry.

1642 ■ *Custom Home Outdoors*
Hanley-Wood L.L.C.
1 Thomas Cir. NW, Ste. 600
Washington, DC 20005-5803
Ph: (202)452-0800
Fax: (202)785-1974
URL: http://www.customhomemediakit.com/r5/
   showkiosk.asp?listing_i

Quarterly. $36.00/year for individuals; $66.00/year for Canada; $192.00/year for other countries. Magazine featuring latest trends and products for building professionals.

1643 ■ *Green Home Builder*
Peninsula Publishing Inc.
1602 Monrovia Ave.
Newport Beach, CA 92663
Ph: (949)631-0308
Fax: (949)631-2475
URL: http://www.greenhomebuildermag.com/

Quarterly. Magazine for home builders and home building industry.

1644 ■ *Masonry Magazine*
Mason Contractors Association of America
1481 Merchant Dr.
Algonquin, IL 60102
Ph: (224)678-9709
Fax: (224)678-9714
Fr: 800-536-2225
URL: http://www.masoncontractors.org

Monthly. $43.00/2 years; $29.00/year. Covers every aspect of the mason contractor profession, from equipment and techniques to building codes and standards, training the future masonry labor force, business planning, promoting business, job interviewing, negotiation and legal issues.

1645 ■ *Professional Builder*
SGC Horizon LLC
3030 W Salt Creek Ln., Ste. 201
Arlington Heights, IL 60005
Ph: (847)391-1000
Fax: (847)390-0408
URL: http://www.housingzone.com/pb/pubhome/

Monthly. Free. The integrated engineering magazine of the building construction industry.

1646 ■ *Residential Concrete*
Hanley-Wood L.L.C.
1 Thomas Cir. NW, Ste. 600
Washington, DC 20005-5803
Ph: (202)452-0800
Fax: (202)785-1974
URL: http://www.hanleywood.com/
   default.aspx?page=b2bresconcrete

Bimonthly. $30.00/year for individuals; $46.00/year for two years; $39.00/year for Canada and Mexico; $64.00/year for two years, Canada & Mexico; $93.00/year for other countries; $162.00/year for other countries, two years. Magazine featuring the use of concrete in residential concrete construction.

1647 ■ *Residential Design & Build*
Cygnus Business Media Inc.
3 Huntington Quadrangle, Ste. 301 N
Melville, NY 11747
Ph: (631)845-2700
Fax: (631)845-7109
Fr: 800-308-6397
URL: http://www.rdbmagazine.com

Magazine providing advice and insight on the design/build project delivery method, as well as information on the latest design trends, new products and home building professionals.

1648 ■ *Tools of the Trade*
Hanley-Wood L.L.C.
1 Thomas Cir. NW, Ste. 600
Washington, DC 20005-5803
Ph: (202)452-0800
Fax: (202)785-1974
URL: http://www.hanleywood.com/
   ?page=toolsofthetrade&section=res_

Bimonthly. $36.00/year for individuals; $66.00/year for Canada; $192.00/year for other countries; $70.00/year for two years. Magazine featuring tools for commercial and residential construction.

EMPLOYER DIRECTORIES AND NETWORKING LISTS

1649 ■ *ABC Today—Associated Builders and Contractors National Membership Directory Issue*
Associated Builders and Contractors Inc.
4250 N Fairfax Dr., 9th Fl.
Arlington, VA 22203-1607
Ph: (703)812-2000
Fax: (703)812-8235
URL: http://www.abc.org

Annual, December. $150.00. Publication includes: List of approximately 19,000 member construction contractors and suppliers.

1650 ■ *ENR—Top 400 Construction Contractors Issue*
McGraw-Hill Inc.
PO Box 182604
Columbus, OH 43218
Ph: (614)430-4000
Fax: (614)759-3749
Fr: 877-833-5524
URL: http://enr.construction.com/toplists/Contractors/
   001-100.asp

Annual, Latest edition 2011. $35.00 for individuals. Publication includes: List of 400 United States contractors receiving largest dollar volumes of contracts in preceding calendar year. Separate lists of 50 largest design/construct management firms; 50 largest program and construction managers; 25 building contractors; 25 heavy contractors.

ONLINE JOB SOURCES AND SERVICES

1651 ■ Bricklayer Jobs
URL: http://www.bricklayerjobs.org
Description: Features a searchable database of employment opportunities for bricklayers.

1652 ■ CementMasonConcreteFinisher.com
URL: http://www.cementmasonconcretefinisher.com
Description: Features job listings for cement masons and concrete finishers.

1653 ■ IHireBuildingTrades
URL: http://www.ihirebuildingtrades.com
Description: Serves as a job posting board that specializes in matching building jobs and construction candidates.

TRADESHOWS

1654 ■ World of Concrete
Hanley-Wood Exhibitions
8600 Freeport Parkway
Irving, TX 75063
Ph: (972)536-6300
Fax: (972)536-6301
Fr: 800-869-8522
URL: http://www.hanley-wood.com

Annual. Primary Exhibits: Equipment and services for the construction industry.

OTHER SOURCES

1655 ■ Associated Builders and Contractors (ABC)
4250 N Fairfax Dr., 9th Fl.
Arlington, VA 22203-1607
Ph: (703)812-2000
Fax: (703)812-8201
E-mail: gotquestions@abc.org
URL: http://www.abc.org

Description: Construction contractors, subcontractors, suppliers and associates. Aims to foster and perpetuate the principles of rewarding construction workers and management on the basis of merit. Sponsors management education programs and craft training; also sponsors apprenticeship and skill training programs. Disseminates technological and labor relations information.

1656 ■ Associated General Contractors of America (AGC)
2300 Wilson Blvd., Ste. 400
Arlington, VA 22201
Ph: (703)548-3118
Fax: (703)548-3119
Fr: 800-242-1767
E-mail: info@agc.org
URL: http://www.agc.org

Description: General construction contractors; subcontractors; industry suppliers; service firms. Provides market services through its divisions. Conducts special conferences and seminars designed specifically for construction firms. Compiles statistics on job accidents reported by member firms. Maintains 65 committees, including joint cooperative committees with other associations and liaison committees with federal agencies.

1657 ■ Associated Specialty Contractors (ASC)
3 Bethesda Metro Ctr., Ste. 1100
Bethesda, MD 20814
E-mail: dgw@necanet.org
URL: http://www.assoc-spec-con.org

Description: Works to promote efficient management and productivity. Coordinates the work of specialized branches of the industry in management information, research, public information, government relations and construction relations. Serves as a liaison among specialty trade associations in the areas of public relations, government relations, and with other organizations. Seeks to avoid unnecessary duplication of effort and expense or conflicting programs among affiliates. Identifies areas of interest and problems shared by members, and develops positions and approaches on such problems.

1658 ■ Mason Contractors Association of America (MCAA)
1481 Merchant Dr.
Algonquin, IL 60102
Ph: (224)678-9709
Fax: (224)678-9714
Fr: 800-536-2225
URL: http://www.masoncontractors.org

Description: Masonry construction firms. Conducts specialized education and research programs. Compiles statistics.

1659 ■ The Masonry Society (TMS)
3970 Broadway, Ste. 201-D
Boulder, CO 80304-1135
Ph: (303)939-9700

Fax: (303)541-9215
E-mail: info@masonrysociety.org
URL: http://www.masonrysociety.org

Description: Represents individuals interested in the art and science of masonry. Serves as professional, technical, and educational association dedicated to the advancement and knowledge of masonry. Gathers and disseminates technical information.

1660 ■ National Association of Home Builders (NAHB)
1201 15th St. NW
Washington, DC 20005
Ph: (202)266-8200
Fax: (202)266-8400
Fr: 800-368-5242
E-mail: jhoward@nahb.com
URL: http://www.nahb.org

Description: Single and multifamily home builders, commercial builders, and others associated with the building industry. Lobbies on behalf of the housing industry and conducts public affairs activities to increase public understanding of housing and the economy. Collects and disseminates data on current developments in home building and home builders' plans through its Economics Department and nationwide Metropolitan Housing Forecast. Maintains NAHB Research Center, which functions as the research arm of the home building industry. Sponsors seminars and workshops on construction, mortgage credit, labor relations, cost reduction, land use, remodeling, and business management. Compiles statistics; offers charitable program, spokesman training, and placement service; maintains speakers' bureau, and Hall of Fame. Subsidiaries include the National Council of the Housing Industry. Maintains over 50 committees in many areas of construction; operates National Commercial Builders Council, National Council of the Multifamily Housing Industry, National Remodelers Council, and National Sales and Marketing Council.

1661 ■ National Association of Women in Construction (NAWIC)
327 S Adams St.
Fort Worth, TX 76104
Ph: (817)877-5551
Fax: (817)877-0324
Fr: 800-552-3506
E-mail: nawic@nawic.org
URL: http://www.nawic.org

Description: Seeks to enhance the success of women in the construction industry.

Sources of Help-Wanted Ads

1662 ■ *Advanced Imaging*
Cygnus Business Media Inc.
3 Huntington Quadrangle, Ste. 301 N
Melville, NY 11747
Ph: (631)845-2700
Fax: (631)845-7109
Fr: 800-308-6397
URL: http://www.advancedimagingpro.com/
magazine.jsp

Magazine covering the full range of electronic imaging technology and its uses.

1663 ■ *AV Video & Multimedia Producer*
Access Intelligence L.L.C.
4 Choke Cherry Rd., 2nd Fl.
Rockville, MD 20850-4024
Ph: (301)354-2000
Fax: (301)309-3847
Fr: 800-777-5006
URL: http://www.accessintel.com/

Monthly. Magazine covering audio-visual, video and multimedia production, presentation, people, technology and techniques.

1664 ■ *Broadcasting & Cable*
Reed Business Information (New York, New York)
360 Park Ave. S
New York, NY 10010
Ph: (646)746-6400
Fax: (646)746-7431
Fr: 800-446-6551
URL: http://www.reedbusiness.com

$199.00/year for individuals; $249.99/year for Canada; $360.99/year for other countries. News magazine covering The Fifth Estate (radio, TV, cable, and satellite), and the regulatory commissions involved.

1665 ■ *Communications Engineering & Design (CED)*
Communications Engineering & Design
PO Box 266007
Highlands Ranch, CO 80163-6007
Ph: (303)470-4800
Fax: (303)470-4890
URL: http://www.cedmagazine.com

Monthly. $64.00/year for individuals; $85.00/year for Canada; $92.00/year for other countries; $116.00/year for two years; $153.00/year for two years, in Canada; $166.00/year for two years, elsewhere. Technical/business publication serving the engineering/management community within broadband/cable TV networks, telecommunications carriers, data and interactive networks.

1666 ■ *Community Radio News*
National Federation of Community Broadcasters
1970 Broadway, Ste. 1000
Oakland, CA 94612

Ph: (510)451-8200
Fax: (510)451-8208
E-mail: newsletter@nfcb.org
URL: http://www.nfcb.org

Description: Monthly. Serves as a medium of communication for independent, community-licensed radio stations. Contains brief articles and news items on such topics as public broadcasting and programming, legislative developments, activities of the Federal Communications Commission, and local stations. Recurring features include notices of grants and awards, job openings, and a calendar of events/conferences for noncommercial broadcasters.

1667 ■ *Entertainment Employment Journal*
Studiolot Publishing
5632 Van Nuys Blvd., Ste. 320
Van Nuys, CA 91401-4600
Ph: (818)776-2800
Fr: 800-640-4836
E-mail: support@eejonline.com
URL: http://www.eej.com

Semimonthly. $109.00/year for individuals; $67.00/year for individuals, 6 months; $39.00/year for individuals, 3 months. Trade magazine covering business and technical careers in broadcast, electronic media, and motion pictures.

1668 ■ *Feminist Media Studies*
Routledge Journals
270 Madison Ave.
New York, NY 10016-0601
Ph: (212)216-7800
Fax: (212)563-2269
URL: http://www.tandf.co.uk/journals/titles/
14680777.asp

Quarterly. $700.00/year for institutions, print + online; $129.00/year for individuals, print only; $630.00/year for institutions, online only. Journal covering media and communication studies.

1669 ■ *Journal of the Audio Engineering Society*
Audio Engineering Society Inc.
60 E 42nd St., Rm. 2520
New York, NY 10165-2520
Ph: (212)661-8528
Fax: (212)682-0477
URL: http://www.aes.org/journal

Monthly. $50.00/year for members; $280.00/year for nonmembers, print; $525.00/year for nonmembers, online; $695.00/year for nonmembers, print and online. Newsletter reporting engineering developments and scientific progress in audio engineering for audio professionals, educators, executives, consumers, and students.

1670 ■ *Millimeter*
NewBay Media, LLC
28 E 28th St., 12th Fl.
New York, NY 10016
Ph: (212)378-0400

Fax: (917)281-4704
URL: http://digitalcontentproducer.com/mil/

Monthly. Magazine focusing on the process of motion picture and television production.

1671 ■ *Post*
Post Pro Publishing Inc.
One Park Ave.
New York, NY 10016
Ph: (212)951-6600
Fax: (212)951-6793
URL: http://www.postmagazine.com/

Monthly. Magazine serving the field of television, film, video production and post-production.

1672 ■ *Producers Masterguide*
Producers Masterguide
60 E 8th St., 34th Fl.
New York, NY 10003-6514
Ph: (212)777-4002
Fax: (212)777-4101
URL: http://www.producers.masterguide.com/
cover.html

Annual. $185.00/year for U.S.; $175.00/year for Canada; $205.00/year for other countries. An international film and TV production directory and guide for the professional motion picture, broadcast television, feature film, TV commercial, cable/satellite, digital and videotape industries in the U.S., Canada, the UK, the Caribbean Islands, Mexico, Australia, New Zealand, Europe, Israel, Morocco, the Far East, and South America.

1673 ■ *QST*
Amateur Radio Relay League Inc.
225 Main St.
Newington, CT 06111-1400
Ph: (860)594-0200
Fax: (860)594-0259
Fr: 888-277-5289
E-mail: qst@arrl.org
URL: http://www.arrl.org/qst/

Monthly. $34.00/year for individuals. Amateur radio magazine.

1674 ■ *Radio and Records*
Nielsen Business Media
770 Broadway
New York, NY 10003-9595
E-mail: nbb@omeda.com
URL: http://www.radioandrecords.com

Weekly. $24.95/year for individuals, monthly, print & online; $299.00/year for individuals, print & online; $19.95/year for individuals, monthly, online. Magazine covering every format of music radio, regulatory developments, news radio, talk radio, and satellite radio.

1675 ■ *SMPTE Motion Imaging Journal*
Society of Motion Picture and Television Engineers
3 Barker Ave., 5th Fl.
White Plains, NY 10601

Ph: (914)761-1100
Fax: (914)761-3115
URL: http://www.smpte.org

Monthly. $130.00/year for individuals. Peer-reviewed journal containing articles pertaining to new developments in motion picture and television technology; standards and recommended practices; general news of the industry.

1676 ■ Telecommunications and Radio Engineering
Begell House Inc.
50 Cross Hwy.
Redding, CT 06896
Ph: (203)938-1300
Fax: (203)938-1304
URL: http://www.begellhouse.com/journals/0632a9d54950b268

$4,518.00/year for institutions. Journal covering telecommunications and radio engineering.

1677 ■ TelevisionWeek
Crain Communications Inc. (Detroit, Michigan)
1155 Gratiot Ave.
Detroit, MI 48207-2997
Ph: (313)446-6000
Fax: (313)567-7681
URL: http://www.tvweek.com/

Weekly. $119.00/year for individuals; $171.00/year for Canada, incl. GST; $309.00/year for other countries, airmail. Newspaper covering management, programming, cable and trends in the television and the media industry.

EMPLOYER DIRECTORIES AND NETWORKING LISTS

1678 ■ Bacon's Metro California Media
Cision US Inc.
332 S Michigan Ave., Ste. 900
Chicago, IL 60604
Ph: (312)363-9793
Fax: (312)922-9387
Fr: (866)639-5087
URL: http://us.cision.com/

Annual, Latest edition 2012. $445.00 for individuals. Covers: Consumer media in the state of California including newspapers, radio television & cable stations, magazines, and broadcast programs, ethnic media, news services & syndicates. Entries include: Name, address, phone, names of editors and creative staff, with titles or indication of assignments. Arrangement: Geographical, classified by type of outlet. Indexes: Alphabetical.

1679 ■ Bacon's Radio/TV/Cable Directory, Volume 1
Cision US Inc.
332 S Michigan Ave., Ste. 900
Chicago, IL 60604
Ph: (312)363-9793
Fax: (312)922-9387
Fr: (866)639-5087
URL: http://us.cision.com/

Annual, Latest edition 2012. $650.00 for individuals. Covers: over 13,500 radio and television stations, including college radio and public television stations, and cable companies. Entries include: For radio and television stations—Call letters, address, phone, names and titles of key personnel, programs, times broadcast, name of contact, network affiliation, frequency or channel number, target audience data. For cable companies—Name, address, phone, description of activities. Arrangement: Geographical.

1680 ■ BIA's Television Yearbook
BIA Financial Network Inc.
15120 Enterprise Ct., Ste. 100
Chantilly, VA 20151
Ph: (703)818-2425
Fax: (703)803-3299

Fr: 800-331-5086
E-mail: sales@bia.com
URL: http://www.bia.com

Annual, Latest edition 2011. $630.00 for individuals. Covers: U.S. Television markets and their inclusive stations, television equipment manufacturers, and related service providers and trade associations. Entries include: For stations—Call letters, address; name and phone of general manager, owner, and other key personnel; technical attributes, rep firm, network affiliation, last acquisition date and price and ratings for total day and prime time. For others—Company or organization name, address, phone, description. Arrangement: Classified by market. Indexes: Numerical by market rank; call letters.

1681 ■ Bowker's News Media Directory
R.R. Bowker L.L.C.
630 Central Ave.
New Providence, NJ 07974
Ph: (908)286-1090
Fr: 888-269-5372
E-mail: wpn@bowker.com
URL: http://www.bowker.com

Annual, Latest edition 2009. $668.00 for individuals. Covers: In three separate volumes, syndicates and over 8,500 daily and weekly newspapers; 1,750 newsletters; over 16,800 radio and television stations; 5,500 magazines; 1,000 internal publications. Entries include: Name of publication or station, address, phone, fax, e-mail and URL, names of executives, editors, writers, etc., as appropriate. Broadcasting and magazine volumes include data on kinds of material accepted. Technical and mechanical requirements for publications are given. Arrangement: Magazines are classified by subject; newspapers and broadcasting stations geographical. Indexes: Newspaper department/editor by interest, metro area, feature syndicate subject; magazine subject, publication title; television director/personnel by subject, radio personnel and director by subject.

1682 ■ Broadcasting & Cable Yearbook
R.R. Bowker L.L.C.
630 Central Ave.
New Providence, NJ 07974
Ph: (908)286-1090
Fr: 888-269-5372
URL: http://www.bowker.com

Annual, latest edition 2010. $395.00 for individuals. Covers: Over 17,000 television and radio stations in the United States, its territories, and Canada; cable MSOs and their individual systems; television and radio networks, broadcast and cable group owners, station representatives, satellite networks and services, film companies, advertising agencies, government agencies, trade associations, schools, and suppliers of professional and technical services, including books, serials, and videos; communications lawyers. Entries include: Company name, address, phone, fax, names of executives. Station listings include broadcast power, other operating details. Arrangement: Stations and systems are geographical, others are alphabetical. Indexes: Alphabetical.

1683 ■ CPB Public Broadcasting Directory
Corporation for Public Broadcasting
401 9th St. NW
Washington, DC 20004-2129
Ph: (202)879-9600
Fax: (202)879-9699
Fr: 800-272-2190
URL: http://www.cpb.org/stations/isis

Annual. Covers: Public television and radio stations, national and regional public broadcasting organizations and networks, state government agencies and commissions, and other related organizations. Entries include: For radio and television stations—Station call letters, frequency or channel, address, phone, licensee name, licensee type, date on air, antenna height, area covered, names and titles of key personnel. For organizations—Name, address, phone, name and title of key personnel. Arrangement: National and regional listings are alphabetical;

state groups and the public radio and television stations are each geographical; other organizations and agencies are alphabetical. Indexes: Geographical, personnel, call letter, licensee type (all in separate indexes for radio and television).

1684 ■ International Motion Picture Almanac
Quigley Publishing Company Inc.
64 Wintergreen Ln.
Groton, MA 01450
Ph: (860)228-0247
Fax: (860)228-0157
Fr: 800-231-8239
URL: http://quigleypublishing.com/

Annual, Latest edition 2011. $235.00 for individuals; $400.00. Covers: Motion picture producing companies, firms serving the industry, equipment manufacturers, casting agencies, literary agencies, advertising and publicity representatives, motion picture theater circuits, buying and booking organizations, independent theaters, international film festivals, associations, theatre equipment supply companies. Entries include: Generally, company name, address, phone. For manufacturers—Products or service provided, name of contact. For producing companies—Additional details. For theaters—Name of owner, screen size. Companion volume is the "International Television and Video Almanac". Arrangement: Classified by service or activity.

1685 ■ International Television and Video Almanac
Quigley Publishing Company Inc.
64 Wintergreen Ln.
Groton, MA 01450-4129
Ph: (978)448-0272
Fax: (978)448-9325
Fr: 800-231-8239
URL: http://quigleypublishing.com/

Annual, January; latest edition 2011. $235.00 for individuals. Covers: "Who's Who in Motion Pictures and Television and Home Video," television networks, major program producers, major group station owners, cable television companies, distributors, firms serving the television and home video industry, equipment manufacturers, casting agencies, literary agencies, advertising and publicity representatives, television stations, associations, list of feature films produced for television; statistics, industry's year in review, award winners, satellite and wireless cable provider, primetime programming, video producers, distributors, wholesalers. Entries include: Generally, company name, address, phone; manufacturer and service listings may include description of products and services and name of contact; producing, distributing, and station listings include additional detail, and contacts for cable and broadcast networks. Arrangement: Classified by service or activity. Indexes: Full.

1686 ■ The R & R Directory
Billboard.biz
PO Box 3595
Northbrook, IL 60065-3595
Ph: (847)559-7531
Fr: 800-658-8372
E-mail: moreinfo@rronline.com
URL: http://www.radioandrecords.com/RRDirectory/Directory_Main.as

Semiannual, Spring and Fall. $75.00. Covers: More than 3,000 radio group owners, equipment manufacturers, jingle producers, TV production houses and spot producers, record companies, representative firms, research companies, consulting firms, media brokers, networks, program suppliers, trade associations, and other organizations involved in the radio and record industry. Entries include: Organization name, address, phone, fax, E-mail, name and title of contacts, branch offices or subsidiary names and locations. Arrangement: Alphabetical; classified by subject. Indexes: Company.

1687 ■ Radio Advertising Source
SRDS
1700 Higgins Rd.
Des Plaines, IL 60018-5605

Ph: (847)375-5000
Fax: (847)375-5001
Fr: 877-883-5524
URL: http://www.srds.com

Quarterly, Latest edition 2011. $699.00 for individuals. Covers: Over 10,500 AM and FM stations, networks, syndicators, group owners, and representative firms. Entries include: Call letters, name of owning company, address, phone; names of representatives and station personnel; demonstration detail, station format, signal strength, programming opportunities, special features. Arrangement: Geographical by state, then Arbitron metro and nonmetro area.

1688 ■ *RTNDA Communicator—Directory Issues*
Radio-Television News Directors Association
1025 F St. NW, Ste. 700
Washington, DC 20004
Ph: (202)467-5214
Fax: (202)223-4007
Fr: 800-80R-TNDA
URL: http://www.rtnda.org

Semiannual, January and July. Number of listings: 3,000; membership includes Canada and some foreign countries. Entries include: Member name, address, phone; and name of radio or television station, network, or other news organization with which affiliated. Arrangement: Same information given in alphabetical and geographical arrangements.

1689 ■ *Television & Cable Factbook*
Warren Communications News
2115 Ward Ct. NW
Washington, DC 20037-1209
Ph: (202)872-9200
Fax: (202)318-8350
Fr: 800-771-9202
URL: http://www.warren-news.com/factbook.htm

Annual, Latest edition 2012. $945.00 for individuals; $295.00 for individuals; $195.00 for individuals; $995.00 for individuals. Covers: Commercial and noncommercial television stations and networks, including educational, low-power and instructional TV stations, and translators; United States cable television systems; cable and television group owners; program and service suppliers; and brokerage and financing companies. Entries include: For stations—Call letters, licensee name and address, studio address and phone; identification of owners, sales and legal representatives and chief station personnel; rates, technical data, map of service area, and Nielsen circulation data. For cable systems—Name, address, basic and pay subscribers, programming and fees, physical plant; names of personnel and ownership. Ownership. Arrangement: Geographical by state, province, city, county, or country. Indexes: Call letters, product/service, name, general subject.

1690 ■ *TV and Cable Source*
SRDS
1700 Higgins Rd.
Des Plaines, IL 60018-5605
Ph: (847)375-5000
Fax: (847)375-5001
Fr: 800-851-7737
URL: http://www.srds.com

Quarterly, Latest edition 2011. $699.00. Covers: All domestic and international commercial television stations and networks; public television stations, cable networks, systems, interconnects, rep firms, and group owners. Includes separate section showing production specifications of stations and systems. Entries include: Call letters, parent company, address, phone, representative, personnel, facilities, special features, programming. Production specifications section shows call letters or system name, address, and preferred specifications for ad copy. Arrangement: Classified by DMA ranking, then by call letters.

HANDBOOKS AND MANUALS

1691 ■ *Careers in Communications*
The McGraw-Hill Companies
PO Box 182604
Columbus, OH 43272

Fax: (614)759-3749
Fr: 877-883-5524
E-mail: customer.service@mcgraw-hill.com
URL: http://www.mhprofessional.com/
    product.php?isbn=0071454764

Shonan Noronha. Fourth edition, 2004. $15.95 (paper). 192 pages. Examines the fields of journalism, photography, radio, television, film, public relations, and advertising. Gives concrete details on job locations and how to secure a job. Suggests many resources for job hunting.

1692 ■ *Great Jobs for Music Majors*
The McGraw-Hill Companies
PO Box 182604
Columbus, OH 43272
Fax: (614)759-3749
Fr: 877-883-5524
E-mail: customer.service@mcgraw-hill.com
URL: http://www.mhprofessional.com/
    product.php?isbn=0071454616

Jan Goldberg. Second edition, 2004. $15.95 (paper). 180 pages.

1693 ■ *Opportunities in Broadcasting Careers*
The McGraw-Hill Companies
PO Box 182604
Columbus, OH 43272
Fax: (614)759-3749
Fr: 877-883-5524
E-mail: customer.service@mcgraw-hill.com
URL: http://www.mhprofessional.com/
    product.php?isbn=0071454578

Elmo I. Ellis. 2004. $13.95. 176 pages. Discusses opportunities and job search techniques in broadcasting, television, and radio. Illustrated.

1694 ■ *Radio Broadcast Technician*
National Learning Corporation
212 Michael Dr.
Syosset, NY 11791
Fr: 800-632-8888
URL: http://www.passbooks.com

2009. $34.95 (paper). Serves as an exam preparation guide for radio broadcast technicians.

1695 ■ *Starting Your Career in Broadcasting: Working On and Off the Air in Radio and Television*
Allworth Press
307 W 36th St., 11th Fl.
New York, NY 10018
Ph: (212)643-6816
Fax: (212)643-6819
URL: http://www.allworth.com

Chris Schneider. 2007. $19.95 (paper). 240 pages. Provides information on how to get into the communications business. Includes chapters on specific on-air and behind-the-scenes jobs, academic programs in broadcasting, what news and program directors seek in job candidates, how an aspiring broadcaster can buy time on the air, weathering the ups and downs of a competitive industry, and how professionals of all kinds can host their own talk shows.

EMPLOYMENT AGENCIES AND SEARCH FIRMS

1696 ■ Baker Scott & Co.
1259 Rte. 46
Parsippany, NJ 07054
Ph: (973)263-3355
Fax: (973)263-9255
E-mail: exec.search@bakerscott.com
URL: http://www.bakerscott.com

Consulting services include executive recruiting, employment attitude surveys, and screening organization plans. Industries served: telecommunication, cable TV, broadcasting entertainment, and financial institutions. The firm is integrated horizontally across

functional discipline such as accounting, administration, call center, data processing, engineering, finance, general operations, marketing and technical and plant operations.

1697 ■ Jim Young & Associates Inc.
Holland Creek
1424 Clear Lake Rd.
Weatherford, TX 76086-5806
Ph: (817)599-7623
Fax: (817)599-4483
Fr: 800-433-2160

Specializes in the placement of cable television, telecommunications, cellular telephone, RF engineering and satellite communications personnel. Industries served: cable television, telecommunications, and cellular.

1698 ■ Warren and Morris Ltd.
463 15th St.
PO Box 1090
Del Mar, CA 92014
Ph: (858)461-0040
Fax: (858)481-6221
E-mail: cmorris@warrenmorrisltd.com
URL: http://www.warrenmorrisltd.com

Offers the following services: executive search and recruitment, providing clients with pre-screened, qualified candidates; and EEO management and labor relations consulting. Industries served: cable TV and wireless communications, multimedia and competitive telephone.

ONLINE JOB SOURCES AND SERVICES

1699 ■ Get Broadcast Technician Jobs
E-mail: contact@getbroadcasttechnicianjobs.com
URL: http://www.getbroadcasttechnicianjobs.com

Description: Provides a searchable database of job postings for broadcast technicians.

1700 ■ Society of Broadcast Engineers Job Line
Ph: (317)846-9000
Fax: (317)846-9120
E-mail: kjones@sbe.org
URL: http://www.sbe.org/career_jobsonline.php

Description: Job Line is one benefit of membership in the Society of Broadcast Engineers. Includes a resume service to distribute resumes to employers, job contact information, and descriptions of job openings. Also accessible via telephone.

TRADESHOWS

1701 ■ National Association of State Telecommunications Directors Conference
National Association of State Telecommunications Directors
2760 Research Pk. Dr.
PO Box 11910
Lexington, KY 40578-1910
Ph: (859)244-8186
Fax: (859)244-8001
E-mail: pjohson@csg.org
URL: http://www.nastd.org

Annual. Primary Exhibits: Exhibits for state telecommunications systems.

1702 ■ SMPTE Technical Conference Exhibition
Society of Motion Picture and Television Engineers
3 Barker Ave.
White Plains, NY 10601
Ph: (914)761-1100
Fax: (914)761-3115
E-mail: smpte@smpte.org
URL: http://www.smpte.org

Annual. Primary Exhibits: Equipment, lights, cameras, film, tape, and lenses.

1703 ■ Society of Broadcast Engineers Engineering Conference
Society of Broadcast Engineers
9102 N. Meridian St., Ste. 150
Indianapolis, IN 46260
Ph: (317)846-9000
Fax: (317)846-9120
URL: http://www.sbe.org

Annual. Primary Exhibits: Equipment, supplies, and services for the broadcast industry.

1704 ■ Southern States Communication Association Convention
Southern States Communication Association
c/o Dr. Carl M. Cates
Valdosta State University
1500 N. Patterson St.
Valdosta, GA 31698
Ph: (229)333-5820
Fax: (229)293-6182
E-mail: director@ncsu.edu
URL: http://www.ssca.net

Annual. Primary Exhibits: Communications equipment; textbooks.

OTHER SOURCES

1705 ■ Association for Educational Communications and Technology (AECT)
1800 N Stonelake Dr., Ste. 2
Bloomington, IN 47404
Ph: (812)335-7675
Fax: (812)335-7678
Fr: 877-677-AECT
E-mail: aect@aect.org
URL: http://www.aect.org

Description: Instructional technology professionals. Provides leadership in educational communications and technology by linking professionals holding a common interest in the use of educational technology and its application of the learning process.

1706 ■ Corporation for Public Broadcasting (CPB)
401 9th St. NW
Washington, DC 20004-2129
Ph: (202)879-9600
Fr: 800-272-2190
URL: http://www.cpb.org

Description: Promotes and finances the growth and development of noncommercial radio and television. Makes grants to local public television and radio stations, program producers, and program distribution networks; studies emerging technologies; works to provide adequate long-range financing from the U.S. government and other sources for public broadcasting. Supports children's services; compiles statistics; sponsors training programs.

1707 ■ Country Radio Broadcasters (CRB)
819 18th Ave. S
Nashville, TN 37203
Ph: (615)327-4487
Fax: (615)329-4492
E-mail: bill@crb.org
URL: http://www.crb.org

Description: Seeks to advance and promote the study of the science of broadcasting through the mutual exchange of ideas by conducting seminars

and workshops, as well as providing scholarships to broadcasting students.

1708 ■ Health Science Communications Association (HeSCA)
39 Wedgewood Dr., Ste. A
Jewett City, CT 06351-2420
Ph: (860)376-5915
Fax: (860)376-6621
E-mail: hescaone@sbcglobal.net
URL: http://www.hesca.org

Description: Represents media managers, graphic artists, biomedical librarians, producers, faculty members of health science and veterinary medicine schools, health professional organizations, and industry representatives. Acts as a clearinghouse for information used by professionals engaged in health science communications. Coordinates Media Festivals Program that recognizes outstanding media productions in the health sciences. Offers placement service.

1709 ■ Media Alliance (MA)
1904 Franklin St., Ste. 500
Oakland, CA 94612
Ph: (510)832-9000
Fax: (510)238-8557
E-mail: information@media-alliance.org
URL: http://www.media-alliance.org

Description: Writers, photographers, editors, broadcast workers, public relations practitioners, videographers, filmmakers, commercial artists and other media workers and aspiring media workers. Supports free press and independent, alternative journalism that services progressive politics and social justice.

1710 ■ National Association of Black Owned Broadcasters (NABOB)
1201 Connecticut Ave. NW, Ste. 200
Washington, DC 20036
Ph: (202)463-8970
Fax: (202)429-0657
E-mail: nabobinfo@nabob.org
URL: http://www.nabob.org

Description: Black broadcast station owners; black formatted stations not owned or controlled by blacks; organizations having an interest in the black consumer market or black broadcast industry; individuals interested in becoming owners; and communications schools, departments and professional groups and associations. Represents the interests of existing and potential black radio and television stations. Works with the Office of Federal Procurement Policy to determine which government contracting major advertisers and advertising agencies are complying with government initiatives to increase the amount of advertising dollars received by minority-owned firms. Conducts lobbying activities; provides legal representation for the protection of minority ownership policies. Sponsors annual Communications Awards Dinner each March. Conducts workshops; compiles statistics.

1711 ■ National Association of Broadcasters (NAB)
1771 N St. NW
Washington, DC 20036
Ph: (202)429-5300
Fax: (202)429-4199
E-mail: nab@nab.org
URL: http://www.nab.org

Description: Serves as the voice for the nation's radio and television broadcasters. Advances the interests of members in federal government, industry and public affairs; improves the quality and profitability of broadcasting; encourages content and technology innovation; and spotlights the important and unique ways stations serve their communities. Delivers value to its members through advocacy, education and innovation. Relies on the grassroots strength of its television and radio members and state broadcast associations. Helps broadcasters seize opportunities in the digital age. Offers broadcasters a variety of programs to help them grow in their careers, promote diversity in the workplace and strengthen their businesses.

1712 ■ National Cable and Telecommunications Association (NCTA)
25 Massachusetts Ave. NW, Ste. 100
Washington, DC 20001-1413
Ph: (202)222-2300
Fax: (202)222-2514
URL: http://www.ncta.com

Description: Franchised cable operators, programmers, and cable networks; associate members are cable hardware suppliers and distributors; affiliate members are brokerage and law firms and financial institutions; state and regional cable television associations cooperate, but are not affiliated, with the organization. Serves as national medium for exchange of experiences and opinions through research, study, discussion, and publications. Represents the cable industry before Congress, the Federal Communications Commission and various courts on issues of primary importance. Conducts research program in conjunction with National Academy of Cable Programming. Sponsors, in conjunction with Motion Picture Association of America, the Coalition Opposing Signal Theft, an organization designed to deter cable signal theft and to develop anti-piracy materials. Provides promotional aids and information on legal, legislative and regulatory matters. Compiles statistics.

1713 ■ National Religious Broadcasters (NRB)
9510 Technology Dr.
Manassas, VA 20110
Ph: (703)330-7000
Fax: (703)330-7100
E-mail: info@nrb.org
URL: http://www.nrb.org

Description: Christian communicators. Fosters electronic media access for the Gospel; promotes standards of excellence; integrity and accountability; and provides networking and fellowship opportunities for members.

1714 ■ Women in Cable Telecommunications (WICT)
14555 Avion Pkwy., Ste. 250
Chantilly, VA 20151
Ph: (703)234-9810
Fax: (703)817-1595
E-mail: mbrennan@wict.org
URL: http://www.wict.org

Description: Empowers and educates women to achieve their professional goals by providing opportunities for leadership, networking and advocacy.

1715 ■ Accounting and Finance
John Wiley & Sons Inc.
350 Main St., Commerce Pl.
Malden, MA 02148-5089
Ph: (781)388-8200
Fax: (781)388-8210
URL: http://www.wiley.com/bw/journal.asp?ref=0810-5391

Quarterly. $442.00/year for institutions, print + online, Australia/New Zealand; $384.00/year for institutions, print or online, Australia/New Zealand; $597.00/year for institutions, print + online; $519.00/year for institutions, print or online; $416.00/year for institutions, other countries, print + online; $361.00/year for institutions, other countries, print or online. Journal focusing on accounting and finance.

1716 ■ Accounting Horizons
American Accounting Association
5717 Bessie Dr.
Sarasota, FL 34233-2399
Ph: (941)921-7747
Fax: (941)923-4093
URL: http://aaahq.org/pubs/horizons.htm

Quarterly. $300.00/year for individuals, print only; $325.00/year for individuals, online, vol. 13 thru current issue; $375.00/year for individuals, online and print. Publication covering the banking, finance, and accounting industries.

1717 ■ Boomer Market Advisor
Summit Business Media
5081 Olympic Blvd.
Erlanger, KY 41018
Ph: (859)692-2100
Fax: (859)692-2000
URL: http://www.advisorone.com

Monthly. Free to qualified subscribers; $120.00/year for Canada; $160.00/year for other countries. Magazine for financial planners who work with variable products.

1718 ■ Brookings Papers on Economic Activity
Brookings Institution Press
1775 Massasshusetts Ave. NW
Washington, DC 20036
Ph: (202)797-6000
URL: http://www.brookings.edu/press/journals.htm#bpea

Semiannual. $55.00/year for individuals; $90.00/year for institutions; $69.00/year for other countries; $104.00/year for institutions, other countries. Publication covering economics and business.

1719 ■ Commercial Lending Review
CCH Inc.
PO Box 4307
Chicago, IL 60680
Fr: 800-248-3248
URL: http://www.commerciallendingreview.com/

Bimonthly. $445.00/year for individuals. Journal covering all aspects of lending for commercial banks, community and regional banks and other financial institutions.

1720 ■ Foundations and Trends in Finance
Now Publishers
PO Box 1024
Hanover, MA 02339-1001
Ph: (781)871-0245
URL: http://www.nowpublishers.com/product.aspx?product=FIN

Irregular. $390.00/year for individuals, online only; $450.00/year for individuals, print and online; $390.00/year for other countries, online only; $450.00/year for other countries, print and online. Academic journal that covers corporate finance, financial markets, asset pricing, and derivatives.

1721 ■ Journal of Applied Finance
INFORMS
7240 Parkway Dr., Ste. 300
Hanover, MD 21076
Ph: (443)757-3500
Fax: (443)757-3515
Fr: 800-446-3676
URL: http://69.175.2.130/~finman/Publications/JAF.htm

Semiannual. Journal for financial practice and education developments.

1722 ■ Journal of Public Budgeting and Finance
American Association for Budget and Program Analysis
PO Box 1157
Falls Church, VA 22041
Ph: (703)941-4300
Fax: (703)941-1535
URL: http://www.aabpa.org/main/pubs.htm

Quarterly. Journal covering public finance.

1723 ■ Strategic Finance
Institute of Management Accountants
10 Paragon Dr., Ste. 1
Montvale, NJ 07645-1718
Ph: (201)573-9000
Fax: (201)474-1600
Fr: 800-638-4427
URL: http://www.imanet.org/publications.asp

Monthly. $210.00/year for nonmembers; $48.00/year for members; $25.00/year for students; $18.00/year for single issue, back issue. Magazine reporting on corporate finance, accounting, cash management, and budgeting.

1724 ■ Wilmott Magazine
John Wiley & Sons Inc.
111 River St.
Hoboken, NJ 07030-5773
Ph: (201)748-6000
Fax: (201)748-6088
Fr: 800-825-7550
URL: http://www.wilmott.com

Bimonthly. $528.00/year for institutions, other countries, print only; $395.00/year for institutions, print only; $695.00/year for institutions, other countries, print only. Journal focusing on the quantitative finance community and concentrating on practicalities.

EMPLOYER DIRECTORIES AND NETWORKING LISTS

1725 ■ Barron's Finance and Investment Handbook
Barron's Educational Series Inc.
250 Wireless Blvd.
Hauppauge, NY 11788-3924
Ph: (631)434-3311
Fax: (631)434-3723
Fr: 800-645-3476
URL: http://barronseduc.stores.yahoo.net/0764162691.html

Latest edition 8th; 2010. $39.99 for individuals; $35.99 for individuals. Covers: More than 6,000 publicly traded corporations in the U.S. and Canada. Entries include: Name, address, phone, fax of all brokerage and mutual funds firms, banks, savings and loan companies, insurance companies, federal and state regulators, and major investment publications.

1726 ■ Career Opportunities in Banking, Finance, and Insurance
Facts On File Inc.
132 W 31st St., 17th Fl.
New York, NY 10001
Ph: (212)967-8800
Fax: 800-678-3633
Fr: 800-322-8755
URL: http://factsonfile.infobasepublishing.com

Latest edition 2nd; Published February, 2007. $49.50 for individuals. Publication includes: Lists of colleges with programs supporting banking, finance, and industry; professional associations; professional certifications; regulatory agencies; and Internet resources for career planning. Principal content of publication is job descriptions for professions in the banking, finance, and insurance industries. Indexes: Alphabetical.

1727 ■ Internet Guide to Personal Finance and Investment
Greenwood Publishing Group Inc.
88 Post Rd. W
PO Box 5007
Westport, CT 06881
Ph: (203)226-3571
Fax: (203)222-1502

Fr: 800-225-5800
URL: http://www.abc-clio.com/
   product.aspx?id=2147495461

$75.00 for single issue. Covers: Over 1,400 Web sites regarding personal finance and investment. Entries include: Name of Web site, URL, sponsor of site, and description of contents. Indexes: Website title; Sponsor; Subject.

HANDBOOKS AND MANUALS

1728 ■ *Assistant Budget Analyst*
National Learning Corporation
212 Michael Dr.
Syosset, NY 11791
Fr: 800-632-8888
URL: http://www.passbooks.com

2009. $34.95 (paper). Serves as an exam preparation guide for assistant budget analysts.

1729 ■ *Associate Budget Analyst*
National Learning Corporation
212 Michael Dr.
Syosset, NY 11791
Fr: 800-632-8888
URL: http://www.passbooks.com

2009. $39.95 (paper). Serves as an exam preparation guide for associate budget analysts.

1730 ■ *Careers in Finance*
The McGraw-Hill Companies
PO Box 182604
Columbus, OH 43272
Fax: (614)759-3749
Fr: 877-883-5524
E-mail: customer.service@mcgraw-hill.com
URL: http://www.mhprofessional.com/
   product.php?isbn=0071454780

Trudy Ring, editor. Third edition, 2004. $15.95. 182 pages. Covers financial careers in such areas as

higher education, corporate and public finance, and commercial and investment banking.

1731 ■ *Opportunities in Financial Careers*
The McGraw-Hill Companies
PO Box 182604
Columbus, OH 43272
Fax: (614)759-3749
Fr: 877-883-5524
E-mail: customer.service@mcgraw-hill.com
URL: http://www.mhprofessional.com/
   product.php?isbn=0071442502

Michael Sumichrast and Martin A. Sumichrast. 2004. $13.95 (paper). 160 pages. A guide to planning for and seeking opportunities in this challenging field.

1732 ■ *The Portable MBA in Finance and Accounting*
John Wiley & Sons Inc.
1 Wiley Dr.
Somerset, NJ 08873
Fax: (732)302-2300
Fr: 800-225-5945
E-mail: custserv@wiley.com
URL: http://as.wiley.com/WileyCDA/WileyTitle/
   productCd-0470481307.html

Theodore Grossman and John Leslie Livingstone. 2009. $34.95. 624 pages. Offers advice to businesses. Includes preparing budgets, implementing business plans, and evaluating acquisition targets.

ONLINE JOB SOURCES AND SERVICES

1733 ■ American Association of Finance and Accounting
URL: http://www.aafa.com

Description: AAFA is the largest and oldest alliance of executive search firms specializing in the recruitment and placement of finance and accounting professionals. Contains career opportunities site with job board for both job seekers and hiring employers.

One does not have to be a member to search for jobs.

1734 ■ Budget Analyst Jobs
URL: http://www.budgetanalystjobs.org

Description: Serves as a niche job board for budget analyst professionals. Offers employment opportunities and candidate recruiting.

1735 ■ The Digital Financier
URL: http://www.dfin.com

Description: Job postings from financial companies. Offers links to major job search websites. Has leads for further training and allows companies to post its own job links.

1736 ■ Financial Job Network
PO Box 55431
Sherman Oaks, CA 91403
Ph: (818)905-5272
E-mail: info@fjn.com
URL: http://www.fjn.com

Description: Contains information on international and national employment opportunities for those in the financial job market. Job listings may be submitted, as well as resumes. Main files include: Testimonials, Calendar, Corporate Listings, FJN Clients, more. Free to candidates.

1737 ■ FinancialServicesCrossing.com
URL: http://www.financialservicescrossing.com

Description: Offers a collection of top financial services job openings carefully researched by analysts. Provides instant access to a comprehensive pool of listings in the industry of financial services.

1738 ■ Get Budget Analyst Jobs
URL: http://www.getbudgetanalystjobs.com

Description: Features job listings for budget analysts. Offers services for employment and staffing needs of hiring and recruitment managers.

Carpenters

SOURCES OF HELP-WANTED ADS

1739 ■ Archetype
Woodwork Institute
PO Box 980247
3188 Industrial Blvd.
West Sacramento, CA 95798-0247
Ph: (916)372-9943
Fax: (916)372-9950
URL: http://www.wicnet.org/publications/
archetype.asp

Semiannual. Journal of the Woodwork Institute.

1740 ■ Builder
Hanley-Wood L.L.C.
1 Thomas Cir. NW, Ste. 600
Washington, DC 20005-5803
Ph: (202)452-0800
Fax: (202)785-1974
E-mail: builder@omeda.com
URL: http://www.hanleywood.com/
default.aspx?page=magazines

$29.95/year for U.S. and Canada; $54.95/year for U.S. and Canada, 2 years; $192.00/year for other countries. Magazine covering housing and construction industry.

1741 ■ Builder and Developer
Peninsula Publishing Inc.
1602 Monrovia Ave.
Newport Beach, CA 92663
Ph: (949)631-0308
Fax: (949)631-2475
URL: http://www.bdmag.com

Magazine for homebuilders.

1742 ■ Concrete & Masonry Construction Products
Hanley Wood L.L.C.
1 Thomas Cir. NW, Ste. 600
Washington, DC 20005-5803
Ph: (202)452-0800
Fax: (202)785-1974
Fr: 877-275-8647
URL: http://www.hanleywoodopportunities.com/
Index.asp?Cat=cc&Pub=

Bimonthly. Free. Publication that covers carpenter tips, tools, and up keep.

1743 ■ Constructor
Associated General Contractors of America
2300 Wilson Blvd., Ste. 400
Arlington, VA 22201
Ph: (703)548-3118
Fax: (703)548-3119
Fr: 800-242-1767
URL: http://constructor.agc.org/

Bimonthly. $95.00/year for individuals. Management magazine for the Construction Industry.

1744 ■ Green Home Builder
Peninsula Publishing Inc.
1602 Monrovia Ave.
Newport Beach, CA 92663
Ph: (949)631-0308
Fax: (949)631-2475
URL: http://www.greenhomebuildermag.com/

Quarterly. Magazine for home builders and home building industry.

1745 ■ Kitchen and Bath Design News
Cygnus Business Media Inc.
3 Huntington Quadrangle, Ste. 301 N
Melville, NY 11747
Ph: (631)845-2700
Fax: (631)845-7109
Fr: 800-308-6397
URL: http://www.cygnusb2b.com/
PropertyPub.cfm?PropertyID=78

Monthly. Trade journal.

1746 ■ Oxymag
Elsevier Science Inc.
360 Park Ave. S
New York, NY 10010-1710
Ph: (212)989-5800
Fax: (212)633-3990
Fr: 888-437-4636
URL: http://www.elsevier.com/wps/find/
journaldescription.cws_home

$124.39/year for institutions, for France; $23,700.00/year for individuals; $190.00/year for institutions, other countries; $155.00/year for institutions, European countries and Iran; $73.46/year for individuals, for France; $89.00/year for U.S. and other countries; $11,100.00/year for individuals; $75.00/year for individuals, European countries and Iran; $51.91/year for students, for France; $63.00/year for students, other countries. Journal related to the construction field covering information in the manufacture of commercial, industrial, spark proof and decorative terrazzo floors, flooring for railroad boxcars, industrial fireproof coatings, fire-resistant marine interior deckings and a variety of building units.

1747 ■ Panel World
Hatton-Brown Publishers Inc.
225 Hanrick St.
PO Box 2268
Montgomery, AL 36102
Ph: (334)834-1170
Fax: (334)834-4525
Fr: 800-669-5613
URL: http://www.panelworldmag.com/

Bimonthly. Free to qualified subscribers. Business magazine serving the worldwide veneer, plywood, and panel board industry.

1748 ■ Professional Builder
SGC Horizon LLC
3030 W Salt Creek Ln., Ste. 201
Arlington Heights, IL 60005

Ph: (847)391-1000
Fax: (847)390-0408
URL: http://www.housingzone.com/pb/pubhome/

Monthly. Free. The integrated engineering magazine of the building construction industry.

1749 ■ Replacement Contractor
Hanley Wood L.L.C.
1 Thomas Cir. NW, Ste. 600
Washington, DC 20005-5803
Ph: (202)452-0800
Fax: (202)785-1974
Fr: 877-275-8647
E-mail: rcon@omeda.com
URL: http://www.omeda.com/rcon/

$29.95/year for individuals; $39.95/year for Canada; $49.95/year for other countries. Magazine for contractors engaged in roofing, siding, decking and window replacement.

1750 ■ Residential Contractor
Peninsula Publishing Inc.
1602 Monrovia Ave.
Newport Beach, CA 92663
Ph: (949)631-0308
Fax: (949)631-2475
URL: http://www.residentialcontractormag.com/

Quarterly. Magazine for small volume residential builders, contractors, and specialty trades.

1751 ■ Wood Digest's Finishing Magazine
Cygnus Business Media Inc.
3 Huntington Quadrangle, Ste. 301 N
Melville, NY 11747
Ph: (631)845-2700
Fax: (631)845-7109
Fr: 800-308-6397
URL: http://www.woodworkingpro.com

Quarterly. Magazine serving commercial and industrial wood finishers of cabinets, furniture and millwork. Providing coverage on technical advances in equipment and supplies to assist its readers in overcoming productivity challenges.

1752 ■ Wood & Wood Products
Vance Publishing Corp.
400 Knightsbridge Pky.
Lincolnshire, IL 60069
Ph: (847)634-2600
Fax: (847)634-4379
URL: http://www.vancepublishing.com

Monthly. Magazine for furniture, cabinet, and woodworking industry.

EMPLOYER DIRECTORIES AND NETWORKING LISTS

1753 ■ ABC Today—Associated Builders and Contractors National Membership Directory Issue
Associated Builders and Contractors Inc.
4250 N Fairfax Dr., 9th Fl.
Arlington, VA 22203-1607

Ph: (703)812-2000
Fax: (703)812-8235
URL: http://www.abc.org

Annual, December. $150.00. Publication includes: List of approximately 19,000 member construction contractors and suppliers.

1754 ■ *ENR—Top 400 Construction Contractors Issue*
McGraw-Hill Inc.
PO Box 182604
Columbus, OH 43218
Ph: (614)430-4000
Fax: (614)759-3749
Fr: 877-833-5524
URL: http://enr.construction.com/toplists/Contractors/ 001-100.asp

Annual, Latest edition 2011. $35.00 for individuals. Publication includes: List of 400 United States contractors receiving largest dollar volumes of contracts in preceding calendar year. Separate lists of 50 largest design/construct management firms; 50 largest program and construction managers; 25 building contractors; 25 heavy contractors.

HANDBOOKS AND MANUALS

1755 ■ *Opportunities in Carpentry Careers*
The McGraw-Hill Companies
PO Box 182604
Columbus, OH 43272
Fax: (614)759-3749
Fr: 877-883-5524
E-mail: customer.service@mcgraw-hill.com
URL: http://www.mhprofessional.com/ product.php?isbn=0071476067

Roger Sheldon. 2007. $13.95 (paper). 221 pages. Discusses how to get started and covers the job market. Illustrated.

ONLINE JOB SOURCES AND SERVICES

1756 ■ CarpenterCareers.com
URL: http://www.carpentercareers.com

Description: Free for job seekers and affordable for employers. Caters to different professionals in the carpentry industry. Allows job seekers to search for jobs in specific locations.

1757 ■ CarpenterJobsite.com
URL: http://www.carpenterjobsite.com

Description: Serves as an online career community for the carpentry industry. Provides new job openings for carpenters, latest research in the construction and extraction employment markets, and career articles.

1758 ■ IHireBuildingTrades
URL: http://www.ihirebuildingtrades.com

Description: Serves as a job posting board that specializes in matching building jobs and construction candidates.

1759 ■ Locate Carpenter Jobs
URL: http://www.locatecarpenterjobs.com

Description: Provides employment opportunities to carpenters nationwide.

TRADESHOWS

1760 ■ Florida Industrial Woodworking Expo
Trade Shows, Inc.
PO Box 2000
Claremont, NC 28610-2000
Ph: (828)459-9894
Fax: (828)459-1312
E-mail: tsi@tsiexpos.com

Biennial. Primary Exhibits: Machinery, tooling, supplies, and services for the furniture, cabinet, casegoods, millwork, and industrial wood products industries.

1761 ■ International Woodworking Machinery and Furniture Supply Fair - USA
Marketing/Association Services Inc.
11110 Ohio Ave., Ste. 208
Los Angeles, CA 90025

Biennial. Primary Exhibits: Woodworking machinery and supplies for furniture, kitchen cabinets, architectural woodwork, and specialty wood products. Dates and Locations: 2012 Aug 22-25; Atlanta, GA; Georgia World Congress Ctr.

1762 ■ Mid-Atlantic Industrial Woodworking Expo
Trade Shows, Inc.
PO Box 2000
Claremont, NC 28610-2000
Ph: (828)459-9894
Fax: (828)459-1312
E-mail: tsi@tsiexpos.com

Annual. Primary Exhibits: Woodworking and furniture industry equipment, supplies, and services.

OTHER SOURCES

1763 ■ Associated Builders and Contractors (ABC)
4250 N Fairfax Dr., 9th Fl.
Arlington, VA 22203-1607
Ph: (703)812-2000
Fax: (703)812-8201
E-mail: gotquestions@abc.org
URL: http://www.abc.org

Description: Construction contractors, subcontractors, suppliers and associates. Aims to foster and perpetuate the principles of rewarding construction workers and management on the basis of merit. Sponsors management education programs and craft training; also sponsors apprenticeship and skill training programs. Disseminates technological and labor relations information.

1764 ■ Associated General Contractors of America (AGC)
2300 Wilson Blvd., Ste. 400
Arlington, VA 22201
Ph: (703)548-3118
Fax: (703)548-3119
Fr: 800-242-1767
E-mail: info@agc.org
URL: http://www.agc.org

Description: General construction contractors; subcontractors; industry suppliers; service firms. Provides market services through its divisions. Conducts special conferences and seminars designed specifically for construction firms. Compiles statistics on job accidents reported by member firms. Maintains 65 committees, including joint cooperative

committees with other associations and liaison committees with federal agencies.

1765 ■ Associated Specialty Contractors (ASC)
3 Bethesda Metro Ctr., Ste. 1100
Bethesda, MD 20814
E-mail: dgw@necanet.org
URL: http://www.assoc-spec-con.org

Description: Works to promote efficient management and productivity. Coordinates the work of specialized branches of the industry in management information, research, public information, government relations and construction relations. Serves as a liaison among specialty trade associations in the areas of public relations, government relations, and with other organizations. Seeks to avoid unnecessary duplication of effort and expense or conflicting programs among affiliates. Identifies areas of interest and problems shared by members, and develops positions and approaches on such problems.

1766 ■ Cabinet Makers Association (CMA)
PO Box 14276
Milwaukee, WI 53214-0276
Ph: (414)377-1340
E-mail: director@cabinetmakers.org
URL: http://www.cabinetmakers.org

Description: Represents cabinetmakers and woodworkers from both the residential and commercial markets who get together and share their knowledge and experience to help one another. Aims to uphold professionalism in the industry by providing its members with networking opportunities, continuing education, and ongoing professional development.

1767 ■ National Association of Home Builders (NAHB)
1201 15th St. NW
Washington, DC 20005
Ph: (202)266-8200
Fax: (202)266-8400
Fr: 800-368-5242
E-mail: jhoward@nahb.com
URL: http://www.nahb.org

Description: Single and multifamily home builders, commercial builders, and others associated with the building industry. Lobbies on behalf of the housing industry and conducts public affairs activities to increase public understanding of housing and the economy. Collects and disseminates data on current developments in home building and home builders' plans through its Economics Department and nationwide Metropolitan Housing Forecast. Maintains NAHB Research Center, which functions as the research arm of the home building industry. Sponsors seminars and workshops on construction, mortgage credit, labor relations, cost reduction, land use, remodeling, and business management. Compiles statistics; offers charitable program, spokesman training, and placement service; maintains speakers' bureau, and Hall of Fame. Subsidiaries include the National Council of the Housing Industry. Maintains over 50 committees in many areas of construction; operates National Commercial Builders Council, National Council of the Multifamily Housing Industry, National Remodelers Council, and National Sales and Marketing Council.

1768 ■ National Association of Women in Construction (NAWIC)
327 S Adams St.
Fort Worth, TX 76104
Ph: (817)877-5551
Fax: (817)877-0324
Fr: 800-552-3506
E-mail: nawic@nawic.org
URL: http://www.nawic.org

Description: Seeks to enhance the success of women in the construction industry.

SOURCES OF HELP-WANTED ADS

1769 ■ *Chow*
Instant Comma Inc.
235 2nd St., 1st Fl.
San Francisco, CA 94105
Ph: (415)344-2000
Fax: (415)344-1219
URL: http://www.chowmag.com/

Bimonthly. $18.95/year for individuals. Magazine that covers food preparation techniques, recipes, columns on specialty food items, how-to articles and editorials.

1770 ■ *Foodservice East*
The Newbury Street Group Inc.
93 Massachusetts Ave., Ste. 306
Boston, MA 02115
Ph: (617)267-2224
Fax: (617)267-5554
URL: http://www.foodserviceeast.com/

Bimonthly. $30.00/year for individuals. Compact Tabloid covering trends and analysis of the foodservice industry in the Northeast. A business-to-business publication featuring news, analysis and trends for the Northeast food service professional.

1771 ■ *Good Things to Eat*
Ogden Publications Inc.
1503 SW 42nd St.
Topeka, KS 66609-1214
Ph: (785)274-4304
Fax: (785)274-4305
Fr: 800-678-5779
URL: http://www.somegoodthingstoeat.com/

Quarterly. $9.95/year for individuals; $28.50/year for Canada. Magazine featuring food and recipes.

1772 ■ *The Gourmet Connection Magazine*
CAPCO Marketing
8417 Oswego Rd., No. 177
Baldwinsville, NY 13027
Ph: (315)699-1687
Fax: (315)699-1689
URL: http://tgcmagazine.com/

Magazine on gourmet food and the finer things in life. Covers a wide range of topics from nutritional information, and diet tips, to recipes, and information on arranging parties.

1773 ■ *Midwest Food Network*
Pinnacle Publishing Group
8205-F Estates Pky.
Plain City, OH 43064
Fax: (614)873-1650
URL: http://www.midwestfoodnetwork.com/

Bimonthly. $24.00/year for free to qualified subscribers; $24.00/year for individuals, others. Food service trade magazine featuring new products and suppliers and other industry news including food news, restau-

rant association updates, news of chefs, restaurant concepts, earnings, and openings and closings.

1774 ■ *The National Culinary Review*
American Culinary Federation Inc.
180 Center Pl. Way
St. Augustine, FL 32095-8859
Ph: (904)824-4468
Fax: (904)825-4758
Fr: 800-624-9458
URL: http://www.acfchefs.org/Content/
NavigationMenu2/About/Media/

Monthly. $60.00/year for individuals; $200.00/year for other countries. Trade magazine covering food and cooking.

1775 ■ *Plate*
Marketing & Technology Group
1415 N Dayton St.
Chicago, IL 60622
Ph: (312)274-2200
Fax: (312)266-3363
URL: http://www.plateonline.com

Bimonthly. Magazine that aims to inform food service professionals and owners food and focuses on how menu items are come up with.

1776 ■ *Real Food*
Greenspring Media Group
600 US Trust Bldg.
730 2nd Ave. S
Minneapolis, MN 55402
Ph: (612)371-5800
Fax: (612)371-5801
Fr: 800-933-4398
URL: http://www.realfoodmag.com/

Quarterly. Magazine featuring food choices.

1777 ■ *Restaurant Business*
VNU Business Publications
770 Broadway
New York, NY 10003
Ph: (646)654-5000
URL: http://www.foodservicetoday.com

Monthly. $119.00/year for individuals; $212.00/year for Canada; $468.00/year for other countries, rest of the world. Trade magazine for restaurants and commercial food service.

1778 ■ *Restaurant Hospitality*
Penton Media Inc.
249 W 17th St.
New York, NY 10011
Ph: (212)204-4200
URL: http://restaurant-hospitality.com

Monthly. Free. Dedicated to the success of full service restaurants and edited for chefs and other commercial foodservice professionals. Includes new food and equipment products and trends, menu and recipe ideas, industry news, new technology, food safety, emerging new concepts, consumer attitudes and

trends, labor and training, and profiles of successful operations.

1779 ■ *Simple & Delicious*
Reiman Publications
5400 S 60th St.
Greendale, WI 53129
Ph: (414)423-0100
URL: http://www.tasteofhome.com/Simple---
Delicious-Magazine

Bimonthly. $14.98/year for individuals; $19.98/year for Canada. Magazine covering recipes and kitchen shortcuts, 10-minute dishes, 5-ingredient recipes, 30-minute meals, and mix and match meal planner.

1780 ■ *Sizzle*
American Culinary Federation Inc.
180 Center Pl. Way
St. Augustine, FL 32095-8859
Ph: (904)824-4468
Fax: (904)825-4758
Fr: 800-624-9458
URL: http://www.acfchefs.org/Content/
NavigationMenu2/About/Media/

Quarterly. $19.95/year for individuals; $34.95/year for two years; $9.95/year for individuals, bulk; $150.00/year for other countries. Magazine for culinary students offering food trends, career information, and how-tos.

HANDBOOKS AND MANUALS

1781 ■ *Career Opportunities in the Food and Beverage Industry*
Facts on File, Inc.
132 W 31st St., 17th Fl.
New York, NY 10001-2006
Ph: (212)967-8800
Fax: 800-678-3633
Fr: 800-322-8755
E-mail: custserv@factsonfile.com
URL: http://www.infobasepublishing.com

Barbara Sims-Bell. 2010. $18.95 (paper). 223 pages. Provides the job seeker with information about locating and landing 80 skilled and unskilled jobs in the industry. Includes detailed job descriptions for many specific positions and lists trade associations, recruiting organizations, and major agencies. Contains index and bibliography.

1782 ■ *Catering on Campus: A Handbook on Catering in Colleges and Universities*
Colman Publishers
1147 Elmwood
Stockton, CA 95204
Ph: (209)464-9503
Fax: (209)262-4257
URL: http://www.paulfairbrook.com

Paul Fairbrook. 2004. $50.00. Designed to help catering managers at colleges do a better job of selling and providing quality and profitable catering services.

1783 ■ *How to Start a Home-Based Catering Business*

The Globe Pequot Press
246 Goose Ln.
Guilford, CT 06437
Ph: (203)458-4500
Fax: 800-820-2329
Fr: 888-249-7586
E-mail: info@globepequot.com
URL: http://www.globepequot.com/

Denise Vivaldo. Sixth edition, 2010. $18.95. 256 pages. Part of the Home-Based Business Series.

1784 ■ *On-Premise Catering: Hotels, Convention Centers, Arenas, Clubs, and More*

John Wiley & Sons, Inc.
111 River St.
Hoboken, NJ 07030-5774
Ph: (201)748-6000
Fax: (201)748-6088
URL: http://www.wiley.com

Patti J. Shock, John M. Stefanelli and Cheryl Sgovio. 2011. $70.00. 496 pages. Covers the essential skills and knowledge a professional needs to succeed in the field. Serves as guide to catering in hotels, banquet halls, wedding facilities, and other venues. Features modern technological trends in the catering industry, such as online marketing, social media and digital proposals. Includes topics on modern decor and effective menu writing.

1785 ■ *Opportunities in Restaurant Careers*

The McGraw-Hill Companies
PO Box 182604
Columbus, OH 43272
Fax: (614)759-3749
Fr: 877-883-5524
E-mail: customer.service@mcgraw-hill.com
URL: http://www.mhprofessional.com/
  product.php?isbn=0071442480

Carol Caprione Chmelynski. 2004. $13.95 (paper). 160 pages. Covers opportunities in the food service industry and details salaries, benefits, training opportunities, and professional associations. Special emphasis is put on becoming a successful restaurant manager by working up through the ranks. Illustrated.

1786 ■ *The Professional Caterer's Handbook: How to Open and Operate a Financially Successful Catering Business*

Atlantic Publishing Company
1210 SW 23rd Pl.
Ocala, FL 34474-7014
Fax: (352)622-1875
Fr: 800-814-1132
E-mail: sales@atlantic-pub.com
URL: http://www.atlantic-pub.com

Douglas Robert Brown and Lora Arduser. 2005. $79.95. Comprehensive guide for planning, starting, and operating a catering business; includes companion CD-ROM. Covers marketing, management, budgeting, home-based catering, ways for restaurants to add catering services to existing businesses, forms, Web sites, and more.

ONLINE JOB SOURCES AND SERVICES

1787 ■ FoodIndustryJobs.com

E-mail: jobboards@hrsmart.com
URL: http://www.foodindustryjobs.com

Description: Job databank and resume submission service for food industry workers.

1788 ■ HCareers.com

E-mail: hospitalitydivision@hcareers.com
URL: http://www.hcareers.com

Description: Connects employers and candidates within the hospitality industry. Enables candidates to search for jobs within a specific industry or location.

1789 ■ New Restaurant and Food Jobs

URL: http://www.newrestaurantandfoodjobs.com

Description: Provides an online listing of companies with available restaurant and food jobs in all specialties.

TRADESHOWS

1790 ■ Annual Hotel, Motel, and Restaurant Supply Show of the Southeast

Leisure Time Unlimited, Inc.
708 Main St.
PO Box 332
Myrtle Beach, SC 29577
Ph: (843)448-9483
Fax: (843)626-1513
Fr: 800-261-5591
E-mail: ltushows@sc.rr.com
URL: http://www.leisuretimeunlimited.com/

Annual. Primary Exhibits: Carpeting, furniture, coffee makers, produce companies, wine and beer and food companies, and services to motels, hotels, and restaurants. Dates and Locations: 2012 Jan 24-26; Myrtle Beach, SC; Myrtle Beach Convention Center.

1791 ■ Institute of Food Technologists Annual Meeting and Food Expo

Institute of Food Technologists
525 W, Van Buren St., Ste. 1000
Chicago, IL 60607
Ph: (312)782-8424
Fax: (312)782-8348
E-mail: info@ift.org
URL: http://www.ift.org

Annual. Primary Exhibits: Food ingredients, equipment, laboratory equipment and supplies, and other services rendered to the food processing industry. Dates and Locations: 2012 Jun 25-28; Las Vegas, NV.

1792 ■ International Baking Industry Exposition

IBIE Exhibition Management
401 N. Michigan Ave.
Chicago, IL 60611
Ph: (312)644-6610
Fax: (312)644-0575
E-mail: pdwyer@smithbucklin.com
URL: http://www.bakingexpo.com

Primary Exhibits: Baking equipment, supplies, and services.

1793 ■ Louisiana Foodservice Expo

Louisiana Restaurant Association
2700 N. Arnoult Rd.
Metairie, LA 70002
Ph: (504)454-2277
Fax: (504)454-2299
Fr: 800-256-4572
E-mail: tomw@lra.org
URL: http://www.lra.org/

Annual. Primary Exhibits: Food service equipment, supplies, and services, food products, furniture, tableware. Dates and Locations: 2012 Aug 11-13; New Orleans, LA; New Orleans Morial Convention Center.

1794 ■ Midsouthwest Foodservice Convention and Exposition

Oklahoma Restaurant Association
3800 N. Portland Ave.
Oklahoma City, OK 73112
Ph: (405)942-8181
Fax: (405)942-0541
Fr: 800-375-8181
URL: http://www.okrestaurants.com

Annual. Primary Exhibits: Providers of foodservice and hospitality products, services and equipment.

1795 ■ National Association of Catering Executives Experience Conference

National Association of Catering Executives
9891 Broken Land Pkwy., Ste. 301
Columbia, MD 21046
Ph: (410)290-5410
Fax: (410)290-5460
URL: http://www.nace.net

Annual. Features educational program, social events, and networking opportunities among peers. 2012 July 15-18; New Orleans, LA; Marriott New Orleans.

1796 ■ National Restaurant Association Restaurant and Hotel-Motel Show

National Restaurant Association Convention Office
1200 17th St., N.W.
Washington, DC 20036
Ph: (202)331-5900
Fax: (202)331-2429
Fr: 800-424-5156
URL: http://www.restaurant.org

Annual. Primary Exhibits: Food service equipment, supplies, and services and food and beverage products for the hospitality industry. Includes international cuisine pavilion. Dates and Locations: 2012 May 05-08; Chicago, IL; McCormick Place.

OTHER SOURCES

1797 ■ International Association of Culinary Professionals (IACP)

1100 Johnson Ferry Rd., Ste. 300
Atlanta, GA 30342
Ph: (404)252-3663
Fax: (404)252-0774
Fr: 800-928-4227
E-mail: info@iacp.com
URL: http://www.iacp.com

Description: Represents cooking school owners, food writers, chefs, caterers, culinary specialists, directors, teachers, cookbook authors, food stylists, food photographers, student/apprentices, and individuals in related industries in 20 countries. Promotes the interests of cooking schools, teachers, and culinary professionals. Encourages the exchange of information and education. Promotes professional standards and accreditation procedures. Maintains a Foundation to award culinary scholarships and grants.

1798 ■ International Council on Hotel, Restaurant, and Institutional Education (CHRIE)

2810 N Parham Rd., Ste. 230
Richmond, VA 23294
Ph: (804)346-4800
Fax: (804)346-5009
E-mail: kmccarty@chrie.org
URL: http://www.chrie.org

Description: Schools and colleges offering specialized education and training in hospitals, recreation, tourism and hotel, restaurant, and institutional administration; individuals, executives, and students. Provides networking opportunities and professional development.

1799 ■ International Flight Services Association (IFSA)

1100 Johnson Ferry Rd., Ste. 300
Atlanta, GA 30342
Ph: (404)252-3663
Fax: (404)252-0774
E-mail: ifsa@kellencompany.com
URL: http://www.ifsanet.com

Description: Works to serve the needs and interests of the airline and railway personnel, in-flight and railway caterers and suppliers responsible for providing passenger foodservice on regularly scheduled travel routes.

1800 ■ Les Amis d'Escoffier Society of New York
787 Ridgewood Rd.
Millburn, NJ 07041
Ph: (212)414-5820
Fax: (973)379-3117
URL: http://www.escoffier-society.com
Description: An educational organization of professionals in the food and wine industries. Maintains museum, speakers' bureau, hall of fame, and placement service. Sponsors charitable programs.

1801 ■ National Association of Catering Executives
9891 Broken Land Pkwy., Ste. 301
Columbia, MD 21046
Ph: (410)290-5410
Fax: (410)290-5460
URL: http://www.nace.net
Description: Serves the catering and special events industries. Promotes career success of members and professionalism in the industry. Offers educational programs, certification, and networking opportunities for members.

1802 ■ National Restaurant Association (NRA)
1200 17th St. NW
Washington, DC 20036
Ph: (202)331-5900
Fax: (202)331-2429
Fr: 800-424-5156
URL: http://www.restaurant.org
Description: Represents restaurants, cafeterias, clubs, contract foodservice management, drive-ins, caterers, institutional food services and other members of the foodservice industry; also represents establishments belonging to non-affiliated state and local restaurant associations in governmental affairs. Supports foodservice education and research in several educational institutions. Is affiliated with the Educational Foundation of the National Restaurant Association to provide training and education for operators, food and equipment manufacturers, distributors and educators. Has 300,000 member locations.

SOURCES OF HELP-WANTED ADS

1803 ■ Chef
Talcott Communication Corp.
233 N Michigan Ave., Ste. 1780
Chicago, IL 60601
Ph: (312)849-2220
Fax: (312)849-2174
E-mail: chef@talcott.com
URL: http://www.chefmagazine.com

$32.00/year for individuals; $47.00/year for two years; $64.00/year for individuals, 3 years; $43.00/year for Canada; $96.00/year for other countries. Food information for chefs.

1804 ■ Chow
Instant Comma Inc.
235 2nd St., 1st Fl.
San Francisco, CA 94105
Ph: (415)344-2000
Fax: (415)344-1219
URL: http://www.chowmag.com/

Bimonthly. $18.95/year for individuals. Magazine that covers food preparation techniques, recipes, columns on specialty food items, how-to articles and editorials.

1805 ■ Field & Feast
Field & Feast
PO Box 205
Four Lakes, WA 99014
URL: http://www.fieldandfeast.net

Quarterly. $19.00/year for individuals. Magazine that offers information on organic food cultivation and its health benefits.

1806 ■ Foodservice East
The Newbury Street Group Inc.
93 Massachusetts Ave., Ste. 306
Boston, MA 02115
Ph: (617)267-2224
Fax: (617)267-5554
URL: http://www.foodserviceeast.com/

Bimonthly. $30.00/year for individuals. Compact Tabloid covering trends and analysis of the foodservice industry in the Northeast. A business-to-business publication featuring news, analysis and trends for the Northeast food service professional.

1807 ■ Good Things to Eat
Ogden Publications Inc.
1503 SW 42nd St.
Topeka, KS 66609-1214
Ph: (785)274-4304
Fax: (785)274-4305
Fr: 800-678-5779
URL: http://www.somegoodthingstoeat.com/

Quarterly. $9.95/year for individuals; $28.50/year for Canada. Magazine featuring food and recipes.

1808 ■ The Gourmet Connection Magazine
CAPCO Marketing
8417 Oswego Rd., No. 177
Baldwinsville, NY 13027
Ph: (315)699-1687
Fax: (315)699-1689
URL: http://tgcmagazine.com/

Magazine on gourmet food and the finer things in life. Covers a wide range of topics from nutritional information, and diet tips, to recipes, and information on arranging parties.

1809 ■ Hotel & Motel Management
Questex Media Group
275 Grove St., 2-130
Newton, MA 02466
Ph: (617)219-8300
Fax: (617)219-8310
Fr: 888-552-4346
URL: http://www.hospitalityworldnetwork.com/hotel-management

$58.85/year for individuals; $81.40/year for Canada and Mexico; $143.00/year for other countries; $75.00/year for individuals, additional airmail shipping; free to qualified subscribers. Magazine (tabloid) covering the global lodging industry.

1810 ■ Midwest Food Network
Pinnacle Publishing Group
8205-F Estates Pky.
Plain City, OH 43064
Fax: (614)873-1650
URL: http://www.midwestfoodnetwork.com/

Bimonthly. $24.00/year for free to qualified subscribers; $24.00/year for individuals, others. Food service trade magazine featuring new products and suppliers and other industry news including food news, restaurant association updates, news of chefs, restaurant concepts, earnings, and openings and closings.

1811 ■ The National Culinary Review
American Culinary Federation Inc.
180 Center Pl. Way
St. Augustine, FL 32095-8859
Ph: (904)824-4468
Fax: (904)825-4758
Fr: 800-624-9458
URL: http://www.acfchefs.org/Content/NavigationMenu2/About/Media/

Monthly. $60.00/year for individuals; $200.00/year for other countries. Trade magazine covering food and cooking.

1812 ■ Plate
Marketing & Technology Group
1415 N Dayton St.
Chicago, IL 60622
Ph: (312)274-2200
Fax: (312)266-3363
URL: http://www.plateonline.com

Bimonthly. Magazine that aims to inform food service professionals and owners food and focuses on how menu items are come up with.

1813 ■ Real Food
Greenspring Media Group
600 US Trust Bldg.
730 2nd Ave. S
Minneapolis, MN 55402
Ph: (612)371-5800
Fax: (612)371-5801
Fr: 800-933-4398
URL: http://www.realfoodmag.com/

Quarterly. Magazine featuring food choices.

1814 ■ Restaurant Business
VNU Business Publications
770 Broadway
New York, NY 10003
Ph: (646)654-5000
URL: http://www.foodservicetoday.com

Monthly. $119.00/year for individuals; $212.00/year for Canada; $468.00/year for other countries, rest of the world. Trade magazine for restaurants and commercial food service.

1815 ■ Restaurant Hospitality
Penton Media Inc.
249 W 17th St.
New York, NY 10011
Ph: (212)204-4200
URL: http://restaurant-hospitality.com

Monthly. Free. Dedicated to the success of full service restaurants and edited for chefs and other commercial foodservice professionals. Includes new food and equipment products and trends, menu and recipe ideas, industry news, new technology, food safety, emerging new concepts, consumer attitudes and trends, labor and training, and profiles of successful operations.

1816 ■ Restaurant Startup & Growth
Specialized Publications Company
5215 Nw Crooked Rd.
Parkville, MO 64152
Ph: (816)741-3120
Fax: (816)741-6458
E-mail: rsg@spc-mag.com
URL: http://www.restaurantowner.com/mag/

Monthly. Magazine about starting and operating a restaurant business.

1817 ■ Simple & Delicious
Reiman Publications
5400 S 60th St.
Greendale, WI 53129
Ph: (414)423-0100
URL: http://www.tasteofhome.com/Simple---Delicious-Magazine

Bimonthly. $14.98/year for individuals; $19.98/year for Canada. Magazine covering recipes and kitchen shortcuts, 10-minute dishes, 5-ingredient recipes, 30-minute meals, and mix and match meal planner.

1818 ■ Sizzle
American Culinary Federation Inc.
180 Center Pl. Way
St. Augustine, FL 32095-8859
Ph: (904)824-4468
Fax: (904)825-4758
Fr: 800-624-9458
URL: http://www.acfchefs.org/Content/
  NavigationMenu2/About/Media/

Quarterly. $19.95/year for individuals; $34.95/year for two years; $9.95/year for individuals, bulk; $150.00/year for other countries. Magazine for culinary students offering food trends, career information, and how-tos.

Employer Directories and Networking Lists

1819 ■ Careers in Focus—Food
Facts On File Inc.
132 W 31st St., 17th Fl.
New York, NY 10001
Ph: (212)967-8800
Fax: 800-678-3633
Fr: 800-322-8755
URL: http://www.infobasepublishing.com

Latest edition 3rd; Published April, 2007. $32.95 for individuals. Covers: An overview of the food industry, followed by a selection of jobs profiled in detail, including the nature of the job, earnings, prospects for employment, what kind of training and skills it requires, and sources for further information.

1820 ■ Discovering Careers for Your Future—Food
Facts On File Inc.
132 W 31st St., 17th Fl.
New York, NY 10001
Ph: (212)967-8800
Fax: 800-678-3633
Fr: 800-322-8755
URL: http://factsonfile.infobasepublishing.com

Published 2005. $21.95 for individuals; $19.75 for libraries. Covers: Brewers, cookbook and recipe writers, cooks and chefs, dietitians and nutritionists, food service workers, supermarket managers, winemakers, and more; links career education to curriculum, helping children investigate the subjects they are interested in, and the careers those subjects might lead to.

Handbooks and Manuals

1821 ■ Becoming a Culinary Arts Professionals
LearningExpress, LLC
2 Rector St., 26th Fl.
New York, NY 10006
Fr: 800-295-9556
E-mail: customerservice@learningexpressllc.com
URL: http://www.learningexpressllc.com

LearningExpress Editors. 2010. $16.95 (paper). 208 pages. Details how to navigate the hundreds of paths to a culinary career available in the United States. Provides many culinary career options and addresses how to develop new skills or refine current skills and how to understand the certification process.

1822 ■ Career Opportunities in the Food and Beverage Industry
Facts on File, Inc.
132 W 31st St., 17th Fl.
New York, NY 10001-2006
Ph: (212)967-8800
Fax: 800-678-3633
Fr: 800-322-8755
E-mail: custserv@factsonfile.com
URL: http://www.infobasepublishing.com

Barbara Sims-Bell. 2010. $18.95 (paper). 223 pages. Provides the job seeker with information about locat-

ing and landing 80 skilled and unskilled jobs in the industry. Includes detailed job descriptions for many specific positions and lists trade associations, recruiting organizations, and major agencies. Contains index and bibliography.

1823 ■ Careers in Travel, Tourism, and Hospitality
The McGraw-Hill Companies
PO Box 182604
Columbus, OH 43272
Fax: (614)759-3749
Fr: 877-883-5524
E-mail: customer.service@mcgraw-hill.com
URL: http://www.mhprofessional.com

Marjorie Eberts, Linda Brothers, and Ann Gisler. Second edition, 2005. $15.95 (paper). 224 pages.

1824 ■ The Cook's Book: Techniques and Tips from the World's Master Chefs
Dorling Kindersley Publishing, Inc.
375 Hudson St., 2nd Fl.
New York, NY 10014
Ph: (646)674-4047
Fax: (646)674-4020
Fr: 800-788-6262
URL: http://us.dk.com

Jill Norman. 2005. $50.00. 648 pages. Tips for home cooks from top chefs around the world; includes concise directions and color photography.

1825 ■ Culinary Careers for Dummies
Wiley
111 River St.
Hoboken, NJ 07030
Ph: (201)748-6000
Fax: (201)748-6088
E-mail: info@wiley.com
URL: http://as.wiley.com/WileyCDA/Section/
  index.html

Michele Thomas, Annette Tomei, Tracey Biscontini. 2011. $22.95 (paper). 384 pages. Provides the essential information every culinary novice needs to enter and excel in the food service industry. Contains expert guidance on planning a career in the food service industry, tips and advice on what to study and information on many career options in the culinary field.

1826 ■ Opportunities in Restaurant Careers
The McGraw-Hill Companies
PO Box 182604
Columbus, OH 43272
Fax: (614)759-3749
Fr: 877-883-5524
E-mail: customer.service@mcgraw-hill.com
URL: http://www.mhprofessional.com/
  product.php?isbn=0071442480

Carol Caprione Chmelynski. 2004. $13.95 (paper). 160 pages. Covers opportunities in the food service industry and details salaries, benefits, training opportunities, and professional associations. Special emphasis is put on becoming a successful restaurant manager by working up through the ranks. Illustrated.

1827 ■ Purchasing for Chefs: A Concise Guide
John Wiley & Sons, Inc.
111 River St.
Hoboken, NJ 07030
Ph: (201)748-6000
Fax: (201)748-6088
E-mail: info@wiley.com
URL: http://as.wiley.com/WileyCDA/Section/
  index.html

Andrew H. Feinstein and John M. Stefanelli. 2010. $51.95. 256 pages. Guide details purchasing principles to chefs and hospitality managers for obtaining goods and services for their business.

Employment Agencies and Search Firms

1828 ■ Boutique Search Firm
1173 Rodeo Dr.
Los Angeles, CA 90035
Ph: (310)552-2221
Fax: (310)552-2224
URL: http://www.boutiquesearchfirm.com

Serves as a recruiting firm specializing in hospitality management. Offers jobs in luxury hotels and resorts worldwide.

1829 ■ Chefs' Professional Agency
870 Market St., 863
San Francisco, CA 94102
Ph: (415)392-1563
E-mail: hospitality@chefsprofessional.com
URL: http://chefsprofessional.com

Locates talent for restaurants, hotels, clubs and resorts. Provides resume kits, career tools, and other candidate resources while also providing resources for employers.

1830 ■ dd factor
2615 190th St., Ste. 221
Redondo Beach, CA 90278
Ph: (310)376-0870
Fax: (310)376-1840
URL: http://ddfactor.com

Operates as a hospitality search firm that specializes in chefs, sous chefs, and kitchen managers.

1831 ■ Food Management Search
235 State St., Ste. 326
Springfield, MA 01103
Ph: (413)732-2666
Fax: (413)732-6466
E-mail: recruiters@foodmanagementsearch.com
URL: http://foodmanagementsearch.com/index.cfm

Specializes in contingency recruiting projects exclusively in the food manufacturing and food service industries. Provides positions covering food production/manufacturing, supply chain, food service, sales and marketing.

1832 ■ Global Hospitality
3579 E Foothill Blvd., Ste. 229
Pasadena, CA 91107
Ph: (626)836-1222
Fax: (626)836-1223
E-mail: mail@globalhospitality.com
URL: http://www.globalhospitality.com

Executive search firm that specializes in identifying, evaluating, and placing leadership and management talent in the hospitality industry.

1833 ■ HospitalityStaff.com
3195 Tamiami Trail, Ste. 204
Port Charlotte, FL 33952
Ph: (941)743-8540
Fax: (941)743-9684
Fr: 800-987-1555
URL: http://www.hospitalitystaff.com

Serves as a placement agency, specializing in the supply of temporary and permanent staff to the hospitality industry.

1834 ■ Prospection Group
PO Box 1999
Santa Monica, CA 90406
Ph: (310)398-3795
URL: http://www.prospectiongroup.com

Executive search firm for the hospitality industry. Searches for hospitality executives ranging from the level of general management to private chefs.

ONLINE JOB SOURCES AND SERVICES

1835 ■ BestfoodJobs.com
URL: http://www.bestfoodjobs.com

Description: Provides information on employment opportunities for the restaurant and food service industry.

1836 ■ ChefCrossing.com
URL: http://www.chefcrossing.com

Description: Shows job listings from employer career pages, job websites, association websites, newspaper classified ads and recruiter sites.

1837 ■ ChefJobs.com
E-mail: info@chefjobs.com
URL: http://www.chefjobs.com

Description: Provides resources to career and recreational culinary education programs worldwide.

1838 ■ ChefJobsNetwork.com
URL: http://chefjobsnetwork.com

Description: Provides employment opportunities for professionals in the culinary industry.

1839 ■ Escoffier.com
URL: http://escoffier.com

Description: Offers a collection of chef job openings, recreational culinary educational resources, resume writing services and career advice for job seekers.

1840 ■ FoodIndustryJobs.com
E-mail: jobboards@hrsmart.com
URL: http://www.foodindustryjobs.com

Description: Job databank and resume submission service for food industry workers.

1841 ■ Foodservice.com
URL: http://www.foodservice.com

Description: Serves as an online community of food-service professionals. Provides services such as a virtual foodshow, employment center, market reports, daily industry news and editorials, discussion forums, culinary school connections, and the weekly foodservice.com express e-Newsletter.

1842 ■ Get Chef Jobs
URL: http://www.getchefjobs.com

Description: Serves as an online job search resource for professional chefs.

1843 ■ HCareers.com
E-mail: hospitalitydivision@hcareers.com
URL: http://www.hcareers.com

Description: Connects employers and candidates within the hospitality industry. Enables candidates to search for jobs within a specific industry or location.

1844 ■ HotelJobs.com
URL: http://www.hoteljobs.com

Description: Provides job postings and resume database for hotel, casino and cruise ship professionals and recruiters.

1845 ■ New Restaurant and Food Jobs
URL: http://www.newrestaurantandfoodjobs.com

Description: Provides an online listing of companies with available restaurant and food jobs in all specialties.

1846 ■ PastryBakerChef.com
URL: http://www.pastrybakerchef.com

Description: Features employment opportunities for bakers and pastry chefs.

1847 ■ RestaurantOperator.com
E-mail: customerservice@restaurantoperator.com
URL: http://www.restaurantoperator.com

Description: Exists as a virtual community created for the benefit of restaurant operators and employees. Offers a variety of services that encompass all facets of the restaurant business. Provides services on product information, distributor and supplier information, professional services, associations and trade show listings, publications, restaurants for sale, business opportunities, and an employment center.

1848 ■ StarChefs.com
E-mail: liz@starchefs.com
URL: http://www.starchefs.com

Description: Contains job board, resume writing service and career advice for job seekers in the culinary arts. Seekers can sign up for free e-mail account and receive job notifications through this service.

TRADESHOWS

1849 ■ ACF National Convention and Trade Show
American Culinary Federation
180 Ctr. Place Way
St. Augustine, FL 32095
Ph: (904)824-4468
Fax: (904)825-4758
Fr: 800-624-9458
E-mail: acf@acfchefs.net
URL: http://www.acfchefs.org

Annual. Includes exhibits featuring apparel, equipment, cookware, books and media, seasonings, packaged goods, and similar merchandise. Provides networking opportunities for attendees. 2012 July 14-17; Sunny Orlando, FL.

1850 ■ Denver Food and Kitchen Expo
Professional Chefs Association
1207 Hawkeye Ct.
Fort Collins, CO 80525
Ph: (970)223-4004
Fax: 877-392-1443
URL: http://www.professionalchef.com

Annual. Features all things related to food, kitchens, and cooking.

1851 ■ International Baking Industry Exposition
IBIE Exhibition Management
401 N. Michigan Ave.
Chicago, IL 60611
Ph: (312)644-6610
Fax: (312)644-0575
E-mail: pdwyer@smithbucklin.com
URL: http://www.bakingexpo.com

Primary Exhibits: Baking equipment, supplies, and services.

1852 ■ National Restaurant Association Restaurant and Hotel-Motel Show
National Restaurant Association Convention Office
1200 17th St., N.W.
Washington, DC 20036
Ph: (202)331-5900
Fax: (202)331-2429
Fr: 800-424-5156
URL: http://www.restaurant.org

Annual. Primary Exhibits: Food service equipment, supplies, and services and food and beverage products for the hospitality industry. Includes international cuisine pavilion. Dates and Locations: 2012 May 05-08; Chicago, IL; McCormick Place.

OTHER SOURCES

1853 ■ American Culinary Federation (ACF)
180 Center Place Way
St. Augustine, FL 32095
Ph: (904)824-4468
Fax: (904)825-4758
Fr: 800-624-9458
E-mail: acf@acfchefs.net
URL: http://www.acfchefs.org

Description: Aims to promote the culinary profession and provide on-going educational training and networking for members. Provides opportunities for competition, professional recognition, and access to educational forums with other culinary experts at local, regional, national, and international events. Operates the National Apprenticeship Program for cooks and pastry cooks. Offers programs that address certification of the individual chef's skills, accreditation of culinary programs, apprenticeship of cooks and pastry cooks, professional development, and the fight against childhood hunger.

1854 ■ Asian Chefs Association (ACA)
3145 Geary Blvd., No. 112
San Francisco, CA 94118
Ph: (408)634-9462
E-mail: contactus@acasf.com
URL: http://www.acasf.com

Description: Aims to increase public and media awareness of Asian-inspired cuisine. Educates chefs about the various aspects of the restaurant and culinary business. Promotes the art of Asian-inspired cuisine. Provides a forum for Asian chefs.

1855 ■ Association for International Practical Training (AIPT)
10400 Little Patuxent Pkwy., Ste. 250
Columbia, MD 21044-3519
Ph: (410)997-2200
Fax: (410)992-3924
E-mail: aipt@aipt.org
URL: http://www.aipt.org

Description: Providers worldwide of on-the-job training programs for students and professionals seeking international career development and life-changing experiences. Arranges workplace exchanges in hundreds of professional fields, bringing employers and trainees together from around the world. Client list ranges from small farming communities to Fortune 500 companies.

1856 ■ International Association of Culinary Professionals (IACP)
1100 Johnson Ferry Rd., Ste. 300
Atlanta, GA 30342
Ph: (404)252-3663
Fax: (404)252-0774
Fr: 800-928-4227
E-mail: info@iacp.com
URL: http://www.iacp.com

Description: Represents cooking school owners, food writers, chefs, caterers, culinary specialists, directors, teachers, cookbook authors, food stylists, food photographers, student/apprentices, and individuals in related industries in 20 countries. Promotes the interests of cooking schools, teachers, and culinary professionals. Encourages the exchange of information and education. Promotes professional standards and accreditation procedures. Maintains a Foundation to award culinary scholarships and grants.

1857 ■ International Council on Hotel, Restaurant, and Institutional Education (CHRIE)
2810 N Parham Rd., Ste. 230
Richmond, VA 23294
Ph: (804)346-4800
Fax: (804)346-5009
E-mail: kmccarty@chrie.org
URL: http://www.chrie.org

Description: Schools and colleges offering specialized education and training in hospitals, recreation, tourism and hotel, restaurant, and institutional administration; individuals, executives, and students. Provides networking opportunities and professional development.

1858 ■ Les Amis d'Escoffier Society of New York
787 Ridgewood Rd.
Millburn, NJ 07041
Ph: (212)414-5820
Fax: (973)379-3117
URL: http://www.escoffier-society.com

Description: An educational organization of professionals in the food and wine industries. Maintains museum, speakers' bureau, hall of fame, and placement service. Sponsors charitable programs.

1859 ■ National Restaurant Association (NRA)
1200 17th St. NW
Washington, DC 20036
Ph: (202)331-5900
Fax: (202)331-2429
Fr: 800-424-5156
URL: http://www.restaurant.org

Description: Represents restaurants, cafeterias, clubs, contract foodservice management, drive-ins, caterers, institutional food services and other members of the foodservice industry; also represents establishments belonging to non-affiliated state and local restaurant associations in governmental affairs. Supports foodservice education and research in several educational institutions. Is affiliated with the Educational Foundation of the National Restaurant Association to provide training and education for operators, food and equipment manufacturers, distributors and educators. Has 300,000 member locations.

1860 ■ Professional Chefs Association
1207 Hawkeye Ct.
Fort Collins, CO 80525
Ph: (970)223-4004
Fax: 877-392-1443
E-mail: support@professionalchef.com
URL: http://www.professionalchef.com

Description: Represents the interests of chefs and those associated with the food service industry. Promotes culinary excellence through the exchange of knowledge among chefs. Offers online education courses and certification programs.

1861 ■ Research Chefs Association
1100 Johnson Ferry Rd., Ste. 300
Atlanta, GA 30342
Ph: (404)252-3663
Fax: (404)252-0774
E-mail: rca@kellencompany.com
URL: http://www.culinology.com

Description: Represents the interests of chefs, food scientists, and other industry professionals in the food research and development industry. Offers resources of culinary and technical information for professionals in the field.

1862 ■ United States Personal Chef Association
7680 Universal Blvd., Ste. 550
Orlando, FL 32819
Fr: 800-995-2138
URL: http://www.uspca.com

Description: Strives to set standards and create guidelines for the industry. Promotes ongoing education.

SOURCES OF HELP-WANTED ADS

1863 ■ Advances in Chemical Engineering and Science
Scientific Research Publishing
PO Box 54821
Irvine, CA 92619-4821
URL: http://www.scirp.org/journal/aces/

Peer-reviewed journal covering advances in chemical engineering and sciences.

1864 ■ American Institute of Chemical Engineers Journal
John Wiley & Sons Inc.
111 River St.
Hoboken, NJ 07030-5773
Ph: (201)748-6000
Fax: (201)748-6088
Fr: 800-825-7550
URL: http://onlinelibrary.wiley.com/journal/10.1002/ (ISSN)1547-59

Monthly. $2,278.00/year for institutions, print only; $2,446.00/year for institutions, Canada and Mexico, print only; $2,401.00/year for other countries, print only; $2,620.00/year for institutions, print with online; $2,788.00/year for institutions, Canada and Mexico, print with online; $2,872.00/year for institutions, other countries, print with online. Peer-reviewed journal focusing on technological advances in core areas of chemical engineering as well as in other relevant engineering disciplines.

1865 ■ American Journal of Analytical Chemistry
Scientific Research Publishing
PO Box 54821
Irvine, CA 92619-4821
E-mail: ajac@scirp.org
URL: http://www.scirp.org/journal/ajac/

Peer-reviewed journal featuring the latest advancements in analytical chemistry.

1866 ■ Chemical Engineering
Access Intelligence L.L.C.
4 Choke Cherry Rd., 2nd Fl.
Rockville, MD 20850-4024
Ph: (301)354-2000
Fr: 888-707-5814
URL: http://www.che.com

Monthly. $109.97/year for individuals, print; $136.97/year for Canada; $239.00/year for other countries. Chemical process industries magazine.

1867 ■ Chemical Engineering Communications
Taylor & Francis Group Journals
325 Chestnut St., Ste. 800
Philadelphia, PA 19106-2608
Ph: (215)625-8900
Fax: (215)625-2940

Fr: 800-354-1420
URL: http://www.tandf.co.uk/journals/titles/ 00986445.asp

Monthly. $2,421.00/year for individuals, print only; $5,298.00/year for institutions, online only; $5,887.00/year for institutions, print and online; $4,536.00/year for institutions, print and online; $4,082.00/year for institutions, online only; $1,461.00/year for individuals, print only. Journal focusing on the results of basic and applied research in chemical engineering.

1868 ■ Chemical Engineering Progress
American Institute of Chemical Engineers
3 Park Ave.
New York, NY 10016-5991
Ph: (646)495-1365
Fax: (646)495-1504
Fr: 800-242-4363
URL: http://www.aiche.org/CEP/index.aspx

Monthly. $170.00/year for nonmembers, in North America; $295.00/year for nonmembers, international; $210.00/year for nonmembers, with online; in North America; $335.00/year for nonmembers, with online; international. Chemical process industries magazine.

1869 ■ Chemical Engineering and Technology
John Wiley & Sons Inc.
111 River St.
Hoboken, NJ 07030-5773
Ph: (201)748-6000
Fax: (201)748-6088
Fr: 800-825-7550
URL: http://onlinelibrary.wiley.com/journal/10.1002/ (ISSN)1521-41

Monthly. $4,750.00/year for institutions, print only; $4,750.00/year for institutions, print only; $5,463.00/year for institutions, print with online; $3,701.00/year for institutions, print only, rest of Europe; $5,755.00/year for institutions, print only, Switzerland and Lichtenstein; $4,750.00/year for institutions, other countries, print only; $2,424.00/year for institutions, print only. Journal focusing on all aspects of chemical and process engineering.

1870 ■ Chemical Equipment
Reed Business Information (New York, New York)
360 Park Ave. S
New York, NY 10010
Ph: (646)746-6400
Fax: (646)746-7431
Fr: 800-446-6551
URL: http://www.reedbusinessinteractive.com

Free for qualified professionals; $72.90/year for individuals, cover price. Tabloid on the chemical process industry.

1871 ■ Chemical Market Reporter
Schnell Publishing Company Inc.
360 Park Ave. S
12th Fl.
New York, NY 10010

Ph: (212)791-4200
Fax: (212)791-4321
URL: http://www.icis.com/v2/magazine/home.aspx

Weekly (Mon.). International tabloid newspaper for the chemical process industries. Includes analytical reports on developments in the chemical marketplace, plant expansions, new technology, corporate mergers, finance, current chemical prices, and regulatory matters.

1872 ■ The Chemical Record
John Wiley & Sons Inc.
111 River St.
Hoboken, NJ 07030-5773
Ph: (201)748-6000
Fax: (201)748-6088
Fr: 800-825-7550
URL: http://onlinelibrary.wiley.com/journal/10.1002/ (ISSN)1528-06

Bimonthly. $105.00/year for U.S., Canada, and Mexico, print only; $153.00/year for other countries, print only; $639.00/year for institutions, print only; $639.00/year for institutions, Canada and Mexico, print only; $639.00/year for institutions, other countries, print only. Journal publishing overviews of new developments at the cutting edge of chemistry of interest to a wide audience of chemists.

1873 ■ The Chemist
American Institute of Chemists Inc.
315 Chestnut St.
Philadelphia, PA 19106-2702
Ph: (215)873-8224
Fax: (215)629-5224
E-mail: info@theaic.org
URL: http://www.theaic.org

Description: Quarterly. Covers news items relating to the chemical profession and membership in the Institute. Reports on legislation, licensure, earnings, awards, and professional education. Recurring features include news of employment opportunities and news of members. Published alternate months as a magazine.

1874 ■ Chemistry & Biology
Elsevier Science Inc.
360 Park Ave. S
New York, NY 10010-1710
Ph: (212)989-5800
Fax: (212)633-3990
Fr: 888-437-4636
URL: http://www.elsevier.com/wps/find/ journaldescription.cws_home

Monthly. $2,137.00/year for institutions, for all countries except Europe, Japan & Iran; $442.00/year for U.S. and Canada; $457.00/year for individuals, for all countries except Europe, Japan and Iran. Journal focused on genetic, computational, or theoretical information of chemistry and biology, substantiating experimental data.

1875 ■ Composites
Begell House Inc.
50 Cross Hwy.
Redding, CT 06896
Ph: (203)938-1300
Fax: (203)938-1304
URL: http://www.begellhouse.com/journals/
   36ff4a142dec9609

$708.00/year for institutions. Journal featuring basic ideas in the mechanics of composite materials and structures between research workers and engineers.

1876 ■ The Electrochemical Society Interface
Electrochemical Society Inc.
65 S Main St., Bldg. D
Pennington, NJ 08534-2839
Ph: (609)737-1902
Fax: (609)737-2743
E-mail: interface@electrochem.org
URL: http://www.electrochem.org/dl/interface/

Quarterly. $64.00/year for individuals, tier 1, print & online; $82.00/year for other countries, tier 1, print & online. Publication featuring news and articles of interest to members of the Electrochemical Society.

1877 ■ Engineering
Scientific Research Publishing
PO Box 54821
Irvine, CA 92619-4821
E-mail: eng@scirp.org
URL: http://www.scirp.org/journal/eng/

Monthly. $708.00/year for individuals. Peer-reviewed journal publishing articles on the latest advancements in engineering.

1878 ■ Engineering in Life Sciences
John Wiley & Sons Inc.
111 River St.
Hoboken, NJ 07030-5773
Ph: (201)748-6000
Fax: (201)748-6088
Fr: 800-825-7550
URL: http://onlinelibrary.wiley.com/journal/10.1002/
   (ISSN)1618-28

Bimonthly. $989.00/year for institutions, European, online only; $1,512.00/year for institutions, online only, Switzerland and Liechtenstein; $1,299.00/year for institutions, other countries, online only; $663.00/year for institutions, European, online only; $1,299.00/year for institutions, online only; $1,299.00/year for institutions, Canada and Mexico, online only. Journal focusing on the field of biotechnology and related topics including microbiology, genetics, biochemistry, and chemistry.

1879 ■ ENR: Engineering News-Record
McGraw-Hill Inc.
PO Box 182604
Columbus, OH 43218
Ph: (614)430-4000
Fax: (614)759-3749
Fr: 877-833-5524
URL: http://enr.construction.com/Default.asp

Weekly. $49.00/year for individuals, print; $89.00/year for Canada, print; $125.00/year for other countries, print. Magazine focusing on engineering and construction.

1880 ■ Graduating Engineer & Computer Careers
Career Recruitment Media
2 LAN Dr., Ste. 100
Westford, MA 01886
Ph: (978)692-5092
Fax: (978)692-4174
URL: http://www.graduatingengineer.com

Quarterly. $16.95/year for individuals. Magazine focusing on employment, education, and career development for entry-level engineers and computer scientists.

1881 ■ High Technology Careers Magazine
HTC
4701 Patrick Henry Dr., No. 1901
Santa Clara, CA 95054
Fax: (408)567-0242
URL: http://www.hightechcareers.com

Bimonthly. $29.00/year; $35.00/year for Canada; $85.00/year for out of country. Magazine (tabloid) containing employment opportunity information for the engineering and technical community.

1882 ■ International Journal of Energetic Materials and Chemical Propulsion
Begell House Inc.
50 Cross Hwy.
Redding, CT 06896
Ph: (203)938-1300
Fax: (203)938-1304
URL: http://www.begellhouse.com/journals/
   17bbb47e377ce023

$1,240.00/year for institutions. Journal promoting scientific investigation, technical advancements and information exchange on energetic materials and chemical propulsion.

1883 ■ International Journal of Organic Chemistry
Scientific Research Publishing
PO Box 54821
Irvine, CA 92619-4821
E-mail: ijoc@scirp.org
URL: http://www.scirp.org/journal/ijoc/

Quarterly. $156.00/year for individuals. Peer-reviewed journal publishing articles in the field of organic chemistry.

1884 ■ Journal of Biomaterials and Nanobiotechnology
Scientific Research Publishing
PO Box 54821
Irvine, CA 92619-4821
URL: http://www.scirp.org/journal/jbnb/

Peer-reviewed journal covering the basic science and engineering aspects of biomaterials and nanotechnology.

1885 ■ Journal of Biophysical Chemistry
Scientific Research Publishing
PO Box 54821
Irvine, CA 92619-4821
URL: http://www.scirp.org/journal/jbpc/

Peer-reviewed journal publishing the latest advancements in biophysical chemistry.

1886 ■ Journal of Chemical Theory and Computation
American Chemical Society
1155 16th St. NW
Washington, DC 20036
Ph: (202)872-4600
Fr: 800-227-5558
URL: http://pubs.acs.org/journals/jctcce

$1,367.00/year for institutions, North America; $1,493.00/year for institutions, outside North America. Journal presenting new theories, methodology, and/or important applications in quantum chemistry, molecular dynamics, and statistical mechanics.

1887 ■ Journal of Crystallization Process and Technology
Scientific Research Publishing
PO Box 54821
Irvine, CA 92619-4821
E-mail: jcpt@scirp.org
URL: http://www.scirp.org/journal/jcpt/

Peer-reviewed journal covering all aspects of the crystallization process, studies and properties of crystalline materials.

1888 ■ Journal of Encapsulation and Adsorption Sciences
Scientific Research Publishing
PO Box 54821
Irvine, CA 92619-4821
URL: http://www.scirp.org/journal/jeas/

Peer-reviewed journal covering all aspects of encapsulation and adsorption sciences.

1889 ■ Journal of Nanomechanics and Micromechanics
American Society of Civil Engineers
1801 Alexander Bell Dr.
Reston, VA 20191-4400
Ph: (703)295-6300
Fax: (703)295-6333
Fr: 800-548-2723
URL: http://ascelibrary.org/nmo/

Quarterly. $373.00/year for institutions, print and online; $393.00/year for institutions, other countries, print and online. Peer-reviewed journal featuring articles on nanomechanics and micromechanics.

1890 ■ Journal of Women and Minorities in Science and Engineering
Begell House Inc.
50 Cross Hwy.
Redding, CT 06896
Ph: (203)938-1300
Fax: (203)938-1304
URL: http://www.begellhouse.com/journals/
   00551c876cc2f027

$248.00/year for institutions. Peer-reviewed journal featuring innovative ideas and programs for classroom teachers, scientific studies, and formulation of concepts related to the education, recruitment, and retention of under-represented groups in science and engineering.

1891 ■ Modern Plastics Worldwide
Canon Communications L.L.C.
11444 W Olympic Blvd., Ste. 900
Los Angeles, CA 90064
Ph: (310)445-4200
Fax: (310)445-4299
URL: http://www.modplas.com

Monthly. $59.00/year for individuals; $99.00/year for two years, U.S. and possessions; $110.00/year for Canada; $199.00/year for two years, for Canada; $150.00/year for other countries; $250.00/year for two years. Magazine for the plastics industry.

1892 ■ Nanomechanics Science and Technology
Begell House Inc.
50 Cross Hwy.
Redding, CT 06896
Ph: (203)938-1300
Fax: (203)938-1304
URL: http://www.begellhouse.com/journals/
   11e12455066dab5d

$748.00/year for institutions. Journal covering the areas of nano- and micromechanics.

1893 ■ Nanoparticle News
BCC Research
49 Walnut St., Bldg. 2
Wellesley, MA 02481
Ph: (781)489-7301
Fax: (781)253-3933
Fr: (866)285-7215
URL: http://www.bccresearch.com/report/
   index.php?rcode=nan

Monthly. $675.00/year for single issue, web access and archive (2 user license); $640.00/year for single issue, print, online, archive (outside North America); $495.00/year for single issue, web access and archive; $590.00/year for single issue, print, web access and archive (North America); $1,485.00/year for individuals, online (enterprise license); $990.00/year for individuals, online (Department license); $750.00/year for individuals, online (5 user license). Publication covering issues in the chemical industry.

1894 ■ *NSBE Magazine*
NSBE Publications
205 Daingerfield Rd.
Alexandria, VA 22314
Ph: (703)549-2207
Fax: (703)683-5312
URL: http://www.nsbe.org/News-Media/Magazines/
   About-NSBE-Magazine

$20.00/year for individuals; $35.00/year for other countries; $15.00/year for students. Journal providing information on engineering careers, self-development, and cultural issues for recent graduates with technical majors.

1895 ■ *PALAIOS*
SEPM Publications
4111 S Darlington, Ste. 100
Tulsa, OK 74135-6373
Ph: (918)610-3361
Fax: (918)621-1685
Fr: 800-865-9765
E-mail: palois@ku.edu
URL: http://palaios.ku.edu/

Monthly. $315.00/year for individuals, for U.S.; online version with CD-ROM; $415.00/year for individuals, for U.S.; print and online version with CD-ROM; $315.00/year for other countries, online version with CD-ROM; $425.00/year for other countries, print and online version with CD-ROM. Journal providing information on the impact of life on Earth history as recorded in the paleontological and sedimentological records. Covers areas such as biogeochemistry, ichnology, sedimentology, stratigraphy, paleoecology, paleoclimatology, and paleoceanography.

1896 ■ *PE*
National Society of Professional Engineers
1420 King St.
Alexandria, VA 22314
Ph: (703)684-2800
Fax: (703)684-4875
URL: http://www.nspe.org/PEmagazine/index.html

Monthly. Magazine (tabloid) covering professional, legislative, and techology issues for an engineering audience.

1897 ■ *Plastics Engineering*
Society of Plastics Engineers
13 Church Hill Rd.
PO Box 403
Newtown, CT 06470
Ph: (203)775-0471
Fax: (203)775-8490
URL: http://www.4spe.org/pub

$142.00/year for nonmembers; $242.00/year for nonmembers, outside North America; $180.00/year for institutions, corporate library; $280.00/year for institutions, corporate library outside North America. Plastics trade magazine.

1898 ■ *Plastics News*
Crain Communications Inc.
77 Franklin St., Ste. 809
Boston, MA 02110-1510
Ph: (617)292-3385
URL: http://www.plasticsnews.com

Weekly. $84.00/year for U.S., print + web; $139.00/year for two years, print + web; $182.00/year for individuals, print + web, Mexico; $292.00/year for other countries, print + web; $99.00/year for other countries, web only; $134.00/year for Canada, print + web; $241.00/year for Canada, two years, print + web. Magazine (tabloid) for the plastics industry providing business news.

1899 ■ *Powder and Bulk Engineering*
CSC Publishing Inc.
1155 Northland Dr.
St. Paul, MN 55120
Ph: (651)287-5650
Fax: (651)287-5600
URL: http://www.powderbulk.com/

Monthly. $100.00/year for individuals, outside North

America, or digital format; free to qualified subscribers. Journal serving chemical, food, plastics, pulp and paper, and electronic industries.

1900 ■ *Rubber World*
Rubber World
1867 W Market St.
Akron, OH 44313-6901
Ph: (330)864-2122
Fax: (330)864-5298
E-mail: jhl@rubberworld.com
URL: http://www.rubberworld.com/

$34.00/year for individuals; $39.00/year for Canada; $89.00/year for other countries, airmail. Rubber manufacturing magazine.

1901 ■ *Soft Nanoscience Letters*
Scientific Research Publishing
PO Box 54821
Irvine, CA 92619-4821
E-mail: snl@scirp.org
URL: http://www.scirp.org/journal/snl/

Quarterly. $156.00/year for individuals. Peer-reviewed journal publishing articles in the field of soft nanoscience.

1902 ■ *Structure Magazine*
American Council of Engineering Companies
1015 15th St. NW, 8th Fl.
Washington, DC 20005-2605
Ph: (202)347-7474
Fax: (202)898-0068
URL: http://www.structuremag.org

Annual. $65.00/year for nonmembers, for U.S residents; $35.00/year for students; $90.00/year for Canada; $125.00/year for other countries. Magazine focused on providing tips, tools, techniques, and innovative concepts for structural engineers.

1903 ■ *SWE, Magazine of the Society of Women Engineers*
Society of Women Engineers
120 S La Salle St., Ste. 1515
Chicago, IL 60603
Ph: (312)596-5223
Fr: 877-793-4636
URL: http://societyofwomenengineers.swe.org/
   index.php

Quarterly. $30.00/year for nonmembers. Magazine for engineering students and for women and men working in the engineering and technology fields. Covers career guidance, continuing development and topical issues.

1904 ■ *WEPANEWS*
Women in Engineering Programs & Advocates
Network
1901 E Asbury Ave., Ste. 220
Denver, CO 80208
Ph: (303)871-4643
Fax: (303)871-4628
E-mail: dmatt@wepan.org
URL: http://www.wepan.org

Description: 2/year. Seeks to provide greater access for women to careers in engineering. Includes news of graduate, undergraduate, freshmen, precollege, and re-entry engineering programs for women. Recurring features include job listings, faculty, grant, and conference news, international engineering program news, action group news, notices of publications available, and a column titled Kudos.

1905 ■ *Woman Engineer*
Equal Opportunity Publications, Inc.
445 Broadhollow Rd., Ste. 425
Melville, NY 11747
Ph: (631)421-9421
Fax: (631)421-1352
E-mail: info@eop.com
URL: http://www.eop.com

Annual. Magazine that is offered at no charge to qualified female engineering, computer-science, and

information-technology students and professionals seeking to find employment and advancement in their careers.

1906 ■ *World Journal of Nano Science and Engineering*
Scientific Research Publishing
PO Box 54821
Irvine, CA 92619-4821
E-mail: wjnse@scirp.org
URL: http://www.scirp.org/journal/wjnse/

Quarterly. $156.00/year for individuals. Peer-reviewed journal publishing articles on applications of physical, chemical and biological sciences to engineering.

EMPLOYER DIRECTORIES AND NETWORKING LISTS

1907 ■ *American Men and Women of Science*
Gale
PO Box 6904
Florence, KY 41022-6904
Fr: 800-354-9706
URL: http://www.gale.cengage.com

Biennial, even years; New edition expected 29th, June 2011. $1,368.00 for individuals. Covers: Over 135,000 U.S. and Canadian scientists active in the physical, biological, mathematical, computer science, and engineering fields; includes references to previous edition for deceased scientists and nonrespondents. Entries include: Name, address, education, personal and career data, memberships, honors and awards, research interest. Arrangement: Alphabetical. Indexes: Discipline (in separate volume).

1908 ■ *Careers in Focus—Engineering*
Facts On File Inc.
132 W 31st St., 17th Fl.
New York, NY 10001
Ph: (212)967-8800
Fax: 800-678-3633
Fr: 800-322-8755
URL: http://www.infobasepublishing.com

Latest edition 3rd; Published July, 2007. $32.95 for individuals. Covers: An overview of engineering, followed by a selection of jobs profiled in detail, including the nature of the job, earnings, prospects for employment, what kind of training and skills it requires, and sources for further information.

1909 ■ *Chemical Week—Buyers Guide Issue*
Chemical Week Associates
2 Grand Central Tower
140 E 45th St., 40th Fl.
New York, NY 10017
Ph: (212)884-9528
Fax: (212)883-9514
URL: http://www.chemweek.com/buyersguide/public

Annual, Latest edition 2008. $115.00. Publication includes: About 4,200 manufacturers and suppliers of chemical raw materials to the chemical process industries; 400 manufacturers of packaging materials; and suppliers of products and services to the chemical process industries, including hazardous waste/environmental services, computer services, plant design, construction, consulting, shipping, and transportation.

1910 ■ *Consulting Services*
Association of Consulting Chemists and Chemical
Engineers Inc.
PO Box 902
Murray Hill, NJ 07974
Ph: (908)464-3182
Fax: (908)464-3182
URL: http://www.chemconsult.org

Biennial, even years. $30.00 for individuals. Covers: About 160 member consultants in chemistry, chemical engineering, metallurgy, etc. Entries include:

Individual name, address, certificate number, qualifications, affiliation, experience, facilities, staff. Arrangement: Classified by area of expertise. Indexes: Personal name, geographical.

1911 ■ *Directory of Chemical Producers—United States*
SRI Consulting
4300 Bohannon Dr., Ste. 200
Menlo Park, CA 94025
Ph: (650)384-4300
Fax: (650)330-1149
E-mail: sric-dcp@ihs.com
URL: http://www.sriconsulting.com/DCP
Annual, latest edition April, 2011. $2,050.00 for U.S.; $1,635.00 for U.S.; $2,100.00. Covers: Over 1,255 United States basic chemical producers manufacturing 7,085 chemicals in commercial quantities at more than 3,205 plant locations. Entries include: For companies—Company name, division or subsidiary names, corporate address, phone, fax, telex, location of each subsidiary, division, and manufacturing plant, and the products made at each plant location. For products—Producer name and plant locations, alternate product names (if any). Subscription price includes bound volume, plus access to the directory staff for inquiries. Arrangement: Companies are alphabetical; products are alphabetical and by group (dyes, pesticides, etc.); manufacturing plants are geographical. Indexes: Geographical, product.

1912 ■ *Directory of Contract Staffing Firms*
C.E. Publications Inc.
PO Box 3006
Bothell, WA 98041-3006
Ph: (425)806-5200
Fax: (425)806-5585
URL: http://www.cjhunter.com/dcsf/overview.html
Annual. Covers: Nearly 1,300 contract firms actively engaged in the employment of engineering, IT/IS, and technical personnel for 'temporary' contract assignments throughout the world. Entries include: Company name, address, phone, name of contact, email, web address. Arrangement: Alphabetical. Indexes: Geographical.

1913 ■ *Directory of World Chemical Producers*
Chemical Information Services Inc.
9101 LBJ Fwy., Ste. 310
PO Box 743512
Dallas, TX 75243
Ph: (214)349-6200
Fax: (214)349-6286
URL: http://www.chemicalinfo.com/_shop/products.plx?product=all
Annual, Latest edition 2011. $1,450.00 for individuals; $3,965.00 for individuals; $4,545.00 for individuals. Covers: Over 20,000 producers of all classes of chemicals worldwide; including bulk pharmaceuticals, fire chemicals, agrochemicals, dyes, pigments, cosmetic, food ingredients, intermediates, etc. Entries include: Company name, address, phone, fax, telex, E-mail address, websites, contact information. Arrangement: Product, CAS#, geographical.

1914 ■ *Indiana Society of Professional Engineers—Directory*
Indiana Society of Professional Engineers
PO Box 20806
Indianapolis, IN 46220
Ph: (317)255-2267
Fax: (317)255-2530
URL: http://www.indspe.org
Annual, fall. Covers: Member registered engineers, land surveyors, engineering students, and engineers in training. Entries include: Member name, address, phone, type of membership, business information, specialty. Arrangement: Alpha by chapter area.

1915 ■ *U.S. National Committee for the International Union of Pure and Applied Chemistry—Directory*
U.S. National Committee for the International Union of Pure and Applied Chemistry
Keck Center
500 5th St., NW
Washington, DC 20001
Ph: (202)334-2000
Fr: 800-624-6242
URL: http://sites.nationalacademies.org/pga/biso/IUPAC/
Annual, July. Covers: 29 member chemists and chemical engineers in the United States.

HANDBOOKS AND MANUALS

1916 ■ *Expert Resumes for Engineers*
JIST Publishing
875 Montreal Way
St. Paul, MN 55102
Fr: 800-648-5478
E-mail: educate@emcp.com
URL: http://www.jist.com
Louise M. Kursmark and Wendy S. Enelow. 2009. $16.95 (softcover). 272 pages. Features a collection of written resume samples for all types of engineers including civil, mechanical, industrial, electrical, electronics, computer, and more. Contains tips and strategies for writing engineering resumes and finding the best jobs.

1917 ■ *Great Jobs for Chemistry Majors*
The McGraw-Hill Companies
PO Box 182604
Columbus, OH 43272
Fax: (614)759-3749
Fr: 877-883-5524
E-mail: customer.service@mcgraw-hill.com
URL: http://www.mhprofessional.com
Mark Rowh. Second edition, 2005. $15.95 (paper). 208 pages.

1918 ■ *Great Jobs for Engineering Majors*
The McGraw-Hill Companies
PO Box 182604
Columbus, OH 43272
Fax: (614)759-3749
Fr: 877-883-5524
E-mail: customer.service@mcgraw-hill.com
URL: http://www.mhprofessional.com/product.php?isbn=0071641963
Geraldine O. Garner. Second edition, 2008. $16.95. 192 pages. Covers all the career options open to students majoring in engineering.

1919 ■ *Resumes for Scientific and Technical Careers*
The McGraw-Hill Companies
PO Box 182604
Columbus, OH 43272
Fax: (614)759-3749
Fr: 877-883-5524
E-mail: customer.service@mcgraw-hill.com
URL: http://www.mhprofessional.com/product.php?isbn=0071482199
Third edition, 2007. $12.95 (paper). 144 pages. Provides resume advice for individuals interested in working in scientific and technical careers. Includes sample resumes and cover letters.

EMPLOYMENT AGENCIES AND SEARCH FIRMS

1920 ■ *Apple and Associates*
PO Box 996
Chapin, SC 29036
Ph: (803)932-2000
E-mail: info@appleassoc.com
URL: http://www.appleassoc.com
Provides staffing services to medical device, plastics, pharmaceutical and performance materials industries.

1921 ■ *The Baer Group*
900 Ashwood Pkwy., Ste. 300
Atlanta, GA 30346
Ph: (770)557-4900
Fax: (770)557-3499
E-mail: info@baergroup.com
URL: http://www.baergroup.com
Executive search firm.

1922 ■ *Capstone Inc.*
971 Albany Shaker Rd.
Latham, NY 12110
Ph: (518)783-9300
Fax: (518)783-9328
E-mail: info@capstone-inc.com
URL: http://www.capstone-inc.com
Executive search firm.

1923 ■ *Career Advocates International*
1539 Ave. A
Katy, TX 77493
Ph: (281)395-9848
Fax: (281)574-3949
URL: http://www.careeradvocates.org
Provides permanent placement and temporary staffing for executive and staff level positions. Specializes in multiple niches including: sales and marketing, accounting and financial services, banking, communications, human resources, chemicals, oil and gas, medical and dental, legal, information technology, energy, technology, engineering, manufacturing, construction, and light industrial.

1924 ■ *Cochran, Cochran & Yale LLC*
955 E Henrietta Rd.
Rochester, NY 14623
Ph: (585)424-6060
E-mail: roch@ccy.com
URL: http://www.ccy.com
Executive search firm. Branches in Denver, CO and Williamsville, NY.

1925 ■ *Conboy Sur Morice & Associates*
15 Churchville Rd., No. 170
Bel Air, MD 21014-3837
E-mail: wks@csma-cons.com
URL: http://www.conboysur.com
Executive search firm.

1926 ■ *CSI Executive Search LLC*
9600 Great Hills Trl., Ste. 150W
Austin, TX 78759
Ph: (512)301-1119
Fax: (512)301-5559
Fr: 877-329-1828
E-mail: info@csi-executivesearch.com
URL: http://www.csi-executivesearch.com
Executive search firm that specializes in the following arenas: accounting, engineering, healthcare, information technology, and legal. Utilizes behavioral, performance, retention variable, social intelligence, and cultural assessments to ensure the best candidate/client fit. Works on a retained, retingency, and contingency search basis.

1927 ■ *ENTEGEE*
70 Blanchard Rd., Ste. 102
Burlington, MA 01803
Fr: 800-368-3433
E-mail: corporate@entegee.com
URL: http://www.entegee.com
Specializes in recruiting experienced professionals in the engineering and technical industries. Features a searchable database of employment opportunities in the engineering and technical fields.

1928 ■ *Executive Directions*
PO Box 5742
Sarasota, FL 34277
Ph: (941)922-9180
E-mail: info@execdir.com
URL: http://www.executivedirections.com
Executive search firm.

1929 ■ Executive Recruiters Agency
PO Box 21810
Little Rock, AR 72211
Ph: (501)224-7000
Fax: (501)224-8534
E-mail: jobs@execrecruit.com
URL: http://www.execrecruit.com

Personnel service firm.

1930 ■ Global Employment Solutions
10375 Park Meadows Dr., Ste. 375
Littleton, CO 80124
Ph: (303)216-9500
Fax: (303)216-9533
URL: http://www.gesnetwork.com

Employment agency.

1931 ■ Ken Clark International
2000 Lenox Dr., Ste. 200
Lawrenceville, NJ 08648
Ph: (609)308-5200
Fax: (609)308-5250
E-mail: info-princeton@kenclark.com
URL: http://www.kenclark.com

Executive search firm. Branches in Newport Beach, CA; Deerfield, IL; Waltham, MA; and Wayne, PA.

1932 ■ Polly Brown Associates Inc.
150 E 57th St., Ste. 25A
New York, NY 10022
E-mail: pbrown@pollybrownassociates.com
URL: http://www.pollybrownassociates.com

Executive search firm.

1933 ■ Quality Search Personnel Inc.
1820 Graham Dr.
Chesterton, IN 46304
Ph: (219)926-7772
Fax: (219)926-7773
E-mail: info@qsjobs.com
URL: http://www.qsjobs.com

Technical recruiting specialists for placing technical and engineering personnel. The current concentration of assignments involves technical and engineering positions with a specialization in packaging and quality control. Assignments are primarily taken on a contingency basis. Industries served: consumer products, food, pharmaceutical and cosmetic, chemical, computer, heavy and light industrial.

ONLINE JOB SOURCES AND SERVICES

1934 ■ American Chemical Society Career Sources
E-mail: help@acs.org
URL: http://portal.acs.org

Description: Offers online interviewing between employers and potential employees, postings for positions available and situations wanted, and regularly updated career advice and information for American Chemical Society members only.

1935 ■ ChemicalEngineer.com
E-mail: info@careermarketplace.com
URL: http://www.chemicalengineer.com

Description: Serves as an employment center where job seekers can find many job opportunities in the field of chemical engineering.

1936 ■ EnergyCentralJobs.com
E-mail: service@energycentral.com
URL: http://www.energycentraljobs.com

Description: Serves as an on-line job resource for candidates and power companies worldwide. Maintains a job search database dedicated to the power, nuclear, oil and gas career fields.

1937 ■ EngineerJobs.com
URL: http://www.engineerjobs.com

Description: Provides job opportunities for engineer-

ing professionals in the following disciplines: aerospace, agricultural, biomedical, chemical, civil, electrical, environmental, industrial, manufacturing, marine, materials, mechanical, mining, nuclear, petroleum, process, project, quality, sales, software, solar, systems, and structural.

1938 ■ PowerPlantPro.com
E-mail: support@powerplantpro.com
URL: http://www.powerplantpro.com/main/sendform/4/18/3472

Description: Dedicated to professionals in the power and energy industry. Features career advice and employer listings.

1939 ■ Spherion
2050 Spectrum Blvd.
Fort Lauderdale, FL 33309
Ph: (954)308-7600
Fr: 800-774-3746
E-mail: help@spherion.com
URL: http://www.spherion.com

Description: Recruitment firm specializing in accounting and finance, sales and marketing, interim executives, technology, engineering, retail and human resources.

1940 ■ ThinkEnergyGroup.com
E-mail: resumes@thinkjobs.com
URL: http://www.thinkenergygroup.com

Description: Serves as a job board for professionals looking for positions in engineering, power plant, energy, and technical fields. Contains advice and tips on interviews, job searching, resume writing, hiring, and management. Provides choices of work location, pay rates in the field of expertise and contract, temp-to-hire, and direct hiring options.

TRADESHOWS

1941 ■ ACS National Meeting and Exposition
American Chemical Society
1155 16th St. N.W.
Washington, DC 20036
Ph: (202)872-4600
Fax: (202)776-8258
Fr: 800-227-5558
E-mail: help@acs.org
URL: http://www.acs.org

Primary Exhibits: Products related to all chemical disciplines. Dates and Locations: 2012 Mar 26-28; San Diego, CA; San Diego Convention Center.

1942 ■ American Chemical Society Southeastern Regional Meeting and Conference
American Chemical Society
1155 16th St. N.W.
Washington, DC 20036
Ph: (202)872-4600
Fax: (202)776-8258
Fr: 800-227-5558
E-mail: help@acs.org
URL: http://www.acs.org

Annual. Primary Exhibits: Chemical equipment, supplies, and services.

1943 ■ American Society for Engineering Education Annual Conference and Exposition
American Society for Engineering Education
1818 N. St. N.W., Ste. 600
Washington, DC 20036-2479
Ph: (202)331-3500
Fax: (202)265-8504
E-mail: conferences@asee.org
URL: http://www.asee.org

Annual. Primary Exhibits: Publications, engineering supplies and equipment, computers, software, and research companies all products and services related

to engineering education. Dates and Locations: 2012 Jun 10-13; San Antonio, TX.

1944 ■ AOCS Annual Meeting & Expo
American Oil Chemist Society
2710 S. Boulder
Urbana, IL 61802-6996
Ph: (217)359-2344
Fax: (217)351-8091
E-mail: general@aocs.org
URL: http://www.aocs.org

Annual. Primary Exhibits: Fat and oil processing plant equipment, supplies, and services; laboratory instrumentation; chemical ingredients for foods, detergents, and personal care products; and publications. Dates and Locations: 2012 Apr 29 - May 02; Long Beach, CA; Long Beach Convention Center; 2013 Apr 28 - May 01; Montreal, QC, Canada; Palais des Congres de Montreal; 2014 May 04-05; San Antonio, TX; Henry B. Gonzalez Convention Center.

OTHER SOURCES

1945 ■ American Academy of Environmental Engineers (AAEE)
130 Holiday Ct., Ste. 100
Annapolis, MD 21401
Ph: (410)266-3311
Fax: (410)266-7653
E-mail: info@aaee.net
URL: http://www.aaee.net

Description: Environmentally oriented registered professional engineers certified by examination as Diplomates of the Academy. Seeks to improve the standards of environmental engineering. Certifies those with special knowledge of environmental engineering. Furnishes lists of those certified to the public. Maintains speakers' bureau. Recognizes areas of specialization: Air Pollution Control; General Environmental; Hazardous Waste Management; Industrial Hygiene; Radiation Protection; Solid Waste Management; Water Supply and Wastewater. Requires written and oral examinations for certification. Works with other professional organizations on environmentally oriented activities. Identifies potential employment candidates through Talent Search Service.

1946 ■ American Association of Engineering Societies (AAES)
1801 Alexander Bell Dr.
Reston, VA 20191
Ph: (202)296-2237
Fax: (202)296-1151
Fr: 888-400-2237
E-mail: dbateson@aaes.org
URL: http://www.aaes.org

Description: Coordinates the efforts of the member societies in the provision of reliable and objective information to the general public concerning issues which affect the engineering profession and the field of engineering as a whole; collects, analyzes, documents, and disseminates data which will inform the general public of the relationship between engineering and the national welfare; provides a forum for the engineering societies to exchange and discuss their views on matters of common interest; and represents the U.S. engineering community abroad through representation in WFEO and UPADI.

1947 ■ American Chemical Society (ACS)
1155 16th St. NW
Washington, DC 20036
Ph: (202)872-4600
Fr: 800-227-5558
E-mail: help@acs.org
URL: http://portal.acs.org/portal/acs/corg/content

Description: Scientific and educational society of chemists and chemical engineers. Conducts: studies and surveys; special programs for disadvantaged persons; legislation monitoring, analysis, and reporting; courses for graduate chemists and chemical engineers; radio and television programming. Offers career guidance counseling; administers the Petroleum Research Fund and other grants and fellowship programs. Operates Employment Clearing Houses. Compiles statistics. Maintains speakers' bureau and 33 divisions.

1948 ■ American Indian Science and Engineering Society (AISES)

PO Box 9828
Albuquerque, NM 87119-9828
Ph: (505)765-1052
Fax: (505)765-5608
E-mail: info@aises.org
URL: http://www.aises.org

Description: Represents American Indian and non-Indian students and professionals in science, technology, and engineering fields; corporations representing energy, mining, aerospace, electronic, and computer fields. Seeks to motivate and encourage students to pursue undergraduate and graduate studies in science, engineering, and technology. Sponsors science fairs in grade schools, teacher training workshops, summer math/science sessions for 8th-12th graders, professional chapters, and student chapters in colleges. Offers scholarships. Adult members serve as role models, advisers, and mentors for students. Operates placement service.

1949 ■ American Institute of Chemical Engineers (AIChE)

3 Park Ave.
New York, NY 10016-5991
Ph: (646)495-1380
Fax: (203)775-5177
Fr: 800-242-4363
E-mail: xpress@aiche.org
URL: http://www.aiche.org

Description: Serves as professional society of chemical engineers. Establishes standards for chemical engineering curricula; offers employment services. Presents technical conferences, petrochemical and refining exposition, and continuing education programs. Sponsors competitions. Offers speakers' bureau; complies statistics.

1950 ■ American Institute of Chemists (AIC)

315 Chestnut St.
Philadelphia, PA 19106-2702
Ph: (215)873-8224
Fax: (215)629-5224
E-mail: info@theaic.org
URL: http://www.theaic.org

Description: Represents chemists and chemical engineers. Promotes advancement of chemical professions in the U.S.; protects public welfare by establishing and enforcing high practice standards; represents professional interests of chemists and chemical engineers. Sponsors National Certification Commission in Chemistry and Chemical Engineering and AIC Foundation.

1951 ■ American Oil Chemists' Society (AOCS)

PO Box 17190
Urbana, IL 61803-7190
Ph: (217)359-2344
Fax: (217)351-8091
E-mail: general@aocs.org
URL: http://www.aocs.org

Description: Chemists, biochemists, chemical engineers, research directors, plant personnel, and others in laboratories and chemical process industries concerned with animal, marine, and vegetable oils and fats, and their extraction, refining, safety, packaging, quality control, and use in consumer and industrial products such as foods, drugs, paints, waxes, lubricants, soaps, and cosmetics. Sponsors short courses; certifies referee chemists; distributes cooperative check samples; sells official reagents. Maintains 100 committees. Operates job placement service for members only.

1952 ■ Association for International Practical Training (AIPT)

10400 Little Patuxent Pkwy., Ste. 250
Columbia, MD 21044-3519
Ph: (410)997-2200
Fax: (410)992-3924
E-mail: aipt@aipt.org
URL: http://www.aipt.org

Description: Providers worldwide of on-the-job training programs for students and professionals seeking international career development and life-changing experiences. Arranges workplace exchanges in hundreds of professional fields, bringing employers and trainees together from around the world. Client list ranges from small farming communities to Fortune 500 companies.

1953 ■ Engineering Society of Detroit (ESD)

20700 Civic Center Dr., Ste. 450
Southfield, MI 48076
Ph: (248)353-0735
Fax: (248)353-0736
E-mail: esd@esd.org
URL: http://ww2.esd.org/home.htm

Description: Engineers from all disciplines; scientists and technologists. Conducts technical programs and engineering refresher courses; sponsors conferences and expositions. Maintains speakers' bureau; offers placement services; although based in Detroit, MI, society membership is international.

1954 ■ International Society of Automation (ISA)

67 Alexander Dr.
PO Box 12277
Research Triangle Park, NC 27709
Ph: (919)549-8411
Fax: (919)549-8288
E-mail: info@isa.org
URL: http://www.isa.org

Description: Sets the standard for automation by helping over 30,000 worldwide members and other professionals solve difficult technical problems, while enhancing their leadership and personal career capabilities. Develops standards; certifies industry professionals; provides education and training; publishes books and technical articles; and hosts the largest conference and exhibition for automation professionals in the Western Hemisphere. Is the founding sponsor of The Automation Federation.

1955 ■ Iranian Chemists' Association of the American Chemical Society (ICA-ACS)

35 Meadowbrook Ln.
Woodbury, CT 06798
Ph: (203)573-3220
Fax: (203)573-3660
E-mail: banijamali@ica-acs.org
URL: http://www.ica-acs.org

Description: Encourages and enhances the interchange and sharing of scientific knowledge and friendship among chemists and chemistry-related professionals of Iranian descent. Provides opportunities for members to assist each other in pursuit of academic and professional development and growth. Promotes awareness of scientific contributions made by Iranian scientists.

1956 ■ Korean-American Scientists and Engineers Association (KSEA)

1952 Gallows Rd., Ste. 300
Vienna, VA 22182
Ph: (703)748-1221
Fax: (703)748-1331
E-mail: sejong@ksea.org
URL: http://www.ksea.org

Description: Represents scientists and engineers holding single or advanced degrees. Promotes friendship and mutuality among Korean and American scientists and engineers; contributes to Korea's scientific, technological, industrial, and economic developments; strengthens the scientific, technological, and cultural bonds between the U.S. and Korea. Sponsors symposium. Maintains speakers' bureau,

placement service, and biographical archives. Compiles statistics.

1957 ■ National Action Council for Minorities in Engineering (NACME)

440 Hamilton Ave., Ste. 302
White Plains, NY 10601-1813
Ph: (914)539-4010
Fax: (914)539-4032
E-mail: info@nacme.org
URL: http://www.nacme.org

Description: Leads the national effort to increase access to careers in engineering and other science-based disciplines. Conducts research and public policy analysis, develops and operates national demonstration programs at precollege and university levels, and disseminates information through publications, conferences and electronic media. Serves as a privately funded source of scholarships for minority students in engineering.

1958 ■ National Organization for the Professional Advancement of Black Chemists and Chemical Engineers (NOBCChE)

PO Box 77040
Washington, DC 20013
Ph: (240)228-1763
Fax: (202)667-1705
Fr: 800-776-1419
E-mail: president@nobcche.org
URL: http://www.nobcche.org

Description: Black professionals in science and chemistry. Seeks to aid black scientists and chemists in reaching their full professional potential; encourages black students to pursue scientific studies and employment; promotes participation of blacks in scientific research. Provides volunteers to teach science courses in selected elementary schools; sponsors scientific field trips for students; maintains speakers' bureau for schools. Conducts technical seminars in Africa. Sponsors competitions; presents awards for significant achievements to individuals in the field. Maintains placement service; compiles statistics.

1959 ■ National Society of Professional Engineers (NSPE)

1420 King St.
Alexandria, VA 22314-2794
Ph: (703)684-2800
Fax: (703)836-4875
Fr: 888-285-6773
E-mail: memserv@nspe.org
URL: http://www.nspe.org

Description: Represents professional engineers and engineers-in-training in all fields registered in accordance with the laws of states or territories of the U.S. or provinces of Canada; qualified graduate engineers, student members, and registered land surveyors. Is concerned with social, professional, ethical, and economic considerations of engineering as a profession; encompasses programs in public relations, employment practices, ethical considerations, education, and career guidance. Monitors legislative and regulatory actions of interest to the engineering profession.

1960 ■ Society of Hispanic Professional Engineers (SHPE)

13181 Crossroads Pkwy. N, Ste. 450
City of Industry, CA 91746-3496
Ph: (323)725-3970
Fax: (323)725-0316
E-mail: shpenational@shpe.org
URL: http://oneshpe.shpe.org/wps/portal/national

Description: Represents engineers, student engineers, and scientists. Aims to increase the number of Hispanic engineers by providing motivation and support to students. Sponsors competitions and educational programs. Maintains placement service and speakers' bureau; compiles statistics.

1961 ■ Society of Women Engineers (SWE)

203 N La Salle St., Ste. 1675

Chicago, IL 60601
Ph: (312)596-5223
Fax: (312)596-5252

Fr: 877-SWE-INFO
E-mail: hq@swe.org
URL: http://societyofwomenengineers.swe.org

Description: Educational and service organization representing both students and professional women in engineering and technical fields.

SOURCES OF HELP-WANTED ADS

1962 ■ AATCC Review
American Association of Textile Chemists and Colorists
1 Davis Dr.
PO Box 12215
Research Triangle Park, NC 27709-2215
Ph: (919)549-8141
Fax: (919)549-8933
URL: http://www.aatcc.org/media/index.htm
Monthly. $200.00/year for nonmembers; $55.00/year for members; $26.00/year for single issue, within U.S.; $36.00/year for single issue, outside U.S. Magazine focusing on dyeing, finishing of fibers and fabrics.

1963 ■ Advances in Chemical Engineering and Science
Scientific Research Publishing
PO Box 54821
Irvine, CA 92619-4821
URL: http://www.scirp.org/journal/aces/
Peer-reviewed journal covering advances in chemical engineering and sciences.

1964 ■ American Biotechnology Laboratory
American Laboratory/Labcompare
30 Controls Dr.
Shelton, CT 06484-0870
Ph: (203)926-9300
Fax: (203)926-9310
URL: http://www.americanbiotechnologylaboratory.com
Biotechnology magazine.

1965 ■ American Institute of Chemical Engineers Journal
John Wiley & Sons Inc.
111 River St.
Hoboken, NJ 07030-5773
Ph: (201)748-6000
Fax: (201)748-6088
Fr: 800-825-7550
URL: http://onlinelibrary.wiley.com/journal/10.1002/(ISSN)1547-59
Monthly. $2,278.00/year for institutions, print only; $2,446.00/year for institutions, Canada and Mexico, print only; $2,401.00/year for other countries, print only; $2,620.00/year for institutions, print with online; $2,788.00/year for institutions, Canada and Mexico, print with online; $2,872.00/year for institutions, other countries, print with online. Peer-reviewed journal focusing on technological advances in core areas of chemical engineering as well as in other relevant engineering disciplines.

1966 ■ American Journal of Analytical Chemistry
Scientific Research Publishing
PO Box 54821
Irvine, CA 92619-4821
E-mail: ajac@scirp.org
URL: http://www.scirp.org/journal/ajac/
Peer-reviewed journal featuring the latest advancements in analytical chemistry.

1967 ■ Biochemistry and Molecular Biology Education
John Wiley & Sons Inc.
111 River St.
Hoboken, NJ 07030-5773
Ph: (201)748-6000
Fax: (201)748-6088
Fr: 800-825-7550
URL: http://onlinelibrary.wiley.com/journal/10.1002/(ISSN)1539-34
Bimonthly. $583.00/year for institutions, print only; $667.00/year for institutions, Canada and Mexico, print only; $709.00/year for institutions, other countries, print only. Journal covering the field of biochemistry, molecular biology, and related sciences.

1968 ■ Chemical Engineering Communications
Taylor & Francis Group Journals
325 Chestnut St., Ste. 800
Philadelphia, PA 19106-2608
Ph: (215)625-8900
Fax: (215)625-2940
Fr: 800-354-1420
URL: http://www.tandf.co.uk/journals/titles/00986445.asp
Monthly. $2,421.00/year for individuals, print only; $5,298.00/year for institutions, online only; $5,887.00/year for institutions, print and online; $4,536.00/year for institutions, print and online; $4,082.00/year for institutions, online only; $1,461.00/year for individuals, print only. Journal focusing on the results of basic and applied research in chemical engineering.

1969 ■ Chemical Engineering and Technology
John Wiley & Sons Inc.
111 River St.
Hoboken, NJ 07030-5773
Ph: (201)748-6000
Fax: (201)748-6088
Fr: 800-825-7550
URL: http://onlinelibrary.wiley.com/journal/10.1002/(ISSN)1521-41
Monthly. $4,750.00/year for institutions, print only; $4,750.00/year for institutions, print only; $5,463.00/year for institutions, print with online; $3,701.00/year for institutions, print only, rest of Europe; $5,755.00/year for institutions, print only, Switzerland and Lichtenstein; $4,750.00/year for institutions, other countries, print only; $2,424.00/year for institutions, print only. Journal focusing on all aspects of chemical and process engineering.

1970 ■ Chemical Equipment
Reed Business Information (New York, New York)
360 Park Ave. S
New York, NY 10010
Ph: (646)746-6400
Fax: (646)746-7431
Fr: 800-446-6551
URL: http://www.reedbusinessinteractive.com
Free for qualified professionals; $72.90/year for individuals, cover price. Tabloid on the chemical process industry.

1971 ■ Chemical Processing
Putman Media
555 W Pierce Rd., Ste. 301
Itasca, IL 60143-2649
Ph: (630)467-1301
Fax: (630)467-1120
URL: http://www.chemicalprocessing.com
Monthly. $68.00/year for U.S. and Canada; $115.00/year for other countries; $200.00/year for other countries, airmail. Magazine for the chemical process industry.

1972 ■ The Chemical Record
John Wiley & Sons Inc.
111 River St.
Hoboken, NJ 07030-5773
Ph: (201)748-6000
Fax: (201)748-6088
Fr: 800-825-7550
URL: http://onlinelibrary.wiley.com/journal/10.1002/(ISSN)1528-06
Bimonthly. $105.00/year for U.S., Canada, and Mexico, print only; $153.00/year for other countries, print only; $639.00/year for institutions, print only; $639.00/year for institutions, Canada and Mexico, print only; $639.00/year for institutions, other countries, print only. Journal publishing overviews of new developments at the cutting edge of chemistry of interest to a wide audience of chemists.

1973 ■ The Chemist
American Institute of Chemists Inc.
315 Chestnut St.
Philadelphia, PA 19106-2702
Ph: (215)873-8224
Fax: (215)629-5224
E-mail: info@theaic.org
URL: http://www.theaic.org
Description: Quarterly. Covers news items relating to the chemical profession and membership in the Institute. Reports on legislation, licensure, earnings, awards, and professional education. Recurring features include news of employment opportunities and news of members. Published alternate months as a magazine.

1974 ■ Chemistry & Biology
Elsevier Science Inc.
360 Park Ave. S
New York, NY 10010-1710
Ph: (212)989-5800
Fax: (212)633-3990
Fr: 888-437-4636
URL: http://www.elsevier.com/wps/find/journaldescription.cws_home

Monthly. $2,137.00/year for institutions, for all countries except Europe, Japan & Iran; $442.00/year for U.S. and Canada; $457.00/year for individuals, for all countries except Europe, Japan and Iran. Journal focused on genetic, computational, or theoretical information of chemistry and biology, substantiating experimental data.

1975 ■ *The Electrochemical Society Interface*
Electrochemical Society Inc.
65 S Main St., Bldg. D
Pennington, NJ 08534-2839
Ph: (609)737-1902
Fax: (609)737-2743
E-mail: interface@electrochem.org
URL: http://www.electrochem.org/dl/interface/

Quarterly. $64.00/year for individuals, tier 1, print & online; $82.00/year for other countries, tier 1, print & online. Publication featuring news and articles of interest to members of the Electrochemical Society.

1976 ■ *Engineering in Life Sciences*
John Wiley & Sons Inc.
111 River St.
Hoboken, NJ 07030-5773
Ph: (201)748-6000
Fax: (201)748-6088
Fr: 800-825-7550
URL: http://onlinelibrary.wiley.com/journal/10.1002/
(ISSN)1618-28

Bimonthly. $989.00/year for institutions, European, online only; $1,512.00/year for institutions, online only, Switzerland and Liechtenstein; $1,299.00/year for institutions, other countries, online only; $663.00/year for institutions, European, online only; $1,299.00/year for institutions, online only; $1,299.00/year for institutions, Canada and Mexico, online only. Journal focusing on the field of biotechnology and related topics including microbiology, genetics, biochemistry, and chemistry.

1977 ■ *International Journal of Organic Chemistry*
Scientific Research Publishing
PO Box 54821
Irvine, CA 92619-4821
E-mail: ijoc@scirp.org
URL: http://www.scirp.org/journal/ijoc/

Quarterly. $156.00/year for individuals. Peer-reviewed journal publishing articles in the field of organic chemistry.

1978 ■ *ISRN Organic Chemistry*
Hindawi Publishing Corporation
410 Park Ave., 15th Fl.
287 PMB
New York, NY 10022
E-mail: oc@isrn.com
URL: http://www.isrn.com/journals/oc

Peer-reviewed journal publishing research in all areas of organic chemistry.

1979 ■ *Journal of Biomaterials and Nanobiotechnology*
Scientific Research Publishing
PO Box 54821
Irvine, CA 92619-4821
URL: http://www.scirp.org/journal/jbnb/

Peer-reviewed journal covering the basic science and engineering aspects of biomaterials and nanotechnology.

1980 ■ *Journal of Biophysical Chemistry*
Scientific Research Publishing
PO Box 54821
Irvine, CA 92619-4821
URL: http://www.scirp.org/journal/jbpc/

Peer-reviewed journal publishing the latest advancements in biophysical chemistry.

1981 ■ *Journal of Chemical Theory and Computation*
American Chemical Society
1155 16th St. NW
Washington, DC 20036
Ph: (202)872-4600
Fr: 800-227-5558
URL: http://pubs.acs.org/journals/jctcce

$1,367.00/year for institutions, North America; $1,493.00/year for institutions, outside North America. Journal presenting new theories, methodology, and/or important applications in quantum chemistry, molecular dynamics, and statistical mechanics.

1982 ■ *Journal of Crystallization Process and Technology*
Scientific Research Publishing
PO Box 54821
Irvine, CA 92619-4821
E-mail: jcpt@scirp.org
URL: http://www.scirp.org/journal/jcpt/

Peer-reviewed journal covering all aspects of the crystallization process, studies and properties of crystalline materials.

1983 ■ *Journal of Electromagnetic Analysis and Applications*
Scientific Research Publishing
PO Box 54821
Irvine, CA 92619-4821
E-mail: jemaa@scirp.org
URL: http://www.scirp.org/journal/jemaa/

Peer-reviewed journal covering the field of electromagnetic analysis testing and application.

1984 ■ *Journal of Encapsulation and Adsorption Sciences*
Scientific Research Publishing
PO Box 54821
Irvine, CA 92619-4821
URL: http://www.scirp.org/journal/jeas/

Peer-reviewed journal covering all aspects of encapsulation and adsorption sciences.

1985 ■ *Journal of Nanomechanics and Micromechanics*
American Society of Civil Engineers
1801 Alexander Bell Dr.
Reston, VA 20191-4400
Ph: (703)295-6300
Fax: (703)295-6333
Fr: 800-548-2723
URL: http://ascelibrary.org/nmo/

Quarterly. $373.00/year for institutions, print and online; $393.00/year for institutions, other countries, print and online. Peer-reviewed journal featuring articles on nanomechanics and micromechanics.

1986 ■ *Journal of Women and Minorities in Science and Engineering*
Begell House Inc.
50 Cross Hwy.
Redding, CT 06896
Ph: (203)938-1300
Fax: (203)938-1304
URL: http://www.begellhouse.com/journals/
00551c876cc2f027

$248.00/year for institutions. Peer-reviewed journal featuring innovative ideas and programs for classroom teachers, scientific studies, and formulation of concepts related to the education, recruitment, and retention of under-represented groups in science and engineering.

1987 ■ *Modern Plastics Worldwide*
Canon Communications L.L.C.
11444 W Olympic Blvd., Ste. 900
Los Angeles, CA 90064
Ph: (310)445-4200
Fax: (310)445-4299
URL: http://www.modplas.com

Monthly. $59.00/year for individuals; $99.00/year for two years, U.S. and possessions; $110.00/year for

Canada; $199.00/year for two years, for Canada; $150.00/year for other countries; $250.00/year for two years. Magazine for the plastics industry.

1988 ■ *Nanomechanics Science and Technology*
Begell House Inc.
50 Cross Hwy.
Redding, CT 06896
Ph: (203)938-1300
Fax: (203)938-1304
URL: http://www.begellhouse.com/journals/
11e12455066dab5d

$748.00/year for institutions. Journal covering the areas of nano- and micromechanics.

1989 ■ *Nanoparticle News*
BCC Research
49 Walnut St., Bldg. 2
Wellesley, MA 02481
Ph: (781)489-7301
Fax: (781)253-3933
Fr: (866)285-7215
URL: http://www.bccresearch.com/report/
index.php?rcode=nan

Monthly. $675.00/year for single issue, web access and archive (2 user license); $640.00/year for single issue, print, online, archive (outside North America); $495.00/year for single issue, web access and archive; $590.00/year for single issue, print, web access and archive (North America); $1,485.00/year for individuals, online (enterprise license); $990.00/year for individuals, online (Department license); $750.00/year for individuals, online (5 user license). Publication covering issues in the chemical industry.

1990 ■ *Nature Biotechnology*
Nature Publishing Group
75 Varick St., 9th Fl.
New York, NY 10013-1917
Ph: (212)726-9200
Fax: (212)696-9006
Fr: 888-331-6288
E-mail: biotech@natureny.com
URL: http://www.nature.com/nbt/index.html

Monthly. $250.00/year for individuals, print + online; $425.00/year for two years, print + online. Scientific research journal.

1991 ■ *Nature International Weekly Journal of Science*
Nature Publishing Group
75 Varick St., 9th Fl.
New York, NY 10013-1917
Ph: (212)726-9200
Fax: (212)696-9006
Fr: 888-331-6288
E-mail: nature@natureny.com
URL: http://www.nature.com/nature/index.html

Weekly. $199.00/year for individuals, print and online; $338.00/year for two years, print and online. Magazine covering science and technology, including the fields of biology, biochemistry, genetics, medicine, earth sciences, physics, pharmacology, and behavioral sciences.

1992 ■ *PALAIOS*
SEPM Publications
4111 S Darlington, Ste. 100
Tulsa, OK 74135-6373
Ph: (918)610-3361
Fax: (918)621-1685
Fr: 800-865-9765
E-mail: palois@ku.edu
URL: http://palaios.ku.edu/

Monthly. $315.00/year for individuals, for U.S.; online version with CD-ROM; $415.00/year for individuals, for U.S.; print and online version with CD-ROM; $315.00/year for other countries, online version with CD-ROM; $425.00/year for other countries, print and online version with CD-ROM. Journal providing information on the impact of life on Earth history as recorded in the paleontological and sedimentological records. Covers areas such as biogeochemistry, ichnology, sedimentology, stratigraphy, paleoecology, paleoclimatology, and paleoceanography.

1993 ■ Paper, Film & Foil Converter

Penton Media Inc.
249 W 17th St.
New York, NY 10011
Ph: (212)204-4200
URL: http://pffc-online.com/

Monthly. Magazine focusing on flexible packaging, paperboard, and film.

1994 ■ Plastics Engineering

Society of Plastics Engineers
13 Church Hill Rd.
PO Box 403
Newtown, CT 06470
Ph: (203)775-0471
Fax: (203)775-8490
URL: http://www.4spe.org/pub

$142.00/year for nonmembers; $242.00/year for nonmembers, outside North America; $180.00/year for institutions, corporate library; $280.00/year for institutions, corporate library outside North America. Plastics trade magazine.

1995 ■ Powder and Bulk Engineering

CSC Publishing Inc.
1155 Northland Dr.
St. Paul, MN 55120
Ph: (651)287-5650
Fax: (651)287-5600
URL: http://www.powderbulk.com/

Monthly. $100.00/year for individuals, outside North America, or digital format; free to qualified subscribers. Journal serving chemical, food, plastics, pulp and paper, and electronic industries.

1996 ■ Science

American Association for the Advancement of Science
1200 New York Ave., NW
Washington, DC 20005
Ph: (202)326-6550
URL: http://www.scienceonline.org

Weekly (Fri.). $146.00/year for members, professional, print & online; $119.00/year for individuals, NPA postdoctoral, print & online; $99.00/year for individuals, postdoctoral/resident, print & online; $75.00/year for students, print & online; $146.00/year for individuals, k-12 teacher, print & online; $310.00/year for individuals, patron, print & online; $115.00/year for individuals, emeritus, print & online; $211.05/year for Canada, professional members, print & online; $161.00/year for Canada, postdoctoral/resident, print & online; $136.50/year for students, Canada, print & online. Magazine devoted to science, scientific research, and public policy.

1997 ■ The Scientist

The Scientist Inc.
121 W 27th St., Ste. 604
New York, NY 10001
Ph: (212)461-4470
Fax: (347)626-2385
URL: http://www.the-scientist.com

Monthly. $39.95/year for individuals, print only; $49.95/year for individuals, print & online; $64.95/year for other countries, print only; $74.95/year for other countries, print & online. News journal (tabloid) for life scientists featuring news, opinions, research, and professional section.

1998 ■ Soft Nanoscience Letters

Scientific Research Publishing
PO Box 54821
Irvine, CA 92619-4821
E-mail: snl@scirp.org
URL: http://www.scirp.org/journal/snl/

Quarterly. $156.00/year for individuals. Peer-reviewed journal publishing articles in the field of soft nanoscience.

1999 ■ World Journal of Nano Science and Engineering

Scientific Research Publishing
PO Box 54821
Irvine, CA 92619-4821
E-mail: wjnse@scirp.org
URL: http://www.scirp.org/journal/wjnse/

Quarterly. $156.00/year for individuals. Peer-reviewed journal publishing articles on applications of physical, chemical and biological sciences to engineering.

EMPLOYER DIRECTORIES AND NETWORKING LISTS

2000 ■ American Men and Women of Science

Gale
PO Box 6904
Florence, KY 41022-6904
Fr: 800-354-9706
URL: http://www.gale.cengage.com

Biennial, even years; New edition expected 29th, June 2011. $1,368.00 for individuals. Covers: Over 135,000 U.S. and Canadian scientists active in the physical, biological, mathematical, computer science, and engineering fields; includes references to previous edition for deceased scientists and nonrespondents. Entries include: Name, address, education, personal and career data, memberships, honors and awards, research interest. Arrangement: Alphabetical. Indexes: Discipline (in separate volume).

2001 ■ Chemical Week—Buyers Guide Issue

Chemical Week Associates
2 Grand Central Tower
140 E 45th St., 40th Fl.
New York, NY 10017
Ph: (212)884-9528
Fax: (212)883-9514
URL: http://www.chemweek.com/buyersguide/public

Annual, Latest edition 2008. $115.00. Publication includes: About 4,200 manufacturers and suppliers of chemical raw materials to the chemical process industries; 400 manufacturers of packaging materials; and suppliers of products and services to the chemical process industries, including hazardous waste/environmental services, computer services, plant design, construction, consulting, shipping, and transportation.

2002 ■ Consulting Services

Association of Consulting Chemists and Chemical Engineers Inc.
PO Box 902
Murray Hill, NJ 07974
Ph: (908)464-3182
Fax: (908)464-3182
URL: http://www.chemconsult.org

Biennial, even years. $30.00 for individuals. Covers: About 160 member consultants in chemistry, chemical engineering, metallurgy, etc. Entries include: Individual name, address, certificate number, qualifications, affiliation, experience, facilities, staff. Arrangement: Classified by area of expertise. Indexes: Personal name, geographical.

2003 ■ Directory of Chemical Producers—United States

SRI Consulting
4300 Bohannon Dr., Ste. 200
Menlo Park, CA 94025
Ph: (650)384-4300
Fax: (650)330-1149
E-mail: sric-dcp@ihs.com
URL: http://www.sriconsulting.com/DCP

Annual, latest edition April, 2011. $2,050.00 for U.S.; $1,635.00 for U.S.; $2,100.00. Covers: Over 1,255 United States basic chemical producers manufacturing 7,085 chemicals in commercial quantities at more than 3,205 plant locations. Entries include: For

companies—Company name, division or subsidiary names, corporate address, phone, fax, telex, location of each subsidiary, division, and manufacturing plant, and the products made at each plant location. For products—Producer name and plant locations, alternate product names (if any). Subscription price includes bound volume, plus access to the directory staff for inquiries. Arrangement: Companies are alphabetical; products are alphabetical and by group (dyes, pesticides, etc.); manufacturing plants are geographical. Indexes: Geographical, product.

2004 ■ U.S. National Committee for the International Union of Pure and Applied Chemistry—Directory

U.S. National Committee for the International Union of Pure and Applied Chemistry
Keck Center
500 5th St., NW
Washington, DC 20001
Ph: (202)334-2000
Fr: 800-624-6242
URL: http://sites.nationalacademies.org/pga/biso/IUPAC/

Annual, July. Covers: 29 member chemists and chemical engineers in the United States.

HANDBOOKS AND MANUALS

2005 ■ Career Management for Chemists

Springer-Verlag New York, Inc.
233 Spring St.
New York, NY 10013
Ph: (212)460-1501
Fax: (212)460-1595
URL: http://www.springer.com/

John Fetzer. 2004. $54.95. Illustrated. 266 pages. Vocational guide for Chemists.

2006 ■ Careers in Focus: Chemistry

Ferguson Publishing
132 W 31st St., 17th Fl.
New York, NY 10001
Fr: 800-322-8755
E-mail: custserv@factsonfile.com
URL: http://factsonfile.infobasepublishing.com

2008. $32.95. 208 pages. Covers jobs profiled in detail, including the nature of the job, earnings, prospects for employment, what kind of training and skills it requires and sources for further information.

2007 ■ Great Jobs for Chemistry Majors

The McGraw-Hill Companies
PO Box 182604
Columbus, OH 43272
Fax: (614)759-3749
Fr: 877-883-5524
E-mail: customer.service@mcgraw-hill.com
URL: http://www.mhprofessional.com

Mark Rowh. Second edition, 2005. $15.95 (paper). 208 pages.

2008 ■ Principal Chemist

National Learning Corporation
212 Michael Dr.
Syosset, NY 11791
Fr: 800-632-8888
URL: http://www.passbooks.com

2009. $34.95 (paper). Serves as an exam preparation guide for principal chemists.

2009 ■ Resumes for Scientific and Technical Careers

The McGraw-Hill Companies
PO Box 182604
Columbus, OH 43272
Fax: (614)759-3749
Fr: 877-883-5524
E-mail: customer.service@mcgraw-hill.com
URL: http://www.mhprofessional.com/product.php?isbn=0071482199

Third edition, 2007. $12.95 (paper). 144 pages. Provides resume advice for individuals interested in working in scientific and technical careers. Includes sample resumes and cover letters.

2010 ■ *Theoretical and Quantum Mechanics: Fundamentals for Chemists*
Springer Publishing Co.
233 Spring St.
New York, NY 10013
Ph: (212)460-1500
Fax: (212)460-1575
Fr: 800-SPR-INGER
E-mail: service-ny@springer.com
URL: http://www.springer.com/chemistry/book/978-1-4020-3365-0

Stefan Ivanov. 2006. $199. 513 pages. Offers an introduction into theoretical and quantum mechanics for chemists. The book focuses on the atom and bridges the gap between classical physics, general and inorganic chemistry, and quantum mechanics.

2011 ■ *What's Cooking in Chemistry?: How Leading Chemists Succeed in the Kitchen*
John Wiley and Sons, Inc.
1 Wiley Dr.
Somerset, NJ 08875-1272
Ph: (732)469-4400
Fax: (732)302-2300
Fr: 800-225-5945
E-mail: custserv@wiley.com
URL: http://as.wiley.com/WileyCDA/WileyTitle/productCd-3527326219.html

Hubertus P. Bell, Tim Feuerstein, Carlos E. Guntner, Soren Holsken and Jan Klaas Lohmann. 2009. $19.95. Illustrated. 243 pages.

Employment Agencies and Search Firms

2012 ■ Amtec Human Capital
2749 Saturn St.
Brea, CA 92821
Ph: (714)993-1900
Fax: (714)993-2419
E-mail: info@amtechc.com
URL: http://www.amtechc.com

Employment agency.

2013 ■ Apple and Associates
PO Box 996
Chapin, SC 29036
Ph: (803)932-2000
E-mail: info@appleassoc.com
URL: http://www.appleassoc.com

Provides staffing services to medical device, plastics, pharmaceutical and performance materials industries.

2014 ■ Biomedical Search Consultants
275 Wyman St., Ste. 110
Waltham, MA 02451
Ph: (781)890-8824
Fax: (781)998-1266
E-mail: kprovost@biomedicalsearch.com
URL: http://www.biomedicalsearchconsultants.com

Employment agency.

2015 ■ The Brentwood Group Inc.
170 Kinnelon Rd.
Kinnelon, NJ 07405
Ph: (973)283-1000
Fax: (973)850-6103
E-mail: officemanager@thebrentwoodgroup.com
URL: http://www.thebrentwoodgroup.com

Executive search firm.

2016 ■ ManpowerGroup
100 Manpower Pl.
Milwaukee, WI 53212
Ph: (414)961-1000

Fax: (414)906-7822
URL: http://us.manpower.com

Specializes in a wide range of employment services including permanent placement, recruitment process outsourcing, managed service programs, outplacement and human resources consulting. Provides companies with workforce solutions that help them increase productivity and improve efficiency.

2017 ■ Professional Placement Associates, Inc.
287 Bowman Ave.
Purchase, NY 10577-2517
Ph: (914)251-1000
Fax: (914)251-1055
E-mail: careers@ppasearch.com
URL: http://www.ppasearch.com

Executive search firm specializing in the health and medical field.

2018 ■ Team Placement Service, Inc.
1414 Prince St., Ste. 202
Alexandria, VA 22314
Ph: (703)820-8618
Fax: (703)820-3368
Fr: 800-495-6767
E-mail: 4jobs@teamplace.com
URL: http://www.teamplace.com

Full-service personnel consultants provide placement for healthcare staff, physician and dentist, private practice, and hospitals. Conduct interviews, tests, and reference checks to select the top 20% of applicants. Survey applicants' skill levels, provide backup information on each candidate, select compatible candidates for consideration, and insure the hiring process minimizes potential legal liability. Industries served: healthcare and government agencies providing medical, dental, biotech, laboratory, hospitals, and physician search.

Online Job Sources and Services

2019 ■ American Chemical Society Career Sources
E-mail: help@acs.org
URL: http://portal.acs.org

Description: Offers online interviewing between employers and potential employees, postings for positions available and situations wanted, and regularly updated career advice and information for American Chemical Society members only.

2020 ■ American Oil Chemists Society Career Opportunities
2710 S Boulder
Urbana, IL 61802-6996
Ph: (217)359-2344
Fax: (217)351-8091
E-mail: general@aocs.org
URL: http://www.aocs.org/aocsbox/jobtarget/index.cfm

Description: Section of the AOCS homepage intended to aid members in finding jobs in the oil chemistry field. Job areas include analytical, health and nutrition, processing, surfactants and detergents, general fats and oils/chemistry, and others. Jobs may be posted and searched.

2021 ■ ChemIndustry.com
E-mail: info@chemindustry.com
URL: http://www.chemindustry.com

Description: Directory and search engine for chemical and related industry professionals. Provides specialized search services for chemical names, jobs, market research and consultants.

2022 ■ Chemist Jobs
URL: http://www.chemistjobs.us

Description: Features nationwide chemist job listings and cost-effective job posting for employers.

2023 ■ ChemistryCrossing.com
URL: http://www.chemistrycrossing.com

Description: Provides employment opportunities for chemists. Locates and classifies jobs on every source and provides specialized research to job seekers, recruiters and other job sites throughout North America.

2024 ■ Discover8.com
E-mail: admin@discover8.com
URL: http://www.discover8.com

Description: Focuses on the dissemination and intelligent discussion of life science news, discoveries, hypotheses, and procedures. Features resume postings and career listings.

2025 ■ Hum-Molgen.org
E-mail: info@hum-molgen.de
URL: http://hum-molgen.org

Description: Provides resources for the latest information in human molecular genetics. Features biotechnical sources, diagnostics, ethical, legal and social implications, meetings and conferences, and positions in bioscience and medicine. Provides the opportunity to communicate with scientists, physicians, and other genetics professionals worldwide.

2026 ■ iHireChemists.com
URL: http://www.ihirechemists.com

Description: Features job listings for chemists. Helps job seekers find employment opportunities and connect with hiring managers in all locations throughout the United States.

2027 ■ ThinkEnergyGroup.com
E-mail: resumes@thinkjobs.com
URL: http://www.thinkenergygroup.com

Description: Serves as a job board for professionals looking for positions in engineering, power plant, energy, and technical fields. Contains advice and tips on interviews, job searching, resume writing, hiring, and management. Provides choices of work location, pay rates in the field of expertise and contract, temp-to-hire, and direct hiring options.

Tradeshows

2028 ■ AOAC International Annual Meeting and Exposition
AOAC International
481 N. Frederick Ave., Ste. 500
Gaithersburg, MD 20877-2417
Ph: (301)924-7077
Fax: (301)924-7089
Fr: 800-379-2622
E-mail: aoac@aoac.org
URL: http://www.aoac.org

Annual. Primary Exhibits: Scientific and laboratory supplies and publications exhibits and posters. Dates and Locations: 2012 Sep 30 - Oct 03; Las Vegas, NV; Planet Hollywood; 2013 Aug 25-28; Chicago, IL; Palmer House Hilton.

Other Sources

2029 ■ AACC International
3340 Pilot Knob Rd.
St. Paul, MN 55121
Ph: (651)454-7250
Fax: (651)454-0766
E-mail: aacc@scisoc.org
URL: http://www.aaccnet.org

Description: Serves as professional society of scientists and other individuals in the grain processing industry (milling, baking, convenience foods, and feeds). Encourages research on cereal grains, oil seeds, pulses, and related materials, and studies their processing, utilization, and products. Seeks to develop and standardize analytical methods used in cereal and seed chemistry and to disseminate scientific and technical information through workshops and publications. Offers honors for outstanding research. Maintains over 20 technical subcommittees. Conducts short courses for continuing education and annual sanitation certification program.

2030 ■ American Academy of Clinical Toxicology (AACT)
110 W Lancaster Ave., Ste. 230
Wayne, PA 19087
Ph: (703)556-9222
Fax: (703)556-8729
E-mail: admin@clintox.org
URL: http://www.clintox.org

Description: Physicians, veterinarians, pharmacists, nurses research scientists, and analytical chemists. Seeks to unite medical scientists and facilitate the exchange of information. Encourages the development of therapeutic methods and technology. Conducts professional training in poison information and emergency service personnel.

2031 ■ American Association of Textile Chemists and Colorists (AATCC)
PO Box 12215
Research Triangle Park, NC 27709-2215
Ph: (919)549-8141
Fax: (919)549-8933
E-mail: danielsj@aatcc.org
URL: http://www.aatcc.org

Description: Professional association for textile design, processing and testing. Works as an authority for industry standard test methods and evaluation procedures.

2032 ■ American Chemical Society (ACS)
1155 16th St. NW
Washington, DC 20036
Ph: (202)872-4600
Fr: 800-227-5558
E-mail: help@acs.org
URL: http://portal.acs.org/portal/acs/corg/content

Description: Scientific and educational society of chemists and chemical engineers. Conducts studies and surveys; special programs for disadvantaged persons; legislation monitoring, analysis, and reporting; courses for graduate chemists and chemical engineers; radio and television programming. Offers career guidance counseling; administers the Petroleum Research Fund and other grants and fellowship programs. Operates Employment Clearing Houses. Compiles statistics. Maintains speakers' bureau and 33 divisions.

2033 ■ American Crystallographic Association (ACA)
PO Box 96 Ellicot Station
Buffalo, NY 14205-0096
Ph: (716)898-8692
Fax: (716)898-8695
E-mail: marcia@hwi.buffalo.edu
URL: http://aca.hwi.buffalo.edu

Description: Chemists, biochemists, physicists, mineralogists, and metallurgists interested in crystallography and in the application of X-ray, electron, and neutron diffraction. Promotes the study of the arrangement of atoms in matter, its causes, its nature, and its consequences, and of the tools and methods used in such studies. Maintains employment clearinghouse for members and employers.

2034 ■ American Institute of Chemists (AIC)
315 Chestnut St.
Philadelphia, PA 19106-2702
Ph: (215)873-8224
Fax: (215)629-5224
E-mail: info@theaic.org
URL: http://www.theaic.org

Description: Represents chemists and chemical engineers. Promotes advancement of chemical professions in the U.S.; protects public welfare by establishing and enforcing high practice standards; represents professional interests of chemists and

chemical engineers. Sponsors National Certification Commission in Chemistry and Chemical Engineering and AIC Foundation.

2035 ■ American Microchemical Society (AMS)
2 June Way
Middlesex, NJ 08846
E-mail: hal1116@netscape.com
URL: http://www.microchem.org

Description: Promotes interest in the practice and teaching of microchemistry. Participates in exhibits and symposia. Maintains placement service.

2036 ■ American Oil Chemists' Society (AOCS)
PO Box 17190
Urbana, IL 61803-7190
Ph: (217)359-2344
Fax: (217)351-8091
E-mail: general@aocs.org
URL: http://www.aocs.org

Description: Chemists, biochemists, chemical engineers, research directors, plant personnel, and others in laboratories and chemical process industries concerned with animal, marine, and vegetable oils and fats, and their extraction, refining, safety, packaging, quality control, and use in consumer and industrial products such as foods, drugs, paints, waxes, lubricants, soaps, and cosmetics. Sponsors short courses; certifies referee chemists; distributes cooperative check samples; sells official reagents. Maintains 100 committees. Operates job placement service for members only.

2037 ■ American Society for Biochemistry and Molecular Biology (ASBMB)
11200 Rockville Pike, Ste. 302
Rockville, MD 20852-3110
Ph: (240)283-6600
Fax: (301)881-2080
E-mail: asbmb@asbmb.org
URL: http://www.asbmb.org

Description: Biochemists and molecular biologists who have conducted and published original investigations in biological chemistry and/or molecular biology. Operates placement service.

2038 ■ American Society of Brewing Chemists
3340 Pilot Knob Rd.
St. Paul, MN 55121
Ph: (651)454-7250
Fax: (651)454-0766
URL: http://www.asbcnet.org

Description: Serves as a group of individual and corporate members worldwide representing large and small brewers, consultants, government agencies, academics, distillers, vintners and those working in allied industries (suppliers of malt, hops, enzymes, brewing syrups, chill proofing, filtration aids, CO2 packaging materials, etc.). Strives to improve and bring uniformity to the brewing industry on a technical level. Provides problem solving on industry-wide issues using chemistry and microbiology and professional development opportunities.

2039 ■ American Society for Neurochemistry (ASN)
9037 Ron Den Ln.
Windermere, FL 34786
Ph: (407)909-9064
Fax: (407)876-0750
E-mail: amazing@iag.net
URL: http://www.asneurochem.org

Description: Represents investigators in the field of neurochemistry and scientists who are qualified specialists in other disciplines and are interested in the activities of the society. Aims to advance and promote the science of neurochemistry and related neurosciences and to increase and enhance neurochemical knowledge; to facilitate the dissemination of information concerning neurochemical research; to

encourage the research of individual neurochemists. Conducts roundtables; distributes research communications. Maintains placement service.

2040 ■ American Society of Plant Biologists (ASPB)
15501 Monona Dr.
Rockville, MD 20855-2768
Ph: (301)251-0560
Fax: (301)279-2996
E-mail: info@aspb.org
URL: http://www.aspb.org

Description: Professional society of plant biologists, plant biochemists, and other plant scientists engaged in research and teaching. Offers placement service for members; conducts educational and public affairs programs.

2041 ■ American Water Works Association (AWWA)
6666 W Quincy Ave.
Denver, CO 80235-3098
Ph: (303)794-7711
Fax: (303)347-0804
Fr: 800-926-7337
E-mail: custsvc@awwa.org
URL: http://www.awwa.org

Description: Water utility managers, superintendents, engineers, chemists, bacteriologists, and other individuals interested in public water supply; municipal- and investor-owned water departments; boards of health; manufacturers of waterworks equipment; government officials and consultants interested in water supply. Develops standards and supports research programs in waterworks design, construction, operation, and management. Conducts in-service training schools and prepares manuals for waterworks personnel. Maintains hall of fame. Offers placement service via member newsletter; compiles statistics. Offers training; children's services; and information center on the water utilities industry, potable water, and water reuse.

2042 ■ Association of Consulting Chemists and Chemical Engineers (ACC&CE)
PO Box 297
Sparta, NJ 07871-0297
Ph: (973)729-6671
Fax: (973)729-7088
E-mail: accce@chemconsult.org
URL: http://www.chemconsult.org

Description: Serves the chemical and related industries through its expertise on a wide variety of technical and business knowledge. Provides experienced counseling for new members.

2043 ■ Association for International Practical Training (AIPT)
10400 Little Patuxent Pkwy., Ste. 250
Columbia, MD 21044-3519
Ph: (410)997-2200
Fax: (410)992-3924
E-mail: aipt@aipt.org
URL: http://www.aipt.org

Description: Providers worldwide of on-the-job training programs for students and professionals seeking international career development and life-changing experiences. Arranges workplace exchanges in hundreds of professional fields, bringing employers and trainees together from around the world. Client list ranges from small farming communities to Fortune 500 companies.

2044 ■ Biomedical Engineering Society (BMES)
8201 Corporate Dr., Ste. 1125
Landover, MD 20785-2224
Ph: (301)459-1999
Fax: (301)459-2444
Fr: 877-871-2637
E-mail: info@bmes.org
URL: http://www.bmes.org

Description: Biomedical, chemical, electrical, civil,

agricultural and mechanical engineers, physicians, managers, and university professors representing all fields of biomedical engineering; students and corporations. Encourages the development, dissemination, integration, and utilization of knowledge in biomedical engineering.

2045 ■ Council for Chemical Research (CCR)
1550 M St. NE, Ste. 500
Washington, DC 20005
Ph: (202)429-3971
Fax: (202)429-3976
E-mail: pmendez@ccrhq.org
URL: http://www.ccrhq.org

Description: Represents universities that grant advanced degrees in chemistry or chemical engineering; chemical companies, government laboratories, and independent research laboratories that employ chemists and chemical engineers in research and development. Aims to promote more effective interactions between university chemistry and chemical engineering departments and the research function of industry and government and to support basic research in chemistry and chemical engineering. Strives for continued vitality of chemical science, engineering, and technology in the U.S., and the greater recognition of the global nature of the chemical research enterprise. Sponsors charitable programs; produces educational materials; compiles statistics. Maintains speakers' bureau.

2046 ■ Electrochemical Society (ECS)
65 S Main St., Bldg. D
Pennington, NJ 08534-2839
Ph: (609)737-1902
Fax: (609)737-2743
E-mail: ecs@electrochem.org
URL: http://www.electrochem.org

Description: Serves as technical society of electrochemists, chemists, chemical and electrochemical engineers, metallurgists and metallurgical engineers, physical chemists, physicists, electrical engineers, research engineers, teachers, technical sales representatives, and patent attorneys. Seeks to advance the science and technology of electrochemistry, electronics, electrothermics, electrometallurgy, and applied subjects.

2047 ■ Engineering Society of Detroit (ESD)
20700 Civic Center Dr., Ste. 450
Southfield, MI 48076
Ph: (248)353-0735
Fax: (248)353-0736
E-mail: esd@esd.org
URL: http://ww2.esd.org/home.htm

Description: Engineers from all disciplines; scientists and technologists. Conducts technical programs and engineering refresher courses; sponsors conferences and expositions. Maintains speakers' bureau; offers placement services; although based in Detroit, MI, society membership is international.

2048 ■ Federation of Analytical Chemistry and Spectroscopy Societies (FACSS)
PO Box 24379
Santa Fe, NM 87502
Ph: (505)820-1648
Fax: (505)989-1073
E-mail: facss@facss.org
URL: http://facss.org/facss/index.php

Description: Professional societies representing 9,000 analytical chemists and spectroscopists. Members are: Analysis Instrumentation Division of the Instrument Society of America; Association of Analytical Chemists; Coblentz Society; Division of Analytical Chemistry of the American Chemical Society; Division of Analytical Chemistry of the Royal Society of Chemistry; Society for Applied Spectroscopy. Aims to provide a forum to address the challenges of analytical chemistry, chromatography, and spectroscopy. Reviews technical papers; maintains placement service.

2049 ■ Geochemical Society (GS)
Washington University
Earth and Planetary Sciences Dept.
One Brookings Dr., CB 1169
St. Louis, MO 63130-4899
Ph: (314)935-4131
Fax: (314)935-4121
E-mail: gsoffice@geochemsoc.org
URL: http://www.geochemsoc.org

Description: Professional society of geochemists, chemists, geologists, physicists, biologists, oceanographers, mathematicians, meteorologists, and other scientists interested in the application of chemistry to the solution of geological and cosmological problems. The Organic Geochemistry Division focuses on biogeochemistry and organic processes at the Earth's surface and subsurface.

2050 ■ International Society of Chemical Ecology (ISCE)
University of Kentucky
Dept. of Entomology
Lexington, KY 40546
Ph: (859)257-1618
Fax: (859)323-1120
E-mail: khaynes@uky.edu
URL: http://www.chemecol.org

Description: Chemists, ecologists, biologists, and others with an interest in chemical ecology. Promotes understanding of the origin, function, and importance of natural chemicals that mediate communication and interactions within and among organisms. Seeks to broaden the scope of chemical ecology and to stimulate cooperation and exchange of information among members of diverse scientific fields. Conducts educational programs designed to foster knowledge in the area of chemical ecology.

2051 ■ Iranian Chemists' Association of the American Chemical Society (ICA-ACS)
35 Meadowbrook Ln.
Woodbury, CT 06798
Ph: (203)573-3220
Fax: (203)573-3660
E-mail: banijamali@ica-acs.org
URL: http://www.ica-acs.org

Description: Encourages and enhances the interchange and sharing of scientific knowledge and friendship among chemists and chemistry-related professionals of Iranian descent. Provides opportunities for members to assist each other in pursuit of academic and professional development and growth. Promotes awareness of scientific contributions made by Iranian scientists.

2052 ■ Korean-American Scientists and Engineers Association (KSEA)
1952 Gallows Rd., Ste. 300
Vienna, VA 22182
Ph: (703)748-1221
Fax: (703)748-1331
E-mail: sejong@ksea.org
URL: http://www.ksea.org

Description: Represents scientists and engineers holding single or advanced degrees. Promotes friendship and mutuality among Korean and American scientists and engineers; contributes to Korea's scientific, technological, industrial, and economic developments; strengthens the scientific, technological, and cultural bonds between Korea and the U.S. Sponsors symposium. Maintains speakers' bureau, placement service, and biographical archives. Compiles statistics.

2053 ■ National Organization for the Professional Advancement of Black Chemists and Chemical Engineers (NOBCChE)
PO Box 77040
Washington, DC 20013
Ph: (240)228-1763
Fax: (202)667-1705

Fr: 800-776-1419
E-mail: president@nobcche.org
URL: http://www.nobcche.org

Description: Black professionals in science and chemistry. Seeks to aid black scientists and chemists in reaching their full professional potential; encourages black students to pursue scientific studies and employment; promotes participation of blacks in scientific research. Provides volunteers to teach science courses in selected elementary schools; sponsors scientific field trips for students; maintains speakers' bureau for schools. Conducts technical seminars in Africa. Sponsors competitions; presents awards for significant achievements to individuals in the field. Maintains placement service; compiles statistics.

2054 ■ National Registry of Certified Chemists (NRCC)
927 S Walter Reed Dr., No. 11
Arlington, VA 22204
Ph: (703)979-9001
E-mail: nrcc6@aol.com
URL: http://www.nrcc6.org

Description: Certifies programs for chemical hygiene officers, clinical chemists, clinical chemistry technologists, environmental analytical chemists, environmental analytical technicians, and toxicological chemists based on education, experience, and examination.

2055 ■ Radiation Research Society (RRS)
PO Box 7050
Lawrence, KS 66044
Fax: (785)843-1274
Fr: 800-627-0326
E-mail: info@radres.org
URL: http://www.radres.org

Description: Professional society of biologists, physicists, chemists, and physicians contributing to knowledge of radiation and its effects. Promotes original research in the natural sciences relating to radiation; facilitates integration of different disciplines in the study of radiation effects.

2056 ■ Radiochemistry Society
PO Box 3091
Richland, WA 99354
Fr: 800-371-0542
E-mail: rad-info@radiochemistry.org
URL: http://www.radiochemistry.org

Description: Aims to promote education and public outreach for the safe use, handling and benefits of radioisotopes in security, energy, agriculture, environment, food safety and medicine. Conducts seminars, trainings, scholarships, meetings and exchange of scientific information.

2057 ■ Society of Cosmetic Chemists (SCC)
120 Wall St., Ste. 2400
New York, NY 10005-4088
Ph: (212)668-1500
Fax: (212)668-1504
E-mail: scc@scconline.org
URL: http://www.scconline.org/website/index.shtml

Description: Serves a professional society of scientists involved in the cosmetic industry. Sponsors educational institution support programs to stimulate growth of cosmetic science-related programs. Maintains placement service.

2058 ■ Society of Flavor Chemists
3301 Rte. 66, Bldg. C, Ste. 205
Neptune, NJ 07753
Ph: (732)922-3393
Fax: (732)922-3590
E-mail: administrator@flavorchemist.org
URL: http://www.flavorchemist.org

Description: Works to advance the field of flavor technology and related sciences. Encourages the exchange of ideas and personal contacts among flavor chemists.

2059 ■ Society for In Vitro Biology (SIVB)
514 Daniels St., Ste. 411
Raleigh, NC 27605-1317
Ph: (919)562-0600
Fax: (919)562-0608
E-mail: sivb@sivb.org
URL: http://www.sivb.org

Description: Fosters exchange of knowledge of in vitro biology of cells, tissues and organs from both plant and animals (including humans). Focuses on biological research, development, and applications of significance to science and society. Accomplishes its mission through the society's publications; national and local conferences, meetings and workshops; and through support of teaching initiatives in cooperation with educational institutions. Creates an environment of scientific exchange and interdisciplinary synergy with the goal of advancing current and future systems for in vitro biology.

2060 ■ Society of Rheology (SOR)
University of Wisconsin
Rheology Research Ctr.
Madison, WI 53706
Ph: (608)262-7473

Fax: (608)265-2316
E-mail: giacomin@wisc.edu
URL: http://www.rheology.org/sor

Description: Professional society of chemical engineers, chemists, physicists, biologists, and others interested in the theory and precise measurement of the deformation and flow of matter and application of the physical data in fields such as biology, food, high polymers and plastics, metals, petroleum products, rubber, paint, printing ink, ceramics and glass, starch, floor preparations, and cosmetics.

2061 ■ Soil Science Society of America (SSSA)
677 S Segoe Rd.
Madison, WI 53711
Ph: (608)273-8080
Fax: (608)273-2021
E-mail: headquarters@soils.org
URL: http://www.soils.org

Description: Professional soil scientists, including soil physicists, soil classifiers, land use and management specialists, chemists, microbiologists, soil fertility specialists, soil cartographers, conservationists, mineralogists, engineers, and others interested in fundamental and applied soil science.

2062 ■ Water Environment Federation (WEF)
601 Wythe St.
Alexandria, VA 22314-1994
Ph: (703)684-2400
Fax: (703)684-2492
Fr: 800-666-0206
E-mail: jeger@wef.org
URL: http://www.wef.org

Description: Technical societies representing chemists, biologists, ecologists, geologists, operators, educational and research personnel, industrial wastewater engineers, consultant engineers, municipal officials, equipment manufacturers, and university professors and students dedicated to the enhancement and preservation of water quality and resources. Seeks to advance fundamental and practical knowledge concerning the nature, collection, treatment, and disposal of domestic and industrial wastewaters, and the design, construction, operation, and management of facilities for these purposes. Disseminates technical information; and promotes good public relations and regulations that improve water quality and the status of individuals working in this field. Conducts educational and research programs.

SOURCES OF HELP-WANTED ADS

2063 ■ Education & Treatment of Children
West Virginia University Press
139 Stansbury Hall
PO Box 6295
Morgantown, WV 26506
Ph: (304)293-8400
Fax: (304)293-6585
URL: http://www.educationandtreatmentofchildren.net

Quarterly. $85.00/year for institutions; $45.00/year for individuals; $100.00/year for institutions, elsewhere; $60.00/year for individuals, elsewhere. Periodical featuring information concerning the development of services for children and youth. Includes reports written for educators and other child care and mental health providers focused on teaching, training, and treatment effectiveness.

PLACEMENT AND JOB REFERRAL SERVICES

2064 ■ 4Nannies.com
2 Pidgeon Hill Dr., No. 550
Potomac Falls, VA 20165
Fr: 800-810-2611
E-mail: support@4nannies.com
URL: http://www.4nannies.com

Description: Exists as an online nanny resource serving both nannies seeking jobs and families seeking nannies through its family-nanny job matching system. Recruits nanny candidates seeking immediate employment and delivers an extensive pool of candidates to choose from.

2065 ■ ABC Nannies & Domestics, Inc.
400 South Colorado Blvd., Ste. 310
Glendale, CO 80246
Ph: (303)321-3866
Fax: (303)321-1395
Fr: 888-33-NANNY
E-mail: info@abcnannies.com
URL: http://www.abcnannies.com

Description: Specializes in nanny and domestic placements. Sponsors quarterly functions such as education seminars, picnics and other events for nannies and domestics.

2066 ■ NannyClassifieds.com
410 W Grand Pkwy. S, Ste. 250
Katy, TX 77494
URL: http://www.nannyclassifieds.com

Description: Exists as an agency that serves the needs of both nannies and working parents through affordable child care services and solutions. Partners with many other nanny and parenting sites to recruit nannies and get their ads the most exposure on the web. Features services and resources such as background screening, nanny payroll tax calculator and other more.

HANDBOOKS AND MANUALS

2067 ■ Basic Training for Residential Childcare Workers: A Practical Guide for Improving Service to Children
Charles C Thomas Publisher, Ltd.
PO Box 19265
Springfield, IL 62794-9265
Ph: (217)789-8980
Fax: (217)789-9130
Fr: 800-258-8980
E-mail: books@ccthomas.com
URL: http://www.ccthomas.com

Beverly Boone. 2011. $36.95 (paper). 224 pages. Contains solid, easy to understand and follow information for residential childcare workers and trainers. Includes exercises designed to help the reader put the material covered into actual use and practice.

2068 ■ Careers in Child Care
The McGraw-Hill Companies
PO Box 182604
Columbus, OH 43272
Fax: (614)759-3749
Fr: 877-883-5524
E-mail: customer.service@mcgraw-hill.com
URL: http://www.mhprofessional.com/
product.php?isbn=0071482113

Marjorie Eberts and Margaret Gisler. Third edition, 2007. $16.95 (paper). $15.95 (hardcover). 192 pages. Know what to expect when you start out. Familiarize yourself with current salaries, benefits, and the best job prospects.

2069 ■ Careers in Focus: Child Care
Ferguson Publishing
132 W 31st St., 17th Fl.
New York, NY 10001
Fr: 800-322-8755
E-mail: custserv@factsonfile.com
URL: http://factsonfile.infobasepublishing.com

2006. $32.95. 176 pages. Profiles 18 jobs in the field of child care and development.

2070 ■ Careers for Kids at Heart and Others Who Adore Children
The McGraw-Hill Companies
PO Box 182604
Columbus, OH 43272
Fax: (614)759-3749
Fr: 877-883-5524
E-mail: customer.service@mcgraw-hill.com
URL: http://www.mhprofessional.com

Marjorie Eberts and Margaret Gisler. Third edition, 2006. $13.95 (paper). 160 pages.

2071 ■ Child and Adult Care Professionals
The McGraw-Hill Companies
PO Box 182604
Columbus, OH 43272
Fax: (614)759-3749
Fr: 877-883-5524
E-mail: customer.service@mcgraw-hill.com
URL: http://www.mhprofessional.com

Karen Stephens and Maxine Hammonds-Smith. Student edition, 2004. $66.64. Illustrated. 688 pages.

2072 ■ Opportunities in Child Care Careers
The McGraw-Hill Companies
PO Box 182604
Columbus, OH 43272
Fax: (614)759-3749
Fr: 877-883-5524
E-mail: customer.service@mcgraw-hill.com
URL: http://www.mhprofessional.com/
product.php?isbn=0071467661

Renee Wittenberg. 2006. $13.95 (paper). 160 pages. Discusses various job opportunities and how to secure a position. Illustrated.

2073 ■ Working with Young Children: Teacher's Resource
Goodheart Willcox Publisher
18604 W Creek Dr.
Tinley Park, IL 60477-6243
Ph: (708)687-5000
Fax: 888-409-3900
Fr: 800-323-0440
E-mail: custserv@g-w.com
URL: http://www.g-w.com

Judy Herr. Seventh edition, 2012. $248.00 (Compact Disc). Educational format.

EMPLOYMENT AGENCIES AND SEARCH FIRMS

2074 ■ Hometown Nannies Plus
250 Post Rd. E, Ste. 110
Westport, CT 06880-3616
Ph: (203)227-3924
E-mail: jobs@hometownnannies.com
URL: http://www.hometownnannies.com

Description: Serves as a full-service domestic placement employment agency that seeks to provide excellence in the referral and placement of child, home, estate, and elder care professionals. Works with family in assessing their job requirements so they can hire and retain the most viable domestic employees possible. Works with job seekers to help them focus their experience, strengths, goals, needs and concerns in their search for a specific type of job with a compatible family in a positive work environment.

ONLINE JOB SOURCES AND SERVICES

2075 ■ AllAboutNannyCare.com
URL: http://nannybizreviews.com

Description: Provides expert assistance in recruitment, screening and retention of quality in-home caregivers and the creation of successful nanny/family relationships. Provides a variety of resources and connection to the larger childcare community. Offers a variety of exclusive tools to help caregivers and families find the right job/nanny match.

2076 ■ ChildcareJob.org
URL: http://childcarejob.org

Description: Offers a searchable database of employment opportunities for child care workers. Enables job seekers to post their resumes online. Facilitates the employers' search for potential candidates through its find-a-resume feature.

2077 ■ ChildcareJobs.net
URL: http://www.childcarejobs.net

Description: Features job opportunities, resume search, postings and employment for childcare workers.

2078 ■ GreatAupair.com
URL: http://www.greataupair.com

Description: Exists as a website created for matching nannies and au pairs with families worldwide. Offers a way for host families, nannies and au pairs to easily find their matches.

2079 ■ The Houseparent Network
E-mail: houseparentnetwork@gmail.com
URL: http://www.houseparent.net

Description: Serves as an online career resource for houseparents and residential child care workers.

2080 ■ NannyJobs.com
URL: http://www.nannyjobs.com

Description: Provides free access to nanny jobs available across the nation. Offers resources and tools, including career information, conferences and event dates for nannies, and more.

2081 ■ NannyLocators.com
E-mail: nannylocators@gmail.com
URL: http://www.nannylocators.com

Description: Allows posting of nanny availabilities and job-wanted ads. Includes key points on evaluating salary offers and other nanny job information.

2082 ■ NannyNeeded.com
URL: http://www.nannyneeded.com

Description: Provides a database of nanny jobs and nanny services. Offers listings and specific requirements of the jobs.

2083 ■ NannyNetwork.com
URL: http://www.nannynetwork.com

Description: Serves as an online resource for nanny placement and referral agencies. Provides information pertaining to nanny recruitment, nanny employment and nanny retention.

OTHER SOURCES

2084 ■ Association of Premier Nanny Agencies (APNA)
400 S Colorado Blvd., Ste. 300
Denver, CO 80246
E-mail: daryl@spnannies.com
URL: http://www.theapna.org

Description: Aims to establish and enforce standards of professional practices within the nanny placement industry. Seeks to address issues and concerns pertinent to domestic services.

2085 ■ International Nanny Association (INA)
PO Box 1299
Hyannis, MA 02601
Ph: (713)526-2670
Fax: (508)638-6462
Fr: 888-878-1477
E-mail: info@nanny.org
URL: http://www.nanny.org

Description: An educational association for nannies and those who educate, place, employ, and support professional in-home child care. Membership is open to those who are directly involved with the in-home child care profession, including nannies, nanny employers, nanny placement agency owners (and staff), nanny educators, and providers of special services related to the nanny profession.

2086 ■ National Association for the Education of Young Children (NAEYC)
PO Box 97156
Washington, DC 20090-7156
Ph: (202)232-8777
Fax: (202)328-1846
Fr: 800-424-2460
E-mail: naeyc@naeyc.org
URL: http://www.naeyc.org

Description: Teachers and directors of preschool and primary schools, kindergartens, child care centers, and early other learning programs for young childhood; early childhood education and child development educators, trainers, and researchers and other professionals dedicated to young children's healthy development.

Sources of Help-Wanted Ads

2087 ■ Chiropractic Economics
Doyle Group
5150 Palm Valley Rd., Ste. 103
Ponte Vedra Beach, FL 32082
Ph: (904)285-6020
Fax: (904)285-9944
URL: http://www.chiroeco.com

18/year. $39.95/year. Provides news and information to practicing chiropractors with a focus on office management; patient relations; personal development; financial planning; legal, clinical, and research data; and wellness/nutrition.

Handbooks and Manuals

2088 ■ Careers in Medicine
The McGraw-Hill Companies
PO Box 182604
Columbus, OH 43272
Fax: (614)759-3749
Fr: 877-883-5524
E-mail: customer.service@mcgraw-hill.com
URL: http://www.mhprofessional.com/product.php?isbn=0071458743

Terence J. Sacks. Third edition, 2006. $15.95 (paper). 192 pages. Examines the many paths open to M.D.s, D.O.s, and M.D./Ph.D.s, including clinical private or group practice, hospitals, public health organizations, the armed forces, emergency rooms, research institutions, medical schools, pharmaceutical companies and private industry, and research/advocacy groups like the World Health Organization. A special chapter on osteopathy and chiropractic explores this branch of medicine.

2089 ■ Core Assessment and Training
Human Kinetics
PO Box 5076
Champaign, IL 61825-5076
Fax: (217)351-1549
Fr: 800-747-4457
E-mail: info@hkusa.com
URL: http://www.humankinetics.com

2010. $42.00 (DVD and paper). 160 pages. Serves as reference for coaches, athletic and personal trainers, and physical therapists. Covers all aspects of core training, from basic to advanced core exercises, stretches, and pylometrics. Includes photos, illustrations and instructions for more than 120 exercises. Accompanying DVD features demonstrations of proper exercise techniques and protocols for review. Helps professionals in the field assess clients' needs and design customized training programs.

2090 ■ Functional Testing in Human Performance
Human Kinetics
PO Box 5076
Champaign, IL 61825-5076

Fax: (217)351-1549
Fr: 800-747-4457
E-mail: info@hkusa.com
URL: http://www.humankinetics.com

Michael Reiman and Robert Manske. 2009. $79.00 (DVD and cloth). 328 pages. Serves as resource for the accurate assessment of an individual's functional abilities. Offers clinicians the compilation of information on clinical and data-based functional testing for sport, exercise and occupational settings. Accompanying DVD features live-action demonstrations of 40 of the most advanced tests.

2091 ■ Opportunities in Chiropractic Careers
The McGraw-Hill Companies
PO Box 182604
Columbus, OH 43272
Fax: (614)759-3749
Fr: 877-883-5524
E-mail: customer.service@mcgraw-hill.com
URL: http://www.mhprofessional.com/product.php?isbn=007141164X

Bart Green, Claire Johnson, and Louis Sportelli. 2004. $13.95 (paper). 160 pages. A guide to planning for and building a career in the field. Illustrated.

2092 ■ Pocket Orthopaedics: Evidence-Based Survival Guide
Jones & Bartlett Learning
5 Wall St.
Burlington, MA 01803
Fax: (978)443-8000
Fr: 800-832-0034
E-mail: info@jblearning.com
URL: http://www.jblearning.com

Michael S. Wong. 2011. $41.95 (spiral/paperback). 412 pages. Serves as learning aide in evidence-based practice for both students and clinicians.

2093 ■ Resumes for Health and Medical Careers
The McGraw-Hill Companies
PO Box 182604
Columbus, OH 43272
Fax: (614)759-3749
Fr: 877-883-5524
E-mail: customer.service@mcgraw-hill.com
URL: http://www.mhprofessional.com/product.php?isbn=0071545352

Third edition, 2008. $12.95 (paper). 144 pages.

Employment Agencies and Search Firms

2094 ■ Chiropractic Staffing Services
1358 Sandpiper Dr.
Corpus Christi, TX 78412
Ph: (361)993-3567

Fax: (361)334-0379
E-mail: info@chiropracticstaffing.com
URL: http://www.chiropracticstaffing.com

Provides permanent and temporary clinical staffing and consulting services to a wide range of clients. Reviews, screens and trains every chiropractic physician and technician to suit the client's workplace environment, patient profiles, and patient needs.

2095 ■ Michael McGurn, D.C. and Associates
450-106 SR 13 N, No. 173
Jacksonville, FL 32259
Fax: (904)230-2349
Fr: 800-501-6111
E-mail: mma@mmachiropractors.com
URL: http://www.mmachiropractors.com

Provides temporary and associate placement services for chiropractors in the United States. Conducts screening of substitute and associate doctors by investigating state board complaints, malpractice and criminal history.

Online Job Sources and Services

2096 ■ ChiroEco.com
URL: http://www.chiroeco.com

Description: Provides online information and resources for the chiropractic community. Features chiropractic news, articles, videos, and job board.

2097 ■ chiropractorjobs.us
URL: http://www.chiropractorjobs.us

Description: Serves as a job board that focuses exclusively on chiropractor employment opportunities and candidate recruiting.

2098 ■ ExploreHealthCareers.org
E-mail: feedback@explorehealthcareers.org
URL: http://explorehealthcareers.org/en/home

Description: Provides employment information in health professions. Includes links to health-related education/training programs, financial aid resources, specialized learning opportunities, and current issues in health care.

2099 ■ HEALTHeCAREERS Network
Fr: 888-884-8242
E-mail: info@healthecareers.com
URL: http://www.healthecareers.com

Description: Career search site for jobs in all health care specialties; educational resources; visa and licensing information for relocation; interesting articles; relocation tools; links to professional organizations and general resources.

2100 ■ ProHealthJobs.com
Ph: (484)443-8545
Fax: (484)443-8549
E-mail: info@prohealthjobs.com
URL: http://prohealthjobs.com/jobboard

Description: Career resources site for the medical and health care field. Lists professional opportunities, product information, continuing education and open positions.

TRADESHOWS

2101 ■ California Chiropractic Association Annual Convention

California Chiropractic Association
1600 Sacramento Inn Way, Ste. 106
Sacramento, CA 95815-3458
Ph: (916)648-2727
Fax: (916)648-2738
E-mail: cca@calchiro.org
URL: http://www.calchiro.org

Annual. Primary Exhibits: Publications, office equipment and supplies, computers, health foods, insurance companies, and x-ray equipment; nutritional, chiropractic equipment, physical therapy, orthopedics. Dates and Locations: 2012 May 04-06; San Diego, CA; Paradise Point Resort & Spa,.

2102 ■ Florida Chiropractic Association National Convention and Expo

Florida Chiropractic Association
30 Remington Rd., Ste. One
Oakland, FL 34787
Ph: (407)654-3225
Fax: (407)656-5433
URL: http://www.fcachiro.org

Annual. Primary Exhibits: Chiropractic examining/adjusting tables; X-ray equipment and products; diagnostic equipment and supplies; office furniture; computer systems and software; nutritional supplements; physical therapy equipment; orthopedic appliances; medical books; patient educational material, and uniforms. Dates and Locations: 2012 Aug 23-26; Orlando, FL; The Peabody Orlando.

2103 ■ North American Spine Society Annual Meeting

North American Spine Society
7075 Veterans Blvd.
Burr Ridge, IL 60527
Ph: (630)230-3600
Fr: (866)960-6277
URL: http://www.spine.org

Annual. Primary Exhibits: Products & services directly and indirectly related to spinal diagnosis, treatment and surgery, the general practice of medicine aid peripheral products and services. Dates and Locations: 2013 Oct 09-02; Dallas, TX; 2014 Nov 12-15; San Francisco, CA; 2015 Oct 14-17; Chicago, IL; 2016 Oct 26-29; Boston, MA.

OTHER SOURCES

2104 ■ American Chiropractic Association (ACA)

1701 Clarendon Blvd.
Arlington, VA 22209
Ph: (703)276-8800
Fax: (703)243-2593
E-mail: memberinfo@acatoday.org
URL: http://www.acatoday.org

Description: Enhances the philosophy, science, and art of chiropractic, and the professional welfare of individuals in the field. Promotes legislation defining chiropractic health care and improves the public's awareness and utilization of chiropractic. Conducts chiropractic survey and statistical study; maintains library. Sponsors Correct Posture Week in May and Spinal Health Month in October. Chiropractic colleges have student groups.

2105 ■ American College of Chiropractic Orthopedists (ACCO)

35 S Lake St.
North East, PA 16428

Ph: (781)665-1497
Fax: (814)665-1032
E-mail: thomasmackdc@gmail.com
URL: http://www.accoweb.org

Description: Certified and non-certified chiropractic orthopedists; students enrolled in a postgraduate chiropractic orthopedic program. Seeks to establish and maintain optimal educational and clinical standards within the field of chiropractic orthopedics. Sponsors educational programs.

2106 ■ Association for Catholic Chiropractors (AFCC)

2049 Kolb Ridge Ct. SW
Marietta, GA 30008
E-mail: afcchiro@bellsouth.net
URL: http://www.catholicchiros.org

Description: Promotes the Catholic faith through the art, science and practice of the chiropractic profession. Supports the chiropractic community-at-large in establishing ethical health care practice principles that will reflect the Church's teachings. Provides spiritual guidance to Catholic chiropractors to help them follow a Christ centered professional and personal life.

2107 ■ Chiropractic Diplomatic Corps

17602 17th St., Ste. 102
Tustin, CA 92780
Fr: 800-600-7032
E-mail: info@chiropracticdiplomatic.com
URL: http://www.chiropracticdiplomatic.com

Description: Seeks to advance chiropractic training and services throughout the world. Aims to establish cooperative alliances with international organizations that are involved with the delivery of chiropractic care.

2108 ■ Chiropractic Orthopedists of North America (CONA)

2048 Montrose Ave.
Montrose, CA 91020
Ph: (818)249-8326
E-mail: rakechiro@ca.rr.com
URL: http://www.conanet.org

Description: Assists in the advancement of chiropractic using scientific and evidence-based research and information. Maintains highest standards of moral and ethical conduct among members. Promotes chiropractic orthopedics with other branches of the healing arts and professions.

2109 ■ Christian Chiropractors Association (CCA)

2550 Stover St., No. B-102
Fort Collins, CO 80525
Ph: (970)482-1404
Fax: (970)482-1538
Fr: 800-999-1970
URL: http://www.christianchiropractors.org

Description: Works to spread the Gospel of Christ throughout the U.S. and abroad. Offers Christian fellowship and works to unify Christian chiropractors around the essentials of the faith, "leaving minor points of doctrine to the conscience of the individual believer." Focuses on world missions; organizing short-term trips and aiding in the placement of Christian chiropractors as missionaries.

2110 ■ Council of Chiropractic Acupuncture

510 Baxter Rd., Ste. 8
Chesterfield, MO 63017
Ph: (636)207-6600
Fax: (636)207-6631
URL: http://councilofchiropracticacupuncture.org

Description: Aims to provide excellent educational opportunities to elevate the quality of care, life and practice of chiropractic acupuncture. Serves as a platform for professional communication regarding the practice of acupuncture in the chiropractic profession.

2111 ■ Council on Chiropractic Education (CCE)

8049 N 85th Way
Scottsdale, AZ 85258-4321
Ph: (480)443-8877
Fax: (480)483-7333
Fr: 888-443-3506
E-mail: cce@cce-usa.org
URL: http://www.cce-usa.org

Description: Advocates high standards in chiropractic education; establishes criteria of institutional excellence for educating chiropractic physicians; acts as national accrediting agency for chiropractic colleges. Conducts workshops for college teams, consultants, and chiropractic college staffs.

2112 ■ Council on Chiropractic Guidelines and Practice Parameters (CCGPP)

PO Box 2542
Lexington, SC 29071
Ph: (803)356-6809
Fax: (803)356-6826
E-mail: ccgpp@sc.rr.com
URL: http://www.ccgpp.org

Description: Advances the development, evaluation and dissemination of clinical practice guidelines and parameters for quality health-care improvement. Promotes the improvement of the quality of chiropractic services and of the professional reputation of doctors of chiropractic. Enhances the intellectual, academic and clinical integrity of chiropractic practice.

2113 ■ Council of Chiropractic Physiological Therapeutics and Rehabilitation (CCPT)

616 N Columbus St.
Lancaster, OH 43130
Ph: (740)653-2973
Fax: (740)653-3249
E-mail: rehabdc18@aol.com
URL: http://www.ccptr.org

Description: Represents chiropractors who use physiotherapy and rehabilitation in their practice and are dedicated to furthering the extended use of physiotherapy in the chiropractic field.

2114 ■ Council on Chiropractic Practice (CCP)

2950 N Dobson Rd., Ste. 1
Chandler, AZ 85224
E-mail: ccp@ccp-guidelines.org
URL: http://www.ccp-guidelines.org

Description: Strives to develop evidence-based guidelines, conduct research and perform other functions to enhance chiropractic practice for the benefit of the consumer. Provides practice guidelines which serve the needs of the consumer and are consistent with chiropractic practice.

2115 ■ Councils on Chiropractic Education International (CCEI)

PO Box 4943
Pocatello, ID 83205
Ph: (208)241-4855
E-mail: ccei@cceintl.org
URL: http://www.cceintl.org

Description: Represents chiropractic accrediting bodies worldwide. Promotes excellence in chiropractic education through emphasis on quality in International Chiropractic Accreditation Standards. Advocates quality education through the dissemination and promotion of information to governments, professional organizations and others.

2116 ■ Holistic Dental Association (HDA)

1825 Ponce de Leon Blvd., No. 148
Coral Gables, FL 33134
Ph: (305)356-7338
Fax: (305)468-6359
E-mail: director@holisticdental.org
URL: http://www.holisticdental.org

Description: Represents dentists, chiropractors, dental hygienists, physical therapists, and medical doctors. Aims to provide a holistic approach to better dental care for patients, and to expand techniques, medications, and philosophies that pertain to extractions, anesthetics, fillings, crowns, and orthodontics. Encourages the use of homeopathic medications, acupuncture, cranial osteopathy, nutritional techniques, and physical therapy in treating patients in addition to conventional treatments. Sponsors training and educational seminars.

2117 ■ International Chiropractors Association (ICA)
6400 Arlington Blvd., Ste. 800
Falls Church, VA 22042
Ph: (703)528-5000
Fax: (703)528-5023
Fr: 800-423-4690
E-mail: chiro@chiropractic.org
URL: http://www.chiropractic.org

Description: Serves as professional society of chiropractors, chiropractic educators, students, and laypersons. Sponsors professional development programs and practice management seminars.

2118 ■ Journey to Solidarity
301 Cottage Grove Ave. SE
Cedar Rapids, IA 52403
Fr: 888-860-9263
E-mail: jay@journeytosolidarity.org
URL: http://journeytosolidarity.org

Description: Seeks to improve the health and well-being of people in developing countries. Promotes chiropractic and wellness care as a profession and healing art to communities in need. Strives to grow the chiropractic profession by facilitating young students so they can get an education and return to their own countries.

2119 ■ Non-Profit Chiropractic Organization (NPCO)
601 Brady St., Ste. 201
Davenport, IA 52803

Ph: (708)459-8080
E-mail: info@npco.org
URL: http://www.npco.org

Description: Provides chiropractic healthcare services to people in underdeveloped countries. Seeks to educate the public about chiropractic through the implementation of various programs.

2120 ■ Professional Football Chiropractic (PFC)
PO Box 842
Sumner, WA 98390
Ph: (253)948-6039
Fax: (253)435-1053
E-mail: footballchiros@gmail.com
URL: http://www.profootballchiros.com

Description: Provides chiropractic health care to professional football athletes. Enhances the perception of chiropractic in sports and with the general public through education and communication. Initiates an understanding of chiropractic for athletes, coaches, administrative and healthcare staff.

SOURCES OF HELP-WANTED ADS

2121 ■ AIE Perspectives Newsmagazine
American Institute of Engineers
4630 Appian Way, Ste. 206
El Sobrante, CA 94803-1875
Ph: (510)758-6240
Fax: (510)758-6240
URL: http://www.members-aie.org

Monthly. Professional magazine covering engineering.

2122 ■ American City and County
Penton Media Inc.
9800 Metcalf Ave.
Overland Park, KS 66212
Ph: (913)341-1300
Fax: (913)967-1898
URL: http://americancityandcounty.com

Monthly. Municipal and county administration magazine.

2123 ■ ASCE News
American Society of Civil Engineers
1801 Alexander Bell Dr.
Reston, VA 20191
Ph: (703)295-6300
Fax: (703)295-6333
E-mail: contacts@mercommawards.com
URL: http://asce-news.asce.org

Description: Monthly. Reports on activities of the society and news of the civil engineering profession.

2124 ■ AWWA Streamlines
American Water Works Association
6666 W Quincy Ave.
Denver, CO 80235
Ph: (303)794-7711
Fax: (303)347-0804
Fr: 800-926-7337
E-mail: streamlines@awwa.org
URL: http://www.awwa.org/publications/
    streamlinescurrent.cfm

Description: Biweekly, online; print issue is quarterly. Carries news of the Association and features about the drinking water industry, including regulations, legislation, conservation, treatment, quality, distribution, management, and utility operations. Recurring features include letters to the editor, a calendar of events, reports of meetings, news of educational opportunities, notices of publications available, education and job opportunities in the industry and legislative news.

2125 ■ Better Roads
James Informational Media Inc.
2720 S River Rd.
Des Plaines, IL 60018-5142
Ph: (847)391-9070
Fax: (847)391-9058

Fr: 800-957-9305
URL: http://www.betterroads.com

Monthly. Free. Magazine serving federal, state, county, city, and township officials involved in road, street, bridge, and airport construction, maintenance and safety.

2126 ■ Civil Engineering
National Technical Information Service
5301 Shawnee Rd.
Alexandria, VA 22312
Ph: (703)605-6040
Fax: (703)605-6900
Fr: 800-553-6847
E-mail: customerservice@ntis.gov
URL: http://www.ntis.gov

Description: Biweekly. $255/year. Publishes abstracts with full bibliographic citations in the areas of highway engineering, civil engineering, soil and rock mechanics, flood control, and construction equipment, materials and supplies. Alerts readers to related published materials available from NTIS and other sources. Also available via e-mail.

2127 ■ Civil Engineering-ASCE
American Society of Civil Engineers (ASCE)
1801 Alexander Bell Dr.
Reston, VA 20191
Fr: 800-548-2723

Monthly. $230.00/year for institutions; $275.00/year for institutions, other countries; $230.00/year for individuals; $275.00/year for other countries; $30.00/year for members, domestic; $69.00/year for other countries, member; $30.00/year for students, member; domestic; $69.00/year for students, member; international. Professional magazine.

2128 ■ Consulting-Specifying Engineer
CFE Media LLC
1111 W 22nd St., Ste. 250
Oak Brook, IL 60523
Ph: (630)571-4070
Fax: (630)214-4504
URL: http://www.csemag.com

The integrated engineering magazine of the building construction industry.

2129 ■ Engineering
Scientific Research Publishing
PO Box 54821
Irvine, CA 92619-4821
E-mail: eng@scirp.org
URL: http://www.scirp.org/journal/eng/

Monthly. $708.00/year for individuals. Peer-reviewed journal publishing articles on the latest advancements in engineering.

**2130 ■ Engineering Conferences
    International Symposium Series**
Berkeley Electronic Press
2809 Telegraph Ave., Ste. 202
Berkeley, CA 94705-1167

Ph: (510)665-1200
Fax: (510)665-1201
URL: http://services.bepress.com/eci/

Journal focusing on advance engineering science.

2131 ■ ENR: Engineering News-Record
McGraw-Hill Inc.
PO Box 182604
Columbus, OH 43218
Ph: (614)430-4000
Fax: (614)759-3749
Fr: 877-833-5524
URL: http://enr.construction.com/Default.asp

Weekly. $49.00/year for individuals, print; $89.00/year for Canada, print; $125.00/year for other countries, print. Magazine focusing on engineering and construction.

**2132 ■ Graduating Engineer & Computer
    Careers**
Career Recruitment Media
2 LAN Dr., Ste. 100
Westford, MA 01886
Ph: (978)692-5092
Fax: (978)692-4174
URL: http://www.graduatingengineer.com

Quarterly. $16.95/year for individuals. Magazine focusing on employment, education, and career development for entry-level engineers and computer scientists.

2133 ■ High Technology Careers Magazine
HTC
4701 Patrick Henry Dr., No. 1901
Santa Clara, CA 95054
Fax: (408)567-0242
URL: http://www.hightechcareers.com

Bimonthly. $29.00/year; $35.00/year for Canada; $85.00/year for out of country. Magazine (tabloid) containing employment opportunity information for the engineering and technical community.

2134 ■ InterJournal
New England Complex Systems Institute
283 Main St., Ste. 319
Cambridge, MA 02142
Ph: (617)547-4100
Fax: (617)661-7711
URL: http://www.interjournal.org/

Journal covering the fields of science and engineering.

2135 ■ ISRN Civil Engineering
Hindawi Publishing Corporation
410 Park Ave., 15th Fl.
287 PMB
New York, NY 10022
E-mail: ce@isrn.com
URL: http://www.isrn.com/journals/ce

Peer-reviewed journal publishing research in all areas of civil engineering.

2136 ■ *ITE Journal*
Institute of Transportation Engineers
1099 14th St. NW, Ste. 300 W
Washington, DC 20005-3419
Ph: (202)289-0222
Fax: (202)289-7722
URL: http://www.ite.org/itejournal/

Monthly. $65.00/year for U.S., Canada, and Mexico; $85.00/year for other countries; $160.00/year for U.S., Canada, and Mexico, 3 years; $200.00/year for other countries, 3 years; $5.00/year for single issue, back issue. Technical magazine focusing on the plan, design, and operation of surface transportation systems.

2137 ■ *Journal of Engineering Education*
American Society for Engineering Education
1818 N St. NW, Ste. 600
Washington, DC 20036-2479
Ph: (202)331-3500
Fax: (202)265-8504
URL: http://www.jee.org

Quarterly. $100.00/year for libraries, online; $160.00/year for other countries, library; $150.00/year for U.S., Canada, and Mexico, library; $160.00/year for other countries, library. Peer-reviewed journal covering scholarly research in engineering education.

2138 ■ *Journal of Women and Minorities in Science and Engineering*
Begell House Inc.
50 Cross Hwy.
Redding, CT 06896
Ph: (203)938-1300
Fax: (203)938-1304
URL: http://www.begellhouse.com/journals/ 00551c876cc2f027

$248.00/year for institutions. Peer-reviewed journal featuring innovative ideas and programs for classroom teachers, scientific studies, and formulation of concepts related to the education, recruitment, and retention of under-represented groups in science and engineering.

2139 ■ *Masonry Magazine*
Mason Contractors Association of America
1481 Merchant Dr.
Algonquin, IL 60102
Ph: (224)678-9709
Fax: (224)678-9714
Fr: 800-536-2225
URL: http://www.masoncontractors.org

Monthly. $43.00/2 years; $29.00/year. Covers every aspect of the mason contractor profession, from equipment and techniques to building codes and standards, training the future masonry labor force, business planning, promoting business, job interviewing, negotiation and legal issues.

2140 ■ *The Military Engineer*
The Society of American Military Engineers
607 Prince St.
Alexandria, VA 22314-3117
Ph: (703)549-3800
Fax: (703)684-0231
URL: http://www.same.org/i4a/pages/ index.cfm?pageid=4273

Bimonthly. $88.00/year for U.S. and Canada, individuals, second class mail; $168.00/year for U.S. and Canada, two years; $222.00/year for U.S. and Canada, three years; $188.00/year for other countries, air mail, individuals; $358.00/year for other countries, two years, air mail; $458.00/year for other countries, three years, air mail; $22.00/year for students, U.S., Canada, and foreign (regular mail). Journal on military and civil engineering.

2141 ■ *Minority Engineer Magazine*
Employment Opportunity Publications
445 Broad Hollow Rd., Ste.
Melville, NY 11747
Ph: (631)421-9421

Fax: (631)421-1352
E-mail: info@eop.com
URL: http://www.eop.com/mags-ME.php

$18.00/year for non-minority engineering student or professional; $34.00/2 years for non-minority engineering student or professional; $49.00/3 years for non-minority engineering student or professional. Provides job listings, company profiles, and articles geared toward the engineering student and professional.

2142 ■ *The Municipality*
League of Wisconsin Municipalities
122 W Washington Ave., Ste. 300
Madison, WI 53703-2715
Ph: (608)267-2380
Fax: (608)267-0645
Fr: 800-991-5502
URL: http://www.lwm-info.org/

Monthly. Magazine for officials of Wisconsin's local municipal governments.

2143 ■ *NSBE Magazine*
NSBE Publications
205 Daingerfield Rd.
Alexandria, VA 22314
Ph: (703)549-2207
Fax: (703)683-5312
URL: http://www.nsbe.org/News-Media/Magazines/ About-NSBE-Magazine

$20.00/year for individuals; $35.00/year for other countries; $15.00/year for students. Journal providing information on engineering careers, self-development, and cultural issues for recent graduates with technical majors.

2144 ■ *PE*
National Society of Professional Engineers
1420 King St.
Alexandria, VA 22314
Ph: (703)684-2800
Fax: (703)684-4875
URL: http://www.nspe.org/PEmagazine/index.html

Monthly. Magazine (tabloid) covering professional, legislative, and techology issues for an engineering audience.

2145 ■ *Public Works*
Hanley Wood L.L.C.
1 Thomas Cir. NW, Ste. 600
Washington, DC 20005-5803
Ph: (202)452-0800
Fax: (202)785-1974
Fr: 877-275-8647
URL: http://www.pwmag.com

$60.00/year for individuals; $75.00/year for Canada; $90.00/year for other countries. Trade magazine covering the public works industry nationwide for city, county, and state.

2146 ■ *Roads & Bridges Magazine*
Scranton Gillette Communications Inc.
3030 W Salt Creek Ln., Ste. 201
Arlington Heights, IL 60005-5025
Ph: (847)391-1000
Fax: (847)390-0408
URL: http://www.roadsbridges.com

Monthly. Free to qualified subscribers. Magazine containing information on highway, road, and bridge design, construction, and maintenance for government agencies, contractors, and consulting engineers.

2147 ■ *SWE, Magazine of the Society of Women Engineers*
Society of Women Engineers
120 S La Salle St., Ste. 1515
Chicago, IL 60603
Ph: (312)596-5223
Fr: 877-793-4636
URL: http://societyofwomenengineers.swe.org/ index.php

Quarterly. $30.00/year for nonmembers. Magazine

for engineering students and for women and men working in the engineering and technology fields. Covers career guidance, continuing development and topical issues.

2148 ■ *WEPANEWS*
Women in Engineering Programs & Advocates Network
1901 E Asbury Ave., Ste. 220
Denver, CO 80208
Ph: (303)871-4643
Fax: (303)871-4628
E-mail: dmatt@wepan.org
URL: http://www.wepan.org

Description: 2/year. Seeks to provide greater access for women to careers in engineering. Includes news of graduate, undergraduate, freshmen, pre-college, and re-entry engineering programs for women. Recurring features include job listings, faculty, grant, and conference news, international engineering program news, action group news, notices of publications available, and a column titled Kudos.

2149 ■ *Western City*
League of California Cities
1400 K St., 4th Fl.
Sacramento, CA 95814
Ph: (916)658-8200
Fax: (916)658-8240
Fr: 800-262-1801
URL: http://www.westerncity.com

Monthly. $39.00/year for individuals; $63.00/year for two years; $52.00/year for other countries; $26.50/year for students. Municipal interest magazine.

2150 ■ *Woman Engineer*
Equal Opportunity Publications, Inc.
445 Broadhollow Rd., Ste. 425
Melville, NY 11747
Ph: (631)421-9421
Fax: (631)421-1352
E-mail: info@eop.com
URL: http://www.eop.com

Annual. Magazine that is offered at no charge to qualified female engineering, computer-science, and information-technology students and professionals seeking to find employment and advancement in their careers.

EMPLOYER DIRECTORIES AND NETWORKING LISTS

2151 ■ *American Men and Women of Science*
Gale
PO Box 6904
Florence, KY 41022-6904
Fr: 800-354-9706
URL: http://www.gale.cengage.com

Biennial, even years; New edition expected 29th, June 2011. $1,368.00 for individuals. Covers: Over 135,000 U.S. and Canadian scientists active in the physical, biological, mathematical, computer science, and engineering fields; includes references to previous edition for deceased scientists and nonrespondents. Entries include: Name, address, education, personal and career data, memberships, honors and awards, research interest. Arrangement: Alphabetical. Indexes: Discipline (in separate volume).

2152 ■ *Careers in Focus—Engineering*
Facts On File Inc.
132 W 31st St., 17th Fl.
New York, NY 10001
Ph: (212)967-8800
Fax: 800-678-3633
Fr: 800-322-8755
URL: http://www.infobasepublishing.com

Latest edition 3rd; Published July, 2007. $32.95 for

individuals. Covers: An overview of engineering, followed by a selection of jobs profiled in detail, including the nature of the job, earnings, prospects for employment, what kind of training and skills it requires, and sources for further information.

2153 ■ *Directory of Contract Staffing Firms*
C.E. Publications Inc.
PO Box 3006
Bothell, WA 98041-3006
Ph: (425)806-5200
Fax: (425)806-5585
URL: http://www.cjhunter.com/dcsf/overview.html

Annual. Covers: Nearly 1,300 contract firms actively engaged in the employment of engineering, IT/IS, and technical personnel for 'temporary' contract assignments throughout the world. Entries include: Company name, address, phone, name of contact, email, web address. Arrangement: Alphabetical. Indexes: Geographical.

2154 ■ *ENR—Top 500 Design Firms Issue*
McGraw-Hill Inc.
PO Box 182604
Columbus, OH 43218
Ph: (614)430-4000
Fax: (614)759-3749
Fr: 877-833-5524
URL: http://enr.construction.com/toplists/
    sourcebooks/2010/design

Annual, latest edition 2010. $82.00 for individuals. Publication includes: List of 500 leading architectural, engineering, and specialty design firms selected on basis of annual billings. Entries include: Company name, headquarters location, type of firm, current and prior year rank in billings, types of services, countries in which operated in preceding year. Arrangement: Ranked by billings.

2155 ■ *Indiana Society of Professional Engineers—Directory*
Indiana Society of Professional Engineers
PO Box 20806
Indianapolis, IN 46220
Ph: (317)255-2267
Fax: (317)255-2530
URL: http://www.indspe.org

Annual, fall. Covers: Member registered engineers, land surveyors, engineering students, and engineers in training. Entries include: Member name, address, phone, type of membership, business information, specialty. Arrangement: Alpha by chapter area.

Handbooks and Manuals

2156 ■ *Changing Our World: True Stories of Women Engineers*
American Society of Civil Engineers
1801 Alexander Bell Dr.
Reston, VA 20191-4400
Ph: (703)295-6300
Fax: (703)295-6222
Fr: 800-548-2723
URL: http://secure.asce.org/ASCEWebSite/
    BOOKSTORE/BookDescription.aspx?ProdId=5436

Sybil E. Hatch. 2006. $54.00. 232 pages.

2157 ■ *Civil Engineer's Handbook of Professional Practice*
John Wiley & Sons, Inc.
111 River St.
Hoboken, NJ 07030-5774
Ph: (201)748-6000
Fax: (201)748-6088
E-mail: info@wiley.com
URL: http://as.wiley.com/WileyCDA

Karen Hansen and Kent Zenobia. 2011. $134.95 (hardcover). 744 pages. Features quotes, techniques, case examples, problems and information that assist in addressing challenges faced by civil engineers. Focuses on business and management aspects of a civil engineer's job.

2158 ■ *Engineering, Mechanics, and Architecture*
Ferguson Publishing
132 W 31st St., 17th Fl.
New York, NY 10001
Fax: 800-678-3633
Fr: 800-322-8755
E-mail: custserv@factsonfile.com
URL: http://www.infobasepublishing.com

Kelly Wiles. 2010. $39.95. 160 pages (hardcover). Serves as a guide for readers interested in switching jobs. Contains useful advice, career tips, interviews and self-asessment questions.

2159 ■ *Expert Resumes for Engineers*
JIST Publishing
875 Montreal Way
St. Paul, MN 55102
Fr: 800-648-5478
E-mail: educate@emcp.com
URL: http://www.jist.com

Louise M. Kursmark and Wendy S. Enelow. 2009. $16.95 (softcover). 272 pages. Features a collection of written resume samples for all types of engineers including civil, mechanical, industrial, electrical, electronics, computer, and more. Contains tips and strategies for writing engineering resumes and finding the best jobs.

2160 ■ *Great Jobs for Engineering Majors*
The McGraw-Hill Companies
PO Box 182604
Columbus, OH 43272
Fax: (614)759-3749
Fr: 877-883-5524
E-mail: customer.service@mcgraw-hill.com
URL: http://www.mhprofessional.com/
    product.php?isbn=0071641963

Geraldine O. Garner. Second edition, 2008. $16.95. 192 pages. Covers all the career options open to students majoring in engineering.

2161 ■ *Preparing for Design-Build Projects: A Primer for Owners, Engineers, and Contractors*
American Society of Civil Engineers
1801 Alexander Bell Dr.
Reston, VA 20191-4400
Ph: (703)295-6300
Fax: (703)295-6222
Fr: 800-548-2723
URL: http://secure.asce.org/ASCEWebSite/
    BOOKSTORE/BookDescription.aspx?ProdId=5427

Douglas D. Gransberg, James E. Koch and Keith R. Molenaar. 2006. $64.00. 296 pages.

2162 ■ *Resumes for Scientific and Technical Careers*
The McGraw-Hill Companies
PO Box 182604
Columbus, OH 43272
Fax: (614)759-3749
Fr: 877-883-5524
E-mail: customer.service@mcgraw-hill.com
URL: http://www.mhprofessional.com/
    product.php?isbn=0071482199

Third edition, 2007. $12.95 (paper). 144 pages. Provides resume advice for individuals interested in working in scientific and technical careers. Includes sample resumes and cover letters.

Employment Agencies and Search Firms

2163 ■ Civil Search International
324 S Bracken Ln., Ste. 2
Chandler, AZ 85224
Ph: (480)820-8663
Fax: (480)820-8709
Fr: 800-737-8182
URL: http://www.csijobs.com

Executive recruiting firm that specializes in the placement of civil engineers. Additional services include preparation of job orders as well as reviewing of prospective candidates.

2164 ■ Claremont-Branan, Inc.
1298 Rockbridge Rd., Ste. B
Stone Mountain, GA 30087
Fr: 800-875-1292
URL: http://cbisearch.com

Employment agency. Executive search firm.

2165 ■ Engineer One, Inc.
PO Box 23037
Knoxville, TN 37933
Fax: (865)691-0110
E-mail: engineerone@engineerone.com
URL: http://www.engineerone.com

Engineering employment service specializing in engineering and management in the chemical process, power utilities, manufacturing, mechanical, electrical, and electronics industries. Maintains an Information Technology Division that works nationwide across all industries. Also provides systems analysis consulting services specializing in VAX based systems.

2166 ■ ENTEGEE
70 Blanchard Rd., Ste. 102
Burlington, MA 01803
Fr: 800-368-3433
E-mail: corporate@entegee.com
URL: http://www.entegee.com

Specializes in recruiting experienced professionals in the engineering and technical industries. Features a searchable database of employment opportunities in the engineering and technical fields.

2167 ■ Global Employment Solutions
10375 Park Meadows Dr., Ste. 375
Littleton, CO 80124
Ph: (303)216-9500
Fax: (303)216-9533
URL: http://www.gesnetwork.com

Employment agency.

2168 ■ International Staffing Consultants
31655 2nd Ave.
Laguna Beach, CA 92651
Ph: (949)255-5857
Fax: (949)767-5959
E-mail: iscinc@iscworld.com
URL: http://www.iscworld.com

Employment agency. Provides placement on regular or temporary basis. Affiliate office in London.

2169 ■ Metzner Group
10130 Harmony Rd.
Myersville, MD 21773
Ph: (301)293-4206
URL: http://www.themetznergroup.com

Specializes in the recruitment of architects, civil engineers, environmental engineers and planners for the A/E/P communities.

2170 ■ Precision Executive Search
977 E Schuylkill Rd., Ste. 201
Pottstown, PA 19465
Ph: (610)704-4942
E-mail: mbarcus@precision-recruiters.com
URL: http://precision-recruiters.com

Executive search firm specializing in the civil engineering, surveying, planning, and landscape architecture industries.

2171 ■ Principal Resource Group
313 Railroad Ave., Ste. 203
Nevada City, CA 95959
Ph: (530)478-6478
Fax: (530)478-6477
E-mail: pat@prgnc.com
URL: http://www.prgnc.com

Executive recruiting firm dedicated to the engineering community. Specializes in various disciplines in civil engineering. Provides personalized and confidential services to professionals with all levels of experience in the civil engineering and technology industries.

2172 ■ Recruiting Partners
3494 Camino Tassajara Rd., No. 404
Danville, CA 94506
Ph: (925)964-0249
E-mail: info@recruitingpartners.com
URL: http://www.recruitingpartners.com

Description: Serves as an executive and technical recruiting firm that specializes in accounting, legal, information technology, engineering, executive management and technical writing.

2173 ■ TRS Staffing Solutions USA
3 Polaris Way
Aliso Viejo, CA 92656
Ph: (949)349-3630
Fax: (949)349-7196
Fr: 800-248-8774
E-mail: info-av@trsstaffing.com
URL: http://www.trsstaffing.com/us

Specializes in engineering recruitment. Maintains a pool of experienced technical, engineering and professional services personnel.

ONLINE JOB SOURCES AND SERVICES

2174 ■ AEJob.com
E-mail: customerservice@aejob.com
URL: http://aejob.com

Description: Provides lists of architectural jobs, engineering jobs and environmental consulting jobs nationwide.

2175 ■ CivilEngineeringCentral.com
URL: http://www.civilengineeringcentral.com

Description: Serves as niche for job board and resume database devoted exclusively to the civil engineering community-from the professionals who visit the site, to the companies, agencies or job recruiters who advertise job opportunities on the site. Offers unique opportunity to reach premier civil engineering professionals without the waste.

2176 ■ CivilEngineeringCrossing.com
URL: http://www.civilengineeringcrossing.com

Description: Locates jobs inside user's niche, conducting a more streamlined job search. Provides instant access to a comprehensive pool of listings based on particular area of focus.

2177 ■ CivilEngineeringJobs.com
URL: http://www.civilengineeringjobs.com/index.htm

Description: Provides job listings, employment information and career resources for civil engineers. Offers help with all civil engineering disciplines including water resources, environmental, research, and others.

2178 ■ CivilEngineerJobSource.com
URL: http://www.civilengineerjobsource.com

Description: Provides direct links to job and career sections of civil engineering firms throughout the United States.

2179 ■ CivilEngineerUSA.com
URL: http://www.civilengineerusa.com

Description: Serves as a career site for civil engineering professionals. Provides listings of jobs, career opportunities, and products to civil engineers and resources for both job seekers and employers.

2180 ■ ConstructionJobs.com
URL: http://www.constructionjobs.com/index_eng.cfm

Description: Serves as an employment job board and resume database built exclusively for the con-struction, design, and building industries. Provides targeted candidate searches by geographic region, specific industries, job titles, education, and experience.

2181 ■ EnergyCentralJobs.com
E-mail: service@energycentral.com
URL: http://www.energycentraljobs.com

Description: Serves as an on-line job resource for candidates and power companies worldwide. Maintains a job search database dedicated to the power, nuclear, oil and gas career fields.

2182 ■ EngineerJobs.com
URL: http://www.engineerjobs.com

Description: Provides job opportunities for engineering professionals in the following disciplines: aerospace, agricultural, biomedical, chemical, civil, electrical, environmental, industrial, manufacturing, marine, materials, mechanical, mining, nuclear, petroleum, process, project, quality, sales, software, solar, systems, and structural.

2183 ■ iCivilEngineer.com
URL: http://www.icivilengineer.com

Description: Serves as a portal for civil engineering professionals and students. Offers civil engineering news, resources, and career center.

2184 ■ PowerPlantPro.com
E-mail: support@powerplantpro.com
URL: http://www.powerplantpro.com/main/sendform/4/18/3472

Description: Dedicated to professionals in the power and energy industry. Features career advice and employer listings.

2185 ■ Spherion
2050 Spectrum Blvd.
Fort Lauderdale, FL 33309
Ph: (954)308-7600
Fr: 800-774-3746
E-mail: help@spherion.com
URL: http://www.spherion.com

Description: Recruitment firm specializing in accounting and finance, sales and marketing, interim executives, technology, engineering, retail and human resources.

2186 ■ ThinkEnergyGroup.com
E-mail: resumes@thinkjobs.com
URL: http://www.thinkenergygroup.com

Description: Serves as a job board for professionals looking for positions in engineering, power plant, energy, and technical fields. Contains advice and tips on interviews, job searching, resume writing, hiring, and management. Provides choices of work location, pay rates in the field of expertise and contract, temp-to-hire, and direct hiring options.

TRADESHOWS

2187 ■ Structures Congress
American Society of Civil Engineers
1801 Alexander Bell Dr.
Reston, VA 20191-4400
Ph: (703)295-6300
Fr: 800-548-2723
URL: http://www.asce.org

Description: Annual. Primary Exhibits: Civil engineering equipment, supplies, and services, including practical design information, landmark bridges, disproportionate collapse, performance-based design, wind design, codes and standards, business and international engineering.

OTHER SOURCES

2188 ■ Acoustical Society of America
2 Huntington Quadrangle, Ste. 1NO1
Melville, NY 11747-4502
Ph: (516)576-2360
Fax: (516)576-2377
E-mail: asa@aip.org
URL: http://acousticalsociety.org

Description: Represents members from various fields related to sound including physics, electrical, mechanical and aeronautical engineering, oceanography, biology, physiology, psychology, architecture, speech, noise and noise control, and music. Aims to increase and diffuse the knowledge of acoustics and its practical applications. Organizes meetings, provides reprints of out-of-print classic texts in acoustics, and translation books.

2189 ■ American Academy of Environmental Engineers (AAEE)
130 Holiday Ct., Ste. 100
Annapolis, MD 21401
Ph: (410)266-3311
Fax: (410)266-7653
E-mail: info@aaee.net
URL: http://www.aaee.net

Description: Environmentally oriented registered professional engineers certified by examination as Diplomates of the Academy. Seeks to improve the standards of environmental engineering. Certifies those with special knowledge of environmental engineering. Furnishes lists of those certified to the public. Maintains speakers' bureau. Recognizes areas of specialization: Air Pollution Control; General Environmental; Hazardous Waste Management; Industrial Hygiene; Radiation Protection; Solid Waste Management; Water Supply and Wastewater. Requires written and oral examinations for certification. Works with other professional organizations on environmentally oriented activities. Identifies potential employment candidates through Talent Search Service.

2190 ■ American Association of Blacks in Energy (AABE)
1625 K St. NW, Ste. 405
Washington, DC 20006
Ph: (202)371-9530
Fax: (202)371-9218
Fr: 800-466-0204
E-mail: info@aabe.org
URL: http://www.aabe.org

Description: Seeks to increase the knowledge, understanding, and awareness of the minority community in energy issues by serving as an energy information source for policymakers, recommending blacks and other minorities to appropriate energy officials and executives, encouraging students to pursue professional careers in the energy industry, and advocating the participation of blacks and other minorities in energy programs and policymaking activities. Updates members on key legislation and regulations being developed by the Department of Energy, the Department of Interior, the Department of Commerce, the Small Business Administration, and other federal and state agencies.

2191 ■ American Association of Engineering Societies (AAES)
1801 Alexander Bell Dr.
Reston, VA 20191
Ph: (202)296-2237
Fax: (202)296-1151
Fr: 888-400-2237
E-mail: dbateson@aaes.org
URL: http://www.aaes.org

Description: Coordinates the efforts of the member societies in the provision of reliable and objective information to the general public concerning issues which affect the engineering profession and the field of engineering as a whole; collects, analyzes, documents, and disseminates data which will inform the general public of the relationship between engineering and the national welfare; provides a forum for the engineering societies to exchange and discuss their views on matters of common interest; and represents the U.S. engineering community abroad through representation in WFEO and UPADI.

2192 ■ American Concrete Institute
PO Box 9094
Farmington Hills, MI 48333-9094
Ph: (248)848-3700
Fax: (248)848-3701
URL: http://www.concrete.org

Description: Comprised of engineers, architects, contractors, educators, and others interested in improving techniques of design construction and maintenance of concrete products and structures. Advances engineering and technical education, scientific investigation and research, and development of standards for design and construction incorporating concrete and related materials. Gathers, correlates, and disseminates information for the improvement of the design, construction, manufacture, use and maintenance of concrete products and structures.

2193 ■ American Engineering Association (AEA)
533 Waterside Blvd.
Monroe Township, NJ 08831
Ph: (201)664-6954
E-mail: aea@aea.org
URL: http://www.aea.org

Description: Members consist of Engineers and engineering professionals. Purpose to advance the engineering profession and U.S. engineering capabilities. Issues of concern include age discrimination, immigration laws, displacement of U.S. Engineers by foreign workers, trade agreements, off shoring of U.S. Engineering and manufacturing jobs, loss of U.S. manufacturing and engineering capability, and recruitment of foreign students. Testifies before Congress. Holds local Chapter meetings.

2194 ■ American Indian Science and Engineering Society (AISES)
PO Box 9828
Albuquerque, NM 87119-9828
Ph: (505)765-1052
Fax: (505)765-5608
E-mail: info@aises.org
URL: http://www.aises.org

Description: Represents American Indian and non-Indian students and professionals in science, technology, and engineering fields; corporations representing energy, mining, aerospace, electronic, and computer fields. Seeks to motivate and encourage students to pursue undergraduate and graduate studies in science, engineering, and technology. Sponsors science fairs in grade schools, teacher training workshops, summer math/science sessions for 8th-12th graders, professional chapters, and student chapters in colleges. Offers scholarships. Adult members serve as role models, advisers, and mentors for students. Operates placement service.

2195 ■ American Road & Transportation Builders Association
1219 28th St., NW
Washington, DC 20007-3389
Ph: (202)289-4434
Fax: (202)289-4435
E-mail: general@artba.org
URL: http://www.artba.org

Description: Advances the interests of the transportation construction industry. Promotes the growth and protection of transportation infrastructure investment to meet the public and business demand for safe and efficient travel. Works to ensure its members' views and business concerns are addressed before Congress, the White House, federal agencies and news media.

2196 ■ American Society of Civil Engineers (ASCE)
1801 Alexander Bell Dr.
Reston, VA 20191-4400
Ph: (703)295-6300
Fax: (703)295-6333

Fr: 800-548-2723
E-mail: pnatale@asce.org
URL: http://www.asce.org

Description: Enhances the welfare of humanity by advancing the science and profession of engineering. Offers continuing education courses and technical specialty conferences. Develops technical codes and standards. Works closely with Congress, the White House and federal agencies to build sound national policy on engineering issues. Supports research of new civil engineering technology and material. Informs the public about various engineering-related topics.

2197 ■ American Water Works Association (AWWA)
6666 W Quincy Ave.
Denver, CO 80235-3098
Ph: (303)794-7711
Fax: (303)347-0804
Fr: 800-926-7337
E-mail: custsvc@awwa.org
URL: http://www.awwa.org

Description: Water utility managers, superintendents, engineers, chemists, bacteriologists, and other individuals interested in public water supply; municipal- and investor-owned water departments; boards of health; manufacturers of waterworks equipment; government officials and consultants interested in water supply. Develops standards and supports research programs in waterworks design, construction, operation, and management. Conducts in-service training schools and prepares manuals for waterworks personnel. Maintains hall of fame. Offers placement service via member newsletter; compiles statistics. Offers training; children's services; and information center on the water utilities industry, potable water, and water reuse.

2198 ■ Asian American Architects and Engineers (AAAE)
1167 Mission St., 4th Fl.
San Francisco, CA 94103
Ph: (415)552-1118
E-mail: info@aaaenc.org
URL: http://www.aaaenc.org

Description: Minorities. Provides contracts and job opportunities for minorities in the architectural and engineering fields. Serves as a network for the promotion in professional fields.

2199 ■ Association for International Practical Training (AIPT)
10400 Little Patuxent Pkwy., Ste. 250
Columbia, MD 21044-3519
Ph: (410)997-2200
Fax: (410)992-3924
E-mail: aipt@aipt.org
URL: http://www.aipt.org

Description: Providers worldwide of on-the-job training programs for students and professionals seeking international career development and life-changing experiences. Arranges workplace exchanges in hundreds of professional fields, bringing employers and trainees together from around the world. Client list ranges from small farming communities to Fortune 500 companies.

2200 ■ Engineering Society of Detroit (ESD)
20700 Civic Center Dr., Ste. 450
Southfield, MI 48076
Ph: (248)353-0735
Fax: (248)353-0736
E-mail: esd@esd.org
URL: http://ww2.esd.org/home.htm

Description: Engineers from all disciplines; scientists and technologists. Conducts technical programs and engineering refresher courses; sponsors conferences and expositions. Maintains speakers' bureau; offers placement services; although based in Detroit, MI, society membership is international.

2201 ■ Intelligent Transportation Society of America
1100 17th St. NW, Ste. 1200
Washington, DC 20036
Ph: (202)484-4847
Fr: 800-374-8472
E-mail: info@itsa.org
URL: http://www.itsa.org

Description: Includes private corporations, public agencies, and academic institutions involved in the research, development, and design of intelligent transportation systems technologies that enhance safety, increase mobility, and sustain the environment.

2202 ■ Korean-American Scientists and Engineers Association (KSEA)
1952 Gallows Rd., Ste. 300
Vienna, VA 22182
Ph: (703)748-1221
Fax: (703)748-1331
E-mail: sejong@ksea.org
URL: http://www.ksea.org

Description: Represents scientists and engineers holding single or advanced degrees. Promotes friendship and mutuality among Korean and American scientists and engineers; contributes to Korea's scientific, technological, industrial, and economic developments; strengthens the scientific, technological, and cultural bonds between Korea and the U.S. Sponsors symposium. Maintains speakers' bureau, placement service, and biographical archives. Compiles statistics.

2203 ■ National Action Council for Minorities in Engineering (NACME)
440 Hamilton Ave., Ste. 302
White Plains, NY 10601-1813
Ph: (914)539-4010
Fax: (914)539-4032
E-mail: info@nacme.org
URL: http://www.nacme.org

Description: Leads the national effort to increase access to careers in engineering and other science-based disciplines. Conducts research and public policy analysis, develops and operates national demonstration programs at precollege and university levels, and disseminates information through publications, conferences and electronic media. Serves as a privately funded source of scholarships for minority students in engineering.

2204 ■ National Association of Traffic Accident Reconstructionists and Investigators (NATARI)
PO Box 2588
West Chester, PA 19382
Ph: (610)696-1919
E-mail: natari@natari.org
URL: http://www.natari.org

Description: Represents engineers, attorneys, police officers, private investigators, medical examiners, and other individuals involved in the analysis of motor vehicle traffic accidents. Gathers and disseminates information on techniques and equipment of potential use to members; reviews literature in the field. Participating Organization of the Accreditation Commission for Traffic Accident Reconstruction.

2205 ■ Society of Hispanic Professional Engineers (SHPE)
13181 Crossroads Pkwy. N, Ste. 450
City of Industry, CA 91746-3496
Ph: (323)725-3970
Fax: (323)725-0316
E-mail: shpenational@shpe.org
URL: http://oneshpe.shpe.org/wps/portal/national

Description: Represents engineers, student engineers, and scientists. Aims to increase the number of Hispanic engineers by providing motivation and support to students. Sponsors competitions and educational programs. Maintains placement service and speakers' bureau; compiles statistics.

2206 ■ Society of Women Engineers (SWE)
203 N La Salle St., Ste. 1675
Chicago, IL 60601
Ph: (312)596-5223
Fax: (312)596-5252
Fr: 877-SWE-INFO
E-mail: hq@swe.org
URL: http://societyofwomenengineers.swe.org

Description: Educational and service organization representing both students and professional women in engineering and technical fields.

2207 ■ Water Environment Federation (WEF)
601 Wythe St.
Alexandria, VA 22314-1994
Ph: (703)684-2400
Fax: (703)684-2492
Fr: 800-666-0206
E-mail: jeger@wef.org
URL: http://www.wef.org

Description: Technical societies representing chemists, biologists, ecologists, geologists, operators, educational and research personnel, industrial wastewater engineers, consultant engineers, municipal officials, equipment manufacturers, and university professors and students dedicated to the enhancement and preservation of water quality and resources. Seeks to advance fundamental and practical knowledge concerning the nature, collection, treatment, and disposal of domestic and industrial wastewaters, and the design, construction, operation, and management of facilities for these purposes. Disseminates technical information; and promotes good public relations and regulations that improve water quality and the status of individuals working in this field. Conducts educational and research programs.

Claims Examiners

SOURCES OF HELP-WANTED ADS

2208 ▪ *Best's Review*
A.M. Best Company, Inc.
Ambest Rd.
Oldwick, NJ 08858
Ph: (908)439-2200
URL: http://www.ambest.com/sales/
newsoverview.asp#br
Monthly. $50.00/year for individuals. Magazine covering issues and trends for the management personnel of life/health insurers, the agents, and brokers who market their products.

2209 ▪ *Business Insurance*
Crain Communications Inc.
1155 Gratiot Ave.
Detroit, MI 48207-2997
Ph: (313)446-6000
URL: http://www.businessinsurance.com
Weekly. $399.00/year for individuals, print; $149.00/year for individuals, print & digital; $69.00/year for individuals, digital edition. International newsweekly reporting on corporate risk and employee benefit management news.

2210 ▪ *Claims*
Claims
15112 64th Ave. W
Edmonds, WA 98026
Ph: (425)745-6394
URL: http://www.propertycasualty360.com/Claims-Magazine
Monthly. $72.00/year for individuals; $93.00/year for Canada; $131.00/year for other countries. Magazine for the property-casualty insurance claims industry.

2211 ▪ *National Underwriter Property and Casualty/Risk and Benefits Management*
National Underwriter Co.
5081 Olympic Blvd.
PO Box 14367
Erlanger, KY 41018
Ph: (859)692-2100
Fax: (859)692-2175
Fr: 800-543-0874
URL: http://www.propertycasualty360.com/National-Underwriter-Prop
Weekly. $94.00/year for individuals, 2nd class; $133.00/year for Canada, air mail; $178.00/year for U.S. and Canada, air mail; $211.00/year for other countries, air mail. Newsweekly for agents, brokers, executives, and managers in risk and benefit insurance.

EMPLOYER DIRECTORIES AND NETWORKING LISTS

2212 ▪ *Best's Insurance Reports*
A.M. Best Co.
Ambest Rd.
Oldwick, NJ 08858

Ph: (908)439-2200
URL: http://www.ambest.com
Annual, Latest edition 2011. Published in three editions—Life-health insurance, covering about 1,750 companies, property-casualty insurance, covering over 3,200 companies; and international, covering more than 1,200 insurers. Each edition lists state insurance commissioners and related companies and agencies (mutual funds, worker compensation funds, underwriting agencies, etc.). Entries include: For each company—Company name, address, phone; history; states in which licensed; names of officers and directors; financial data; financial analysis and Best's rating. Arrangement: Alphabetical.

2213 ▪ *Business Insurance—Third-Party Claims Administrators Issue*
Business Insurance
360 N Michigan Ave.
Chicago, IL 60601-3806
Ph: (312)649-5200
Fax: (312)280-3174
Fr: 888-446-1422
URL: http://businessinsurance.datajoe.com/app/
ecom/pub_products.p
Annual, Latest edition 2009. Publication includes: List of approximately 150 third-party claims administration, adjusting, and auditing firms that process claims for self-insured clients, including employee benefit- and property/casualty claims. Entries include: Company name, address, phone, fax, number of employees, number of claims processing staff, number of clients, method of compensation, prior year's revenues (when available), along with percent attributed to claims administration, adjusting and auditing for self-insured clients; claims volume by number of projects conducted; specialty or area of expertise. Arrangement: Alphabetical by company.

2214 ▪ *Insurance Phone Book*
Briefings Media Group
2807 N Parham Rd., Ste. 200
Richmond, VA 23294
Ph: (570)567-1982
Fr: 800-791-8699
URL: http://www.douglaspublications.com
Annual, latest edition 2009-2010. $195.00; $389.00. Covers: About 3,700 life, accident and health, worker's compensation, auto, fire and casualty, marine, surety, and other insurance companies; 2,300 executive contacts from presidents and CEOs to claims and customer service managers. Entries include: Company name, address, phone, fax, toll-free number, type of insurance provided. Arrangement: Alphabetical.

2215 ▪ *Kirschner's Insurance Directories*
National Underwriter Co.
5081 Olympic Blvd.
PO Box 14367
Erlanger, KY 41018
Ph: (859)692-2100
Fax: (859)692-2175

Fr: 800-543-0874
URL: http://www.nationalunderwriter.com
Annual, Latest edition 2007. Covers: Insurance agents and agencies in all 50 states and the District of Columbia. Published in 24 separate editions for Southern California, Northern California, Pacific Northwest (AK, ID, HI, OR, WA, MT), Michigan, Illinois, New England states (CT, ME, MA, NH, RI, VT), Ohio, Rocky Mountain states (AZ, CO, NV, NM, UT, WY), South Central states (GA, AL, MS), Indiana, Texas, Kentucky/Tennessee, East Central states (VA, WV, NC, SC), South Central West states (AR, OK, LA), Wisconsin, Central states (KS, MO, NE), North Central states (IA, MN, ND, SD), Mid-Atlantic states (DE, MD, NJ, DC), Pennsylvania, Florida. Entries include: For companies—Name, address, key personnel (with addresses and phone numbers). Arrangement: Separate alphabetical sections for insurance companies, wholesalers, field agents, and agencies. Indexes: Type of insurance.

2216 ▪ *Mergent Bank and Finance Manual*
Mergent Inc.
580 Kingsley Park Dr.
Fort Mill, SC 29715
Ph: (704)527-2700
Fax: (704)559-6837
Fr: 800-937-1398
URL: http://www.mergent.com
Annual, July; supplements in 'Mergent Bank & Finance News Reports'. $2,095.00. Covers: In four volumes, over 12,000 national, state, and private banks, savings and loans, mutual funds, unit investment trusts, and insurance and real estate companies in the United States. Entries include: Company name, headquarters and branch offices, phones, names and titles of principal executives, directors, history, Moody's rating, and extensive financial and statistical data. Arrangement: Classified by type of business. Indexes: Company name.

2217 ▪ *National Association of Catastrophe Adjusters—Membership Roster*
National Association of Catastrophe Adjusters Inc.
5217 Cloyce Ct.
PO Box 821864
Fort Worth, TX 76180-6747
Ph: (817)498-3466
Fax: (817)498-0480
URL: http://www.nacatadj.org
Annual, March; latest edition 2006-2007. Covers: About 400 insurance catastrophe claims adjusters and adjusting firms; about 150 related insurance firms (associate members). Entries include: Name, address, phone, spouse's name. Arrangement: Separate geographical sections for regular associate and business associate members. Indexes: Alphabetical; geographical.

2218 ▪ *Yearbook*
American Association of Managing General Agents
150 S Warner Rd., Ste. 156
King of Prussia, PA 19406

Ph: (610)225-1999
Fax: (610)225-1996
URL: http://www.aamga.org

Annual, Latest edition 2006. Covers: 250 managing general agents of insurance companies and their more than 500 branch offices; coverage includes Canada. Entries include: Name, address, names and titles of principal and contact, insurance companies represented. Arrangement: Geographical.

HANDBOOKS AND MANUALS

2219 ■ Associate Claim Examiner
National Learning Corporation
212 Michael Dr.
Syosset, NY 11791
Fr: 800-632-8888
URL: http://www.passbooks.com

2009. $29.95 (paper). Serves as an exam preparation guide for associate claim examiners.

2220 ■ Opportunities in Insurance Careers
The McGraw-Hill Companies
PO Box 182604
Columbus, OH 43272
Fax: (614)759-3749
Fr: 877-883-5524
E-mail: customer.service@mcgraw-hill.com
URL: http://www.mhprofessional.com/
   product.php?isbn=0071482075

Robert M. Schrayer. Revised, 2007. $14.95 (paper). 160 pages. A guide to planning for and seeking opportunities in the field. Contains bibliography and illustrations.

EMPLOYMENT AGENCIES AND SEARCH FIRMS

2221 ■ International Insurance Personnel, Inc.
300 W Wieuca Rd., Bldg. 2, Ste. 101
Atlanta, GA 30342

Ph: (404)255-9710
Fax: (404)255-9864
E-mail: iipjulie@bellsouth.net
URL: http://realpages.com/sites/intlinspersonnel/
   index.html

Employment agency specializing in the area of insurance.

2222 ■ Lear & Associates, Inc.
1235 N Orange Ave.
Orlando, FL 32804
Ph: (407)645-4611
Fax: (407)645-5735
E-mail: info@learsearch.com
URL: http://www.learsearch.com

Serves as recruitment firm specializing in the insurance industry.

2223 ■ Questor Consultants, Inc.
2515 N Broad St.
Colmar, PA 18915
Ph: (215)997-9262
Fax: (215)997-9226
E-mail: sbevivino@questorconsultants.com
URL: http://www.questorconsultants.com

Executive search firm specializing in the insurance and legal fields.

OTHER SOURCES

2224 ■ Insurance Information Institute (III)
110 William St.
New York, NY 10038
Ph: (212)346-5500
E-mail: members@iii.org
URL: http://www.iii.org

Description: Property and casualty insurance companies. Provides information and educational services to mass media, educational institutions, trade associations, businesses, government agencies, and the public.

2225 ■ LOMA
2300 Windy Ridge Pkwy., Ste. 600
Atlanta, GA 30339-8443

Ph: (770)951-1770
Fax: (770)984-0441
Fr: 800-275-5662
E-mail: askloma@loma.org
URL: http://www.loma.org

Description: Life and health insurance companies and financial services in the U.S. and Canada; and overseas in 45 countries; affiliate members are firms that provide professional support to member companies. Provides research, information, training, and educational activities in areas of operations and systems, human resources, financial planning and employee development. Administers FLMI Insurance Education Program, which awards FLMI (Fellow, Life Management Institute) designation to those who complete the ten-examination program.

2226 ■ National Association of Insurance Women International (NAIW)
9343 E 95th Ct. S
Tulsa, OK 74133
Ph: (918)294-3700
Fax: (918)294-3711
Fr: 800-766-6249
E-mail: joinnaiw@naiw.org
URL: http://www.naiw.org

Description: Insurance industry professionals. Promotes continuing education and networking for the professional advancement of its members. Offers education programs, meetings, services, and leadership opportunities. Provides a forum to learn about other disciplines in the insurance industry.

2227 ■ National Association of Public Insurance Adjusters (NAPIA)
21165 Whitfield Pl., No. 105
Potomac Falls, VA 20165
Ph: (703)433-9217
Fax: (703)433-0369
E-mail: info@napia.com
URL: http://www.napia.com

Description: Professional society of public insurance adjusters. Sponsors certification and professional education programs.

Clinical Laboratory Technologists and Technicians

SOURCES OF HELP-WANTED ADS

2228 ■ ACTA Cytologica
Science Printers and Publishers Inc.
8342 Olive Blvd.
St. Louis, MO 63132-2814
Ph: (314)991-4440
Fax: (314)991-4654
E-mail: editor@acta-cytol.com
URL: http://www.acta-cytol.com

Bimonthly. $380.00/year for individuals, print & online; $480.00/year for other countries, print & online; $755.00/year for institutions, print & online; $855.00/year for institutions, other countries, print & online. Journal publishing scientific articles offering significant contributions to the advancement of clinical cytology.

2229 ■ ADVANCE for Medical Laboratory Professionals
Merion Publications Inc.
2900 Horizon Dr.
PO Box 61556
King of Prussia, PA 19406-0956
Ph: (610)278-1400
Fr: 800-355-5627
E-mail: advance@merion.com
URL: http://laboratorian.advanceweb.com/Default.aspx

Biweekly. Free. Magazine that reaches technologists and laboratory managers with professional news and employment opportunities.

2230 ■ Advances in Bioscience and Biotechnology
Scientific Research Publishing
PO Box 54821
Irvine, CA 92619-4821
E-mail: abb@scirp.org
URL: http://www.scirp.org/journal/abb/

Peer-reviewed journal publishing the latest advancements in biosciences.

2231 ■ American Laboratory News
American Laboratory/Labcompare
30 Controls Dr.
Shelton, CT 06484-0870
Ph: (203)926-9300
Fax: (203)926-9310
URL: http://www.americanlaboratory.com

Monthly. Trade magazine for scientists.

2232 ■ ASPB News
American Society of Plant Biologists
15501 Monona Dr.
Rockville, MD 20855-2768
Ph: (301)251-0560
Fax: (301)279-2996
E-mail: info@aspb.org
URL: http://www.aspb.org/newsletter

Description: Bimonthly. $30/year for nonmember.

Offers news of interest to plant physiologists, biochemists, horticulturists, and plant molecular and cell biologists engaged in research and teaching. Alerts members to public policy issues, educational opportunities, meetings, seminars, and conventions pertinent to the field. Recurring features include letters to the editor, reports of meetings, job listings, a calendar of events, news from regional sections, and teaching ideas.

2233 ■ Brain Connectivity
Mary Ann Liebert Inc., Publishers
140 Huguenot St., 3rd Fl.
New Rochelle, NY 10801-5215
Ph: (914)740-2100
Fax: (914)740-2101
Fr: 800-654-3237
URL: http://www.liebertpub.com/products/product.aspx?pid=389

Bimonthly. Peer-reviewed journal publishing research on neurological disorders.

2234 ■ CAP Today
College of American Pathologists
325 Waukegan Rd.
Northfield, IL 60093-2750
Ph: (847)832-7000
Fax: (847)832-8000
Fr: 800-323-4040
URL: http://www.cap.org

Monthly. $110.00/year for individuals; $30.00/year for U.S. and Canada; $135.00/year for individuals, Canada; $135.00/year for other countries; $40.00/year for other countries, single copy. Magazine covering advances in pathology tests and equipment, clinical lab management and operations trends, and related regulatory and legislative changes.

2235 ■ Cell
Cell Press
600 Technology Sq.
Cambridge, MA 02139
Ph: (617)661-7057
Fax: (617)661-7061
Fr: (866)314-2355
E-mail: celleditor@cell.com
URL: http://www.cell.com

$212.00/year for U.S. and Canada, individual, print and online; $320.00/year for other countries, individual, print and online; $212.00/year for U.S. and Canada, online only, individual; $212.00/year for other countries, online only, individual; $1,425.00/year for U.S. and Canada, institution, print only; $1,605.00/year for institutions, other countries, print only. Peer-reviewed journal on molecular and cell biology.

2236 ■ Clinical Laboratory News
American Association of Clinical Chemistry
1850 K St. NW, Ste. 625
Washington, DC 20006-2215
Ph: (202)857-0717

Fax: (202)887-5093
Fr: 800-892-1400
URL: http://www.aacc.org/publications/cln/Pages/default.aspx

Monthly. Free to qualified subscribers, living in US. Scholarly magazine providing current news in the field of clinical laboratory science.

2237 ■ Cytometry, Part A
John Wiley & Sons Inc.
111 River St.
Hoboken, NJ 07030-5773
Ph: (201)748-6000
Fax: (201)748-6088
Fr: 800-825-7550
URL: http://onlinelibrary.wiley.com/journal/10.1002/(ISSN)1552-49

Monthly. $1,748.00/year for institutions, print only; $2,000.00/year for institutions, Canada and Mexico, print only; $2,126.00/year for institutions, other countries, print only. International journal covering all aspects of analytical cytology.

2238 ■ International Journal of Clinical Medicine
Scientific Research Publishing
PO Box 54821
Irvine, CA 92619-4821
E-mail: ijcm@scirp.org
URL: http://www.scirp.org/journal/ijcm/

Quarterly. $156.00/year for individuals. Peer-reviewed journal publishing articles on the latest advancements in clinical medicine.

2239 ■ ISRN Endocrinology
Hindawi Publishing Corporation
410 Park Ave., 15th Fl.
287 PMB
New York, NY 10022
E-mail: endocrinology@isrn.com
URL: http://www.isrn.com/journals/endocrinology

Peer-reviewed, open access journal publishing original research articles, review articles, case reports, and clinical studies in all areas of endocrinology.

2240 ■ ISRN Hematology
Hindawi Publishing Corporation
410 Park Ave., 15th Fl.
287 PMB
New York, NY 10022
E-mail: hematology@isrn.com
URL: http://www.isrn.com/journals/hematology

Peer-reviewed journal covering research in all areas of hematology.

2241 ■ ISRN Neurology
Hindawi Publishing Corporation
410 Park Ave., 15th Fl.
287 PMB
New York, NY 10022
E-mail: neurology@isrn.com
URL: http://www.isrn.com/journals/neurology

Peer-reviewed journal publishing research in all areas of neurology.

2242 ■ *ISRN Oncology*
Hindawi Publishing Corporation
410 Park Ave., 15th Fl.
287 PMB
New York, NY 10022
E-mail: oncology@isrn.com
URL: http://www.isrn.com/journals/oncology

Peer-reviewed journal publishing research articles in all areas of oncology.

2243 ■ *Journal of Adolescent and Young Adult Oncology*
Mary Ann Liebert Inc., Publishers
140 Huguenot St., 3rd Fl.
New Rochelle, NY 10801-5215
Ph: (914)740-2100
Fax: (914)740-2101
Fr: 800-654-3237
URL: http://www.liebertpub.com/products/
product.aspx?pid=387

Quarterly. $336.00/year for individuals, print and online; $758.00/year for institutions, print and online. Peer-reviewed journal focusing on research, education, communication and collaboration between health professionals in adolescent and young adult oncology.

2244 ■ *Journal of Women and Minorities in Science and Engineering*
Begell House Inc.
50 Cross Hwy.
Redding, CT 06896
Ph: (203)938-1300
Fax: (203)938-1304
URL: http://www.begellhouse.com/journals/
00551c876cc2f027

$248.00/year for institutions. Peer-reviewed journal featuring innovative ideas and programs for classroom teachers, scientific studies, and formulation of concepts related to the education, recruitment, and retention of under-represented groups in science and engineering.

2245 ■ *Laboratory Medicine*
American Society for Clinical Pathology
33 W Monroe, Ste. 1600
Chicago, IL 60603
Ph: (312)541-4999
Fax: (312)541-4998
Fr: 800-267-2727
E-mail: labmed@ascp.org
URL: http://labmed.ascpjournals.org/

Monthly. $95.00/year for individuals, online; $120.00/year for individuals, print and online; $120.00/year for institutions, online; $145.00/year for institutions, print and online. Professional journal covering medical technology and pathology.

2246 ■ *Leukemia Supplements*
Nature Publishing Group
75 Varick St., 9th Fl.
New York, NY 10013-1917
Ph: (212)726-9200
Fax: (212)696-9006
Fr: 888-331-6288
URL: http://www.nature.com/leusup/marketing/
index.html

Peer-reviewed journal covering all aspects of the research and treatment of leukemia and allied diseases.

2247 ■ *Medical Laboratory Observer (MLO)*
Nelson Publishing Inc.
2500 Tamiami Trl. N
Nokomis, FL 34275
Ph: (941)966-9521
Fax: (941)966-2590
URL: http://www.mlo-online.com

Monthly. Free to qualified clinical laboratory professionals. Magazine for clinical laboratory professionals.

2248 ■ *MEEN Imaging Technology News*
Reilly Communications Group
16 E Schaumburg Rd.
Schaumburg, IL 60194-3551
Ph: (847)882-6336
Fax: (847)882-0631
URL: http://www.itnonline.net

Trade magazine (tabloid) serving users and buyers of medical imaging technologies and services.

2249 ■ *Nature International Weekly Journal of Science*
Nature Publishing Group
75 Varick St., 9th Fl.
New York, NY 10013-1917
Ph: (212)726-9200
Fax: (212)696-9006
Fr: 888-331-6288
E-mail: nature@natureny.com
URL: http://www.nature.com/nature/index.html

Weekly. $199.00/year for individuals, print and online; $338.00/year for two years, print and online. Magazine covering science and technology, including the fields of biology, biochemistry, genetics, medicine, earth sciences, physics, pharmacology, and behavioral sciences.

2250 ■ *Neuroscience and Medicine*
Scientific Research Publishing
PO Box 54821
Irvine, CA 92619-4821
E-mail: nm@scirp.org
URL: http://www.scirp.org/journal/nm/

Quarterly. $156.00/year for individuals. Peer-reviewed journal publishing the latest advancements in neuroscience.

2251 ■ *Vantage Point*
Clinical Laboratory Management Association
401 N Michigan Ave., Ste. 2200
Chicago, IL 60611
Ph: (312)321-5111
Fax: (312)673-6927
E-mail: srobinson@clma.org
URL: http://www.clma.org

Description: Semimonthly. Features general, health care, and laboratory management tips, trends, and legislative news. Recurring features include news of educational opportunities, job listings, and columns titled Manager's Workshop, Healthcare Management Briefs, Career Corner, Online Update and Legislative Update.

EMPLOYER DIRECTORIES AND NETWORKING LISTS

2252 ■ *AGT International Membership Directory*
Association of Genetic Technologists
AGT Executive Office
PO Box 19193
Lenexa, KS 66285
Ph: (913)895-4605
Fax: (913)895-4652
URL: http://www.agt-info.org/IntMembershipDir.aspx

Monthly. Covers: About 520 laboratories studying heritable and acquired chromosomal disorders using cytogenetic, genetics, and cellular biology techniques. Entries include: Laboratory name, address, phone, areas of specialization, techniques, numbers and types of laboratory tests performed, and names of director and cytogenetic technologists. Arrangement: Geographical. Indexes: Director name, ACT member name.

2253 ■ *Directory of Accredited Laboratories*
American Association for Laboratory Accreditation
5301 Buckeystown Pike, Ste. 350
Frederick, MD 21704-8307
Ph: (301)644-3248

Fax: (301)662-2974
URL: http://www.a2la.org

Weekly, on Web site. Free. Covers: Over 1,600 testing and calibration laboratories and inspection agencies accredited for technical competence as measured against national and international standards in the following fields of testing: metrology, acoustics and vibration, construction materials, biology, chemistry, electricity, environmental, geotechnical, mechanical, thermal, and nondestructive. Entries include: Name of laboratory, address, phone, contact, certificate number, current period of accreditation, fields of accreditation technologies and methodologies. Arrangement: Alphabetical. Indexes: Fields of accreditation.

2254 ■ *Directory of Hospital Personnel*
Grey House Publishing
4919 Rte. 22
PO Box 56
Amenia, NY 12501
Ph: (518)789-8700
Fax: (518)789-0556
Fr: 800-562-2139
URL: http://www.greyhouse.com/hospital_
personnel.htm

Annual, Latest edition 2011. $325.00 for individuals. Covers: 200,000 executives at 6,000 U.S. Hospitals. Entries include: Name of hospital, address, phone, number of beds, type and JCAHO status of hospital, names and titles of key department heads and staff, medical and nursing school affiliations; number of residents, interns, and nursing students. Arrangement: Geographical. Indexes: Hospital name, personnel, hospital size.

2255 ■ *Hospital Blue Book*
Billian Publishing Inc. and Trans World Publishing Inc.
2100 River Edge Pky.
Atlanta, GA 30328
Ph: (770)955-5656
Fax: (770)952-0669
Fr: 800-800-5668
E-mail: blu-book@billian.com
URL: http://www.billianshealthdata.com/Products/
bluebook.html

Annual, Latest edition 2010. $575.00 for individuals; $575.00 for individuals. Covers: More than 6,500 hospitals; some listings also appear in a separate southern edition of this publication. Entries include: Name of hospital, accreditation, mailing address, phone, fax, number of beds, type of facility (nonprofit, general, state, etc.); list of administrative personnel and chiefs of medical services, with specific titles. Arrangement: Geographical.

2256 ■ *Medical and Health Information Directory*
Gale
PO Box 6904
Florence, KY 41022-6904
Fr: 800-354-9706
URL: http://www.gale.cengage.com

Annual, Latest edition April 2011. $1190.00 for individuals; $501.00 for individuals. Covers: In volume 1, more than 33,000 medical and health oriented associations, organizations, institutions, and government agencies, including health maintenance organizations (HMOs), preferred provider organizations (PPOs), insurance companies, pharmaceutical companies, research centers, and medical and allied health schools. In Volume 2, over 20,000 medical book publishers; medical periodicals, directories, audiovisual producers and services, medical libraries and information centers, electronic resources, and health-related internet search engines. In Volume 3, more than 40,500 clinics, treatment centers, care programs, and counseling/diagnostic services for 34 subject areas. Entries include: Institution, service, or firm name, address, phone, fax, email and URL; many include names of key personnel and, when pertinent, descriptive annotation. Volume 3 was formerly listed separately as Health Services

Directory. Arrangement: Classified by organization activity, service, etc. Indexes: Each volume has a complete alphabetical name and keyword index.

HANDBOOKS AND MANUALS

2257 ■ Careers in Health Care
The McGraw-Hill Companies
PO Box 182604
Columbus, OH 43272
Fax: (614)759-3749
Fr: 877-883-5524
E-mail: customer.service@mcgraw-hill.com
URL: http://www.mhprofessional.com/
   product.php?isbn=0071466533

Barbara M. Swanson. Fifth edition, 2005. $19.95 (paper). 192 pages. Describes job duties, work settings, salaries, licensing and certification requirements, educational preparation, and future outlook. Gives ideas on how to secure a job.

2258 ■ Opportunities in Health and Medical Careers
The McGraw-Hill Companies
PO Box 182604
Columbus, OH 43272
Fax: (614)759-3749
Fr: 877-883-5524
E-mail: customer.service@mcgraw-hill.com
URL: http://www.mhprofessional.com/
   product.php?isbn=0071437274

I. Donald Snook, Jr. and Leo D'Orazio. 2004. $14.95 (paper). 157 pages. Covers the full range of medical and health occupations. Illustrated.

2259 ■ Opportunities in Medical Imaging Careers
The McGraw-Hill Companies
PO Box 182604
Columbus, OH 43272
Fax: (614)759-3749
Fr: 877-883-5524
E-mail: customer.service@mcgraw-hill.com
URL: http://www.mhprofessional.com/
   product.php?isbn=0071458719

Clifford J. Sherry. 2006. $13.95. 160 pages.

2260 ■ Resumes for Health and Medical Careers
The McGraw-Hill Companies
PO Box 182604
Columbus, OH 43272
Fax: (614)759-3749
Fr: 877-883-5524
E-mail: customer.service@mcgraw-hill.com
URL: http://www.mhprofessional.com/
   product.php?isbn=0071545352

Third edition, 2008. $12.95 (paper). 144 pages.

EMPLOYMENT AGENCIES AND SEARCH FIRMS

2261 ■ The Coelyn Group
1 Park Plaza, Ste. 600
Irvine, CA 92614
Ph: (949)553-8855
Fax: (866)436-2171
E-mail: contact@coelyngroup.com
URL: http://www.coelyngroup.com

Executive search firm.

2262 ■ CompHealth
PO Box 713100
Salt Lake City, UT 84171-3100
Ph: (801)930-3000
Fax: (801)930-4517
Fr: 800-453-3030
E-mail: info@comphealth.com
URL: http://www.comphealth.com

Provides healthcare staffing and recruiting services covering certified registered nurse anesthetist, dosimetrist, imaging and radiation therapy, laboratory technology, medical physicist, nurse practitioner, nursing, pharmacy, physician, physician assistant, rehab therapy and respiratory therapy.

2263 ■ Durakis Executive Search
PO Box 1382
Brooklandville, MD 21022-1382
Ph: (410)252-2055
E-mail: resumes@durakis.com
URL: http://www.durakis.com

Executive search firm.

2264 ■ Flannery & Associates, LLC
N27 W23953 Paul Rd., Ste. 204
Pewaukee, WI 53072
Ph: (262)523-1206
Fax: (262)523-1873
E-mail: peter@flannerysearch.com
URL: http://flannerysearch.com

Executive search firm.

ONLINE JOB SOURCES AND SERVICES

2265 ■ BiosciRegister.com
URL: http://www.biosciregister.com

Description: Serves as an online directory or reference database of suppliers of products and services used in the biotechnology and life sciences industries. Contains job listings.

2266 ■ HEALTHeCAREERS Network
Fr: 888-884-8242
E-mail: info@healthecareers.com
URL: http://www.healthecareers.com

Description: Career search site for jobs in all health care specialties; educational resources; visa and licensing information for relocation; interesting articles; relocation tools; links to professional organizations and general resources.

2267 ■ Hospital Jobs OnLine
E-mail: support@hospitaljobsonline.com
URL: http://www.hospitaljobsonline.com

Description: Serves as a niche healthcare job board designed exclusively for hospitals, healthcare companies, and healthcare job seekers.

2268 ■ MedicalTechnologistsCentral.com
URL: http://www.medicaltechnologistscentral.com

Description: Offers medical technologist jobs and products in the healthcare industry.

2269 ■ MedTechJobsite.com
URL: http://www.medtechjobsite.com

Description: Provides new job openings for medical techs, in addition to insightful research into the healthcare and medical employment market, and a career articles section, written and frequented by industry professionals.

2270 ■ ProHealthJobs.com
Ph: (484)443-8545
Fax: (484)443-8549
E-mail: info@prohealthjobs.com
URL: http://prohealthjobs.com/jobboard

Description: Career resources site for the medical and health care field. Lists professional opportunities, product information, continuing education and open positions.

2271 ■ TechniciansNow.com
URL: http://www.techniciansnow.com

Description: Provides an avenue to showcase jobs and products vital to the mechanical and technical trade communities.

TRADESHOWS

2272 ■ American Association of Blood Banks Annual Meeting and TXPO
American Association of Blood Banks
8101 Glenbrook Rd.
Bethesda, MD 20814-2749
Ph: (301)907-6977
Fax: (301)907-6895
E-mail: aabb@aabb.org
URL: http://www.aabb.org

Annual. Primary Exhibits: Products related to blood banking and transfusion medicine: gloves, donor coaches, chairs, recruitment articles. Dates and Locations: 2012 Oct 06-09; Boston, MA.

2273 ■ APIC Annual Meeting and Educational Conference
Hachero Hill Conference and Exhibition Managers, Inc.
11260 Roger Bacon Dr., Ste. 500
Reston, VA 20190
Ph: (703)964-1240
Fax: (703)964-1246
URL: http://conferencemanagers.com/

Annual. Primary Exhibits: Pharmaceuticals, disinfectants, soaps, data processing software, sterilization devices, chemicals, housekeeping equipment and supplies, and related products. Dates and Locations: 2012 Jun 03-07; San Antonio, TX.

OTHER SOURCES

2274 ■ Accrediting Bureau of Health Education Schools (ABHES)
7777 Leesburg Pike, Ste. 314 N
Falls Church, VA 22043
Ph: (703)917-9503
Fax: (703)917-4109
E-mail: info@abhes.org
URL: http://www.abhes.org

Description: Serves as a nationally recognized accrediting agency of health education institutions and schools conducting medical laboratory technician and medical assistant education programs. Establishes criteria and standards for the administration and operation of health education institutions. Seeks to enhance the profession through the improvement of schools, courses, and the competence of graduates. Schools must apply voluntarily for accreditation; once accredited, they must report to the bureau annually and be reexamined at least every 6 years. Has accredited 15 programs for medical laboratory technicians, 124 medical assistants, and 80 institutions of allied health.

2275 ■ American Association for Clinical Chemistry (AACC)
1850 K St. NW, Ste. 625
Washington, DC 20006
Ph: (202)857-0717
Fax: (202)887-5093
Fr: 800-892-1400
E-mail: custserv@aacc.org
URL: http://www.aacc.org

Description: Clinical laboratory scientists and others engaged in the practice of clinical laboratory science in independent laboratories, hospitals, and allied institutions. Sponsors education programs; publishes books.

2276 ■ American Medical Technologists (AMT)
10700 W Higgins Rd., Ste. 150
Rosemont, IL 60018
Ph: (847)823-5169
Fax: (847)823-0458
Fr: 800-275-1268
E-mail: membership@amt1.com
URL: http://www.amt1.com

Description: Represents medical technologists, medical laboratory technicians, medical assistants, medical administrative specialists, dental assistants, office laboratory technicians, phlebotomy technicians, laboratory consultants, and allied health instructors. Provides allied health professionals with professional certification services and membership programs to enhance their professional and personal growth. Aims to issue certification credentials to medical and dental assistants, clinical laboratory personnel, laboratory consultants, and allied health instructors.

2277 ■ American Society for Clinical Laboratory Science (ASCLS)
2025 M St. NW, Ste. 800
Washington, DC 20036
Ph: (202)367-1174
Fax: (301)657-2909
E-mail: ascls@ascls.org
URL: http://www.ascls.org

Description: Primarily clinical laboratory personnel who have an associate or baccalaureate degree and clinical training and specialists who hold at least a master's degree in one of the major fields of clinical laboratory science such as bacteriology, mycology, or biochemistry; also includes technicians, specialists, and educators with limited certificates and students enrolled in approved programs of clinical laboratory studies and military medical technology schools.

Promotes and maintains high standards in clinical laboratory methods and research and advances standards of education and training of personnel. Conducts educational program of seminars and workshops. Approves programs of continuing education and maintains records on participation in continuing education programs for members.

2278 ■ American Society of Cytopathology (ASC)
100 W 10th St., Ste. 605
Wilmington, DE 19801
Ph: (302)543-6583
Fax: (302)543-6597
E-mail: asc@cytopathology.org
URL: http://www.cytopathology.org

Description: Represents physicians, cytotechnologists, and scientists dedicated to the cytologic method of diagnostic pathology.

2279 ■ Clinical Laboratory Management Association
401 N Michigan Ave., Ste. 2200
Chicago, IL 60611
Ph: (312)321-5111
Fax: (312)673-6927
E-mail: info@clma.org
URL: http://www.clma.org

Description: Represents the interests of clinical laboratory professionals. Promotes the clinical laboratory profession and supports members in their careers. Empowers laboratory professionals through educational, networking, and advocacy opportunities.

2280 ■ Commission on Accreditation of Allied Health Education Programs (CAAHEP)
1361 Park St.
Clearwater, FL 33756
Ph: (727)210-2350
Fax: (727)210-2354
E-mail: megivern@caahep.org
URL: http://www.caahep.org

Description: Serves as a nationally recognized accrediting agency for allied health programs in 23 occupational areas.

2281 ■ Endocrine Society
8401 Connecticut Ave., Ste. 900
Chevy Chase, MD 20815-5817
Ph: (301)941-0200
Fax: (301)941-0259
Fr: 888-363-6274
E-mail: societyservices@endo-society.org
URL: http://www.endo-society.org

Description: Promotes excellence in research, education, and clinical practice in endocrinology and related disciplines. Maintains placement service.

2282 ■ Journal of Environmental Pathology, Toxicology and Oncology
Begell House Inc.
50 Cross Hwy.
Redding, CT 06896
Ph: (203)938-1300
Fax: (203)938-1304
URL: http://www.begellhouse.com/journals/
0ff459a57a4c08d0

$940.00/year for institutions. Journal covering research and reviews of factors and conditions that affect human and animal carcinogenesis.

2283 ■ Journal of Skin Cancer
Hindawi Publishing Corp.
410 Park Ave., 15th Fl.
287 PMB
New York, NY 10022-4407
Fax: (215)893-4392
E-mail: jsc@hindawi.com
URL: http://www.hindawi.com/journals/jsc/

$195.00/year for individuals. Peer-reviewed journal publishing original research and review articles, case reports and clinical studies related to all aspects of skin cancer.

Employment Agencies and Search Firms

2284 ■ PMD Research, Inc.
PO Box 61231
Raleigh, NC 27661-1231
Fax: (919)877-9937
E-mail: info@pmdresearch.com
URL: http://www.pmdresearch.com

Maintains an extensive network between experienced clinical research professionals and the business systems that match career opportunities.

Other Sources

2285 ■ International Cellular Medicine Society (ICMS)
PO Box 4423
Salem, OR 97302
E-mail: info@cellmedicinesociety.org
URL: http://www.cellmedicinesociety.org

Description: Aims to advance the field of adult cell based medicine through developing international best practice standards that ensure patient safety, facilitate physician education, and provide peer oversight. Strives to provide unbiased, objective information regarding the medical use of autologous adult stem cells.

2286 ■ International Society for Cardiovascular Translational Research (ISCTR)
5580 La Jolla Blvd., Ste. 605
La Jolla, CA 92037
Ph: (858)774-0206
E-mail: ndib@isctr.org
URL: http://www.isctr.org

Description: Strives to provide an environment for collaboration and guidance among basic and clinical scientists. Promotes research and development of guidelines for training and certification in translational research. Influences health care policy and educates the public about discoveries in cardiovascular translational research.

2287 ■ International Society of Gastrointestinal Oncology (ISGIO)
200 Broadhollow Rd., Ste. 207
Melville, NY 11747
Ph: (631)390-8390
Fax: (631)393-5026
E-mail: willet@radonc.duke.edu
URL: http://www.isgio.org

Description: Facilitates gastrointestinal cancer research and education. Promotes dissemination of new gastrointestinal oncology-related knowledge and discovery. Provides a platform to build international and regional consensuses on therapy and research in gastrointestinal oncology.

2288 ■ Society for Heart Brain Medicine
9500 Euclid Ave.
Mail Code JJ40
Cleveland, OH 44195
Ph: (216)636-2424
Fax: (216)636-0271
E-mail: info@heartbrain.org
URL: http://www.heartbrain.org

Description: Educates clinicians and scientists about the physiology, pathophysiology and medical aspects of heart-brain interactions. Promotes and fosters research into the heart-brain relationship. Educates the public about the physiology, pathophysiology and medical aspects of heart-brain interactions.

2289 ■ Society for Translational Oncology (STC)
318 Blackwell St., Ste. 270
Durham, NC 27701
Ph: (919)433-0489
Fax: (919)680-4411
E-mail: admin@sto-online.org
URL: http://sto-online.org

Description: Aims to speed up the discovery and translation of treatments in the field of cancer medicine. Brings knowledge and strategies for critical new developments in cancer treatment to the practice of the community oncologist. Provides educational activities to improve physician competencies and strategies for screening, prevention, diagnosis, treatment and management of patients with cancer.

Sources of Help-Wanted Ads

2290 ■ *AATSEEL Newsletter*
American Association of Teachers of Slavic and East European Languages (AATSEEL)
PO Box 1116
San Juan Bautista, CA 95045-1116
Ph: (831)578-0290
Fax: (831)886-2486
URL: http://www.aatseel.org

Description: 4/academic year. Carries articles of interest to teachers of Slavic languages. Reports on study programs, teaching innovations, and Association news. Recurring features include news of members, notices of employment opportunities, a calendar of events, reviews of materials, and columns titled Chapter Minutes, Computer Information, Communicative Corner, and Russian Language Features.

2291 ■ *About Campus*
John Wiley & Sons Inc.
111 River St.
Hoboken, NJ 07030-5773
Ph: (201)748-6000
Fax: (201)748-6088
Fr: 800-825-7550
URL: http://onlinelibrary.wiley.com/journal/10.1002/(ISSN)1536-06

Bimonthly. $207.00/year for institutions, print only; $267.00/year for institutions, Canada and Mexico, print only; $318.00/year for institutions, other countries, print only; $60.00/year for U.S., Canada, and Mexico, print only; $96.00/year for other countries, print only. Journal focused on the critical issues faced by both student affairs and academic affairs staff as they work on helping students learn.

2292 ■ *Academician Magazine*
National Association of State Approved Colleges and Universities
808 17th St. NW, Ste. 410
Washington, DC 20006
Ph: (202)293-0090

Monthly. Magazine covering higher education.

2293 ■ *The Accounting Review*
American Accounting Association
5717 Bessie Dr.
Sarasota, FL 34233-2399
Ph: (941)921-7747
Fax: (941)923-4093
E-mail: tar@mccombs.utexas.edu
URL: http://aaahq.org/pubs/acctrev.htm

Quarterly. $395.00/year for institutions, print; $385.00/year for institutions, online from volume 74 through current issue; $445.00/year for institutions, online and print. Accounting education, research, financial reporting, and book reviews.

2294 ■ *American Academic*
American Federation of Teachers
555 New Jersey Ave. NW
Washington, DC 20001
Ph: (202)879-4400
URL: http://www.aft.org/pubs-reports/american_academic/index.htm

Higher education policy journal.

2295 ■ *The American Biology Teacher*
National Association of Biology Teachers
1313 Dolley Madison Blvd., Ste. 402
McLean, VA 22101
Ph: (703)264-9696
Fax: (703)264-7778
Fr: 800-406-0775
URL: http://www.nabt.org/websites/institution/index.php?p=26

$9.00/year for members; $24.00/year for nonmembers; $24.00/year for institutions. Peer-reviewed journal featuring articles on biology, science, and education for elementary, high school and college level biology teachers. Includes audio-visual, book, computer, and research reviews.

2296 ■ *American School & University*
Penton Media Inc.
9800 Metcalf Ave.
Overland Park, KS 66212
Ph: (913)341-1300
Fax: (913)967-1898
URL: http://asumag.com/

Monthly. Trade magazine.

2297 ■ *Annals of Medicine*
Informa Healthcare
52 Vanderbilt Ave., 7th Fl.
New York, NY 10017-3846
Ph: (212)520-2777
URL: http://informahealthcare.com/ann

$595.00/year for institutions; $980.00/year for institutions; $780.00/year for institutions. Journal covering health science and medical education.

2298 ■ *Assessment & Evaluation in Higher Education*
Routledge Journals
270 Madison Ave.
New York, NY 10016-0601
Ph: (212)216-7800
Fax: (212)563-2269
URL: http://www.tandf.co.uk/journals/titles/02602938.asp

Bimonthly. $1,316.00/year for institutions, online only; $2,547.00/year for institutions, print + online; $1,462.00/year for individuals, print + online; $2,292.00/year for institutions, online only; $578.00/year for individuals, print only; $314.00/year for individuals, print only. Peer-reviewed journal focusing on publishing papers and reports on all aspects of assessment and evaluation within higher education.

2299 ■ *Brookings Papers on Education Policy*
Brookings Institution Press
1775 Massashusetts Ave. NW
Washington, DC 20036
Ph: (202)797-6000
URL: http://www.brookings.edu/press/Journals/2007/brookingspapers

$36.00/year for individuals. Journal dealing with all aspects of American education.

2300 ■ *Change*
Heldref Publications
325 Chestnut St., Ste. 800
Philadelphia, PA 19106
Ph: (215)625-8900
Fr: 800-354-1420
E-mail: ch@heldref.org
URL: http://www.heldref.org/change.php

Bimonthly. $52.00/year for individuals, print only; $39.00/year for institutions, print only; $64.00/year for individuals, print and online; $207.00/year for institutions, print and online. Magazine dealing with contemporary issues in higher learning.

2301 ■ *The Chronicle of Higher Education*
The Chronicle of Higher Education
1255 23rd St. NW, 7th Fl.
Washington, DC 20037-1125
Ph: (202)466-1000
Fax: (202)452-1033
Fr: 800-728-2803
URL: http://chronicle.com

Weekly. $82.50/year for individuals, 43 issues; $45.00/year for individuals, 21 issues; $140.00/year for individuals, 86 issues. Higher education magazine (tabloid).

2302 ■ *Collegiate Aviation News Newsletter*
University Aviation Association
3410 Skyway Dr.
Auburn, AL 36830-6444
Ph: (334)844-2434
Fax: (334)844-2432
E-mail: uaamail@uaa.aero
URL: http://www.uaa.aero/

Description: Quarterly. $42/yr. for non-members. Provides information on Association activities and projects, events of other aviation organizations that bear on higher education, and the future impact of collegiate aviation education. Recurring features include feature articles on outstanding individual and institutional members, statistics, a calendar of events, news of members, news of research, an editorial, letters to the editor, book reviews, employment information, and the president's report.

2303 ■ *Columbia Journalism Review*
Columbia Journalism Review
2950 Broadway, Journalism Bldg.
Columbia University
New York, NY 10027

Ph: (212)854-1881
Fax: (212)854-8367
URL: http://www.cjr.org/

Bimonthly. $19.95/year for individuals; $27.95/year for other countries. Magazine focusing on journalism.

2304 ■ Community Colleges Journal
American Association of Community Colleges
1 Dupont Cir. NW, Ste. 410
Washington, DC 20036-1145
Ph: (202)728-0200
Fax: (202)833-2467
URL: http://www.aacc.nche.edu/Publications/CCJ/Pages/default.aspx

$34.00/year for nonmembers; $34.00/year for members; $39.00/year for nonmembers, International; $39.00/year for members, International; $24.00/year for single issue, non-member; $24.00/year for single issue, member. Educational magazine.

2305 ■ Connections
Association of Jesuit Colleges and Universities
1 Dupont Cir., Ste. 405
Washington, DC 20036
Ph: (202)862-9893
Fax: (202)862-8523
E-mail: dhowes@ajcunet.edu
URL: http://www.ajcunet.edu

Description: Monthly, except June, July and August. Furnishes information on legislative action affecting higher education and on Jesuit colleges and universities in the U.S. Recurring features include news of research, calendar of events, reports of meetings, notices of publications available, and columns titled Federal Relations, New Programs, and News from the Campuses. Only available online.

2306 ■ Education & Treatment of Children
West Virginia University Press
139 Stansbury Hall
PO Box 6295
Morgantown, WV 26506
Ph: (304)293-8400
Fax: (304)293-6585
URL: http://www.educationandtreatmentofchildren.net

Quarterly. $85.00/year for institutions; $45.00/year for individuals; $100.00/year for institutions, elsewhere; $60.00/year for individuals, elsewhere. Periodical featuring information concerning the development of services for children and youth. Includes reports written for educators and other child care and mental health providers focused on teaching, training, and treatment effectiveness.

2307 ■ Educational Research and Evaluation
Routledge Journals
270 Madison Ave.
New York, NY 10016-0601
Ph: (212)216-7800
Fax: (212)563-2269
URL: http://www.tandf.co.uk/journals/titles/13803611.asp

Bimonthly. $428.00/year for institutions, print + online; $385.00/year for institutions, online only; $165.00/year for individuals, print only; $731.00/year for institutions, print + online; $658.00/year for institutions, online only; $275.00/year for individuals, print only. Peer-reviewed journal on theory and practice.

2308 ■ Educational Researcher
American Educational Research Association
1430 K St. NW, Ste. 1200
Washington, DC 20005
Ph: (202)238-3200
Fax: (202)238-3250
URL: http://www.aera.net/publications/?id=317

Monthly. $48.00/year for individuals, plus foreign mailing charges; $150.00/year for institutions, plus foreign mailing charges. Educational research journal.

2309 ■ Environmental Education Research
Routledge Journals
270 Madison Ave.
New York, NY 10016-0601
Ph: (212)216-7800
Fax: (212)563-2269
URL: http://www.tandf.co.uk/journals/titles/13504622.asp

Bimonthly. $1,373.00/year for institutions, print + online; $1,236.00/year for institutions, online only; $364.00/year for individuals, print only. Journal covering all aspects of environmental education.

2310 ■ Essays in Education
University of South Carolina
471 University Pky.
Aiken, SC 29801
Ph: (803)648-6851
URL: http://www.usca.edu/essays/

Monthly. Journal covering issues that impact and influence education.

2311 ■ Financial Management
Financial Management Association International
4202 E Fowler Ave.
BSN 3331
Tampa, FL 33620-5500
Ph: (813)974-2084
Fax: (813)974-3318
E-mail: fma@coba.usf.edu
URL: http://www.fma.org/

Quarterly. $300.00/year for institutions, print + premium online; $95.00/year for institutions, premium online; $167.00/year for institutions, Europe, print + premium online; $158.00/year for institutions, Europe, premium online; $167.00/year for institutions, rest of world, print + premium online; $158.00/year for institutions, rest of world, premium online. Journal covering business, economics, finance and management.

2312 ■ Hematology
American Society of Hematology
2021 L St. NW, Ste. 900
Washington, DC 20036
Ph: (202)776-0544
Fax: (202)776-0545
URL: http://asheducationbook.hematologylibrary.org

Annual. $75.00/year for members; $125.00/year for nonmembers. Journal providing continuing medical education for physicians.

2313 ■ Interdisciplinary Journal of Teaching and Learning
Southern University at Baton Rouge
PO Box 9942
Baton Rouge, LA 70813
Ph: (225)711-4500
Fax: (225)771-4400
URL: http://www.subr.edu/CollegeofEducation/COE%20ONLINE%20Journa

Online academic journal that publishes research and scholarly articles in the field of education and learning.

2314 ■ The International Electronic Journal of Health Education
American Alliance for Health, Physical Education, Recreation & Dance
1900 Association Dr.
Reston, VA 20191-1598
Ph: (703)476-3400
Fax: (703)476-9527
Fr: 800-213-7193
URL: http://www.aahperd.org/aahe/publications/iejhe/

Annual. Free, health education professionals and students. Journal promoting health through education and other systematic strategies.

2315 ■ International Journal of Early Years Education
Routledge Journals
270 Madison Ave.
New York, NY 10016-0601

Ph: (212)216-7800
Fax: (212)563-2269
URL: http://www.tandf.co.uk/journals/titles/09669760.asp

$705.00/year for institutions, online only; $783.00/year for institutions, print + online; $271.00/year for individuals, print only. Journal focusing on education world-wide.

2316 ■ International Journal of Inclusive Education
Routledge Journals
270 Madison Ave.
New York, NY 10016-0601
Ph: (212)216-7800
Fax: (212)563-2269
URL: http://www.tandf.co.uk/journals/titles/13603116.asp

$589.00/year for individuals, print only; $1,135.00/year for institutions, online only; $1,261.00/year for individuals, print + online; $355.00/year for individuals, print only; $694.00/year for institutions, online only; $771.00/year for institutions, print + online. Journal providing information on the nature of schools, universities and technical colleges for the educators and educational policy-makers.

2317 ■ International Journal of Leadership in Education
Routledge
711 3 Ave., 8 Fl.
New York, NY 10016
Ph: (212)216-7800
Fax: (212)563-2269
Fr: 800-634-7064
E-mail: ijle@txstate.edu
URL: http://www.tandf.co.uk/journals/tf/13603124.html

Quarterly. $240.00/year for individuals, print only; $612.00/year for institutions, online only; $680.00/year for institutions, print and online; $408.00/year for institutions, print and online; $367.00/year for institutions, online only; $142.00/year for individuals, print only. Journal dealing with leadership in education.

2318 ■ International Journal of Progressive Education
International Journal of Progressive Education
c/o Alex Jean-Charles, PhD, Asst. Mng. Ed.
320 Fitzelle Hall, Ravine Pky.
Oneonta, NY 13820
URL: http://www.inased.org/ijpe.htm

$35.00/year for members; $45.00/year for individuals; $140.00/year for institutions, library; $35.00/year for students; $25.00/year for single issue; $50.00/year for students, other countries. Peer-reviewed online journal that aims to create an open and continuing dialogue about current educational issues and future conceptions of educational theory.

2319 ■ International Journal of Whole Schooling
Whole Schooling Press
Wayne State University
217 Education
Detroit, MI 48202
URL: http://www.wholeschooling.net/Journal_of_Whole_Schooling/IJW

Free. International, refereed academic journal dedicated to exploring ways to improve learning and schooling for all children.

2320 ■ Journal of Academic Leadership
Academic Leadership
600 Park St.
Rarick Hall 219
Hays, KS 67601-4099
Ph: (785)628-4547
URL: http://www.academicleadership.org/

Journal focusing on the leadership issues in the academic world.

2321 ■ *Journal of Cases in Educational Leadership*
Sage Publications Inc.
2455 Teller Rd.
Thousand Oaks, CA 91320-2218
Ph: (805)499-9774
Fax: (805)583-2665
Fr: 800-818-7243
URL: http://jel.sagepub.com

Quarterly. $411.00/year for institutions, e-access; $94.00/year for individuals, e-access. Journal covering cases appropriate for use in programs that prepare educational leaders.

2322 ■ *Journal of College Teaching & Learning*
The Clute Institute for Academic Research
6901 S Pierce St., Ste. 239
Littleton, CO 80128
Ph: (303)904-4750
Fax: (303)259-2420
URL: http://www.cluteinstitute.com/journals/TLC.html

Monthly. $495.00/year for institutions, with airmail postage. Refereed academic journal covering all areas of college level teaching, learning and administration.

2323 ■ *The Journal of Continuing Education in Nursing*
SLACK Incorporated
6900 Grove Rd.
Thorofare, NJ 08086-9447
Ph: (856)848-1000
Fax: (856)848-6091
E-mail: jcen@slackinc.com
URL: http://www.slackjournals.com/jcen

Monthly. $124.00/year for individuals; $248.00/year for two years; $29.00/year for single issue; $355.00/year for institutions. Peer-reviewed journal for nurses involved in planning and implementing educational programs for the practitioner and others in patient care.

2324 ■ *Journal of Curriculum and Supervision*
Association for Supervision and Curriculum Development
1703 N Beauregard St.
Alexandria, VA 22311-1714
Ph: (703)578-9600
Fax: (703)575-5400
Fr: 800-933-2723
URL: http://www.ascd.org/publications/jcs/fall2002/On_Community.a

Scholarly journal focusing on curriculum and supervision.

2325 ■ *Journal of Direct Instruction*
Association for Direct Instruction
PO Box 10252
Eugene, OR 97440
Ph: (541)485-1293
Fax: (541)868-1397
Fr: 800-995-2464
URL: http://www.adihome.org/index.php?option=com_content&view=art

Quarterly. Included in membership. Journal covering education.

2326 ■ *Journal of Engineering Education*
American Society for Engineering Education
1818 N St. NW, Ste. 600
Washington, DC 20036-2479
Ph: (202)331-3500
Fax: (202)265-8504
URL: http://www.jee.org

Quarterly. $100.00/year for libraries, online; $160.00/year for other countries, library; $150.00/year for U.S., Canada, and Mexico, library; $160.00/year for other countries, library. Peer-reviewed journal covering scholarly research in engineering education.

2327 ■ *Journal of Higher Education Outreach and Engagement (JHEOE)*
Institute of Higher Education (IHE)
Meigs Hall
Athens, GA 30602
Ph: (706)542-3464
Fax: (706)542-7588
URL: http://openjournals.libs.uga.edu/index.php/jheoe/

Semiannual. $60.00/year for individuals; $95.00/year for other countries; $30.00/year for students; $65.00/year for students, other countries; $100.00/year for institutions; $199.00/year for institutions, other countries. Journal covering higher education outreach and engagement for scholars, practitioners, and professionals.

2328 ■ *Journal of Language, Identity, and Education*
Routledge Journals
270 Madison Ave.
New York, NY 10016-0601
Ph: (212)216-7800
Fax: (212)563-2269
URL: http://www.tandf.co.uk/journals/titles/15348458.asp

$316.00/year for institutions, print + online; $284.00/year for institutions, online; $43.00/year for individuals, print + online; $527.00/year for institutions, print + online; $474.00/year for institutions, online; $71.00/year for individuals, print + online; $421.00/year for institutions, print + online; $379.00/year for institutions, online; $57.00/year for individuals, print + online. Scholarly, interdisciplinary journal covering issues in language, identity and education worldwide for academics, educators and policy specialists in a variety of disciplines, and others.

2329 ■ *Journal of Latinos and Education*
Routledge Journals
270 Madison Ave.
New York, NY 10016-0601
Ph: (212)216-7800
Fax: (212)563-2269
URL: http://www.tandf.co.uk/journals/titles/15348431.asp

Quarterly. $286.00/year for institutions, print + online; $257.00/year for institutions, online; $38.00/year for individuals, print + online; $480.00/year for institutions, print + online; $432.00/year for institutions, online; $63.00/year for individuals, print + online; $331.00/year for institutions, print + online; $343.00/year for institutions, online; $51.00/year for individuals, print + online. Scholarly, multidisciplinary journal covering educational issues that impact Latinos for researchers, teaching professionals, academics, scholars, institutions, and others.

2330 ■ *Journal of STEM Education*
Auburn University
9088 Haley Ctr.
Auburn, AL 36849
Ph: (334)844-9088
Fax: (334)844-9027
URL: http://ojs.jstem.org/index.php?journal=JSTEM

Semiannual. Journal for educators in Science, Technology, Engineering, and Mathematics (STEM) education.

2331 ■ *Leadership and Policy in Schools*
Routledge Journals
270 Madison Ave.
New York, NY 10016-0601
Ph: (212)216-7800
Fax: (212)563-2269
URL: http://www.tandf.co.uk/journals/titles/15700763.asp

Quarterly. $567.00/year for institutions, print and online; $260.00/year for individuals, print only; $510.00/year for institutions, online only. Journal providing information about leadership and policy in primary and secondary education.

2332 ■ *NAIA News*
National Association of Intercollegiate Athletics
1200 Grand Blvd.
Kansas City, MO 64106
Ph: (816)595-8000
Fax: (816)595-8200
E-mail: naianews@naia.org
URL: http://naia.cstv.com

Description: Daily. Provides news and information on the Association, which strives to "develop intercollegiate athletic programs as an integral part of the total educational program of the college rather than as a separate commercial or promotional adjunct." Aims toward uniformity and equity in policies and practices. Recurring features include news of members and events, notices of awards, and job listings.

2333 ■ *NewsNet, the Newsletter of the ASEEES*
Association for Slavic, East European, and Eurasian Studies
203C Bellefield Hall
Pittsburgh, PA 15260
Ph: (412)648-9911
Fax: (412)648-9815
E-mail: aseees@pitt.edu
URL: http://www.aseees.org

Description: Bimonthly. Reports on Association activities and on Slavic study research in institutions throughout the world. Alerts readers to research grants, internships, and fellowship opportunities as well as to employment opportunities in universities across the country. Announces awards, upcoming conferences, courses, new scholarly publications, and annual research.

2334 ■ *Notices of the American Mathematical Society*
American Mathematical Society
201 Charles St.
Providence, RI 02904-2294
Ph: (401)455-4000
Fax: (401)331-3842
Fr: 800-321-4267
E-mail: notices@math.wustl.edu
URL: http://www.ams.org/notices

$488.00/year for nonmembers; free to members. Peer-reviewed AMS journal publishing programs, meeting reports, new publications, announcements, upcoming mathematical meetings, scientific development trends, computer software reviews, and federal funding reports.

2335 ■ *OECD Observer*
Organisation for Economic Co-operation and Development
2001 L St. NW, Ste. 650
Washington, DC 20036-4922
Ph: (202)785-6323
Fax: (202)785-0350
Fr: 800-456-6323
E-mail: observer@oecd.org
URL: http://www.oecdobserver.org

$90.00/year for individuals, print + online; $70.00/year for individuals, print + online; $55.00/year for individuals, print + online; $9,800.00/year for individuals, print + online. Magazine on economic affairs, science, and technology.

2336 ■ *Oxford Review of Education*
Routledge Journals
270 Madison Ave.
New York, NY 10016-0601
Ph: (212)216-7800
Fax: (212)563-2269
URL: http://www.tandf.co.uk/journals/titles/03054985.asp

$709.00/year for institutions, print + online; $1,224.00/year for institutions, print + online; $249.00/year for individuals, print only; $454.00/year for individuals, print only. Journal covering advance study of education.

2337 ■ The Physics Teacher
American Association of Physics Teachers
1 Physics Ellipse
College Park, MD 20740-3845
Ph: (301)209-3311
Fax: (301)209-0845
URL: http://tpt.aapt.org

; $434.00/year for nonmembers, domestic; $469.00/year for nonmembers, international. Scientific education magazine.

2338 ■ School Effectiveness and School Improvement
Routledge
711 3 Ave., 8 Fl.
New York, NY 10016
Ph: (212)216-7800
Fax: (212)563-2269
Fr: 800-634-7064
URL: http://www.tandf.co.uk/journals/titles/09243453.asp

Quarterly. $387.00/year for institutions, print and online; $348.00/year for institutions, online only; $186.00/year for individuals, print only; $660.00/year for institutions, print and online; $594.00/year for institutions, online only; $312.00/year for individuals, print only. Journal focusing on educational progress of all students.

2339 ■ The Science Teacher
National Science Teachers Association
1840 Wilson Blvd.
Arlington, VA 22201-3000
Ph: (703)243-7100
Fax: (703)243-7177
URL: http://www.nsta.org/highschool/

Peer-reviewed journal for secondary science teachers.

2340 ■ Teaching and Learning in Nursing
Elsevier Science Inc.
360 Park Ave. S
New York, NY 10010-1710
Ph: (212)989-5800
Fax: (212)633-3990
Fr: 888-437-4636
URL: http://www.elsevier.com/wps/find/journaldescription.cws_home

Quarterly. $232.00/year for institutions, other countries; $134.00/year for other countries; $160.00/year for institutions; $91.00/year for individuals. Journal devoted to associate degree nursing education and practice.

2341 ■ Technology and Engineering Teacher
International Technology Education Association
1914 Association Dr., Ste. 201
Reston, VA 20191-1539
Ph: (703)860-2100
Fax: (703)860-0353
URL: http://www.iteaconnect.org/Publications/ttt.htm

$35.00/year for individuals, professional U.S., 2 years; $70.00/year for individuals, professional U.S.; $30.00/year for students, undergrad student- first time member; $35.00/year for students, full-time grad/renewing undergrad student; $55.00/year for students, bridge - one-time student to professional; $410.00/year for institutions, group membership, 2 years; $210.00/year for institutions, group membership; $690.00/year for individuals, group membership, 2 years; $350.00/year for individuals, group membership; $270.00/year for individuals, group membership, 2 years. Magazine on technology education.

2342 ■ Theory and Research in Education
Sage Publications Inc.
2455 Teller Rd.
Thousand Oaks, CA 91320-2218
Ph: (805)499-9774
Fax: (805)583-2665
Fr: 800-818-7243
URL: http://www.sagepub.com/journalsProdDesc.nav?prodId=Journal20

$546.00/year for institutions, print and e-access; $491.00/year for institutions, e-access; $535.00/year for institutions, print; $85.00/year for individuals, print; $196.00/year for single issue, institutional; $37.00/year for single issue, individual. Interdisciplinary journal covering normative and theoretical issues concerning education including multi-faceted philosophical analysis of moral, social, political and epistemological problems and issues arising from educational practice.

2343 ■ Weatherwise
Routledge
711 3 Ave., 8 Fl.
New York, NY 10016
Ph: (212)216-7800
Fax: (212)563-2269
Fr: 800-634-7064
URL: http://www.weatherwise.org/

Bimonthly. $48.00/year for individuals, print and online; $162.00/year for institutions, print and online; $162.00/year for institutions, print only. Popular weather magazine for students, teachers, and professionals.

2344 ■ Wisconsin Lawyer
State Bar of Wisconsin
PO Box 7158
Madison, WI 53707-7158
Ph: (608)257-3838
Fax: (608)257-5502
Fr: 800-728-7788
E-mail: wislawyer@wisbar.org
URL: http://www.wisbar.org/wislawmag

Monthly. $35.00/year for members; $53.00/year for nonmembers; $3.50/year for single issue. Official monthly publication of the State Bar of Wisconsin.

EMPLOYER DIRECTORIES AND NETWORKING LISTS

2345 ■ Accredited Institutions of Postsecondary Education
Oryx Press
88 Post Rd. W
PO Box 5007
Westport, CT 06881
Fax: (203)222-1502
URL: http://www.greenwood.com/catalog/OXAIPE05.aspx

Annual, latest edition 2006. $89.95 for individuals; $49.95 for individuals. Covers: More than 7,000 accredited institutions and programs of postsecondary education in the United States and U.S. -chartered schools in 14 countries. Entries include: Institution name, address, phone, whether public or private, any religious affiliation, type of institution and student body, branch campuses or affiliated institutions, date of first accreditation and latest reaffirmation of accrediting body, accredited programs in professional fields, level of degrees offered, name of chief executive officer, size and composition of enrollment, type of academic calendar. Arrangement: Geographical. Indexes: Institution.

2346 ■ Association of American University Presses—Directory
Association of American University Presses
28 W 36th St., Ste. 602
New York, NY 10018
Ph: (212)989-1010
Fax: (212)989-0975
URL: http://www.aaupnet.org

Annual, Latest edition 2011. $30.00 for individuals. Covers: 124 presses and affiliates worldwide. Entries include: Press name, address, phone, e-mail, URL; titles and names of complete editorial and managerial staffs; editorial program; mailing, warehouse, printing, and/or customer service addresses; other details. Arrangement: Classified by press affiliation,

alphabetical by press name. Indexes: Personal name.

2347 ■ Chronicle Four-Year College Databook
Chronicle Guidance Publications Inc.
66 Aurora St.
Moravia, NY 13118-3569
Ph: (315)497-0330
Fax: (315)497-0339
Fr: 800-622-7284
URL: http://www.chronicleguidance.com

Annual, latest edition 2009-2010. $26.75 for individuals. Covers: More than 825 baccalaureate, master's, doctoral, and first professional programs offered by more than 2,528 colleges and universities in the United States. Entries include: College charts section gives college name, address, phone; accreditation, enrollment, admissions, costs, financial aid; accreditation associations' names, addresses, and phone numbers. Appendices gives details on admissions and other information special to each college. Arrangement: Part I, classified by college major; part II, geographical. Indexes: College name.

2348 ■ Chronicle Two-Year College Databook
Chronicle Guidance Publications Inc.
66 Aurora St.
Moravia, NY 13118-3569
Ph: (315)497-0330
Fax: (315)497-0339
Fr: 800-622-7284
URL: http://www.chronicleguidance.com

Annual, latest edition 2009-2010. $26.74 for individuals. Covers: Over 954 associate, certificate, occupational, and transfer programs offered by more than 2,509 technical institutes, two-year colleges, and universities in the United States. Entries include: College charts section gives college name, address, phone; accreditation, enrollment, admissions, costs, financial aid; accrediting associations' names, addresses, and phone numbers. Arrangement: Part I is classified by college major; part II is geographical. Indexes: College name.

2349 ■ Employment Information in the Mathematical Sciences
American Mathematical Society
201 Charles St.
Providence, RI 02904-2294
Ph: (401)455-4000
Fax: (401)331-3842
Fr: 800-321-4267
E-mail: eims-info@ams.org
URL: http://www.ams.org/profession/employment-services/eims/eims

Five times a year. $190.00 for individuals; $114.00 for individuals. Covers: Colleges and universities with departments in the mathematical sciences, and non-academic and foreign organizations with employment openings. Entries include: For departments—Name, address, name and title of contact; job title, job description, salary (if applicable). Arrangement: Classified as academic or nonacademic, then geographical.

2350 ■ Fulbright Scholar Program Grants for U.S. Faculty and Professionals
Council for International Exchange of Scholars
3007 Tilden St. NW, Ste. 5L
Washington, DC 20008-3009
Ph: (202)686-4000
Fax: (202)362-3442
URL: http://www.cies.org/

Annual, March. Free. Covers: about 800 grants available for postdoctoral university lecturing and advanced research by American citizens in more than 140 countries. Entries include: Periods in which grants are tenable; number of grants available for the country; language or other requirement; fields in which lectures and research are desired; stipend, housing; additional income for dependents, applications and reference forms. Arrangement: Geographical. Indexes: Professional, discipline.

2351 ■ Grants, Fellowships, and Prizes of Interest to Historians
American Historical Association
400 A St. SE
Washington, DC 20003-3889
Ph: (202)544-2422
Fax: (202)544-8307
E-mail: grantguide@theaha.org
URL: http://www.historians.org

Annual, latest edition 2006. for members. Covers: Over 450 sources of funding (scholarships, fellowships, internships, awards, and book and essay prizes) in the United States and abroad for graduate students, postdoctoral researchers, and institutions in the humanities. Entries include: Name of source, institution name or contact, address, phone, eligibility and proposal requirements, award or stipend amount, location requirements for research, application deadlines. Arrangement: Alphabetical in three categories: support for individual research and teaching; grants for groups and organizations for research and education; and book, article, essay, and manuscript prizes.

2352 ■ Higher Education Directory
Higher Education Publications Inc.
1801 Robert Fulton Dr., Ste. 340
Reston, VA 20191
Ph: (571)313-0478
Fax: (571)313-0526
Fr: 888-349-9715
URL: http://www.hepinc.com

Annual, latest edition 2011. $75.00 for individuals. Covers: Over 4,364 degree granting colleges and universities accredited by approved agencies recognized by the U.S. Secretary of Education and by the Council of Higher Education Accreditation (CHEA); 103 systems offices; over 550 related associations and state government agencies; recognized accrediting agencies. Entries include: For institutions—Name, address, congressional district, phone, fax, year established; Carnegie classification; enrollment; type of student body; religious or other affiliation; undergraduate tuition and fees; type of academic calendar; highest degree offered; accreditations; IRS status; names, titles and job classification codes for academic and administrative officers. For associations and state agencies—Name, address, phone, name of chief executive officer. Same content and coverage as the base volume of the Department of Education's publication "Directory of Postsecondary Institutions". Arrangement: Geographical, alphabetical by state. Indexes: Administrator name (with phone and e-mail addresses), accreditation, FICE numbers, college or university name.

2353 ■ Mathematical Sciences Professional Directory
American Mathematical Society
201 Charles St.
Providence, RI 02904-2294
Ph: (401)455-4000
Fax: (401)331-3842
Fr: 800-321-4267
URL: http://www.ams.org

Annual, latest edition 2010. $44.00 for institutions; $55.00 for individuals. Covers: 37 professional organizations concerned with mathematics, government agencies, academic institutions with department in the mathematical sciences, nonacademic organizations, and individuals. Entries include: For professional organizations and government agencies—Name, address, names and titles of key personnel. For institutions—Name, address; name, title, and address of department chair. Arrangement: Classified by type of organization; institutions are then geographical; others, alphabetical. Indexes: University or college name.

2354 ■ Modern Language Association of America—Job Information List
Modern Language Association of America
26 Broadway, 3rd Fl.
New York, NY 10004-1789

Ph: (646)576-5000
Fax: (646)458-0030
E-mail: jileditor@mla.org
URL: http://www.mla.org/jil

Quarterly, February, April, October, and December. Covers: Available positions for college teachers of English and foreign languages in four-year colleges and universities; February issue includes separate section of openings in two-year institutions. Separate editions for English and American language and literature and for foreign language openings. Entries include: Department chair statement, including institution name; contact name, address, phone; definite or possible openings; related information for job seekers (change in deadline date, or job description, notice of a vacancy filled, etc.). Arrangement: First section—Statements of department chairmen. Second section (in October and February only)—List of departments reporting no vacancies.

2355 ■ National Directory of College Athletics
Collegiate Directories Inc.
PO Box 450640
Cleveland, OH 44145
Ph: (440)835-1172
Fax: (440)835-8835
Fr: 800-426-2232
URL: http://www.collegiatedirectories.com/shopping/index.asp

Annual, Latest edition 2010-2012. $49.95 for individuals; $29.95. Covers: Men's athletic departments of 2,100 senior and junior colleges in the United States and Canada. Entries include: School name, address, enrollment, colors, team nicknames, stadium and/or gym capacity; names of president, men's athletic director, athletic administrative staff, physical education director and coaches for each sport; athletic department phones, faxes, etc.; association affiliations. Arrangement: Alphabetical. Indexes: Schools by program and division; Alphabetical by advertisers and products.

2356 ■ National Faculty Directory
Gale
PO Box 6904
Florence, KY 41022-6904
Fr: 800-354-9706
URL: http://www.gale.cengage.com

Annual, Latest edition 43rd; October, 2011. $1,391.00 for individuals. Covers: More than 900,000 (60,000 more in supplement) teaching faculty members at over 4,600 junior colleges, colleges, and universities in the United States and those in Canada that give instruction in English. Entries include: Name, department name, institution, address, and phone and fax numbers. Directory combines main edition and supplement. Arrangement: Alphabetical.

2357 ■ Patterson's Schools Classified
Educational Directories Inc.
1025 W Wise Rd., Ste. 101
PO Box 68097
Schaumburg, IL 60168-0097
Ph: (847)891-1250
Fax: (847)891-0945
Fr: 800-357-6183
URL: http://www.ediusa.com

Annual, Latest edition 2010, volume 60. $23.00 for individuals. Covers: Over 6,000 accredited colleges, universities, community colleges, junior colleges, career schools and teaching hospitals. Entries include: School name, address, phone, URL, e-mail, name of administrator or admissions officer, description, professional accreditation (where applicable). Updated from previous year's edition of 'Patterson's American Education'. Arrangement: Classified by area of study, then geographical by state. Indexes: Alphabetical by name.

2358 ■ School Guide
School Guide Publications
210 North Ave.
New Rochelle, NY 10801-6402

Ph: (914)632-7771
Fax: (914)632-3412
Fr: 800-433-7771
URL: http://distance.schoolguides.com

Annual, Latest edition 2008. Covers: Over 3,000 colleges, vocational schools, and nursing schools in the United States. Entries include: Institution name, address, phone, courses offered, degrees awarded. Arrangement: Classified by type of institution, then geographical. Indexes: Subject.

2359 ■ Who's Who in American Law
Marquis Who's Who L.L.C.
300 Connell Dr., Ste. 2000
Berkeley Heights, NJ 07922
Ph: (908)673-1000
Fax: (908)673-1189
Fr: 800-473-7020
E-mail: law@marquiswhoswho.com
URL: http://www.marquiswhoswho.com

Biennial, Latest edition 17th; 2011-2012. $365.00 for individuals. Covers: Over 19,000 lawyers, judges, law school deans and professors, and other legal professionals. Entries include: Name, home and office addresses, place and date of birth, educational background, career history, civic positions, professional memberships, publications, awards, special achievements. Arrangement: Alphabetical. Indexes: Fields of practice, professional area.

HANDBOOKS AND MANUALS

2360 ■ Academic Job Search Handbook
University of Pennsylvania Press
3905 Spruce St.
Philadelphia, PA 19104-4112
Ph: (215)898-6261
Fax: (215)898-0404
E-mail: custserv@pobox.upenn.edu
URL: http://www.upenn.edu/pennpress/book/14469.html

Julia Miller Vick and Jennifer S. Furlong. 2008. $18.95 (paper). 296 pages. Includes information on aspects of the search that are common to all levels, with tips for those seeking their first or second faculty position. Provides advice and addresses topics in the job market, including the challenges faced by dual-career couples, job search issues for pregnant candidates, and advice on how to deal with gaps in a CV.

2361 ■ Careers in Horticulture and Botany
The McGraw-Hill Companies
PO Box 182604
Columbus, OH 43272
Fax: (614)759-3749
Fr: 877-883-5524
E-mail: customer.service@mcgraw-hill.com
URL: http://www.mhprofessional.com/product.php?isbn=0071467734

Jerry Garner. 2006. 16.95 (paper). 192 pages. Includes bibliographical references.

2362 ■ Careers in Journalism
The McGraw-Hill Companies
PO Box 182604
Columbus, OH 43272
Fax: (614)759-3749
Fr: 877-883-5524
E-mail: customer.service@mcgraw-hill.com
URL: http://www.mhprofessional.com/product.php?isbn=0071466371

Jan Goldberg. Third edition, 2005. $15.95 (paper). 192 pages.

2363 ■ Educational Pathways: A Faculty Development Resource
Cengage Learning
PO Box 6904
Florence, KY 41022
Fax: 800-487-8488

Fr: 800-354-9706
E-mail: esales@cengage.com
URL: http://www.cengage.com

Kathryn Kalanick. 2007. $73.49. 368 pages. Provides a three-track approach to address the training needs of instructors and educators by following the experiences of three educators from various backgrounds.

2364 ■ Great Jobs for English Majors
The McGraw-Hill Companies
PO Box 182604
Columbus, OH 43272
Fax: (614)759-3749
Fr: 877-883-5524
E-mail: customer.service@mcgraw-hill.com
URL: http://www.mhprofessional.com

Julie DeGalan and Stephen Lambert. Third edition, 2006. $15.95 (paper). 192 pages.

2365 ■ Great Jobs for History Majors
The McGraw-Hill Companies
PO Box 182604
Columbus, OH 43272
Fax: (614)759-3749
Fr: 877-883-5524
E-mail: customer.service@mcgraw-hill.com
URL: http://www.mhprofessional.com

Julie DeGalan and Stephen Lambert. 2007. $16.95 (paper). 192 pages.

2366 ■ Great Jobs for Liberal Arts Majors
The McGraw-Hill Companies
PO Box 182604
Columbus, OH 43272
Fax: (614)759-3749
Fr: 877-883-5524
E-mail: customer.service@mcgraw-hill.com
URL: http://www.mhprofessional.com/
    product.php?isbn=0071482148

Blythe Camenson. Second edition, 2007. $16.95 (paper). 192 pages.

2367 ■ Great Jobs for Music Majors
The McGraw-Hill Companies
PO Box 182604
Columbus, OH 43272
Fax: (614)759-3749
Fr: 877-883-5524
E-mail: customer.service@mcgraw-hill.com
URL: http://www.mhprofessional.com/
    product.php?isbn=0071454616

Jan Goldberg. Second edition, 2004. $15.95 (paper). 180 pages.

2368 ■ Great Jobs for Sociology Majors
The McGraw-Hill Companies
PO Box 182604
Columbus, OH 43272
Fax: (614)759-3749
Fr: 877-883-5524
E-mail: customer.service@mcgraw-hill.com
URL: http://www.mhprofessional.com/
    product.php?isbn=0071642056

Stephen Lambert. Second edition, 2008. $16.95 (paper). 192 pages.

2369 ■ Great Jobs for Theater Majors
The McGraw-Hill Companies
PO Box 182604
Columbus, OH 43272
Fax: (614)759-3749
Fr: 877-883-5524
E-mail: customer.service@mcgraw-hill.com
URL: http://www.mhprofessional.com/
    product.php?isbn=007143853X

Jan Goldberg and Julie DeGalan. 2005. $15.95 (paper). 192 pages.

2370 ■ Idea-Based Learning
Stylus Publishing, LLC
22883 Quicksilver Dr.
Sterling, VA 20166-2012
Ph: (703)661-1504

Fax: (703)661-1547
E-mail: stylusinfo@styluspub.com
URL: http://www.styluspub.com

Edmund J. Hansen. 2011. $75.00 (hardback); $24.95 (paperback). Serves as guide in developing college instruction that has clear purpose, is well integrated into the curriculum, and improves student learning.

2371 ■ Job Search in Academe: How to Get the Position You Deserve
Stylus Publishing
22883 Quicksilver Dr.
Sterling, VA 20166-2012
Ph: (703)661-1504
Fax: (703)661-1547
E-mail: stylusinfo@styluspub.com
URL: http://stylus.styluspub.com

Dawn M. Formo and Cheryl Reed. 2011. $49.95 (cloth) and $22.50 (paper). 268 pages. Covers the process for Masters and PhDs level job-seekers of all disciplines: from identifying sources of information about positions, to advising on the preparation of effective CVs and portfolios, through guidance on the process of interview to final negotiation of terms. Includes sample application letters and vitae.

2372 ■ Opportunities in Overseas Careers
The McGraw-Hill Companies
PO Box 182604
Columbus, OH 43272
Fax: (614)759-3749
Fr: 877-883-5524
E-mail: customer.service@mcgraw-hill.com
URL: http://www.mhprofessional.com/
    product.php?isbn=0071454470

Blythe Camenson. 2004. $13.95 (paper). 173 pages.

2373 ■ Opportunities in Teaching Careers
The McGraw-Hill Companies
PO Box 182604
Columbus, OH 43272
Fax: (614)759-3749
Fr: 877-883-5524
E-mail: customer.service@mcgraw-hill.com
URL: http://www.mhprofessional.com/
    product.php?isbn=0071438173

Janet Fine. 2005. $13.95 (paper). 160 pages. Discusses licensing and accreditation programs, sources of placement information, job-seeking correspondence, selection procedures, and paths to advancement. Also covers professional associations, non-traditional teaching opportunities, and jobs abroad.

2374 ■ A Survival Guide for New Faculty Members: Outlining the Keys to Success for Promotion and Tenure
Charles C Thomas Publisher, Ltd.
PO Box 19265
Springfield, IL 62794-9265
Ph: (217)789-8980
Fax: (217)789-9130
Fr: 800-258-8980
E-mail: books@ccthomas.com
URL: http://www.ccthomas.com

Jeffrey P. Bakken and Cynthia G. Simpson. 2011. $35.95 (paper). 258 pages. Serves as a guide for new faculty members in higher education. Contains practical, down-to-earth advice and suggestions for successfully working through to tenure and promotion.

EMPLOYMENT AGENCIES AND SEARCH FIRMS

2375 ■ Boston Search Group Inc.
224 Clarendon St., Ste. 41
Boston, MA 02116-3729
Ph: (617)266-4333

Fax: (781)735-0562
E-mail: ralph@bsgtv.com
URL: http://www.bostonsearchgroup.com

Executive search firm.

2376 ■ Compass Group Ltd.
Birmingham Place Bldg.
401 S Old Woodward, Ste. 310
Birmingham, MI 48009-6613
Ph: (248)540-9110
Fax: (248)647-8288
URL: http://www.compassgroup.com

Executive search firm. Second location in Oak Brook, IL.

2377 ■ The Dalley Hewitt Company
PO Box 19973
Atlanta, GA 30325
Ph: (404)992-5065
Fax: (404)355-6136
E-mail: rives@dalleyhewitt.com
URL: http://www.dalleyhewitt.com

Executive search firm.

2378 ■ Deerfield Associates
572 Washington St., Ste. 15
Wellesley, MA 02482
Ph: (781)237-2800
Fax: (781)237-5600
E-mail: jobs@deerfieldassociates.com
URL: http://www.deerfieldassociates.com

Executive search firm.

2379 ■ Development Resource Group Inc (DRG)
130 E 40th St., Ste. 800
New York, NY 10016
Ph: (212)983-1600
Fax: (212)983-1687
E-mail: search@drgnyc.com
URL: http://www.drgnyc.com

Executive search firm.

2380 ■ Dunn Associates
229 Limberline Dr.
Greensburg, PA 15601
Ph: (724)832-9822
E-mail: maddunn@aol.com
URL: http://www.dunnassociatesinc.com

Executive search firm.

2381 ■ EFL Associates
11440 Tomahawk Creek Pky.
Leawood, KS 66211
Ph: (913)234-1560
URL: http://www.cbiz.com/eflassociates

Executive search firm. Locations in Englewood, CO and Lake Forest, IL.

2382 ■ Ford Webb Associates Inc.
60 Thoreau St.
Concord, MA 01742
Ph: (978)371-4900
Fax: (978)334-5544
E-mail: twebb@fordwebb.com
URL: http://www.fordwebb.com

Executive search firm.

2383 ■ Perez-Arton Consultants Inc.
23 Spring St., Ste. 204B
Ossining, NY 10562
Ph: (914)762-2103
Fax: (914)762-7834
E-mail: perezart@bestweb.net

Provides executive searches for major academic and administrative units. Conducts institutional evaluations and executive staff assessments. Firm works for colleges, universities and education-related non-profits only.

2384 ■ Witt/Kieffer
2015 Spring Rd., Ste. 510
Oak Brook, IL 60523
Ph: (630)990-1370
Fax: (630)990-1382
E-mail: info@wittkieffer.com
URL: http://www.wittkieffer.com

Executive search firm with five locations throughout the United States.

ONLINE JOB SOURCES AND SERVICES

2385 ■ Academic Careers Online
E-mail: info@academiccareers.com
URL: http://www.academiccareers.com

Description: Serves as an academic job site for teaching jobs, education jobs, research jobs, and professional jobs in education and academia.

2386 ■ Academic Employment Network
URL: http://www.academploy.com

Description: Online position announcement service. Lists available positions in colleges, primary and secondary educational institutions for faculty, staff, and administrative professionals. Fee: Free searching and browsing features.

2387 ■ Academic360.com
URL: http://www.academic360.com

Description: Site is a collection of internet resources gathered for the academic job hunter. Contains links to over 1,400 colleges and universities that advertise job openings online. Positions listed are not limited to teaching positions.

2388 ■ AcademicKeys.com
URL: http://www.academickeys.com

Description: Provides resources for job seekers who are looking for academic employment. Offers higher education jobs and jobs at universities, colleges, and other institutions of higher education.

2389 ■ Adjunctnation.com
URL: http://adjunctadvocate.com

Description: Focuses on faculty job postings within higher education for both part-time, as well as full-time temporary college faculty appointments.

2390 ■ ChristianUniversityJobs.com
URL: http://www.christianuniversityjobs.com

Description: Features an online job search database focused on higher education jobs in Christian schools including universities, colleges, seminaries, and theological schools.

2391 ■ HigherEdJobs.com
E-mail: jobseeker@higheredjobs.com
URL: http://www.higheredjobs.com

Description: Exists as a job database focused exclusively on college and university positions. Provides a recruitment tool that adds value to the job seeker and recruiter by offering cost-effective, innovative, useful, and timely services.

2392 ■ National Educators Employment Review
URL: http://www.thereview.com

Description: Matches qualified educators with employment for teachers, specialists, and administrators from kindergarten through college.

2393 ■ TedJob.com
E-mail: contact@tedjob.com
URL: http://www.tedjob.com

Description: Serves as a higher-education job marketplace designed to meet the unique, recruitment requirements for universities, colleges, and other academic organizations.

2394 ■ UniversityJobs.com
E-mail: staff@universityjobs.com
URL: http://www.universityjobs.com

Description: Provides an online recruitment solution for colleges and universities to hire new faculty and administrators or staff.

2395 ■ UnivJobs.com
E-mail: univjobs@yahoo.com
URL: http://www.univjobs.com

Description: Serves as a site to find jobs at universities and colleges nationwide. Provides information on faculty, staff, and student positions at university and college campuses in all 50 states.

TRADESHOWS

2396 ■ American Association of Physics Teachers Winter Meeting
American Association of Physics Teachers AAPT
1 Physics Ellipse
College Park, MD 20740-3845
Ph: (301)209-3311
Fax: (301)209-0845
E-mail: aapt-web@aapt.org
URL: http://www.aapt.org

Annual. Primary Exhibits: Physics textbooks, apparatus, and software. Dates and Locations: 2012 Feb 04-08; Ontario, CA; 2013 Jan 05-09; New Orleans, LA.

2397 ■ American Society for Engineering Education Annual Conference and Exposition
American Society for Engineering Education
1818 N. St. N.W., Ste. 600
Washington, DC 20036-2479
Ph: (202)331-3500
Fax: (202)265-8504
E-mail: conferences@asee.org
URL: http://www.asee.org

Annual. Primary Exhibits: Publications, engineering supplies and equipment, computers, software, and research companies all products and services related to engineering education. Dates and Locations: 2012 Jun 10-13; San Antonio, TX.

2398 ■ American Technical Education Association National Conference on Technical Education
American Technical Education Association
c/o North Dakota State College of Science
800 N. 6th St.
Wahpeton, ND 58076-0002
Ph: (701)671-2301
Fax: (701)671-2260
URL: http://www.ateaonline.org

Annual. Primary Exhibits: Supplies and services related to post secondary technical education. Dates and Locations: 2012 Mar 21-23; Biloxi, MS.

2399 ■ Association for Education in Journalism and Mass Communication Annual Convention
Association for Education in Journalism and Mass Communication
234 Outlet Point Blvd.
Columbia, SC 29210-5667
Ph: (803)798-0271
Fax: (803)772-3509
E-mail: aejmcmemsub@aol.com
URL: http://www.aejmc.org

Annual. Primary Exhibits: Publications, information retrieval services, and special programs. Dates and Locations: 2012 Aug 09-12; Chicago, IL; Chicago Marriott Downtown ; 2013 Aug 08-11; Washington, DC; The Renaissance Hotel.

2400 ■ Council of Graduate Schools Annual Meeting
Council of Graduate Schools
1 Dupont Cir. NW, Ste. 230
Washington, DC 20036
Ph: (202)223-3791
Fax: (202)331-7157
E-mail: ngaffney@cgs.nche.edu
URL: http://www.cgsnet.org

Annual. Primary Exhibits: Exhibits related to the improvement and advancement of graduate education.

2401 ■ National Association for Bilingual Education Conference
National Association for Bilingual Education
8701 Georgia Ave., Ste. 611
Silver Spring, MD 20910
Ph: (240)450-3700
Fax: (240)450-3799
E-mail: nabe@nabe.org
URL: http://www.nabe.org

Annual. Features speakers, sessions, product exhibits, and job fair.

2402 ■ National Association for Developmental Education Conference
National Association for Developmental Education
PMB 412
500 N Estrella Pkwy.
Goodyear, AZ 85338
Fax: (623)792-5747
Fr: 877-233-9455
E-mail: office@nade.net
URL: http://www.nade.net

Annual. Offers an opportunity for personal and professional growth. Includes job fair. 2013 February 27-March 2; Denver, CO; Sheraton Denver Hotel. 2014 March 5-8; Dallas, TX; Hilton Anatole.

2403 ■ Southwestern Federation of Administrative Disciplines Convention
Southwestern Federation of Administrative Disciplines
2700 Bay Area Blvd.
Houston, TX 77058

Annual. Primary Exhibits: Educational materials and services.

2404 ■ UCEA Annual Conference
National University Continuing Education Association
1 Dupont Cir., Ste. 615
Washington, DC 20036
Ph: (202)659-3130
Fax: (202)785-0374
URL: http://www.ucea.edu

Annual. Primary Exhibits: Exhibits related to continuing education and online learning at institutions of higher learning.

OTHER SOURCES

2405 ■ Academy of International Business (AIB)
Michigan State University
The Eli Broad College of Business
7 Eppley Center
East Lansing, MI 48824-1121
Ph: (517)432-1452
Fax: (517)432-1009
E-mail: aib@aib.msu.edu
URL: http://aib.msu.edu

Description: Consists primarily of university professors, doctoral students, researchers, writers, consultants, executives, and policy setters in the international business/trade research and education fields. Facilitates information exchange among people in academia, business, and government and encourages research activities that advance the knowledge of international business operations and increase the available body of teaching materials. Compiles an inventory of collegiate courses in international business, a survey of research projects, and statistics.

2406 ■ Academy of Legal Studies in Business (ALSB)

Miami University
Dept. of Finance
3111 Farmer School of Business
Oxford, OH 45056
Fr: 800-831-2903
E-mail: herrondj@muohio.edu
URL: http://www.alsb.org

Description: Teachers of business law and legal environment in colleges and universities. Promotes and encourages business law scholarship and teaching outside of the law school environment.

2407 ■ Academy of Management (AOM)

PO Box 3020
Briarcliff Manor, NY 10510-8020
Ph: (914)923-2607
Fax: (914)923-2615
E-mail: nurbanowicz@pace.edu
URL: http://www.aomonline.org

Description: Professors in accredited universities and colleges who teach management; selected business executives who have made significant written contributions to the literature in the field of management and organization. Offers placement service.

2408 ■ Academy of Marketing Science (AMS)

PO Box 3072
Ruston, LA 71272
Ph: (318)257-2612
Fax: (318)257-4253
E-mail: ams@latech.edu
URL: http://www.ams-web.org

Description: Marketing academicians and practitioners; individuals interested in fostering education in marketing science. Aims to promote the advancement of knowledge and the furthering of professional standards in the field of marketing. Explores the special application areas of marketing science and its responsibilities as an economic, ethical, and social force; promotes research and the widespread dissemination of findings. Facilitates exchange of information and experience among members, and the transfer of marketing knowledge and technology to developing countries; promotes marketing science on an international level. Provides a forum for discussion and refinement of concepts, methods and applications, and the opportunity to publish papers in the field. Assists member educators in the development of improved teaching methods, devices, directions, and materials. Offers guidance and direction in marketing practice and reviewer assistance on scholarly works. Contributes to the solution of marketing problems encountered by individual firms, industries, and society as a whole. Encourages members to utilize their marketing talents to the fullest through redirection, reassignment, and relocation. Sponsors competitions.

2409 ■ American Academy of Religion (AAR)

825 Houston Mill Rd. NE, Ste. 300
Atlanta, GA 30329
Ph: (404)727-3049
Fax: (404)727-7959
E-mail: jfitzmier@aarweb.org
URL: http://www.aarweb.org

Description: Professional society of scholars and teachers in the field of religion. Encourages scholarship, research, and publications in the study of religion, and stimulates effective teaching. Hosts annual meeting, publishes academic journal, offers research grants and placement services to members; compiles statistics.

2410 ■ American Association of Community Colleges (AACC)

1 Dupont Cir. NW, Ste. 410
Washington, DC 20036-1176
Ph: (202)728-0200

Fax: (202)833-2467
E-mail: wbumphus@aacc.nche.edu
URL: http://www.aacc.nche.edu

Description: Community colleges; individual associates interested in community college development; corporate, educational, foundation, and international associate members. Office of Federal Relations monitors federal educational programming and legislation. Compiles statistics through data collection and policy analysis. Conducts seminars and professional training programs.

2411 ■ American Association for Employment in Education (AAEE)

3040 Riverside Dr., Ste. 117
Columbus, OH 43221
Ph: (614)485-1111
Fax: (614)485-9609
E-mail: execdir@aaee.org
URL: http://www.aaee.org

Description: Represents colleges, universities, and other post-secondary educational institutions, which are not-for-profit. Prepares teachers and other educational personnel for service in public and private educational institutions, organizations and agencies. Provides information or services relating to career planning, placement, and recruitment activities in education.

2412 ■ American Association for Health Education (AAHE)

1900 Association Dr.
Reston, VA 20191-1599
Ph: (703)476-3400
Fax: (703)476-9527
Fr: 800-213-7193
E-mail: aahe@aahperd.org
URL: http://www.aahperd.org/aahe

Description: Professionals who have responsibility for health education in schools, colleges, communities, hospitals and clinics, and industries. Aims to advance the health education through program activities and federal legislation; encourage close working relationships between all health education and health service organizations; achieve good health and well-being for all Americans automatically, without conscious thought and endeavor. Member of the American Alliance for Health, Physical Education, Recreation and Dance.

2413 ■ American Association of Teachers of French (AATF)

Southern Illinois University
Mail Code 4510
Carbondale, IL 62901
Ph: (618)453-5731
Fax: (618)453-5733
E-mail: aatf@frenchteachers.org
URL: http://www.frenchteachers.org

Description: Teachers of French in public and private elementary and secondary schools, colleges and universities. Sponsors National French Week each November to take French out of the classroom and into the schools and community. Conducts National French Contest in elementary and secondary schools and awards prizes at all levels. Maintains Materials Center with promotional and pedagogical materials; National French Honor Society (high school), Placement Bureau, summer scholarships.

2414 ■ American Association of Teachers of German (AATG)

112 Haddontowne Ct., No. 104
Cherry Hill, NJ 08034-3668
Ph: (856)795-5553
Fax: (856)795-9398
E-mail: headquarters@aatg.org
URL: http://www.aatg.org

Description: Represents teachers of German at all levels; individuals interested in German language and culture. Offers in-service teacher-training workshops, materials, student honor society, national German examination and stipends/scholarships.

2415 ■ American Association of Teachers of Spanish and Portuguese (AATSP)

900 Ladd Rd.
Walled Lake, MI 48390
Ph: (248)960-2180
Fax: (248)960-9570
E-mail: aatspoffice@aatsp.org
URL: http://www.aatsp.org

Description: Teachers of Spanish and Portuguese languages and literatures and others interested in Hispanic culture. Operates placement bureau and maintains pen pal registry. Sponsors honor society, Sociedad Honoraria Hispanica and National Spanish Examinations for secondary school students.

2416 ■ American Association of University Professors

1133 19th St. NW, Ste. 200
Washington, DC 20036
Ph: (202)737-5900
Fax: (202)737-5526
E-mail: aaup@aaup.org
URL: http://www.aaup.org

Description: Serves as a group of college and university teachers, research scholars, and academic librarians. Aims to advance academic freedom and shared governance, to define fundamental professional values and standards for higher education, and to ensure higher education's contribution to the common good. Develops standards and procedures to maintain quality in education and academic freedom in colleges and universities.

2417 ■ American Association for Women in Community Colleges (AAWCC)

PO Box 30808
Salt Lake City, UT 84130-0808
Ph: (801)975-4225
Fax: (801)957-4440
E-mail: aawccsupport@gmail.com
URL: http://www.aawccnatl.org

Description: Women faculty members, administrators, staff members, students, and trustees of community colleges. Objectives are to: develop communication and disseminate information among women in community, junior, and technical colleges; encourage educational program development; obtain grants for educational projects for community college women. Disseminates information on women's issues and programs. Conducts regional and state professional development workshops and forums. Recognizes model programs that assist women in community colleges. An affiliate council of the American Association of Community Colleges.

2418 ■ American Catholic Philosophical Association (ACPA)

University of St. Thomas
Center for Thomistic Studies
3800 Montrose Blvd.
Houston, TX 77006
Ph: (713)942-3483
Fax: (713)525-6964
E-mail: osborntm@stthom.edu
URL: http://www.acpaweb.org

Description: College and university teachers of philosophy; students engaged in research; writers and others interested in philosophical knowledge.

2419 ■ American Classical League (ACL)

Miami University
422 Wells Mills Dr.
Oxford, OH 45056-1694
Ph: (513)529-7741
Fax: (513)529-7742
E-mail: info@aclclassics.org
URL: http://www.aclclassics.org

Description: Teachers of classical languages in high schools and colleges. Works to promote the teaching of Latin and other classical languages. Presents scholarship. Maintains placement service, teaching materials, and resource center at Miami University in Oxford, OH to sell teaching aids to Latin and Greek teachers.

2420 ■ American Mathematical Society (AMS)
201 Charles St.
Providence, RI 02904-2213
Ph: (401)455-4000
Fax: (401)331-3842
Fr: 800-321-4AMS
E-mail: ams@ams.org
URL: http://www.ams.org

Description: Professional society of mathematicians and educators. Promotes the interests of mathematical scholarship and research. Holds institutes, seminars, short courses, and symposia to further mathematical research; awards prizes. Offers placement services; compiles statistics.

2421 ■ American Philosophical Association (APA)
University of Delaware
31 Amstel Ave.
Newark, DE 19716-4797
Ph: (302)831-1112
Fax: (302)831-8690
E-mail: apaonline@udel.edu
URL: http://www.apaonline.org

Description: College and university teachers of philosophy and others with an interest in philosophy. Facilitates exchange of ideas in philosophy, encourages creative and scholarly activity in philosophy, and fosters the professional work of teachers of philosophy. Participates in international congresses of philosophy and maintains affiliations with national and international philosophical organizations. Maintains placement service; sponsors competitions. Oversees selection of Romanell, Schutz and Carus lecturers and other prizes and awards.

2422 ■ American Political Science Association (APSA)
1527 New Hampshire Ave. NW
Washington, DC 20036-1206
Ph: (202)483-2512
Fax: (202)483-2657
E-mail: apsa@apsanet.org
URL: http://www.apsanet.org

Description: College and university teachers of political science, public officials, research workers, and businessmen. Encourages the impartial study and promotes the development of the art and science of government. Develops research projects of public interest and educational programs for political scientists and journalists; seeks to improve the knowledge of and increase citizen participation in political and governmental affairs. Serves as clearinghouse for teaching and research positions in colleges, universities, and research bureaus in the U.S. and abroad and for positions open to political scientists in government and private business; conducts Congressional Fellowship Program. Conducts Committee on Professional Ethic, and Rights and Freedom. Offers placement service.

2423 ■ Art Directors Club (ADC)
106 W 29th St.
New York, NY 10001
Ph: (212)643-1440
Fax: (212)643-4266
E-mail: info@adcglobal.org
URL: http://www.adcglobal.org

Description: Art directors of advertising magazines and agencies, visual information specialists, and graphic designers; associate members are artists, cinematographers, photographers, copywriters, educators, journalists, and critics. Promotes and stimulates interest in the practice of art direction. Sponsors Annual Exhibition of Advertising, Editorial and Television Art and Design; International Traveling Exhibition. Provides educational, professional, and entertainment programs; on-premise art exhibitions; portfolio review program. Conducts panels for students and faculty.

2424 ■ Association of American Law Schools (AALS)
1201 Connecticut Ave. NW, Ste. 800
Washington, DC 20036-2717
Ph: (202)296-8851
Fax: (202)296-8869
E-mail: aals@aals.org
URL: http://www.aals.org

Description: Law schools association. Seeks to improve the legal profession through legal education. Interacts for law professors with state and federal government, other legal education and professional associations, and other national higher education and learned society organizations. Compiles statistics; sponsors teacher placement service. Presents professional development programs.

2425 ■ Association of Departments of English (ADE)
26 Broadway, 3rd Fl.
New York, NY 10004-1789
Ph: (646)576-5130
Fax: (646)835-4056
E-mail: dlaurence@mla.org
URL: http://www.ade.org

Description: Administrators of college and university departments of English, humanities, rhetoric, and communications. Works to improve the teaching of English and the administration of English departments. Conducts studies and surveys of literature and writing courses. Sponsors sessions at major English conventions and conferences nationwide. Sponsored by Modern Language Association of America.

2426 ■ Association for Direct Instruction (ADI)
PO Box 10252
Eugene, OR 97440
Ph: (541)485-1293
Fax: (541)868-1397
Fr: 800-995-2464
E-mail: brywick@adihome.org
URL: http://www.adihome.org

Description: Public school regular and special education teachers and university instructors. Encourages, promotes, and engages in research aimed at improving educational methods. Promotes dissemination of developmental information and skills that facilitate the education of adults and children. Administers a preschool for developmentally delayed children. Offers educational training workshops for instructors. Maintains speaker's bureau and placement service.

2427 ■ Association for Education in Journalism and Mass Communication (AEJMC)
234 Outlet Pointe Blvd.
Columbia, SC 29210-5667
Ph: (803)798-0271
Fax: (803)772-3509
E-mail: aejmchq@aol.com
URL: http://www.aejmc.org

Description: Professional organization of college and university journalism and communication teachers. Works to improve methods and standards of teaching and stimulate research. Compiles statistics on enrollments and current developments in journalism education. Maintains a listing of journalism and communication teaching positions available and teaching positions wanted, revised bimonthly.

2428 ■ Association for Institutional Research
1435 E Piedmont Dr., Ste. 211
Tallahassee, FL 32308
Ph: (850)385-4155
Fax: (850)385-5180
E-mail: air@airweb.org
URL: http://www.airweb.org

Description: Serves as a professional organization for institutional researchers that provides educational resources and professional-development opportunities. Supports its members in the process of facilitating quality, data-informed decisions for the enhancement of higher education.

2429 ■ Association for Library and Information Science Education (ALISE)
65 E Wacker Pl., Ste. 1900
Chicago, IL 60601-7246
Ph: (312)795-0996
Fax: (312)419-8950
E-mail: contact@alise.org
URL: http://www.alise.org

Description: Graduate schools offering degree programs in library science and their faculties. Seeks to: promote excellence in education for library and information science as a means of increasing the effectiveness of library and information services; provide a forum for the active interchange of ideas and information among library educators; promote research related to teaching and to library and information science; formulate and promulgate positions on matters related to library education. Offers employment program at annual conference.

2430 ■ Association for the Study of Higher Education (ASHE)
4505 S Maryland Pkwy.
UNLV Box 453068
Las Vegas, NV 89154
Ph: (702)895-2737
Fax: (702)895-4269
E-mail: ashe@unlv.edu
URL: http://www.ashe.ws

Description: Professors, researchers, administrators, policy analysts, graduate students, and others concerned with the study of higher education. Aims to advance the study of higher education and facilitate and encourage discussion of priority issues for research in the study of higher education.

2431 ■ Association of University Professors of Ophthalmology (AUPO)
PO Box 193030
San Francisco, CA 94119
Ph: (415)561-8548
Fax: (415)561-8531
E-mail: aupo@aao.org
URL: http://www.aupo.org

Description: Heads of departments or divisions of ophthalmology in accredited medical schools throughout the U.S. and Canada; directors of ophthalmology residency programs in institutions not connected to medical schools. Promotes medical education, research, and patient care relating to ophthalmology. Operates Ophthalmology Matching Program and faculty placement service, which aids ophthalmologists interested in being associated with university ophthalmology programs to locate such programs.

2432 ■ College Language Association (CLA)
University of South Carolina Upstate
Division of Academic Affairs
Administration 222
Spartanburg, SC 29303
Ph: (864)503-5634
Fax: (864)503-5262
E-mail: wcarson@uscupstate.edu
URL: http://www.clascholars.org

Description: Teachers of English and modern foreign languages, primarily in historically black colleges and universities. Maintains placement service.

2433 ■ College Media Advisers (CMA)
University of Memphis
Department of Journalism
3711 Veterans Ave., Rm. 300
Memphis, TN 38152-6661
Ph: (901)678-2403
Fax: (901)678-4798
E-mail: rsplbrgr@memphis.edu
URL: http://www.collegemedia.org

Description: Professional association serving advisers, directors, and chairmen of boards of college student media (newspapers, yearbooks, magazines, handbooks, directories, and radio and television stations); heads of schools and departments of journalism; and others interested in junior college, college, and university student media. Serves as a clearinghouse for student media; acts as consultant on student theses and dissertations on publications. Encourages high school journalism and examines its relationships to college and professional journalism. Conducts national survey of student media in rotation each year by type: newspapers, magazines, and yearbooks; radio and television stations. Compiles statistics. Maintains placement service and speakers' bureau.

2434 ■ College Reading and Learning Association (CRLA)

2 Caracal St.
Belen, NM 87002
Ph: (505)861-2142
E-mail: annwolf@crla.net
URL: http://www.crla.net

Description: Professionals involved in college/adult reading, learning assistance, developmental education, and tutorial services. Promotes communication for the purpose of professional growth.

2435 ■ Conference on College Composition and Communication (CCCC)

1111 W Kenyon Rd.
Urbana, IL 61801-1096
Ph: (217)328-3870
Fr: 800-369-6283
E-mail: public_info@ncte.org
URL: http://www.ncte.org/cccc

Description: Represents college and university educators involved in teaching composition and communication.

2436 ■ Decision Sciences Institute (DSI)

75 Piedmont Ave., Ste. 340
Atlanta, GA 30303
Ph: (404)413-7710
Fax: (404)413-7714
E-mail: clatta@gsu.edu
URL: http://www.decisionsciences.org

Description: Businesspersons and members of business school faculties. Maintains placement service.

2437 ■ Eastern Finance Association (EFA)

Auburn Montgomery
School of Business
PO Box 244023
Montgomery, AL 36124-4023
E-mail: membershipservices@
  blackwellpublishers.co.uk
URL: http://etnpconferences.net/efa

Description: College and university professors and financial officers; libraries. Provides a meeting place for persons interested in any aspect of finance, including financial management, investments, and banking. Sponsors research competitions.

2438 ■ Financial Management Association International (FMA)

University of South Florida
College of Business Administration
4202 E Fowler Ave., BSN 3331
Tampa, FL 33620-5500
Ph: (813)974-2084
Fax: (813)974-3318
E-mail: fma@coba.usf.edu
URL: http://www.fma.org

Description: Professors of financial management; corporate financial officers. Facilitates exchange of ideas among persons involved in financial management or the study thereof. Conducts workshops for comparison of current research projects and development of cooperative ventures in writing and research. Sponsors honorary society for superior students at 300 colleges and universities. Offers placement services.

2439 ■ Friends Council on Education (FCE)

1507 Cherry St.
Philadelphia, PA 19102
Ph: (215)241-7245
Fax: (215)241-7299
E-mail: info@friendscouncil.org
URL: http://www.friendscouncil.org

Description: Representatives appointed by Friends Yearly Meetings; heads of Quaker secondary and elementary schools and colleges; members-at-large. Acts as a clearinghouse for information on Quaker schools and colleges. Holds meetings and conferences on education and provides in-service training for teachers, administrators and trustees in Friends schools.

2440 ■ International Association of Baptist Colleges and Universities (IABCU)

8120 Sawyer Brown Rd., Ste. 108
Nashville, TN 37221-1410
Ph: (615)673-1896
Fax: (615)662-1396
E-mail: marrington@baptistschools.org
URL: http://www.baptistschools.org

Description: Southern Baptist senior colleges, universities, junior colleges, academies, and Bible schools. Promotes Christian education through literature, faculty workshops, student recruitment, teacher placement, trustee orientation, statistical information, and other assistance to members.

2441 ■ International Association for Computer and Information Science (ACIS)

735 Meadowbrook Dr.
Mount Pleasant, MI 48858
Ph: (989)774-1175
Fax: (989)774-1174
E-mail: acis@acisinternational.org
URL: http://www.acisinternational.org

Description: Represents individuals in the fields of computer and information science. Disseminates the latest developments in the fields of computer and information science. Provides a forum for researchers in education and computer and information science industries.

2442 ■ The International Educator (TIE)

PO Box 513
Cummaquid, MA 02637
Ph: (508)790-1990
Fax: (508)790-1922
Fr: 877-375-6668
E-mail: tie@tieonline.com
URL: http://www.tieonline.com

Description: Facilitates the placement of teachers and administrators in American, British, and international schools. Seeks to create a network that provides for professional development opportunities and improved financial security of members. Offers advice and information on international school news, recent educational developments, job placement, and investment, consumer, and professional development opportunities. Makes available insurance and travel benefits. Operates International Schools Internship Program.

2443 ■ Modern Language Association of America (MLA)

26 Broadway, 3rd Fl.
New York, NY 10004-1789
Ph: (646)576-5000
Fax: (646)458-0030
E-mail: execdirector@mla.org
URL: http://www.mla.org

Description: Provides opportunities for the members to share their scholarly findings and teaching experiences with colleagues and to discuss trends in the academy. Works to strengthen the study and teaching of language and literature.

2444 ■ NAFSA: Association of International Educators (NAFSA)

1307 New York Ave. NW, 8th Fl.
Washington, DC 20005-4701
Ph: (202)737-3699
Fax: (202)737-3657
E-mail: inbox@nafsa.org
URL: http://www.nafsa.org

Description: Individuals, organizations, and institutions dealing with international educational exchange, including foreign student advisers, overseas educational advisers, credentials and admissions officers, administrators and teachers of English as a second language, community support personnel, study-abroad administrators, and embassy cultural or educational personnel. Promotes self-regulation standards and responsibilities in international educational exchange; offers professional development opportunities primarily through publications, workshops, grants, and regional and national conferences. Advocates for increased awareness and support of international education and exchange on campuses, in government, and in communities. Offers services including: a job registry for employers and professionals involved with international education; a consultant referral service. Sponsors joint liaison activities with a variety of other educational and government organizations to conduct a census of foreign student enrollment in the U.S.; conducts workshops about specific subjects and countries.

2445 ■ National Alliance of Black School Educators (NABSE)

310 Pennsylvania Ave. SE
Washington, DC 20003
Ph: (202)608-6310
Fax: (202)608-6319
Fr: 800-221-2654
E-mail: info@nabse.org
URL: http://www.nabse.org

Description: Black educators from all levels; others indirectly involved in the education of black youth. Promotes awareness, professional expertise, and commitment among black educators. Goals are to: eliminate and rectify the results of racism in education; work with state, local, and national leaders to raise the academic achievement level of all black students; increase members' involvement in legislative activities; facilitate the introduction of a curriculum that more completely embraces black America; improve the ability of black educators to promote problem resolution; create a meaningful and effective network of strength, talent, and professional support. Sponsors workshops, commission meetings, and special projects. Encourages research, especially as it relates to blacks, and the presentation of papers during national conferences. Plans to establish a National Black Educators Data Bank and offer placement service.

2446 ■ National Art Education Association (NAEA)

1806 Robert Fulton Dr., Ste. 300
Reston, VA 20191
Ph: (703)860-8000
Fax: (703)860-2960
Fr: 800-299-8321
E-mail: info@arteducators.org
URL: http://www.arteducators.org

Description: Teachers of art at elementary, middle, secondary, and college levels; colleges, libraries, museums, and other educational institutions. Studies problems of teaching art; encourages research and experimentation. Serves as a clearinghouse for information on art education programs, materials, and methods of instruction. Sponsors special institutes. Cooperates with other national organizations for the furtherance of creative art experiences for youth.

2447 ■ National Association for Bilingual Education

8701 Georgia Ave., Ste. 611
Silver Spring, MD 20910

Ph: (240)450-3700
Fax: (240)450-3799
E-mail: nabe@nabe.org
URL: http://www.nabe.org

Description: Comprised of bilingual and English language learner (ELL) teachers, parents, paraprofessionals, administrators, professors, advocates, researchers, and policy makers. Promotes English proficiency and respect for cultural and linguistic diversity. Creates and supports policies, programs, research, pedagogy, and professional development to achieve bilingualism and biliteracy.

2448 ■ National Association of Blind Teachers (NABT)
2200 Wilson Blvd., Ste. 650
Arlington, VA 22201
Ph: (202)467-5081
Fax: (703)465-5085
Fr: 800-424-8666
E-mail: info@acb.org
URL: http://www.acb.org

Description: Public school teachers, teachers of the visually impaired, college and university professors, and teachers in residential schools for the blind. Promotes employment and professional goals of blind persons entering the teaching profession or those established in their respective teaching fields. Serves as a vehicle for the dissemination of information and the exchange of ideas addressing special problems of members.

2449 ■ National Association of College and University Business Officers (NACUBO)
1110 Vermont Ave. NW, Ste. 800
Washington, DC 20005
Ph: (202)861-2500
Fax: (202)861-2583
Fr: 800-462-4916
E-mail: john.walda@nacubo.org
URL: http://www.nacubo.org

Description: Colleges, universities, and companies that are members of a regional association. Develops and maintains national interest in improving the principles and practices of business and financial administration in higher education. Sponsors workshops in fields such as cash management, grant and contract maintenance, accounting, investment, student loan administration, and costing. Conducts research and information exchange programs between college and university personnel; compiles statistics.

2450 ■ National Association of Deans and Directors of Schools of Social Work (NADD)
1701 Duke St., Ste. 200
Alexandria, VA 22314
Ph: (703)683-8080
Fax: (703)683-8099
E-mail: naddssw@cswe.org
URL: http://www.naddssw.org

Description: Represents deans and directors of graduate social work programs that are in candidacy or accredited by CSWE. Works to promote excellence in social work education. Supports deans and directors in their professional development and effectiveness as academic administrators.

2451 ■ National Association for Developmental Education
PMB 412
500 N Estrella Pkwy.
Goodyear, AZ 85338
Fax: (623)792-5747
Fr: 877-233-9455
E-mail: office@nade.net
URL: http://www.nade.net

Description: Seeks to improve the theory and practice of developmental education. Enhances the

professional capabilities of development educators. Facilitates communication among developmental education professionals.

2452 ■ National Association for Sport and Physical Education (NASPE)
1900 Association Dr.
Reston, VA 20191-1598
Ph: (703)476-3410
Fax: (703)476-8316
Fr: 800-213-7193
E-mail: naspe@aahperd.org
URL: http://www.naspeinfo.org

Description: Men and women professionally involved with physical activity and sports. Seeks to improve the total sport and physical activity experience in America. Conducts research and education programs in such areas as sport psychology, curriculum development, kinesiology, history, philosophy, sport sociology, and the biological and behavioral basis of human activity. Develops and distributes public information materials which explain the value of physical education programs. Supports councils involved in organizing and supporting elementary, secondary, and college physical education and sport programs; administers the National Council of Athletic Training in conjunction with the National Association for Girls and Women in Sport; serves the professional interests of coaches, trainers, and officials. Maintains hall of fame, placement service, and media resource center for public information and professional preparation. Member benefits include group insurance and discounts.

2453 ■ National Communication Association (NCA)
1765 N St. NW
Washington, DC 20036
Ph: (202)464-4622
Fax: (202)464-4600
E-mail: nkidd@natcom.org
URL: http://www.natcom.org

Description: Elementary, secondary, college, and university teachers, speech clinicians, media specialists, communication consultants, students, theater directors, and other interested persons; libraries and other institutions. Works to promote study, criticism, research, teaching, and application of the artistic, humanistic, and scientific principles of communication, particularly speech communication. Sponsors the publication of scholarly volumes in speech. Conducts international debate tours in the U.S. and abroad. Maintains placement service.

2454 ■ National Council for Geographic Education (NCGE)
1145 17th St. NW, Rm. 7620
Washington, DC 20036
Ph: (202)857-7695
Fax: (202)618-6249
E-mail: ncge@ncge.org
URL: http://www.ncge.org

Description: Teachers of geography and social studies in elementary and secondary schools, colleges and universities; geographers in governmental agencies and private businesses. Encourages the training of teachers in geographic concepts, practices, teaching methods and techniques; works to develop effective geographic educational programs in schools and colleges and with adult groups; stimulates the production and use of accurate and understandable geographic teaching aids and materials.

2455 ■ National Council of Teachers of Mathematics (NCTM)
1906 Association Dr.
Reston, VA 20191-1502
Ph: (703)620-9840
Fax: (703)476-2970

Fr: 800-235-7566
E-mail: nctm@nctm.org
URL: http://www.nctm.org

Description: Aims to improve teaching and learning of mathematics.

2456 ■ Organization of American Historians (OAH)
112 N Bryan Ave.
Bloomington, IN 47408-4141
Ph: (812)855-7311
Fax: (812)855-0696
E-mail: questions@oah.org
URL: http://www.oah.org

Description: Professional historians, including college faculty members, secondary school teachers, graduate students, and other individuals in related fields; institutional subscribers are college, university, high school and public libraries, and historical agencies. Promotes historical research and study. Sponsors 12 prize programs for historical writing; maintains speakers' bureau. Conducts educational programs.

2457 ■ *Overseas Employment Opportunities for Educators: Department of Defense Dependents Schools*
DIANE Publishing Co.
PO Box 617
Darby, PA 19023-0617
Fr: 800-782-3833
URL: http://www.dianepublishing.net

Barry Leonard, editor. $20.00. 52 pages. An introduction to teachings positions in the Dept. of Defense Dependents Schools (DoDDS), a worldwide school system, operated by the DoD in 14 countries.

2458 ■ U.S.-China Education Foundation (USCEF)
4140 Oceanside Blvd., Ste. 159, No. 112
Oceanside, CA 92056-6005
E-mail: info@sage-usa.net
URL: http://www.sage-usa.net

Description: Aims to promote the learning of the Chinese languages (including Mandarin, Cantonese, and minority languages such as Mongolian) by Americans, and the learning of English by Chinese. Conducts short-term travel-study program to prepare Americans and Chinese for stays of four, six, or eight months or one to four years in China or the U.S., respectively. Operates teacher placement service and speakers' bureau. A project of The Society for the Development of Global Education (S.A.G.E. Inc.).

2459 ■ University Photographers Association of America (UPAA)
Community College
9000 W College Pkwy.
Palos Hills, IL 60465
E-mail: carpenter@morainevalley.edu
URL: http://www.upaa.org

Description: College and university personnel engaged professionally in photography, audiovisual work, or journalism for universities. Seeks to advance applied photography and the profession through the exchange of thoughts and opinions among its members. Awards fellowship for exceptional work in the advancement of photography. Provides a medium for exchange of ideas and technical information on photography, especially university photographic work. Sponsors exhibits. Provides placement service for members.

2460 ■ ACM Transactions on Internet Technology
Association for Computing Machinery
PO Box 30777
New York, NY 10087
Ph: (212)626-0500
Fax: (212)944-1318
Fr: 800-342-6626
URL: http://toit.acm.org

Quarterly. $190.00/year for nonmembers, print only; $152.00/year for nonmembers, online only; $228.00/year for nonmembers, online and print. Publication of the Association for Computing Machinery. Brings together many computing disciplines including computer software engineering, computer programming languages, middleware, database management, security, knowledge discovery and data mining, networking and distributed systems, communications, performance and scalability, and more. Covers the results and roles of the individual disciplines and the relationships among them.

2461 ■ AVIOS Journal
Applied Voice Input/Output Society
PO Box 20817
San Jose, CA 95160
Ph: (408)323-1783
Fax: (408)323-1782
URL: http://www.avios.com/

Annual. Journal covering issues in computer science.

2462 ■ Communications of the ACM
Association for Computing Machinery
PO Box 30777
New York, NY 10087
Ph: (212)626-0500
Fax: (212)944-1318
Fr: 800-342-6626
URL: http://cacm.acm.org

Monthly. $99.00/year for members, professional. Computing news magazine.

2463 ■ Communications and Network
Scientific Research Publishing
PO Box 54821
Irvine, CA 92619-4821
E-mail: cn@scirp.org
URL: http://www.scirp.org/journal/cn/

Quarterly. $236.00/year for individuals. Journal publishing articles on the latest advancements in communications and network technologies.

2464 ■ Computer Economics Report
Computer Economics Inc.
2082 Business Center Dr., Ste 240
Irvine, CA 92612
Ph: (949)831-8700
Fax: (949)442-7688

Fr: 800-326-8100
URL: http://www.computereconomics.com

Description: Monthly. $695. 20 pages. Provides analyses of new IBM technologies and acquisitions and financial management strategies from an end-user perspective. Recurring features include cost comparisons, price/performance analyses, new product forecasts, and evaluations of acquisition techniques for medium and large computer systems. Also available in international edition.

2465 ■ Computers and Composition
Elsevier Science Inc.
360 Park Ave. S
New York, NY 10010-1710
Ph: (212)989-5800
Fax: (212)633-3990
Fr: 888-437-4636
URL: http://www.elsevier.com/wps/find/journaldescription.cws_home

$454.00/year for institutions, all countries except Europe, Japan and Iran; $405.00/year for institutions, European countries and Iran; $53,500.00/year for institutions, Japan; $82.00/year for individuals, all countries except Europe, Japan and Iran; $62.00/year for individuals, European countries and Iran; $8,900.00/year for individuals, Japan. Journal covering computers in writing classes, programs, and research.

2466 ■ Computers Programs/PC World
IDG Communications Inc.
3 Speen St.
Framingham, MA 01701
Ph: (508)875-5000
URL: http://www.idg.com

Magazine devoted to IT specialists, covering practical questions of computing including purchase and usage of the computer technology, software, computer components and peripherals.

2467 ■ Computerworld/Correio Informatico
IDG Communications Inc.
3 Speen St.
Framingham, MA 01701
Ph: (508)875-5000
URL: http://www.idg.com/www/IDGProducts.nsf/0/B1E40F5ABD0169AB852

Weekly. Magazine providing news on latest developments in computer industry.

2468 ■ Computerworld Top 100
IDG Communications Inc.
3 Speen St.
Framingham, MA 01701
Ph: (508)875-5000
URL: http://www.idg.com/www/IDGProducts.nsf/0/E7EDD4EC98463F2C852

Annual. Magazine for analyzing trends and events of information technology business.

2469 ■ Computing SA
IDG Communications Inc.
3 Speen St.
Framingham, MA 01701
Ph: (508)875-5000
URL: http://www.idg.com/www/IDGProducts.nsf/0/12C44C74D05A07DF852

Monthly. Newspaper focusing computer hardware, software, networking, telecommunications, channel management and online computing.

2470 ■ Cutter IT Journal
Cutter Information Corp.
37 Broadway, Ste. 1
Arlington, MA 02474
Ph: (781)648-8700
Fax: (781)648-8707
E-mail: service@cutter.com
URL: http://www.cutter.com/itjournal.html

Description: Monthly. $485. Provides IT managers with practical and objective views on the latest technology and management trends.

2471 ■ CXO
IDG Communications Inc.
3 Speen St.
Framingham, MA 01701
Ph: (508)875-5000
URL: http://www.idg.com/www/IDGProducts.nsf/0/022796185EED5984852

Monthly. Magazine providing technology information for chief officers and managers.

2472 ■ Eclipse Review
BZ Media L.L.C.
7 High St., Ste. 407
Huntington, NY 11743
Ph: (631)421-4158
Fax: (631)421-4130
URL: http://www.eclipsesource.com/contact.htm

Magazine for IT professionals.

2473 ■ Foundations and Trends in Networking
Now Publishers
PO Box 1024
Hanover, MA 02339-1001
Ph: (781)871-0245
URL: http://www.nowpublishers.com/product.aspx?product=NET

$390.00/year for individuals, online only; $450.00/year for individuals, print and online; $390.00/year for other countries, online only; $450.00/year for other countries, print and online. Academic journal publishing new research in computer networking.

2474 ■ Government Computer News
PostNewsweek Tech Media
10 G St. NE, Ste. 500
Washington, DC 20002-4228
Ph: (202)772-2500
Fax: (202)772-2511

Fr: (866)447-6864
URL: http://gcn.com/

Semimonthly. Magazine for professionals interested in government IT.

2475 ■ HIMSS Insider
Healthcare Information and Management Systems Society
230 E Ohio St., Ste. 500
Chicago, IL 60611-3270
Ph: (312)664-4467
Fax: (312)664-6143
E-mail: himss@himss.org
URL: http://www.himss.org/ASP/index.asp

Description: Monthly. Reports the news of the Healthcare Information and Management Systems Society (HIMSS), which provides leadership in healthcare for the management of technology, information, and change through publications, educational opportunities, and member services.

2476 ■ IEEE Security & Privacy Magazine
IEEE Computer Society
10662 Los Vaqueros Cir.
PO Box 3014
Los Alamitos, CA 90720-1314
Ph: (714)821-8380
Fax: (714)821-4010
Fr: 800-272-6657
URL: http://www.computer.org/portal/site/security/

Bimonthly. $735.00/year for individuals, online; $770.00/year for individuals, print; $965.00/year for individuals, print and online. Journal that aims to explore role and importance of networked infrastructure and developing lasting security solutions.

2477 ■ IEEE Transactions on Terahertz Science and Technology
IEEE Microwave Theory and Techniques Society
c/o Edward C. Niehenke
Niehenke Consulting
5829 Bellanca Dr.
Elkridge, MD 21075
Ph: (410)796-5866
Fax: (410)796-5829
E-mail: thz.editors@ieee.org
URL: http://www.mtt.org/publications/118-terahertz.html

Peer-reviewed journal covering terahertz science and applications.

2478 ■ Information Executive
Association of Information Technology Professionals
401 N Michigan Ave., Ste. 2400
Chicago, IL 60611-4267
Ph: (312)245-1070
Fax: (312)673-6659
Fr: 800-224-9371
E-mail: aitp_hq@aitp.org
URL: http://www.aitp.org

Description: Ten issues/year. Provides up-to-date information on the changes and developments of the information systems industry.

2479 ■ Information Security
TechTarget
117 Kendrick St., Ste. 800
Needham, MA 02494
Ph: (781)657-1000
Fax: (781)657-1100
Fr: 888-274-4111
URL: http://searchsecurity.techtarget.com/

Monthly. Free to qualified subscribers. Magazine covering information security topics.

2480 ■ Information Technology Adviser
Progressive Business Publications
370 Technology Dr.
Malvern, PA 19355
Fax: (610)647-8089
Fr: 800-220-5000
E-mail: customer_service@pbp.com
URL: http://www.pbp.com/ITA.asp

Description: Semimonthly. $299/year. Presents information to keep IT/IS managers up-to-date on how technology cuts costs, boosts productivity, and makes companies more successful. Recurring features include interviews, news of research, a calendar of events, news of educational opportunities, and a column titled Sharpen Your Judgment.

2481 ■ InfoWorld
InfoWorld Media Group
501 2nd St.
San Francisco, CA 94107
Fr: 800-227-8365
E-mail: letters@infoworld.com
URL: http://www.infoworld.com/

Weekly. Free to qualified subscribers; $180.00/year for individuals. Weekly publication.

2482 ■ Intelligent Information Management
Scientific Research Publishing
PO Box 54821
Irvine, CA 92619-4821
E-mail: iim@scirp.org
URL: http://www.scirp.org/journal/iim/

Bimonthly. $354.00/year for individuals. Peer-reviewed journal publishing articles on the latest advancements in intelligent information management.

2483 ■ International Journal of Communications, Network and System Sciences
Scientific Research Publishing
PO Box 54821
Irvine, CA 92619-4821
E-mail: ijcns@scirp.org
URL: http://www.scirp.org/journal/ijcns/

Monthly. $948.00/year for individuals. Peer-reviewed journal publishing articles on the latest advancements in communications and network technologies.

2484 ■ IT Solutions Guide
SYS-CON Media
577 Chestnut Ridge Rd.
Woodcliff Lake, NJ 07677
Ph: (201)802-3000
Fax: (201)782-9601
URL: http://itsolutions.sys-con.com/

Quarterly. Magazine for IT professionals.

2485 ■ Journal of Computer Science
Science Publications
Vails Gate Heights Dr.
PO Box 879
Vails Gate, NY 12584-0879
URL: http://thescipub.com/jcs.toc

Scholarly journal covering many areas of computer science, including: concurrent, parallel and distributed processing; artificial intelligence; image and voice processing; quality software and metrics; computer-aided education; wireless communication; real time processing; evaluative computation; and data bases and information recovery and neural networks.

2486 ■ Journal of Computer Systems, Networks, and Communications
Hindawi Publishing Corp.
410 Park Ave., 15th Fl.
287 PMB
New York, NY 10022-4407
Fax: (215)893-4392
E-mail: jcsnc@hindawi.com
URL: http://www.hindawi.com/journals/jcsnc/

$195.00/year for individuals, print & online. Journal covering important areas of information technology.

2487 ■ Journal of Information Security
Scientific Research Publishing
PO Box 54821
Irvine, CA 92619-4821
E-mail: jis@scirp.org
URL: http://www.scirp.org/journal/jis/

Quarterly. $156.00/year for individuals. Peer-reviewed

journal publishing articles on different areas of information security.

2488 ■ Journal of Intelligent Learning Systems and Applications
Scientific Research Publishing
PO Box 54821
Irvine, CA 92619-4821
URL: http://www.scirp.org/journal/jilsa/

Peer-reviewed journal covering all aspects of intelligent learning systems and applications.

2489 ■ Monitor
Capital PC User Group
19209 Mt. Airey Rd.
Brookeville, MD 20833
Ph: (301)560-6442
Fax: (301)760-3303
E-mail: editor@cpcug.org
URL: http://monitor.cpcug.org/index.html

Quarterly. Magazine covering computer hardware and software reviews, special interest user group news, advertisers and author/subject index, and calendar of events.

2490 ■ PC WORLD
101 Communications
9121 Oakdale Ave., Ste. 101
Chatsworth, CA 91311
Ph: (818)814-5200
Fax: (818)734-1522
E-mail: pcwletters@pcworld.com
URL: http://www.pcworld.com

Quarterly. $19.97/year for individuals; $29.97/year for two years. Technology or business magazine meeting the informational needs of tech-savvy managers, both at work and at home.

2491 ■ Positioning
Scientific Research Publishing
PO Box 54821
Irvine, CA 92619-4821
E-mail: pos@scirp.org
URL: http://www.scirp.org/journal/pos/

Quarterly. $156.00/year for individuals. Peer-reviewed journal publishing articles on different areas of navigation and positioning.

2492 ■ Queue
Association for Computing Machinery
PO Box 30777
New York, NY 10087
Ph: (212)626-0500
Fax: (212)944-1318
Fr: 800-342-6626
E-mail: queue@acm.org
URL: http://queue.acm.org/

Monthly. Free, U.S./Canadian residents and all members. Online magazine aimed at the computer professional. Magazine editorial does not provide solutions for the "here-and-now", but instead helps decision-makers plan future projects by examining the challenges and problems they are most likely to face.

2493 ■ Report on IBM
DataTrends Publications Inc.
PO Box 3221
Leesburg, VA 20177
Ph: (571)313-9916
Fax: (703)771-9091
E-mail: sarah@datatrendspublications.com
URL: http://www.datatrendspublications.com

Description: Biweekly. $495. Involved with International Business Machines Corporation (IBM) activities and lines of business, with emphasis on information systems in businesses, factories and homes. Contains news and articles on new IBM introductions, new markets and market strategies, and industry trends.

2494 ■ *Revenue*
Montgomery Media International
55 New Montgomery St., Ste. 617
San Francisco, CA 94105
Ph: (415)371-8800
URL: http://www.revenuetoday.com/

Free to qualified subscribers. Magazine covering internet marketing strategies.

**2495 ■ *SIGMIS Management Information
Systems***
Association for Computing Machinery
2 Penn Pl., Ste. 701
New York, NY 10121-0701
Ph: (212)626-0500
Fax: (212)944-1318
Fr: 800-342-6626
E-mail: infodir_sigmis@acm.org
URL: http://www.sigmis.org

Description: Quarterly. Covers information systems and technologies for management.

2496 ■ *Systems Management News*
BZ Media L.L.C.
7 High St., Ste. 407
Huntington, NY 11743
Ph: (631)421-4158
Fax: (631)421-4130
URL: http://www.sysmannews.com/

Monthly. Magazine providing news, analysis and strategic technology articles that help IT managers understand.

2497 ■ *Ubiquity*
Association for Computing Machinery
PO Box 30777
New York, NY 10087
Ph: (212)626-0500
Fax: (212)944-1318
Fr: 800-342-6626
URL: http://ubiquity.acm.org

Weekly. Free. Web-based magazine of the Association for Computing Machinery dedicated to fostering critical analysis and in-depth commentary, including book reviews, on issues relating to the nature, constitution, structure, science, engineering, cognition, technology, practices and paradigms of the IT profession.

2498 ■ *WITI FastTrack*
United business Media L.L.C
240 W 35th St.
New York, NY 10001
Ph: (516)562-5000
URL: http://www.witi.com/corporate/fasttrack.php

Semiannual. Semiannual publication featuring in-depth content on the issues facing today's women professionals in technology.

Placement and Job Referral Services

2499 ■ Randstad Engineering
225 Scientific Dr.
Norcross, GA 30092
Ph: (770)390-9888
URL: http://www.thinkresources.com/tr.nsf/
    Welcome.xsp

Description: Provides staffing solutions for companies that have needs for qualified technical professionals. Serves as a vital link between technical professionals and the companies that need technical personnel.

Employer Directories and Networking Lists

**2500 ■ *Career Opportunities in Computers
and Cyberspace***
Facts On File Inc.
132 W 31st St., 17th Fl.
New York, NY 10001

Ph: (212)967-8800
Fax: 800-678-3633
Fr: 800-322-8755
URL: http://www.infobasepublishing.com

Published March, 2004. Covers: Nearly 200 professions, clustering them by skill, objectives, and work conditions. Entries include: Education, salaries, employment prospects.

2501 ■ *Careers in Focus—Computers*
Facts On File Inc.
132 W 31st St., 17th Fl.
New York, NY 10001
Ph: (212)967-8800
Fax: 800-678-3633
Fr: 800-322-8755
URL: http://www.infobasepublishing.com

Latest edition 5th; Published August, 2008. $32.95 for individuals. Covers: An overview of computers, followed by a selection of jobs profiled in detail, including the nature of the job, earnings, prospects for employment, what kind of training and skills it requires, and sources for further information.

**2502 ■ *Discovering Careers for Your
Future—Computers***
Facts On File Inc.
132 W 31st St., 17th Fl.
New York, NY 10001
Ph: (212)967-8800
Fax: 800-678-3633
Fr: 800-322-8755
URL: http://factsonfile.infobasepublishing.com

Latest edition 2nd, 2008. $21.95 for individuals. Covers: Computer operators, programmers, database specialists, and software engineers; links career education to curriculum, helping children investigate the subjects they are interested in, and the careers those subjects might lead to.

**2503 ■ *Vault Guide to the Top Tech
Employers***
Vault.com Inc.
150 W 22nd St., 5th Fl.
New York, NY 10011
Ph: (212)366-4212
Fax: (212)366-6117
Fr: 888-562-8285
URL: http://www.vault.com/store/book_
    preview.jsp?product_id=38814

Latest edition June, 2009. $19.95 for individuals; $19.95 for members. Covers: Technology industry employers. Entries include: Name, address, phone, fax, website, and other branch office location. Also include company overviews, recent company news, information on the hiring process, key competitors, and employment contact.

Handbooks and Manuals

**2504 ■ *America's Top 100 Computer and
Technical Jobs***
Jist Publishing
875 Montreal Way
St. Paul, MN 55102
Fr: 800-648-5478
E-mail: info@jist.com
URL: http://www.jist.com/shop/
    product.php?productid=16453&cat=0&page=1

Michael J. Farr. 2009. $17.95. 400 pages. Job hunting in computer and technical industries.

Employment Agencies and Search Firms

2505 ■ ATR Technology
1230 Oakmead Pkwy.
Sunnyvale, CA 94085
Ph: (408)328-8000

Fax: (408)328-8001
Fr: 877-412-1100
E-mail: corporate@atr1.com
URL: http://www.atr-technology.com

Description: Serves as an executive search firm specializing in the placement of information technology professionals ranging from complex software application development and infrastructure support to enterprise-wide project management.

2506 ■ Busch International
1000 Fremont Ave., Ste. 195
Los Altos, CA 94024
Ph: (650)949-6500
E-mail: olga@buschint.com
URL: http://www.buschint.com

Executive search firm focused solely on high-technology electronics.

2507 ■ Carol Maden Group
2019 Cunningham Dr., Ste. 218
Hampton, VA 23666-3316
Ph: (757)827-9010
Fax: (757)827-9081
E-mail: cmaden@hroads.net

Personnel consultants offering placement service in computer technology and engineering; servicing manufacturing and private industries nationwide. Temporary placement servicing clerical and light industrial.

2508 ■ cFour Partners
100 Wilshire Blvd., Ste. 1840
Santa Monica, CA 90401
Ph: (310)471-5444
Fax: (310)388-0411
E-mail: info@cfour.com
URL: http://www.cfour.com/web/default.asp

Executive search firm.

2509 ■ Chaves & Associates
418 Meadow St.
Fairfield, CT 06824
Ph: (203)222-2222
Fax: (203)341-8844
E-mail: info@asinsitesearch.com
URL: http://www.insitesearch.com

Executive search firm.

2510 ■ Clovis, LLC
10411 Motor City Dr., Ste. 450
Bethesda, MD 20817
Ph: (301)365-8480
Fax: (301)576-3579
Fr: 888-925-6847
E-mail: solutions@clovisgroup.com
URL: http://www.clovisgroup.com

Description: Serves as recruitment outsourcing staffing firm for information technology, accounting and finance professionals.

2511 ■ CNR Search & Services
30752 Via Conquista
San Juan Capistrano, CA 92675
Ph: (949)488-0065
Fax: (775)851-4514
E-mail: cnrkenmiller@juno.com
URL: http://www.cnrsearch.com

Provides staffing services of permanent and temporary employees. Works primarily on a retained basis. Contingency on a limited basis. Services include human resources consulting, mergers and acquisitions in high technology firms. Industries served: computer; information services; insurance, pharmaceutical and health care. Provides staffing services of permanent and temporary employees. Works primarily on a retained basis. Contingency on a limited basis. Services include human resources consulting, mergers and acquisitions in high technology firms. Industries served: computer; information services; insurance, pharmaceutical and health care.

2512 ▪ Computer Management
7982 Honeygo Blvd., No. 23
Baltimore, MD 21236
Ph: (410)679-7000
E-mail: info@technicaljobs.com
URL: http://www.technicaljobs.com

Search firm focusing on filling jobs for database administration, network administration, web development, and software.

2513 ▪ CyberCoders, Inc.
6591 Irvine Center Dr., Ste. 200
Irvine, CA 92618
Ph: (866)421-0200
Fax: (949)885-5150
E-mail: info@cybercoders.com
URL: http://www.cybercoders.com

Description: Recruitment and job search firm specializing in engineering, executive, financial, accounting and sales.

2514 ▪ Dahl-Morrow International
1821 Michael Faraday Dr., Ste. 202
Reston, VA 20190
Ph: (703)787-8117
E-mail: info@dahl-morrowintl.com
URL: http://www.dahl-morrowintl.com

Executive search firm specializing in high technology.

2515 ▪ DillonGray
1796 Equestrian Dr.
Pleasanton, CA 94588
Ph: (925)846-9396
E-mail: info@dillongray.com
URL: http://www.dillongray.com

Executive search firm focused on technology related companies.

2516 ▪ Doleman Enterprises
11160-F S Lakes Dr., Ste. 326
Reston, VA 22091
Ph: (703)742-5454
Fax: (703)708-6992
E-mail: doleman@patriot.net

Human resources firm specializes in recruiting for the high-tech, data and computer engineering and pharmaceutical industries.

2517 ▪ Durakis Executive Search
PO Box 1382
Brooklandville, MD 21022-1382
Ph: (410)252-2055
E-mail: resumes@durakis.com
URL: http://www.durakis.com

Executive search firm.

2518 ▪ Dynamic Search Systems Inc.
220 W Campus Dr., Ste. 201
PO Box 1188
Arlington Heights, IL 60004-1499
Ph: (847)304-0700
Fax: (847)304-5859
E-mail: candidate@dssjobs.com
URL: http://www.dssjobs.com

Provides executive and professional search services to the IT community. Firm specializes in the placement of developers, programmers, programmer analysts, systems analysts, project leaders, project managers, systems programmers, data processing consultants, IT directors, and other information technology related candidates. Industries served: all.

2519 ▪ EDP Staffing, LLC
PO Box 651
Hebron, CT 06231
Fr: (860)781-6064
E-mail: info@edpstaffingllc.com
URL: http://www.edpstaffingllc.com

Description: Serves as an e-commerce and IT management search firm. Provides staffing solutions for contingency, retained, contract or temporary staffing. Specializes in the recruitment and placement

of e-commerce applications specialists, core IT staff members or IT management professionals.

2520 ▪ Effective Search Inc.
301 N Main St., Ste. 1320
Wichita, KS 67202-4813
Ph: (316)267-9180
Fax: (316)267-9187
Fr: 800-844-8456
E-mail: effsrch@aol.com

Conducts executive professional level searches only. Firm specializes in information technology IT.

2521 ▪ Executive Directions Inc.
PO Box 5742
Sarasota, CA 34277
Ph: (941)922-9180
E-mail: info@execdir.com
URL: http://www.execdir.com

Executive search firm.

2522 ▪ Focus Learning Corp.
173 Cross St., Ste. 200
San Luis Obispo, CA 93401
Ph: (805)543-4895
Fax: (805)543-4897
Fr: 800-458-5116
E-mail: info@focuslearning.com
URL: http://www.focuslearning.com

Provides professional services to corporations for the development and implementation of training programs. Assists clients with needs assessment related to training and professional development, goals definition, and development of training materials. Industries served include: government, utility, aerospace, business, and computer.

2523 ▪ Howard Fischer Associates International Inc.
1800 Kennedy Blvd., Ste. 700
Philadelphia, PA 19103
Ph: (215)568-8363
Fax: (215)568-4815
E-mail: search@hfischer.com
URL: http://www.hfischer.com

Executive search firm. Branches in Campbell, CA and Boston, MA.

2524 ▪ Integrisource
1689 Mahan Center Blvd., Ste. B
Tallahassee, FL 32308
Ph: (850)575-5454
Fax: (850)575-0984
Fr: 877-575-5454
E-mail: recruiting@integrisource.net
URL: http://www.integrisource.net

Provides information technology staffing services to public and private organizations.

2525 ▪ JES Search Firm Inc.
1021 Stovall Blvd., Ste. 600
Atlanta, GA 30319
Ph: (404)812-0622
Fax: (404)812-1910
E-mail: admin@jessearch.com
URL: http://www.jessearch.com

Contract and permanent information technology search firm specializing in placing software developers as well as other information systems professionals.

2526 ▪ Louis Rudzinsky Associates Inc.
394 Lowell St., Ste. 17
PO Box 640
Lexington, MA 02420-2551
Ph: (781)862-6727
Fax: (781)862-6868
E-mail: lra@lra.com
URL: http://www.lra.com

Provides recruitment, placement, and executive search to industry (software, electronics, optics) covering positions in general management, manufacturing, engineering, and marketing. Personnel con-

sulting activities include counsel to small and startup companies. Industries served: electronics, aerospace, optical, laser, computer, software, imaging, electro-optics, biotechnology, advanced materials, and solid-state/semiconductor.

2527 ▪ LW Foote Company
PO Box 52762
Bellevue, WA 98004
Ph: (425)451-1660
E-mail: email@lwfoote.com
URL: http://www.lwfoote.com

Executive search firm.

2528 ▪ Management Architects
6484 Washington St., Ste. B
Yountville, CA 94599
Ph: (707)945-1340
Fax: (707)945-1345
E-mail: doug@managementarchitects.net
URL: http://www.managementarchitects.net

Executive search firm. Focuses on networking industries.

2529 ▪ Michael Anthony Associates Inc.
44 Washington St., Ste. 250
Wellesley, MA 02481-1802
Ph: (781)237-4950
Fax: (781)237-6811
Fr: 800-337-4950
E-mail: manthony@maainc.com
URL: http://www.maainc.com

Applications development, systems programming, communications, and database specialists servicing the IBM mainframe, midrange, and PC marketplace. Provides technical expertise of conversions, system software installation and upgrades, performance and tuning, capacity planning, and data communications. In addition to contract services also provide retained search and contingency placement of computer professionals ranging from senior staff to senior management. Also act as brokers for independent consultants and small consulting firms requiring the services of marketing specialists. Industries served: banking, financial services, hospitals, HMO's, manufacturers, software development, universities, defense, and consulting firms.

2530 ▪ Penn Search Inc.
1045 1st Ave., Ste. 110
PO Box 688
King of Prussia, PA 19406
Ph: (610)964-8820
Fax: (610)964-8916
E-mail: charlied@pennsearch.com
URL: http://www.pennsearch.com

Assists in recruiting and hiring accounting and financial professionals from staff accountant to chief financial officer. Industries served: all.

2531 ▪ Pro Staff
14300 Nicollet Ct., Ste. 208
Burnsville, MN 55306
Ph: (952)892-3240
Fax: (952)892-7304
Fr: 800-938-WORK
E-mail: burnsville@prostaff.com
URL: http://www.prostaff.com

Description: Strives to enhance the success and development of client-companies through cost-efficient, comprehensive workforce management solutions. Focuses on the employment market, labor trends, and best practices in administrative, finance and accounting, information technology, technical, and creative services.

2532 ▪ Spectrum Group, LLC
1919 Gallows Rd., Ste. 600
Vienna, VA 22182
Ph: (703)738-1200
Fax: (703)761-9477
E-mail: web@spectrumcareers.com
URL: http://www.spectrumcareers.com

Description: Serves as executive search firm for accounting and finance, information technology and sales and marketing industries.

2533 ■ TRC Staffing Services Inc.

115 Perimeter Center Pl. NE, Ste. 855
Atlanta, GA 30346
Ph: (770)392-1411
Fax: (770)392-7926
E-mail: info@trcstaff.com
URL: http://www.trcstaff.com

A full-service executive search company with permanent placements encompassing engineering, industrial sales, financial and computer science positions. Screen, interview, and verify past employment for all candidates prior to referral. Also assist personnel staffs in the attainment of their EEO/AAP goals with the placement of talented individuals in positions which were underutilized with minorities and/or women. Industries served: all.

ONLINE JOB SOURCES AND SERVICES

2534 ■ Benchfolks.com

URL: http://www.benchfolks.com

Description: Provides a one-stop shop for IT professionals, companies/clients and vendors/suppliers by catering to their employment needs. Caters to individual needs like professional standing in terms of qualification, level of expertise, experience gained and requirement of the industry.

2535 ■ ComputerWork.com

Fr: 800-691-8413
URL: http://www.computerwork.com

Description: Job search and resume submission service for professionals in information technology.

2536 ■ Computerworld Careers

URL: http://www.computerworld.com/careertopics/careers

Description: Offers career opportunities for IT (information technology) professionals. Job seekers may search the jobs database, register at the site, and read about job surveys and employment trends. Employers may post jobs.

2537 ■ Computing Research Association Job Announcements

1828 L St. NW, Ste. 800
Washington, DC 20036-4632
Ph: (202)234-2111
Fax: (202)667-1066
E-mail: info@cra.org
URL: http://www.cra.org/ads

Description: Contains dated links to national college and university computer technology positions.

2538 ■ Dice.com

URL: http://www.dice.com

Description: Job search database for computer consultants and high-tech professionals, listing thousands of high tech permanent contract and consulting jobs for programmers, software engineers, systems administrators, web developers, and hardware engineers. Also free career advice e-mail newsletter and job posting e-alerts.

2539 ■ Guru.com

5001 Baum Blvd., Ste. 760
Pittsburgh, PA 15213
Fax: (412)687-4466
Fr: 888-687-1316
URL: http://www.guru.com

Description: Job board specializing in contract jobs for creative and information technology professionals. Also provides online incorporation and educational opportunities for independent contractors along with articles and advice.

2540 ■ InformationTechnologyCrossing.com

URL: http://www.informationtechnologycrossing.com

Description: Provides information on IT jobs.

2541 ■ IT Classifieds

URL: http://www.itclassifieds.com

Description: Serves as career site for information technology professionals.

2542 ■ ItJobs.com

E-mail: comments@itjobsllc.com
URL: http://www.itjobs.com

Description: Provides information technology employment opportunities for the following categories: internet/intranet/extranet, network systems, open systems, client/server, software engineering and development, software QA and testing, ERP applications and management consulting, and legacy systems.

2543 ■ JustTechJobs.com

E-mail: support@justtechjobs.com
URL: http://www.justtechjobs.com

Description: Serves as a jobsite that provides employers with a technology specific focus and provides job seekers with job postings aimed at those specific tech jobs. Offers a community of 15 million tech professionals and also supports several technology websites.

2544 ■ Spherion

2050 Spectrum Blvd.
Fort Lauderdale, FL 33309
Ph: (954)308-7600
Fr: 800-774-3746
E-mail: help@spherion.com
URL: http://www.spherion.com

Description: Recruitment firm specializing in accounting and finance, sales and marketing, interim executives, technology, engineering, retail and human resources.

2545 ■ Tech-Engine.com

URL: http://techengine.com

Description: Features employment listings concerning the IT and engineering fields. Features employers and recruiters information, resume posting and career resources.

2546 ■ TechCareers

URL: http://www.techcareers.com

Description: Features career-related resources, news, and job postings for information technology and engineering professionals.

2547 ■ ZDNet Tech Jobs

URL: http://www.zdnet.com

Description: Site houses a listing of national employment opportunities for professionals in high tech fields. Also contains resume building tips and relocation resources.

TRADESHOWS

2548 ■ Information Architecture Summit

American Society for Information Science and Technology
1320 Fenwick Ln., Ste. 510
Silver Spring, MD 20910
Ph: (301)495-0900
Fax: (301)495-0810
E-mail: asis@asis.org
URL: http://www.asis.org

Annual. Features presentations from research and industry leaders, and opportunities for personal interaction among information architects and other user experience professionals.

2549 ■ Large Installation System Administration Conference

USENIX, the Advanced Computing Systems Association
2560 9th St., Ste. 215
Berkeley, CA 94710
Ph: (510)528-8649
Fax: (510)548-5738
E-mail: office@usenix.org
URL: http://www.usenix.org

Annual. Includes exhibits of books, products, and services that can optimize systems, networks, and internet management. 2012 December 9-14; San Diego, CA; 2013 November 3-8; Washington, DC; 2014 November 9-14; Seattle, WA; 2015 November 8-13; Washington, DC; 2016 December 4-9; Boston, MA. Provides networking opportunities for computing professionals.

2550 ■ Urban and Regional Information Systems Association Annual Conference and Exhibition

Urban and Regional Information Systems Association
701 Lee St., Ste. 680
Des Plaines, IL 60016
Ph: (847)824-6300
Fax: (847)824-6363
URL: http://www.urisa.org

Annual. Features management and policy discussions of IT/GIS issues affecting urban and regional governments.

2551 ■ USENIX Annual Technical Conference

USENIX, the Advanced Computing Systems Association
2560 9th St., Ste. 215
Berkeley, CA 94710
Ph: (510)528-8649
Fax: (510)548-5738
E-mail: office@usenix.org
URL: http://www.usenix.org

Annual. Includes exhibits of products and services for the advancement of computing systems.

2552 ■ XPLOR International Conference and Vendor Forum

XPLOR International
24156 State Rd. 54, Ste. 4
Lutz, FL 33559
Ph: (813)929-8100
Fax: (813)929-8524
Fr: 800-669-7567
E-mail: info@xplor.org
URL: http://www.xplor.org

Annual. Primary Exhibits: Equipment, supplies, and services for users and manufacturers of advanced electronic document systems. Dates and Locations: 2012 May 27-29; Tampa, FL; TradeWinds Island Grand Hotel and Conference Center.

OTHER SOURCES

2553 ■ AFCOM

742 E Chapman Ave.
Orange, CA 92866
Ph: (714)997-7966
Fax: (714)997-9743
E-mail: afcom@afcom.com
URL: http://www.afcom.com

Description: Data center, networking and enterprise systems management professionals from medium and large scale mainframe, midrange and client/server data centers worldwide. Works to meet the professional needs of the enterprise system management community. Provides information and support through educational events, research and assistance hotlines, and surveys.

2554 ■ Association of Information Technology Professionals (AITP)

401 N Michigan Ave., Ste. 2400
Chicago, IL 60611-4267
Ph: (312)245-1070
Fax: (312)673-6659
Fr: 800-224-9371
E-mail: aitp_hq@aitp.org
URL: http://www.aitp.org

Description: Managerial personnel, staff, educators, and individuals interested in the management of information resources. Founder of the Certificate in Data Processing examination program, now administered by an intersociety organization. Maintains Legislative Communications Network. Professional education programs include EDP-oriented business and management principles self-study courses and a series of videotaped management development seminars. Sponsors student organizations around the country interested in information technology and encourages members to serve as counselors for the Scout computer merit badge. Conducts research projects, including a business information systems curriculum for two- and four-year colleges.

2555 ■ Association for Women in Computing (AWC)

PO Box 2768
Oakland, CA 94602
E-mail: info@awc-hq.org
URL: http://www.awc-hq.org

Description: Individuals interested in promoting the education, professional development, and advancement of women in computing.

2556 ■ Computer Society (CS)

IEEE
2001 L St. NW, Ste. 700
Washington, DC 20036-4910
Ph: (202)371-0101
Fax: (202)728-9614
Fr: 800-272-6657
E-mail: help@computer.org
URL: http://www.computer.org

Description: Computer professionals. Promotes the development of computer and information sciences and fosters communication within the information processing community. Sponsors conferences, symposia, workshops, tutorials, technical meetings, and seminars. Operates Computer Society Press.

Presents scholarships; bestows technical achievement and service awards and certificates.

2557 ■ Computing Technology Industry Association (CompTIA)

3500 Lacey Rd., Ste. 100
Downers Grove, IL 60515
Ph: (630)678-8300
Fax: (630)678-8384
E-mail: membership@comptia.org
URL: http://www.comptia.org

Description: Trade association of more than 19,000 companies and professional IT members in the rapidly converging computing and communications market. Has members in more than 89 countries and provides a unified voice for the industry in the areas of e-commerce standards, vendor-neutral certification, service metrics, public policy and workforce development. Serves as information clearinghouse and resource for the industry; sponsors educational programs.

2558 ■ EC-Council

6330 Riverside Plaza Ln. NW, Ste. 210
Albuquerque, NM 87120
Ph: (505)341-3228
Fax: (505)341-0050
E-mail: info@eccouncil.org
URL: http://www.eccouncil.org

Description: Supports and enhances the role of individuals and organizations who design, create, manage or market security and e-business solutions. Offers Electronic Commerce Consultant certification and educational, technical, placement, and discounted services to its members. Provides a forum where discussion and information exchange can operate freely in the context of mutual trust and benefit.

2559 ■ International Association for Computer and Information Science (ACIS)

735 Meadowbrook Dr.
Mount Pleasant, MI 48858
Ph: (989)774-1175
Fax: (989)774-1174
E-mail: acis@acisinternational.org
URL: http://www.acisinternational.org

Description: Represents individuals in the fields of computer and information science. Disseminates the latest developments in the fields of computer and information science. Provides a forum for researchers in education and computer and information science industries.

2560 ■ IT Service Management Forum USA (itSMF USA)

150 E Colorado Blvd., Ste. 215
Pasadena, CA 91105
Ph: (626)449-3300
Fax: (626)449-3341
E-mail: info@itsmfusa.org
URL: http://www.itsmfusa.org

Description: Promotes IT Service Management best practices through knowledge sharing and educational and networking opportunities. Advances the credibility and professionalism of all its members. Assists with the planning, development and implementation strategies of IT service management best practices.

2561 ■ Urban and Regional Information Systems Association

701 Lee St., Ste. 680
Des Plaines, IL 60016
Ph: (847)824-6300
Fax: (847)824-6363
URL: http://www.urisa.org

Description: Represents professionals using Geographic Information Systems (GIS) and other information technologies to solve challenges in state and local government agencies. Promotes the effective and ethical use of spatial information and information technologies for the understanding and management of urban and regional systems. Produces a number of educational conferences and publications.

2562 ■ USENIX, the Advanced Computing Systems Association

2560 9th St., Ste. 215
Berkeley, CA 94710
Ph: (510)528-8649
Fax: (510)548-5738
E-mail: office@usenix.org
URL: http://www.usenix.org

Description: Represents the community of engineers, system administrators, scientists, and technicians working on the cutting edge of the computing world. Aims to foster technical excellence and innovation that pertains to computer systems. Supports and disseminates research with a practical bias. Provides a neutral forum for discussion of technical issues and encourages computing outreach into the community at large.

Computer Operators

Sources of Help-Wanted Ads

2563 ■ *ACM Transactions on Internet Technology*
Association for Computing Machinery
PO Box 30777
New York, NY 10087
Ph: (212)626-0500
Fax: (212)944-1318
Fr: 800-342-6626
URL: http://toit.acm.org

Quarterly. $190.00/year for nonmembers, print only; $152.00/year for nonmembers, online only; $228.00/year for nonmembers, online and print. Publication of the Association for Computing Machinery. Brings together many computing disciplines including computer software engineering, computer programming languages, middleware, database management, security, knowledge discovery and data mining, networking and distributed systems, communications, performance and scalability, and more. Covers the results and roles of the individual disciplines and the relationships among them.

2564 ■ *AVIOS Journal*
Applied Voice Input/Output Society
PO Box 20817
San Jose, CA 95160
Ph: (408)323-1783
Fax: (408)323-1782
URL: http://www.avios.com/

Annual. Journal covering issues in computer science.

2565 ■ *Communications of the ACM*
Association for Computing Machinery
PO Box 30777
New York, NY 10087
Ph: (212)626-0500
Fax: (212)944-1318
Fr: 800-342-6626
URL: http://cacm.acm.org

Monthly. $99.00/year for members, professional. Computing news magazine.

2566 ■ *Communications and Network*
Scientific Research Publishing
PO Box 54821
Irvine, CA 92619-4821
E-mail: cn@scirp.org
URL: http://www.scirp.org/journal/cn/

Quarterly. $236.00/year for individuals. Journal publishing articles on the latest advancements in communications and network technologies.

2567 ■ *Computers and Composition*
Elsevier Science Inc.
360 Park Ave. S
New York, NY 10010-1710
Ph: (212)989-5800
Fax: (212)633-3990

Fr: 888-437-4636
URL: http://www.elsevier.com/wps/find/journaldescription.cws_home

$454.00/year for institutions, all countries except Europe, Japan and Iran; $405.00/year for institutions, European countries and Iran; $53,500.00/year for institutions, Japan; $82.00/year for individuals, all countries except Europe, Japan and Iran; $62.00/year for individuals, European countries and Iran; $8,900.00/year for individuals, Japan. Journal covering computers in writing classes, programs, and research.

2568 ■ *Computers Programs/PC World*
IDG Communications Inc.
3 Speen St.
Framingham, MA 01701
Ph: (508)875-5000
URL: http://www.idg.com

Magazine devoted to IT specialists, covering practical questions of computing including purchase and usage of the computer technology, software, computer components and peripherals.

2569 ■ *Computerworld*
101 Communications
9121 Oakdale Ave., Ste. 101
Chatsworth, CA 91311
Ph: (818)814-5200
Fax: (818)734-1522
URL: http://www.computerworld.com

Weekly. $129.00/year for individuals; $129.00/year for Canada; $295.00/year for other countries; $250.00/year for individuals, Mexico/Central/South America; $29.00/year for individuals, digital edition. Newspaper for information systems executives.

2570 ■ *Computerworld/Correio Informatico*
IDG Communications Inc.
3 Speen St.
Framingham, MA 01701
Ph: (508)875-5000
URL: http://www.idg.com/www/IDGProducts.nsf/0/B1E40F5ABD0169AB852

Weekly. Magazine providing news on latest developments in computer industry.

2571 ■ *Computerworld Top 100*
IDG Communications Inc.
3 Speen St.
Framingham, MA 01701
Ph: (508)875-5000
URL: http://www.idg.com/www/IDGProducts.nsf/0/E7EDD4EC98463F2C852

Annual. Magazine for analyzing trends and events of information technology business.

2572 ■ *Computing SA*
IDG Communications Inc.
3 Speen St.
Framingham, MA 01701

Ph: (508)875-5000
URL: http://www.idg.com/www/IDGProducts.nsf/0/12C44C74D05A07DF852

Monthly. Newspaper focusing computer hardware, software, networking, telecommunications, channel management and online computing.

2573 ■ *Cutter IT Journal*
Cutter Information Corp.
37 Broadway, Ste. 1
Arlington, MA 02474
Ph: (781)648-8700
Fax: (781)648-8707
E-mail: service@cutter.com
URL: http://www.cutter.com/itjournal.html

Description: Monthly. $485. Provides IT managers with practical and objective views on the latest technology and management trends.

2574 ■ *CXO*
IDG Communications Inc.
3 Speen St.
Framingham, MA 01701
Ph: (508)875-5000
URL: http://www.idg.com/www/IDGProducts.nsf/0/022796185EED5984852

Monthly. Magazine providing technology information for chief officers and managers.

2575 ■ *Datamation*
Reed Business Information
360 Park Ave. S
New York, NY 10010-1710
Ph: (646)746-6400
URL: http://www.datamation.com

Semimonthly. Magazine on computers and information processing.

2576 ■ *Eclipse Review*
BZ Media L.L.C.
7 High St., Ste. 407
Huntington, NY 11743
Ph: (631)421-4158
Fax: (631)421-4130
URL: http://www.eclipsesource.com/contact.htm

Magazine for IT professionals.

2577 ■ *Foundations and Trends in Networking*
Now Publishers
PO Box 1024
Hanover, MA 02339-1001
Ph: (781)871-0245
URL: http://www.nowpublishers.com/product.aspx?product=NET

$390.00/year for individuals, online only; $450.00/year for individuals, print and online; $390.00/year for other countries, online only; $450.00/year for other countries, print and online. Academic journal publishing new research in computer networking.

2578 ■ Government Computer News
PostNewsweek Tech Media
10 G St. NE, Ste. 500
Washington, DC 20002-4228
Ph: (202)772-2500
Fax: (202)772-2511
Fr: (866)447-6864
URL: http://gcn.com/

Semimonthly. Magazine for professionals interested in government IT.

2579 ■ IEEE Security & Privacy Magazine
IEEE Computer Society
10662 Los Vaqueros Cir.
PO Box 3014
Los Alamitos, CA 90720-1314
Ph: (714)821-8380
Fax: (714)821-4010
Fr: 800-272-6657
URL: http://www.computer.org/portal/site/security/

Bimonthly. $735.00/year for individuals, online; $770.00/year for individuals, print; $965.00/year for individuals, print and online. Journal that aims to explore role and importance of networked infrastructure and developing lasting security solutions.

2580 ■ IEEE Software
IEEE Computer Society
10662 Los Vaqueros Cir.
PO Box 3014
Los Alamitos, CA 90720-1314
Ph: (714)821-8380
Fax: (714)821-4010
Fr: 800-272-6657
E-mail: software@computer.org
URL: http://www.computer.org/portal/web/software/home

Bimonthly. $990.00/year for individuals, online; $1,040.00/year for individuals, print; $1,300.00/year for individuals, print and online. Magazine covering the computer software industry for the community of leading software practitioners.

2581 ■ Information Security
TechTarget
117 Kendrick St., Ste. 800
Needham, MA 02494
Ph: (781)657-1000
Fax: (781)657-1100
Fr: 888-274-4111
URL: http://searchsecurity.techtarget.com/

Monthly. Free to qualified subscribers. Magazine covering information security topics.

2582 ■ International Journal of Communications, Network and System Sciences
Scientific Research Publishing
PO Box 54821
Irvine, CA 92619-4821
E-mail: ijcns@scirp.org
URL: http://www.scirp.org/journal/ijcns/

Monthly. $948.00/year for individuals. Peer-reviewed journal publishing articles on the latest advancements in communications and network technologies.

2583 ■ iSeries News Magazine
Penton Media
249 W 17th St.
New York, NY 10011
Ph: (212)024-4200
E-mail: service@iseriesnetwork.com
URL: http://www.systeminetwork.com/info/networkpubs/news400/about

$149.00/year for U.S. and Canada; $199.00/year for other countries. Trade magazine for programmers and data processing managers who use IBM iSeries.

2584 ■ IT Solutions Guide
SYS-CON Media
577 Chestnut Ridge Rd.
Woodcliff Lake, NJ 07677
Ph: (201)802-3000

Fax: (201)782-9601
URL: http://itsolutions.sys-con.com/
Quarterly. Magazine for IT professionals.

2585 ■ Journal of Computer Science
Science Publications
Vails Gate Heights Dr.
PO Box 879
Vails Gate, NY 12584-0879
URL: http://thescipub.com/jcs.toc

Scholarly journal covering many areas of computer science, including: concurrent, parallel and distributed processing; artificial intelligence; image and voice processing; quality software and metrics; computer-aided education; wireless communication; real time processing; evaluative computation; and data bases and information recovery and neural networks.

2586 ■ Journal of Computer Systems, Networks, and Communications
Hindawi Publishing Corp.
410 Park Ave., 15th Fl.
287 PMB
New York, NY 10022-4407
Fax: (215)893-4392
E-mail: jcsnc@hindawi.com
URL: http://www.hindawi.com/journals/jcsnc/

$195.00/year for individuals, print & online. Journal covering important areas of information technology.

2587 ■ Monitor
Capital PC User Group
19209 Mt. Airey Rd.
Brookeville, MD 20833
Ph: (301)560-6442
Fax: (301)760-3303
E-mail: editor@cpcug.org
URL: http://monitor.cpcug.org/index.html

Quarterly. Magazine covering computer hardware and software reviews, special interest user group news, advertisers and author/subject index, and calendar of events.

2588 ■ Queue
Association for Computing Machinery
PO Box 30777
New York, NY 10087
Ph: (212)626-0500
Fax: (212)944-1318
Fr: 800-342-6626
E-mail: queue@acm.org
URL: http://queue.acm.org/

Monthly. Free, U.S./Canadian residents and all members. Online magazine aimed at the computer professional. Magazine editorial does not provide solutions for the "here-and-now", but instead helps decision-makers plan future projects by examining the challenges and problems they are most likely to face.

2589 ■ Revenue
Montgomery Media International
55 New Montgomery St., Ste. 617
San Francisco, CA 94105
Ph: (415)371-8800
URL: http://www.revenuetoday.com/

Free to qualified subscribers. Magazine covering internet marketing strategies.

2590 ■ Ubiquity
Association for Computing Machinery
PO Box 30777
New York, NY 10087
Ph: (212)626-0500
Fax: (212)944-1318
Fr: 800-342-6626
URL: http://ubiquity.acm.org

Weekly. Free. Web-based magazine of the Association for Computing Machinery dedicated to fostering critical analysis and in-depth commentary, including book reviews, on issues relating to the nature, constitution, structure, science, engineering, cogni-

tion, technology, practices and paradigms of the IT profession.

2591 ■ WITI FastTrack
United business Media L.L.C
240 W 35th St.
New York, NY 10001
Ph: (516)562-5000
URL: http://www.witi.com/corporate/fasttrack.php

Semiannual. Semiannual publication featuring in-depth content on the issues facing today's women professionals in technology.

EMPLOYER DIRECTORIES AND NETWORKING LISTS

2592 ■ Computer Directory
Computer Directories Inc.
23815 Nichols Sawmill Rd.
Hockley, TX 77447
Ph: (281)259-5959
Fax: (281)259-5959
Fr: 800-234-4353
URL: http://www.compdirinc.com

Annual, fall. Covers: Approximately 130,000 computer installations; 19 separate volumes for Alaska/Hawaii, Connecticut/New Jersey, Dallas/Ft. Worth, Eastern Seaboard, Far Midwest, Houston, Illinois, Midatlantic, Midcentral, Mideast, Minnesota/Wisconsin, North Central, New England, New York Metro, Northwest, Ohio, Pennsylvania/West Virginia, Southeast, and Southwest Texas. Entries include: Company name, address, phone, fax, email, name and title of contact, hardware used, software application, operating system, programming language, computer graphics, networking system. Arrangement: Geographical. Indexes: Alphabetical, industry, hardware.

2593 ■ Directory of Top Computer Executives
Applied Computer Research Inc.
PO Box 41730
Phoenix, AZ 85080-1730
Ph: (623)937-4700
Fax: (623)937-3115
Fr: 800-234-2227
URL: http://www.itmarketintelligence.com

Semiannual, June and December. $345.00 for individuals; $520.00 for U.S. and Canada; $620.00 for individuals; $930.00 for U.S. and Canada; $925.00 for individuals; $1390.00 for U.S. and Canada. Covers: In three volumes, over 65,000 U.S. and Canadian executives with major information technology or communications responsibilities in over 35,500 U.S. and Canadian companies. Entries include: Company name, address, phone, subsidiary and/or division names, major systems installed, names and titles of top information system executives, number of IT employees, number of PCs, and web address. Arrangement: Geographical within separate eastern, western, and Canadian volumes. Indexes: Industry; alphabetical by company name.

2594 ■ Discovering Careers for Your Future—Computers
Facts On File Inc.
132 W 31st St., 17th Fl.
New York, NY 10001
Ph: (212)967-8800
Fax: 800-678-3633
Fr: 800-322-8755
URL: http://factsonfile.infobasepublishing.com

Latest edition 2nd, 2008. $21.95 for individuals. Covers: Computer operators, programmers, database specialists, and software engineers; links career education to curriculum, helping children investigate the subjects they are interested in, and the careers those subjects might lead to.

2595 ■ Vault Guide to the Top Internet Industry Employers
Vault.com Inc.
150 W 22nd St., 5th Fl.
New York, NY 10011
Ph: (212)366-4212
Fax: (212)366-6117
Fr: 888-562-8285
URL: http://www.vault.com

Latest edition February, 2006. $19.95 for individuals; $19.95 for members. Covers: Top employers in the Internet industry in United States. Entries include: Company name, contact person, address, location, phone and fax numbers, statistics and emails.

2596 ■ Vault Guide to the Top Tech Employers
Vault.com Inc.
150 W 22nd St., 5th Fl.
New York, NY 10011
Ph: (212)366-4212
Fax: (212)366-6117
Fr: 888-562-8285
URL: http://www.vault.com/store/book_
    preview.jsp?product_id=38814

Latest edition June, 2009. $19.95 for individuals; $19.95 for members. Covers: Technology industry employers. Entries include: Name, address, phone, fax, website, and other branch office location. Also include company overviews, recent company news, information on the hiring process, key competitors, and employment contact.

HANDBOOKS AND MANUALS

2597 ■ America's Top 100 Computer and Technical Jobs
Jist Publishing
875 Montreal Way
St. Paul, MN 55102
Fr: 800-648-5478
E-mail: info@jist.com
URL: http://www.jist.com/shop/
    product.php?productid=16453&cat=0&page=1

Michael J. Farr. 2009. $17.95. 400 pages. Job hunting in computer and technical industries.

2598 ■ Careers for Computer Buffs and Other Technological Types
The McGraw-Hill Companies
PO Box 182604
Columbus, OH 43272
Fax: (614)759-3749
Fr: 877-883-5524
E-mail: customer.service@mcgraw-hill.com
URL: http://www.mhprofessional.com/
    product.php?isbn=0071458778

Marjorie Eberts and Margaret Gisler. Third edition, 2006. $13.95 (paper). 160 pages. Suggested jobs in a wide range of settings, from the office to the outdoors.

2599 ■ Chief Electronic Computer Operator
National Learning Corporation
212 Michael Dr.
Syosset, NY 11791
Fr: 800-632-8888
URL: http://www.passbooks.com

2009. $34.95 (paper). Serves as an exam preparation guide for chief electronic computer operators.

2600 ■ Expert Resumes for Computer and Web Jobs
Jist Publishing
875 Montreal Way
St. Paul, MN 55102
Fr: 800-648-5478
E-mail: info@jist.com
URL: http://www.jist.com

Wendy Enelow and Louise Kursmark. Third edition, 2011. $17.95 (paper). 304 pages.

EMPLOYMENT AGENCIES AND SEARCH FIRMS

2601 ■ The Aspire Group
711 Boylston St.
Boston, MA 02116-2616
Fax: (617)500-7284
Fr: 800-487-2967
URL: http://www.bmanet.com/Aspire/index.html

Employment agency.

2602 ■ KForce
Fr: 877-4KF-ORCE
URL: http://www.kforce.com

Executive search firm. More than 41 locations throughout the United States and two in the Philippines.

2603 ■ Worlco Computer Resources, Inc.
901 Rte. 38
Cherry Hill, NJ 08002
Ph: (610)293-9070
Fax: (856)665-8903
E-mail: recruiter@worlco.com
URL: http://www.worlco.com

Employment agency and executive search firm. Second location in Cherry Hill, New Jersey.

ONLINE JOB SOURCES AND SERVICES

2604 ■ ComputerJobs.com
URL: http://www.computerjobs.com

Description: Provides listings of computer-related job opportunities.

2605 ■ ComputerWork.com
Fr: 800-691-8413
URL: http://www.computerwork.com

Description: Job search and resume submission service for professionals in information technology.

2606 ■ Computerworld Careers
URL: http://www.computerworld.com/careertopics/
    careers

Description: Offers career opportunities for IT (information technology) professionals. Job seekers may search the jobs database, register at the site, and read about job surveys and employment trends. Employers may post jobs.

2607 ■ Computing Research Association Job Announcements
1828 L St. NW, Ste. 800
Washington, DC 20036-4632
Ph: (202)234-2111
Fax: (202)667-1066
E-mail: info@cra.org
URL: http://www.cra.org/ads

Description: Contains dated links to national college and university computer technology positions.

2608 ■ Guru.com
5001 Baum Blvd., Ste. 760
Pittsburgh, PA 15213
Fax: (412)687-4466
Fr: 888-687-1316
URL: http://www.guru.com

Description: Job board specializing in contract jobs for creative and information technology professionals. Also provides online incorporation and educational opportunities for independent contractors along with articles and advice.

2609 ■ InformationTechnologyCrossing.com
URL: http://www.informationtechnologycrossing.com

Description: Provides information on IT jobs.

2610 ■ ItJobs.com
E-mail: comments@itjobsllc.com
URL: http://www.itjobs.com

Description: Provides information technology employment opportunities for the following categories: internet/intranet/extranet, network systems, open systems, client/server, software engineering and development, software QA and testing, ERP applications and management consulting, and legacy systems.

2611 ■ JustTechJobs.com
E-mail: support@justtechjobs.com
URL: http://www.justtechjobs.com

Description: Serves as a jobsite that provides employers with a technology specific focus and provides job seekers with job postings aimed at those specific tech jobs. Offers a community of 15 million tech professionals and also supports several technology websites.

2612 ■ Tech-Engine.com
URL: http://techengine.com

Description: Features employment listings concerning the IT and engineering fields. Features employers and recruiters information, resume posting and career resources.

2613 ■ ThinkEnergyGroup.com
E-mail: resumes@thinkjobs.com
URL: http://www.thinkenergygroup.com

Description: Serves as a job board for professionals looking for positions in engineering, power plant, energy, and technical fields. Contains advice and tips on interviews, job searching, resume writing, hiring, and management. Provides choices of work location, pay rates in the field of expertise and contract, temp-to-hire, and direct hiring options.

2614 ■ ZDNet Tech Jobs
URL: http://www.zdnet.com

Description: Site houses a listing of national employment opportunities for professionals in high tech fields. Also contains resume building tips and relocation resources.

TRADESHOWS

2615 ■ XPLOR International Conference and Vendor Forum
XPLOR International
24156 State Rd. 54, Ste. 4
Lutz, FL 33559
Ph: (813)929-8100
Fax: (813)929-8524
Fr: 800-669-7567
E-mail: info@xplor.org
URL: http://www.xplor.org

Annual. Primary Exhibits: Equipment, supplies, and services for users and manufacturers of advanced electronic document systems. Dates and Locations: 2012 May 27-29; Tampa, FL; TradeWinds Island Grand Hotel and Conference Center.

OTHER SOURCES

2616 ■ AFCOM
742 E Chapman Ave.
Orange, CA 92866
Ph: (714)997-7966
Fax: (714)997-9743
E-mail: afcom@afcom.com
URL: http://www.afcom.com

Description: Data center, networking and enterprise systems management professionals from medium and large scale mainframe, midrange and client/server data centers worldwide. Works to meet the professional needs of the enterprise system management community. Provides information and support through educational events, research and assistance hotlines, and surveys.

2617 ■ Association of Information Technology Professionals (AITP)
401 N Michigan Ave., Ste. 2400
Chicago, IL 60611-4267
Ph: (312)245-1070
Fax: (312)673-6659
Fr: 800-224-9371
E-mail: aitp_hq@aitp.org
URL: http://www.aitp.org

Description: Managerial personnel, staff, educators, and individuals interested in the management of information resources. Founder of the Certificate in Data Processing examination program, now administered by an intersociety organization. Maintains Legislative Communications Network. Professional education programs include EDP-oriented business and management principles self-study courses and a series of videotaped management development seminars. Sponsors student organizations around the country interested in information technology and encourages members to serve as counselors for the Scout computer merit badge. Conducts research projects, including a business information systems curriculum for two- and four-year colleges.

2618 ■ Association for Women in Computing (AWC)
PO Box 2768
Oakland, CA 94602
E-mail: info@awc-hq.org
URL: http://www.awc-hq.org

Description: Individuals interested in promoting the education, professional development, and advancement of women in computing.

2619 ■ Black Data Processing Associates (BDPA)
9500 Arena Dr., Ste. 350
Largo, MD 20774
Ph: (301)584-3135
Fax: (301)560-8300
Fr: 800-727-BDPA
E-mail: office@bdpa.org
URL: http://www.bdpa.org

Description: Represents persons employed in the information processing industry, including electronic data processing, electronic word processing and data communications; others interested in information processing. Seeks to accumulate and share information processing knowledge and business expertise to increase the career and business potential of minorities in the information processing field. Conducts professional seminars, workshops, tutoring services and community introductions to data processing. Makes annual donation to the United Negro College Fund.

2620 ■ Computing Research Association (CRA)
1828 L St. NW, Ste. 800
Washington, DC 20036-4632
Ph: (202)234-2111
Fax: (202)667-1066
E-mail: info@cra.org
URL: http://www.cra.org

Description: An association of more than 200 North American academic departments of computer science, computer engineering, and related fields; laboratories and centers in industry government, and academia engaging in basic computing research; and affiliated professional societies.

2621 ■ MIT Computer Science and Artificial Intelligence Laboratory
32 Vassar St.
Cambridge, MA 02139
Ph: (617)253-5851
Fax: (617)258-8682
URL: http://www.csail.mit.edu

Description: Active since 1959. Interdisciplinary laboratory of over 200 people that spans several academic departments and has active projects ongoing with members of every academic school at MIT. Offers research, current job listings, and educational outreach.

2622 ■ National Association of Government Webmasters (NAGW)
86 Woodstone Rd.
Rockaway, NJ 07866
Ph: (973)594-6249
E-mail: board@nagw.org
URL: http://www.nagw.org

Description: Provides a way for local and state government webmasters to share knowledge, ideas and resources with others who have similar positions. Coordinates national conferences, monthly webinars, and facilitates the networking of all members with a listserv. Strives to merge the combined efforts of state and local webmasters into one strong voice.

2623 ■ Special Interest Group on Accessible Computing (SIGACCESS)
2 Penn Plz., Ste. 701
New York, NY 10121-0701
Ph: (212)626-0500
Fax: (212)944-1318
Fr: 800-342-6626
E-mail: chair_sigaccess@acm.org
URL: http://www.sigaccess.org

Description: Promotes the professional interests of computing personnel with physical disabilities and the application of computing and information technology in solving relevant disability problems. Works to educate the public to support careers for the disabled.

Computer Programmers

SOURCES OF HELP-WANTED ADS

2624 ■ *ACM Transactions on Graphics (TOG)*
Association for Computing Machinery
PO Box 30777
New York, NY 10087
Ph: (212)626-0500
Fax: (212)944-1318
Fr: 800-342-6626
URL: http://tog.acm.org/

Quarterly. $215.00/year for nonmembers; $172.00/year for nonmembers, online; $258.00/year for nonmembers, online & print. Computer graphics journal.

2625 ■ *ACM Transactions on Internet Technology*
Association for Computing Machinery
PO Box 30777
New York, NY 10087
Ph: (212)626-0500
Fax: (212)944-1318
Fr: 800-342-6626
URL: http://toit.acm.org

Quarterly. $190.00/year for nonmembers, print only; $152.00/year for nonmembers, online only; $228.00/year for nonmembers, online and print. Publication of the Association for Computing Machinery. Brings together many computing disciplines including computer software engineering, computer programming languages, middleware, database management, security, knowledge discovery and data mining, networking and distributed systems, communications, performance and scalability, and more. Covers the results and roles of the individual disciplines and the relationships among them.

2626 ■ *Advances in Internet of Things*
Scientific Research Publishing
PO Box 54821
Irvine, CA 92619-4821
E-mail: ait@scirp.org
URL: http://www.scirp.org/journal/ait/

Peer-reviewed journal discussing issues on the impact of internet to society.

2627 ■ *AVIOS Journal*
Applied Voice Input/Output Society
PO Box 20817
San Jose, CA 95160
Ph: (408)323-1783
Fax: (408)323-1782
URL: http://www.avios.com/

Annual. Journal covering issues in computer science.

2628 ■ *Communications of the ACM*
Association for Computing Machinery
PO Box 30777
New York, NY 10087
Ph: (212)626-0500

Fax: (212)944-1318
Fr: 800-342-6626
URL: http://cacm.acm.org

Monthly. $99.00/year for members, professional. Computing news magazine.

2629 ■ *Communications and Network*
Scientific Research Publishing
PO Box 54821
Irvine, CA 92619-4821
E-mail: cn@scirp.org
URL: http://www.scirp.org/journal/cn/

Quarterly. $236.00/year for individuals. Journal publishing articles on the latest advancements in communications and network technologies.

2630 ■ *Computers and Composition*
Elsevier Science Inc.
360 Park Ave. S
New York, NY 10010-1710
Ph: (212)989-5800
Fax: (212)633-3990
Fr: 888-437-4636
URL: http://www.elsevier.com/wps/find/journaldescription.cws_home

$454.00/year for institutions, all countries except Europe, Japan and Iran; $405.00/year for institutions, European countries and Iran; $53,500.00/year for institutions, Japan; $82.00/year for individuals, all countries except Europe, Japan and Iran; $62.00/year for individuals, European countries and Iran; $8,900.00/year for individuals, Japan. Journal covering computers in writing classes, programs, and research.

2631 ■ *Computers Programs/PC World*
IDG Communications Inc.
3 Speen St.
Framingham, MA 01701
Ph: (508)875-5000
URL: http://www.idg.com

Magazine devoted to IT specialists, covering practical questions of computing including purchase and usage of the computer technology, software, computer components and peripherals.

2632 ■ *Computerworld*
101 Communications
9121 Oakdale Ave., Ste. 101
Chatsworth, CA 91311
Ph: (818)814-5200
Fax: (818)734-1522
URL: http://www.computerworld.com

Weekly. $129.00/year for individuals; $129.00/year for Canada; $295.00/year for other countries; $250.00/year for individuals, Mexico/Central/South America; $29.00/year for individuals, digital edition. Newspaper for information systems executives.

2633 ■ *Computerworld/Correio Informatico*
IDG Communications Inc.
3 Speen St.
Framingham, MA 01701
Ph: (508)875-5000
URL: http://www.idg.com/www/IDGProducts.nsf/0/B1E40F5ABD0169AB852

Weekly. Magazine providing news on latest developments in computer industry.

2634 ■ *Computerworld Top 100*
IDG Communications Inc.
3 Speen St.
Framingham, MA 01701
Ph: (508)875-5000
URL: http://www.idg.com/www/IDGProducts.nsf/0/E7EDD4EC98463F2C852

Annual. Magazine for analyzing trends and events of information technology business.

2635 ■ *Computing SA*
IDG Communications Inc.
3 Speen St.
Framingham, MA 01701
Ph: (508)875-5000
URL: http://www.idg.com/www/IDGProducts.nsf/0/12C44C74D05A07DF852

Monthly. Newspaper focusing computer hardware, software, networking, telecommunications, channel management and online computing.

2636 ■ *Computing Surveys (CSUR)*
Association for Computing Machinery
PO Box 30777
New York, NY 10087
Ph: (212)626-0500
Fax: (212)944-1318
Fr: 800-342-6626
URL: http://surveys.acm.org/

Quarterly. $205.00/year for nonmembers, print only; $164.00/year for nonmembers, online only; $246.00/year for nonmembers, online & print. Journal presenting surveys and tutorials in computer science.

2637 ■ *Cutter IT Journal*
Cutter Information Corp.
37 Broadway, Ste. 1
Arlington, MA 02474
Ph: (781)648-8700
Fax: (781)648-8707
E-mail: service@cutter.com
URL: http://www.cutter.com/itjournal.html

Description: Monthly. $485. Provides IT managers with practical and objective views on the latest technology and management trends.

2638 ■ *CXO*
IDG Communications Inc.
3 Speen St.
Framingham, MA 01701

Ph: (508)875-5000
URL: http://www.idg.com/www/IDGProducts.nsf/0/
022796185EED5984852

Monthly. Magazine providing technology information for chief officers and managers.

2639 ■ Datamation
Reed Business Information
360 Park Ave. S
New York, NY 10010-1710
Ph: (646)746-6400
URL: http://www.datamation.com

Semimonthly. Magazine on computers and information processing.

2640 ■ Eclipse Review
BZ Media L.L.C.
7 High St., Ste. 407
Huntington, NY 11743
Ph: (631)421-4158
Fax: (631)421-4130
URL: http://www.eclipsesource.com/contact.htm

Magazine for IT professionals.

2641 ■ Foundations and Trends in Networking
Now Publishers
PO Box 1024
Hanover, MA 02339-1001
Ph: (781)871-0245
URL: http://www.nowpublishers.com/
product.aspx?product=NET

$390.00/year for individuals, online only; $450.00/year for individuals, print and online; $390.00/year for other countries, online only; $450.00/year for other countries, print and online. Academic journal publishing new research in computer networking.

2642 ■ Government Computer News
PostNewsweek Tech Media
10 G St. NE, Ste. 500
Washington, DC 20002-4228
Ph: (202)772-2500
Fax: (202)772-2511
Fr: (866)447-6864
URL: http://gcn.com/

Semimonthly. Magazine for professionals interested in government IT.

2643 ■ iBusiness
Scientific Research Publishing
PO Box 54821
Irvine, CA 92619-4821
E-mail: ib@scirp.org
URL: http://www.scirp.org/journal/ib/

Quarterly. $236.00/year for individuals. Peer-reviewed journal publishing articles on the latest advancements in internet and business, and the intersection of economics with business applications.

2644 ■ IEEE Computer Graphics and Applications
IEEE Computer Society
10662 Los Vaqueros Cir.
PO Box 3014
Los Alamitos, CA 90720-1314
Ph: (714)821-8380
Fax: (714)821-4010
Fr: 800-272-6657
E-mail: cga-ma@computer.org
URL: http://www.computer.org/portal/web/cga

Bimonthly. $1,020.00/year for individuals, online; $1,065.00/year for individuals, print; $1,330.00/year for individuals, print and online. Magazine addressing the interests and needs of professional designers and users of computer graphics hardware, software, and systems.

2645 ■ IEEE Security & Privacy Magazine
IEEE Computer Society
10662 Los Vaqueros Cir.
PO Box 3014
Los Alamitos, CA 90720-1314

Ph: (714)821-8380
Fax: (714)821-4010
Fr: 800-272-6657
URL: http://www.computer.org/portal/site/security/

Bimonthly. $735.00/year for individuals, online; $770.00/year for individuals, print; $965.00/year for individuals, print and online. Journal that aims to explore role and importance of networked infrastructure and developing lasting security solutions.

2646 ■ IEEE Software
IEEE Computer Society
10662 Los Vaqueros Cir.
PO Box 3014
Los Alamitos, CA 90720-1314
Ph: (714)821-8380
Fax: (714)821-4010
Fr: 800-272-6657
E-mail: software@computer.org
URL: http://www.computer.org/portal/web/software/
home

Bimonthly. $990.00/year for individuals, online; $1,040.00/year for individuals, print; $1,300.00/year for individuals, print and online. Magazine covering the computer software industry for the community of leading software practitioners.

2647 ■ IEEE Transactions on Terahertz Science and Technology
IEEE Microwave Theory and Techniques Society
c/o Edward C. Niehenke
Niehenke Consulting
5829 Bellanca Dr.
Elkridge, MD 21075
Ph: (410)796-5866
Fax: (410)796-5829
E-mail: thz.editors@ieee.org
URL: http://www.mtt.org/publications/118-
terahertz.html

Peer-reviewed journal covering terahertz science and applications.

2648 ■ Information Security
TechTarget
117 Kendrick St., Ste. 800
Needham, MA 02494
Ph: (781)657-1000
Fax: (781)657-1100
Fr: 888-274-4111
URL: http://searchsecurity.techtarget.com/

Monthly. Free to qualified subscribers. Magazine covering information security topics.

2649 ■ InfoWorld
InfoWorld Media Group
501 2nd St.
San Francisco, CA 94107
Fr: 800-227-8365
E-mail: letters@infoworld.com
URL: http://www.infoworld.com/

Weekly. Free to qualified subscribers; $180.00/year for individuals. Weekly publication.

2650 ■ International Journal of Communications, Network and System Sciences
Scientific Research Publishing
PO Box 54821
Irvine, CA 92619-4821
E-mail: ijcns@scirp.org
URL: http://www.scirp.org/journal/ijcns/

Monthly. $948.00/year for individuals. Peer-reviewed journal publishing articles on the latest advancements in communications and network technologies.

2651 ■ International Journal for Multiscale Computational Engineering
Begell House Inc.
50 Cross Hwy.
Redding, CT 06896
Ph: (203)938-1300

Fax: (203)938-1304
URL: http://www.begellhouse.com/journals/
61fd1b191cf7e96f

$1,245.00/year for institutions. Journal featuring the advancement of multiscale computational science and engineering.

2652 ■ iSeries News Magazine
Penton Media
249 W 17th St.
New York, NY 10011
Ph: (212)024-4200
E-mail: service@iseriesnetwork.com
URL: http://www.systeminetwork.com/info/
networkpubs/news400/about

$149.00/year for U.S. and Canada; $199.00/year for other countries. Trade magazine for programmers and data processing managers who use IBM iSeries.

2653 ■ IT Solutions Guide
SYS-CON Media
577 Chestnut Ridge Rd.
Woodcliff Lake, NJ 07677
Ph: (201)802-3000
Fax: (201)782-9601
URL: http://itsolutions.sys-con.com/

Quarterly. Magazine for IT professionals.

2654 ■ Journal of Computer Science
Science Publications
Vails Gate Heights Dr.
PO Box 879
Vails Gate, NY 12584-0879
URL: http://thescipub.com/jcs.toc

Scholarly journal covering many areas of computer science, including: concurrent, parallel and distributed processing; artificial intelligence; image and voice processing; quality software and metrics; computer-aided education; wireless communication; real time processing; evaluative computation; and data bases and information recovery and neural networks.

2655 ■ Journal of Computer Systems, Networks, and Communications
Hindawi Publishing Corp.
410 Park Ave., 15th Fl.
287 PMB
New York, NY 10022-4407
Fax: (215)893-4392
E-mail: jcsnc@hindawi.com
URL: http://www.hindawi.com/journals/jcsnc/

$195.00/year for individuals, print & online. Journal covering important areas of information technology.

2656 ■ Journal of Software Engineering and Applications
Scientific Research Publishing
PO Box 54821
Irvine, CA 92619-4821
URL: http://www.scirp.org/journal/jsea/

Peer-reviewed journal covering software engineering and applications.

2657 ■ Monitor
Capital PC User Group
19209 Mt. Airey Rd.
Brookeville, MD 20833
Ph: (301)560-6442
Fax: (301)760-3303
E-mail: editor@cpcug.org
URL: http://monitor.cpcug.org/index.html

Quarterly. Magazine covering computer hardware and software reviews, special interest user group news, advertisers and author/subject index, and calendar of events.

2658 ■ PC Today
Sandhills Publishing
120 W Harvest Dr.
Lincoln, NE 68521
Ph: (402)479-2181
Fax: (402)479-2195

Fr: 800-331-1978
E-mail: editor@pctoday.com
URL: http://www.pctoday.com/

Monthly. $29.00/year for individuals; $37.00/year for Canada; $64.00/year for Canada, 2 years; $2.42/year for individuals, print; $17.00/year for individuals, online only; $69.00/year for other countries; $48.00/year for individuals, 2 years; $64.00/year for individuals, 3 years; $82.00/year for Canada, 3 years; $64.00/year for Canada, 2 years. Magazine for personal computer users.

2659 ■ PC WORLD
101 Communications
9121 Oakdale Ave., Ste. 101
Chatsworth, CA 91311
Ph: (818)814-5200
Fax: (818)734-1522
E-mail: pcwletters@pcworld.com
URL: http://www.pcworld.com

Quarterly. $19.97/year for individuals; $29.97/year for two years. Technology or business magazine meeting the informational needs of tech-savvy managers, both at work and at home.

2660 ■ Positioning
Scientific Research Publishing
PO Box 54821
Irvine, CA 92619-4821
E-mail: pos@scirp.org
URL: http://www.scirp.org/journal/pos/

Quarterly. $156.00/year for individuals. Peer-reviewed journal publishing articles on different areas of navigation and positioning.

2661 ■ Queue
Association for Computing Machinery
PO Box 30777
New York, NY 10087
Ph: (212)626-0500
Fax: (212)944-1318
Fr: 800-342-6626
E-mail: queue@acm.org
URL: http://queue.acm.org/

Monthly. Free, U.S./Canadian residents and all members. Online magazine aimed at the computer professional. Magazine editorial does not provide solutions for the "here-and-now", but instead helps decision-makers plan future projects by examining the challenges and problems they are most likely to face.

2662 ■ Revenue
Montgomery Media International
55 New Montgomery St., Ste. 617
San Francisco, CA 94105
Ph: (415)371-8800
URL: http://www.revenuetoday.com/

Free to qualified subscribers. Magazine covering internet marketing strategies.

2663 ■ Ubiquity
Association for Computing Machinery
PO Box 30777
New York, NY 10087
Ph: (212)626-0500
Fax: (212)944-1318
Fr: 800-342-6626
URL: http://ubiquity.acm.org

Weekly. Free. Web-based magazine of the Association for Computing Machinery dedicated to fostering critical analysis and in-depth commentary, including book reviews, on issues relating to the nature, constitution, structure, science, engineering, cognition, technology, practices and paradigms of the IT profession.

2664 ■ WITI FastTrack
United business Media L.L.C
240 W 35th St.
New York, NY 10001
Ph: (516)562-5000
URL: http://www.witi.com/corporate/fasttrack.php

Semiannual. Semiannual publication featuring in-depth content on the issues facing today's women professionals in technology.

Employer Directories and Networking Lists

2665 ■ Careers in Focus—Computer & Video Game Design
Facts On File Inc.
132 W 31st St., 17th Fl.
New York, NY 10001
Ph: (212)967-8800
Fax: 800-678-3633
Fr: 800-322-8755
URL: http://factsonfile.infobasepublishing.com

Latest edition 5th; 2009. $32.95 for individuals. Covers: An overview of computer and video game design, followed by a selection of jobs profiled in detail, including the nature of the job, earnings, prospects for employment, what kind of training and skills it requires, and sources for further information.

2666 ■ Careers in Focus—Computers
Facts On File Inc.
132 W 31st St., 17th Fl.
New York, NY 10001
Ph: (212)967-8800
Fax: 800-678-3633
Fr: 800-322-8755
URL: http://www.infobasepublishing.com

Latest edition 5th; Published August, 2008. $32.95 for individuals. Covers: An overview of computers, followed by a selection of jobs profiled in detail, including the nature of the job, earnings, prospects for employment, what kind of training and skills it requires, and sources for further information.

2667 ■ Computer Directory
Computer Directories Inc.
23815 Nichols Sawmill Rd.
Hockley, TX 77447
Ph: (281)259-5959
Fax: (281)259-5959
Fr: 800-234-4353
URL: http://www.compdirinc.com

Annual, fall. Covers: Approximately 130,000 computer installations; 19 separate volumes for Alaska/Hawaii, Connecticut/New Jersey, Dallas/Ft. Worth, Eastern Seaboard, Far Midwest, Houston, Illinois, Midatlantic, Midcentral, Mideast, Minnesota/Wisconsin, North Central, New England, New York Metro, Northwest, Ohio, Pennsylvania/West Virginia, Southeast, and Southwest Texas. Entries include: Company name, address, phone, fax, email, name and title of contact, hardware used, software application, operating system, programming language, computer graphics, networking system. Arrangement: Geographical. Indexes: Alphabetical, industry, hardware.

2668 ■ Directory of Top Computer Executives
Applied Computer Research Inc.
PO Box 41730
Phoenix, AZ 85080-1730
Ph: (623)937-4700
Fax: (623)937-3115
Fr: 800-234-2227
URL: http://www.itmarketintelligence.com

Semiannual, June and December. $345.00 for individuals; $520.00 for U.S. and Canada; $620.00 for individuals; $930.00 for U.S. and Canada; $925.00 for individuals; $1390.00 for U.S. and Canada. Covers: In three volumes, over 65,000 U.S. and Canadian executives with major information technology or communications responsibilities in over 35,500 U.S. and Canadian companies. Entries include: Company name, address, phone, subsidiary and/or division names, major systems installed, names and titles of top information system executives, number of IT employees, number of PCs, and web address. Arrangement: Geographical within separate eastern,

western, and Canadian volumes. Indexes: Industry; alphabetical by company name.

2669 ■ Discovering Careers for Your Future—Computers
Facts On File Inc.
132 W 31st St., 17th Fl.
New York, NY 10001
Ph: (212)967-8800
Fax: 800-678-3633
Fr: 800-322-8755
URL: http://factsonfile.infobasepublishing.com

Latest edition 2nd, 2008. $21.95 for individuals. Covers: Computer operators, programmers, database specialists, and software engineers; links career education to curriculum, helping children investigate the subjects they are interested in, and the careers those subjects might lead to.

2670 ■ Vault Guide to the Top Tech Employers
Vault.com Inc.
150 W 22nd St., 5th Fl.
New York, NY 10011
Ph: (212)366-4212
Fax: (212)366-6117
Fr: 888-562-8285
URL: http://www.vault.com/store/book_preview.jsp?product_id=38814

Latest edition June, 2009. $19.95 for individuals; $19.95 for members. Covers: Technology industry employers. Entries include: Name, address, phone, fax, website, and other branch office location. Also include company overviews, recent company news, information on the hiring process, key competitors, and employment contact.

Handbooks and Manuals

2671 ■ America's Top 100 Computer and Technical Jobs
Jist Publishing
875 Montreal Way
St. Paul, MN 55102
Fr: 800-648-5478
E-mail: info@jist.com
URL: http://www.jist.com/shop/product.php?productid=16453&cat=0&page=1

Michael J. Farr. 2009. $17.95. 400 pages. Job hunting in computer and technical industries.

2672 ■ Careers for Computer Buffs and Other Technological Types
The McGraw-Hill Companies
PO Box 182604
Columbus, OH 43272
Fax: (614)759-3749
Fr: 877-883-5524
E-mail: customer.service@mcgraw-hill.com
URL: http://www.mhprofessional.com/product.php?isbn=0071458778

Marjorie Eberts and Margaret Gisler. Third edition, 2006. $13.95 (paper). 160 pages. Suggested jobs in a wide range of settings, from the office to the outdoors.

2673 ■ Careers in the Computer Game Industry
The Rosen Publishing Group Inc.
29 E 21st St.
New York, NY 10010
Ph: (212)777-3017
Fax: (212)777-0277
Fr: 800-237-9932
URL: http://www.rosenpublishing.com/

Peter Suciu, David Gerardi. 2005. $33.25. 144 pages. Careers in mathematics.

2674 ■ Expert Resumes for Computer and Web Jobs
Jist Publishing
875 Montreal Way
St. Paul, MN 55102
Fr: 800-648-5478
E-mail: info@jist.com
URL: http://www.jist.com

Wendy Enelow and Louise Kursmark. Third edition, 2011. $17.95 (paper). 304 pages.

2675 ■ New Programmer's Survival Manual
The Pragmatic Bookshelf
c/o Dave Thomas
PO Box 293325
Lewisville, TX 75029-3325
Ph: (214)233-6543
Fax: (214)206-9982
E-mail: sales@pragmaticprogrammer.com
URL: http://pragprog.com

Josh Carter. 2011. $29.00 (paper). 250 pages. Offers an in-depth look at the professional programming industry. Introduces novice programmers to professional practices for working on large-scale programs. Includes tips and tools for navigating the corporate environment, working with teammates, and dealing with other people from other departments.

2676 ■ Practices of an Agile Developer: Working in the Real World
Pragamatic Bookshelf
9650 Strickland Rd., Ste. 103, PMB 255
Raleigh, NC 27615
Ph: (919)847-3884
Fr: 800-699-7764
E-mail: sales@pragmaticprogrammer.com
URL: http://pragprog.com/titles/pad/practices-of-an-agile-developer

Venkat Subramaniam and Andy Hunt. 2006. $29.95. 208 pages. Provides expertise in the areas of development processes, coding techniques, developer attitudes, project and team management, and iterative and incremental learning techniques in the field of computer programming.

2677 ■ Principal Computer Programmer
National Learning Corporation
212 Michael Dr.
Syosset, NY 11791
Fr: 800-632-8888
URL: http://www.passbooks.com

2009. $34.95 (paper). Serves as an exam preparation guide for principal computer programmers.

EMPLOYMENT AGENCIES AND SEARCH FIRMS

2678 ■ Access Staffing
360 Lexington Ave., 8th Fl.
New York, NY 10017
Ph: (212)687-5440
Fax: (212)557-2544
URL: http://www.accessstaffingco.com

Serves as a staffing firm covering accounting/financial, advertising, bilingual Japanese, creative, event planning, fashion/retail, healthcare/ human services, human resources, information technology, insurance, legal, light industrial and office support.

2679 ■ The Aspire Group
711 Boylston St.
Boston, MA 02116-2616
Fax: (617)500-7284
Fr: 800-487-2967
URL: http://www.bmanet.com/Aspire/index.html

Employment agency.

2680 ■ ATR Technology
1230 Oakmead Pkwy.
Sunnyvale, CA 94085
Ph: (408)328-8000
Fax: (408)328-8001
Fr: 877-412-1100
E-mail: corporate@atr1.com
URL: http://www.atr-technology.com

Description: Serves as an executive search firm specializing in the placement of information technology professionals ranging from complex software application development and infrastructure support to enterprise-wide project management.

2681 ■ Busch International
1000 Fremont Ave., Ste. 195
Los Altos, CA 94024
Ph: (650)949-6500
E-mail: olga@buschint.com
URL: http://www.buschint.com

Executive search firm focused solely on high-technology electronics.

2682 ■ C Associates
1619 G St. SE
PO Box 73868
Washington, DC 20056-3868
Ph: (202)518-8595
Fax: (202)387-7033
E-mail: john@cassociates.com

Personnel consultants specialize in the placement of computer professionals, concentrating in UNIX/C++ candidates. Serves private industries as well as government contractors. Also focus on oracle, ASP, and visual basic developers, programmers, system administrators and web developers.

2683 ■ Carol Maden Group
2019 Cunningham Dr., Ste. 218
Hampton, VA 23666-3316
Ph: (757)827-9010
Fax: (757)827-9081
E-mail: cmaden@hroads.net

Personnel consultants offering placement service in computer technology and engineering; servicing manufacturing and private industries nationwide. Temporary placement servicing clerical and light industrial.

2684 ■ Computer Management
7982 Honeygo Blvd., No. 23
Baltimore, MD 21236
Ph: (410)679-7000
E-mail: info@technicaljobs.com
URL: http://www.technicaljobs.com

Search firm focusing on filling jobs for database administration, network administration, web development, and software.

2685 ■ Dahl-Morrow International
1821 Michael Faraday Dr., Ste. 202
Reston, VA 20190
Ph: (703)787-8117
E-mail: info@dahl-morrowintl.com
URL: http://www.dahl-morrowintl.com

Executive search firm specializing in high technology.

2686 ■ The Datafinders Group, Inc.
PO Box 1624
Fort Lee, NJ 07024
Ph: (201)845-7700
Fax: (201)969-1065
E-mail: info@datafinders.net
URL: http://www.datafinders.net

Executive search firm.

2687 ■ DillonGray
1796 Equestrian Dr.
Pleasanton, CA 94588
Ph: (925)846-9396
E-mail: info@dillongray.com
URL: http://www.dillongray.com

Executive search firm focused on technology related companies.

2688 ■ Dynamic Search Systems Inc.
220 W Campus Dr., Ste. 201
PO Box 1188
Arlington Heights, IL 60004-1499
Ph: (847)304-0700
Fax: (847)304-5859
E-mail: candidate@dssjobs.com
URL: http://www.dssjobs.com

Provides executive and professional search services to the IT community. Firm specializes in the placement of developers, programmers, programmer analysts, systems analysts, project leaders, project managers, systems programmers, data processing consultants, IT directors, and other information technology related candidates. Industries served: all.

2689 ■ KForce
Fr: 877-4KF-ORCE
URL: http://www.kforce.com

Executive search firm. More than 41 locations throughout the United States and two in the Philippines.

2690 ■ Michael Anthony Associates Inc.
44 Washington St., Ste. 250
Wellesley, MA 02481-1802
Ph: (781)237-4950
Fax: (781)237-6811
Fr: 800-337-4950
E-mail: manthony@maainc.com
URL: http://www.maainc.com

Applications development, systems programming, communications, and database specialists servicing the IBM mainframe, midrange, and PC marketplace. Provides technical expertise of conversions, system software installation and upgrades, performance and tuning, capacity planning, and data communications. In addition to contract services also provide retained search and contingency placement of computer professionals ranging from senior staff to senior management. Also act as brokers for independent consultants and small consulting firms requiring the services of marketing specialists. Industries served: banking, financial services, hospitals, HMO's, manufacturers, software development, universities, defense, and consulting firms.

2691 ■ Recruiting Partners
3494 Camino Tassajara Rd., No. 404
Danville, CA 94506
Ph: (925)964-0249
E-mail: info@recruitingpartners.com
URL: http://www.recruitingpartners.com

Description: Serves as an executive and technical recruiting firm that specializes in accounting, legal, information technology, engineering, executive management and technical writing.

2692 ■ Strategic Staffing Solutions Inc.
Penobscot Bldg., 645 Griswold, Ste. 2900
Detroit, MI 48226-4206
Ph: (313)596-6900
Fax: (313)596-6905
Fr: 888-738-3261
E-mail: s3corporate@strategicstaff.com
URL: http://www.strategicstaff.com

Provides staffing for customized systems development, contract programming, customer specific training programs, and alternate staffing options. Industries served: banking, retail, health care, manufacturing, telecommunications, and automotive.

2693 ■ Technical Talent Locators Ltd.
5570 Sterrett Pl., Ste. 208
Columbia, MD 21044
Ph: (410)740-0091
E-mail: steve@ttlgroup.com
URL: http://www.ttlgroup.com

Permanent employment agency working within the following fields: software and database engineering; computer, communication, and telecommunication system engineering; and other computer-related disciplines.

2694 ■ TRC Staffing Services Inc.
115 Perimeter Center Pl. NE, Ste. 855
Atlanta, GA 30346
Ph: (770)392-1411
Fax: (770)392-7926
E-mail: info@trcstaff.com
URL: http://www.trcstaff.com

A full-service executive search company with permanent placements encompassing engineering, industrial sales, financial and computer science positions.
Screen, interview, and verify past employment for all
candidates prior to referral. Also assist personnel
staffs in the attainment of their EEO/AAP goals with
the placement of talented individuals in positions
which were underutilized with minorities and/or
women. Industries served: all.

2695 ■ Wallach Associates Inc.
7811 Montrose Rd., Ste. 505
Potomac, MD 20854
Ph: (301)340-0300
Fax: (301)340-8008
Fr: 800-296-2084
URL: http://www.wallach.org

Specialists in recruitment of professional personnel,
primarily in information technology and electronic
systems and engineering, energy research and
development, management consulting, operations
research, computers, defense systems, and
programmers. Specializes in Internet and software
engineer for intelligence community.

2696 ■ Worlco Computer Resources, Inc.
901 Rte. 38
Cherry Hill, NJ 08002
Ph: (610)293-9070
Fax: (856)665-8903
E-mail: recruiter@worlco.com
URL: http://www.worlco.com

Employment agency and executive search firm.
Second location in Cherry Hill, New Jersey.

Online Job Sources and Services

2697 ■ ComputerJobs.com
URL: http://www.computerjobs.com

Description: Provides listings of computer-related
job opportunities.

2698 ■ ComputerWork.com
Fr: 800-691-8413
URL: http://www.computerwork.com

Description: Job search and resume submission
service for professionals in information technology.

2699 ■ Computerworld Careers
URL: http://www.computerworld.com/careertopics/
careers

Description: Offers career opportunities for IT
(information technology) professionals. Job seekers
may search the jobs database, register at the site,
and read about job surveys and employment trends.
Employers may post jobs.

**2700 ■ Computing Research Association Job
Announcements**
1828 L St. NW, Ste. 800
Washington, DC 20036-4632
Ph: (202)234-2111
Fax: (202)667-1066
E-mail: info@cra.org
URL: http://www.cra.org/ads

Description: Contains dated links to national college
and university computer technology positions.

2701 ■ Dice.com
URL: http://www.dice.com

Description: Job search database for computer
consultants and high-tech professionals, listing
thousands of high tech permanent contract and
consulting jobs for programmers, software engineers,

systems administrators, web developers, and hardware engineers. Also free career advice e-mail
newsletter and job posting e-alerts.

2702 ■ Guru.com
5001 Baum Blvd., Ste. 760
Pittsburgh, PA 15213
Fax: (412)687-4466
Fr: 888-687-1316
URL: http://www.guru.com

Description: Job board specializing in contract jobs
for creative and information technology professionals.
Also provides online incorporation and educational
opportunities for independent contractors along with
articles and advice.

2703 ■ InformationTechnologyCrossing.com
URL: http://www.informationtechnologycrossing.com

Description: Provides information on IT jobs.

2704 ■ ItJobs.com
E-mail: comments@itjobsllc.com
URL: http://www.itjobs.com

Description: Provides information technology employment opportunities for the following categories:
internet/intranet/extranet, network systems, open
systems, client/server, software engineering and
development, software QA and testing, ERP applications and management consulting, and legacy
systems.

2705 ■ Jobs for Programmers
E-mail: support@jfpresources.com
URL: http://www.prgjobs.com

Description: Job board site for computer programmers that allows them to browse through thousands
of programming jobs, even search for special jobs
with sign-on bonuses, relocation funding, and 4-day
work weeks. Resume posting is free.

2706 ■ Jobs4IT.com
URL: http://www.jobs4it.com

Description: Features information technology job
opportunities, job fairs, business opportunities, news,
events, continuing education guide, resume database, distribution services and other career
resources.

2707 ■ JustTechJobs.com
E-mail: support@justtechjobs.com
URL: http://www.justtechjobs.com

Description: Serves as a jobsite that provides
employers with a technology specific focus and
provides job seekers with job postings aimed at those
specific tech jobs. Offers a community of 15 million
tech professionals and also supports several technology websites.

2708 ■ PrgJobs.com
URL: http://www.prgjobs.com

Description: Serves as an employment site for
programmers.

2709 ■ ProgrammingCareers.com
URL: http://www.programmingcareers.com

Description: Provides programming jobs to computer
software developers and programmers. Functions
mainly as an advertiser, and is not involved in the hiring process. Connects job seekers in related professions with employers and employment recruiters.

2710 ■ Tech-Engine.com
URL: http://techengine.com

Description: Features employment listings concerning the IT and engineering fields. Features employers
and recruiters information, resume posting and career
resources.

2711 ■ TechCareers
URL: http://www.techcareers.com

Description: Features career-related resources,

news, and job postings for information technology
and engineering professionals.

2712 ■ ZDNet Tech Jobs
URL: http://www.zdnet.com

Description: Site houses a listing of national employment opportunities for professionals in high tech
fields. Also contains resume building tips and relocation resources.

Tradeshows

**2713 ■ XPLOR International Conference and
Vendor Forum**
XPLOR International
24156 State Rd. 54, Ste. 4
Lutz, FL 33559
Ph: (813)929-8100
Fax: (813)929-8524
Fr: 800-669-7567
E-mail: info@xplor.org
URL: http://www.xplor.org

Annual. Primary Exhibits: Equipment, supplies, and
services for users and manufacturers of advanced
electronic document systems. Dates and Locations:
2012 May 27-29; Tampa, FL; TradeWinds Island
Grand Hotel and Conference Center.

Other Sources

**2714 ■ American Indian Science and
Engineering Society (AISES)**
PO Box 9828
Albuquerque, NM 87119-9828
Ph: (505)765-1052
Fax: (505)765-5608
E-mail: info@aises.org
URL: http://www.aises.org

Description: Represents American Indian and non-
Indian students and professionals in science, technology, and engineering fields; corporations representing energy, mining, aerospace, electronic, and
computer fields. Seeks to motivate and encourage
students to pursue undergraduate and graduate studies in science, engineering, and technology. Sponsors science fairs in grade schools, teacher training
workshops, summer math/science sessions for 8th-
12th graders, professional chapters, and student
chapters in colleges. Offers scholarships. Adult
members serve as role models, advisers, and mentors for students. Operates placement service.

**2715 ■ Association of Information
Technology Professionals (AITP)**
401 N Michigan Ave., Ste. 2400
Chicago, IL 60611-4267
Ph: (312)245-1070
Fax: (312)673-6659
Fr: 800-224-9371
E-mail: aitp_hq@aitp.org
URL: http://www.aitp.org

Description: Managerial personnel, staff, educators,
and individuals interested in the management of
information resources. Founder of the Certificate in
Data Processing examination program, now administered by an intersociety organization. Maintains
Legislative Communications Network. Professional
education programs include EDP-oriented business
and management principles self-study courses and a
series of videotaped management development
seminars. Sponsors student organizations around the
country interested in information technology and
encourages members to serve as counselors for the
Scout computer merit badge. Conducts research
projects, including a business information systems
curriculum for two- and four-year colleges.

**2716 ■ Association for Women in Computing
(AWC)**
PO Box 2768
Oakland, CA 94602
E-mail: info@awc-hq.org
URL: http://www.awc-hq.org

Description: Individuals interested in promoting the education, professional development, and advancement of women in computing.

2717 ■ Black Data Processing Associates (BDPA)
9500 Arena Dr., Ste. 350
Largo, MD 20774
Ph: (301)584-3135
Fax: (301)560-8300
Fr: 800-727-BDPA
E-mail: office@bdpa.org
URL: http://www.bdpa.org

Description: Represents persons employed in the information processing industry, including electronic data processing, electronic word processing and data communications; others interested in information processing. Seeks to accumulate and share information processing knowledge and business expertise to increase the career and business potential of minorities in the information processing field. Conducts professional seminars, workshops, tutoring services and community introductions to data processing. Makes annual donation to the United Negro College Fund.

2718 ■ Computer Society (CS)
IEEE
2001 L St. NW, Ste. 700
Washington, DC 20036-4910
Ph: (202)371-0101
Fax: (202)728-9614
Fr: 800-272-6657
E-mail: help@computer.org
URL: http://www.computer.org

Description: Computer professionals. Promotes the development of computer and information sciences and fosters communication within the information processing community. Sponsors conferences, symposia, workshops, tutorials, technical meetings, and seminars. Operates Computer Society Press. Presents scholarships; bestows technical achievement and service awards and certificates.

2719 ■ Computing Research Association (CRA)
1828 L St. NW, Ste. 800
Washington, DC 20036-4632
Ph: (202)234-2111
Fax: (202)667-1066
E-mail: info@cra.org
URL: http://www.cra.org

Description: An association of more than 200 North American academic departments of computer science, computer engineering, and related fields; laboratories and centers in industry government, and academia engaging in basic computing research; and affiliated professional societies.

2720 ■ Large Installation System Administration Conference
USENIX, the Advanced Computing Systems Association
2560 9th St., Ste. 215
Berkeley, CA 94710
Ph: (510)528-8649
Fax: (510)548-5738
E-mail: office@usenix.org
URL: http://www.usenix.org

Annual. Includes exhibits of books, products, and services that can optimize systems, networks, and internet management. 2012 December 9-14; San Diego, CA; 2013 November 3-8; Washington, DC; 2014 November 9-14; Seattle, WA; 2015 November 8-13; Washington, DC; 2016 December 4-9; Boston, MA. Provides networking opportunities for computing professionals.

2721 ■ MIT Computer Science and Artificial Intelligence Laboratory
32 Vassar St.
Cambridge, MA 02139
Ph: (617)253-5851
Fax: (617)258-8682
URL: http://www.csail.mit.edu

Description: Active since 1959. Interdisciplinary laboratory of over 200 people that spans several academic departments and has active projects ongoing with members of every academic school at MIT. Offers research, current job listings, and educational outreach.

2722 ■ Special Interest Group on Accessible Computing (SIGACCESS)
2 Penn Plz., Ste. 701
New York, NY 10121-0701
Ph: (212)626-0500
Fax: (212)944-1318
Fr: 800-342-6626
E-mail: chair_sigaccess@acm.org
URL: http://www.sigaccess.org

Description: Promotes the professional interests of computing personnel with physical disabilities and the application of computing and information technology in solving relevant disability problems. Works to educate the public to support careers for the disabled.

2723 ■ USENIX, the Advanced Computing Systems Association
2560 9th St., Ste. 215
Berkeley, CA 94710
Ph: (510)528-8649
Fax: (510)548-5738
E-mail: office@usenix.org
URL: http://www.usenix.org

Description: Represents the community of engineers, system administrators, scientists, and technicians working on the cutting edge of the computing world. Aims to foster technical excellence and innovation that pertains to computer systems. Supports and disseminates research with a practical bias. Provides a neutral forum for discussion of technical issues and encourages computing outreach into the community at large.

2724 ■ USENIX Annual Technical Conference
USENIX, the Advanced Computing Systems Association
2560 9th St., Ste. 215
Berkeley, CA 94710
Ph: (510)528-8649
Fax: (510)548-5738
E-mail: office@usenix.org
URL: http://www.usenix.org

Annual. Includes exhibits of products and services for the advancement of computing systems.

Sources of Help-Wanted Ads

2725 ■ ACM Transactions on Internet Technology
Association for Computing Machinery
PO Box 30777
New York, NY 10087
Ph: (212)626-0500
Fax: (212)944-1318
Fr: 800-342-6626
URL: http://toit.acm.org

Quarterly. $190.00/year for nonmembers, print only; $152.00/year for nonmembers, online only; $228.00/year for nonmembers, online and print. Publication of the Association for Computing Machinery. Brings together many computing disciplines including computer software engineering, computer programming languages, middleware, database management, security, knowledge discovery and data mining, networking and distributed systems, communications, performance and scalability, and more. Covers the results and roles of the individual disciplines and the relationships among them.

2726 ■ AVIOS Journal
Applied Voice Input/Output Society
PO Box 20817
San Jose, CA 95160
Ph: (408)323-1783
Fax: (408)323-1782
URL: http://www.avios.com/

Annual. Journal covering issues in computer science.

2727 ■ Communications of the ACM
Association for Computing Machinery
PO Box 30777
New York, NY 10087
Ph: (212)626-0500
Fax: (212)944-1318
Fr: 800-342-6626
URL: http://cacm.acm.org

Monthly. $99.00/year for members, professional. Computing news magazine.

2728 ■ Communications and Network
Scientific Research Publishing
PO Box 54821
Irvine, CA 92619-4821
E-mail: cn@scirp.org
URL: http://www.scirp.org/journal/cn/

Quarterly. $236.00/year for individuals. Journal publishing articles on the latest advancements in communications and network technologies.

2729 ■ Computers and Composition
Elsevier Science Inc.
360 Park Ave. S
New York, NY 10010-1710
Ph: (212)989-5800
Fax: (212)633-3990

Fr: 888-437-4636
URL: http://www.elsevier.com/wps/find/
journaldescription.cws_home

$454.00/year for institutions, all countries except Europe, Japan and Iran; $405.00/year for institutions, European countries and Iran; $53,500.00/year for institutions, Japan; $82.00/year for individuals, all countries except Europe, Japan and Iran; $62.00/year for individuals, European countries and Iran; $8,900.00/year for individuals, Japan. Journal covering computers in writing classes, programs, and research.

2730 ■ Computers Programs/PC World
IDG Communications Inc.
3 Speen St.
Framingham, MA 01701
Ph: (508)875-5000
URL: http://www.idg.com

Magazine devoted to IT specialists, covering practical questions of computing including purchase and usage of the computer technology, software, computer components and peripherals.

2731 ■ Computerworld
101 Communications
9121 Oakdale Ave., Ste. 101
Chatsworth, CA 91311
Ph: (818)814-5200
Fax: (818)734-1522
URL: http://www.computerworld.com

Weekly. $129.00/year for individuals; $129.00/year for Canada; $295.00/year for other countries; $250.00/year for individuals, Mexico/Central/South America; $29.00/year for individuals, digital edition. Newspaper for information systems executives.

2732 ■ Computerworld/Correio Informatico
IDG Communications Inc.
3 Speen St.
Framingham, MA 01701
Ph: (508)875-5000
URL: http://www.idg.com/www/IDGProducts.nsf/0/
B1E40F5ABD0169AB852

Weekly. Magazine providing news on latest developments in computer industry.

2733 ■ Computerworld Top 100
IDG Communications Inc.
3 Speen St.
Framingham, MA 01701
Ph: (508)875-5000
URL: http://www.idg.com/www/IDGProducts.nsf/0/
E7EDD4EC98463F2C852

Annual. Magazine for analyzing trends and events of information technology business.

2734 ■ Computing SA
IDG Communications Inc.
3 Speen St.
Framingham, MA 01701

Ph: (508)875-5000
URL: http://www.idg.com/www/IDGProducts.nsf/0/
12C44C74D05A07DF852

Monthly. Newspaper focusing computer hardware, software, networking, telecommunications, channel management and online computing.

2735 ■ CXO
IDG Communications Inc.
3 Speen St.
Framingham, MA 01701
Ph: (508)875-5000
URL: http://www.idg.com/www/IDGProducts.nsf/0/
022796185EED5984852

Monthly. Magazine providing technology information for chief officers and managers.

2736 ■ Eclipse Review
BZ Media L.L.C.
7 High St., Ste. 407
Huntington, NY 11743
Ph: (631)421-4158
Fax: (631)421-4130
URL: http://www.eclipsesource.com/contact.htm

Magazine for IT professionals.

2737 ■ Foundations and Trends in Networking
Now Publishers
PO Box 1024
Hanover, MA 02339-1001
Ph: (781)871-0245
URL: http://www.nowpublishers.com/
product.aspx?product=NET

$390.00/year for individuals, online only; $450.00/year for individuals, print and online; $390.00/year for other countries, online only; $450.00/year for other countries, print and online. Academic journal publishing new research in computer networking.

2738 ■ Government Computer News
PostNewsweek Tech Media
10 G St. NE, Ste. 500
Washington, DC 20002-4228
Ph: (202)772-2500
Fax: (202)772-2511
Fr: (866)447-6864
URL: http://gcn.com/

Semimonthly. Magazine for professionals interested in government IT.

2739 ■ IEEE Security & Privacy Magazine
IEEE Computer Society
10662 Los Vaqueros Cir.
PO Box 3014
Los Alamitos, CA 90720-1314
Ph: (714)821-8380
Fax: (714)821-4010
Fr: 800-272-6657
URL: http://www.computer.org/portal/site/security/

Bimonthly. $735.00/year for individuals, online;

$770.00/year for individuals, print; $965.00/year for individuals, print and online. Journal that aims to explore role and importance of networked infrastructure and developing lasting security solutions.

2740 ■ Information Security
TechTarget
117 Kendrick St., Ste. 800
Needham, MA 02494
Ph: (781)657-1000
Fax: (781)657-1100
Fr: 888-274-4111
URL: http://searchsecurity.techtarget.com/

Monthly. Free to qualified subscribers. Magazine covering information security topics.

2741 ■ International Journal of Communications, Network and System Sciences
Scientific Research Publishing
PO Box 54821
Irvine, CA 92619-4821
E-mail: ijcns@scirp.org
URL: http://www.scirp.org/journal/ijcns/

Monthly. $948.00/year for individuals. Peer-reviewed journal publishing articles on the latest advancements in communications and network technologies.

2742 ■ IT Solutions Guide
SYS-CON Media
577 Chestnut Ridge Rd.
Woodcliff Lake, NJ 07677
Ph: (201)802-3000
Fax: (201)782-9601
URL: http://itsolutions.sys-con.com/

Quarterly. Magazine for IT professionals.

2743 ■ Journal of Computer Science
Science Publications
Vails Gate Heights Dr.
PO Box 879
Vails Gate, NY 12584-0879
URL: http://thescipub.com/jcs.toc

Scholarly journal covering many areas of computer science, including: concurrent, parallel and distributed processing; artificial intelligence; image and voice processing; quality software and metrics; computer-aided education; wireless communication; real time processing; evaluative computation; and data bases and information recovery and neural networks.

2744 ■ Journal of Computer Systems, Networks, and Communications
Hindawi Publishing Corp.
410 Park Ave., 15th Fl.
287 PMB
New York, NY 10022-4407
Fax: (215)893-4392
E-mail: jcsnc@hindawi.com
URL: http://www.hindawi.com/journals/jcsnc/

$195.00/year for individuals, print & online. Journal covering important areas of information technology.

2745 ■ Machine Design
Penton Media Inc.
249 W 17th St.
New York, NY 10011
Ph: (212)204-4200
URL: http://machinedesign.com/

Magazine on design engineering function.

2746 ■ Monitor
Capital PC User Group
19209 Mt. Airey Rd.
Brookeville, MD 20833
Ph: (301)560-6442
Fax: (301)760-3303
E-mail: editor@cpcug.org
URL: http://monitor.cpcug.org/index.html

Quarterly. Magazine covering computer hardware and software reviews, special interest user group news, advertisers and author/subject index, and calendar of events.

2747 ■ PC WORLD
101 Communications
9121 Oakdale Ave., Ste. 101
Chatsworth, CA 91311
Ph: (818)814-5200
Fax: (818)734-1522
E-mail: pcwletters@pcworld.com
URL: http://www.pcworld.com

Quarterly. $19.97/year for individuals; $29.97/year for two years. Technology or business magazine meeting the informational needs of tech-savvy managers, both at work and at home.

2748 ■ Queue
Association for Computing Machinery
PO Box 30777
New York, NY 10087
Ph: (212)626-0500
Fax: (212)944-1318
Fr: 800-342-6626
E-mail: queue@acm.org
URL: http://queue.acm.org/

Monthly. Free, U.S./Canadian residents and all members. Online magazine aimed at the computer professional. Magazine editorial does not provide solutions for the "here-and-now", but instead helps decision-makers plan future projects by examining the challenges and problems they are most likely to face.

2749 ■ Revenue
Montgomery Media International
55 New Montgomery St., Ste. 617
San Francisco, CA 94105
Ph: (415)371-8800
URL: http://www.revenuetoday.com/

Free to qualified subscribers. Magazine covering internet marketing strategies.

2750 ■ Ubiquity
Association for Computing Machinery
PO Box 30777
New York, NY 10087
Ph: (212)626-0500
Fax: (212)944-1318
Fr: 800-342-6626
URL: http://ubiquity.acm.org

Weekly. Free. Web-based magazine of the Association for Computing Machinery dedicated to fostering critical analysis and in-depth commentary, including book reviews, on issues relating to the nature, constitution, structure, science, engineering, cognition, technology, practices and paradigms of the IT profession.

2751 ■ WITI FastTrack
United business Media L.L.C
240 W 35th St.
New York, NY 10001
Ph: (516)562-5000
URL: http://www.witi.com/corporate/fasttrack.php

Semiannual. Semiannual publication featuring in-depth content on the issues facing today's women professionals in technology.

EMPLOYER DIRECTORIES AND NETWORKING LISTS

2752 ■ Computer Directory
Computer Directories Inc.
23815 Nichols Sawmill Rd.
Hockley, TX 77447
Ph: (281)259-5959
Fax: (281)259-5959
Fr: 800-234-4353
URL: http://www.compdirinc.com

Annual, fall. Covers: Approximately 130,000 computer installations; 19 separate volumes for Alaska/Hawaii, Connecticut/New Jersey, Dallas/Ft. Worth, Eastern Seaboard, Far Midwest, Houston, Illinois, Midatlantic, Midcentral, Mideast, Minnesota/Wisconsin, North

Central, New England, New York Metro, Northwest, Ohio, Pennsylvania/West Virginia, Southeast, and Southwest Texas. Entries include: Company name, address, phone, fax, email, name and title of contact, hardware used, software application, operating system, programming language, computer graphics, networking system. Arrangement: Geographical. Indexes: Alphabetical, industry, hardware.

2753 ■ Directory of Top Computer Executives
Applied Computer Research Inc.
PO Box 41730
Phoenix, AZ 85080-1730
Ph: (623)937-4700
Fax: (623)937-3115
Fr: 800-234-2227
URL: http://www.itmarketintelligence.com

Semiannual, June and December. $345.00 for individuals; $520.00 for U.S. and Canada; $620.00 for individuals; $930.00 for U.S. and Canada; $925.00 for individuals; $1390.00 for U.S. and Canada. Covers: In three volumes, over 65,000 U.S. and Canadian executives with major information technology or communications responsibilities in over 35,500 U.S. and Canadian companies. Entries include: Company name, address, phone, subsidiary and/or division names, major systems installed, names and titles of top information system executives, number of IT employees, number of PCs, and web address. Arrangement: Geographical within separate eastern, western, and Canadian volumes. Indexes: Industry; alphabetical by company name.

HANDBOOKS AND MANUALS

2754 ■ America's Top 100 Computer and Technical Jobs
Jist Publishing
875 Montreal Way
St. Paul, MN 55102
Fr: 800-648-5478
E-mail: info@jist.com
URL: http://www.jist.com/shop/
product.php?productid=16453&cat=0&page=1

Michael J. Farr. 2009. $17.95. 400 pages. Job hunting in computer and technical industries.

2755 ■ Careers for Computer Buffs and Other Technological Types
The McGraw-Hill Companies
PO Box 182604
Columbus, OH 43272
Fax: (614)759-3749
Fr: 877-883-5524
E-mail: customer.service@mcgraw-hill.com
URL: http://www.mhprofessional.com/
product.php?isbn=0071458778

Marjorie Eberts and Margaret Gisler. Third edition, 2006. $13.95 (paper). 160 pages. Suggested jobs in a wide range of settings, from the office to the outdoors.

2756 ■ Expert Resumes for Computer and Web Jobs
Jist Publishing
875 Montreal Way
St. Paul, MN 55102
Fr: 800-648-5478
E-mail: info@jist.com
URL: http://www.jist.com

Wendy Enelow and Louise Kursmark. Third edition, 2011. $17.95 (paper). 304 pages.

EMPLOYMENT AGENCIES AND SEARCH FIRMS

2757 ■ Recruiting Partners
3494 Camino Tassajara Rd., No. 404
Danville, CA 94506

Ph: (925)964-0249
E-mail: info@recruitingpartners.com
URL: http://www.recruitingpartners.com

Description: Serves as an executive and technical recruiting firm that specializes in accounting, legal, information technology, engineering, executive management and technical writing.

ONLINE JOB SOURCES AND SERVICES

2758 ■ ComputerJobs.com
URL: http://www.computerjobs.com

Description: Provides listings of computer-related job opportunities.

2759 ■ ComputerWork.com
Fr: 800-691-8413
URL: http://www.computerwork.com

Description: Job search and resume submission service for professionals in information technology.

2760 ■ Computerworld Careers
URL: http://www.computerworld.com/careertopics/careers

Description: Offers career opportunities for IT (information technology) professionals. Job seekers may search the jobs database, register at the site, and read about job surveys and employment trends. Employers may post jobs.

2761 ■ Computing Research Association Job Announcements
1828 L St. NW, Ste. 800
Washington, DC 20036-4632
Ph: (202)234-2111
Fax: (202)667-1066
E-mail: info@cra.org
URL: http://www.cra.org/ads

Description: Contains dated links to national college and university computer technology positions.

2762 ■ Guru.com
5001 Baum Blvd., Ste. 760
Pittsburgh, PA 15213
Fax: (412)687-4466
Fr: 888-687-1316
URL: http://www.guru.com

Description: Job board specializing in contract jobs for creative and information technology professionals. Also provides online incorporation and educational opportunities for independent contractors along with articles and advice.

2763 ■ InformationTechnologyCrossing.com
URL: http://www.informationtechnologycrossing.com

Description: Provides information on IT jobs.

2764 ■ Jobs4IT.com
URL: http://www.jobs4it.com

Description: Features information technology job opportunities, job fairs, business opportunities, news, events, continuing education guide, resume database, distribution services and other career resources.

2765 ■ JustTechJobs.com
E-mail: support@justtechjobs.com
URL: http://www.justtechjobs.com

Description: Serves as a jobsite that provides employers with a technology specific focus and provides job seekers with job postings aimed at those specific tech jobs. Offers a community of 15 million tech professionals and also supports several technology websites.

2766 ■ TechniciansNow.com
URL: http://www.techniciansnow.com

Description: Provides an avenue to showcase jobs and products vital to the mechanical and technical trade communities.

2767 ■ ZDNet Tech Jobs
URL: http://www.zdnet.com

Description: Site houses a listing of national employment opportunities for professionals in high tech fields. Also contains resume building tips and relocation resources.

OTHER SOURCES

2768 ■ Association of Information Technology Professionals (AITP)
401 N Michigan Ave., Ste. 2400
Chicago, IL 60611-4267
Ph: (312)245-1070
Fax: (312)673-6659
Fr: 800-224-9371
E-mail: aitp_hq@aitp.org
URL: http://www.aitp.org

Description: Managerial personnel, staff, educators, and individuals interested in the management of information resources. Founder of the Certificate in Data Processing examination program, now administered by an intersociety organization. Maintains Legislative Communications Network. Professional education programs include EDP-oriented business and management principles self-study courses and a series of videotaped management development seminars. Sponsors student organizations around the country interested in information technology and encourages members to serve as counselors for the Scout computer merit badge. Conducts research projects, including a business information systems curriculum for two- and four-year colleges.

2769 ■ Association for Women in Computing (AWC)
PO Box 2768
Oakland, CA 94602
E-mail: info@awc-hq.org
URL: http://www.awc-hq.org

Description: Individuals interested in promoting the education, professional development, and advancement of women in computing.

2770 ■ Computing Research Association (CRA)
1828 L St. NW, Ste. 800
Washington, DC 20036-4632
Ph: (202)234-2111
Fax: (202)667-1066
E-mail: info@cra.org
URL: http://www.cra.org

Description: An association of more than 200 North American academic departments of computer science, computer engineering, and related fields; laboratories and centers in industry government, and academia engaging in basic computing research; and affiliated professional societies.

2771 ■ Electronics Technicians Association International (ETA)
5 Depot St.
Greencastle, IN 46135
Ph: (765)653-8262
Fax: (765)653-4287
Fr: 800-288-3824
E-mail: eta@eta-i.org
URL: http://www.eta-i.org

Description: Skilled electronics technicians. Provides placement service; offers certification examinations for electronics technicians and satellite, fiber optics, and data cabling installers. Compiles wage and manpower statistics. Administers FCC Commercial License examinations and certification of computer network systems technicians and web and internet specialists.

2772 ■ International Society of Certified Electronics Technicians (ISCET)
3608 Pershing Ave.
Fort Worth, TX 76107-4527
Ph: (817)921-9101

Fax: (817)921-3741
Fr: 800-946-0201
E-mail: info@iscet.org
URL: http://www.iscet.org

Description: Technicians in 50 countries who have been certified by the society. Seeks to provide a fraternal bond among certified electronics technicians, raise their public image and improve the effectiveness of industry education programs for technicians. Offers training programs in new electronics information. Maintains library of service literature for consumer electronic equipment, including manuals and schematics for out-of-date equipment. Offers all FCC licenses. Sponsors testing program for certification of electronics technicians in the fields of audio, communications, computer, consumer, industrial, medical electronics, radar, radio-television and video.

2773 ■ Large Installation System Administration Conference
USENIX, the Advanced Computing Systems Association
2560 9th St., Ste. 215
Berkeley, CA 94710
Ph: (510)528-8649
Fax: (510)548-5738
E-mail: office@usenix.org
URL: http://www.usenix.org

Annual. Includes exhibits of books, products, and services that can optimize systems, networks, and internet management. 2012 December 9-14; San Diego, CA; 2013 November 3-8; Washington, DC; 2014 November 9-14; Seattle, WA; 2015 November 8-13; Washington, DC; 2016 December 4-9; Boston, MA. Provides networking opportunities for computing professionals.

2774 ■ MIT Computer Science and Artificial Intelligence Laboratory
32 Vassar St.
Cambridge, MA 02139
Ph: (617)253-5851
Fax: (617)258-8682
URL: http://www.csail.mit.edu

Description: Active since 1959. Interdisciplinary laboratory of over 200 people that spans several academic departments and has active projects ongoing with members of every academic school at MIT. Offers research, current job listings, and educational outreach.

2775 ■ National Electronics Service Dealers Association (NESDA)
3608 Pershing Ave.
Fort Worth, TX 76107-4527
Ph: (817)921-9061
Fax: (817)921-3741
Fr: 800-797-9197
E-mail: info@nesda.com
URL: http://www.nesda.com

Description: Local and state electronic service associations and companies. Supplies technical service information on business management training to electronic service dealers. Offers certification and training programs through International Society of Certified Electronics Technicians. Conducts technical service and business management seminars.

2776 ■ Special Interest Group on Accessible Computing (SIGACCESS)
2 Penn Plz., Ste. 701
New York, NY 10121-0701
Ph: (212)626-0500
Fax: (212)944-1318
Fr: 800-342-6626
E-mail: chair_sigaccess@acm.org
URL: http://www.sigaccess.org

Description: Promotes the professional interests of computing personnel with physical disabilities and the application of computing and information technology in solving relevant disability problems. Works to educate the public to support careers for the disabled.

2777 ■ USENIX, the Advanced Computing Systems Association

2560 9th St., Ste. 215
Berkeley, CA 94710
Ph: (510)528-8649
Fax: (510)548-5738
E-mail: office@usenix.org
URL: http://www.usenix.org

Description: Represents the community of engineers, system administrators, scientists, and technicians working on the cutting edge of the computing world. Aims to foster technical excellence and innovation that pertains to computer systems. Supports and disseminates research with a practical bias. Provides a neutral forum for discussion of technical issues and encourages computing outreach into the community at large.

2778 ■ USENIX Annual Technical Conference
USENIX, the Advanced Computing Systems Association

2560 9th St., Ste. 215
Berkeley, CA 94710
Ph: (510)528-8649
Fax: (510)548-5738
E-mail: office@usenix.org
URL: http://www.usenix.org

Annual. Includes exhibits of products and services for the advancement of computing systems.

2560 9th St., Ste. 215
Berkeley, CA 94710
Ph: (510)528-8649
Fax: (510)548-5738

2779 ■ ACM Transactions on Internet Technology
Association for Computing Machinery
PO Box 30777
New York, NY 10087
Ph: (212)626-0500
Fax: (212)944-1318
Fr: 800-342-6626
URL: http://toit.acm.org

Quarterly. $190.00/year for nonmembers, print only; $152.00/year for nonmembers, online only; $228.00/year for nonmembers, online and print. Publication of the Association for Computing Machinery. Brings together many computing disciplines including computer software engineering, computer programming languages, middleware, database management, security, knowledge discovery and data mining, networking and distributed systems, communications, performance and scalability, and more. Covers the results and roles of the individual disciplines and the relationships among them.

2780 ■ AVIOS Journal
Applied Voice Input/Output Society
PO Box 20817
San Jose, CA 95160
Ph: (408)323-1783
Fax: (408)323-1782
URL: http://www.avios.com/

Annual. Journal covering issues in computer science.

2781 ■ Communications of the ACM
Association for Computing Machinery
PO Box 30777
New York, NY 10087
Ph: (212)626-0500
Fax: (212)944-1318
Fr: 800-342-6626
URL: http://cacm.acm.org

Monthly. $99.00/year for members, professional. Computing news magazine.

2782 ■ Communications and Network
Scientific Research Publishing
PO Box 54821
Irvine, CA 92619-4821
E-mail: cn@scirp.org
URL: http://www.scirp.org/journal/cn/

Quarterly. $236.00/year for individuals. Journal publishing articles on the latest advancements in communications and network technologies.

2783 ■ Computers and Composition
Elsevier Science Inc.
360 Park Ave. S
New York, NY 10010-1710
Ph: (212)989-5800
Fax: (212)633-3990

Fr: 888-437-4636
URL: http://www.elsevier.com/wps/find/journaldescription.cws_home

$454.00/year for institutions, all countries except Europe, Japan and Iran; $405.00/year for institutions, European countries and Iran; $53,500.00/year for institutions, Japan; $82.00/year for individuals, all countries except Europe, Japan and Iran; $62.00/year for individuals, European countries and Iran; $8,900.00/year for individuals, Japan. Journal covering computers in writing classes, programs, and research.

2784 ■ Computers in Libraries
Information Today Inc.
143 Old Marlton Pike
Medford, NJ 08055-8750
Ph: (609)654-6266
Fax: (609)654-4309
Fr: 800-300-9868
URL: http://www.infotoday.com/cilmag/default.shtml

$99.95/year for individuals, computers in libraries; $188.00/year for individuals, 2 years, U.S.; $288.00/year for individuals, 3 year, U.S.; $118.00/year for Canada and Mexico; $131.00/year for individuals, outside North America; $69.95/year for individuals; $132.00/year for two years; $201.00/year for individuals, 3 years; $88.00/year for Canada and Mexico; $101.00/year for individuals, outside North America. Library science magazine that provides complete coverage of the news and issues in the rapidly evolving field of library information technology.

2785 ■ Computers Programs/PC World
IDG Communications Inc.
3 Speen St.
Framingham, MA 01701
Ph: (508)875-5000
URL: http://www.idg.com

Magazine devoted to IT specialists, covering practical questions of computing including purchase and usage of the computer technology, software, computer components and peripherals.

2786 ■ Computerworld/Correio Informatico
IDG Communications Inc.
3 Speen St.
Framingham, MA 01701
Ph: (508)875-5000
URL: http://www.idg.com/www/IDGProducts.nsf/0/B1E40F5ABD0169AB852

Weekly. Magazine providing news on latest developments in computer industry.

2787 ■ Computerworld Top 100
IDG Communications Inc.
3 Speen St.
Framingham, MA 01701
Ph: (508)875-5000
URL: http://www.idg.com/www/IDGProducts.nsf/0/E7EDD4EC98463F2C852

Annual. Magazine for analyzing trends and events of information technology business.

2788 ■ Computing SA
IDG Communications Inc.
3 Speen St.
Framingham, MA 01701
Ph: (508)875-5000
URL: http://www.idg.com/www/IDGProducts.nsf/0/12C44C74D05A07DF852

Monthly. Newspaper focusing computer hardware, software, networking, telecommunications, channel management and online computing.

2789 ■ CXO
IDG Communications Inc.
3 Speen St.
Framingham, MA 01701
Ph: (508)875-5000
URL: http://www.idg.com/www/IDGProducts.nsf/0/022796185EED5984852

Monthly. Magazine providing technology information for chief officers and managers.

2790 ■ Eclipse Review
BZ Media L.L.C.
7 High St., Ste. 407
Huntington, NY 11743
Ph: (631)421-4158
Fax: (631)421-4130
URL: http://www.eclipsesource.com/contact.htm

Magazine for IT professionals.

2791 ■ Foundations and Trends in Networking
Now Publishers
PO Box 1024
Hanover, MA 02339-1001
Ph: (781)871-0245
URL: http://www.nowpublishers.com/product.aspx?product=NET

$390.00/year for individuals, online only; $450.00/year for individuals, print and online; $390.00/year for other countries, online only; $450.00/year for other countries, print and online. Academic journal publishing new research in computer networking.

2792 ■ Government Computer News
PostNewsweek Tech Media
10 G St. NE, Ste. 500
Washington, DC 20002-4228
Ph: (202)772-2500
Fax: (202)772-2511
Fr: (866)447-6864
URL: http://gcn.com/

Semimonthly. Magazine for professionals interested in government IT.

2793 ■ IEEE Security & Privacy Magazine
IEEE Computer Society
10662 Los Vaqueros Cir.
PO Box 3014
Los Alamitos, CA 90720-1314

Ph: (714)821-8380
Fax: (714)821-4010
Fr: 800-272-6657
URL: http://www.computer.org/portal/site/security/

Bimonthly. $735.00/year for individuals, online; $770.00/year for individuals, print; $965.00/year for individuals, print and online. Journal that aims to explore role and importance of networked infrastructure and developing lasting security solutions.

2794 ■ Information Security
TechTarget
117 Kendrick St., Ste. 800
Needham, MA 02494
Ph: (781)657-1000
Fax: (781)657-1100
Fr: 888-274-4111
URL: http://searchsecurity.techtarget.com/

Monthly. Free to qualified subscribers. Magazine covering information security topics.

2795 ■ International Journal of Communications, Network and System Sciences
Scientific Research Publishing
PO Box 54821
Irvine, CA 92619-4821
E-mail: ijcns@scirp.org
URL: http://www.scirp.org/journal/ijcns/

Monthly. $948.00/year for individuals. Peer-reviewed journal publishing articles on the latest advancements in communications and network technologies.

2796 ■ IT Solutions Guide
SYS-CON Media
577 Chestnut Ridge Rd.
Woodcliff Lake, NJ 07677
Ph: (201)802-3000
Fax: (201)782-9601
URL: http://itsolutions.sys-con.com/

Quarterly. Magazine for IT professionals.

2797 ■ Journal of Computer Science
Science Publications
Vails Gate Heights Dr.
PO Box 879
Vails Gate, NY 12584-0879
URL: http://thescipub.com/jcs.toc

Scholarly journal covering many areas of computer science, including: concurrent, parallel and distributed processing; artificial intelligence; image and voice processing; quality software and metrics; computer-aided education; wireless communication; real time processing; evaluative computation; and data bases and information recovery and neural networks.

2798 ■ Journal of Computer Systems, Networks, and Communications
Hindawi Publishing Corp.
410 Park Ave., 15th Fl.
287 PMB
New York, NY 10022-4407
Fax: (215)893-4392
E-mail: jcsnc@hindawi.com
URL: http://www.hindawi.com/journals/jcsnc/

$195.00/year for individuals, print & online. Journal covering important areas of information technology.

2799 ■ Monitor
Capital PC User Group
19209 Mt. Airey Rd.
Brookeville, MD 20833
Ph: (301)560-6442
Fax: (301)760-3303
E-mail: editor@cpcug.org
URL: http://monitor.cpcug.org/index.html

Quarterly. Magazine covering computer hardware and software reviews, special interest user group news, advertisers and author/subject index, and calendar of events.

2800 ■ PC Today
Sandhills Publishing
120 W Harvest Dr.
Lincoln, NE 68521
Ph: (402)479-2181
Fax: (402)479-2195
Fr: 800-331-1978
E-mail: editor@pctoday.com
URL: http://www.pctoday.com/

Monthly. $29.00/year for individuals; $37.00/year for Canada; $64.00/year for Canada, 2 years; $2.42/year for individuals, print; $17.00/year for individuals, online only; $69.00/year for other countries; $48.00/year for individuals, 2 years; $64.00/year for individuals, 3 years; $82.00/year for Canada, 3 years; $64.00/year for Canada, 2 years. Magazine for personal computer users.

2801 ■ PC WORLD
101 Communications
9121 Oakdale Ave., Ste. 101
Chatsworth, CA 91311
Ph: (818)814-5200
Fax: (818)734-1522
E-mail: pcwletters@pcworld.com
URL: http://www.pcworld.com

Quarterly. $19.97/year for individuals; $29.97/year for two years. Technology or business magazine meeting the informational needs of tech-savvy managers, both at work and at home.

2802 ■ Queue
Association for Computing Machinery
PO Box 30777
New York, NY 10087
Ph: (212)626-0500
Fax: (212)944-1318
Fr: 800-342-6626
E-mail: queue@acm.org
URL: http://queue.acm.org/

Monthly. Free, U.S./Canadian residents and all members. Online magazine aimed at the computer professional. Magazine editorial does not provide solutions for the "here-and-now", but instead helps decision-makers plan future projects by examining the challenges and problems they are most likely to face.

2803 ■ Revenue
Montgomery Media International
55 New Montgomery St., Ste. 617
San Francisco, CA 94105
Ph: (415)371-8800
URL: http://www.revenuetoday.com/

Free to qualified subscribers. Magazine covering internet marketing strategies.

2804 ■ Ubiquity
Association for Computing Machinery
PO Box 30777
New York, NY 10087
Ph: (212)626-0500
Fax: (212)944-1318
Fr: 800-342-6626
URL: http://ubiquity.acm.org

Weekly. Free. Web-based magazine of the Association for Computing Machinery dedicated to fostering critical analysis and in-depth commentary, including book reviews, on issues relating to the nature, constitution, structure, science, engineering, cognition, technology, practices and paradigms of the IT profession.

2805 ■ WITI FastTrack
United business Media L.L.C
240 W 35th St.
New York, NY 10001
Ph: (516)562-5000
URL: http://www.witi.com/corporate/fasttrack.php

Semiannual. Semiannual publication featuring in-depth content on the issues facing today's women professionals in technology.

EMPLOYER DIRECTORIES AND NETWORKING LISTS

2806 ■ Career Opportunities in Computers and Cyberspace
Facts On File Inc.
132 W 31st St., 17th Fl.
New York, NY 10001
Ph: (212)967-8800
Fax: 800-678-3633
Fr: 800-322-8755
URL: http://www.infobasepublishing.com

Published March, 2004. Covers: Nearly 200 professions, clustering them by skill, objectives, and work conditions. Entries include: Education, salaries, employment prospects.

2807 ■ Careers in Focus—Computers
Facts On File Inc.
132 W 31st St., 17th Fl.
New York, NY 10001
Ph: (212)967-8800
Fax: 800-678-3633
Fr: 800-322-8755
URL: http://www.infobasepublishing.com

Latest edition 5th; Published August, 2008. $32.95 for individuals. Covers: An overview of computers, followed by a selection of jobs profiled in detail, including the nature of the job, earnings, prospects for employment, what kind of training and skills it requires, and sources for further information.

2808 ■ Computer Directory
Computer Directories Inc.
23815 Nichols Sawmill Rd.
Hockley, TX 77447
Ph: (281)259-5959
Fax: (281)259-5959
Fr: 800-234-4353
URL: http://www.compdirinc.com

Annual, fall. Covers: Approximately 130,000 computer installations; 19 separate volumes for Alaska/Hawaii, Connecticut/New Jersey, Dallas/Ft. Worth, Eastern Seaboard, Far Midwest, Houston, Illinois, Midatlantic, Midcentral, Mideast, Minnesota/Wisconsin, North Central, New England, New York Metro, Northwest, Ohio, Pennsylvania/West Virginia, Southeast, and Southwest Texas. Entries include: Company name, address, phone, fax, email, name and title of contact, hardware used, software application, operating system, programming language, computer graphics, networking system. Arrangement: Geographical. Indexes: Alphabetical, industry, hardware.

2809 ■ Vault Guide to the Top Tech Employers
Vault.com Inc.
150 W 22nd St., 5th Fl.
New York, NY 10011
Ph: (212)366-4212
Fax: (212)366-6117
Fr: 888-562-8285
URL: http://www.vault.com/store/book_preview.jsp?product_id=38814

Latest edition June, 2009. $19.95 for individuals; $19.95 for members. Covers: Technology industry employers. Entries include: Name, address, phone, fax, website, and other branch office location. Also include company overviews, recent company news, information on the hiring process, key competitors, and employment contact.

HANDBOOKS AND MANUALS

2810 ■ America's Top 100 Computer and Technical Jobs
Jist Publishing
875 Montreal Way
St. Paul, MN 55102

Fr: 800-648-5478
E-mail: info@jist.com
URL: http://www.jist.com/shop/
product.php?productid=16453&cat=0&page=1
Michael J. Farr. 2009. $17.95. 400 pages. Job hunting in computer and technical industries.

EMPLOYMENT AGENCIES AND SEARCH FIRMS

2811 ■ Carol Maden Group
2019 Cunningham Dr., Ste. 218
Hampton, VA 23666-3316
Ph: (757)827-9010
Fax: (757)827-9081
E-mail: cmaden@hroads.net

Personnel consultants offering placement service in computer technology and engineering; servicing manufacturing and private industries nationwide. Temporary placement servicing clerical and light industrial.

2812 ■ Chaves & Associates
418 Meadow St.
Fairfield, CT 06824
Ph: (203)222-2222
Fax: (203)341-8844
E-mail: info@asinsitesearch.com
URL: http://www.insitesearch.com

Executive search firm.

2813 ■ CNR Search & Services
30752 Via Conquista
San Juan Capistrano, CA 92675
Ph: (949)488-0065
Fax: (775)851-4514
E-mail: cnrkenmiller@juno.com
URL: http://www.cnrsearch.com

Provides staffing services of permanent and temporary employees. Works primarily on a retained basis. Contingency on a limited basis. Services include human resources consulting, mergers and acquisitions in high technology firms. Industries served: computer; information services; insurance, pharmaceutical and health care. Provides staffing services of permanent and temporary employees. Works primarily on a retained basis. Contingency on a limited basis. Services include human resources consulting, mergers and acquisitions in high technology firms. Industries served: computer; information services; insurance, pharmaceutical and health care.

2814 ■ Doleman Enterprises
11160-F S Lakes Dr., Ste. 326
Reston, VA 22091
Ph: (703)742-5454
Fax: (703)708-6992
E-mail: doleman@patriot.net

Human resources firm specializes in recruiting for the high-tech, data and computer engineering and pharmaceutical industries.

2815 ■ EDP Staffing, LLC
PO Box 651
Hebron, CT 06231
Fr: (860)781-6064
E-mail: info@edpstaffingllc.com
URL: http://www.edpstaffingllc.com

Description: Serves as an e-commerce and IT management search firm. Provides staffing solutions for contingency, retained, contract or temporary staffing. Specializes in the recruitment and placement of e-commerce applications specialists, core IT staff members or IT management professionals.

2816 ■ Louis Rudzinsky Associates Inc.
394 Lowell St., Ste. 17
PO Box 640
Lexington, MA 02420-2551
Ph: (781)862-6727

Fax: (781)862-6868
E-mail: lra@lra.com
URL: http://www.lra.com

Provides recruitment, placement, and executive search to industry (software, electronics, optics) covering positions in general management, manufacturing, engineering, and marketing. Personnel consulting activities include counsel to small and startup companies. Industries served: electronics, aerospace, optical, laser, computer, software, imaging, electro-optics, biotechnology, advanced materials, and solid-state/semiconductor.

2817 ■ Michael Anthony Associates Inc.
44 Washington St., Ste. 250
Wellesley, MA 02481-1802
Ph: (781)237-4950
Fax: (781)237-6811
Fr: 800-337-4950
E-mail: manthony@maainc.com
URL: http://www.maainc.com

Applications development, systems programming, communications, and database specialists servicing the IBM mainframe, midrange, and PC marketplace. Provides technical expertise of conversions, system software installation and upgrades, performance and tuning, capacity planning, and data communications. In addition to contract services also provide retained search and contingency placement of computer professionals ranging from senior staff to senior management. Also act as brokers for independent consultants and small consulting firms requiring the services of marketing specialists. Industries served: banking, financial services, hospitals, HMO's, manufacturers, software development, universities, defense, and consulting firms.

2818 ■ Professional Computer Resources Inc.
1500 S Blvd., No. 201B
Charlotte, NC 28203
Ph: (980)216-6152
Fax: (704)332-7288
Fr: 888-727-2458
URL: http://www.pcr.net

Executive search firm.

2819 ■ Wallach Associates Inc.
7811 Montrose Rd., Ste. 505
Potomac, MD 20854
Ph: (301)340-0300
Fax: (301)340-8008
Fr: 800-296-2084
URL: http://www.wallach.org

Specialists in recruitment of professional personnel, primarily in information technology and electronic systems and engineering, energy research and development, management consulting, operations research, computers, defense systems, and programmers. Specializes in Internet and software engineer for intelligence community.

ONLINE JOB SOURCES AND SERVICES

2820 ■ ComputerJobs.com
URL: http://www.computerjobs.com

Description: Provides listings of computer-related job opportunities.

2821 ■ ComputerWork.com
Fr: 800-691-8413
URL: http://www.computerwork.com

Description: Job search and resume submission service for professionals in information technology.

2822 ■ Computerworld Careers
URL: http://www.computerworld.com/careertopics/careers

Description: Offers career opportunities for IT (information technology) professionals. Job seekers may search the jobs database, register at the site,

and read about job surveys and employment trends. Employers may post jobs.

2823 ■ Computing Research Association Job Announcements
1828 L St. NW, Ste. 800
Washington, DC 20036-4632
Ph: (202)234-2111
Fax: (202)667-1066
E-mail: info@cra.org
URL: http://www.cra.org/ads

Description: Contains dated links to national college and university computer technology positions.

2824 ■ Guru.com
5001 Baum Blvd., Ste. 760
Pittsburgh, PA 15213
Fax: (412)687-4466
Fr: 888-687-1316
URL: http://www.guru.com

Description: Job board specializing in contract jobs for creative and information technology professionals. Also provides online incorporation and educational opportunities for independent contractors along with articles and advice.

2825 ■ InformationTechnologyCrossing.com
URL: http://www.informationtechnologycrossing.com

Description: Provides information on IT jobs.

2826 ■ JustTechJobs.com
E-mail: support@justtechjobs.com
URL: http://www.justtechjobs.com

Description: Serves as a jobsite that provides employers with a technology specific focus and provides job seekers with job postings aimed at those specific tech jobs. Offers a community of 15 million tech professionals and also supports several technology websites.

2827 ■ Tech-Engine.com
URL: http://techengine.com

Description: Features employment listings concerning the IT and engineering fields. Features employers and recruiters information, resume posting and career resources.

2828 ■ ZDNet Tech Jobs
URL: http://www.zdnet.com

Description: Site houses a listing of national employment opportunities for professionals in high tech fields. Also contains resume building tips and relocation resources.

TRADESHOWS

2829 ■ XPLOR International Conference and Vendor Forum
XPLOR International
24156 State Rd. 54, Ste. 4
Lutz, FL 33559
Ph: (813)929-8100
Fax: (813)929-8524
Fr: 800-669-7567
E-mail: info@xplor.org
URL: http://www.xplor.org

Annual. Primary Exhibits: Equipment, supplies, and services for users and manufacturers of advanced electronic document systems. Dates and Locations: 2012 May 27-29; Tampa, FL; TradeWinds Island Grand Hotel and Conference Center.

OTHER SOURCES

2830 ■ Association of Information Technology Professionals (AITP)
401 N Michigan Ave., Ste. 2400
Chicago, IL 60611-4267
Ph: (312)245-1070

Fax: (312)673-6659
Fr: 800-224-9371
E-mail: aitp_hq@aitp.org
URL: http://www.aitp.org

Description: Managerial personnel, staff, educators, and individuals interested in the management of information resources. Founder of the Certificate in Data Processing examination program, now administered by an intersociety organization. Maintains Legislative Communications Network. Professional education programs include EDP-oriented business and management principles self-study courses and a series of videotaped management development seminars. Sponsors student organizations around the country interested in information technology and encourages members to serve as counselors for the Scout computer merit badge. Conducts research projects, including a business information systems curriculum for two- and four-year colleges.

2831 ■ Association for Women in Computing (AWC)
PO Box 2768
Oakland, CA 94602
E-mail: info@awc-hq.org
URL: http://www.awc-hq.org

Description: Individuals interested in promoting the education, professional development, and advancement of women in computing.

2832 ■ Computing Research Association (CRA)
1828 L St. NW, Ste. 800
Washington, DC 20036-4632
Ph: (202)234-2111

Fax: (202)667-1066
E-mail: info@cra.org
URL: http://www.cra.org

Description: An association of more than 200 North American academic departments of computer science, computer engineering, and related fields; laboratories and centers in industry government, and academia engaging in basic computing research; and affiliated professional societies.

2833 ■ Large Installation System Administration Conference
USENIX, the Advanced Computing Systems Association
2560 9th St., Ste. 215
Berkeley, CA 94710
Ph: (510)528-8649
Fax: (510)548-5738
E-mail: office@usenix.org
URL: http://www.usenix.org

Annual. Includes exhibits of books, products, and services that can optimize systems, networks, and internet management. 2012 December 9-14; San Diego, CA; 2013 November 3-8; Washington, DC; 2014 November 9-14; Seattle, WA; 2015 November 8-13; Washington, DC; 2016 December 4-9; Boston, MA. Provides networking opportunities for computing professionals.

2834 ■ MIT Computer Science and Artificial Intelligence Laboratory
32 Vassar St.
Cambridge, MA 02139
Ph: (617)253-5851

Fax: (617)258-8682
URL: http://www.csail.mit.edu

Description: Active since 1959. Interdisciplinary laboratory of over 200 people that spans several academic departments and has active projects ongoing with members of every academic school at MIT. Offers research, current job listings, and educational outreach.

2835 ■ USENIX, the Advanced Computing Systems Association
2560 9th St., Ste. 215
Berkeley, CA 94710
Ph: (510)528-8649
Fax: (510)548-5738
E-mail: office@usenix.org
URL: http://www.usenix.org

Description: Represents the community of engineers, system administrators, scientists, and technicians working on the cutting edge of the computing world. Aims to foster technical excellence and innovation that pertains to computer systems. Supports and disseminates research with a practical bias. Provides a neutral forum for discussion of technical issues and encourages computing outreach into the community at large.

2836 ■ USENIX Annual Technical Conference
USENIX, the Advanced Computing Systems Association
2560 9th St., Ste. 215
Berkeley, CA 94710
Ph: (510)528-8649
Fax: (510)548-5738
E-mail: office@usenix.org
URL: http://www.usenix.org

Annual. Includes exhibits of products and services for the advancement of computing systems.

Computer Systems Analysts

SOURCES OF HELP-WANTED ADS

2837 ■ ACM Transactions on Internet Technology
Association for Computing Machinery
PO Box 30777
New York, NY 10087
Ph: (212)626-0500
Fax: (212)944-1318
Fr: 800-342-6626
URL: http://toit.acm.org

Quarterly. $190.00/year for nonmembers, print only; $152.00/year for nonmembers, online only; $228.00/year for nonmembers, online and print. Publication of the Association for Computing Machinery. Brings together many computing disciplines including computer software engineering, computer programming languages, middleware, database management, security, knowledge discovery and data mining, networking and distributed systems, communications, performance and scalability, and more. Covers the results and roles of the individual disciplines and the relationships among them.

2838 ■ AVIOS Journal
Applied Voice Input/Output Society
PO Box 20817
San Jose, CA 95160
Ph: (408)323-1783
Fax: (408)323-1782
URL: http://www.avios.com/

Annual. Journal covering issues in computer science.

2839 ■ Communications of the ACM
Association for Computing Machinery
PO Box 30777
New York, NY 10087
Ph: (212)626-0500
Fax: (212)944-1318
Fr: 800-342-6626
URL: http://cacm.acm.org

Monthly. $99.00/year for members, professional. Computing news magazine.

2840 ■ Communications and Network
Scientific Research Publishing
PO Box 54821
Irvine, CA 92619-4821
E-mail: cn@scirp.org
URL: http://www.scirp.org/journal/cn/

Quarterly. $236.00/year for individuals. Journal publishing articles on the latest advancements in communications and network technologies.

2841 ■ Computers and Composition
Elsevier Science Inc.
360 Park Ave. S
New York, NY 10010-1710
Ph: (212)989-5800
Fax: (212)633-3990

Fr: 888-437-4636
URL: http://www.elsevier.com/wps/find/journaldescription.cws_home

$454.00/year for institutions, all countries except Europe, Japan and Iran; $405.00/year for institutions, European countries and Iran; $53,500.00/year for institutions, Japan; $82.00/year for individuals, all countries except Europe, Japan and Iran; $62.00/year for individuals, European countries and Iran; $8,900.00/year for individuals, Japan. Journal covering computers in writing classes, programs, and research.

2842 ■ Computers Programs/PC World
IDG Communications Inc.
3 Speen St.
Framingham, MA 01701
Ph: (508)875-5000
URL: http://www.idg.com

Magazine devoted to IT specialists, covering practical questions of computing including purchase and usage of the computer technology, software, computer components and peripherals.

2843 ■ Computerworld
101 Communications
9121 Oakdale Ave., Ste. 101
Chatsworth, CA 91311
Ph: (818)814-5200
Fax: (818)734-1522
URL: http://www.computerworld.com

Weekly. $129.00/year for individuals; $129.00/year for Canada; $295.00/year for other countries; $250.00/year for individuals, Mexico/Central/South America; $29.00/year for individuals, digital edition. Newspaper for information systems executives.

2844 ■ Computerworld/Correio Informatico
IDG Communications Inc.
3 Speen St.
Framingham, MA 01701
Ph: (508)875-5000
URL: http://www.idg.com/www/IDGProducts.nsf/0/B1E40F5ABD0169AB852

Weekly. Magazine providing news on latest developments in computer industry.

2845 ■ Computerworld Top 100
IDG Communications Inc.
3 Speen St.
Framingham, MA 01701
Ph: (508)875-5000
URL: http://www.idg.com/www/IDGProducts.nsf/0/E7EDD4EC98463F2C852

Annual. Magazine for analyzing trends and events of information technology business.

2846 ■ Computing SA
IDG Communications Inc.
3 Speen St.
Framingham, MA 01701

Ph: (508)875-5000
URL: http://www.idg.com/www/IDGProducts.nsf/0/12C44C74D05A07DF852

Monthly. Newspaper focusing computer hardware, software, networking, telecommunications, channel management and online computing.

2847 ■ Computing Surveys (CSUR)
Association for Computing Machinery
PO Box 30777
New York, NY 10087
Ph: (212)626-0500
Fax: (212)944-1318
Fr: 800-342-6626
URL: http://surveys.acm.org/

Quarterly. $205.00/year for nonmembers, print only; $164.00/year for nonmembers, online only; $246.00/year for nonmembers, online & print. Journal presenting surveys and tutorials in computer science.

2848 ■ Cutter IT Journal
Cutter Information Corp.
37 Broadway, Ste. 1
Arlington, MA 02474
Ph: (781)648-8700
Fax: (781)648-8707
E-mail: service@cutter.com
URL: http://www.cutter.com/itjournal.html

Description: Monthly. $485. Provides IT managers with practical and objective views on the latest technology and management trends.

2849 ■ CXO
IDG Communications Inc.
3 Speen St.
Framingham, MA 01701
Ph: (508)875-5000
URL: http://www.idg.com/www/IDGProducts.nsf/0/022796185EED5984852

Monthly. Magazine providing technology information for chief officers and managers.

2850 ■ Datamation
Reed Business Information
360 Park Ave. S
New York, NY 10010-1710
Ph: (646)746-6400
URL: http://www.datamation.com

Semimonthly. Magazine on computers and information processing.

2851 ■ Eclipse Review
BZ Media L.L.C.
7 High St., Ste. 407
Huntington, NY 11743
Ph: (631)421-4158
Fax: (631)421-4130
URL: http://www.eclipsesource.com/contact.htm

Magazine for IT professionals.

2852 ■ *Foundations and Trends in Networking*
Now Publishers
PO Box 1024
Hanover, MA 02339-1001
Ph: (781)871-0245
URL: http://www.nowpublishers.com/
product.aspx?product=NET

$390.00/year for individuals, online only; $450.00/year for individuals, print and online; $390.00/year for other countries, online only; $450.00/year for other countries, print and online. Academic journal publishing new research in computer networking.

2853 ■ *Government Computer News*
PostNewsweek Tech Media
10 G St. NE, Ste. 500
Washington, DC 20002-4228
Ph: (202)772-2500
Fax: (202)772-2511
Fr: (866)447-6864
URL: http://gcn.com/

Semimonthly. Magazine for professionals interested in government IT.

2854 ■ *IEEE Security & Privacy Magazine*
IEEE Computer Society
10662 Los Vaqueros Cir.
PO Box 3014
Los Alamitos, CA 90720-1314
Ph: (714)821-8380
Fax: (714)821-4010
Fr: 800-272-6657
URL: http://www.computer.org/portal/site/security/

Bimonthly. $735.00/year for individuals, online; $770.00/year for individuals, print; $965.00/year for individuals, print and online. Journal that aims to explore role and importance of networked infrastructure and developing lasting security solutions.

2855 ■ *IEEE Software*
IEEE Computer Society
10662 Los Vaqueros Cir.
PO Box 3014
Los Alamitos, CA 90720-1314
Ph: (714)821-8380
Fax: (714)821-4010
Fr: 800-272-6657
E-mail: software@computer.org
URL: http://www.computer.org/portal/web/software/
home

Bimonthly. $990.00/year for individuals, online; $1,040.00/year for individuals, print; $1,300.00/year for individuals, print and online. Magazine covering the computer software industry for the community of leading software practitioners.

2856 ■ *IEEE Transactions on Terahertz Science and Technology*
IEEE Microwave Theory and Techniques Society
c/o Edward C. Niehenke
Niehenke Consulting
5829 Bellanca Dr.
Elkridge, MD 21075
Ph: (410)796-5866
Fax: (410)796-5829
E-mail: thz.editors@ieee.org
URL: http://www.mtt.org/publications/118-terahertz.html

Peer-reviewed journal covering terahertz science and applications.

2857 ■ *Information Security*
TechTarget
117 Kendrick St., Ste. 800
Needham, MA 02494
Ph: (781)657-1000
Fax: (781)657-1100
Fr: 888-274-4111
URL: http://searchsecurity.techtarget.com/

Monthly. Free to qualified subscribers. Magazine covering information security topics.

2858 ■ *InfoWorld*
InfoWorld Media Group
501 2nd St.
San Francisco, CA 94107
Fr: 800-227-8365
E-mail: letters@infoworld.com
URL: http://www.infoworld.com/

Weekly. Free to qualified subscribers; $180.00/year for individuals. Weekly publication.

2859 ■ *International Journal of Communications, Network and System Sciences*
Scientific Research Publishing
PO Box 54821
Irvine, CA 92619-4821
E-mail: ijcns@scirp.org
URL: http://www.scirp.org/journal/ijcns/

Monthly. $948.00/year for individuals. Peer-reviewed journal publishing articles on the latest advancements in communications and network technologies.

2860 ■ *IT Solutions Guide*
SYS-CON Media
577 Chestnut Ridge Rd.
Woodcliff Lake, NJ 07677
Ph: (201)802-3000
Fax: (201)782-9601
URL: http://itsolutions.sys-con.com/

Quarterly. Magazine for IT professionals.

2861 ■ *Journal of Computer Science*
Science Publications
Vails Gate Heights Dr.
PO Box 879
Vails Gate, NY 12584-0879
URL: http://thescipub.com/jcs.toc

Scholarly journal covering many areas of computer science, including: concurrent, parallel and distributed processing; artificial intelligence; image and voice processing; quality software and metrics; computer-aided education; wireless communication; real time processing; evaluative computation; and data bases and information recovery and neural networks.

2862 ■ *Journal of Computer Systems, Networks, and Communications*
Hindawi Publishing Corp.
410 Park Ave., 15th Fl.
287 PMB
New York, NY 10022-4407
Fax: (215)893-4392
E-mail: jcsnc@hindawi.com
URL: http://www.hindawi.com/journals/jcsnc/

$195.00/year for individuals, print & online. Journal covering important areas of information technology.

2863 ■ *Monitor*
Capital PC User Group
19209 Mt. Airey Rd.
Brookeville, MD 20833
Ph: (301)560-6442
Fax: (301)760-3303
E-mail: editor@cpcug.org
URL: http://monitor.cpcug.org/index.html

Quarterly. Magazine covering computer hardware and software reviews, special interest user group news, advertisers and author/subject index, and calendar of events.

2864 ■ *PC Today*
Sandhills Publishing
120 W Harvest Dr.
Lincoln, NE 68521
Ph: (402)479-2181
Fax: (402)479-2195
Fr: 800-331-1978
E-mail: editor@pctoday.com
URL: http://www.pctoday.com/

Monthly. $29.00/year for individuals; $37.00/year for Canada; $64.00/year for Canada, 2 years; $2.42/year for individuals, print; $17.00/year for individuals, online only; $69.00/year for other countries; $48.00/

year for individuals, 2 years; $64.00/year for individuals, 3 years; $82.00/year for Canada, 3 years; $64.00/year for Canada, 2 years. Magazine for personal computer users.

2865 ■ *PC WORLD*
101 Communications
9121 Oakdale Ave., Ste. 101
Chatsworth, CA 91311
Ph: (818)814-5200
Fax: (818)734-1522
E-mail: pcwletters@pcworld.com
URL: http://www.pcworld.com

Quarterly. $19.97/year for individuals; $29.97/year for two years. Technology or business magazine meeting the informational needs of tech-savvy managers, both at work and at home.

2866 ■ *Positioning*
Scientific Research Publishing
PO Box 54821
Irvine, CA 92619-4821
E-mail: pos@scirp.org
URL: http://www.scirp.org/journal/pos/

Quarterly. $156.00/year for individuals. Peer-reviewed journal publishing articles on different areas of navigation and positioning.

2867 ■ *Queue*
Association for Computing Machinery
PO Box 30777
New York, NY 10087
Ph: (212)626-0500
Fax: (212)944-1318
Fr: 800-342-6626
E-mail: queue@acm.org
URL: http://queue.acm.org/

Monthly. Free, U.S./Canadian residents and all members. Online magazine aimed at the computer professional. Magazine editorial does not provide solutions for the "here-and-now", but instead helps decision-makers plan future projects by examining the challenges and problems they are most likely to face.

2868 ■ *Revenue*
Montgomery Media International
55 New Montgomery St., Ste. 617
San Francisco, CA 94105
Ph: (415)371-8800
URL: http://www.revenuetoday.com/

Free to qualified subscribers. Magazine covering internet marketing strategies.

2869 ■ *Ubiquity*
Association for Computing Machinery
PO Box 30777
New York, NY 10087
Ph: (212)626-0500
Fax: (212)944-1318
Fr: 800-342-6626
URL: http://ubiquity.acm.org

Weekly. Free. Web-based magazine of the Association for Computing Machinery dedicated to fostering critical analysis and in-depth commentary, including book reviews, on issues relating to the nature, constitution, structure, science, engineering, cognition, technology, practices and paradigms of the IT profession.

2870 ■ *WITI FastTrack*
United business Media L.L.C
240 W 35th St.
New York, NY 10001
Ph: (516)562-5000
URL: http://www.witi.com/corporate/fasttrack.php

Semiannual. Semiannual publication featuring in-depth content on the issues facing today's women professionals in technology.

EMPLOYER DIRECTORIES AND NETWORKING LISTS

2871 ■ Career Opportunities in Computers and Cyberspace
Facts On File Inc.
132 W 31st St., 17th Fl.
New York, NY 10001
Ph: (212)967-8800
Fax: 800-678-3633
Fr: 800-322-8755
URL: http://www.infobasepublishing.com

Published March, 2004. Covers: Nearly 200 professions, clustering them by skill, objectives, and work conditions. Entries include: Education, salaries, employment prospects.

2872 ■ Computer Directory
Computer Directories Inc.
23815 Nichols Sawmill Rd.
Hockley, TX 77447
Ph: (281)259-5959
Fax: (281)259-5959
Fr: 800-234-4353
URL: http://www.compdirinc.com

Annual, fall. Covers: Approximately 130,000 computer installations; 19 separate volumes for Alaska/Hawaii, Connecticut/New Jersey, Dallas/Ft. Worth, Eastern Seaboard, Far Midwest, Houston, Illinois, Midatlantic, Midcentral, Mideast, Minnesota/Wisconsin, North Central, New England, New York Metro, Northwest, Ohio, Pennsylvania/West Virginia, Southeast, and Southwest Texas. Entries include: Company name, address, phone, fax, email, name and title of contact, hardware used, software application, operating system, programming language, computer graphics, networking system. Arrangement: Geographical. Indexes: Alphabetical, industry, hardware.

2873 ■ Directory of Top Computer Executives
Applied Computer Research Inc.
PO Box 41730
Phoenix, AZ 85080-1730
Ph: (623)937-4700
Fax: (623)937-3115
Fr: 800-234-2227
URL: http://www.itmarketintelligence.com

Semiannual, June and December. $345.00 for individuals; $520.00 for U.S. and Canada; $620.00 for individuals; $930.00 for U.S. and Canada; $925.00 for individuals; $1390.00 for U.S. and Canada. Covers: In three volumes, over 65,000 U.S. and Canadian executives with major information technology or communications responsibilities in over 35,500 U.S. and Canadian companies. Entries include: Company name, address, phone, subsidiary and/or division names, major systems installed, names and titles of top information system executives, number of IT employees, number of PCs, and web address. Arrangement: Geographical within separate eastern, western, and Canadian volumes. Indexes: Industry; alphabetical by company name.

2874 ■ Discovering Careers for Your Future—Computers
Facts On File Inc.
132 W 31st St., 17th Fl.
New York, NY 10001
Ph: (212)967-8800
Fax: 800-678-3633
Fr: 800-322-8755
URL: http://factsonfile.infobasepublishing.com

Latest edition 2nd, 2008. $21.95 for individuals. Covers: Computer operators, programmers, database specialists, and software engineers; links career education to curriculum, helping children investigate the subjects they are interested in, and the careers those subjects might lead to.

2875 ■ Vault Guide to the Top Tech Employers
Vault.com Inc.
150 W 22nd St., 5th Fl.
New York, NY 10011
Ph: (212)366-4212
Fax: (212)366-6117
Fr: 888-562-8285
URL: http://www.vault.com/store/book_
preview.jsp?product_id=38814

Latest edition June, 2009. $19.95 for individuals; $19.95 for members. Covers: Technology industry employers. Entries include: Name, address, phone, fax, website, and other branch office location. Also include company overviews, recent company news, information on the hiring process, key competitors, and employment contact.

HANDBOOKS AND MANUALS

2876 ■ America's Top 100 Computer and Technical Jobs
Jist Publishing
875 Montreal Way
St. Paul, MN 55102
Fr: 800-648-5478
E-mail: info@jist.com
URL: http://www.jist.com/shop/
product.php?productid=16453&cat=0&page=1

Michael J. Farr. 2009. $17.95. 400 pages. Job hunting in computer and technical industries.

2877 ■ Careers for Computer Buffs and Other Technological Types
The McGraw-Hill Companies
PO Box 182604
Columbus, OH 43272
Fax: (614)759-3749
Fr: 877-883-5524
E-mail: customer.service@mcgraw-hill.com
URL: http://www.mhprofessional.com/
product.php?isbn=0071458778

Marjorie Eberts and Margaret Gisler. Third edition, 2006. $13.95 (paper). 160 pages. Suggested jobs in a wide range of settings, from the office to the outdoors.

2878 ■ Computer Systems Analyst
National Learning Corporation
212 Michael Dr.
Syosset, NY 11791
Fr: 800-632-8888
URL: http://www.passbooks.com

2009. $34.95 (paper). Serves as an exam preparation guide for computer systems analysts.

2879 ■ Expert Resumes for Computer and Web Jobs
Jist Publishing
875 Montreal Way
St. Paul, MN 55102
Fr: 800-648-5478
E-mail: info@jist.com
URL: http://www.jist.com

Wendy Enelow and Louise Kursmark. Third edition, 2011. $17.95 (paper). 304 pages.

EMPLOYMENT AGENCIES AND SEARCH FIRMS

2880 ■ The Aspire Group
711 Boylston St.
Boston, MA 02116-2616
Fax: (617)500-7284
Fr: 800-487-2967
URL: http://www.bmanet.com/Aspire/index.html

Employment agency.

2881 ■ ATR Technology
1230 Oakmead Pkwy.
Sunnyvale, CA 94085
Ph: (408)328-8000
Fax: (408)328-8001
Fr: 877-412-1100
E-mail: corporate@atr1.com
URL: http://www.atr-technology.com

Description: Serves as an executive search firm specializing in the placement of information technology professionals ranging from complex software application development and infrastructure support to enterprise-wide project management.

2882 ■ The Datafinders Group, Inc.
PO Box 1624
Fort Lee, NJ 07024
Ph: (201)845-7700
Fax: (201)969-1065
E-mail: info@datafinders.net
URL: http://www.datafinders.net

Executive search firm.

2883 ■ Dynamic Search Systems Inc.
220 W Campus Dr., Ste. 201
PO Box 1188
Arlington Heights, IL 60004-1499
Ph: (847)304-0700
Fax: (847)304-5859
E-mail: candidate@dssjobs.com
URL: http://www.dssjobs.com

Provides executive and professional search services to the IT community. Firm specializes in the placement of developers, programmers, programmer analysts, systems analysts, project leaders, project managers, systems programmers, data processing consultants, IT directors, and other information technology related candidates. Industries served: all.

2884 ■ EDP Staffing, LLC
PO Box 651
Hebron, CT 06231
Fr: (860)781-6064
E-mail: info@edpstaffingllc.com
URL: http://www.edpstaffingllc.com

Description: Serves as an e-commerce and IT management search firm. Provides staffing solutions for contingency, retained, contract or temporary staffing. Specializes in the recruitment and placement of e-commerce applications specialists, core IT staff members or IT management professionals.

2885 ■ JES Search Firm Inc.
1021 Stovall Blvd., Ste. 600
Atlanta, GA 30319
Ph: (404)812-0622
Fax: (404)812-1910
E-mail: admin@jessearch.com
URL: http://www.jessearch.com

Contract and permanent information technology search firm specializing in placing software developers as well as other information systems professionals.

2886 ■ KForce
Fr: 877-4KF-ORCE
URL: http://www.kforce.com

Executive search firm. More than 41 locations throughout the United States and two in the Philippines.

2887 ■ Michael Anthony Associates Inc.
44 Washington St., Ste. 250
Wellesley, MA 02481-1802
Ph: (781)237-4950
Fax: (781)237-6811
Fr: 800-337-4950
E-mail: manthony@maainc.com
URL: http://www.maainc.com

Applications development, systems programming, communications, and database specialists servicing the IBM mainframe, midrange, and PC marketplace. Provides technical expertise of conversions, system software installation and upgrades, performance and tuning, capacity planning, and data communications. In addition to contract services also provide retained search and contingency placement of computer professionals ranging from senior staff to senior management. Also act as brokers for independent consultants and small consulting firms requiring the services of marketing specialists. Industries served: banking, financial services, hospitals, HMO's, manufacturers, software development, universities, defense, and consulting firms.

2888 ■ Sullivan and Cogliano
230 2nd Ave.
Waltham, MA 02451
Ph: (781)890-7890
Fax: (781)906-7801
Fr: 888-785-2641
E-mail: jobs@sullivancogliano.com
URL: http://www.sullivancogliano.com

Technical staffing firm.

2889 ■ Technical Talent Locators Ltd.
5570 Sterrett Pl., Ste. 208
Columbia, MD 21044
Ph: (410)740-0091
E-mail: steve@ttlgroup.com
URL: http://www.ttlgroup.com

Permanent employment agency working within the following fields: software and database engineering; computer, communication, and telecommunication system engineering; and other computer-related disciplines.

2890 ■ TRC Staffing Services Inc.
115 Perimeter Center Pl. NE, Ste. 855
Atlanta, GA 30346
Ph: (770)392-1411
Fax: (770)392-7926
E-mail: info@trcstaff.com
URL: http://www.trcstaff.com

A full-service executive search company with permanent placements encompassing engineering, industrial sales, financial and computer science positions. Screen, interview, and verify past employment for all candidates prior to referral. Also assist personnel staffs in the attainment of their EEO/AAP goals with the placement of talented individuals in positions which were underutilized with minorities and/or women. Industries served: all.

2891 ■ Wallach Associates Inc.
7811 Montrose Rd., Ste. 505
Potomac, MD 20854
Ph: (301)340-0300
Fax: (301)340-8008
Fr: 800-296-2084
URL: http://www.wallach.org

Specialists in recruitment of professional personnel, primarily in information technology and electronic systems and engineering, energy research and development, management consulting, operations research, computers, defense systems, and programmers. Specializes in Internet and software engineer for intelligence community.

2892 ■ Worlco Computer Resources, Inc.
901 Rte. 38
Cherry Hill, NJ 08002
Ph: (610)293-9070
Fax: (856)665-8903
E-mail: recruiter@worlco.com
URL: http://www.worlco.com

Employment agency and executive search firm. Second location in Cherry Hill, New Jersey.

ONLINE JOB SOURCES AND SERVICES

2893 ■ Computer Systems Analyst Jobs
URL: http://computer-systems-analyst-jobs.intellego-publishing.com

Description: Contains statistics, informative articles and updated list of current open positions for computer systems analysts. Includes news concerning prospects for a career in computer systems analysis.

2894 ■ ComputerWork.com
Fr: 800-691-8413
URL: http://www.computerwork.com

Description: Job search and resume submission service for professionals in information technology.

2895 ■ Computerworld Careers
URL: http://www.computerworld.com/careertopics/careers

Description: Offers career opportunities for IT (information technology) professionals. Job seekers may search the jobs database, register at the site, and read about job surveys and employment trends. Employers may post jobs.

2896 ■ Computing Research Association Job Announcements
1828 L St. NW, Ste. 800
Washington, DC 20036-4632
Ph: (202)234-2111
Fax: (202)667-1066
E-mail: info@cra.org
URL: http://www.cra.org/ads

Description: Contains dated links to national college and university computer technology positions.

2897 ■ Guru.com
5001 Baum Blvd., Ste. 760
Pittsburgh, PA 15213
Fax: (412)687-4466
Fr: 888-687-1316
URL: http://www.guru.com

Description: Job board specializing in contract jobs for creative and information technology professionals. Also provides online incorporation and educational opportunities for independent contractors along with articles and advice.

2898 ■ InformationTechnologyCrossing.com
URL: http://www.informationtechnologycrossing.com

Description: Provides information on IT jobs.

2899 ■ ItJobs.com
E-mail: comments@itjobsllc.com
URL: http://www.itjobs.com

Description: Provides information technology employment opportunities for the following categories: internet/intranet/extranet, network systems, open systems, client/server, software engineering and development, software QA and testing, ERP applications and management consulting, and legacy systems.

2900 ■ Jobs for Programmers
E-mail: support@jfpresources.com
URL: http://www.prgjobs.com

Description: Job board site for computer programmers that allows them to browse through thousands of programming jobs, even search for special jobs with sign-on bonuses, relocation funding, and 4-day work weeks. Resume posting is free.

2901 ■ Jobs4IT.com
URL: http://www.jobs4it.com

Description: Features information technology job opportunities, job fairs, business opportunities, news, events, continuing education guide, resume database, distribution services and other career resources.

2902 ■ JustTechJobs.com
E-mail: support@justtechjobs.com
URL: http://www.justtechjobs.com

Description: Serves as a jobsite that provides employers with a technology specific focus and provides job seekers with job postings aimed at those specific tech jobs. Offers a community of 15 million

tech professionals and also supports several technology websites.

2903 ■ Tech-Engine.com
URL: http://techengine.com

Description: Features employment listings concerning the IT and engineering fields. Features employers and recruiters information, resume posting and career resources.

2904 ■ ZDNet Tech Jobs
URL: http://www.zdnet.com

Description: Site houses a listing of national employment opportunities for professionals in high tech fields. Also contains resume building tips and relocation resources.

TRADESHOWS

2905 ■ XPLOR International Conference and Vendor Forum
XPLOR International
24156 State Rd. 54, Ste. 4
Lutz, FL 33559
Ph: (813)929-8100
Fax: (813)929-8524
Fr: 800-669-7567
E-mail: info@xplor.org
URL: http://www.xplor.org

Annual. Primary Exhibits: Equipment, supplies, and services for users and manufacturers of advanced electronic document systems. Dates and Locations: 2012 May 27-29; Tampa, FL; TradeWinds Island Grand Hotel and Conference Center.

OTHER SOURCES

2906 ■ American Indian Science and Engineering Society (AISES)
PO Box 9828
Albuquerque, NM 87119-9828
Ph: (505)765-1052
Fax: (505)765-5608
E-mail: info@aises.org
URL: http://www.aises.org

Description: Represents American Indian and non-Indian students and professionals in science, technology, and engineering fields; corporations representing energy, mining, aerospace, electronic, and computer fields. Seeks to motivate and encourage students to pursue undergraduate and graduate studies in science, engineering, and technology. Sponsors science fairs in grade schools, teacher training workshops, summer math/science sessions for 8th-12th graders, professional chapters, and student chapters in colleges. Offers scholarships. Adult members serve as role models, advisers, and mentors for students. Operates placement service.

2907 ■ Association of Information Technology Professionals (AITP)
401 N Michigan Ave., Ste. 2400
Chicago, IL 60611-4267
Ph: (312)245-1070
Fax: (312)673-6659
Fr: 800-224-9371
E-mail: aitp_hq@aitp.org
URL: http://www.aitp.org

Description: Managerial personnel, staff, educators, and individuals interested in the management of information resources. Founder of the Certificate in Data Processing examination program, now administered by an intersociety organization. Maintains Legislative Communications Network. Professional education programs include EDP-oriented business and management principles self-study courses and a series of videotaped management development seminars. Sponsors student organizations around the country interested in information technology and encourages members to serve as counselors for the

Scout computer merit badge. Conducts research projects, including a business information systems curriculum for two- and four-year colleges.

2908 ■ Association for Women in Computing (AWC)
PO Box 2768
Oakland, CA 94602
E-mail: info@awc-hq.org
URL: http://www.awc-hq.org

Description: Individuals interested in promoting the education, professional development, and advancement of women in computing.

2909 ■ Black Data Processing Associates (BDPA)
9500 Arena Dr., Ste. 350
Largo, MD 20774
Ph: (301)584-3135
Fax: (301)560-8300
Fr: 800-727-BDPA
E-mail: office@bdpa.org
URL: http://www.bdpa.org

Description: Represents persons employed in the information processing industry, including electronic data processing, electronic word processing and data communications; others interested in information processing. Seeks to accumulate and share information processing knowledge and business expertise to increase the career and business potential of minorities in the information processing field. Conducts professional seminars, workshops, tutoring services and community introductions to data processing. Makes annual donation to the United Negro College Fund.

2910 ■ Computer Society (CS)
IEEE
2001 L St. NW, Ste. 700
Washington, DC 20036-4910
Ph: (202)371-0101
Fax: (202)728-9614
Fr: 800-272-6657
E-mail: help@computer.org
URL: http://www.computer.org

Description: Computer professionals. Promotes the development of computer and information sciences and fosters communication within the information processing community. Sponsors conferences, symposia, workshops, tutorials, technical meetings, and seminars. Operates Computer Society Press. Presents scholarships; bestows technical achievement and service awards and certificates.

2911 ■ Large Installation System Administration Conference
USENIX, the Advanced Computing Systems Association
2560 9th St., Ste. 215
Berkeley, CA 94710
Ph: (510)528-8649
Fax: (510)548-5738
E-mail: office@usenix.org
URL: http://www.usenix.org

Annual. Includes exhibits of books, products, and services that can optimize systems, networks, and internet management. 2012 December 9-14; San Diego, CA; 2013 November 3-8; Washington, DC; 2014 November 9-14; Seattle, WA; 2015 November 8-13; Washington, DC; 2016 December 4-9; Boston, MA. Provides networking opportunities for computing professionals.

2912 ■ Special Interest Group on Accessible Computing (SIGACCESS)
2 Penn Plz., Ste. 701
New York, NY 10121-0701
Ph: (212)626-0500
Fax: (212)944-1318
Fr: 800-342-6626
E-mail: chair_sigaccess@acm.org
URL: http://www.sigaccess.org

Description: Promotes the professional interests of computing personnel with physical disabilities and the application of computing and information technology in solving relevant disability problems. Works to educate the public to support careers for the disabled.

2913 ■ USENIX, the Advanced Computing Systems Association
2560 9th St., Ste. 215
Berkeley, CA 94710
Ph: (510)528-8649
Fax: (510)548-5738
E-mail: office@usenix.org
URL: http://www.usenix.org

Description: Represents the community of engineers, system administrators, scientists, and technicians working on the cutting edge of the computing world. Aims to foster technical excellence and innovation that pertains to computer systems. Supports and disseminates research with a practical bias. Provides a neutral forum for discussion of technical issues and encourages computing outreach into the community at large.

2914 ■ USENIX Annual Technical Conference
USENIX, the Advanced Computing Systems Association
2560 9th St., Ste. 215
Berkeley, CA 94710
Ph: (510)528-8649
Fax: (510)548-5738
E-mail: office@usenix.org
URL: http://www.usenix.org

Annual. Includes exhibits of products and services for the advancement of computing systems.

SOURCES OF HELP-WANTED ADS

2915 ■ American City and County
Penton Media Inc.
9800 Metcalf Ave.
Overland Park, KS 66212
Ph: (913)341-1300
Fax: (913)967-1898
URL: http://americancityandcounty.com

Monthly. Municipal and county administration magazine.

2916 ■ American Professional Constructor
American Institute of Constructors
700 N Fairfax St.
Alexandria, VA 22314
Ph: (703)683-4999
Fax: (571)527-3105
URL: http://www.professionalconstructor.org/aic/publications/

Biennial. $112.00/year for individuals. Journal covering general interest and technical articles for construction professionals.

2917 ■ BIA News
Brick Industry Association
1850 Centennial Park Dr., Ste. 301
Reston, VA 20191
Ph: (703)620-0010
Fax: (703)620-3928
URL: http://www.gobrick.com/html/pr.html

Monthly. $30.00/year for individuals. Trade publication covering issues for the brick industry.

2918 ■ Builder
Hanley-Wood L.L.C.
1 Thomas Cir. NW, Ste. 600
Washington, DC 20005-5803
Ph: (202)452-0800
Fax: (202)785-1974
E-mail: builder@omeda.com
URL: http://www.hanleywood.com/default.aspx?page=magazines

$29.95/year for U.S. and Canada; $54.95/year for U.S. and Canada, 2 years; $192.00/year for other countries. Magazine covering housing and construction industry.

2919 ■ Building Systems Magazine
Active Interest Media
300 Continental Blvd., Ste. 650
El Segundo, CA 90245-5067
Ph: (310)356-4100
Fax: (310)356-4110
URL: http://www.buildingsystems.com

Bimonthly. Magazine featuring innovative construction technologies for builders, developers and general contractors.

2920 ■ Civil Engineering-ASCE
American Society of Civil Engineers (ASCE)
1801 Alexander Bell Dr.
Reston, VA 20191
Fr: 800-548-2723

Monthly. $230.00/year for institutions; $275.00/year for institutions, other countries; $230.00/year for individuals; $275.00/year for other countries; $30.00/year for members, domestic; $69.00/year for other countries, member; $30.00/year for students, member; domestic; $69.00/year for students, member; international. Professional magazine.

2921 ■ Construction
Reed Business Information (New York, New York)
360 Park Ave. S
New York, NY 10010
Ph: (646)746-6400
Fax: (646)746-7431
Fr: 800-446-6551
URL: http://www.acppubs.com/community/835.html

Semimonthly. $106.00/year for individuals; $126.00/year for Canada; $166.00/year for other countries. Regional construction publication covering Maryland, the District of Columbia, Virginia, North Carolina and South Carolina. Geared toward those engaged in engineering (heavy and highway), non-residential building construction and allied fields relating to construction or requiring the use of construction equipment. Containing "how to" job stories, product news, industry news and bid and award information.

2922 ■ Construction Business Owner
Cahaba Media Group
1900 28th Ave. S
Birmingham, AL 35209
Ph: (205)212-9402
URL: http://www.constructionbusinessowner.com/

Monthly. Free. Magazine that provides information for construction management and industry business information.

2923 ■ Construction Claims Monthly
Business Publishers Inc.
2222 Sedwick Dr., Ste. 101
Durham, NC 27713
Fr: 800-223-8720
E-mail: custserv@bpinews.com
URL: http://www.bpinews.com

Description: Monthly. $402/year. Covers significant legal developments governing contract payment and performance. Features an article on construction claims law; summaries of recent decisions with expert commentary; and highlights of actions by the federal boards of contract appeals and the Comptroller General.

2924 ■ Constructor
Associated General Contractors of America
2300 Wilson Blvd., Ste. 400
Arlington, VA 22201
Ph: (703)548-3118

Fax: (703)548-3119
Fr: 800-242-1767
URL: http://constructor.agc.org/
Bimonthly. $95.00/year for individuals. Management magazine for the Construction Industry.

2925 ■ Consulting-Specifying Engineer
CFE Media LLC
1111 W 22nd St., Ste. 250
Oak Brook, IL 60523
Ph: (630)571-4070
Fax: (630)214-4504
URL: http://www.csemag.com

The integrated engineering magazine of the building construction industry.

2926 ■ ENR: Engineering News-Record
McGraw-Hill Inc.
PO Box 182604
Columbus, OH 43218
Ph: (614)430-4000
Fax: (614)759-3749
Fr: 877-833-5524
URL: http://enr.construction.com/Default.asp

Weekly. $49.00/year for individuals, print; $89.00/year for Canada, print; $125.00/year for other countries, print. Magazine focusing on engineering and construction.

2927 ■ ISHN
BNP Media
2401 W Big Beaver Rd., Ste. 700
Troy, MI 48084-3333
Ph: (847)763-9534
Fax: (847)763-9538
URL: http://www.ishn.com/

Monthly. Free. Business-to-business magazine for safety and health managers at high-hazard worksites in manufacturing, construction, health facilities, and service industries. Content covering OSHA and EPA regulations, howto features, safety and health management topics, and the latest product news.

2928 ■ Journal of Green Building
College Publishing
12309 Lynwood Dr.
Glen Allen, VA 23059
Ph: (804)364-8410
Fax: (804)364-8408
Fr: 800-827-0723
URL: http://www.collegepublishing.us/journal.htm

$149.00/year for individuals; $589.00/year for institutions; $589.00/year for libraries. Peer-reviewed journal covering green, sustainable, or high-performance built facilities and infrastructure systems.

2929 ■ Kitchen and Bath Business
Nielsen Business Media
770 Broadway
New York, NY 10003-9595
E-mail: kbb@mediabrains.com
URL: http://www.kitchen-bath.com/kbb/index.jsp

Monthly. $10.00/year for individuals, cover; $79.00/ year for individuals, domestic; $94.00/year for Canada and Mexico; $139.00/year for other countries. Trade magazine on kitchen and bath remodeling and construction.

2930 ■ Landscape Construction
Moose River Media
374 Emerson Falls Rd.
St. Johnsbury, VT 05819
Fax: (802)748-1866
Fr: 800-422-7147
URL: http://www.lcmmagazine.com/

Monthly. Magazine featuring landscaping.

2931 ■ MetalMag
Hanley Wood L.L.C.
1 Thomas Cir. NW, Ste. 600
Washington, DC 20005-5803
Ph: (202)452-0800
Fax: (202)785-1974
Fr: 877-275-8647
E-mail: mtm@omeda.com
URL: http://www.metalmag.com/

Bimonthly. Free to qualified subscribers. Magazine for industrial construction professionals.

2932 ■ The Municipality
League of Wisconsin Municipalities
122 W Washington Ave., Ste. 300
Madison, WI 53703-2715
Ph: (608)267-2380
Fax: (608)267-0645
Fr: 800-991-5502
URL: http://www.lwm-info.org/

Monthly. Magazine for officials of Wisconsin's local municipal governments.

2933 ■ NAHRO Monitor
National Association of Housing and Redevelopment Officials
630 Eye St. NW
Washington, DC 20001
Ph: (202)289-3500
Fax: (202)289-8181
Fr: 877-866-2476
E-mail: nahro@nahro.org
URL: http://www.nahro.org/nahro_monitor

Description: Biweekly. Disseminates news on low-income housing and community development issues. Intended for member professionals and government officials.

2934 ■ The NAWIC Image
National Association of Women in Construction
327 S Adams St.
Fort Worth, TX 76104
Ph: (817)877-5551
Fax: (817)877-0324
Fr: 800-552-3506
E-mail: nawic@nawic.org
URL: http://www.nawic.org

Description: Bimonthly. Fosters career advancement for women in construction. Features women business owners, training for construction trades and educational programs. Recurring features include columns titled "Issues and Trends," "Road to Success," "Chapter Highlights," "Members on the Move," and "Q&A."

2935 ■ PE
National Society of Professional Engineers
1420 King St.
Alexandria, VA 22314
Ph: (703)684-2800
Fax: (703)684-4875
URL: http://www.nspe.org/PEmagazine/index.html

Monthly. Magazine (tabloid) covering professional, legislative, and techology issues for an engineering audience.

2936 ■ Professional Builder
SGC Horizon LLC
3030 W Salt Creek Ln., Ste. 201
Arlington Heights, IL 60005
Ph: (847)391-1000
Fax: (847)390-0408
URL: http://www.housingzone.com/pb/pubhome/

Monthly. Free. The integrated engineering magazine of the building construction industry.

2937 ■ Remodeling
Hanley-Wood L.L.C.
1 Thomas Cir. NW, Ste. 600
Washington, DC 20005-5803
Ph: (202)452-0800
Fax: (202)785-1974
E-mail: rm@omeda.com
URL: http://www.remodeling.hw.net

$25.00/year for individuals; $40.00/year for individuals, Canadian residents; $192.00/year for individuals, international residents. Trade magazine for the professional remodeling industry.

2938 ■ Residential Architect
Hanley-Wood L.L.C.
1 Thomas Cir. NW, Ste. 600
Washington, DC 20005-5803
Ph: (202)452-0800
Fax: (202)785-1974
E-mail: res@omeda.com
URL: http://www.residentialarchitectmediakit.com/r5/ home.asp

$39.95/year for individuals; $66.00/year for Canada; $132.50/year for other countries. Magazine for architects, designers, and building professionals.

2939 ■ Residential Concrete
Hanley-Wood L.L.C.
1 Thomas Cir. NW, Ste. 600
Washington, DC 20005-5803
Ph: (202)452-0800
Fax: (202)785-1974
URL: http://www.hanleywood.com/ default.aspx?page=b2bresconcrete

Bimonthly. $30.00/year for individuals; $46.00/year for two years; $39.00/year for Canada and Mexico; $64.00/year for two years, Canada & Mexico; $93.00/ year for other countries; $162.00/year for other countries, two years. Magazine featuring the use of concrete in residential concrete construction.

2940 ■ Tools of the Trade
Hanley-Wood L.L.C.
1 Thomas Cir. NW, Ste. 600
Washington, DC 20005-5803
Ph: (202)452-0800
Fax: (202)785-1974
URL: http://www.hanleywood.com/ ?page=toolsofthetrade&section=res_

Bimonthly. $36.00/year for individuals; $66.00/year for Canada; $192.00/year for other countries; $70.00/ year for two years. Magazine featuring tools for commercial and residential construction.

2941 ■ Western City
League of California Cities
1400 K St., 4th Fl.
Sacramento, CA 95814
Ph: (916)658-8200
Fax: (916)658-8240
Fr: 800-262-1801
URL: http://www.westerncity.com

Monthly. $39.00/year for individuals; $63.00/year for two years; $52.00/year for other countries; $26.50/ year for students. Municipal interest magazine.

EMPLOYER DIRECTORIES AND NETWORKING LISTS

2942 ■ ABC Today—Associated Builders and Contractors National Membership Directory Issue
Associated Builders and Contractors Inc.
4250 N Fairfax Dr., 9th Fl.
Arlington, VA 22203-1607

Ph: (703)812-2000
Fax: (703)812-8235
URL: http://www.abc.org

Annual, December. $150.00. Publication includes: List of approximately 19,000 member construction contractors and suppliers.

2943 ■ ENR—Top 400 Construction Contractors Issue
McGraw-Hill Inc.
PO Box 182604
Columbus, OH 43218
Ph: (614)430-4000
Fax: (614)759-3749
Fr: 877-833-5524
URL: http://enr.construction.com/toplists/Contractors/ 001-100.asp

Annual, Latest edition 2011. $35.00 for individuals. Publication includes: List of 400 United States contractors receiving largest dollar volumes of contracts in preceding calendar year. Separate lists of 50 largest design/construct management firms; 50 largest program and construction managers; 25 building contractors; 25 heavy contractors.

HANDBOOKS AND MANUALS

2944 ■ Career Opportunities in Engineering
Facts On File Inc.
132 W 31st St., 17th Fl.
New York, NY 10001
Fr: 800-322-8755
E-mail: custserv@factsonfile.com
URL: http://factsonfile.infobasepublishing.com

2006. $49.50. 336 pages. Provides an overview of engineering, followed by a selection of jobs profiled in detail, including the nature of the job, earnings, prospects for employment, what kind of training and skills it requires and sources for further information.

2945 ■ Senior Construction Inspector
National Learning Corporation
212 Michael Dr.
Syosset, NY 11791
Fr: 800-632-8888
URL: http://www.passbooks.com

2009. $39.95 (paper). Serves as an exam preparation guide for senior construction inspectors.

EMPLOYMENT AGENCIES AND SEARCH FIRMS

2946 ■ 20-20 Foresight Executive Search Inc.
150 N Michigan Ave., Ste. 2800
Chicago, IL 60601
Ph: (708)246-2100
E-mail: bcavoto@202-4.com
URL: http://www.2020-4.com

Executive search firm. Affiliate offices in California and Washington DC.

2947 ■ Cook Associates Inc.
212 W Kinzie St.
Chicago, IL 60610
Ph: (312)329-0900
Fax: (312)329-1528
E-mail: info@cookassociates.com
URL: http://www.cookassociates.com

Management and executive recruiting specialists offering a commitment to clients to find the best candidates and to find those candidates as efficiently as possible. Approach provides a flexible and effective structure that serves the special needs of both large and small companies. Serves the following industries: industrial, equipment manufacturer, food processing, graphic arts, chemical process, retailing, mechanical products, healthcare services, financial and professional services, legal, consumer products, construction and engineering, packaging, pulp and paper.

2948 ■ Frank Palma Associates
17 Beechwood Lane
Kinnelon, NJ 07405
Ph: (973)884-1498
Fax: (973)884-1499
E-mail: fpalma@fpassocs.com
URL: http://www.fpassocs.com

Executive search firm. Additional location in Duluth, GA.

2949 ■ Golden Gate Staffing
1422 Springs Rd., Ste. B
Vallejo, CA 94591
Ph: (707)552-6767
E-mail: info@goldengatestaffing.com
URL: http://www.goldengatestaffing.com

Provides project based, temporary, full-time and permanent placement staffing services.

2950 ■ Real Estate Executive Search, Inc.
225 E Dania Beach Blvd. Ste., 200
Dania Beach, FL 33004
Ph: (954)927-6000
Fax: (954)927-6003
E-mail: reesearch954@aol.com
URL: http://reesearchinc.com

Executive search firm for the real estate and finance fields.

2951 ■ Synergy Professionals
1029 N Peachtree Pkwy., Ste. 252
Peachtree City, GA 30269
Ph: (770)632-6585
E-mail: contact@synergyprof.com
URL: http://www.synergyprof.com

Serves as a professional recruiting firm devoted exclusively to the construction industry.

ONLINE JOB SOURCES AND SERVICES

2952 ■ Building Inspector Jobs
URL: http://www.buildinginspectorjobs.org

Description: Serves as a job board for building inspector employment opportunities.

2953 ■ Construction Inspector Jobs
URL: http://www.constructioninspectorjobs.org

Description: Serves as a job board for construction inspector employment opportunities.

2954 ■ ConstructionCrossing.com
URL: http://www.constructioncrossing.com

Description: Lists new employment opportunities specifically related to the construction personnel profession.

2955 ■ ConstructionEducation.com
Ph: (828)226-8299
E-mail: ceo@constructioneducation.com
URL: http://www.constructioneducation.com

Description: Includes link page with list of professional resources, employment opportunities listed by company, and construction-related recruiters' pages, as well as general job search websites. Also contains on-site job bank.

2956 ■ GeneralConstructionJobs.com
URL: http://www.generalconstructionjobs.com/JobSeeker/Jobs.aspx

Description: Serves as a job board for online employment advertising built exclusively for the general construction industry.

2957 ■ Great Green Careers
URL: http://www.greatgreencareers.com

Description: Serves as online resource that connects employers and job seekers in the green jobs industries.

OTHER SOURCES

2958 ■ American Society of Home Inspectors (ASHI)
932 Lee St., Ste. 101
Des Plaines, IL 60016
Ph: (847)759-2820
Fax: (847)759-1620
Fr: 800-743-2744
E-mail: jeffa@ashi.org
URL: http://www.ashi.org

Description: Professional home inspectors whose goals are to: establish home inspector qualifications; set standards of practice for home inspections; adhere to a code of ethics; keep the concept of "objective third party" intact; inform members of the most advanced methods and techniques, and educate consumers on the value of home inspections. Conducts seminars through local chapters.

2959 ■ Associated Builders and Contractors (ABC)
4250 N Fairfax Dr., 9th Fl.
Arlington, VA 22203-1607
Ph: (703)812-2000
Fax: (703)812-8201
E-mail: gotquestions@abc.org
URL: http://www.abc.org

Description: Construction contractors, subcontractors, suppliers and associates. Aims to foster and perpetuate the principles of rewarding construction workers and management on the basis of merit. Sponsors management education programs and craft training; also sponsors apprenticeship and skill training programs. Disseminates technological and labor relations information.

2960 ■ Associated General Contractors of America (AGC)
2300 Wilson Blvd., Ste. 400
Arlington, VA 22201
Ph: (703)548-3118
Fax: (703)548-3119
Fr: 800-242-1767
E-mail: info@agc.org
URL: http://www.agc.org

Description: General construction contractors; subcontractors; industry suppliers; service firms. Provides market services through its divisions. Conducts special conferences and seminars designed specifically for construction firms. Compiles statistics on job accidents reported by member firms. Maintains 65 committees, including joint cooperative committees with other associations and liaison committees with federal agencies.

2961 ■ National Association of Black Women in Construction (NABWIC)
1910 NW 105 Ave.
Pembroke Pines, FL 33026
E-mail: info@nabwic.org
URL: http://nabwic.org

Description: Promotes the advancement of black women in the construction industry. Supports aspiring construction executives. Provides advocacy, mentorship and professional development for its members.

2962 ■ National Association of Home Builders (NAHB)
1201 15th St. NW
Washington, DC 20005
Ph: (202)266-8200
Fax: (202)266-8400
Fr: 800-368-5242
E-mail: jhoward@nahb.com
URL: http://www.nahb.org

Description: Single and multifamily home builders, commercial builders, and others associated with the building industry. Lobbies on behalf of the housing industry and conducts public affairs activities to increase public understanding of housing and the economy. Collects and disseminates data on current developments in home building and home builders' plans through its Economics Department and nationwide Metropolitan Housing Forecast. Maintains NAHB Research Center, which functions as the research arm of the home building industry. Sponsors seminars and workshops on construction, mortgage credit, labor relations, cost reduction, land use, remodeling, and business management. Compiles statistics; offers charitable program, spokesman training, and placement service; maintains speakers' bureau, and Hall of Fame. Subsidiaries include the National Council of the Housing Industry. Maintains over 50 committees in many areas of construction; operates National Commercial Builders Council, National Council of the Multifamily Housing Industry, National Remodelers Council, and National Sales and Marketing Council.

2963 ■ National Association of Women in Construction (NAWIC)
327 S Adams St.
Fort Worth, TX 76104
Ph: (817)877-5551
Fax: (817)877-0324
Fr: 800-552-3506
E-mail: nawic@nawic.org
URL: http://www.nawic.org

Description: Seeks to enhance the success of women in the construction industry.

2964 ■ National Center for Construction Education and Research (NCCER)
3600 NW 43rd St., Bldg. G
Gainesville, FL 32606
Ph: (352)334-0911
Fax: (352)334-0932
Fr: 888-622-3720
E-mail: marketing@nccer.org
URL: http://www.nccer.org

Description: Education foundation committed to the development and publication of Contren(TM) Learning Series, the source of craft training, management education and safety resources for the construction industry.

2965 ■ Professional Women in Construction (PWC)
315 E 56th St.
New York, NY 10022-3730
Ph: (212)486-4712
Fax: (212)486-0228
E-mail: pwc@pwcusa.org
URL: http://www.pwcusa.org

Description: Management-level women and men in construction and allied industries; owners, suppliers, architects, engineers, field personnel, office personnel and bonding/surety personnel. Provides a forum for exchange of ideas and promotion of political and legislative action, education and job opportunities for women in construction and related fields; forms liaisons with other trade and professional groups; develops research programs. Strives to reform abuses and to assure justice and equity within the construction industry. Sponsors mini-workshops. Maintains Action Line, which provides members with current information on pertinent legislation and on the association's activities and job referrals.

Construction Managers

Sources of Help-Wanted Ads

2966 ■ ABC Newsline
Associated Builders & Contractors Inc.
4250 N Fairfax Dr., 9th Fl.
Arlington, VA 22203-1607
Ph: (703)812-2000
E-mail: gotquestions@abc.org
URL: http://www.abc.org
Description: Weekly. Designed to keep readers alerted to important changes within ABC and the construction industry. Reports on legislative issues, construction trends, conferences and meetings, and ABC services. Recurring features include news of members and columns titled Labor Relations, Construction Law, Computer Corner, Bottom Line, and Chapter News.

2967 ■ American Institute of Constructors and the Constructor Commission Newsletter
American Institute of Constructors and the Constructor Commission
PO Box 26334
Alexandria, VA 22314
Ph: (703)683-4999
Fax: (571)527-3105
E-mail: dwright@professionalconstructor.org
URL: http://www.professionalconstructor.org
Description: Bimonthly. Concerned with construction practice, design, administration, and teaching. Carries news of members, listings of job opportunities, local chapter reports, notices of new publications, and conferences on construction topics.

2968 ■ American Professional Constructor
American Institute of Constructors
700 N Fairfax St.
Alexandria, VA 22314
Ph: (703)683-4999
Fax: (571)527-3105
URL: http://www.professionalconstructor.org/aic/publications/
Biennial. $112.00/year for individuals. Journal covering general interest and technical articles for construction professionals.

2969 ■ Asphalt Roofing Manufacturers Association Newsletter
Asphalt Roofing Manufacturers Association
750 National Press Bldg.
529 14th St., NW
Washington, DC 20045
Ph: (202)207-0917
Fax: (202)223-9741
URL: http://www.asphaltroofing.org/
Description: Semi-annual. Reports news and information of interest to professionals in the asphalt roofing industry. Highlights Association activities and discusses developments in the industry, including occupational safety and health measures, changes in

industry codes and standards, environmental issues, and legislative and regulatory actions.

2970 ■ BIA News
Brick Industry Association
1850 Centennial Park Dr., Ste. 301
Reston, VA 20191
Ph: (703)620-0010
Fax: (703)620-3928
URL: http://www.gobrick.com/html/pr.html
Monthly. $30.00/year for individuals. Trade publication covering issues for the brick industry.

2971 ■ Builder and Developer
Peninsula Publishing Inc.
1602 Monrovia Ave.
Newport Beach, CA 92663
Ph: (949)631-0308
Fax: (949)631-2475
URL: http://www.bdmag.com
Magazine for homebuilders.

2972 ■ Building Industry Technology
National Technical Information Service
5301 Shawnee Rd.
Alexandria, VA 22312
Ph: (703)605-6585
Fax: (703)605-6900
Fr: 800-553-6847
E-mail: info@ntis.gov
URL: http://www.ntis.gov/products/alerts.aspx
Description: Biweekly. $255. Consists of abstracts of reports on architectural and environmental design, building standards, construction materials and equipment, and structural analyses. Recurring features include a form for ordering reports from NTIS. Also available via e-mail.

2973 ■ Building Systems Magazine
Active Interest Media
300 Continental Blvd., Ste. 650
El Segundo, CA 90245-5067
Ph: (310)356-4100
Fax: (310)356-4110
URL: http://www.buildingsystems.com
Bimonthly. Magazine featuring innovative construction technologies for builders, developers and general contractors.

2974 ■ CM Advisor
Construction Management Association of America Inc.
7926 Jones Branch Dr., Ste. 800
Mc Lean, VA 22102
Ph: (703)356-2622
Fax: (703)356-6388
E-mail: info@cmaanet.org
URL: http://www.cmaanet.org
Description: Bimonthly. Provides information on construction management and its technical, legal, and legislative issues. Recurring features include letters to the editor, news of research, a calendar of

events, reports of meetings, news of educational opportunities, book reviews, notices of publications available, and columns titled Government Affairs and For Your Information.

2975 ■ Concrete & Masonry Construction Products
Hanley Wood L.L.C.
1 Thomas Cir. NW, Ste. 600
Washington, DC 20005-5803
Ph: (202)452-0800
Fax: (202)785-1974
Fr: 877-275-8647
URL: http://www.hanleywoodopportunities.com/Index.asp?Cat=cc&Pub=
Bimonthly. Free. Publication that covers carpenter tips, tools, and up keep.

2976 ■ Construction
Reed Business Information (New York, New York)
360 Park Ave. S
New York, NY 10010
Ph: (646)746-6400
Fax: (646)746-7431
Fr: 800-446-6551
URL: http://www.acppubs.com/community/835.html
Semimonthly. $106.00/year for individuals; $126.00/year for Canada; $166.00/year for other countries. Regional construction publication covering Maryland, the District of Columbia, Virginia, North Carolina and South Carolina. Geared toward those engaged in engineering (heavy and highway), non-residential building construction and allied fields relating to construction or requiring the use of construction equipment. Containing "how to" job stories, product news, industry news and bid and award information.

2977 ■ Construction Business Owner
Cahaba Media Group
1900 28th Ave. S
Birmingham, AL 35209
Ph: (205)212-9402
URL: http://www.constructionbusinessowner.com/
Monthly. Free. Magazine that provides information for construction management and industry business information.

2978 ■ Construction Claims Monthly
Business Publishers Inc.
2222 Sedwick Dr., Ste. 101
Durham, NC 27713
Fr: 800-223-8720
E-mail: custserv@bpinews.com
URL: http://www.bpinews.com
Description: Monthly. $402/year. Covers significant legal developments governing contract payment and performance. Features an article on construction claims law; summaries of recent decisions with expert commentary; and highlights of actions by the federal boards of contract appeals and the Comptroller General.

2979 ■ *Construction Superintendent*
Inform Publishing Group L.L.C.
8040 E Morgan Trl., Ste. 23
Scottsdale, AZ 85258
Ph: (480)361-6300
Fax: (480)361-6394
URL: http://www.consupt.com/

Bimonthly. Magazine featuring current news, technology, and methods in the construction field.

2980 ■ *Design Cost Data*
DC & D Technologies Inc.
PO Box 948
Valrico, FL 33595-0948
Ph: (813)662-6830
Fax: (813)662-6793
Fr: 800-533-5680
URL: http://www.dcd.com

Bimonthly. $94.00/year for individuals, silver; $157.00/year for two years, silver; $149.00/year for individuals, gold; $239.00/year for two years, gold. Publication providing real cost data case studies of various types completed around the country for design and building professionals.

2981 ■ *Environmental Building News*
Building Green Inc.
122 Birge St., Ste. 30
Brattleboro, VT 05301-3206
Ph: (802)257-7300
Fax: (802)257-7304
Fr: 800-861-0954
E-mail: info@buildinggreen.com
URL: http://www.buildinggreen.com/landing/
ebnperformance1102.html

Description: Monthly. $99/year. Covers the building trade with an environmental slant. Covers nontoxic materials, better landscaping and water use, and resources for energy conservation in a technical manner.

2982 ■ *Equipment World*
Randall-Reilly Publishing Co.
3200 Rice Mine Rd. NE
Tuscaloosa, AL 35406
Fr: 800-633-5953
URL: http://www.equipmentworld.com

Monthly. Magazine featuring construction contractors, equipment manufacturers, and dealers and providers of services and supplies to the construction industry.

2983 ■ *EUCA Magazine*
Engineering & Utility Contractors Association
17 Crow Canyon Ct., Ste. 100
San Ramon, CA 94583
Ph: (925)855-7900
Fax: (925)855-7909
E-mail: eucaxinfo@euca.com
URL: http://www.euca.com

Description: Monthly. Supports the Association in its efforts to "provide innovative ideas and strong leadership" to those in the contracting industry. Focuses on various issues pertinent to members and industry executives, including legislative and regulatory developments, occupational safety concerns, new products and technologies, and industry trends and developments. Recurring features include interviews, news of research, reports of meetings, news of educational opportunities, notices of publications available, and a calendar of events. Contains member profiles and news of members, Association elections, and administrative decisions.

2984 ■ *Green Home Builder*
Peninsula Publishing Inc.
1602 Monrovia Ave.
Newport Beach, CA 92663
Ph: (949)631-0308
Fax: (949)631-2475
URL: http://www.greenhomebuildermag.com/

Quarterly. Magazine for home builders and home building industry.

2985 ■ *ISHN*
BNP Media
2401 W Big Beaver Rd., Ste. 700
Troy, MI 48084-3333
Ph: (847)763-9534
Fax: (847)763-9538
URL: http://www.ishn.com/

Monthly. Free. Business-to-business magazine for safety and health managers at high-hazard worksites in manufacturing, construction, health facilities, and service industries. Content covering OSHA and EPA regulations, howto features, safety and health management topics, and the latest product news.

2986 ■ *Journal of Green Building*
College Publishing
12309 Lynwood Dr.
Glen Allen, VA 23059
Ph: (804)364-8410
Fax: (804)364-8408
Fr: 800-827-0723
URL: http://www.collegepublishing.us/journal.htm

$149.00/year for individuals; $589.00/year for institutions; $589.00/year for libraries. Peer-reviewed journal covering green, sustainable, or high-performance built facilities and infrastructure systems.

2987 ■ *Kitchen and Bath Business*
Nielsen Business Media
770 Broadway
New York, NY 10003-9595
E-mail: kbb@mediabrains.com
URL: http://www.kitchen-bath.com/kbb/index.jsp

Monthly. $10.00/year for individuals, cover; $79.00/year for individuals, domestic; $94.00/year for Canada and Mexico; $139.00/year for other countries. Trade magazine on kitchen and bath remodeling and construction.

2988 ■ *Landscape Construction*
Moose River Media
374 Emerson Falls Rd.
St. Johnsbury, VT 05819
Fax: (802)748-1866
Fr: 800-422-7147
URL: http://www.lcmmagazine.com/

Monthly. Magazine featuring landscaping.

2989 ■ *MetalMag*
Hanley Wood L.L.C.
1 Thomas Cir. NW, Ste. 600
Washington, DC 20005-5803
Ph: (202)452-0800
Fax: (202)785-1974
Fr: 877-275-8647
E-mail: mtm@omeda.com
URL: http://www.metalmag.com/

Bimonthly. Free to qualified subscribers. Magazine for industrial construction professionals.

2990 ■ *Offshore Field Development International*
ODS-Petrodata
3200 Wilcrest Dr., Ste. 170
Houston, TX 77042
Ph: (832)463-3000
Fax: (832)463-3100
E-mail: ksmith@ods-petrodata.com
URL: http://www.ods-petrodata.com

Description: Monthly. Reports on petroleum-related offshore construction projects worldwide, from the planning stage through final installation. Covers platforms, pipelines, subsea completions, and mooring terminals. Recurring features include sections on construction barge locations and possible areas for future development.

2991 ■ *Remodeling*
Hanley-Wood L.L.C.
1 Thomas Cir. NW, Ste. 600
Washington, DC 20005-5803
Ph: (202)452-0800

Fax: (202)785-1974
E-mail: rm@omeda.com
URL: http://www.remodeling.hw.net

$25.00/year for individuals; $40.00/year for individuals, Canadian residents; $192.00/year for individuals, international residents. Trade magazine for the professional remodeling industry.

2992 ■ *Replacement Contractor*
Hanley Wood L.L.C.
1 Thomas Cir. NW, Ste. 600
Washington, DC 20005-5803
Ph: (202)452-0800
Fax: (202)785-1974
Fr: 877-275-8647
E-mail: rcon@omeda.com
URL: http://www.omeda.com/rcon/

$29.95/year for individuals; $39.95/year for Canada; $49.95/year for other countries. Magazine for contractors engaged in roofing, siding, decking and window replacement.

2993 ■ *Residential Architect*
Hanley-Wood L.L.C.
1 Thomas Cir. NW, Ste. 600
Washington, DC 20005-5803
Ph: (202)452-0800
Fax: (202)785-1974
E-mail: res@omeda.com
URL: http://www.residentialarchitectmediakit.com/r5/
home.asp

$39.95/year for individuals; $66.00/year for Canada; $132.50/year for other countries. Magazine for architects, designers, and building professionals.

2994 ■ *Residential Concrete*
Hanley-Wood L.L.C.
1 Thomas Cir. NW, Ste. 600
Washington, DC 20005-5803
Ph: (202)452-0800
Fax: (202)785-1974
URL: http://www.hanleywood.com/
default.aspx?page=b2bresconcrete

Bimonthly. $30.00/year for individuals; $46.00/year for two years; $39.00/year for Canada and Mexico; $64.00/year for two years, Canada & Mexico; $93.00/year for other countries; $162.00/year for other countries, two years. Magazine featuring the use of concrete in residential concrete construction.

2995 ■ *Residential Contractor*
Peninsula Publishing Inc.
1602 Monrovia Ave.
Newport Beach, CA 92663
Ph: (949)631-0308
Fax: (949)631-2475
URL: http://www.residentialcontractormag.com/

Quarterly. Magazine for small volume residential builders, contractors, and specialty trades.

2996 ■ *Residential Design & Build*
Cygnus Business Media Inc.
3 Huntington Quadrangle, Ste. 301 N
Melville, NY 11747
Ph: (631)845-2700
Fax: (631)845-7109
Fr: 800-308-6397
URL: http://www.rdbmagazine.com

Magazine providing advice and insight on the design/build project delivery method, as well as information on the latest design trends, new products and home building professionals.

2997 ■ *Tools of the Trade*
Hanley-Wood L.L.C.
1 Thomas Cir. NW, Ste. 600
Washington, DC 20005-5803
Ph: (202)452-0800
Fax: (202)785-1974
URL: http://www.hanleywood.com/
?page=toolsofthetrade&section=res_

Bimonthly. $36.00/year for individuals; $66.00/year for Canada; $192.00/year for other countries; $70.00/

year for two years. Magazine featuring tools for commercial and residential construction.

EMPLOYER DIRECTORIES AND NETWORKING LISTS

2998 ■ *Athletic Business—Professional Directory Section*
Athletic Business Publications Inc.
4130 Lien Rd.
Madison, WI 53704
Ph: (608)249-0186
Fax: (608)249-1153
Fr: 800-722-8764
URL: http://www.athleticbusiness.com

Monthly, Latest edition 2010. $8.00. Publication includes: List of architects, engineers, contractors, and consultants in athletic facility planning and construction; all listings are paid. Entries include: Company name, address, phone, fax and short description of company. Arrangement: Alphabetical.

2999 ■ *Career Ideas for Teens in Architecture and Construction*
Facts On File Inc.
132 W 31st St., 17th Fl.
New York, NY 10001
Ph: (212)967-8800
Fax: 800-678-3633
Fr: 800-322-8755
URL: http://www.infobasepublishing.com

Published August, 2005. Covers: A multitude of career possibilities based on a teenager's specific interests and skills and links his/her talents to a wide variety of actual professions.

3000 ■ *Careers in Focus—Construction*
Facts On File Inc.
132 W 31st St., 17th Fl.
New York, NY 10001
Ph: (212)967-8800
Fax: 800-678-3633
Fr: 800-322-8755
URL: http://www.infobasepublishing.com

Latest edition 5th; Published May, 2010. $32.95 for individuals. Covers: An overview of construction, followed by a selection of jobs profiled in detail, including the nature of the job, earnings, prospects for employment, what kind of training and skills it requires, and sources for further information.

3001 ■ *Contractor's Directory*
Government Data Publications Inc.
2300 M St. NW
Washington, DC 20037
Fax: (718)998-5960
Fr: 800-275-4688
URL: http://www.govdata.com

Annual, February. $49.50; $15.00; $49.50. Covers: Contractors who have received government contract under Public Law 95-507, which requires preferential treatment of small business for subcontracts. Entries include: Contractor name and address. Supplementary to 'Small Business Preferential Subcontracts Opportunities Monthly,' which lists companies with government contracts over $500,000 ($1,000,000 for construction). Arrangement: Same information given alphabetically and by ZIP code.

3002 ■ *Discovering Careers for Your Future—Construction*
Facts On File Inc.
132 W 31st St., 17th Fl.
New York, NY 10001
Ph: (212)967-8800
Fax: 800-678-3633
Fr: 800-322-8755
URL: http://factsonfile.infobasepublishing.com

Latest edition 2nd, 2008. $21.95 for individuals. Covers: Architects, carpenters, drafters, engineers, painters and roofers; links career education to curriculum,

helping children investigate the subjects they are interested in, and the careers those subjects might lead to.

HANDBOOKS AND MANUALS

3003 ■ *Becoming a Construction Manager*
John Wiley & Sons, Inc.
111 River St.
Hoboken, NJ 07030-5774
Ph: (201)748-6000
Fax: (201)748-6088
E-mail: info@wiley.com
URL: http://www.wiley.com

John J. McKeon. 2012. $39.95 (paper). 224 pages. Serves as a guide for job seekers interested in or beginning a career in construction management. Provides an overview of the profession, educational requirements, and specialties. Includes interviewing tips and resource section on professional organizations and educational opportunities.

3004 ■ *Information Technologies for Construction Managers, Architects, and Engineers*
Cengage Learning
PO Box 6904
Florence, KY 41022
Fax: 800-487-8488
Fr: 800-354-9706
E-mail: esales@cengage.com
URL: http://www.cengage.com

Trefor Williams. 2007. $102.95. 256 pages. Profiles information technology applications in construction trades, from traditional computer applications to emerging Web-based and mobile technologies.

3005 ■ *Preparing for Design-Build Projects: A Primer for Owners, Engineers, and Contractors*
American Society of Civil Engineers
1801 Alexander Bell Dr.
Reston, VA 20191-4400
Ph: (703)295-6300
Fax: (703)295-6222
Fr: 800-548-2723
URL: http://secure.asce.org/ASCEWebSite/BOOKSTORE/BookDescription.aspx?ProdId=5427

Douglas D. Gransberg, James E. Koch and Keith R. Molenaar. 2006. $64.00. 296 pages.

EMPLOYMENT AGENCIES AND SEARCH FIRMS

3006 ■ *20-20 Foresight Executive Search Inc.*
150 N Michigan Ave., Ste. 2800
Chicago, IL 60601
Ph: (708)246-2100
E-mail: bcavoto@202-4.com
URL: http://www.2020-4.com

Executive search firm. Affiliate offices in California and Washington DC.

3007 ■ *Career Advocates International*
1539 Ave. A
Katy, TX 77493
Ph: (281)395-9848
Fax: (281)574-3949
URL: http://www.careeradvocates.org

Provides permanent placement and temporary staffing for executive and staff level positions. Specializes in multiple niches including: sales and marketing, accounting and financial services, banking, communications, human resources, chemicals, oil and gas, medical and dental, legal, information technology, energy, technology, engineering, manufacturing, construction, and light industrial.

3008 ■ The Cherbonnier Group Inc.
1 Riverway, Ste. 1700
Houston, TX 77056
Ph: (713)688-4701
E-mail: consult@thecherbonniergroup.com
URL: http://www.thecherbonniergroup.com
Executive search firm.

3009 ■ The Consulting Group
757 Third Ave., 23rd Fl.
New York, NY 10017
Ph: (212)751-8484
E-mail: research@consultinggroupny.com
URL: http://www.consultinggroupny.com
Executive search firm.

3010 ■ Contractor Marketing
346 Dayton St.
Dayton, OH 45387-1704
Ph: (937)767-2876
Fax: (937)767-7281
E-mail: larry@contractormarketing.com
URL: http://www.contractormarketing.com
Executive search firm.

3011 ■ Contractors & Builders
8888 Clairemont Mesa Blvd., Ste. J
San Diego, CA 92123
Ph: (858)874-7500
Fr: 877-862-2632
E-mail: sandiego@contractorsandbuilders.com
URL: http://www.contractorsandbuilders.com

Description: Specializes in connecting construction workers and managers with direct-hire and temporary positions.

3012 ■ Cook Associates Inc.
212 W Kinzie St.
Chicago, IL 60610
Ph: (312)329-0900
Fax: (312)329-1528
E-mail: info@cookassociates.com
URL: http://www.cookassociates.com

Management and executive recruiting specialists offering a commitment to clients to find the best candidates and to find those candidates as efficiently as possible. Approach provides a flexible and effective structure that serves the special needs of both large and small companies. Serves the following industries: industrial, equipment manufacturer, food processing, graphic arts, chemical process, retailing, mechanical products, healthcare services, financial and professional services, legal, consumer products, construction and engineering, packaging, pulp and paper.

3013 ■ Crown Advisors Inc.
100 McKnight Park Dr., Ste. 110
Pittsburgh, PA 15212
Ph: (412)348-1540
E-mail: info@crownsearch.com
URL: http://www.crownsearch.com
Executive search firm.

3014 ■ Edward Dellon Associates Inc.
450 N Brand Blvd., Ste. 600
Glendale, CA 91203
Ph: (310)286-0625
E-mail: edward_dellon@yahoo.com
URL: http://edwarddellonassociatesinc.com
Executive search firm.

3015 ■ HardHatJobs Inc.
1200 Executive Dr. E, Ste. 127A
Richardson, TX 75081-2231
Ph: (972)808-9200
Fax: (972)808-9203
E-mail: bill@hardhatjobs.com
URL: http://www.hardhatjobs.com

Executive search and consulting for Commercial Construction, Construction Engineering and Construction Management professionals. Presidents,

CEO's, COO's, Business Development, Executive Vice Presidents, VP, CFO's, Program, Project and Construction Managers, Superintendents, Schedulers, Project Accountants, Cost Controllers and Safety Engineers.

3016 ■ Kimmel & Associates
25 Page Ave.
Asheville, NC 28801
Ph: (828)251-9900
Fax: (828)251-9955
E-mail: kimmel@kimmel.com
URL: http://www.kimmel.com

Specializes in the construction, waste, architecture, engineering, logistics and supply chain industries.

3017 ■ McNichol Associates
8419 Germantown Ave.
Philadelphia, PA 19118
Ph: (215)922-4142
Fax: (215)922-0178
E-mail: mailbox@mcnicholassoc.com

Performs executive search for middle and senior-level management, marketing, and technical personnel for professional design firms; construction, management, and general contractors; engineering-construction organizations; environmental firms, and others needing technical management personnel.

3018 ■ Oliver & Rozner Associates
598 Madison Ave., Ste. 11
New York, NY 10022
Ph: (212)688-1850

Performs executive search for top tiers of management including presidents, general management, advertising account management, division management, group executive and vice presidential line positions in such areas as marketing, research, operations, sales, finance, human resources and others; hard-to-find specialists including specific marketing/advertising executives, research and development expertise, computer/data processing knowledge, scientific, physicians-product efficacy and occupational medicine and engineering. Industries served include pharmaceutical, health care, hospital, advertising, consumer products and packaged goods, house wares, direct selling, cosmetics/toiletries, industrial products, high technology products, forest products, engineering, construction, environment/resource recovery, graphic arts, chemical and government agencies.

3019 ■ Robert Howe and Associates
3331 Bolero Dr.
Atlanta, GA 30341
Ph: (770)270-1211

Provides consulting services in the area of executive search and recruitment. Industries served: healthcare, hospitality, chemical, metals, electronics, construction, and food processing.

3020 ■ Specialty Consultants Inc.
2710 Gateway Towers
Pittsburgh, PA 15222-1189
Ph: (412)355-8200
Fax: (412)355-0498
E-mail: info@specialtyconsultants.com
URL: http://www.specon.com

Provides executive recruiting services for companies in the construction and real estate industry. Identifies candidates through an extensive research database and industry contacts. Services also include compensation surveys, organizational development and executive coaching.

3021 ■ Synergy Professionals
1029 N Peachtree Pkwy., Ste. 252
Peachtree City, GA 30269
Ph: (770)632-6585
E-mail: contact@synergyprof.com
URL: http://www.synergyprof.com

Serves as a professional recruiting firm devoted exclusively to the construction industry.

ONLINE JOB SOURCES AND SERVICES

3022 ■ AECWorkForce.com
E-mail: jclarke@zweigwhite.com
URL: http://aecworkforce.com

Description: Serves as job board for professionals and employers in architecture, engineering and construction.

3023 ■ Builder Jobs
URL: http://www.builderjobs.com

Description: Serves as an online career resource for home building professionals. Features career development articles, salary tools, home building and construction job listings, resume postings, and job alerts.

3024 ■ Construction Executive Online
URL: http://www.constructionexecutive.com

Description: Serves as a career management center for construction executives. Provides members access to a job board of executive construction jobs and to career counseling from top executive coaches.

3025 ■ ConstructionCrossing.com
URL: http://www.constructioncrossing.com

Description: Lists new employment opportunities specifically related to the construction personnel profession.

3026 ■ ConstructionEducation.com
Ph: (828)226-8299
E-mail: ceo@constructioneducation.com
URL: http://www.constructioneducation.com

Description: Includes link page with list of professional resources, employment opportunities listed by company, and construction-related recruiters' pages, as well as general job search websites. Also contains on-site job bank.

3027 ■ ConstructionJobs.com
URL: http://www.constructionjobs.com/index_eng.cfm

Description: Serves as an employment job board and resume database built exclusively for the construction, design, and building industries. Provides targeted candidate searches by geographic region, specific industries, job titles, education, and experience.

3028 ■ GeneralConstructionJobs.com
URL: http://www.generalconstructionjobs.com/JobSeeker/Jobs.aspx

Description: Serves as a job board for online employment advertising built exclusively for the general construction industry.

3029 ■ IHireBuildingTrades
URL: http://www.ihirebuildingtrades.com

Description: Serves as a job posting board that specializes in matching building jobs and construction candidates.

TRADESHOWS

3030 ■ American Institute of Constructors Annual Forum
American Institute of Constructors
466 94th Ave. North
St. Petersburg, FL 33702
Ph: (727)578-0317
Fax: (727)578-9982
E-mail: admin@aicnet.org
URL: http://www.aicnet.org/

Annual. Primary Exhibits: Exhibits related to professionals engaged in construction practice, education and research.

3031 ■ The Builders' Show
National Association of Home Builders of the United States
1201 15th St. N.W.
Washington, DC 20005
Ph: (202)266-8200
Fax: (202)266-8400
Fr: 800-368-5242
E-mail: exposales@nahb.com
URL: http://www.nahb.org

Annual. Primary Exhibits: Building products, equipment, and services.

3032 ■ The Building Industry Show
Building Industry Association of Southern California
17744 Sky Pk. Cir., Ste. 170
Irvine, CA 92614
Ph: (949)553-9500
Fax: (949)769-8942
URL: http://www.biasc.org

Annual. Primary Exhibits: Products and services for the building industry.

3033 ■ Buildings Show
Merchandise Mart Properties Inc.
222 Merchandise Mart, Ste. 470
Chicago, IL 60654
Fr: 800-677-6278
URL: http://www.merchandisemart.com

Annual. Primary Exhibits: Building products, commercial furnishings, and finishes. Dates and Locations: 2012 Jun 24-26; Seattle, WA.

3034 ■ CONEXPO-CON/AGG
Association of Equipment Manufacturers AEM
6737 W. Washington St., Ste. 2400
Milwaukee, WI 53214-5647
Ph: (414)272-0943
Fax: (414)272-1170
E-mail: aem@aem.org
URL: http://www.aem.org

Annual. Primary Exhibits: Construction and construction materials industry equipment, supplies, and services. Dates and Locations: 2014 Mar 04-08; Las Vegas, NV; Las Vegas Convention Center.

3035 ■ Construct and The CSI Annual Convention
Construction Specifications Institute
110 S. Union St., Ste. 100
Alexandria, VA 22314-3351
Ph: 800-689-2900
Fax: (703)236-4600
E-mail: csi@csinet.org
URL: http://www.csinet.org

Annual. Primary Exhibits: Products and services used in non-residential construction.

3036 ■ Construction Financial Management Association Annual Conference and Exhibition
Construction Financial Management Association
100 Village Blvd., Ste. 200
Princeton, NJ 08540
Ph: (609)452-8000
Fax: (609)452-0474
URL: http://www.cfma.org

Annual. Primary Exhibits: Equipment, supplies, and services for the construction industry. Dates and Locations: 2012 Jun 23-27; Orlando, FL; Hilton Orlando Bonnet Creek ; 2013 Jun 22-26; San Diego, CA; Hilton San Diego Bayfront.

3037 ■ Constructo - International Exhibition of the Construction Industry
APEX
207 E. Franklin Ave., Ste. B
El Segundo, CA 90245
E-mail: apexcommunity@apex.org
URL: http://www.apex.org

Annual. Primary Exhibits: Construction equipment, supplies, and services.

3038 ■ International Construction and Utility Equipment Exposition
Association of Equipment Manufacturers AEM
6737 W. Washington St., Ste. 2400
Milwaukee, WI 53214-5647
Ph: (414)272-0943
Fax: (414)272-1170
E-mail: aem@aem.org
URL: http://www.aem.org

Biennial. Primary Exhibits: Utility and construction equipment, supplies, and services. Dates and Locations: 2013 Oct 01-03; Louisville, KY; Kentucky Exposition Center.

3039 ■ JLC LIVE Residential Construction Show - Pacific Northwest
Hanley-Wood Exhibitions
8600 Freeport Parkway
Irving, TX 75063
Ph: (972)536-6300
Fax: (972)536-6301
Fr: 800-869-8522
URL: http://www.hanley-wood.com

Annual. Primary Exhibits: Housing and construction industry equipment, supplies, and services.

3040 ■ MIACON - Miami International Construction Show/Expo
MIACON Construction Show, Inc.
2921 Coral Way
Miami, FL 33145
Ph: (305)441-2865
Fax: (305)529-9217
E-mail: mail@miacon.com
URL: http://www.miacon.com

Annual. Primary Exhibits: Equipment, machinery, building supplies, and services for the construction industry.

3041 ■ Michigan Construction & Design Tradeshow
Construction Association of Michigan
43636 Woodward Ave.
PO Box 3204
Bloomfield Hills, MI 48302
Ph: (248)972-1000
Fax: (248)972-1001
E-mail: marketing@cam-online.com
URL: http://www.cam-online.com

Annual. Primary Exhibits: Construction industry equipment, supplies, and services.

3042 ■ National Association of Demolition Contractors Annual Convention
National Association of Demolition Contractors
16 N. Franklin St., Ste. 203
Doylestown, PA 18901-3536
Ph: (215)348-4949
Fax: (215)348-8422
Fr: 800-541-2412
URL: http://www.demolitionassociation.com

Annual. Primary Exhibits: Demolition equipment, supplies, and services. Dates and Locations: 2012 Mar 10-13; San Antonio, TX; Convention Center & Grand Hyatt Hotel.

3043 ■ Power Show Ohio
Ohio-Michigan Equipment Dealers Association
6124 Avery Rd.
PO Box 68
Dublin, OH 43017
Ph: (614)889-1309
Fax: (614)889-0463
E-mail: info@amgllcusa.com
URL: http://www.omeda.org

Annual. Primary Exhibits: Construction equipment, agricultural equipment, and outdoor power equipment.

3044 ■ Sunbelt Builders Show
National Association of Home Builders of the United States
1201 15th St. N.W.
Washington, DC 20005
Ph: (202)266-8200
Fax: (202)266-8400
Fr: 800-368-5242
E-mail: exposales@nahb.com
URL: http://www.nahb.org

Annual. Primary Exhibits: Residential building industry exhibits.

3045 ■ Women Construction Owners and Executives, U.S.A Annual Meeting
Women Construction Owners and Executives, U.S.A.
4401A Connecticut Ave. NW
Washington, DC 20008
Fax: (650)551-5584
Fr: 800-788-3548
E-mail: info@wcoeusa.org
URL: http://www.wcoeusa.org

Annual. Primary Exhibits: Exhibits relating to women construction owners.

3046 ■ World of Masonry
Ecobuild Federal, LCC
1645 Falmouth Rd., Ste. 1A
Centerville, MA 02632
Ph: (508)790-4751
Fax: (508)790-4750
Fr: 800-996-3863
E-mail: support@ecobuildamerica.com
URL: http://www.aececobuild.com/

Annual. Primary Exhibits: Concrete and masonry construction products and equipment.

OTHER SOURCES

3047 ■ American Concrete Institute
PO Box 9094
Farmington Hills, MI 48333-9094
Ph: (248)848-3700
Fax: (248)848-3701
URL: http://www.concrete.org

Description: Comprised of engineers, architects, contractors, educators, and others interested in improving techniques of design construction and maintenance of concrete products and structures. Advances engineering and technical education, scientific investigation and research, and development of standards for design and construction incorporating concrete and related materials. Gathers, correlates, and disseminates information for the improvement of the design, construction, manufacture, use and maintenance of concrete products and structures.

3048 ■ American Road & Transportation Builders Association
1219 28th St., NW
Washington, DC 20007-3389
Ph: (202)289-4434
Fax: (202)289-4435
E-mail: general@artba.org
URL: http://www.artba.org

Description: Advances the interests of the transportation construction industry. Promotes the growth and protection of transportation infrastructure investment to meet the public and business demand for safe and efficient travel. Works to ensure its members' views and business concerns are addressed before Congress, the White House, federal agencies and news media.

3049 ■ American Society of Home Inspectors (ASHI)
932 Lee St., Ste. 101
Des Plaines, IL 60016
Ph: (847)759-2820
Fax: (847)759-1620

Fr: 800-743-2744
E-mail: jeffa@ashi.org
URL: http://www.ashi.org

Description: Professional home inspectors whose goals are to: establish home inspector qualifications; set standards of practice for home inspections; adhere to a code of ethics; keep the concept of "objective third party" intact; inform members of the most advanced methods and techniques, and educate consumers on the value of home inspections. Conducts seminars through local chapters.

3050 ■ American Society of Professional Estimators (ASPE)
2525 Perimeter Place Dr., Ste. 103
Nashville, TN 37214
Ph: (615)316-9200
Fax: (615)316-9800
Fr: 888-EST-MATE
E-mail: psmith@aspenational.org
URL: http://www.aspenational.org

Description: Construction cost estimators. Develops professional and ethical standards in construction estimating. Offers continuing education to established professionals; provides certification for estimators.

3051 ■ Associated Builders and Contractors (ABC)
4250 N Fairfax Dr., 9th Fl.
Arlington, VA 22203-1607
Ph: (703)812-2000
Fax: (703)812-8201
E-mail: gotquestions@abc.org
URL: http://www.abc.org

Description: Construction contractors, subcontractors, suppliers and associates. Aims to foster and perpetuate the principles of rewarding construction workers and management on the basis of merit. Sponsors management education programs and craft training; also sponsors apprenticeship and skill training programs. Disseminates technological and labor relations information.

3052 ■ Associated General Contractors of America (AGC)
2300 Wilson Blvd., Ste. 400
Arlington, VA 22201
Ph: (703)548-3118
Fax: (703)548-3119
Fr: 800-242-1767
E-mail: info@agc.org
URL: http://www.agc.org

Description: General construction contractors; subcontractors; industry suppliers; service firms. Provides market services through its divisions. Conducts special conferences and seminars designed specifically for construction firms. Compiles statistics on job accidents reported by member firms. Maintains 65 committees, including joint cooperative committees with other associations and liaison committees with federal agencies.

3053 ■ Construction Industry Round Table (CIRT)
8115 Old Dominion Dr., Ste. 210
McLean, VA 22102-2324
Ph: (202)466-6777
E-mail: cirt@cirt.org
URL: http://www.cirt.org

Description: Represents the interests of CEOs from architectural, engineering and construction firms doing business in the United States. Enhances and develops strong management approaches through networking and peer interaction. Seeks to improve the industry's image and relationships with public and private clients.

3054 ■ Construction Management Association of America
7926 Jones Branch Dr., Ste. 800
McLean, VA 22102
Ph: (703)356-2622

Fax: (703)356-6388
E-mail: info@cmaanet.org
URL: http://cmaanet.org

Description: Association website contains a job databank, professional resources books for sale, and career development seminars to attend. Must be a member to fully utilize site, which also includes more project leads, discussion forums, and more.

3055 ■ National Association of Black Women in Construction (NABWIC)
1910 NW 105 Ave.
Pembroke Pines, FL 33026
E-mail: info@nabwic.org
URL: http://nabwic.org

Description: Promotes the advancement of black women in the construction industry. Supports aspiring construction executives. Provides advocacy, mentorship and professional development for its members.

3056 ■ National Association of Home Builders (NAHB)
1201 15th St. NW
Washington, DC 20005
Ph: (202)266-8200

Fax: (202)266-8400
Fr: 800-368-5242
E-mail: jhoward@nahb.com
URL: http://www.nahb.org

Description: Single and multifamily home builders, commercial builders, and others associated with the building industry. Lobbies on behalf of the housing industry and conducts public affairs activities to increase public understanding of housing and the economy. Collects and disseminates data on current developments in home building and home builders' plans through its Economics Department and nationwide Metropolitan Housing Forecast. Maintains NAHB Research Center, which functions as the research arm of the home building industry. Sponsors seminars and workshops on construction, mortgage credit, labor relations, cost reduction, land use, remodeling, and business management. Compiles statistics; offers charitable program, spokesman training, and placement service; maintains speakers' bureau, and Hall of Fame. Subsidiaries include the National Council of the Housing Industry. Maintains over 50 committees in many areas of construction; operates

National Commercial Builders Council, National Council of the Multifamily Housing Industry, National Remodelers Council, and National Sales and Marketing Council.

3057 ■ Residential Construction Workers' Association (ASTRACOR)
3660D Wheeler Ave.
Alexandria, VA 22304
Ph: (703)212-8294
Fax: (703)212-8295
E-mail: info@astracor.org
URL: http://www.astracor.org

Description: Represents the interests of residential construction workers. Aims to improve the lives of all workers employed in residential construction. Provides job and social service referrals. Informs workers of their rights and benefits and provides training in different construction trades.

SOURCES OF HELP-WANTED ADS

3058 ■ ACJS Today
Academy of Criminal Justice Sciences (ACJS)
PO Box 960
Greenbelt, MD 20768-0960
Ph: (301)446-6300
Fax: (301)446-2819
Fr: 800-757-2257
E-mail: info@acjs.org
URL: http://www.acjs.org/
Description: Four issues/year. Circulation is 2,000. Contains criminal justice information.

3059 ■ American City and County
Penton Media Inc.
9800 Metcalf Ave.
Overland Park, KS 66212
Ph: (913)341-1300
Fax: (913)967-1898
URL: http://americancityandcounty.com
Monthly. Municipal and county administration magazine.

3060 ■ Law and Order
Hendon Publishing
130 N Waukegan Rd., Ste. 202
Deerfield, IL 60015-5652
Ph: (847)444-3300
Fax: (847)444-3333
Fr: 800-843-9764
E-mail: law&ordermag@halldata.com
URL: http://www.hendonpub.com/publications/
  lawandorder/
Monthly. $22.00/year for individuals. Law enforcement trade magazine.

3061 ■ The Municipality
League of Wisconsin Municipalities
122 W Washington Ave., Ste. 300
Madison, WI 53703-2715
Ph: (608)267-2380
Fax: (608)267-0645
Fr: 800-991-5502
URL: http://www.lwm-info.org/
Monthly. Magazine for officials of Wisconsin's local municipal governments.

3062 ■ On the Line
American Correctional Association
206 N Washington St., Ste. 200
Alexandria, VA 22314
Ph: (703)224-0000
Fax: (703)224-0179
Fr: 800-222-5646
E-mail: execoffice@aca.org
URL: http://www.aca.org/
Description: Five issues/year. Provides updates on the Association's efforts to improve correctional standards and to develop adequate physical facilities.

Presents national news of the corrections field. Recurring features include job listings, news of research, notices of publications available, reports of meetings, and a calendar of events.

3063 ■ Western City
League of California Cities
1400 K St., 4th Fl.
Sacramento, CA 95814
Ph: (916)658-8200
Fax: (916)658-8240
Fr: 800-262-1801
URL: http://www.westerncity.com
Monthly. $39.00/year for individuals; $63.00/year for two years; $52.00/year for other countries; $26.50/year for students. Municipal interest magazine.

EMPLOYER DIRECTORIES AND NETWORKING LISTS

3064 ■ National Directory of Law Enforcement Administrators, Correctional Institutions & Related Agencies
National Public Safety Information Bureau
601 Main St.
PO Box 365
Stevens Point, WI 54481-2617
Ph: (715)345-2772
Fax: (715)345-7288
Fr: 800-647-7579
URL: http://www.safetysource.com
Annual, Latest edition 44th, Published 2008. $149.00 for individuals; $189.00. Covers: Police departments, sheriffs, coroners, criminal prosecutors, child support agencies, state law enforcement and criminal investigation agencies; federal criminal investigation and related agencies; state and federal correctional institutions; campus law enforcement departments; County jails, airport and harbor police, Bureau of Indian Affairs officials, plus new homeland security section. Entries include: Name, address, phone, fax, names and titles of key personnel, number of officers, population served. Arrangement: Separate geographical sections for police chiefs, coroners, sheriffs, prosecutors, prisons and state criminal investigation agencies; also separate sections for federal agencies and miscellaneous law enforcement and related agencies. Indexes: Departments.

3065 ■ Who's Who in Jail Management Jail Directory, 5th Edition
American Jail Association
1135 Professional Ct.
Hagerstown, MD 21740
Ph: (301)790-3930
Fax: (301)790-2941
URL: http://www.aja.org
Provides information on local jails in the United

States. $75.00 for members; $85.00 for nonmembers.

HANDBOOKS AND MANUALS

3066 ■ The Correctional Officer: A Practical Guide
Carolina Academic Press
700 Kent St.
Durham, NC 27701
Ph: (919)489-7486
Fax: (919)493-5668
URL: http://www.cap-press.com
Gary F. Cornelius. 2010. $40.00 (paper). 406 pages. Provides a clear, realistic understanding of a correctional officer's job. Includes information on maintaining positive traits and job skills that can enhance the career of a correctional officer.

3067 ■ Master the Corrections Officer Exams
Peterson's Publishing
Peterson's Nelnet LLC
2000 Lenox Dr., 2nd Fl., Ste. 203
Lawrenceville, NJ 08648
Ph: (609)896-1800
E-mail: onlinestore@petersons.com
URL: http://www.petersonsbooks.com
2010. $18.95. 312 pages. Provides detailed information and review to help aspirants pass the corrections officer exam. Includes latest information on job requirements, application procedure and officer screening process, as well as practice tests and guidelines for the oral interview.

ONLINE JOB SOURCES AND SERVICES

3068 ■ Corrections.com
URL: http://www.corrections.com
Description: Serves as an online community for the corrections industry. Features a news site dealing with prison and parole issues, including jobs that are available across the country.

TRADESHOWS

3069 ■ American Jail Association Training Conference & Jail Expo
American Jail Association
1135 Professional Ct.
Hagerstown, MD 21740-5853
Ph: (301)790-3930
Fax: (301)790-2941
URL: http://www.aja.org
Annual. Primary Exhibits: Jail supplies & services for correctional facilities; construction design; training; officer equipment and correctional equipment, supplies, and services.

3070 ■ International Community Corrections Association Research Conference

International Community Corrections Association
8701 Georgia Ave., Ste. 402
Silver Spring, MD 20910
Ph: (301)585-6090
Fax: (301)585-6094
E-mail: info@iccaweb.org
URL: http://www.iccaweb.org

Annual. Presents research findings of evidence-based best practices in prisoner reentry, juvenile justice, treatment, and organizational management. 2012 September 7-13; Orlando, FL; Caribe Royale Resort and Conference Center.

OTHER SOURCES

3071 ■ American Correctional Association (ACA)

206 N Washington St., Ste. 200
Alexandria, VA 22314
Ph: (703)224-0000
Fax: (703)224-0179
Fr: 800-222-5646
E-mail: execoffice@aca.org
URL: http://www.aca.org

Description: Correctional administrators, wardens, superintendents, members of prison and parole boards, probation officers, psychologists, educators, sociologists, and other individuals; institutions and associations involved in the correctional field. Promotes improved correctional standards, including selection of personnel, care, supervision, education, training, employment, treatment, and post-release adjustment of inmates. Studies causes of crime and juvenile delinquency and methods of crime control

and prevention through grants and contracts. Compiles statistics. Conducts research programs and training of correctional professionals. Offers accreditation of institutions and certification for correctional executive, manager, supervisor, and officer.

3072 ■ American Probation & Parole Association

PO Box 11910
Lexington, KY 40578-1910
Ph: (859)244-8203
Fax: (859)244-8001
E-mail: appa@csg.org
URL: http://www.appa-net.org

Description: Comprises of probation/parole executives, line officers, and other interested individuals. Seeks to improve and advance progressive probation/parole practices through the development of knowledge, skills, resources, and legislation. Promotes legislative programs, sponsors research programs, and conducts regional workshops.

3073 ■ American Society of Criminology (ASC)

1314 Kinnear Rd., Ste. 212
Columbus, OH 43212-1156
Ph: (614)292-9207
Fax: (614)292-6767
E-mail: asc@asc41.com
URL: http://www.asc41.com

Description: Represents professional and academic criminologists, students of criminology in accredited universities, psychiatrists, psychologists, and sociologists. Develops criminology as a science and academic discipline. Aids in the construction of criminological curricula in accredited universities. Upgrades the practitioner in criminological fields (police, prisons, probation, parole, delinquency

workers). Conducts research programs and sponsors three student paper competitions. Provides placement service at annual convention.

3074 ■ International Community Corrections Association

8701 Georgia Ave., Ste. 402
Silver Spring, MD 20910
Ph: (301)585-6090
Fax: (301)585-6094
E-mail: info@iccaweb.org
URL: http://www.iccaweb.org

Description: Represents agencies and individuals working in community-based correctional programs. Promotes the development of community-based correctional programs and treatment. Assists members through the exchange of information regarding management and treatment.

3075 ■ Nine Lives Associates (NLA)

Executive Protection Institute
16 Penn Pl., Ste. 1570
New York, NY 10001
Ph: (212)268-4555
Fax: (212)563-4783
Fr: 800-947-5827
E-mail: info@personalprotection.com
URL: http://www.personalprotection.com/nla.cfm

Description: Law enforcement, correctional, military, and security professionals who have been granted Personal Protection Specialist Certification through completion of the protective services program offered by the Executive Protection Institute; conducts research; EPI programs emphasize personal survival skills and techniques for the protection of others. Provides professional recognition for qualified individuals engaged in executive protection assignments. Maintains placement service. Operates speakers' bureau; compiles statistics.

Cosmetologists and Hairdressers

SOURCES OF HELP-WANTED ADS

3076 ■ Beauty Launchpad
Creative Age Publications Inc.
7628 Densmore Ave.
Van Nuys, CA 91406-2042
Ph: (818)782-7328
Fax: (818)782-7450
Fr: 800-442-5667
URL: http://www.beautylaunchpad.com/index.php
Fashion magazine.

3077 ■ Beauty Store Business
Creative Age Publications Inc.
7628 Densmore Ave.
Van Nuys, CA 91406-2042
Ph: (818)782-7328
Fax: (818)782-7450
Fr: 800-442-5667
URL: http://www.beautystorebusiness.com/

Monthly. Business magazine for beauty industry professionals and beauty store owners.

3078 ■ Cosmetics & Toiletries
Allured Publishing Corp.
336 Gundersen Dr., Ste. A
Carol Stream, IL 60188-2403
Ph: (630)653-2155
Fax: (630)653-2192
E-mail: lhince@allured.com
URL: http://www.cosmeticsandtoiletries.com

Monthly. $98.00/year for individuals; $137.00/year for Canada; $189.00/year for other countries; $169.00/year for two years; $231.00/year for Canada, two years; $330.00/year for other countries, two years. Trade magazine on cosmetic and toiletries manufacturing with an emphasis on product research and development issues.

3079 ■ Global Cosmetic Industry
Allured Publishing Corp.
336 Gundersen Dr., Ste. A
Carol Stream, IL 60188-2403
Ph: (630)653-2155
Fax: (630)653-2192
URL: http://www.gcimagazine.com/

Monthly. Free to qualified subscribers, U.S. and Canada; $98.00/year for other countries; $176.00/year for two years, other countries. Trade publication covering the cosmetics industry worldwide.

3080 ■ Hair Gallery
Multi-Media International
13915 W 107th St.
Lenexa, KS 66215
Ph: (913)469-6800
Fax: (913)469-6805
URL: http://mmimags.com/HairGallery.html

$9.99/year for single issue; $12.99/year for single is-

sue, Canada. Magazine featuring gallery of hairstyles.

3081 ■ Journal of Cosmetics, Dermatological Sciences and Applications
Scientific Research Publishing
PO Box 54821
Irvine, CA 92619-4821
URL: http://www.scirp.org/journal/jcdsa/

Peer-reviewed journal covering the basic sciences, engineering aspects and applied technology of cosmetics, toiletries, perfumery and related fields.

3082 ■ Live Design
Penton Media Inc.
9800 Metcalf Ave.
Overland Park, KS 66212
Ph: (913)341-1300
Fax: (913)967-1898
URL: http://livedesignonline.com

The business of entertainment technology and design.

3083 ■ Modern Salon
Vance Publishing Corp.
400 Knightsbridge Pky.
Lincolnshire, IL 60069
Ph: (847)634-2600
Fax: (847)634-4379
URL: http://www.modernsalon.com/

Monthly. Magazine focusing on hairstyling salons for men and women.

3084 ■ Nailpro
Creative Age Publications Inc.
7628 Densmore Ave.
Van Nuys, CA 91406-2042
Ph: (818)782-7328
Fax: (818)782-7450
Fr: 800-442-5667
E-mail: nailpro@creativeage.com
URL: http://www.nailpro.com

Monthly. Salon owners and nail technicians read Nailpro for continuing education in techniques and services, marketing and management tips, product information and industry news.

3085 ■ Skin Inc.
Allured Publishing Corp.
336 Gundersen Dr., Ste. A
Carol Stream, IL 60188-2403
Ph: (630)653-2155
Fax: (630)653-2192
E-mail: customerservice@allured.com
URL: http://www.skininc.com/

Monthly. $49.00/year for individuals; $57.00/year for Canada; $98.00/year for other countries. The complete business guide for face and body care.

3086 ■ Soap and Cosmetics
Chemical Week Associates
2 Grand Central Tower
140 E 45th St., 40th Fl.
New York, NY 10017
Ph: (212)884-9528
Fax: (212)883-9514
URL: http://www.chemweek.com/verticals/sc/

Monthly. $225.97/year for individuals, print + online; $259.97/year for Canada, print + online; $629.00/year for other countries, print + online. Trade publication covering the cosmetics industry.

3087 ■ Spa 20/20
Virgo Publishing Inc.
PO Box 40079
Phoenix, AZ 85067-0079
Ph: (480)990-1101
Fax: (480)990-0819
URL: http://www.spa20-20.com

Bimonthly. $14.00/year for individuals, in U.S.; $26.00/year for Canada; $82.00/year for elsewhere. Magazine covering the spa industry, including skin care, cosmetics, and sunless tanning.

EMPLOYER DIRECTORIES AND NETWORKING LISTS

3088 ■ Careers in Focus—Cosmetology
Facts On File Inc.
132 W 31st St., 17th Fl.
New York, NY 10001
Ph: (212)967-8800
Fax: 800-678-3633
Fr: 800-322-8755
URL: http://www.infobasepublishing.com

Latest edition 4th; Published February, 2008. $32.95 for individuals. Covers: An overview of cosmetology, followed by a selection of jobs profiled in detail, including the nature of the job, earnings, prospects for employment, what kind of training and skills it requires, and sources for further information.

HANDBOOKS AND MANUALS

3089 ■ Cosmetologist
National Learning Corporation
212 Michael Dr.
Syosset, NY 11791
Fr: 800-632-8888
URL: http://www.passbooks.com

2009. $34.95 (paper). Serves as an exam preparation guide for cosmetologists.

3090 ■ The Makeup Artist Handbook: Techniques for Film, Television, Photography, and Theatre
Focal Press
225 Wyman St.
Waltham, MA 02451

Fr: 800-545-2522
E-mail: usbkinfo@elsevier.com
URL: http://www.elsevier.com

Gretchen Davis and Mindy Hall. 2012. $44.95 (paperback). 320 pages. 2nd edition. Contains Hollywood-style makeup tips and techniques for aspiring and professional makeup artists. Includes full reference section with relevant websites, business listings and contacts.

TRADESHOWS

3091 ■ American Association of Cosmetology Schools Annual Conference - AACS Annual Convention & Expo
American Association of Cosmetology Schools
15825 N. 71st St., Ste. 100
Scottsdale, AZ 85254-1521
Ph: (480)281-0431
Fax: (480)905-0993
Fr: 800-831-1086
E-mail: dilsah@beautyschools.org
URL: http://www.beautyschools.org

Annual. Primary Exhibits: Beauty supplies and products, and cosmetology services.

3092 ■ American Electrology Association Annual Convention
American Electrology Association
PO Box 687
Bodega Bay, CA 94923
Ph: (707)875-9135
E-mail: infoaea@electrology.com
URL: http://www.electrology.com

Annual. Primary Exhibits: Electrology equipment, supplies, and services.

3093 ■ Cosmoprof North America
Professional Beauty Association
15825 N 71st St., Ste. 100
Scottsdale, AZ 85254
Ph: (480)281-0424
Fax: (480)905-0708
Fr: 800-468-2274
E-mail: info@probeauty.org
URL: http://www.probeauty.org

Annual. Promotes emerging trends from within all segments of the beauty industry. Features guest speakers. Fosters the establishment of new contacts and renewal of old business connections. 2012 July 22-24; Las Vegas, NV.

3094 ■ International Beauty Show, New York
Advanstar Communications
641 Lexington Ave., 8th Fl.
New York, NY 10022
Ph: (212)951-6600
Fax: (212)951-6793
E-mail: info@advantstar.com
URL: http://www.advanstar.com

Annual. Primary Exhibits: Beauty and health related equipment, supplies, and services.

3095 ■ Midwest Beauty Show
Chicago Cosmetologists Inc.
401 N. Michigan Ave.
Chicago, IL 60611
Ph: (312)321-6809
Fax: (312)245-1080

Fr: 800-648-2505
E-mail: info@americasbeautyshow.com
URL: http://www.isnow.com

Annual. Primary Exhibits: Goods and services for the beauty trade. Dates and Locations: 2012 Mar 03-05; Chicago, IL; McCormick Place.

3096 ■ National Beauty Show - HAIRWORLD
National Cosmetology Association
15825 N. 71st St., Ste. 100
Scottsdale, AZ 85254
Ph: (480)281-0424
Fax: (480)905-0708
Fr: 800-468-2274
E-mail: info@probeauty.org
URL: http://www.probeauty.org/nca/

Annual. Primary Exhibits: Hair products, cosmetics, and jewelry.

3097 ■ Premiere Orlando
Premiere Shows, Inc.
1049 Willa Springs Dr., Ste. 1001
Winter Springs, FL 32708
Ph: (407)265-3131
Fax: (407)265-3134
Fr: 800-335-7469
E-mail: sales@premiereshows.com
URL: http://www.premiereshows.com

Annual. Primary Exhibits: Products and services for hair, nail, and skin care professionals and the beauty industry. Dates and Locations: 2012 Jun 04-04; Orlando, FL; Orlando/Orange County Convention Center.

OTHER SOURCES

3098 ■ American Association of Cosmetology Schools (AACS)
9927 E Bell Rd., Ste. 110
Scottsdale, AZ 85260
Ph: (480)281-0431
Fax: (480)905-0993
Fr: 800-831-1086
E-mail: jim@beautyschools.org
URL: http://www.beautyschools.org

Description: Owners and teachers in cosmetology schools.

3099 ■ Intercoiffure America
1303 Campbell Rd.
Houston, TX 77055
Ph: (713)984-8800
Fax: (713)935-4409
Fr: 800-442-3007
E-mail: maryanne@visiblechanges.com
URL: http://www.intercoiffure.us

Description: Owners of beauty salons in the United States and Canada who meet the ethical standards set down by Intercoiffure. Seeks to make the women of America the best in hair fashion.

3100 ■ International SalonSpa Business Network (ISBN)
207 E Ohio St., No. 361
Chicago, IL 60611
Fax: (866)444-5139
Fr: (866)444-ICSA
E-mail: margie@salonspanetwork.org
URL: http://salonspanetwork.org

Description: Beauty salon chains. Collects and

processes data on industry standards; proactively works to affect the outcome of pending legislation and regulations governing the cosmetology industry; provides continuing education programs on management issues to members; works for free exchange of corporate information, solutions to common problems, advertising ideas, and incentive programs amongst members; takes part in and supports other industry associations.

3101 ■ National Beauty Culturists' League (NBCL)
25 Logan Cir. NW
Washington, DC 20005-3725
Ph: (202)332-2695
Fax: (202)332-0940
E-mail: nbcl@bellsouth.net
URL: http://www.nbcl.org

Description: Beauticians, cosmetologists, and beauty products manufacturers. Encourages standardized, scientific, and approved methods of hair, scalp, and skin treatments. Offers scholarships and plans to establish a research center. Sponsors: National Institute of Cosmetology, a training course in operating and designing and business techniques. Maintains hall of fame; conducts research program.

3102 ■ National Coalition of Estheticians, Manufacturers/Distributors and Associations (NCEA)
484 Spring Ave.
Ridgewood, NJ 07450
Ph: (201)670-4100
Fax: (201)670-4265
E-mail: nceaorg@aol.com
URL: http://www.ncea.tv

Description: Establishes standards and practices for skin care industry. Provides political representation for estheticians to state legislators and licensing boards. Provides a forum to discuss issues that affect the skin care industry and individual licensees.

3103 ■ National Cosmetology Association (PBA)
Professional Beauty Association
15825 N 71st St., Ste. 100
Scottsdale, AZ 85254
Ph: (480)281-0424
Fax: (480)905-0708
Fr: 800-468-2274
E-mail: info@probeauty.org
URL: http://www.probeauty.org

Description: Manufacturers and manufacturers' representatives of beauty and barber products, cosmetics, equipment, and supplies used in or resold by beauty salons or barbershops. Promotes the beauty industry; works to ensure product safety; disseminates information. Holds educational seminars; organizes charity events.

3104 ■ National Latino Cosmetology Association
PO Box 401285
Las Vegas, NV 89140
Ph: (702)448-5020
Fax: (702)448-8993
Fr: 877-658-3801
E-mail: info@nlcamerican.org
URL: http://www.nlcamerican.org

Description: Represents Latino beauty industry professionals and businesses. Enhances professional knowledge, business growth, and career focus in the beauty industry. Offers resources, strategies, and tools to meet the needs of businesses, professionals, and other individuals in the beauty industry.

Cost Estimators

Sources of Help-Wanted Ads

3105 ■ Builder
Hanley-Wood L.L.C.
1 Thomas Cir. NW, Ste. 600
Washington, DC 20005-5803
Ph: (202)452-0800
Fax: (202)785-1974
E-mail: builder@omeda.com
URL: http://www.hanleywood.com/
default.aspx?page=magazines

$29.95/year for U.S. and Canada; $54.95/year for U.S. and Canada, 2 years; $192.00/year for other countries. Magazine covering housing and construction industry.

3106 ■ Constructor
Associated General Contractors of America
2300 Wilson Blvd., Ste. 400
Arlington, VA 22201
Ph: (703)548-3118
Fax: (703)548-3119
Fr: 800-242-1767
URL: http://constructor.agc.org/

Bimonthly. $95.00/year for individuals. Management magazine for the Construction Industry.

3107 ■ Cost Engineering
AACE International
1265 Suncrest Towne Centre Dr.
Morgantown, WV 26505
Ph: (304)296-8444
Fax: (304)291-5728
Fr: 800-858-2678
URL: http://www.aacei.org/resources/CE/
welcome.shtml

Monthly. $65.00/year for individuals; $82.00/year for other countries; $8.00/year for single issue, for members; $12.00/year for nonmembers. Magazine.

3108 ■ Design Cost Data
DC & D Technologies Inc.
PO Box 948
Valrico, FL 33595-0948
Ph: (813)662-6830
Fax: (813)662-6793
Fr: 800-533-5680
URL: http://www.dcd.com

Bimonthly. $94.00/year for individuals, silver; $157.00/year for two years, silver; $149.00/year for individuals, gold; $239.00/year for two years, gold. Publication providing real cost data case studies of various types completed around the country for design and building professionals.

3109 ■ ENR: Engineering News-Record
McGraw-Hill Inc.
PO Box 182604
Columbus, OH 43218
Ph: (614)430-4000
Fax: (614)759-3749

Fr: 877-833-5524
URL: http://enr.construction.com/Default.asp

Weekly. $49.00/year for individuals, print; $89.00/year for Canada, print; $125.00/year for other countries, print. Magazine focusing on engineering and construction.

3110 ■ Professional Builder
SGC Horizon LLC
3030 W Salt Creek Ln., Ste. 201
Arlington Heights, IL 60005
Ph: (847)391-1000
Fax: (847)390-0408
URL: http://www.housingzone.com/pb/pubhome/

Monthly. Free. The integrated engineering magazine of the building construction industry.

Employer Directories and Networking Lists

3111 ■ ABC Today—Associated Builders and Contractors National Membership Directory Issue
Associated Builders and Contractors Inc.
4250 N Fairfax Dr., 9th Fl.
Arlington, VA 22203-1607
Ph: (703)812-2000
Fax: (703)812-8235
URL: http://www.abc.org

Annual, December. $150.00. Publication includes: List of approximately 19,000 member construction contractors and suppliers.

3112 ■ ENR—Top 400 Construction Contractors Issue
McGraw-Hill Inc.
PO Box 182604
Columbus, OH 43218
Ph: (614)430-4000
Fax: (614)759-3749
Fr: 877-833-5524
URL: http://enr.construction.com/toplists/Contractors/
001-100.asp

Annual, Latest edition 2011. $35.00 for individuals. Publication includes: List of 400 United States contractors receiving largest dollar volumes of contracts in preceding calendar year. Separate lists of 50 largest design/construct management firms; 50 largest program and construction managers; 25 building contractors; 25 heavy contractors.

3113 ■ ENR—Top 500 Design Firms Issue
McGraw-Hill Inc.
PO Box 182604
Columbus, OH 43218
Ph: (614)430-4000
Fax: (614)759-3749
Fr: 877-833-5524
URL: http://enr.construction.com/toplists/
sourcebooks/2010/design

Annual, latest edition 2010. $82.00 for individuals. Publication includes: List of 500 leading architectural, engineering, and specialty design firms selected on basis of annual billings. Entries include: Company name, headquarters location, type of firm, current and prior year rank in billings, types of services, countries in which operated in preceding year. Arrangement: Ranked by billings.

Handbooks and Manuals

3114 ■ From Product Description to Cost: A Practical Approach for Cost Estimators
Springer Publishing Co.
11 West 42nd St., 15th Fl.
New York, NY 10036
Ph: (212)460-1500
Fax: (212)473-6272
Fr: 877-687-7476
E-mail: contactus@springerpub.com
URL: http://www.springer.com/series/7232

Pierre Foussier. 2006. $205.00. Profiles cost estimating, covering data preparation, general cost estimating, the use of cost models, and risk analysis used in cost estimations.

Employment Agencies and Search Firms

3115 ■ Kimmel & Associates
25 Page Ave.
Asheville, NC 28801
Ph: (828)251-9900
Fax: (828)251-9955
E-mail: kimmel@kimmel.com
URL: http://www.kimmel.com

Specializes in the construction, waste, architecture, engineering, logistics and supply chain industries.

3116 ■ Real Estate Executive Search, Inc.
225 E Dania Beach Blvd. Ste., 200
Dania Beach, FL 33004
Ph: (954)927-6000
Fax: (954)927-6003
E-mail: reesearch954@aol.com
URL: http://reesearchinc.com

Executive search firm for the real estate and finance fields.

3117 ■ Synergy Professionals
1029 N Peachtree Pkwy., Ste. 252
Peachtree City, GA 30269
Ph: (770)632-6585
E-mail: contact@synergyprof.com
URL: http://www.synergyprof.com

Serves as a professional recruiting firm devoted exclusively to the construction industry.

ONLINE JOB SOURCES AND SERVICES

3118 ■ Construction Executive Online
URL: http://www.constructionexecutive.com

Description: Serves as a career management center for construction executives. Provides members access to a job board of executive construction jobs and to career counseling from top executive coaches.

OTHER SOURCES

3119 ■ AACE International
1265 Suncrest Towne Ctr Dr.
Morgantown, WV 26505-1876
Ph: (304)296-8444
Fax: (304)291-5728
E-mail: info@aacei.org
URL: http://www.aacei.org

Description: Professional society of cost managers, cost engineers, estimators, schedulers and planners, project managers, educators, representatives of all branches of engineering, engineering students, and others. Conducts technical and educational programs. Offers placement service. Compiles statistics. Operates certification program for Certified Cost Engineers (CCE); Certified Cost Consultants (CCC); Interim Cost Consultants (ICC); Planning & Scheduling Professionals (PSP); and Earned Value Professionals (EVP).

3120 ■ American Road & Transportation Builders Association
1219 28th St., NW
Washington, DC 20007-3389
Ph: (202)289-4434
Fax: (202)289-4435
E-mail: general@artba.org
URL: http://www.artba.org

Description: Advances the interests of the transportation construction industry. Promotes the growth and protection of transportation infrastructure investment to meet the public and business demand for safe and efficient travel. Works to ensure its members' views and business concerns are addressed before Congress, the White House, federal agencies and news media.

3121 ■ American Society of Professional Estimators (ASPE)
2525 Perimeter Place Dr., Ste. 103
Nashville, TN 37214
Ph: (615)316-9200
Fax: (615)316-9800
Fr: 888-EST-MATE
E-mail: psmith@aspenational.org
URL: http://www.aspenational.org

Description: Construction cost estimators. Develops professional and ethical standards in construction estimating. Offers continuing education to established professionals; provides certification for estimators.

3122 ■ Associated Builders and Contractors (ABC)
4250 N Fairfax Dr., 9th Fl.
Arlington, VA 22203-1607
Ph: (703)812-2000
Fax: (703)812-8201
E-mail: gotquestions@abc.org
URL: http://www.abc.org

Description: Construction contractors, subcontrac-

tors, suppliers and associates. Aims to foster and perpetuate the principles of rewarding construction workers and management on the basis of merit. Sponsors management education programs and craft training; also sponsors apprenticeship and skill training programs. Disseminates technological and labor relations information.

3123 ■ Associated General Contractors of America (AGC)
2300 Wilson Blvd., Ste. 400
Arlington, VA 22201
Ph: (703)548-3118
Fax: (703)548-3119
Fr: 800-242-1767
E-mail: info@agc.org
URL: http://www.agc.org

Description: General construction contractors; subcontractors; industry suppliers; service firms. Provides market services through its divisions. Conducts special conferences and seminars designed specifically for construction firms. Compiles statistics on job accidents reported by member firms. Maintains 65 committees, including joint cooperative committees with other associations and liaison committees with federal agencies.

3124 ■ International Society of Parametric Analysts (ISPA)
527 Maple Ave. E, Ste. 301
Vienna, VA 22180
Ph: (703)938-5090
Fax: (703)938-5091
Fr: 877-734-2726
E-mail: ispa@sceaonline.net
URL: http://www.ispa-cost.org

Description: Engineers, designers, statisticians, estimators, and managers in industry, the military, and government who develop and use computerized, parametric cost-estimating models. Conducts educational activities to promote usage of parametric modeling techniques for purposes of cost estimating, risk analysis, and technology forecasting. Sponsors placement service.

3125 ■ National Association of Home Builders (NAHB)
1201 15th St. NW
Washington, DC 20005
Ph: (202)266-8200
Fax: (202)266-8400
Fr: 800-368-5242
E-mail: jhoward@nahb.com
URL: http://www.nahb.org

Description: Single and multifamily home builders, commercial builders, and others associated with the building industry. Lobbies on behalf of the housing industry and conducts public affairs activities to increase public understanding of housing and the economy. Collects and disseminates data on current developments in home building and home builders' plans through its Economics Department and nationwide Metropolitan Housing Forecast. Maintains NAHB Research Center, which functions as the research arm of the home building industry. Sponsors seminars and workshops on construction, mortgage credit, labor relations, cost reduction, land use, remodeling, and business management. Compiles statistics; offers charitable program, spokesman training, and placement service; maintains speakers' bureau, and Hall of Fame. Subsidiaries include the National Council of the Housing Industry. Maintains over 50 committees in many areas of construction; operates National Commercial Builders Council, National

Council of the Multifamily Housing Industry, National Remodelers Council, and National Sales and Marketing Council.

3126 ■ National Association of Women in Construction (NAWIC)
327 S Adams St.
Fort Worth, TX 76104
Ph: (817)877-5551
Fax: (817)877-0324
Fr: 800-552-3506
E-mail: nawic@nawic.org
URL: http://www.nawic.org

Description: Seeks to enhance the success of women in the construction industry.

3127 ■ National Center for Construction Education and Research (NCCER)
3600 NW 43rd St., Bldg. G
Gainesville, FL 32606
Ph: (352)334-0911
Fax: (352)334-0932
Fr: 888-622-3720
E-mail: marketing@nccer.org
URL: http://www.nccer.org

Description: Education foundation committed to the development and publication of Contren(TM) Learning Series, the source of craft training, management education and safety resources for the construction industry.

3128 ■ Professional Women in Construction (PWC)
315 E 56th St.
New York, NY 10022-3730
Ph: (212)486-4712
Fax: (212)486-0228
E-mail: pwc@pwcusa.org
URL: http://www.pwcusa.org

Description: Management-level women and men in construction and allied industries; owners, suppliers, architects, engineers, field personnel, office personnel and bonding/surety personnel. Provides a forum for exchange of ideas and promotion of political and legislative action, education and job opportunities for women in construction and related fields; forms liaisons with other trade and professional groups; develops research programs. Strives to reform abuses and to assure justice and equity within the construction industry. Sponsors mini-workshops. Maintains Action Line, which provides members with current information on pertinent legislation and on the association's activities and job referrals.

3129 ■ Society of Cost Estimating and Analysis (SCEA)
527 Maple Ave. E, Ste. 301
Vienna, VA 22180
Ph: (703)938-5090
Fax: (703)938-5091
E-mail: scea@sceaonline.org
URL: http://www.sceaonline.net

Description: Works to improve cost estimating and analysis in government and industry and to enhance the professional competence and achievements of its members. Administers a professional certification program leading to the designation of Certified Cost Estimator/Analyst; offers extensive literature in the field through its Professional Development Program. Goals of the Society include enhancing the profession of cost estimating and analysis, fostering the professional growth of its members, enhancing the understanding and application of cost estimating, analysis and related disciplines throughout government and industry and providing forums and media through which current issues of interest to the profession can be addressed and advances in the state-of-the-art can be shared.

SOURCES OF HELP-WANTED ADS

3130 ■ *Addiction Professional*
Vendome Group L.L.C.
6 E 32nd St.
New York, NY 10016
Ph: (212)812-8420
E-mail: addiction_professional@halldata.com
URL: http://www.addictionpro.com/ME2/default.asp
Bimonthly. $67.00/year for individuals. Magazine that publishes innovations and trends in the clinical care of persons with substance use and dependence disorders.

3131 ■ *Alcoholism*
John Wiley & Sons Inc.
350 Main St., Commerce Pl.
Malden, MA 02148-5089
Ph: (781)388-8200
Fax: (781)388-8210
E-mail: mnewcomb-acer@earthlink.net
URL: http://www.wiley.com/bw/journal.asp?ref=0145-6008&site=1
Monthly. $506.00/year for individuals, print & online; $1,341.00/year for institutions, print & online; $1,166.00/year for institutions, print or online; $327.00/year for individuals, UK, print & online; $819.00/year for institutions, UK, print & online; $327.00/year for other countries, print & online; $1,041.00/year for institutions, Europe, print & online; $905.00/year for institutions, Europe, print or online; $712.00/year for institutions, UK, print or online. Publishing original clinical and research studies on alcoholism and alcohol-induced organ damage.

3132 ■ *American Annals of the Deaf*
Conference of Educational Administrators Serving the Deaf
Gallaudet University Press
Denison House
Washington, DC 20002
Ph: (202)651-5488
Fax: (202)651-5489
URL: http://gupress.gallaudet.edu/annals/
Quarterly. $55.00/year for individuals; $95.00/year for institutions; $50.00/year for members. Journal focusing on education of the deaf.

3133 ■ *Career Planning & Adult Development Network Newsletter*
Career Planning & Adult Development Network
543 Vista Mar Ave.
Pacifica, CA 94044
Ph: (650)773-0982
Fax: 877-270-0215
E-mail: admin@careernetwork.org
URL: http://www.careernetwork.org
Description: Bimonthly. Contains features and news items on career development and human resources: theory, methodology, research, practices, and techniques. Deals with manpower, organizational planning, counseling, training, equal opportunity, career transition, marketing skills, and adult learning. Recurring features include notices of resources, materials, publications of interest, conferences, workshops, seminars, employment opportunities, book reviews, network news, and a column on publishers of career development books.

3134 ■ *The Chronicle of Higher Education*
The Chronicle of Higher Education
1255 23rd St. NW, 7th Fl.
Washington, DC 20037-1125
Ph: (202)466-1000
Fax: (202)452-1033
Fr: 800-728-2803
URL: http://chronicle.com
Weekly. $82.50/year for individuals, 43 issues; $45.00/year for individuals, 21 issues; $140.00/year for individuals, 86 issues. Higher education magazine (tabloid).

3135 ■ *Counseling Today*
American Counseling Association
5999 Stevenson Ave.
Alexandria, VA 22304
Ph: (703)823-6862
Fax: (703)823-0252
Fr: 800-347-6647
URL: http://www.counseling.org
Description: Monthly. Covers news and issues relevant to the counseling profession.

3136 ■ *Counselor Education and Supervision*
American Counseling Association
5999 Stevenson Ave.
Alexandria, VA 22304
Ph: (703)823-6862
Fax: (703)823-0252
Fr: 800-347-6647
E-mail: ces@unco.edu
URL: http://www.counseling.org/Publications/Journals.aspx
Quarterly. $53.00/year for nonmembers; $84.00/year for institutions, non-member; print only. Journal covering research in counselor teaching, training, and trends.

3137 ■ *International Journal of Play Therapy*
American Psychological Association
750 1st St. NE
Washington, DC 20002-4242
Ph: (202)336-5500
Fax: (202)336-5549
Fr: 800-374-2721
URL: http://www.apa.org/pubs/journals/pla/index.aspx
Quarterly. $65.00/year for members; $89.00/year for other countries, members; $65.00/year for students; $454.00/year for institutions; $518.00/year for institutions, other countries, by mail; $120.00/year for nonmembers; $149.00/year for other countries, nonmembers. Journal for mental health professionals specializing on play therapy.

3138 ■ *Journal of Career Development*
Sage Publications Inc.
2455 Teller Rd.
Thousand Oaks, CA 91320-2218
Ph: (805)499-9774
Fax: (805)583-2665
Fr: 800-818-7243
URL: http://www.sagepub.com/journalsProdDesc.nav?prodId=Journal20
Quarterly. $719.00/year for institutions, current volume print and online; $654.00/year for institutions, print and e-access; $589.00/year for institutions, e-access; $641.00/year for institutions, print only; $118.00/year for institutions, single print; $23.00/year for individuals, single print. Journal for professionals in counseling, psychology, education, student personnel, human resources, and business management.

3139 ■ *Journal of Counseling Psychology*
American Psychological Association
750 1st St. NE
Washington, DC 20002-4242
Ph: (202)336-5500
Fax: (202)336-5549
Fr: 800-374-2721
E-mail: journals@apa.org
URL: http://www.apa.org/pubs/journals/cou/index.aspx
Quarterly. $55.00/year for members, domestic; $77.00/year for members, foreign, surface; $89.00/year for members, foreign, air mail; $44.00/year for students, domestic; $66.00/year for students, foreign, surface; $78.00/year for students, foreign, air mail; $145.00/year for nonmembers, domestic; $172.00/year for nonmembers, foreign, surface; $183.00/year for nonmembers, foreign, air mail; $415.00/year for institutions, domestic. Journal presenting empirical studies about counseling processes and interventions, theoretical articles about counseling, and studies dealing with evaluation of counseling applications and programs.

3140 ■ *Journal of Family Psychology*
American Psychological Association
750 1st St. NE
Washington, DC 20002-4242
Ph: (202)336-5500
Fax: (202)336-5549
Fr: 800-374-2721
E-mail: journals@apa.org
URL: http://www.apa.org/journals/fam.html
Bimonthly. $55.00/year for members, domestic; $78.00/year for members, surface; $97.00/year for members, airmail; $47.00/year for students, domestic; $70.00/year for students, foreign, surface; $89.00/year for students, foreign, air mail; $156.00/year for nonmembers, domestic; $187.00/year for nonmembers, surface, airmail; $202.00/year for nonmembers, airmail; $465.00/year for institutions, domestic. Journal reporting on theory, research, and clinical

practice in family psychology; including articles on family and marital theory and concepts, research and evaluation, therapeutic frameworks and methods, and policies and legal matters concerning family and marriage.

3141 ■ Journal of Family Psychotherapy
Routledge Journals
270 Madison Ave.
New York, NY 10016-0601
Ph: (212)216-7800
Fax: (212)563-2269
URL: http://www.tandf.co.uk/journals/WJFP

Quarterly. $110.00/year for individuals, online only; $118.00/year for individuals, print + online; $624.00/year for institutions, online only; $693.00/year for institutions, print + online. Journal includes case studies, treatment reports, and strategies in clinical practice for psychotherapists.

3142 ■ Monitor on Psychology
American Psychological Association
750 1st St. NE
Washington, DC 20002-4242
Ph: (202)336-5500
Fax: (202)336-5549
Fr: 800-374-2721
E-mail: journals@apa.org
URL: http://www.apa.org/monitor/

$50.00/year for nonmembers; $99.00/year for individuals, foreign, surface freight; $126.00/year for individuals, foreign, air mail; $93.00/year for institutions; $190.00/year for institutions, surface freight; $217.00/year for institutions, air freight; $20.00/year for single issue. Magazine of the APA. Reports on the science, profession, and social responsibility of psychology, including latest legislative developments affecting mental health, education, and research support.

3143 ■ NACE Journal
National Association of Colleges and Employers
62 Highland Ave.
Bethlehem, PA 18017-9085
Ph: (610)868-1421
Fax: (610)868-0208
Fr: 800-544-5272
URL: http://www.naceweb.org/
KnowledgeCenter.aspx

Quarterly. $70.00/year for individuals, print; $20.00/year for single issue; $25.00/year for other countries, airmail postage; $12.50/year for individuals, additional copies. Journal on career planning, and recruitment of the college educated work force.

3144 ■ National Association of Advisors for the Health Professions-Advisor
National Association of Advisors for the Health Professions Inc.
PO Box 1518
Champaign, IL 61824-1518
Ph: (217)355-0063
Fax: (217)355-1287
E-mail: naahpja@aol.com
URL: http://www.naahp.org/

Description: Quarterly. Intended for college and university faculty who advise undergraduate students on health careers. Focuses on manpower statistics, financial aid, admission procedures, curriculum, advising, recruitment, counseling practice, and ethics. Covers Association and legislative news and announcements from affiliated organizations. Recurring features include interviews, statistics, book reviews, news of research, editorials, opinion, and items on awards, meetings, and membership.

3145 ■ NCC
National Board for Certified Counselors
3 Terrace Way, Ste. D
PO Box 77699
Greensboro, NC 27417-7699
Ph: (336)547-0607

Fax: (336)547-0017
E-mail: nbcc@nbcc.org
URL: http://www.nbcc.org/newsletter

Description: Three issues/year. Includes updates on counselor licensure and continuing education information.

3146 ■ The New Social Worker
White Hat Communications
2001 N Front St., Blvd. 2, Ste. 325
PO Box 5390
Harrisburg, PA 17110-0390
Ph: (717)238-3787
Fax: (717)238-2090
URL: http://www.socialworker.com

Quarterly. $15.00/year for individuals. Publication offering career guidance for social work students.

3147 ■ The NonProfit Times
NPT Publishing Group Inc.
201 Littleton Rd., 2nd Fl.
Morris Plains, NJ 07950
Ph: (973)401-0202
Fax: (973)401-0404
E-mail: ednchief@nptimes.com
URL: http://www.nptimes.com/

$49.95/year for individuals, print; $19.95/year for individuals, digital only; $59.95/year for individuals, digital & print. Trade journal serving nonprofit organizations.

3148 ■ Psychology of Violence
American Psychological Association
750 1st St. NE
Washington, DC 20002-4242
Ph: (202)336-5500
Fax: (202)336-5549
Fr: 800-374-2721
URL: http://www.apa.org/pubs/journals/vio/index.aspx

Quarterly. $65.00/year for members; $89.00/year for other countries, members; $65.00/year for students; $110.00/year for nonmembers; $139.00/year for other countries, nonmembers; $441.00/year for institutions; $490.00/year for institutions, other countries. Multidisciplinary research journal concerning topics on the psychology of violence and extreme aggression.

3149 ■ Spectrum
Association for Counselor Education and Supervision (ACES)
5999 Stevenson Ave.
Alexandria, VA 22304
Ph: (703)212-2237
Fr: (866)815-2237
E-mail: aces@counseling.org
URL: http://www.acesonline.net

Description: Quarterly. Focuses on "the need for quality education and supervision of counselors in all work settings," the accreditation process, and professional development activities for counselors. Recurring features include news of the activities, programs, and members of ACES and related organizations.

3150 ■ Washington Counseletter
Chronicle Guidance Publications Inc.
66 Aurora St.
Moravia, NY 13118-3569
Fax: (315)497-0339
Fr: 800-622-7284
E-mail: customerservice@chronicleguidance.com
URL: http://www.chronicleguidance.com/
store.asp?pid=14382&catid=19626

Description: Monthly. Provides information on new developments in education and the behavioral sciences for guidance counselors. Emphasizes government materials, actions, and issues affecting education. Recurring features include items concerning scholarships, financial aid, and educational and employment opportunities.

EMPLOYER DIRECTORIES AND NETWORKING LISTS

3151 ■ American Group Psychotherapy Association—Membership Directory
American Group Psychotherapy Association Inc.
25 E 21st St., 6th Fl.
New York, NY 10010
Ph: (212)477-2677
Fax: (212)979-6627
Fr: 877-668-2472
URL: http://www.agpa.org

Covers: 4,500 physicians, psychologists, clinical social workers, psychiatric nurses, and other mental health professionals interested in treatment of emotional problems by group methods. Entries include: Name, office or home address, highest degree held, office or home phone number. Arrangement: Alphabetical. Indexes: Geographical.

3152 ■ American Society for Adolescent Psychiatry—Membership Directory
American Society for Adolescent Psychiatry
PO Box 570218
Dallas, TX 75357-0218
Ph: (972)613-0985
Fax: (972)613-5532
URL: http://www.adolpsych.org

Covers: 1,500 members. Entries include: Name, office address and phone, fax, home address and phone (when given). Arrangement: Alphabetical. Indexes: Geographical, chapter.

3153 ■ Boarding Schools Directory
The Association of Boarding Schools
9 SW Pack Sq., Ste. 201
Asheville, NC 28801-3526
Ph: (828)258-5354
Fax: (828)258-6428
URL: http://www.schools.com

Annual, Latest edition 2007-2008. for U.S. and Canada. Covers: Boarding schools that are members of the Association of Boarding Schools. Entries include: School name, address, phone, e-mail and url's, grades for which boarding students are accepted, enrollment, brief description. Arrangement: Classified by type of school. Indexes: Geographical; program; Alphabetical.

3154 ■ Christian Association for Psychological Studies International—Membership Directory
Christian Association for Psychological Studies
PO Box 365
Batavia, IL 60510-0365
Ph: (630)639-9478
Fax: (630)454-3799
URL: http://www.caps.net

Annual, June. $12.00 for Canada; $12.00 for other countries. Covers: 2,300 Christians involved in psychology, psychiatry, counseling, sociology, social work, ministry, and nursing. Entries include: Name, office address and phone number, highest degree held, area of occupational specialization, and career data. Arrangement: Geographical. Indexes: Alphabetical.

3155 ■ Christian Schools International—Directory
Christian Schools International
3350 E Paris Ave. SE
Grand Rapids, MI 49512-2907
Ph: (616)957-1070
Fax: (616)957-5022
Fr: 800-635-8288
URL: http://www.store.csionline.org/index.php?main_page=index&cPath=

Annual, Latest edition 2007-2008. $15.00 for members. Covers: Nearly 450 Reformed Christian elementary and secondary schools; related associations; societies without schools. Entries include: For schools—School name, address, phone; name, title, and address of officers; names of faculty members. Arrangement: Geographical.

3156 ■ Directory of Accredited Counseling Services

International Association of Counseling Services
101 S Whiting St., Ste. 211
Alexandria, VA 22304-3416
Ph: (703)823-9840
Fax: (703)823-9843
URL: http://iacsinc.org/iacsmem.html

Annual, September. $50.00. Covers: About 200 accredited services in the United States and Canada concerned with psychological, educational, and vocational counseling, including those at colleges and universities, and public and private agencies. Entries include: Name, address, phone, hours of operation, director's name, service, clientele served. Arrangement: Geographical.

3157 ■ Directory of Public School Systems in the U.S.

American Association for Employment in Education
3040 Riverside Dr., Ste. 117
Columbus, OH 43221
Ph: (614)485-1111
Fax: (360)244-7802
E-mail: office@aaee.org
URL: http://www.aaee.org/

Annual, Winter; latest edition 2004-2005 edition. $55.00 for members; $80.00 for nonmembers. Covers: About 14,000 public school systems in the United States and their administrative personnel. Entries include: System name, address, phone, website address, name and title of personnel administrator, levels taught and approx. Student population. Arrangement: Geographical by state.

3158 ■ Handbook of Private Schools

Porter Sargent Publishers Inc.
11 Beacon St., Ste. 1400
Boston, MA 02108-3099
Ph: (617)523-1670
Fax: (617)523-1021
Fr: 800-342-7470
URL: http://www.portersargent.com

Annual, latest edition 92nd, 2011-2012. $99.00 for individuals. Covers: More than 1,700 elementary and secondary boarding and day schools in the United States. Entries include: School name, address, phone, fax, E-mail, URL, type of school (boarding or day), sex and age range, names and titles of administrators, grades offered, academic orientation, curriculum, new admissions yearly, tests required for admission, enrollment and faculty, graduate record, number of alumni, tuition and scholarship figures, summer session, plant evaluation and endowment, date of establishment, calendar, association membership, description of school's offerings and history, test score averages, uniform requirements, geographical, and demographic date. Arrangement: Geographical. Indexes: Alphabetical by school name, cross indexed by state, region, grade range, sexes accepted, school features and enrollment.

3159 ■ MDR's School Directories

Market Data Retrieval
6 Armstrong Rd., Ste. 301
Shelton, CT 06484-4722
Ph: (203)926-4800
Fax: (203)926-1826
Fr: 800-333-8802
URL: http://www.schooldata.com/mdrdir.asp

Annual, Latest edition 2008-2009. Covers: Over 90,000 public, 8,000 Catholic, and 15,000 other private schools (grades K-12) in the United States; over 15,000 school district offices, and 76,000 school librarians; and 27,000 media specialists, 33,000 technology coordinators. Includes names of over 165,000 school district administrators and staff members in county and state education administration. Entries include: District name and address; telephone and fax number; number of schools;

number of teachers in the district; district enrollment; special Ed students; limited-English proficient students; minority percentage by race, college bound students; expenditures per student for instructional materials; poverty level; title 1 dollars; site-based management; district open/close dates; construction indicator; technologies and quantities; district-level administrators, *new superintendents shaded*; school name and address—new public shaded; telephone and fax number; principal new principal shaded; librarian, media specialist and technology coordinator; grade span; special programs and school type; student enrollment; technologies and quantities (instructional computer brand noting predominant brand); Multi-Media Computers; Internet connection or access; Tech Sophistication Index. Arrangement: Geographical. Indexes: District County; District Personnel; Principal; New Public Schools and Key Personnel; District and School Telephone; District URLs.

3160 ■ National Directory for Employment in Education

American Association for Employment in Education
3040 Riverside Dr., Ste. 117
Columbus, OH 43221
Ph: (614)485-1111
Fax: (360)244-7802
URL: http://www.aaee.org/

Annual, winter; latest edition 2008-2009. $20.00 for nonmembers; $10.00 for members. Covers: about 600 placement offices maintained by teacher-training institutions and 300 school district personnel officers and/or superintendents responsible for hiring professional staff. Entries include: Institution name, address, phone, contact name, email address, and website. Arrangement: Geographical. Indexes: Personal name, subject-field of teacher training, institutions which provide vacancy bulletins and placement services to non-enrolled students.

3161 ■ National Register

American Association of Sexuality Educators, Counselors, and Therapists
PO Box 1960
Ashland, VA 23005-1960
Fax: (804)752-0056
E-mail: aasect@worldnet.att.net
URL: http://www.aasect.org

Annual. Covers: about 1,600 association members. Entries include: Name, address, phone, highest degree, certification status. Arrangement: Separate geographical sections for educators, therapists, and counselors.

3162 ■ Private Independent Schools

Bunting and Lyon Inc.
615 Broad Swamp Rd.
Cheshire, CT 06410
Ph: (203)668-1897
Fax: (203)269-8908
URL: http://www.buntingandlyon.com

Annual, Latest edition 2010. $115.00 for individuals. Covers: 1,200 English-speaking elementary and secondary private schools and summer programs in North America and abroad. Entries include: School name, address, phone, fax, e-mail, website, enrollment, tuition and other fees, financial aid information, administrator's name and educational background, director of admission, regional accreditation, description of programs, curriculum, activities, learning differences grid. Arrangement: Geographical. Indexes: School name; geographical. Summer programs, general classification grid, learning differences reference grid.

3163 ■ Public Human Services Directory

American Public Human Services Association
1133 19th St., NW, Ste. 400
Washington, DC 20036-3631
Ph: (202)682-0100
Fax: (202)289-6555
URL: http://www.aphsa.org

Annual, Latest edition 2009. $225.00 for individuals;

$200.00 for members; $350.00 for institutions. Covers: Federal, state, territorial, county, and major municipal public human service agencies. Entries include: Agency name, address, phone, fax, e-mail address, web site address, names of key personnel, program area. Arrangement: Geographical.

3164 ■ Requirements for Certification of Teachers, Counselors, Librarians, Administrators for Elementary and Secondary Schools

University of Chicago Press
Journals Division
1427 E 60th St.
Chicago, IL 60637-2954
Ph: (773)702-7636
Fax: (773)702-9756
URL: http://www.press.uchicago.edu

Annual, Latest edition 74th. $53.00. Publication includes: List of state and local departments of education. Entries include: Office name, address, phone. Principal content of publication is summaries of each state's teaching and administrative certification requirements. Arrangement: Geographical.

3165 ■ State Vocational Rehabilitation Agencies

U.S. Office of Special Education and Rehabilitative Services
400 Maryland Ave. SW
Washington, DC 20202-7100
Ph: (202)245-7468
Fax: (202)401-0689
Fr: 800-437-0833
URL: http://www.ed.gov/index.jhtml

Quarterly. Covers: state government agencies responsible for vocational rehabilitation activities. Entries include: Agency name, address, phone, name and title of director, federal Rehabilitation Services Administration region number, fax, tty, and e-mail address. Arrangement: Geographical.

HANDBOOKS AND MANUALS

3166 ■ The Career Counselor's Handbook

Ten Speed Press
6001 Shellmound St.
Emeryville, CA 94608
Ph: (510)285-3000
Fax: (510)285-2979
Fr: 800-841-2665
URL: http://www.randomhouse.com

Richard Nelson Bolles. 2007. $19.99 (2nd ed.). 320 pages. Features an overall view of how career counseling works. Offers advice for counselors and job seekers alike.

3167 ■ Careers for Good Samaritans and Other Humanitarian Types

The McGraw-Hill Companies
PO Box 182604
Columbus, OH 43272
Fax: (614)759-3749
Fr: 877-883-5524
E-mail: customer.service@mcgraw-hill.com
URL: http://www.mhprofessional.com

Marjorie Eberts and Margaret Gisler. Third edition, 2006. $16.95 (paper). 160 pages. Contains hundreds of ideas for turning good work into paid work. Inventories opportunities in service organizations like the Red Cross, Goodwill, and the Salvation Army; religious groups, VISTA, the Peace Corps, and UNICEF; and agencies at all levels of the government. Part of Careers for You series.

3168 ■ Careers in Health Care

The McGraw-Hill Companies
PO Box 182604
Columbus, OH 43272
Fax: (614)759-3749

Fr: 877-883-5524
E-mail: customer.service@mcgraw-hill.com
URL: http://www.mhprofessional.com/
    product.php?isbn=0071466533

Barbara M. Swanson. Fifth edition, 2005. $19.95 (paper). 192 pages. Describes job duties, work settings, salaries, licensing and certification requirements, educational preparation, and future outlook. Gives ideas on how to secure a job.

3169 ■ Careers in Social and Rehabilitation Services

The McGraw-Hill Companies
PO Box 182604
Columbus, OH 43272
Fax: (614)759-3749
Fr: 877-883-5524
E-mail: customer.service@mcgraw-hill.com
URL: http://www.mhprofessional.com/
    product.php?isbn=0071641955

Geraldine O. Garner. 2008. $16.95. 192 pages.

3170 ■ Clinical Supervision in Alcohol and Drug Abuse Counseling: Principles, Models, Methods

Jossey-Bass
989 Market St.
San Francisco, CA 94103
Ph: (415)433-1740
Fax: (415)433-0499
Fr: 800-255-5945
E-mail: custserv@wiley.com
URL: http://www.josseybass.com/WileyCDA/

David J. Powell, Archie Brodsky. 2004. $51.50. 448 pages.

3171 ■ Employment and Training Counselor

National Learning Corporation
212 Michael Dr.
Syosset, NY 11791
Ph: (516)921-8888
Fax: (516)921-8743
Fr: 800-632-8888
URL: http://www.passbooks.com/

Jack Rudman. 2005. $34.95. Career explorations.

3172 ■ Great Jobs for Liberal Arts Majors

The McGraw-Hill Companies
PO Box 182604
Columbus, OH 43272
Fax: (614)759-3749
Fr: 877-883-5524
E-mail: customer.service@mcgraw-hill.com
URL: http://www.mhprofessional.com/
    product.php?isbn=0071482148

Blythe Camenson. Second edition, 2007. $16.95 (paper). 192 pages.

3173 ■ Guidance Counselor, Elementary School

National Learning Corporation
212 Michael Dr.
Syosset, NY 11791
Ph: (516)921-8888
Fax: (516)921-8743
Fr: 800-632-8888
URL: http://www.passbooks.com/

Jack Rudman. 2005. $29.95. 204 pages

3174 ■ Opportunities in Health and Medical Careers

The McGraw-Hill Companies
PO Box 182604
Columbus, OH 43272
Fax: (614)759-3749
Fr: 877-883-5524
E-mail: customer.service@mcgraw-hill.com
URL: http://www.mhprofessional.com/
    product.php?isbn=0071437274

I. Donald Snook, Jr. and Leo D'Orazio. 2004. $14.95 (paper). 157 pages. Covers the full range of medical and health occupations. Illustrated.

3175 ■ The Secrets to Being a Great School Counselor

CreateSpace
7290 B. Investment Dr.
Charleston, SC 29418
E-mail: info@createspace.com
URL: http://www.createspace.com

Richard P. O'Connell. 2011. $24.95 (paper). 405 pages. Features strategies, approaches, and organizational skills that help make an effective school counselor. Includes anecdotes that provide real-life applications.

ONLINE JOB SOURCES AND SERVICES

3176 ■ CounselingCrossing.com

URL: http://www.counselingcrossing.com

Description: Offers instant access to a comprehensive pool of job listings in the counseling field. Shows jobs from employer career pages, job websites, association websites, newspaper classified ads and recruiter sites.

3177 ■ Delta T Group

E-mail: cfassl@deltatg.com
URL: http://www.delta-tgroup.com

Description: Specialized contract temporary staffing source for healthcare professionals in the fields of social service, psychiatry, mental health, and substance abuse. Organizations may request services and staffing; job seekers may view services provided, submit a resume, or peruse jobs available.

3178 ■ Get School Counselor Jobs

URL: http://www.getschoolcounselorjobs.com

Description: Serves as a one-stop resource for finding and filling school counselor positions.

3179 ■ RehabWorld.com

URL: http://www.rehabworld.com

Description: Site for rehabilitation professionals to learn about the profession and locate jobs. Includes user groups, salary surveys, and chat capabilities. Main files include: Physical Therapy, Occupational Therapy, Speech Therapy, Mental Health, Employer World, Student World, International World, Forum.

3180 ■ School Counselor Jobs

URL: http://www.schoolcounselorjobs.org

Description: Features listings for school counselor employment opportunities and candidate recruiting.

3181 ■ StudentAffairs.com

URL: http://www.studentaffairs.com

Description: Serves as an online guide for college student affairs professionals. Maintains position listings, online exhibit hall, conference center, online courses, and an online e-journal.

TRADESHOWS

3182 ■ American Counseling Association Conference and Exposition

American Counseling Association
5999 Stevenson Ave.
Alexandria, VA 22304-3300
Fax: 800-473-2329
Fr: 800-347-6647
E-mail: membership@counseling.org
URL: http://www.counseling.org

Annual. Primary Exhibits: Books, career development information, college selection, student financial aid, testing and measurement techniques, practice management companies, software, rehabilitation aids, and community agencies and private clinics specializing in substance abuse and mental health. Dates and Locations: 2012 Mar 21-25; San Francisco, CA.

3183 ■ Association for Counselor Education and Supervision National Conference

Association for Counselor Education and Supervision
5999 Stevenson Ave.
Alexandria, VA 22304
Ph: (703)212-2237
Fr: (866)815-2237
URL: http://www.acesonline.net

Annual. Primary Exhibits: Exhibits relating to the professional preparation of counselors.

OTHER SOURCES

3184 ■ Alliance for Children and Families

11700 W Lake Park Dr.
Milwaukee, WI 53224-3099
Ph: (414)359-1040
Fax: (414)359-1074
E-mail: severson@alliance1.org
URL: http://www.alliance1.org

Description: Membership organization of local agencies in thousands of communities providing family counseling, family life education, residential treatment, and family advocacy services, and other programs to help families with parent-child, marital, mental health, and other problems. Assists member agencies in developing capacity and maintaining high performance. Compiles statistics; conducts research. Maintains extensive files of unpublished materials from member agencies.

3185 ■ American Association of Psychiatric Technicians (AAPT)

1220 S St., Ste. 100
Sacramento, CA 95811-7138
Fax: (916)329-9145
Fr: 800-391-7589
E-mail: aapt@psychtechs.net
URL: http://www.psychtechs.org

Description: Administers the Nationally Certified Psychiatric Technician examination to non-licensed direct-care workers in the fields of mental illness, developmental disabilities and substance abuse.

3186 ■ American College Counseling Association (ACCA)

5999 Stevenson Ave.
Alexandria, VA 22304-3300
Ph: (703)823-9800
Fax: (703)823-0252
Fr: 800-347-6647
E-mail: brian.vanbrunt@wku.edu
URL: http://www.collegecounseling.org

Description: Works to advance the practice of college counseling. Promotes ethical practice and communication among members; encourages cooperation with other related organizations; provides advocacy for the profession.

3187 ■ American College of Counselors (ACC)

273 Glossip Ave.
Highlandville, MO 65669-8133
Ph: (417)885-4030
Fax: (417)443-3002
URL: http://acconline.us

Description: Represents individuals who are active in counseling in related fields of human services. Fosters values that enrich human growth and development. Works to establish guidelines and standards that will be in common with all specialties. Aims to increase knowledge and awareness of complex behavioral and emotional problems. Promotes objectivity and integrity; high standards of inquiry and communication; responsibility and competence in objectively reporting findings.

3188 ■ American College Personnel Association (ACPA)

1 Dupont Cir. NW, Ste. 300
Washington, DC 20036-1188

Ph: (202)835-2272
Fax: (202)296-3286
E-mail: info@acpa.nche.edu
URL: http://www.acpa.nche.edu

Description: Represents individuals employed in higher education and involved in student personnel work, including administration, counseling, research, and teaching. Fosters student development in higher education in areas of service, advocacy, and standards by offering professional programs for educators committed to the overall development of postsecondary students. Sponsors professional and educational activities in cooperation with other organizations. Offers placement services.

3189 ■ American Counseling Association (ACA)
5999 Stevenson Ave.
Alexandria, VA 22304
Fax: (703)823-0252
Fr: 800-347-6647
E-mail: ryep@counseling.org
URL: http://www.counseling.org

Description: Counseling professionals in elementary and secondary schools, higher education, community agencies and organizations, rehabilitation programs, government, industry, business, private practice, career counseling, and mental health counseling. Conducts professional development institutes and provides liability insurance. Maintains Counseling and Human Development Foundation to fund counseling projects.

3190 ■ American Family Therapy Academy (AFTA)
1608 20th St. NW, 4th Fl.
Washington, DC 20009
Ph: (202)483-8001
Fax: (202)483-8002
E-mail: afta@afta.org
URL: http://www.afta.org

Description: Family therapy teachers, researchers, and practitioners working to advance theory and therapy that regards the family as a unit. Promotes research and professional education in family therapy and allied fields. Disseminates information to practitioners, scientists, and the public. Focuses on improving the knowledge of how families function and how to treat them.

3191 ■ American Mental Health Alliance (AMHA)
PO Box 4075
Portland, OR 97208-4075
Ph: (503)227-2027
Fr: 888-826-3682
E-mail: memberinfo@americanmentalhealth.com
URL: http://www.americanmentalhealth.com

Description: Represents mental health professionals licensed or certified for independent practice. Creates a professional community that provides therapy of the highest quality and ethical standards. Supports and markets competent, ethical mental health services that preserve privacy and confidentiality. Supports education, supervision, and research opportunities for members. Opposes legislation and regulations that invade patent privacy and confidentiality.

3192 ■ American Mental Health Counselors Association (AMHCA)
801 N Fairfax St., Ste. 304
Alexandria, VA 22314
Ph: (703)548-6002
Fax: (703)548-4775
Fr: 800-326-2642
E-mail: mhamilton@amhca.org
URL: http://www.amhca.org

Description: Professional counselors employed in mental health services; students. Aims to: deliver quality mental health services to children, youth, adults, families, and organizations; improve the availability and quality of counseling services through licensure and certification, training standards, and consumer advocacy. Supports specialty and special

interest networks. Fosters communication among members. A division of the American Counseling Association.

3193 ■ American Psychiatric Nurses Association
1555 Wilson Blvd., Ste. 530
Arlington, VA 22209
Ph: (703)243-2443
Fax: (703)243-3390
Fr: (866)243-2443
E-mail: ncroce@apna.org
URL: http://www.apna.org

Description: Represents psychiatric nurses who are at all levels of education from basic to doctoral and work in a variety of settings including inpatient, outpatient, research, education, administration, clinical, private practice, military, and forensic.

3194 ■ American Psychological Association (APA)
750 First St. NE
Washington, DC 20002-4242
Ph: (202)336-5500
Fax: (202)336-6069
Fr: 800-374-2721
E-mail: president@apa.org
URL: http://www.apa.org

Description: Scientific and professional society of psychologists; students participate as affiliates. Advances psychology as a science, a profession, and as a means of promoting health, education and the human welfare.

3195 ■ American School Counselor Association (ASCA)
1101 King St., Ste. 625
Alexandria, VA 22314
Ph: (703)683-2722
Fax: (703)683-1619
Fr: 800-306-4722
E-mail: asca@schoolcounselor.org
URL: http://www.schoolcounselor.org

Description: Supports school counselors' efforts to help students focus on academic, personal/social and career development so they not only achieve success in school but are prepared to lead fulfilling lives as responsible members of society; provides professional development, publications and other resources, research and advocacy, governmental and public relations. Serves as liaison among members and counselors in other settings; disseminates educational, professional, and scientific materials.

3196 ■ Art Therapy Connection (ATC)
1800 Ridge Ave., Unit 211
Evanston, IL 60201
E-mail: info@arttherapyconnection.net
URL: http://www.arttherapyconnection.net

Description: Promotes art therapy as a form of psychotherapy. Works with children and teenagers to develop self-awareness and self-management skills by integrating art and creativity with therapy. Increases the concentration levels, self-control and interpersonal skills of youth and children.

3197 ■ Association for Counselor Education and Supervision (ACES)
5999 Stevenson Ave.
Alexandria, VA 22304
Ph: (703)212-2237
Fr: (866)815-2237
E-mail: aces@counseling.org
URL: http://www.acesonline.net

Description: Represents the interests of persons engaged in the professional preparation of counselors or who are responsible for supervising professional counselors in a wide variety of work settings. Works to improve the education, credentialing and supervision of counselors through accreditation and professional development activities. Disseminates information on current and relevant research, practices, ethical standards and problems related to the profession.

Maintains archives on counselor education and supervision.

3198 ■ Association for Counselors and Educators in Government (ACEG)
5999 Stevenson Ave.
Alexandria, VA 22304-3300
Fax: 800-473-2329
Fr: 800-347-6647
E-mail: donald.hill8@us.army.mil
URL: http://www.dantes.doded.mil/dantes_web/organizations/aceg/index.htm

Description: Professional counselors who work in the U.S. Armed Services. Encourages and provides counseling to individuals in the service and their dependents, veterans, and civilians employed by the military. Promotes and maintains improved communication with the non-military community. Provides representation for counseling and education professionals working in and for the U.S. Department of Defense. Offers programs to enhance individual growth and development.

3199 ■ Association on Higher Education and Disability (AHEAD)
107 Commerce Center Dr., Ste. 204
Huntersville, NC 28078
Ph: (704)947-7779
Fax: (704)948-7779
E-mail: ahead@ahead.org
URL: http://www.ahead.org

Description: Individuals interested in promoting the equal rights and opportunities of disabled postsecondary students, staff, faculty, and graduates. Provides an exchange of communication for those professionally involved with disabled students; collects, evaluates, and disseminates information; encourages and supports legislation for the benefit of disabled students. Conducts surveys on issues pertinent to college students with disabilities; offers resource referral system and employment exchange for positions in disability student services. Conducts research programs; compiles statistics.

3200 ■ Association for Humanistic Counseling
PO Box 791006
Baltimore, MD 21279-1006
Ph: (703)823-9800
Fax: 800-473-2329
Fr: 800-347-6647
E-mail: cmalchiodi@insightbb.com
URL: http://www.c-ahead.com

Description: A division of the American Counseling Association. Teachers, educational administrators, community agency workers, counselors, school social workers, and psychologists; others interested in the area of human development. Aims to assist individuals in improving their quality of life. Provides forum for the exchange of information about humanistically-oriented administrative and instructional practices. Supports humanistic practices and research on instructional and organizational methods for facilitating humanistic education; encourages cooperation among related professional groups.

3201 ■ Association for Specialists in Group Work (ASGW)
Indiana University-Purdue University Fort Wayne
2101 E Coliseum Blvd.
Fort Wayne, IN 46805-1499
Fr: 800-347-6647
E-mail: nitzaa@ipfw.edu
URL: http://www.asgw.org

Description: A division of the American Counseling Association. Individuals interested in group counseling holding master's or doctoral degrees, and engaged in practice, teaching, or research in group work; persons holding undergraduate degrees who are interested in group work, but not actively engaged in practice, teaching, or research; students. Seeks to assist and further interests of children, youth, and adults by providing effective services through the group medium, preventing problems, providing maximum development, and remediating disabling behaviors. Sponsors programs to advance group work in schools, clinics, universities, private practice, and mental health institutions. Conducts placement service.

3202 ■ Employee Assistance Society of North America (EASNA)
2001 Jefferson Davis Hwy., Ste. 1004
Arlington, VA 22202-3617
Ph: (703)416-0060
Fax: (703)416-0014
E-mail: bmclean@easna.org
URL: http://www.easna.org

Description: Individuals in the field of employee assistance, including psychiatrists, psychologists, and managers. Facilitates communication among members; provides resource information; serves as a network for employee assistance programs nationwide. Conducts research.

3203 ■ Family Therapy Section of the National Council on Family Relations (FTSNCFR)
1201 W River Pkwy., Ste. 200
Minneapolis, MN 55454
Ph: (763)231-2891
Fax: (763)781-9348
Fr: 888-781-9331
E-mail: blume@oakland.edu
URL: http://www.ncfr.org/sections/ft

Description: A section of the National Council on Family Relations. Practicing family therapists and family therapy supervisors, educators, and researchers. Seeks to improve the practice of family therapy through the development of theory, research, and training. Promotes communication between family therapy researchers and clinicians; functions as a network for family therapy research projects; conducts educational programs.

3204 ■ International Association of Biblical Counselors (IABC)
11500 Sheridan Blvd.
Westminster, CO 80020
Ph: (303)469-4222
E-mail: information@iabc.net
URL: http://www.iabc.net

Description: Represents organizations and individuals who saw the need for basic standards, beliefs and practices in counseling. Promotes Biblical Counseling through seminars, conferences and workshops. Encourages the development of Biblical research and offers a counselor network for the exchange of information and client referral.

3205 ■ International Association of Counselors and Therapists (IACT)
8852 SR 3001
Laceyville, PA 18623
Ph: (570)869-1021
Fax: (570)869-1249
Fr: 800-553-6886
E-mail: info@iact.org
URL: http://www.iact.org

Description: Mental health professionals, medical professionals, social workers, clergy, educators, hypnotherapists, counselors, and individuals interested in the helping professions. Promotes enhanced professional image and prestige for complementary therapy. Provides a forum for exchange of information and ideas among practitioners of traditional and nontraditional therapies and methodologies; fosters unity among "grassroots" practitioners and those with advanced academic credentials. Facilitates the development of new therapy programs. Conducts educational, research, and charitable programs. Awards credits for continuing education. Maintains speakers' bureau and library; operates referral and placement services; compiles statistics. Assists in the development of local chapters.

3206 ■ The International Educator (TIE)
PO Box 513
Cummaquid, MA 02637
Ph: (508)790-1990
Fax: (508)790-1922
Fr: 877-375-6668
E-mail: tie@tieonline.com
URL: http://www.tieonline.com

Description: Facilitates the placement of teachers and administrators in American, British, and international schools. Seeks to create a network that provides for professional development opportunities and improved financial security of members. Offers advice and information on international school news, recent educational developments, job placement, and investment, consumer, and professional development opportunities. Makes available insurance and travel benefits. Operates International Schools Internship Program.

3207 ■ International Mentoring Network Organization (IMNO)
766 E 560 N, No. 206
Provo, UT 84606
Ph: (801)361-9942
E-mail: contact@imno.org
URL: http://www.imno.org/imno.asp

Description: Aims to solve the worldwide need for professional mentoring. Serves as an open source mentoring movement. Gives help and direction to the career development of aspiring professionals.

3208 ■ National Academic Advising Association (NACADA)
Kansas State University
2323 Anderson Ave., Ste. 225
Manhattan, KS 66502-2912
Ph: (785)532-5717
Fax: (785)532-7732
E-mail: nacada@ksu.edu
URL: http://www.nacada.ksu.edu

Description: Academic program advisors, faculty, administrators, counselors, and others concerned with the intellectual, personal, and career development of students in all types of postsecondary educational institutions. Works to support and promotes professional growth of academic advising and academic advisers. Provides a forum for discussion, debate, and exchange of ideas regarding academic advising. Serves as advocate for standards and quality programs in academic advising. Operates consultants' bureau to assist advising services on college campuses. Maintains placement service, speakers' bureau, and information clearinghouse.

3209 ■ National Association for College Admission Counseling
1050 N Highland St., Ste. 400
Arlington, VA 22201
Ph: (703)836-2222
Fax: (703)243-9375
Fr: 800-822-6285
E-mail: info@nacacnet.org
URL: http://www.nacacnet.org

Description: Comprised of secondary-school counselors, independent counselors, college admission and financial aid officers, enrollment managers, and organizations engaged in guiding students through the secondary-to-higher-education transition process. Supports and advances the work of counseling and enrollment professionals as they help all students realize their full educational potential, with particular emphasis on the transition to postsecondary education. Promotes high professional standards that foster ethical and social responsibility.

3210 ■ National Career Development Association (NCDA)
305 N Beech Cir.
Broken Arrow, OK 74012
Ph: (918)663-7060
Fax: (918)663-7058

Fr: (866)367-6232
E-mail: dpennington@ncda.org
URL: http://associationdatabase.com/aws/NCDA/pt/sp/Home_Page

Description: Represents professionals and others interested in career development or counseling in various work environments. Supports counselors, education and training personnel, and allied professionals working in schools, colleges, business/industry, community and government agencies, and in private practice. Provides publications, support for state and local activities, human equity programs, and continuing education and training for these professionals. Provides networking opportunities for career professionals in business, education, and government.

3211 ■ National Council for Accreditation of Teacher Education (NCATE)
2010 Massachusetts Ave. NW, Ste. 500
Washington, DC 20036
Ph: (202)466-7496
Fax: (202)296-6620
E-mail: ncate@ncate.org
URL: http://www.ncate.org

Description: Representatives from constituent colleges and universities, state departments of education, school boards, teacher, and other professional groups. Voluntary accrediting body devoted exclusively to: evaluation and accreditation of institutions for preparation of elementary and secondary school teachers; preparation of school service personnel, including school principals, supervisors, superintendents, school psychologists, instructional technologists, and other specialists for school-oriented positions.

3212 ■ National Council on Rehabilitation Education (NCRE)
497 N Clovis Ave., Ste. 202
Clovis, CA 93611
Ph: (559)906-0787
Fax: (559)412-2550
E-mail: info@rehabeducators.org
URL: http://www.rehabeducators.org

Description: Represents academic institutions and organizations, professional educators, researchers, and students. Seeks to: assist in the documentation of the effect of education in improving services to persons with disability; determine the skills and training necessary for effective rehabilitation services; develop models, standards, and uniform licensure and certification requirements for rehabilitation personnel; interact with consumers and public and private sector policy makers. Disseminates information and provides forum for discussion. Sponsors specialized education and placement service. Compiles statistics. Works closely with agencies and associations serving persons with disabilities.

3213 ■ National Employment Counseling Association (NECA)
6836 Bee Cave Rd., Ste. 260
Austin, TX 78746
Fr: 800-347-6647
E-mail: kimberly@encompasswf.com
URL: http://www.employmentcounseling.org

Description: Serves as a division of the American Counseling Association. Represents individuals who are engaged in employment counseling, counselor education, research, administration or supervision in business and industry, colleges and universities, and federal and state governments; students. Offers professional leadership and development services; provides opportunities for professional growth through workshops and special projects.

3214 ■ National Rehabilitation Association (NRA)
633 S Washington St.
Alexandria, VA 22314
Ph: (703)836-0850

Fax: (703)836-0848
E-mail: info@nationalrehab.org
URL: http://www.nationalrehab.org

Description: Provides opportunities through knowledge and diversity for professionals in the fields of rehabilitation of people with disabilities.

3215 ■ National Rehabilitation Counseling Association (NRCA)
PO Box 4480
Manassas, VA 20108
Ph: (703)361-2077
Fax: (703)361-2489
E-mail: info@nrca-net.org
URL: http://nrca-net.org

Description: An independent Association of Professional and student rehabilitation counselors. Works to expand the role of counselors in the rehabilitation process and seeks to advance members' professional development. Supports legislation favoring the profession.

3216 ■ *Overseas Employment Opportunities for Educators: Department of Defense Dependents Schools*
DIANE Publishing Co.
PO Box 617
Darby, PA 19023-0617
Fr: 800-782-3833
URL: http://www.dianepublishing.net

Barry Leonard, editor. $20.00. 52 pages. An introduction to teachings positions in the Dept. of Defense Dependents Schools (DoDDS), a worldwide school system, operated by the DoD in 14 countries.

3217 ■ Society for Vocational Psychology (SVP)
Southern Illinois University at Carbondale
Dept. of Psychology
Life Science II, Rm. 222C
Carbondale, IL 62901
Ph: (618)453-3573
E-mail: rpatrick@siu.edu
URL: http://www.div17.org/vocpsych

Description: Encourages, promotes and facilitates contributions to research, teaching, practice and public interest in vocational psychology and career interventions. Promotes quality research and practice of vocational psychology and career counseling. Supports the diversity of characteristics, work settings, roles and activities of counselling psychologists involved in vocational psychology and career intervention.

Sources of Help-Wanted Ads

3218 ■ *Homeland Response*
Penton Media Inc.
249 W 17th St.
New York, NY 10011
Ph: (212)204-4200
URL: http://www.respondersafetyonline.com/
Bimonthly. Magazine covering homeland security.

3219 ■ *International Counterterrorism & Security*
Counterterrorism & Security Inc.
PO Box 10265
Arlington, VA 22210
Ph: (703)243-0993
Fax: (703)243-1197
URL: http://www.iacsp.com/publications.php
Quarterly. Journal covering terrorism and security analysis.

3220 ■ *Studies in Conflict and Terrorism*
Routledge
711 3 Ave., 8 Fl.
New York, NY 10016
Ph: (212)216-7800
Fax: (212)563-2269
Fr: 800-634-7064
URL: http://www.tandf.co.uk/journals/titles/1057610x.asp
$478.00/year for individuals, print only; $1,251.00/year for individuals, online only; $1,390.00/year for individuals, print and online. Journal publishing research on all forms of conflict and terrorism.

Placement and Job Referral Services

3221 ■ *Security and Investigative Placement*
7710 Woodmont Ave., No. 209
Bethesda, MD 20814
Ph: (301)229-6360
E-mail: klavinder@siplacement.com
URL: http://www.siplacement.com
Places professionals in security and investigation positions within corporate, financial, legal, accounting and consulting firms. Candidates possess backgrounds in financial investigation, fraud, anti-money laundering, forensic accounting, investigative research, computer forensics and cyber investigation, security management, threat assessment, and global risk mitigation.

Employer Directories and Networking Lists

3222 ■ *Counterterrorism*
ABC-CLIO
PO Box 1911
Santa Barbara, CA 93102-1911

Ph: (805)968-1911
Fax: (866)270-3856
Fr: 800-368-6868
URL: http://www.abc-clio.com

Latest edition 2004. $55.00 for individuals. Covers: The wave of terrorism in the post-Cold War era and the ways in which states and societies are responding.

Handbooks and Manuals

3223 ■ *Counterterrorism Handbook: Tactics, Procedures, and Techniques, 3rd Ed.*
CRC Press
6000 Broken Sound Pkwy., Ste. 300
Boca Raton, FL 33487
Ph: (561)994-0555
Fax: 800-374-3401
Fr: 800-272-7737
URL: http://www.crcpress.com/product/isbn/9780849330230

Frank Bolz, Jr., Kenneth J. Dudonis, and David P. Schulz. 2005. $78.36. 432 pages. Experts provide information to assist in understanding tactics, strategies and techniques to counter terrorism; topics include all aspects of terrorism, bomb threats, risk assessment, hostage situations, and weapons of mass destruction. Part of the Practical Aspects of Criminal and Forensic Investigations series, Volume 41.

3224 ■ *Democracy and Counterterrorism: Lessons from the Past*
United States Institute of Peace Press
2301 Constitution Ave. NW
Washington, DC 20037
Ph: (202)457-1700
Fax: (202)429-6063
URL: http://bookstore.usip.org/books/BookDetail.aspx?productID=146835

Robert J. Art and Louise Richardson. January 2007. $65.00 hardcopy, $28 (paper). 481 pages. A comparative study of the policies, strategies, and instruments used by various democratic governments in the fight against terrorism.

3225 ■ *First Responder Chem-Bio Handbook*
Tempest Publishing
PO Box 22572
Alexandria, VA 22304-9257
Ph: (703)370-2962
Fax: (703)370-1571
E-mail: info@tempestpublishing.com
URL: http://www.chem-bio.com

$49.00 CD-ROM. Provides critical information to help analysts counter chem-bio terrorism threats. Also available in CD-ROM which contains fully searchable and indexed electronic versions of the handbook.

3226 ■ *Terror on the Internet: The New Arena, the New Challenges*
United States Institute of Peace Press
2301 Constitution Ave. NW
Washington, DC 20037
Ph: (202)457-1700
Fax: (202)429-6063
URL: http://bookstore.usip.org/books/BookDetail.aspx?productID=134280

Gabriel Weimann. April 2006. $20.00. 320 pages. Examination of the new psychology of terrorists and the ways in which they use the Internet to accomplish their goals.

3227 ■ *The War of Ideas: Jihadism against Democracy*
Palgrave Macmillan
175 Fifth Ave.
New York, NY 10010
Ph: (646)307-5151
URL: http://us.macmillan.com/thewarofideas/WalidPhares

Required reading for senior intelligence managers to help understand the game plan, goals and denial and deception of Jihadism against the U.S.

Online Job Sources and Services

3228 ■ *ClearedConnections.com*
URL: http://www.clearedconnections.com

Online resource lists jobs for those security-cleared professionals including counterintelligence specialists.

3229 ■ *CollegeRecruiter.com*
URL: http://www.collegerecruiter.com

Job listings.

3230 ■ *IntelligenceCareers.com*
Fax: (703)995-0863
Fr: 800-919-8284
E-mail: customerservice@intelligencecareers.com
URL: http://www.intelligencecareers.com

Provides an online job search for intelligence positions by state, U.S. Forces overseas, and worldwide.

3231 ■ *US Army Recruiting Command: GoArmy.com*
URL: http://www.goarmy.com

Online resource lists jobs, particularly those in the field of counterintelligence.

3232 ■ *USADefenseIndustryJobs.com*
E-mail: resumes@defensecareers.com
URL: http://usadefenseindustryjobs.com

Provides an online job search for intelligence positions with the American defense industry.

TRADESHOWS

3233 ■ AFCEA Intelligence Annual Fall and Spring Classified Symposia
4400 Fair Lakes Ct.
Fairfax, VA 22033
Ph: (703)631-6219
Fax: (703)631-6133
URL: http://www.afcea.org

U.S. intelligence professionals in government and industry explore issues involving the challenges and opportunities in the intelligence community as well as national security issues.

3234 ■ International Association of Crime Analysts Annual Training Conference
9218 Metcalf Ave., Ste. 364
Overland Park, KS 66212
Fr: 800-609-3419
E-mail: iaca@iaca.net
URL: http://www.iaca.net

Annual. Focuses on training in the areas of analysis and law enforcement and offers the IACA Certification Exam. 2012 September 10-13; Henderson, NV; The Ravella.

OTHER SOURCES

3235 ■ AFCEA Intelligence
4400 Fair Lakes Ct.
Fairfax, VA 22033-3899
Ph: (703)631-6219
Fax: (703)631-6133
URL: http://www.afcea.org/mission/intel

As part of the AFCEA International, the Association was established in 1981 to enhance outreach to the U.S. Intelligence Community and to support intelligence professionals in the government, military and private sector.

3236 ■ Association of Former Intelligence Officers (AFIO)
6723 Whittier Ave., Ste. 200
McLean, VA 22101-4533
Ph: (703)790-0320
Fax: (703)991-1278
E-mail: afio@afio.com
URL: http://www.afio.com

Description: Represents educational association of current and former intelligence professionals, security and counterterrorism practitioners and some U.S. citizens. Enhances public understanding of the role and importance of intelligence for national security, counterterrorism and to deal with threats in the contemporary world. Engages in career guidance for young people who are interested in intelligence or homeland security careers.

3237 ■ Central Intelligence Agency
Office of Public Affairs
Washington, DC 20505
Ph: (703)482-0623
Fax: (703)482-1739
URL: http://www.cia.gov

Independent United States government agency providing national security intelligence to senior U.S. policymakers.

3238 ■ Central Valley Crime and Intelligence Analysts Association
c/o Kim Miller
PO Box 20756
Bakersfield, CA 93390
Ph: (661)391-7466
E-mail: info@cvciaa.org
URL: http://cvciaa.org

Works to enhance crime and intelligence analysis as a tool in law enforcement.

3239 ■ Centre for Counterintelligence and Security System
PO Box 11221
Alexandria, VA 22312
Ph: (703)642-7450
Fax: (703)642-7451
Fr: 800-779-4007
URL: http://cicentre.com

Provides advanced counterintelligence, counterterrorism and security training, analysis and consulting.

3240 ■ IntelCenter
PO Box 22572
Alexandria, VA 22304-9257
Ph: (703)370-2962
Fax: (703)370-1571
E-mail: info@intelcenter.com
URL: http://www.intelcenter.com

Assists intelligence, counterterrorism and first responder professionals to prevent every act of terrorism, including the use of biological agents, chemical weapons, dirty devices or hijacked airliners. The firm studies terrorist groups and other threat actors as well as capabilities and intentions, warnings and indicators, operational characteristics and other points to better understand how to interdict terrorist operations and reduce the likelihood of future attacks.

3241 ■ International Association of Crime Analysts
9218 Metcalf Ave., Ste. 364
Overland Park, KS 66212
Fr: 800-609-3419
E-mail: iaca@iaca.net
URL: http://www.iaca.net

Crime analysts, intelligence analysts, police officers of all ranks, educators and students.

3242 ■ International Association of Law Enforcement Intelligence Analysts
PO Box 13857
Richmond, VA 23225
Fax: (804)565-2059
E-mail: admin@ialeia.org
URL: http://www.ialeia.org

Promotes the development and enhancement of law enforcement intelligence analysts.

3243 ■ International Counter-Terrorism Officers Association (ICTOA)
PO Box 580009
Flushing, NY 11358
Ph: (212)564-5048

Fax: (718)661-4044
E-mail: info@ictoa.org
URL: http://www.ictoa.org

Description: Promotes unity to combat and understand terrorism. Provides training, education and networking to enhance terrorism awareness. Supports members with advanced counter-terrorism measures. Ensures safety and security through international networking.

3244 ■ Law Enforcement Intelligence Unit
4949 Broadway
Sacramento, CA 95820
Ph: (916)227-7881
E-mail: leiu@doj.ca.gov
URL: http://leiu.org

Provides leadership and promotes professionalism in the criminal intelligence community.

3245 ■ Memorial Institute for the Prevention of Terrorism
621 N Robinson Ave., 4th Fl.
PO Box 889
Oklahoma City, OK 73102
Ph: (405)278-6300
Fax: (405)232-5132
URL: http://www.mipt.org

Works to provide information about terrorism prevention and responder preparedness to better understand existing and growing terrorist threats.

3246 ■ National Geospatial-Intelligence Agency
Office of Corporate Communications
Public Affairs Branch, MS N73-OCCAE
7500 GEOINT Dr.
Springfield, VA 22150-7500
E-mail: recruitment@nga.mil
URL: http://www.nga.mil

Provides timely, relevant and accurate geospatial intelligence in support of national security.

3247 ■ Student Association on Terrorism and Security Analysis
402 MacNaughton Hall
Syracuse, NY 13244-1030
E-mail: satsa@maxwell.syr.edu
URL: http://satsa.us

Dedicated to the critical analysis of terrorism, counterterrorism policy, and national and international security issues.

3248 ■ United States Institute of Peace
2301 Constitution Ave., NW
Washington, DC 20037
Ph: (202)457-1700
Fax: (202)429-6063
URL: http://www.usip.org

Independent, nonpartisan, national institution funded by Congress to help prevent, manage and resolve threats to security and development worldwide, including interstate wars, internal armed conflicts, ethnic and religious strife, extremism, terrorism, and the proliferation of weapons of mass destruction.

SOURCES OF HELP-WANTED ADS

3249 ■ American Shipper
American Shipper
200 W Forsyth St., Ste. 1000
Jacksonville, FL 32202
Ph: (904)355-2601
Fax: (904)791-8836
Fr: 800-874-6422
URL: http://www.americanshipper.com

Monthly. $36.00/year for individuals. Transportation and shipping magazine.

3250 ■ OAG Air Cargo Guide
OAG Worldwide
3025 Highland Pky., Ste. 200
Downers Grove, IL 60515-5561
Ph: (630)515-5300
Fax: (630)515-5301
Fr: 888-589-6340
URL: http://www.oag.com

Monthly. Guide to shipping freight by air containing current domestic, international and combination passenger cargo flight schedules.

EMPLOYER DIRECTORIES AND NETWORKING LISTS

3251 ■ Air Cargo World—Express Delivery Guide Issue
Air Cargo World
1080 Holcomb Bridge Rd.
Roswell Summit, Bldg. 200, Ste. 255
Roswell, GA 30076
Ph: (770)642-9170
Fax: (770)642-9982
URL: http://www.aircargoworld.com/Resources/Air-Express

Annual, Latest edition 2009. Publication includes: List of approximately 200 air and truck express carriers. Entries include: Company name, address, contact person, phone, telex, services offered, mode of transportation, maximum size of package, method of payment, areas served. Arrangement: Alphabetical. Indexes: Organization name.

3252 ■ DACA Directory
Distributors & Consolidators of America
2240 Bernays Dr.
York, PA 17404
Fax: (717)764-6531
Fr: 888-519-9195
URL: http://www.dacacarriers.com

Latest edition 2008. Covers: firms and individuals active in the shipping, warehousing, receiving, distribution, or consolidation of freight shipments.

3253 ■ International Air Cargo Association Membership Directory
5600 NW 36th St., Ste. 620
Miami, FL 33122
Ph: (786)265-7011
Fax: (786)265-7012
E-mail: secgen@tiaca.org
URL: http://www.tiaca.org

Directory of membership organizations listed alphabetically by category and industry.

3254 ■ Messenger Courier Association of America—Network Guide and Membership Directory
Messenger Courier Association of America
1156 Fifteenth St. NW, Ste. 900
Washington, DC 20005
Ph: (202)785-3298
Fax: (202)223-9741
URL: http://www.mcaa.com

Annual, January. $235.00. Covers: Approximately 500 member air courier companies. Entries include: Company name, office personnel, warehouse facilities area served. Arrangement: Geographical by airport city.

3255 ■ Smart Mail
Pitney-Bowes
1 Elmcroft Rd.
Stamford, CT 06926-0700
Ph: (203)356-5000
URL: http://www.pitneybowes.com

Quarterly. Covers: Courier companies that provide same day, overnight and second-day delivery service of small packages throughout the United States. Entries include: Courier name, rates, phone, destinations, delivery times, types of service, hours of operation, company profile. Arrangement: Geographical.

HANDBOOKS AND MANUALS

3256 ■ Common Support Data Dictionary (CSDD)
Airlines for America
Publications Department
1301 Pennsylvania Ave. NW, Ste. 1100
Washington, DC 20004
Ph: (202)626-4062
Fax: (202)626-4081
E-mail: pubs@airlines.org
URL: http://publications.airlines.org/
    CommerceProductDetail.aspx?Product=124

CD-ROM single user: $255.00 member, $365.00 non-member; CD-ROM multi user: $550.00 member, $785 non-member. Catalog of all data elements, terms, and tags that are used in association specifications; provides standardized names, definitions, and properties for data used within the air transport industry.

ONLINE JOB SOURCES AND SERVICES

3257 ■ Messenger Jobs
URL: http://www.messengerjobs.org

Description: Provides a searchable database of available jobs for messengers, couriers and delivery personnel.

OTHER SOURCES

3258 ■ Air Cargo Annual Conference
Express Delivery & Logistics Association
400 Admiral Blvd.
Kansas City, MO 64106
Ph: (816)221-0254
E-mail: info@expressassociation.org
URL: http://www.expressassociation.org

Conference held annually in March in cooperation with the Air and Expedited Motor Carriers Association and the Airforwarders Association.

3259 ■ Air and Expedited Motor Carriers Association
9532 Liberia Ave., No. 705
Manassas, VA 20110
Ph: (703)361-5208
Fax: (703)361-5274
E-mail: fiona@aemca.org
URL: http://aemca.org

Advocates for air and expedited cargo trucking companies that provide ground transportation services, including airport-to-airport connecting runs and local air and expedited cargo pickup and delivery. Members include firms using a variety of equipment including tractor-trailers and straight trucks while serving an entire region or group of states or provinces; firms using mainly straight trucks and vans, serving metropolitan areas around one major regional airport; firms working with airports nationwide, running line hauls day and night providing connecting service; and ancillary providers of goods and services to the air and expedited freight trucking industry, such as computer software, communications equipment, roller bed equipment, truck bodies, insurance, legal counsel, etc.

3260 ■ Air Transport Association of America
1301 Pennsylvania Ave. NW, Ste. 1100
Washington, DC 20004
Ph: (202)626-4000
E-mail: ata@airlines.org
URL: http://www.airlines.org

Trade organization representing principle U.S. airlines and their affiliates responsible for transporting airline passenger and cargo traffic.

3261 ■ Airforwarders Association
750 National Press Bldg.
529 14th St., NW
Washington, DC 20045

Ph: (202)393-2818
Fax: (202)223-9741
E-mail: bfried@airforwarders.org
URL: http://www.airforwarders.org

Works as an alliance for the airforwarding industry, including indirect air carriers, cargo airlines, and affiliated businesses located in the U.S.

3262 ■ Courier Association of Seattle
756 Garfield St.
Seattle, WA 98109
Ph: (206)969-2267
E-mail: el_gato@speakeasy.org
URL: http://www.scn.org/caos

Promotes the interests of the bicycle messenger industry in Seattle, Washington.

3263 ■ Express Delivery and Logistics Association (XLA)
400 Admiral Blvd.
Kansas City, MO 64106
Ph: (816)221-0254
Fax: (816)472-7765
Fr: 888-838-0761
E-mail: jim@expressassociation.org
URL: http://www.expressassociation.org

Description: Represents air couriers, small package express delivery companies, airlines and associated industry members (75); supports companies and facilities such as airlines and airports. Seeks to: provide industry forum for ideas, educate members about new technologies within the industry; represent air couriers before governmental bodies; inform

members of legislation affecting the industry; develop and maintain relationships among members. Conducts seminars and workshops.

3264 ■ International Air Cargo Association
5600 NW 36th St., Ste. 620
Miami, FL 33122
Ph: (786)265-7011
Fax: (786)265-7012
E-mail: secgen@tiaca.org
URL: http://www.tiaca.org

Supports and assists the air cargo industry and works to improve its role in world trade expansion.

3265 ■ Messenger Courier Association of America (MCAA)
750 National Press Bldg.
529 14th St. NW
Washington, DC 20045
Ph: (202)785-3298
Fax: (202)223-9741
E-mail: bdecaprio@mcaa.com
URL: http://www.mcaa.com

Description: Trade organization of local and international messenger courier companies. Addresses issues facing the industry, including municipal traffic ordinances that impede industry operations. Works to establish driver pools and to develop centralized core computer service bureaus for smaller courier companies. Provides training, discount purchasing programs, and legislative and regulatory issue monitoring. Conducts educational and research programs; compiles statistics.

3266 ■ New York Bike Messenger Foundation
303 W 42nd St., Ste. 316
New York, NY 10036
URL: http://www.nybmf.org

Supports bicycle messengers in New York City by providing assistance and financial support to injured messengers and promoting programs that assist in the research and advancement of the messenger workforce.

3267 ■ New York State Messenger and Courier Association
150 Main St.
Port Washington, NY 11050
Ph: (516)883-1583
Fax: (516)883-1584
E-mail: info@nysmca.org
URL: http://www.nysmca.org

Promotes the interests of the messenger and courier industry in New York.

3268 ■ San Francisco Bike Messenger Association
255 9th St.
San Francisco, CA 94103
E-mail: naccc07@nacc07sf.com
URL: http://www.ahalenia.com/sfbma

Promotes unity and solidarity among bicycle messengers in the San Francisco Bay Area and seeks to raise the status of the profession.

Sources of Help-Wanted Ads

3269 ■ Accounting Horizons
American Accounting Association
5717 Bessie Dr.
Sarasota, FL 34233-2399
Ph: (941)921-7747
Fax: (941)923-4093
URL: http://aaahq.org/pubs/horizons.htm

Quarterly. $300.00/year for individuals, print only; $325.00/year for individuals, online, vol. 13 thru current issue; $375.00/year for individuals, online and print. Publication covering the banking, finance, and accounting industries.

3270 ■ American Banker
Banking Group
1 State Street Plz., 27th Fl.
New York, NY 10004-1483
Ph: (212)803-8200
Fax: (212)843-9600
Fr: 800-221-1809
URL: http://www.americanbanker.com

Daily. $995.00/year for individuals. Newspaper for senior executives in banking and other financial services industries. Coverage includes trends, analysis, and statistics of the legislative scene in Washington; finance; mortgages; technology; small business; and regional banking.

3271 ■ Brookings Papers on Economic Activity
Brookings Institution Press
1775 Massachusetts Ave. NW
Washington, DC 20036
Ph: (202)797-6000
URL: http://www.brookings.edu/press/
journals.htm#bpea

Semiannual. $55.00/year for individuals; $90.00/year for institutions; $69.00/year for other countries; $104.00/year for institutions, other countries. Publication covering economics and business.

3272 ■ Business Credit
National Association of Credit Management
8840 Columbia 100 Pkwy.
Columbia, MD 21045-2158
Ph: (410)740-5560
Fax: (410)740-5574
URL: http://www.nacm.org/index.php?option=com_
content&view=catego

$60.00/year for Canada; $65.00/year for other countries; $54.00/year for individuals; $48.00/year for libraries; $7.00/year for single issue. Magazine covering finance, business risk management, providing information for the extension of credit, maintenance of accounts receivable, and cash asset management.

3273 ■ Commercial Lending Review
CCH Inc.
PO Box 4307
Chicago, IL 60680

Fr: 800-248-3248
URL: http://www.commerciallendingreview.com/

Bimonthly. $445.00/year for individuals. Journal covering all aspects of lending for commercial banks, community and regional banks and other financial institutions.

3274 ■ Financial Management
Financial Management Association International
4202 E Fowler Ave.
BSN 3331
Tampa, FL 33620-5500
Ph: (813)974-2084
Fax: (813)974-3318
E-mail: fma@coba.usf.edu
URL: http://www.fma.org/

Quarterly. $300.00/year for institutions, print + premium online; $95.00/year for institutions, premium online; $167.00/year for institutions, Europe, print + premium online; $158.00/year for institutions, Europe, premium online; $167.00/year for institutions, rest of world, print + premium online; $158.00/year for institutions, rest of world, premium online. Journal covering business, economics, finance and management.

3275 ■ Northwestern Financial Review
NFR Communications Inc.
7400 Metro Blvd., Ste. 217
Minneapolis, MN 55439
Ph: (952)835-2275
URL: http://www.northwesternfinancialreview.com

$99.00/year for individuals. Trade publication covering commercial banking.

3276 ■ U.S. Banker
SourceMedia Inc.
1 State St. Plz., 27th Fl.
New York, NY 10004-1561
Ph: (212)803-8200
Fax: (646)264-6828
URL: http://www.americanbanker.com/usb.html

Monthly. $109.00/year for individuals; $139.00/year for individuals, Canada; $139.00/year for individuals, outside North America; $179.00/year for two years; $239.00/year for two years, Canada; $239.00/year for two years, outside North America. Magazine serving the financial services industry.

Employer Directories and Networking Lists

3277 ■ The Bank Directory
Accuity Inc.
4709 Golf Rd.
Skokie, IL 60076
Ph: (847)676-9600
Fax: (847)933-8101
Fr: 800-321-3373
URL: http://store.accuitysolutions.com/order.html

Semiannual, June and December. $1,195.00 for individuals. Covers: In five volumes, about 11,000 banks and 50,000 branches of United States banks, and 60,000 foreign banks and branches engaged in foreign banking; Federal Reserve system and other United States government and state government banking agencies; 500 largest North American and International commercial banks; paper and automated clearinghouses. Volumes 1 and 2 contain North American listings; volumes 3 and 4, international listings (also cited as "M Thomson International Bank Directory"); volume 5, Worldwide Correspondents Guide containing key correspondent data to facilitate funds transfer. Entries include: For domestic banks—Bank name, address, phone, telex, cable, date established, routing number, charter type, bank holding company affiliation, memberships in Federal Reserve System and other banking organizations, principal officers by function performed, principal correspondent banks, and key financial data (deposits, etc.). For international banks—Bank name, address, phone, fax, telex, cable, SWIFT address, transit or sort codes within home country, ownership, financial data, names and titles of key personnel, branch locations. For branches—Bank name, address, phone, charter type, ownership and other details comparable to domestic bank listings. Arrangement: Geographical. Indexes: Alphabetical, geographical.

3278 ■ Career Opportunities in Banking, Finance, and Insurance
Facts On File Inc.
132 W 31st St., 17th Fl.
New York, NY 10001
Ph: (212)967-8800
Fax: 800-678-3633
Fr: 800-322-8755
URL: http://factsonfile.infobasepublishing.com

Latest edition 2nd; Published February, 2007. $49.50 for individuals. Publication includes: Lists of colleges with programs supporting banking, finance, and industry; professional associations; professional certifications; regulatory agencies; and Internet resources for career planning. Principal content of publication is job descriptions for professions in the banking, finance, and insurance industries. Indexes: Alphabetical.

3279 ■ Corporate Finance Sourcebook
LexisNexis Group
9443 Springboro Pike
Dayton, OH 45342
Fr: 888-285-3947
E-mail: nrpsales@marquiswhoswho.com
URL: http://www.financesourcebook.com

Annual, Latest edition 2010. $695.00 for individuals; $556.00 for individuals. Covers: Securities research analysts; major private lenders; investment banking firms; commercial banks; United States-based foreign banks; commercial finance firms; leasing companies; foreign investment bankers in the United States; pension managers; banks that offer master trusts; cash managers; business insurance brokers; business real estate specialists; lists about 3,500 firms; 14,500 key financial experts. Entries include: All entries include firm name, address, phone, e-mail, and names and titles of officers, contacts, or specialists in corporate finance. Additional details are given as appropriate, including names of major clients, number of companies served, services, total assets, branch locations, years in business. Arrangement: Classified by line of business and then alphabetized within that line of business. Indexes: Firm name, personnel name, geographical.

3280 ■ North American Financial Institutions Directory

Accuity Inc.
4709 Golf Rd.
Skokie, IL 60076
Ph: (847)676-9600
Fax: (847)933-8101
Fr: 800-321-3373
URL: http://store.accuitysolutions.com/order.html

Semiannual, January and July. $955.00 for individuals. Covers: 15,000 banks and their branches; over 2,000 head offices, and 15,500 branches of savings and loan associations; over 5,500 credit unions with assets over $5 million; Federal Reserve System and other U.S. government and state government banking agencies; bank holding, commercial finance, and leasing companies; coverage includes the United States, Canada, Mexico, and Central America. Entries include: Bank name, address, phone, fax, telex, principal officers and directors, date established, financial data, association memberships, attorney or counsel, correspondent banks, out-of-town branch, holding company affiliation, ABA transit number and routing symbol, MICR number with check digit, credit card(s) issued, trust powers, current par value and dividend of common stock, kind of charter. Arrangement: Geographical. Indexes: Alphabetical.

3281 ■ Who's Who in Finance and Business

Marquis Who's Who L.L.C.
300 Connell Dr., Ste. 2000
Berkeley Heights, NJ 07922
Ph: (908)673-1000
Fax: (908)673-1189
Fr: 800-473-7020
E-mail: finance@marquiswhoswho.com
URL: http://www.marquiswhoswho.com

Biennial, latest edition 37th; 2009-2010. $349.00 for individuals. Covers: Over 24,000 individuals. Entries include: Name, home and office addresses, personal, career, and family data; civic and political activities; memberships, publications, awards. Arrangement: Alphabetical.

HANDBOOKS AND MANUALS

3282 ■ The Million-Dollar Financial Services Practice: A Proven System for Becoming a Top Producer

AMACOM Publishing
c/o American Management Association
1601 Broadway
New York, NY 10019-7434
Ph: (212)586-8100
Fax: (518)891-0368
Fr: 800-714-6395
E-mail: pubs_cust_serv@amanet.org
URL: http://www.amacombooks.org

David J. Mullen. 2007. $30.00 (hardback). 352 pages. Features information on how to become a financial advisor using the methods given in the book. Combines marketing, prospecting, sales, and time management techniques into a system that will help readers build a successful and lucrative practice.

3283 ■ Opportunities in Hospital Administration Careers

The McGraw-Hill Companies
PO Box 182604
Columbus, OH 43272

Fax: (614)759-3749
Fr: 877-883-5524
E-mail: customer.service@mcgraw-hill.com
URL: http://www.mhprofessional.com/ product.php?isbn=0071467688

I. Donald Snook. 2006. $13.95. 160 pages. Discusses opportunities for administrators in a variety of management settings: hospital, department, clinic, group practice, HMO, mental health, and extended care facilities.

EMPLOYMENT AGENCIES AND SEARCH FIRMS

3284 ■ Adams Inc. Financial Recruiting

17330 Wright St., Ste. 101
Omaha, NE 68130
Ph: (402)333-3009
Fax: (402)333-3448
Fr: 800-536-4933
E-mail: info@adams-inc.com
URL: http://www.adams-inc.com

Description: Provides recruitment and candidate placement in the banking/financial, trust/investment, and credit card industries.

3285 ■ Butterfass, Pepe & MacCallan Inc.

PO Box 179
Franklin Lakes, NJ 07417
Ph: (201)560-9500
Fax: (201)560-9506
E-mail: staff@bpmi.com
URL: http://www.bpmi.com

Executive search firm.

3286 ■ Cheryl Alexander & Associates

8588 Shadow Creek Dr.
Maple Grove, MN 55311
Ph: (763)416-4570
E-mail: cheryl@cherylalexander.com
URL: http://www.cherylalexander.com

Executive search firm.

3287 ■ Cross Hill Partners LLC

845 Third Ave., 6th Fl.
New York, NY 10022
Ph: (646)405-7500
Fax: (866)927-4449
E-mail: info@crosshillpartners.com
URL: http://www.crosshillpartners.com

Executive search firm.

3288 ■ Douglas-Allen Inc.

Tower Square, 24th Fl.
PO Box 15368
Springfield, MA 01115
Ph: (413)739-0900
E-mail: research@douglas-allen.com
URL: http://www.douglas-allen.com

Executive search firm.

3289 ■ Financial Professionals

4100 Spring Valley Rd., Ste. 250
Dallas, TX 75244
Ph: (972)991-8999
Fax: (972)702-0776
E-mail: rita@fpstaff.net
URL: http://www.fpstaff.net

Executive search consultants with additional offices in Forth Worth and Houston.

ONLINE JOB SOURCES AND SERVICES

3290 ■ BankingCareers.com

URL: http://www.bankingcareers.com

Description: Provides lists of jobs and products to bankers in the banking and finance community.

3291 ■ FinancialServicesCrossing.com

URL: http://www.financialservicescrossing.com

Description: Offers a collection of top financial services job openings carefully researched by analysts. Provides instant access to a comprehensive pool of listings in the industry of financial services.

TRADESHOWS

3292 ■ Pennsylvania Association of Community Bankers Convention

Pennsylvania Association of Community Bankers
2405 N. Front St.
Harrisburg, PA 17110
Ph: (717)231-7447
Fax: (717)231-7445
Fr: 800-443-5076
E-mail: pacb@pacb.org
URL: http://www.pacb.org

Annual. Primary Exhibits: Equipment, supplies, and services for community banks, thrifts, and associate firms.

OTHER SOURCES

3293 ■ American Bankers Association (ABA)

1120 Connecticut Ave. NW
Washington, DC 20036
Ph: (202)663-5564
Fax: (202)663-7543
Fr: 800-226-5377
E-mail: custserv@aba.com
URL: http://www.aba.com

Description: Members are principally commercial banks and trust companies; combined assets of members represent approximately 90% of the U.S. banking industry; approximately 94% of members are community banks with less than $500 million in assets. Seeks to enhance the role of commercial bankers as preeminent providers of financial services through communications, research, legal action, lobbying of federal legislative and regulatory bodies, and education and training programs. Serves as spokesperson for the banking industry; facilitates exchange of information among members. Maintains the American Institute of Banking, an industry-sponsored adult education program. Conducts educational and training programs for bank employees and officers through a wide range of banking schools and national conferences. Maintains liaison with federal bank regulators; lobbies Congress on issues affecting commercial banks; testifies before congressional committees; represents members in U.S. postal rate proceedings. Serves as secretariat of the International Monetary Conference and the Financial Institutions Committee for the American National Standards Institute. Files briefs and lawsuits in major court cases affecting the industry. Conducts teleconferences with state banking associations on such issues as regulatory compliance; works to build consensus and coordinate activities of leading bank and financial service trade groups. Provides services to members including: public advocacy; news media contact; insurance program providing directors and officers with liability coverage, financial institution bond, and trust errors and omissions coverage; research service operated through ABA Center for Banking Information; fingerprint set processing in conjunction with the Federal Bureau of Investigation; discounts on operational and income-producing projects through the Corporation for American Banking. Conducts conferences, forums, and workshops covering subjects such as small business, consumer credit, agricultural and community banking, trust management, bank operations, and automation. Sponsors ABA Educational Foundation and the Personal Economics Program, which educates schoolchildren and the community on banking, economics, and personal finance.

3294 ■ American Credit Union Mortgage Association (ACUMA)

PO Box 400955
Las Vegas, NV 89140
Fax: (702)823-3950
Fr: 877-442-2862
E-mail: bdorsa@acuma.org
URL: http://www.acuma.org/wp

Description: Credit unions providing real estate lending services. Promotes adherence to high standards of ethics and practice in the issuing of mortgage loans. Represents members' interests before regulatory agencies and industrial associations; conducts research and educational programs; maintains speakers' bureau; compiles statistics.

3295 ■ American Financial Services Association (AFSA)

919 18th St. NW, Ste. 300
Washington, DC 20006-5526
Ph: (202)296-5544
Fax: (202)223-0321
E-mail: susie@afsamail.org
URL: http://www.afsaonline.org

Description: Represents companies whose business is primarily direct credit lending to consumers and/or the purchase of sales finance paper on consumer goods. Has members that have insurance and retail subsidiaries; some are themselves subsidiaries of highly diversified parent corporations. Encourages the business of financing individuals and families for necessary and useful purposes at reasonable charges, including interest; promotes consumer understanding of basic money management principles as well as constructive uses of consumer credit. Includes educational services such as films, textbooks and study units for the classroom and budgeting guides for individuals and families. Compiles statistical reports; offers seminars.

3296 ■ Association for Financial Professionals (AFP)

4520 E West Hwy., Ste. 750
Bethesda, MD 20814
Ph: (301)907-2862
Fax: (301)907-2864
E-mail: afp@afponline.org
URL: http://www.afponline.org

Description: Seeks to establish a national forum for the exchange of concepts and techniques related to improving the management of treasury and the careers of professionals through research, education, publications and recognition of the treasury management profession through a certification program. Conducts educational programs. Operates career center.

3297 ■ Commercial Finance Association (CFA)

370 7th Ave., Ste. 1801
New York, NY 10001-3979
Ph: (212)792-9390
Fax: (212)564-6053
E-mail: info@cfa.com
URL: http://www.cfa.com

Description: Organizations engaged in asset-based financial services including commercial financing and factoring and lending money on a secured basis to small- and medium-sized business firms. Acts as a forum for information and consideration about ideas, opportunities and legislation concerning asset-based financial services. Seeks to improve the industry's legal and operational procedures. Offers job placement and reference services for members. Sponsors School for Field Examiners and other educational programs. Compiles statistics; conducts seminars and surveys; maintains speakers' bureau and 21 committees.

3298 ■ Consumer Data Industry Association (CDIA)

1090 Vermont Ave. NW, Ste. 200
Washington, DC 20005-4964
Ph: (202)371-0910
Fax: (202)371-0134
E-mail: cdia@cdiaonline.org
URL: http://www.cdiaonline.org

Description: Serves as international association of credit reporting and collection service offices. Maintains hall of fame and biographical archives; conducts specialized educational programs. Offers computerized services and compiles statistics.

3299 ■ Credit Professionals International (CPI)

10726 Manchester Rd., Ste. 210
St. Louis, MO 63122
Ph: (314)821-9393
Fax: (314)821-7171
E-mail: creditpro@creditprofessionals.org
URL: http://www.creditprofessionals.org

Description: Represents individuals employed in credit or collection departments of business firms or professional offices. Conducts educational program in credit work. Sponsors Career Club composed of members who have been involved in credit work for at least 25 years.

3300 ■ Credit Union Executives Society (CUES)

PO Box 14167
Madison, WI 53708-0167
Ph: (608)271-2664
Fax: (608)271-2303
Fr: 800-252-2664
E-mail: cues@cues.org
URL: http://www.cues.org

Description: Advances the professional development of credit union CEOs, senior management and directors. Serves as an international membership association dedicated to the professional development of credit union CEOs, senior management and directors.

3301 ■ National Association of Credit Management (NACM)

8840 Columbia 100 Pkwy.
Columbia, MD 21045-2158
Ph: (410)740-5560
Fax: (410)740-5574
Fr: 800-955-8815
URL: http://www.nacm.org

Description: Credit and financial executives representing manufacturers, wholesalers, financial institutions, insurance companies, utilities, and other businesses interested in business credit. Promotes sound credit practices and legislation. Conducts Graduate School of Credit and Financial Management at Dartmouth College, Hanover, NH.

3302 ■ National Association of Credit Union Services Organizations (NACUSO)

3419 Via Lido
PMB 135
Newport Beach, CA 92663
Ph: (949)645-5296
Fax: (949)645-5297
Fr: 888-462-2870
E-mail: info@nacuso.org
URL: http://www.nacuso.org

Description: Credit union service organizations and their employees. Promotes professional advancement of credit union service organization staff; seeks to insure adherence to high standards of ethics and practice among members. Conducts research and educational programs; formulates and enforces standards of conduct and practice; maintains speakers' bureau; compiles statistics.

3303 ■ National Association of Federal Credit Unions (NAFCU)

3138 10th St. N
Arlington, VA 22201-2149
Ph: (703)522-4770
Fax: (703)524-1082
Fr: 800-336-4644
URL: http://www.nafcu.org

Description: Serves as federally-chartered credit unions. Offers legislative and regulatory advocacy, compliance assistance, training and professional development and a range of products. Provides information on the latest industry developments and proposed and final regulations. Represents members' interests before federal regulatory bodies and Congress. Compiles statistics and holds educational conferences.

3304 ■ National Bankers Association (NBA)

1513 P St. NW
Washington, DC 20005
Ph: (202)588-5432
Fax: (202)588-5443
E-mail: mgrant@nationalbankers.org
URL: http://www.nationalbankers.org

Description: Minority banking institutions owned by minority individuals and institutions. Serves as an advocate for the minority banking industry. Organizes banking services, government relations, marketing, scholarship, and technical assistance programs. Offers placement services; compiles statistics.

3305 ■ Risk Management Association

1801 Market St., Ste. 300
Philadelphia, PA 19103-1628
Ph: (215)446-4000
Fax: (215)446-4101
Fr: 800-677-7621
E-mail: member@rmahq.org
URL: http://www.rmahq.org/RMA

Description: Commercial and savings banks, and savings and loan, and other financial services companies. Conducts research and professional development activities in areas of loan administration, asset management, and commercial lending and credit to increase professionalism.

Dancers and Choreographers

SOURCES OF HELP-WANTED ADS

3306 ■ AAHPERD UpdatePLUS
American Alliance for Health, Physical Education, Recreation & Dance
1900 Association Dr.
Reston, VA 20191
Ph: (703)476-3400
Fax: (703)476-9527
Fr: 800-213-7193
E-mail: info@aahperd.org
URL: http://www.aahperd.org

Description: Six issues/year. Provides news and information on the Alliance. Discusses current issues and research in the areas of health, physical education, recreation, dances, fitness, and adapted physical education. Recurring features include a calendar of events, reports of meetings, news of educational opportunities, job listings, notices of publications available, and columns titled President's Message, Membership Corner, and From the EVP's Desk.

3307 ■ ArtSEARCH
Theatre Communications Group
520 8th Ave., 24th Fl.
New York, NY 10018-4156
Ph: (212)609-5900
Fax: (212)609-5901
E-mail: tcg@tcg.org
URL: http://www.tcg.org

Description: Biweekly. Publishes classified listings for job opportunities in the arts, especially theatre, dance, music, and educational institutions. Listings include opportunities in administration, artistic, education, production, and career development.

3308 ■ Daily Variety
Reed Business Information
360 Park Ave. S
New York, NY 10010-1710
Ph: (646)746-7764
Fax: (646)746-7583
URL: http://www.reedbusiness.com/
index.asp?layout=theListProfile&

Daily. $329.99/year for individuals. Global entertainment newspaper (tabloid).

3309 ■ Dance Magazine
Dance Magazine Inc.
333 7th Ave., 11th Fl.
PO Box 678
New York, NY 10001
Ph: (646)459-4800
Fax: (646)459-4900
Fr: 800-331-1750
URL: http://www.dancemagazine.com

Monthly. $34.95/year for individuals; $64.90/year for two years; $46.95/year for Canada; $88.90/year for Canada, 2 years; $66.95/year for other countries; $128.90/year for other countries, 2 years. Performing arts magazine featuring all forms of dance with

profiles, news, photos, reviews of performances, and information on books, videos, films, schools, health, and technique.

3310 ■ Music and Media
Nielsen Business Media
770 Broadway
New York, NY 10003-9595
URL: http://www.vnubusinessmedia.com

Weekly. Publication covering the music and entertainment industries.

3311 ■ Ross Reports Television and Film
Nielsen Business Media
770 Broadway
New York, NY 10003-9595
URL: http://www.backstage.com

Bimonthly. $65.00/year for individuals; $10.00/year for individuals. Trade publication covering talent agents and casting directors in New York and Los Angeles, as well as television and film production. Special national issue of agents and casting directors is published annually. Sister publication to Back Stage, Back Stage West.

3312 ■ Strategies
American Alliance for Health, Physical Education, Recreation & Dance
1900 Association Dr.
Reston, VA 20191-1598
Ph: (703)476-3400
Fax: (703)476-9527
Fr: 800-213-7193
E-mail: strategies@aahperd.org
URL: http://www.aahperd.org/naspe/publications/
journals/strategie

Bimonthly. $130.00/year for U.S. and Canada, institutions, schools & libraries; print & online; $50.00/year for U.S. and Canada, add $5 GST; $62.00/year for other countries, schools & libraries, print & online; $130.00/year for institutions, other countries, schools & libraries, online; $142.00/year for institutions, other countries, schools & libraries, print; $162.00/year for institutions, other countries, schools & libraries, print & online. Peer-reviewed journal providing practical, hands-on information to physical educators and coaches.

3313 ■ Variety
Reed Business Information
360 Park Ave. S
New York, NY 10010-1710
Ph: (646)746-7764
Fax: (646)746-7583
URL: http://www.reedbusiness.com/us.html

Weekly. $259.00/year for individuals; $25.00/year for individuals, monthly. Newspaper (tabloid) reporting on theatre, television, radio, music, records, and movies.

EMPLOYER DIRECTORIES AND NETWORKING LISTS

3314 ■ Contemporary Theatre, Film, and Television
Gale
PO Box 6904
Florence, KY 41022-6904
Fr: 800-354-9706
URL: http://www.gale.cengage.com

Bimonthly, Latest edition December, 2011. $293.00 for individuals. Covers: 116 volumes, more than 20,000 leading and up-and-coming performers, directors, writers, producers, designers, managers, choreographers, technicians, composers, executives, and dancers in the United States, Canada, Great Britain and the world. Each volume includes updated biographies for people listed in previous volumes and in "Who's Who in the Theatre," which this series has superseded. Entries include: Name, agent and/or office addresses, personal and career data; stage, film, and television credits; writings, awards, other information. Arrangement: Alphabetical. Indexes: Cumulative name index also covers entries in "Who's Who in the Theatre" editions 1-17 and in "Who Was Who in the Theatre.".

3315 ■ National Directory of Arts Internships
National Network for Artist Placement
935 West Ave. 37
Los Angeles, CA 90065
Ph: (323)222-4035
E-mail: info@artistplacement.com
URL: http://www.artistplacement.com

Biennial, odd years; latest edition 11th. $95.00 for individuals. Covers: Over 5,000 internship opportunities in dance, music, theater, art, design, film, and video & over 1,250 host organizations Entries include: Name of sponsoring organization, address, name of contact; description of positions available, eligibility requirements, stipend or salary (if any), application procedures. Arrangement: Classified by discipline, then geographical.

3316 ■ Regional Theater Directory
American Theatre Works Inc.
2349 West Rd.
PO Box 159
Dorset, VT 05251
Ph: (802)867-9333
Fax: (802)867-2297
URL: http://www.theatredirectories.com

Annual, May. $38.50 for individuals. Covers: Regional theater companies and dinner theatres with employment opportunities in acting, design, production, and management. Entries include: Company name, address, phone, name and title of contact; type of company, activities, and size of house; whether union affiliated, whether nonprofit or commercial; year established; hiring procedure and number of positions hired annually, season; description of stage; internships, description of artistic policy and audience. Arrangement: Geographical. Indexes: Company name, type of plays produced.

3317 ■ *Summer Theater Directory*
American Theatre Works Inc.
2349 West Rd.
PO Box 159
Dorset, VT 05251
Ph: (802)867-9333
Fax: (802)867-2297
URL: http://www.theatredirectories.com

Annual, Latest edition 2009. $38.50 for individuals. Covers: Summer theater companies, theme parks and cruise lines that offer employment opportunities in acting, design, production, and management; summer theater training programs. Entries include: Company name, address, phone, name and title of contact; type of company, activities and size of house; whether union affiliated, whether nonprofit or commercial; year established; hiring procedure and number of positions hired annually, season; description of stage; internships; description of company's artistic goals and audience. Arrangement: Geographical. Indexes: Company name.

HANDBOOKS AND MANUALS

3318 ■ *Ballet Dancers in Career Transition: Sixteen Success Stories*
McFarland & Company, Inc. Publishers
PO Box 611
Jefferson, NC 28640
Ph: (336)246-4460
Fax: (336)246-5018
Fr: 800-253-2187
E-mail: info@mcfarlandpub.com
URL: http://www.mcfarlandpub.com/

Nancy Upper. May 2004. $39.95 (paper). Illustrated. 278 Pages.

3319 ■ *Careers for the Stagestruck and Other Dramatic Types*
The McGraw-Hill Companies
PO Box 182604
Columbus, OH 43272
Fax: (614)759-3749
Fr: 877-883-5524
E-mail: customer.service@mcgraw-hill.com
URL: http://www.mhprofessional.com/
    product.php?isbn=007144243X

Lucia Mauro. Second edition, 2004. $13.95 (paper). 160 pages. Includes bibliographical references.

3320 ■ *Creative Careers: Paths for Aspiring Actors, Artists, Dancers, Musicians and Writers*
SuperCollege, LLC
3286 Oak Ct.
Belmont, CA 94002
Ph: (650)618-2221
URL: http://www.supercollege.com

Elaina Loveland. 2009. $17.95. 352 pages. Provides tips and advice for job seekers aiming for a career in the field of arts. Includes details on salaries, job descriptions, job outlook, training and education requirements for each artistic career.

3321 ■ *The Dancer's Survival Manual: Everything You Need to Know from the First Class to Career Change*
University Press of Florida
15 NW 15th St.
Gainesville, FL 32611
Ph: (352)392-1351
Fax: (352)392-0590
Fr: 800-226-3822
URL: http://www.upf.com

Marian Horosko and Judith Kupersmith. 2009. $27.50 (paperback). 224 pages. Covers every aspect of a

career in dance, including the major decisions and challenges dancers face throughout their careers.

3322 ■ *Resumes for Performing Arts Careers*
The McGraw-Hill Companies
PO Box 182604
Columbus, OH 43272
Fax: (614)759-3749
Fr: 877-883-5524
E-mail: customer.service@mcgraw-hill.com
URL: http://www.mhprofessional.com/
    product.php?isbn=0071442464

2004. $10.95 (paper). 160 pages.

3323 ■ *Starting Your Career as a Dancer*
Allworth Press
307 W 36th St., 11th Fl.
New York, NY 10018
Ph: (212)643-6816
Fax: (212)643-6819
URL: http://www.skyhorsepublishing.com

Mande Dagenais. 2012. $19.95 (paper). 256 pages. Serves as a comprehensive and practical guide for dancers. Offers insider advice and knowledge on what it really takes to get into the business, be in the business, and survive in the business.

ONLINE JOB SOURCES AND SERVICES

3324 ■ Answers4Dancers.com
URL: http://www.answers4dancers.com

Description: Provides resources such as listings of auditions and jobs, tips and secrets, tools and training, videos, and success stories to job seekers in the dance and choreography industry.

3325 ■ Dance.net
URL: http://www.dance.net

Description: Strives to offer dancers a place on the internet to learn about all dance forms and meet fellow students, dancers, instructors, coaches, choreographers, and studio owners. Provides a database of jobs.

TRADESHOWS

3326 ■ Texas Association for Health, Physical Education, Recreation, and Dance Annual State Convention
Texas Association for Health, Physical Education, Recreation, and Dance
7910 Cameron Rd.
Austin, TX 78754
Ph: (512)459-1299
Fax: (512)459-1290
Fr: 800-880-7300
E-mail: lynda@tahperd.org
URL: http://www.tahperd.org

Annual. Primary Exhibits: Publications, equipment, and supplies for health, physical education, recreation, and dance.

OTHER SOURCES

3327 ■ American Dance Guild (ADG)
240 W 14th St.
New York, NY 10011
Ph: (212)627-9407
E-mail: info@americandanceguild.org
URL: http://www.americandanceguild.org

Description: Serves the dance professional by providing: a networking system between dance artists and dance educators; an informed voice on behalf of the dance field to governmental, educational and corporate institutions and the general public; international dance festivals, conferences and dance film festivals; educational publications and videos;

the ADG Fannie Weiss Scholarship; the ADG Harkness Resource for Dance Study.

3328 ■ Dance Notation Bureau (DNB)
111 John St., Ste. 704
New York, NY 10038
Ph: (212)571-7011
Fax: (212)571-7012
E-mail: dnbinfo@dancenotation.org
URL: http://www.dancenotation.org

Description: Documents and preserves dance works through the use of graphic notation. Conducts research into movement-related analysis techniques and programs. Maintains extension at Ohio State University, Columbus. Maintains placement service; assists choreographers in copyrighting, licensing, and restaging of their dance works. Offers service for dance reconstructors and circulating library materials to members. Maintains archive of original Labanotated dance scores in the world.

3329 ■ Dance/USA
1111 16th St. NW, Ste. 300
Washington, DC 20036
Ph: (202)833-1717
Fax: (202)833-2686
URL: http://www.danceusa.org

Description: Comprised of dancers, dance companies, artists, and others involved in non-profit professional dance. Sustains and advances professional dance by addressing the needs, concerns, and interests of artists, administrators, and organizations. Enhances the infrastructure for dance creation and distribution, education, and dissemination of information.

3330 ■ Institute of American Indian Arts (IAIA)
83 Avan Nu Po Rd.
Santa Fe, NM 87508
Ph: (505)424-2300
Fax: (505)424-3900
Fr: 800-804-6423
E-mail: setzel@iaia.edu
URL: http://www.iaia.edu

Description: Federally chartered private institution. Offers 4-year degrees in Creative Writing, New Media Arts, Museum Studies, Indigenous Studies and Studio arts primarily to Native American and Alaska Natives (but school is open enrollment). Emphasis is placed upon Indian traditions as the basis for creative expression in fine arts including painting, sculpture, museum studies, creative writing, printmaking, photography, communications, design, and dance, as well as training in metal crafts, jewelry, ceramics, textiles, and various traditional crafts. Students are encouraged to identify with their heritage and to be aware of themselves as members of a culture rich in architecture, the fine arts, music, pageantry, and the humanities. All programs are based on elements of the Native American cultural heritage that emphasizes differences between Native American and non-Native American cultures. Sponsors Indian arts-oriented junior college offering Associate of Fine Arts degrees in various fields as well as seminars, an exhibition program, and traveling exhibits. Maintains extensive library, museum, and biographical archives. Provides placement service. Conventions/Meetings: varies.

3331 ■ International Tap Association (ITA)
PO Box 150574
Austin, TX 78715
Ph: (303)443-7989
E-mail: info@tapdance.org
URL: http://www.tapdance.org

Description: Represents the interests of tap dancers, performers, studios, choreographers, teachers, scholars, historians, students, and other tap enthusiasts. Promotes understanding, preservation, and development of tap dance as an art form. Encourages the creation of new tap performance venues and touring circuits. Preserves the history of tap through archival documentation and research.

Establishes support mechanisms and communication networks for tap.

3332 ■ National Dance Association (NDA)
1900 Association Dr.
Reston, VA 20191
Ph: (703)476-3400
Fax: (703)476-9527
Fr: 800-213-7193
E-mail: nda@aahperd.org
URL: http://www.aahperd.org/nda

Description: Dance educators, choreographers, schools and dance/arts administrators, researchers, performers, dance medicine/science specialists, technologists, therapists and others associated with dance/arts education. Works with 160 federal and state agencies, arts and education associations, foundations, and businesses and corporations to ensure that: (1) quality dance/arts education is available to all Americans regardless of age, sex, ability, interest, or culture; and (2) quality dance/arts education becomes a part of U.S. education for all children.

3333 ■ North American Irish Dance Federation (NAIDF)
2317 Peppermill Pointe Ct.
Springfield, IL 62712
E-mail: achillacademy@yahoo.com
URL: http://www.naidf.com

Description: Fosters the growth and development of Irish dance and culture. Encourages the pursuit of excellence among teachers and performers. Offers certification programs for teachers who are interested in furthering their dance education.

3334 ■ Texas International Theatrical Arts Society (TITAS)
3625 N Hall St., Ste. 740
Dallas, TX 75219
Ph: (214)528-6112
Fax: (214)528-2617
E-mail: csantos@titas.org
URL: http://www.titas.org

Description: Theatrical agencies working to book entertainers and international acts into all live music venues. Provides placement service; conducts educational seminars.

Sources of Help-Wanted Ads

3335 ■ Communications of the ACM
Association for Computing Machinery
PO Box 30777
New York, NY 10087
Ph: (212)626-0500
Fax: (212)944-1318
Fr: 800-342-6626
URL: http://cacm.acm.org

Monthly. $99.00/year for members, professional. Computing news magazine.

3336 ■ Computerworld
101 Communications
9121 Oakdale Ave., Ste. 101
Chatsworth, CA 91311
Ph: (818)814-5200
Fax: (818)734-1522
URL: http://www.computerworld.com

Weekly. $129.00/year for individuals; $129.00/year for Canada; $295.00/year for other countries; $250.00/year for individuals, Mexico/Central/South America; $29.00/year for individuals, digital edition. Newspaper for information systems executives.

3337 ■ Computing Surveys (CSUR)
Association for Computing Machinery
PO Box 30777
New York, NY 10087
Ph: (212)626-0500
Fax: (212)944-1318
Fr: 800-342-6626
URL: http://surveys.acm.org/

Quarterly. $205.00/year for nonmembers, print only; $164.00/year for nonmembers, online only; $246.00/year for nonmembers, online & print. Journal presenting surveys and tutorials in computer science.

3338 ■ Datamation
Reed Business Information
360 Park Ave. S
New York, NY 10010-1710
Ph: (646)746-6400
URL: http://www.datamation.com

Semimonthly. Magazine on computers and information processing.

3339 ■ InfoWorld
InfoWorld Media Group
501 2nd St.
San Francisco, CA 94107
Fr: 800-227-8365
E-mail: letters@infoworld.com
URL: http://www.infoworld.com/

Weekly. Free to qualified subscribers; $180.00/year for individuals. Weekly publication.

3340 ■ iSeries News Magazine
Penton Media
249 W 17th St.
New York, NY 10011
Ph: (212)024-4200
E-mail: service@iseriesnetwork.com
URL: http://www.systeminetwork.com/info/
networkpubs/news400/about

$149.00/year for U.S. and Canada; $199.00/year for other countries. Trade magazine for programmers and data processing managers who use IBM iSeries.

Employer Directories and Networking Lists

3341 ■ Computer Directory
Computer Directories Inc.
23815 Nichols Sawmill Rd.
Hockley, TX 77447
Ph: (281)259-5959
Fax: (281)259-5959
Fr: 800-234-4353
URL: http://www.compdirinc.com

Annual, fall. Covers: Approximately 130,000 computer installations; 19 separate volumes for Alaska/Hawaii, Connecticut/New Jersey, Dallas/Ft. Worth, Eastern Seaboard, Far Midwest, Houston, Illinois, Midatlantic, Midcentral, Mideast, Minnesota/Wisconsin, North Central, New England, New York Metro, Northwest, Ohio, Pennsylvania/West Virginia, Southeast, and Southwest Texas. Entries include: Company name, address, phone, fax, email, name and title of contact, hardware used, software application, operating system, programming language, computer graphics, networking system. Arrangement: Geographical. Indexes: Alphabetical, industry, hardware.

3342 ■ Information Sources
Software & Information Industry Association
1090 Vermont Ave. NW, 6th Fl.
Washington, DC 20005-4095
Ph: (202)289-7442
Fax: (202)289-7097
Fr: 800-388-7478
URL: http://www.siia.net

Continuous. Covers: More than 800 companies involved in the creation, distribution, and use of information products, services, and technology. Entries are prepared by companies described. Entries include: Company name, address, phone, names of executives, international partners, regional offices, trade and brand names, and description of products and services. Arrangement: Alphabetical. Indexes: Product, personal name, trade name, geographical, corporate parents, international and niche markets.

3343 ■ Signal Magazine—AFCEA Source Book Issue
Armed Forces Communications & Electronics Association
4400 Fair Lakes Ct.
Fairfax, VA 22033-3899

Ph: (703)631-6192
Fax: (703)631-6169
Fr: 800-336-4583
E-mail: signal@afcea.org
URL: http://www.afcea.org/sourcebook

Annual, Latest edition 2010. Publication includes: List of member companies concerned with communications, design, production, maintenance and operation of communications, electronics, command and control, computers, intelligence systems and imagery. Entries include: Company name, address, phone, names and titles of key personnel, financial keys, trade and brand names, products or services, affiliations, description of organizational purpose, objectives. Arrangement: Alphabetical. Indexes: By disciplines.

Handbooks and Manuals

3344 ■ Careers for Computer Buffs and Other Technological Types
The McGraw-Hill Companies
PO Box 182604
Columbus, OH 43272
Fax: (614)759-3749
Fr: 877-883-5524
E-mail: customer.service@mcgraw-hill.com
URL: http://www.mhprofessional.com/
product.php?isbn=0071458778

Marjorie Eberts and Margaret Gisler. Third edition, 2006. $13.95 (paper). 160 pages. Suggested jobs in a wide range of settings, from the office to the outdoors.

3345 ■ DBA Survivor: Become a Rock Star DBA
Apress, Inc.
233 Spring St.
New York, NY 10013
Ph: (212)460-1500
Fax: (212)460-1575
E-mail: support@apress.com
URL: http://www.apress.com

Thomas LaRock. 2010. $39.99. 250 pages. Helps new database administrators understand more about the field. Features basics of database administration and different types of database support. Provides tips and advice to get ahead in the profession.

Employment Agencies and Search Firms

3346 ■ ATR Technology
1230 Oakmead Pkwy.
Sunnyvale, CA 94085
Ph: (408)328-8000
Fax: (408)328-8001

Fr: 877-412-1100
E-mail: corporate@atr1.com
URL: http://www.atr-technology.com

Description: Serves as an executive search firm specializing in the placement of information technology professionals ranging from complex software application development and infrastructure support to enterprise-wide project management.

3347 ■ Cardinal Mark Inc.
17113 Minnetonka Blvd., Ste. 112
Minnetonka, MN 55345
Ph: (952)314-4636
Fax: (610)228-7390
E-mail: jimz@cardinalmark.com
URL: http://www.cardinalmark.com

Executive search firm concentrated on telecommunication industry.

3348 ■ Career Development Services
150 State St.
Rochester, NY 14614
Ph: (585)244-0765
Fr: 800-736-6710
E-mail: info@careerdev.org
URL: http://www.careerdev.org

Employment agency.

3349 ■ Computer Management
7982 Honeygo Blvd., No. 23
Baltimore, MD 21236
Ph: (410)679-7000
E-mail: info@technicaljobs.com
URL: http://www.technicaljobs.com

Search firm focusing on filling jobs for database administration, network administration, web development, and software.

3350 ■ Conselium
14850 Montfort Dr., Ste. 106
Dallas, TX 75254
Ph: (972)934-8444
E-mail: maurice@conselium.com
URL: http://www.conselium.com

Executive search firm with a core expertise in corporate compliance, audit and information technology security.

3351 ■ Integrisource
1689 Mahan Center Blvd., Ste. B
Tallahassee, FL 32308
Ph: (850)575-5454
Fax: (850)575-0984
Fr: 877-575-5454
E-mail: recruiting@integrisource.net
URL: http://www.integrisource.net

Provides information technology staffing services to public and private organizations.

3352 ■ ManpowerGroup
100 Manpower Pl.
Milwaukee, WI 53212
Ph: (414)961-1000
Fax: (414)906-7822
URL: http://us.manpower.com

Specializes in a wide range of employment services including permanent placement, recruitment process outsourcing, managed service programs, outplacement and human resources consulting. Provides companies with workforce solutions that help them increase productivity and improve efficiency.

3353 ■ Recruiting Partners
3494 Camino Tassajara Rd., No. 404
Danville, CA 94506
Ph: (925)964-0249
E-mail: info@recruitingpartners.com
URL: http://www.recruitingpartners.com

Description: Serves as an executive and technical recruiting firm that specializes in accounting, legal, information technology, engineering, executive management and technical writing.

ONLINE JOB SOURCES AND SERVICES

3354 ■ ComputerWork.com
Fr: 800-691-8413
URL: http://www.computerwork.com

Description: Job search and resume submission service for professionals in information technology.

3355 ■ Database Administrator Jobs
URL: http://www.databaseadministratorjobs.net

Description: Features a searchable database of employment opportunities for database administrators.

3356 ■ DatabaseAnalyst.com
E-mail: info@careermarketplace.com
URL: http://www.databaseanalyst.com

Description: Features database analyst jobs and products for the software development industry.

3357 ■ Guru.com
5001 Baum Blvd., Ste. 760
Pittsburgh, PA 15213
Fax: (412)687-4466
Fr: 888-687-1316
URL: http://www.guru.com

Description: Job board specializing in contract jobs for creative and information technology professionals. Also provides online incorporation and educational opportunities for independent contractors along with articles and advice.

3358 ■ ItJobs.com
E-mail: comments@itjobsllc.com
URL: http://www.itjobs.com

Description: Provides information technology employment opportunities for the following categories: internet/intranet/extranet, network systems, open systems, client/server, software engineering and development, software QA and testing, ERP applications and management consulting, and legacy systems.

3359 ■ Jobs4IT.com
URL: http://www.jobs4it.com

Description: Features information technology job opportunities, job fairs, business opportunities, news, events, continuing education guide, resume database, distribution services and other career resources.

3360 ■ NetworkEngineer.com
URL: http://www.networkengineer.com

Description: Provides lists of job and career opportunities for network engineers.

3361 ■ ThinkEnergyGroup.com
E-mail: resumes@thinkjobs.com
URL: http://www.thinkenergygroup.com

Description: Serves as a job board for professionals looking for positions in engineering, power plant, energy, and technical fields. Contains advice and tips on interviews, job searching, resume writing, hiring, and management. Provides choices of work location, pay rates in the field of expertise and contract, temp-to-hire, and direct hiring options.

3362 ■ ZDNet Tech Jobs
URL: http://www.zdnet.com

Description: Site houses a listing of national employment opportunities for professionals in high tech fields. Also contains resume building tips and relocation resources.

OTHER SOURCES

3363 ■ Meta-Data Professional Organization (MPO)
PO Box 170445
Boston, MA 02117
Ph: (973)379-7212
E-mail: president@metadataprofessional.org
URL: http://www.metadataprofessional.org

Description: Represents business and IT professionals in all areas of meta-data practice including administrators, developers, architects and managers. Brings together individuals with interests, expertise, or hands-on experience in meta-data use from all areas of private and public enterprise throughout the world. Seeks to disseminate technical and professional information to meta-data practitioners of all levels of experience. Provides meta-data professionals with a community that fosters discussion, advancement and increased understanding of meta-data as it is applied in the field.

SOURCES OF HELP-WANTED ADS

3364 ■ *ACD News*
American College of Dentists
839J Quince Orchard Blvd.
Gaithersburg, MD 20878-1614
Ph: (301)977-3223
Fax: (301)977-3330
E-mail: office@acd.org
URL: http://www.acd.org/publications.htm

Description: Tri-annual. Presents accounts of College meetings, as well as remarks from the College's president. Publishes notices of scheduled events, spotlights individuals recognized or given awards by the College, and profiles convocation speakers, and other dental organizations. Recurring features include reports of meetings.

3365 ■ *AGD Impact*
Academy of General Dentistry
211 E Chicago Ave., Ste. 900
Chicago, IL 60611-1999
Fax: (312)440-0559
Fr: 888-AGD-DENT
E-mail: impact@agd.org
URL: http://www.agd.org/publications/?pubID=4

Description: Monthly. Covers the issues and trends that impact on general dentists and the profession. Includes CDE course list and fact sheets for patients.

3366 ■ *American Academy of Implant Dentistry Newsletter*
American Academy of Implant Dentistry
211 E Chicago Ave., Ste. 750
Chicago, IL 60611
Ph: (312)335-1550
Fax: (312)335-9090
Fr: 877-335-AAID
E-mail: info@aaid.com
URL: http://www.aaid-implant.org

Description: Quarterly. Covers current activities in the field of implant dentistry, particularly the educational programs of the Academy.

3367 ■ *American Dental Hygienists' Association Access*
American Dental Hygienists' Association
444 N Michigan Ave., Ste. 3400
Chicago, IL 60611
Ph: (312)440-8900
Fr: 800-243-ADHA
URL: http://www.adha.org/publications/index.html

$48.00/year for individuals; $85.00/year for two years; $120.00/year for individuals, for 3 years. Magazine covering current dental hygiene topics, regulatory and legislative developments, and association news.

3368 ■ *Bulletin of Dental Education*
American Dental Education Association
1400 K St., NW, Ste. 1100
Washington, DC 20005
Ph: (202)289-7201
Fax: (202)289-7204
E-mail: publications@adea.org
URL: http://www.adea.org

Description: Monthly. Contains news and information on dental education. Recurring features include a calendar of events, reports of meetings, news of educational opportunities, job listings, and notices of publications available.

3369 ■ *CDS Review*
Chicago Dental Society
401 N Michigan Ave., Ste. 200
Chicago, IL 60611
Ph: (312)836-7300
Fax: (312)836-7337
URL: http://www.cds.org/cds_review/

$25.00/year for individuals; $30.00/year for institutions, and schools in USA & Canada; $45.00/year for other countries; $5.00/year for single issue. Dental journal.

3370 ■ *Dental Economics*
PennWell Corp.
1421 S Sheridan Rd.
Tulsa, OK 74112
Ph: (918)835-3161
Fax: (918)831-9497
Fr: 800-331-4463
URL: http://www.dentaleconomics.com/index.html

Monthly. $132.00/year for individuals; $179.00/year for Canada and Mexico; $248.00/year for other countries; $211.00/year for two years; $312.00/year for Canada and Mexico; $428.00/year for other countries, two years; $65.00/year online. Magazine featuring business-related articles for dentists.

3371 ■ *Dental Town*
Dental Town
9633 S 48th St., Ste. 200
Phoenix, AZ 85044
Ph: (480)598-0001
Fax: (480)598-3450
URL: http://www.dentaltown.com/

Monthly. Free to qualified subscribers. Magazine that offers information on the dental industry and latest dental equipment.

3372 ■ *Hawaii Dental Journal*
Hawaii Medical Journal
1360 S Beretania St., Ste. 200
Honolulu, HI 96814
Ph: (808)536-7702
Fax: (808)536-2376
E-mail: hda@hawaiidentalassociation.net
URL: http://www.hawaiidentalassociation.net/index.html

Bimonthly. $55.00/year for individuals. Dental journal.

3373 ■ *Illinois Dental News*
Illinois State Dental Society
1010 S Second St.
Springfield, IL 62704
Ph: (217)525-1406
URL: http://www.isds.org/memberBenefits/publications/IllinoisDent

Monthly. $10.00/year for single issue, outside United States; $45.00/year for individuals; $90.00/year for other countries; $5.00/year for single issue. Dental magazine.

3374 ■ *InterFace*
American Society for Geriatric Dentistry
401 N Michigan Ave., Ste. 2200
Chicago, IL 60611
Ph: (312)527-6764
Fax: (312)673-6663
E-mail: scda@scdaonline.org
URL: http://www.scdonline.org/displaynewsletter.cfm

Description: Quarterly. Publishes news of geriatric dentistry as well as news of the Society, its members and activities. Recurring features include legislative updates, a calendar of events, news of members, book reviews, editorials, a message from the president, bibliographies, and biographies.

3375 ■ *Journal of the American Dental Association*
ADA Publishing
211 E Chicago Ave.
Chicago, IL 60611-2678
Ph: (312)440-2500
URL: http://jada.ada.org/

Monthly. $128.00/year for individuals, U.S. and Mexico; $161.00/year for institutions, U.S. and Mexico; $16.00/year for single issue, U.S. and Mexico; $141.00/year for Canada, U.S. and Mexico; $183.00/year for institutions, Canada, plus airmail; $24.00/year for single issue, Canada, plus airmail; $161.00/year for individuals, Canada, plus airmail; $204.00/year for institutions, Canada, plus airmail; $24.00/year; $22.00/year for single issue, Canada, plus airmail. Trade journal for the dental profession.

3376 ■ *Journal of the California Dental Association*
California Dental Association
1201 K St.
Sacramento, CA 95814
Fr: 800-232-7645
URL: http://www.cda.org/publications/journal_of_the_california_de

Monthly. $18.00/year for members; $40.00/year for members, domestic; $75.00/year for nonmembers, ADA; $80.00/year for other countries; $10.00/year for members, back issue. Professional magazine for dentists.

3377 ■ *Journal of Dental Education*
American Dental Education Association
1400 K St. NW, Ste. 1100
Washington, DC 20005
Ph: (202)289-7201

Fax: (202)289-7204
URL: http://www.adea.org/publications/jde/Pages/
default.aspx

Monthly. $80.00/year for members, print, online is free; $160.00/year for nonmembers, U.S., print; $190.00/year for nonmembers, Canada, print; $220.00/year for nonmembers, other countries, print; $390.00/year for institutions, Tier 1; $515.00/year for institutions, Tier 2; $665.00/year for institutions, Tier 3; $885.00/year for institutions, Tier 4; $1,100.00/year for institutions, Tier 5. Peer-reviewed journal for scholarly research and reviews on dental education.

3378 ■ *Journal of Dental Hygiene*
American Dental Hygienists' Association
444 N Michigan Ave., Ste. 3400
Chicago, IL 60611
Ph: (312)440-8900
Fr: 800-243-ADHA
E-mail: communications@adha.net
URL: http://www.adha.org/publications/index.html

Quarterly. $45.00/year for individuals; $65.00/year for two years; $90.00/year for individuals, 3 years. Professional journal on dental hygiene.

3379 ■ *Journal of Dental Research*
Sage Publications Inc.
2455 Teller Rd.
Thousand Oaks, CA 91320-2218
Ph: (805)499-9774
Fax: (805)583-2665
Fr: 800-818-7243
URL: http://www.dentalresearch.org/i4a/pages/
index.cfm?pageid=332

Monthly. $877.00/year for institutions, print & online; $427.00/year for individuals, print only; $789.00/year for institutions, online only; $859.00/year for institutions, print only. Peer-reviewed dental science journal.

3380 ■ *Journal of Operative Dentistry*
American Academy of Gold Foil Operators
c/o Dr. Robert C. Keene, Sec.-Treas.
1 Woods End Rd.
Etna, NH 03750-4318
URL: http://academyofoperativedentistry.com/
journal.html

Bimonthly. $75.00/year for individuals, online only; $200.00/year for institutions, online or print; $110.00/year for individuals, online or print; $85.00/year for other countries, online only; $115.00/year for other countries, print only; $250.00/year for institutions, other countries. Peer-reviewed professional journal covering issues in dentistry.

3381 ■ *Maryland State Dental Association Newsletter*
Maryland State Dental Association
6410F Dobbin Rd.
Columbia, MD 21045
Ph: (410)964-2880
Fax: (410)964-0583
E-mail: mddent@msda.com
URL: http://www.msda.com

Description: Monthly. Reports on health, legislative, economic, and medical issues that are pertinent to dentistry. Recurring features include letters to the editor, interviews, news of research, a calendar of events, reports of meetings, news of educational opportunities, and job listings.

3382 ■ *MDS Connection*
Massachusetts Dental Society
Two Willow St., Ste. 200
Southborough, MA 01745-1027
Fax: (508)480-0002
Fr: 800-342-8747
URL: http://www.massdental.org/

Description: Bimonthly. Provides news on the Society's activities and articles on the dental profession. Recurring features include reports of meetings, news of educational opportunities, job listings, and notices of publications available.

3383 ■ *News From The NIDCR*
National Institute of Dental and Craniofacial Research
National Institutes of Health
Bethesda, MD 20892-2190
Fax: (301)480-4098
E-mail: nidcrinfo@mail.nih.gov
URL: http://www.nidcr.nih.gov

Description: Bimonthly. Includes the latest news about funding opportunities, training and career development opportunities, NIDCR and NIH news, and science advances.

3384 ■ *Pediatric Dentistry Today*
American Academy of Pediatric Dentistry
211 E Chicago Ave., Ste. 1700
Chicago, IL 60611-2637
Ph: (312)337-2169
Fax: (312)337-6329
E-mail: aapdinfo@aapd.org
URL: http://www.aapd.org

Description: Bimonthly. Reports on the activities of the Academy, which seeks to advance the specialty of pediatric dentistry through practice, education, and research. Recurring features include news of research, profiles of members, and legislative updates.

3385 ■ *Pennsylvania Dental Journal*
Pennsylvania Dental Association
3501 N Front St.
PO Box 3341
Harrisburg, PA 17105
Ph: (717)234-5941
Fax: (717)234-2186
URL: http://www.padental.org/AM/
Template.cfm?Section=Publications

Bimonthly. Professional dentistry magazine containing treatment/procedure news, PDA activities information, continuing education courses, and legislation updates.

3386 ■ *RDH*
PennWell Publishing Co.
1421 S Sheridan Rd.
Tulsa, OK 74112
Ph: (918)835-3161
Fr: 800-331-4463
URL: http://www.rdhmag.com/index.html

Monthly. $79.00/year for individuals; $112.00/year for Canada; $141.00/year for other countries; $40.00/year for U.S. and other countries, digital. Magazine for dental hygiene professionals covering practice management, patient motivation, practice options, financial planning, personal development, preventive oral health care and treatment, home care instruction, radiology, anesthesia, nutrition, and new products.

3387 ■ *Washington State Dental Laboratory Association Newsletter*
PO Box 385
Graham, WA 98338
Ph: (360)832-2471
Fax: (360)832-2471
Fr: 800-652-2212
E-mail: peg2@mashell.com
URL: http://www.wsdla.com

Association newsletter featuring articles of interest to dental laboratory technicians as well as classified advertising for technical positions available.

3388 ■ *Westviews*
Western Los Angeles Dental Society
14722 Hawthorne Blvd., Ste. B
Lawndale, CA 90260
Ph: (310)349-2199
Fax: (310)349-2175
E-mail: wlads@pacbell.net
URL: http://www.westernlads.org

Description: Six issues/year. Carries items relating to organized dentistry and the clinical aspects of dentistry. Covers local community events involving

the organization or the profession; provides updates of states agency actions affecting dentistry.

3389 ■ *WSDA News*
Washington State Dental Association (WSDA)
126 NW Canal St.
Seattle, WA 98107
Ph: (206)448-1914
Fax: (206)443-9266
Fr: 800-448-3368
E-mail: info@wsda.org
URL: http://www.wsda.org/news

Description: Monthly. $67 per year. Contains information of interest to dentists on legislation, regulations, state boards and government, and business of the association. Recurring features include letters to the editor, editorial and op-ed columns, President's message, obituaries, practice opportunities, news of educational opportunities, and job listings.

EMPLOYER DIRECTORIES AND NETWORKING LISTS

3390 ■ *American Academy of Pediatric Dentistry—Membership Directory*
American Academy of Pediatric Dentistry
211 E Chicago Ave., Ste. 1700
Chicago, IL 60611-2663
Ph: (312)337-2169
Fax: (312)337-6329
URL: http://www.aapd.org

Annual, November. Covers: 5,600 pediatric dentists and several dentists in practice, teaching, and research. Entries include: Name, address, phone. Arrangement: Alphabetical. Indexes: Geographical.

3391 ■ *International Association for Orthodontics—Membership Directory*
International Association for Orthodontics
750 N Lincoln Memorial Dr., Ste. 422
Milwaukee, WI 53202
Ph: (414)272-2757
Fax: (414)272-2754
URL: http://www.iaortho.org

Annual, June. Covers: 2,500 general and children's dentists who also work to correct facial and jaw irregularities. Entries include: Name, office address and phone, orthodontic techniques practiced. Arrangement: Geographical. Indexes: Personal name.

3392 ■ *Washington Physicians Directory*
The Washington Physicians Directory
13912 Overton Ln.
PO Box 4436
Silver Spring, MD 20904
Ph: (301)384-1506
Fax: (301)384-6854
E-mail: wpd@wpdnetwork.com
URL: http://www.wpdnetwork.com

Annual, Latest edition 50th Anniversary Edition; 2012. Covers: 9,800 physicians in private practice or on full-time staff at hospitals in the Washington, D.C., metropolitan area. Entries include: Name, medical school and year of graduation; up to four office addresses with phone numbers for each; up to four medical specialties (indicating board certifications), Unique Physician Identification Numbers (UPIN), and e-mail. Arrangement: Alphabetical. Indexes: Geographical (within medical specialty); foreign language.

3393 ■ *Worldwide Online Search Directory*
402 W Wilson St.
Madison, WI 53703
Ph: (608)222-8583
Fax: (608)222-9540
Fr: 800-543-9220
E-mail: info@aacd.com
URL: http://www.aacd.com/professional/
membershipbenefits.asp#4

Provides a worldwide listing of members of the American Academy of Cosmetic Dentistry.

HANDBOOKS AND MANUALS

3394 ■ Careers in Health Care
The McGraw-Hill Companies
PO Box 182604
Columbus, OH 43272
Fax: (614)759-3749
Fr: 877-883-5524
E-mail: customer.service@mcgraw-hill.com
URL: http://www.mhprofessional.com/
product.php?isbn=0071466533

Barbara M. Swanson. Fifth edition, 2005. $19.95 (paper). 192 pages. Describes job duties, work settings, salaries, licensing and certification requirements, educational preparation, and future outlook. Gives ideas on how to secure a job.

3395 ■ Clinical Primer: A Pocket Guide for Dental Assistants
Lippincott Williams & Wilkins
16522 Hunters Green Pkwy.
Hagerstown, MD 21740
Ph: (301)223-2300
Fax: (301)223-2398
Fr: 800-638-3030
E-mail: customerservice@lww.com
URL: http://www.lww.com

Melanie Mitchell. 2006. $41.95. Help you learn and retain important information you need as a dental assistant

3396 ■ Dental Assisting: A Comprehensive Approach
Cengage Learning
PO Box 6904
Florence, KY 41022
Fax: 800-487-8488
Fr: 800-354-9706
URL: http://www.cengage.com

Donna J. Phinney, Judy H. Halstead. Third edition, 2008. $132.95. Designed to help you prepare for and pass the DANB certification exam, as well as to manage the challenges of working in the modern day dental office. Illustrated. 976 pages.

3397 ■ Levison's Textbook for Dental Nurses
Blackwell Publishers
350 Main St., 6th Fl.
Malden, MA 02148-5018
Ph: (781)388-8200
Fax: (781)388-8210
URL: http://as.wiley.com/WileyCDA/WileyTitle/
productCd-1405175575.html

Carole Hollins. Tenth edition, 2008. Illustrated. $41.99. 440 Pages. Educational.

3398 ■ Materials and Procedures for Today's Dental Assistant
Cengage Learning
PO Box 6904
Florence, KY 41022
Fax: 800-487-8488
Fr: 800-354-9706
E-mail: esales@cengage.com
URL: http://www.cengage.com

Ellen Dietz-Bourguignon. 2006. $73.25. 296 pages. Profiles training and skills for individuals interested in a career as a dental assistant.

3399 ■ Opportunities in Dental Care Careers
McGraw-Hill Professional
PO Box 182604
Columbus, OH 43272
Ph: 877-833-5524
Fax: (614)759-3749
E-mail: pbg.ecommerce_custserv@mcgraw-hill.com
URL: http://www.mhprofessional.com/
product.php?isbn=0071388346

Bonnie Kendall. $12.95 (e-book). 160 pages. Provides a complete overview of the job possibilities in dental industry. Includes the skill and training requirements to current salary figures.

3400 ■ Opportunities in Health and Medical Careers
The McGraw-Hill Companies
PO Box 182604
Columbus, OH 43272
Fax: (614)759-3749
Fr: 877-883-5524
E-mail: customer.service@mcgraw-hill.com
URL: http://www.mhprofessional.com/
product.php?isbn=0071437274

I. Donald Snook, Jr. and Leo D'Orazio. 2004. $14.95 (paper). 157 pages. Covers the full range of medical and health occupations. Illustrated.

3401 ■ Resumes for Health and Medical Careers
The McGraw-Hill Companies
PO Box 182604
Columbus, OH 43272
Fax: (614)759-3749
Fr: 877-883-5524
E-mail: customer.service@mcgraw-hill.com
URL: http://www.mhprofessional.com/
product.php?isbn=0071545352

Third edition, 2008. $12.95 (paper). 144 pages.

EMPLOYMENT AGENCIES AND SEARCH FIRMS

3402 ■ Actuary Resources
115 N Castle Heights Ave., Ste. 202
Lebanon, TN 37087-2768
Ph: (615)360-5171
Fax: (615)360-5173
E-mail: info@actuaryresources.org
URL: http://www.actuaryresources.org

Provides staffing services to several different types of industries. Offers a free screening service to clients.

3403 ■ DDS Staffing Resources, Inc.
9755 Dogwood Rd., Ste. 200
Roswell, GA 30075
Ph: (770)998-7779
Fax: (770)552-0176
Fr: 888-668-7779
URL: http://msrstaffing.com

Dental staffing agency.

3404 ■ Team Placement Service, Inc.
1414 Prince St., Ste. 202
Alexandria, VA 22314
Ph: (703)820-8618
Fax: (703)820-3368
Fr: 800-495-6767
E-mail: 4jobs@teamplace.com
URL: http://www.teamplace.com

Full-service personnel consultants provide placement for healthcare staff, physician and dentist, private practice, and hospitals. Conduct interviews, tests, and reference checks to select the top 20% of applicants. Survey applicants' skill levels, provide backup information on each candidate, select compatible candidates for consideration, and insure the hiring process minimizes potential legal liability. Industries served: healthcare and government agencies providing medical, dental, biotech, laboratory, hospitals, and physician search.

ONLINE JOB SOURCES AND SERVICES

3405 ■ CareersInDental.com
URL: http://www.careersindental.com

Description: Serves as a job board for the dental industry. Features listings of employment opportunities and job openings in the field.

3406 ■ DentalAssistantJobs.com
E-mail: targetedjobsites@yahoo.com
URL: http://www.dentalassistantjobs.com

Description: Features job opportunities, resume search, postings and employment for dental assistant professionals.

3407 ■ DentalCrossing.com
URL: http://www.dentalcrossing.com

Description: Provides employment opportunities for dentists, dental assistants, dental hygienists, and dental lab technicians.

3408 ■ DentalJobsBoard.net
URL: http://www.dentaljobsboard.net

Description: Features dentist jobs, dental hygiene jobs, dental assistant jobs, and jobs for dental lab technicians.

3409 ■ DentalPortal.com
URL: http://www.dentalportal.com

Description: Search engine for finding dentists, orthodontists, oral surgeons, and other dental professionals.

3410 ■ DentalPost.net
URL: http://www.dentalpost.net

Description: Lists dental jobs including dentist jobs, dental hygienist jobs, dental assistant jobs, dental lab technician jobs, and dental front office jobs.

3411 ■ DentalWorkers.com
URL: http://www.dentalworkers.com/employment

Description: Serves as an online employment resource among dental professionals. Provides classified ads for dental jobs, and free resume posting for workers.

3412 ■ Dentist Job Cafe
URL: http://www.dentistjobcafe.com

Description: Features dental job listings. Provides employment services for dentists, dental hygienists, and dental assistants.

3413 ■ DentistJobsNow.com
URL: http://www.dentist-jobs-now.com

Description: Provides assistance to new and practicing dentists, hygienists, and dental assistants in finding employment.

3414 ■ DentistryJob.com
URL: http://www.dentistryjob.com

Description: Serves as a job board for dentistry professionals.

3415 ■ HEALTHeCAREERS Network
Fr: 888-884-8242
E-mail: info@healthecareers.com
URL: http://www.healthecareers.com

Description: Career search site for jobs in all health care specialties; educational resources; visa and licensing information for relocation; interesting articles; relocation tools; links to professional organizations and general resources.

3416 ■ iHireDental
URL: http://www.ihiredental.com

Description: Features dental jobs in different specialty areas.

3417 ■ ProHealthJobs.com
Ph: (484)443-8545
Fax: (484)443-8549
E-mail: info@prohealthjobs.com
URL: http://prohealthjobs.com/jobboard

Description: Career resources site for the medical and health care field. Lists professional opportunities, product information, continuing education and open positions.

TRADESHOWS

3418 ■ American Academy of Pediatric Dentistry Annual Session

American Academy of Pediatric Dentistry
211 E. Chicago Ave., Ste. 1700
Chicago, IL 60611-2637
Ph: (312)337-2169
Fax: (312)337-6329
URL: http://www.aapd.org

Annual. Primary Exhibits: Dental products and publications. Dates and Locations: 2012 May 24-27; San Diego, CA; San Diego Marriott Hotel & Marina; 2013 May 23-26; Orlando, FL; Walt Disney World Swan Dolphin Resort; 2014 May 22-25; Boston, MA; Hynes Convention Center.

3419 ■ Star of the North Meeting

Minnesota Dental Association
1335 Industrial Blvd., Ste. 200
Minneapolis, MN 55413-4801
Ph: (612)767-8400
Fax: (612)767-8500
Fr: 800-950-3368
E-mail: info@mndental.org
URL: http://www.mndental.org

Annual. Primary Exhibits: Dental equipment and supplies, dental laboratory equipment, office equipment, and service organizations. Dates and Locations: 2012 Apr 26-28; 2013 Apr 25-27; 2014 Apr 24-26; 2015 Apr 23-25.

3420 ■ Thomas P. Hinman Dental Meeting & Exhibits

Thomas P. Hinman Dental Society of Atlanta
33 Lenox Pte.
Atlanta, GA 30324-3172
Ph: (404)231-1663
Fax: (404)231-9638
URL: http://www.hinman.org

Annual. Primary Exhibits: Dental equipment, supplies, and services. Dates and Locations: 2012 Mar 22-24; 2013 Mar 21-23.

3421 ■ Yankee Dental Congress

Massachusetts Dental Society
2 Willow St., No. 200
Southborough, MA 01745-1027
Ph: (508)480-9797
Fax: (508)480-0002
Fr: 800-342-8747
E-mail: madental@massdental.org
URL: http://www.massdental.org

Annual. Primary Exhibits: Dental products, equipment, and services. Dates and Locations: 2012 Jan 25-29; Boston, MA; Boston Convention & Exhibition Center.

OTHER SOURCES

3422 ■ American Academy of Cosmetic Dentistry

402 W Wilson St.
Madison, WI 53703
Ph: (608)222-8583
Fax: (608)222-9540
Fr: 800-543-9220
E-mail: info@aacd.com
URL: http://www.aacd.com

Members include more than 8,000 cosmetic and reconstructive dentists, dental laboratory technicians, dental auxiliaries, dental hygienists, educators, researchers and students. Membership benefits include AACD accreditation, registration to AACD's Annual Scientific Session, publications, online search directory, marketing materials, and more.

3423 ■ American College of Prosthodontists

211 E Chicago Ave., Ste. 1000
Chicago, IL 60611
Ph: (312)573-1260
Fax: (312)573-1257
URL: http://www.prosthodontics.org

Membership includes more than 3,300 prosthodontists, dental technicians, dental students and other dental professionals contributing to the specialty. Committed to the esthetic restoration of teeth, including bridges, crowns/caps, dental implants, dentures, partial dentures, whitening and veneers. Membership includes free subscriptions to the Journal of Prosthodontics, the Messenger, and e-blasts.

3424 ■ American Dental Assistants Association (ADAA)

35 E Wacker Dr., Ste. 1730
Chicago, IL 60601-2211
Ph: (312)541-1550
Fax: (312)541-1496
Fr: 877-874-3785
E-mail: adaahelp@aol.com
URL: http://www.dentalassistant.org

Description: Individuals employed as dental assistants in dental offices, clinics, hospitals, or institutions; instructors of dental assistants; dental students. Sponsors workshops and seminars; maintains governmental liaison. Offers group insurance; maintains scholarship trust fund. Dental Assisting National Board examines members who are candidates for title of Certified Dental Assistant.

3425 ■ American Dental Association (ADA)

211 E Chicago Ave.
Chicago, IL 60611-2678
Ph: (312)440-2500
Fax: (312)440-2800
E-mail: membership@ada.org
URL: http://www.ada.org

Description: Professional society of dentists. Encourages the improvement of the health of the public and promotes the art and science of dentistry in matters of legislation and regulations. Inspects and accredits dental schools and schools for dental hygienists, assistants, and laboratory technicians. Conducts research programs at ADA Foundation Research Institute. Produces dental health education material used in the U.S. Sponsors National Children's Dental Health Month and Give Kids a Smile Day. Compiles statistics on personnel, practice, and dental care needs and attitudes of patients with regard to dental health.

3426 ■ American Dental Education Association (ADEA)

1400 K St. NW, Ste. 1100
Washington, DC 20005
Ph: (202)289-7201
Fax: (202)289-7204
E-mail: valachovicr@adea.org
URL: http://www.adea.org

Description: Individuals interested in dental education; schools of dentistry, advanced dental and allied dental education in the U.S., Canada, and Puerto Rico; affiliated institutions of the federal government and corporations. Works to promote better teaching and education in dentistry and dental research and to facilitate exchange of ideas among dental educators. Sponsors meetings, conferences, and workshops; conducts surveys, studies, and special projects and publishes their results. Maintains 37 sections and 8 special interest groups representing many different aspects of dental education.

3427 ■ American Medical Technologists (AMT)

10700 W Higgins Rd., Ste. 150
Rosemont, IL 60018
Ph: (847)823-5169
Fax: (847)823-0458
Fr: 800-275-1268
E-mail: membership@amt1.com
URL: http://www.amt1.com

Description: Represents medical technologists, medical laboratory technicians, medical assistants, medical administrative specialists, dental assistants, office laboratory technicians, phlebotomy technicians, laboratory consultants, and allied health instructors. Provides allied health professionals with professional certification services and membership programs to enhance their professional and personal growth. Aims to issue certification credentials to medical and dental assistants, clinical laboratory personnel, laboratory consultants, and allied health instructors.

3428 ■ American Public Health Association (APHA)

800 I St. NW
Washington, DC 20001
Ph: (202)777-2742
Fax: (202)777-2534
E-mail: comments@apha.org
URL: http://www.apha.org

Description: Professional organization of physicians, nurses, educators, academicians, environmentalists, epidemiologists, new professionals, social workers, health administrators, optometrists, podiatrists, pharmacists, dentists, nutritionists, health planners, other community and mental health specialists, and interested consumers. Seeks to protect and promote personal, mental, and environmental health. Services include: promulgation of standards; establishment of uniform practices and procedures; development of the etiology of communicable diseases; research in public health; exploration of medical care programs and their relationships to public health. Sponsors job placement service.

3429 ■ American School Health Association (ASHA)

4340 East West Hwy., Ste. 403
Bethesda, MD 20814
Ph: (301)652-8072
Fax: (301)652-8077
Fr: 800-445-2742
E-mail: info@ashaweb.org
URL: http://www.ashaweb.org

Description: School physicians, school nurses, counselors, nutritionists, psychologists, social workers, administrators, school health coordinators, health educators, and physical educators working in schools, professional preparation programs, public health, and community-based organizations. Promotes coordinated school health programs that include health education, health services, a healthful school environment, physical education, nutrition services, and psycho-social health services offered in schools collaboratively with families and other members of the community. Offers professional reference materials and professional development opportunities. Conducts pilot programs that inform materials development, provides technical assistance to school professionals, advocates for school health.

3430 ■ Crown Council

975 Woodoak Ln., Ste. 200
Salt Lake City, UT 84117
Ph: (801)293-8522
Fax: (801)293-8524
Fr: 800-276-9658
E-mail: success@crowncouncil.com
URL: http://www.mycrowncouncil.com

Description: Seeks to improve independent dental practices. Promotes oral health and the fight against oral cancer. Provides patient care and offers state-of-the-art dental procedure facilities.

3431 ■ Holistic Dental Association (HDA)

1825 Ponce de Leon Blvd., No. 148
Coral Gables, FL 33134
Ph: (305)356-7338
Fax: (305)468-6359
E-mail: director@holisticdental.org
URL: http://www.holisticdental.org

Description: Represents dentists, chiropractors, dental hygienists, physical therapists, and medical doctors. Aims to provide a holistic approach to better dental care for patients, and to expand techniques, medications, and philosophies that pertain to extractions, anesthetics, fillings, crowns, and orthodontics.

Encourages the use of homeopathic medications, acupuncture, cranial osteopathy, nutritional techniques, and physical therapy in treating patients in addition to conventional treatments. Sponsors training and educational seminars.

3432 ■ National Dental Assistants Association (NDAA)
3517 16th St. NW
Washington, DC 20010
Ph: (202)588-1697
Fax: (202)588-1244
E-mail: deboffmgr@aol.com
URL: http://www.ndaonline.org/
index.php?option=com_
content&view=article&id=90&Itemid=96

Description: An auxiliary of the National Dental Association. Works to encourage education and certification among dental assistants. Conducts clinics and workshops to further the education of members. Bestows annual Humanitarian Award; offers scholarships.

3433 ■ National Rural Health Association (NRHA)
Administrative Office
521 E 63rd St.
Kansas City, MO 64110-3329
Ph: (816)756-3140
Fax: (816)756-3144
E-mail: mail@nrharural.org
URL: http://www.ruralhealthweb.org

Description: Administrators, physicians, nurses, physician assistants, health planners, academicians, and others interested or involved in rural health care. Creates a better understanding of health care problems unique to rural areas; utilizes a collective approach in finding positive solutions; articulates and represents the health care needs of rural America; supplies current information to rural health care providers; serves as a liaison between rural health care programs throughout the country. Offers continuing education credits for medical, dental, nursing, and management courses.

SOURCES OF HELP-WANTED ADS

3434 ■ *ACD News*
American College of Dentists
839J Quince Orchard Blvd.
Gaithersburg, MD 20878-1614
Ph: (301)977-3223
Fax: (301)977-3330
E-mail: office@acd.org
URL: http://www.acd.org/publications.htm
Description: Tri-annual. Presents accounts of College meetings, as well as remarks from the College's president. Publishes notices of scheduled events, spotlights individuals recognized or given awards by the College, and profiles convocation speakers, and other dental organizations. Recurring features include reports of meetings.

3435 ■ *AGD Impact*
Academy of General Dentistry
211 E Chicago Ave., Ste. 900
Chicago, IL 60611-1999
Fax: (312)440-0559
Fr: 888-AGD-DENT
E-mail: impact@agd.org
URL: http://www.agd.org/publications/?pubID=4
Description: Monthly. Covers the issues and trends that impact on general dentists and the profession. Includes CDE course list and fact sheets for patients.

3436 ■ *American Dental Hygienists' Association Access*
American Dental Hygienists' Association
444 N Michigan Ave., Ste. 3400
Chicago, IL 60611
Ph: (312)440-8900
Fr: 800-243-ADHA
URL: http://www.adha.org/publications/index.html
$48.00/year for individuals; $85.00/year for two years; $120.00/year for individuals, for 3 years. Magazine covering current dental hygiene topics, regulatory and legislative developments, and association news.

3437 ■ *Bulletin of Dental Education*
American Dental Education Association
1400 K St., NW, Ste. 1100
Washington, DC 20005
Ph: (202)289-7201
Fax: (202)289-7204
E-mail: publications@adea.org
URL: http://www.adea.org
Description: Monthly. Contains news and information on dental education. Recurring features include a calendar of events, reports of meetings, news of educational opportunities, job listings, and notices of publications available.

3438 ■ *CDS Review*
Chicago Dental Society
401 N Michigan Ave., Ste. 200
Chicago, IL 60611

Ph: (312)836-7300
Fax: (312)836-7337
URL: http://www.cds.org/cds_review/
$25.00/year for individuals; $30.00/year for institutions, and schools in USA & Canada; $45.00/year for other countries; $5.00/year for single issue. Dental journal.

3439 ■ *Dental Economics*
PennWell Corp.
1421 S Sheridan Rd.
Tulsa, OK 74112
Ph: (918)835-3161
Fax: (918)831-9497
Fr: 800-331-4463
URL: http://www.dentaleconomics.com/index.html
Monthly. $132.00/year for individuals; $179.00/year for Canada and Mexico; $248.00/year for other countries; $211.00/year for two years; $312.00/year for Canada and Mexico; $428.00/year for other countries, two years; $65.00/year online. Magazine featuring business-related articles for dentists.

3440 ■ *Dental Town*
Dental Town
9633 S 48th St., Ste. 200
Phoenix, AZ 85044
Ph: (480)598-0001
Fax: (480)598-3450
URL: http://www.dentaltown.com/
Monthly. Free to qualified subscribers. Magazine that offers information on the dental industry and latest dental equipment.

3441 ■ *Hawaii Dental Journal*
Hawaii Medical Journal
1360 S Beretania St., Ste. 200
Honolulu, HI 96814
Ph: (808)536-7702
Fax: (808)536-2376
E-mail: hda@hawaiidentalassociation.net
URL: http://www.hawaiidentalassociation.net/index.html
Bimonthly. $55.00/year for individuals. Dental journal.

3442 ■ *Illinois Dental News*
Illinois State Dental Society
1010 S Second St.
Springfield, IL 62704
Ph: (217)525-1406
URL: http://www.isds.org/memberBenefits/publications/IllinoisDent
Monthly. $10.00/year for single issue, outside United States; $45.00/year for individuals; $90.00/year for other countries; $5.00/year for single issue. Dental magazine.

3443 ■ *InterFace*
American Society for Geriatric Dentistry
401 N Michigan Ave., Ste. 2200
Chicago, IL 60611
Ph: (312)527-6764

Fax: (312)673-6663
E-mail: scda@scdaonline.org
URL: http://www.scdonline.org/displaynewsletter.cfm
Description: Quarterly. Publishes news of geriatric dentistry as well as news of the Society, its members and activities. Recurring features include legislative updates, a calendar of events, news of members, book reviews, editorials, a message from the president, bibliographies, and biographies.

3444 ■ *Journal of the American Dental Association*
ADA Publishing
211 E Chicago Ave.
Chicago, IL 60611-2678
Ph: (312)440-2500
URL: http://jada.ada.org/
Monthly. $128.00/year for individuals, U.S. and Mexico; $161.00/year for institutions, U.S. and Mexico; $16.00/year for single issue, U.S. and Mexico; $141.00/year for Canada, U.S. and Mexico; $183.00/year for institutions, Canada, plus airmail; $24.00/year for single issue, Canada, plus airmail; $161.00/year for individuals, Canada, plus airmail; $204.00/year for institutions, Canada, plus airmail; $24.00/year; $22.00/year for single issue, Canada, plus airmail. Trade journal for the dental profession.

3445 ■ *Journal of the California Dental Association*
California Dental Association
1201 K St.
Sacramento, CA 95814
Fr: 800-232-7645
URL: http://www.cda.org/publications/journal_of_the_california_de
Monthly. $18.00/year for members; $40.00/year for members, domestic; $75.00/year for nonmembers, ADA; $80.00/year for other countries; $10.00/year for members, back issue. Professional magazine for dentists.

3446 ■ *Journal of Dental Education*
American Dental Education Association
1400 K St. NW, Ste. 1100
Washington, DC 20005
Ph: (202)289-7201
Fax: (202)289-7204
URL: http://www.adea.org/publications/jde/Pages/default.aspx
Monthly. $80.00/year for members, print, online is free; $160.00/year for nonmembers, U.S., print; $190.00/year for nonmembers, Canada, print; $220.00/year for nonmembers, other countries, print; $390.00/year for institutions, Tier 1; $515.00/year for institutions, Tier 2; $665.00/year for institutions, Tier 3; $885.00/year for institutions, Tier 4; $1,100.00/year for institutions, Tier 5. Peer-reviewed journal for scholarly research and reviews on dental education.

3447 ■ *Journal of Dental Hygiene*
American Dental Hygienists' Association
444 N Michigan Ave., Ste. 3400
Chicago, IL 60611

Ph: (312)440-8900
Fr: 800-243-ADHA
E-mail: communications@adha.net
URL: http://www.adha.org/publications/index.html

Quarterly. $45.00/year for individuals; $65.00/year for
two years; $90.00/year for individuals, 3 years.
Professional journal on dental hygiene.

3448 ■ Journal of Dental Research
Sage Publications Inc.
2455 Teller Rd.
Thousand Oaks, CA 91320-2218
Ph: (805)499-9774
Fax: (805)583-2665
Fr: 800-818-7243
URL: http://www.dentalresearch.org/i4a/pages/
    index.cfm?pageid=332

Monthly. $877.00/year for institutions, print & online;
$427.00/year for individuals, print only; $789.00/year
for institutions, online only; $859.00/year for institu-
tions, print only. Peer-reviewed dental science journal.

3449 ■ Journal of Operative Dentistry
American Academy of Gold Foil Operators
c/o Dr. Robert C. Keene, Sec.-Treas.
1 Woods End Rd.
Etna, NH 03750-4318
URL: http://academyofoperativedentistry.com/
    journal.html

Bimonthly. $75.00/year for individuals, online only;
$200.00/year for institutions, online or print; $110.00/
year for individuals, online or print; $85.00/year for
other countries, online only; $115.00/year for other
countries, print only; $250.00/year for institutions,
other countries. Peer-reviewed professional journal
covering issues in dentistry.

**3450 ■ Maryland State Dental Association
    Newsletter**
Maryland State Dental Association
6410F Dobbin Rd.
Columbia, MD 21045
Ph: (410)964-2880
Fax: (410)964-0583
E-mail: mddent@msda.com
URL: http://www.msda.com

Description: Monthly. Reports on health, legislative,
economic, and medical issues that are pertinent to
dentistry. Recurring features include letters to the
editor, interviews, news of research, a calendar of
events, reports of meetings, news of educational opportunities, and job listings.

3451 ■ MDS Connection
Massachusetts Dental Society
Two Willow St., Ste. 200
Southborough, MA 01745-1027
Fax: (508)480-0002
Fr: 800-342-8747
URL: http://www.massdental.org/

Description: Bimonthly. Provides news on the
Society's activities and articles on the dental
profession. Recurring features include reports of
meetings, news of educational opportunities, job listings, and notices of publications available.

3452 ■ Pediatric Dentistry Today
American Academy of Pediatric Dentistry
211 E Chicago Ave., Ste. 1700
Chicago, IL 60611-2637
Ph: (312)337-2169
Fax: (312)337-6329
E-mail: aapdinfo@aapd. org
URL: http://www.aapd.org

Description: Bimonthly. Reports on the activities of
the Academy, which seeks to advance the specialty
of pediatric dentistry through practice, education, and
research. Recurring features include news of research, profiles of members, and legislative updates.

3453 ■ Pennsylvania Dental Journal
Pennsylvania Dental Association
3501 N Front St.
PO Box 3341
Harrisburg, PA 17105
Ph: (717)234-5941
Fax: (717)234-2186
URL: http://www.padental.org/AM/
    Template.cfm?Section=Publications

Bimonthly. Professional dentistry magazine containing treatment/procedure news, PDA activities information, continuing education courses, and legislation
updates.

3454 ■ RDH
PennWell Publishing Co.
1421 S Sheridan Rd.
Tulsa, OK 74112
Ph: (918)835-3161
Fr: 800-331-4463
URL: http://www.rdhmag.com/index.html

Monthly. $79.00/year for individuals; $112.00/year for
Canada; $141.00/year for other countries; $40.00/
year for U.S. and other countries, digital. Magazine
for dental hygiene professionals covering practice
management, patient motivation, practice options,
financial planning, personal development, preventive
oral health care and treatment, home care instruction, radiology, anesthesia, nutrition, and new
products.

**3455 ■ Washington State Dental Laboratory
    Association Newsletter**
PO Box 385
Graham, WA 98338
Ph: (360)832-2471
Fax: (360)832-2471
Fr: 800-652-2212
E-mail: peg2@mashell.com
URL: http://www.wsdla.com

Association newsletter featuring articles of interest to
dental laboratory technicians as well as classified
advertising for technical positions available.

3456 ■ Westviews
Western Los Angeles Dental Society
14722 Hawthorne Blvd., Ste. B
Lawndale, CA 90260
Ph: (310)349-2199
Fax: (310)349-2175
E-mail: wlads@pacbell.net
URL: http://www.westernlads.org

Description: Six issues/year. Carries items relating
to organized dentistry and the clinical aspects of
dentistry. Covers local community events involving
the organization or the profession; provides updates
of states agency actions affecting dentistry.

3457 ■ WSDA News
Washington State Dental Association (WSDA)
126 NW Canal St.
Seattle, WA 98107
Ph: (206)448-1914
Fax: (206)443-9266
Fr: 800-448-3368
E-mail: info@wsda.org
URL: http://www.wsda.org/news

Description: Monthly. $67 per year. Contains infor-
mation of interest to dentists on legislation, regulations, state boards and government, and business of
the association. Recurring features include letters to
the editor, editorial and op-ed columns, President's
message, obituaries, practice opportunities, news of
educational opportunities, and job listings.

EMPLOYER DIRECTORIES AND
NETWORKING LISTS

**3458 ■ American Academy of Pediatric
    Dentistry—Membership Directory**
American Academy of Pediatric Dentistry
211 E Chicago Ave., Ste. 1700
Chicago, IL 60611-2663

Ph: (312)337-2169
Fax: (312)337-6329
URL: http://www.aapd.org

Annual, November. Covers: 5,600 pediatric dentists
and several dentists in practice, teaching, and
research. Entries include: Name, address, phone. Arrangement: Alphabetical. Indexes: Geographical.

**3459 ■ International Association for
    Orthodontics—Membership Directory**
International Association for Orthodontics
750 N Lincoln Memorial Dr., Ste. 422
Milwaukee, WI 53202
Ph: (414)272-2757
Fax: (414)272-2754
URL: http://www.iaortho.org

Annual, June. Covers: 2,500 general and children's
dentists who also work to correct facial and jaw
irregularities. Entries include: Name, office address
and phone, orthodontic techniques practiced. Arrangement: Geographical. Indexes: Personal name.

3460 ■ Washington Physicians Directory
The Washington Physicians Directory
13912 Overton Ln.
PO Box 4436
Silver Spring, MD 20904
Ph: (301)384-1506
Fax: (301)384-6854
E-mail: wpd@wpdnetwork.com
URL: http://www.wpdnetwork.com

Annual, Latest edition 50th Anniversary Edition; 2012.
Covers: 9,800 physicians in private practice or on
full-time staff at hospitals in the Washington, D.C.,
metropolitan area. Entries include: Name, medical
school and year of graduation; up to four office addresses with phone numbers for each; up to four
medical specialties (indicating board certifications),
Unique Physician Identification Numbers (UPIN), and
e-mail. Arrangement: Alphabetical. Indexes: Geographical (within medical specialty); foreign language.

3461 ■ Worldwide Online Search Directory
402 W Wilson St.
Madison, WI 53703
Ph: (608)222-8583
Fax: (608)222-9540
Fr: 800-543-9220
E-mail: info@aacd.com
URL: http://www.aacd.com/professional/
    membershipbenefits.asp#4

Provides a worldwide listing of members of the
American Academy of Cosmetic Dentistry.

HANDBOOKS AND MANUALS

3462 ■ Careers in Health Care
The McGraw-Hill Companies
PO Box 182604
Columbus, OH 43272
Fax: (614)759-3749
Fr: 877-883-5524
E-mail: customer.service@mcgraw-hill.com
URL: http://www.mhprofessional.com/
    product.php?isbn=0071466533

Barbara M. Swanson. Fifth edition, 2005. $19.95
(paper). 192 pages. Describes job duties, work settings, salaries, licensing and certification requirements, educational preparation, and future outlook.
Gives ideas on how to secure a job.

**3463 ■ Dental Assisting: A Comprehensive
    Approach**
Cengage Learning
PO Box 6904
Florence, KY 41022
Fax: 800-487-8488
Fr: 800-354-9706
URL: http://www.cengage.com

Donna J. Phinney, Judy H. Halstead. Third edition,
2008. $132.95. Designed to help you prepare for and
pass the DANB certification exam, as well as to man-

age the challenges of working in the modern day dental office. Illustrated. 976 pages.

3464 ■ *Dental Hygienist*
National Learning Corporation
212 Michael Dr.
Syosset, NY 11791
Fr: 800-632-8888
URL: http://www.passbooks.com

2009. $39.95 (paper). Serves as an exam preparation guide for dental hygienists.

3465 ■ *Kaplan Dental Hygienist Licensure Exam*
Kaplan Publishing
1 Liberty Plaza, 24th Fl.
New York, NY 10006
Ph: (212)618-2405
Fax: (212)618-2499
Fr: 800-527-4836
URL: http://www.kaplanpublishing.com

Paula Tomko. 2007. $59.95. Provides a complete review for individuals taking the National Dental Hygienist Licensure exam, including a full-length simulated test and explanations of answers.

3466 ■ *Levison's Textbook for Dental Nurses*
Blackwell Publishers
350 Main St., 6th Fl.
Malden, MA 02148-5018
Ph: (781)388-8200
Fax: (781)388-8210
URL: http://as.wiley.com/WileyCDA/WileyTitle/productCd-1405175575.html

Carole Hollins. Tenth edition, 2008. Illustrated. $41.99. 440 Pages. Educational.

3467 ■ *Master the Dental Hygienist Exam*
Peterson's Publishing
Peterson's Nelnet LLC
2000 Lenox Dr., 2nd Fl., Ste. 203
Lawrenceville, NJ 08648
Ph: (609)896-1800
E-mail: onlinestore@petersons.com
URL: http://www.petersonsbooks.com

2011. $18.95. 352 pages. Offers test preparation strategies and skill-building review for test takers seeking career advancement in dental hygiene. Includes practice tests, step-by-step career plan and topics covering the dental hygienist's tasks, duties, necessary education and experience, and ethical and legal requirements.

3468 ■ *Opportunities in Dental Care Careers*
McGraw-Hill Professional
PO Box 182604
Columbus, OH 43272
Ph: 877-833-5524
Fax: (614)759-3749
E-mail: pbg.ecommerce_custserv@mcgraw-hill.com
URL: http://www.mhprofessional.com/product.php?isbn=0071388346

Bonnie Kendall. $12.95 (e-book). 160 pages. Provides a complete overview of the job possibilities in dental industry. Includes the skill and training requirements to current salary figures.

3469 ■ *Opportunities in Health and Medical Careers*
The McGraw-Hill Companies
PO Box 182604
Columbus, OH 43272
Fax: (614)759-3749
Fr: 877-883-5524
E-mail: customer.service@mcgraw-hill.com
URL: http://www.mhprofessional.com/product.php?isbn=0071437274

I. Donald Snook, Jr. and Leo D'Orazio. 2004. $14.95 (paper). 157 pages. Covers the full range of medical and health occupations. Illustrated.

3470 ■ *Practice Management for Dental Hygienists*
Lippincott Williams & Wilkins
351 W Camden St.
Baltimore, MD 21201
Ph: (301)223-2300
Fr: 800-638-3030
URL: http://www.lww.com

Esther Andrews. 2006. $54.95. 372 pages. Prepares dental hygiene students and dental hygienists to handle the business and operational aspects of the dental office.

3471 ■ *Resumes for Health and Medical Careers*
The McGraw-Hill Companies
PO Box 182604
Columbus, OH 43272
Fax: (614)759-3749
Fr: 877-883-5524
E-mail: customer.service@mcgraw-hill.com
URL: http://www.mhprofessional.com/product.php?isbn=0071545352

Third edition, 2008. $12.95 (paper). 144 pages.

EMPLOYMENT AGENCIES AND SEARCH FIRMS

3472 ■ Actuary Resources
115 N Castle Heights Ave., Ste. 202
Lebanon, TN 37087-2768
Ph: (615)360-5171
Fax: (615)360-5173
E-mail: info@actuaryresources.org
URL: http://www.actuaryresources.org

Provides staffing services to several different types of industries. Offers a free screening service to clients.

3473 ■ DDS Resources
16020 Swingley Ridge Rd., Ste. 340
Chesterfield, MO 63017
Ph: (636)536-6656
Fax: (636)536-6667
Fr: 877-337-0563
E-mail: info@mdr-inc.com
URL: http://www.mdr-inc.com/dentists.aspx

Serves as a dental recruitment agency in the United States. Specializes in matching qualified dentists with dental employers.

3474 ■ DDS Staffing Resources, Inc.
9755 Dogwood Rd., Ste. 200
Roswell, GA 30075
Ph: (770)998-7779
Fax: (770)552-0176
Fr: 888-668-7779
URL: http://msrstaffing.com

Dental staffing agency.

3475 ■ Team Placement Service, Inc.
1414 Prince St., Ste. 202
Alexandria, VA 22314
Ph: (703)820-8618
Fax: (703)820-3368
Fr: 800-495-6767
E-mail: 4jobs@teamplace.com
URL: http://www.teamplace.com

Full-service personnel consultants provide placement for healthcare staff, physician and dentist, private practice, and hospitals. Conduct interviews, tests, and reference checks to select the top 20% of applicants. Survey applicants' skill levels, provide backup information on each candidate, select compatible candidates for consideration, and insure the hiring process minimizes potential legal liability. Industries served: healthcare and government agencies providing medical, dental, biotech, laboratory, hospitals, and physician search.

ONLINE JOB SOURCES AND SERVICES

3476 ■ CareersInDental.com
URL: http://www.careersindental.com

Description: Serves as a job board for the dental industry. Features listings of employment opportunities and job openings in the field.

3477 ■ DentalCrossing.com
URL: http://www.dentalcrossing.com

Description: Provides employment opportunities for dentists, dental assistants, dental hygienists, and dental lab technicians.

3478 ■ DentalJobsBoard.net
URL: http://www.dentaljobsboard.net

Description: Features dentist jobs, dental hygiene jobs, dental assistant jobs, and jobs for dental lab technicians.

3479 ■ DentalPortal.com
URL: http://www.dentalportal.com

Description: Search engine for finding dentists, orthodontists, oral surgeons, and other dental professionals.

3480 ■ DentalPost.net
URL: http://www.dentalpost.net

Description: Lists dental jobs including dentist jobs, dental hygienist jobs, dental assistant jobs, dental lab technician jobs, and dental front office jobs.

3481 ■ DentalWorkers.com
URL: http://www.dentalworkers.com/employment

Description: Serves as an online employment resource among dental professionals. Provides classified ads for dental jobs, and free resume posting for workers.

3482 ■ Dentist Job Cafe
URL: http://www.dentistjobcafe.com

Description: Features dental job listings. Provides employment services for dentists, dental hygienists, and dental assistants.

3483 ■ DentistJobsNow.com
URL: http://www.dentist-jobs-now.com

Description: Provides assistance to new and practicing dentists, hygienists, and dental assistants in finding employment.

3484 ■ DentistryJob.com
URL: http://www.dentistryjob.com

Description: Serves as a job board for dentistry professionals.

3485 ■ HEALTHeCAREERS Network
Fr: 888-884-8242
E-mail: info@healthecareers.com
URL: http://www.healthecareers.com

Description: Career search site for jobs in all health care specialties; educational resources; visa and licensing information for relocation; interesting articles; relocation tools; links to professional organizations and general resources.

3486 ■ iHireDental
URL: http://www.ihiredental.com

Description: Features dental jobs in different specialty areas.

3487 ■ Medjobsdata.com
URL: http://www.medjobsdata.com

Description: Helps jobseekers find a health profession from clinical to administrative.

3488 ■ ProHealthJobs.com
Ph: (484)443-8545
Fax: (484)443-8549
E-mail: info@prohealthjobs.com
URL: http://prohealthjobs.com/jobboard

Description: Career resources site for the medical and health care field. Lists professional opportunities, product information, continuing education and open positions.

TRADESHOWS

3489 ■ American Academy of Pediatric Dentistry Annual Session
American Academy of Pediatric Dentistry
211 E. Chicago Ave., Ste. 1700
Chicago, IL 60611-2637
Ph: (312)337-2169
Fax: (312)337-6329
URL: http://www.aapd.org

Annual. Primary Exhibits: Dental products and publications. Dates and Locations: 2012 May 24-27; San Diego, CA; San Diego Marriott Hotel & Marina; 2013 May 23-26; Orlando, FL; Walt Disney World Swan Dolphin Resort; 2014 May 22-25; Boston, MA; Hynes Convention Center.

3490 ■ National Dental Association Annual Convention
National Dental Association, Inc.
3517 16th St., N.W.
Washington, DC 20010
Ph: (202)588-1697
Fax: (202)588-1244
E-mail: admin@ndaonline.org
URL: http://www.ndaonline.org

Annual. Primary Exhibits: Dental and Pharmaceutical equipment, supplies, and services. Dates and Locations: 2012 Jul 20-24.

3491 ■ Star of the North Meeting
Minnesota Dental Association
1335 Industrial Blvd., Ste. 200
Minneapolis, MN 55413-4801
Ph: (612)767-8400
Fax: (612)767-8500
Fr: 800-950-3368
E-mail: info@mndental.org
URL: http://www.mndental.org

Annual. Primary Exhibits: Dental equipment and supplies, dental laboratory equipment, office equipment, and service organizations. Dates and Locations: 2012 Apr 26-28; 2013 Apr 25-27; 2014 Apr 24-26; 2015 Apr 23-25.

3492 ■ Thomas P. Hinman Dental Meeting & Exhibits
Thomas P. Hinman Dental Society of Atlanta
33 Lenox Pte.
Atlanta, GA 30324-3172
Ph: (404)231-1663
Fax: (404)231-9638
URL: http://www.hinman.org

Annual. Primary Exhibits: Dental equipment, supplies, and services. Dates and Locations: 2012 Mar 22-24; 2013 Mar 21-23.

3493 ■ Three Rivers Dental Conference
Dental Society of Western Pennsylvania
900 Cedar Ave.
Pittsburgh, PA 15212
Ph: (412)321-5810
Fax: (412)321-7719
URL: http://www.dswp.org

Annual. Primary Exhibits: Dental products and equipment, computers, office equipment, and insurance.

3494 ■ Yankee Dental Congress
Massachusetts Dental Society
2 Willow St., No. 200
Southborough, MA 01745-1027

Ph: (508)480-9797
Fax: (508)480-0002
Fr: 800-342-8747
E-mail: madental@massdental.org
URL: http://www.massdental.org

Annual. Primary Exhibits: Dental products, equipment, and services. Dates and Locations: 2012 Jan 25-29; Boston, MA; Boston Convention & Exhibition Center.

OTHER SOURCES

3495 ■ American Academy of Cosmetic Dentistry
402 W Wilson St.
Madison, WI 53703
Ph: (608)222-8583
Fax: (608)222-9540
Fr: 800-543-9220
E-mail: info@aacd.com
URL: http://www.aacd.com

Members include more than 8,000 cosmetic and reconstructive dentists, dental laboratory technicians, dental auxiliaries, dental hygienists, educators, researchers and students. Membership benefits include AACD accreditation, registration to AACD's Annual Scientific Session, publications, online search directory, marketing materials, and more.

3496 ■ American Academy of Dental Group Practice (AADGP)
2525 E Arizona Biltmore Cir., Ste. 127
Phoenix, AZ 85016
Ph: (602)381-1185
Fax: (602)381-1093
E-mail: aadgp@aadgp.org
URL: http://www.aadgp.org

Description: Represents active dentists and dental group practices. Aims to improve the level of dental service provided by members through exchanging and expanding of ideas and techniques for patient treatment and practice administration. Promotes group practice and research; accumulates and disseminates information; seeks to achieve the proper recognition for the aims and goals of group practice. Helps support an accreditation program as a system of voluntary peer review.

3497 ■ American Association of Dental Boards
211 E Chicago Ave., Ste. 760
Chicago, IL 60611
Ph: (312)440-7464
Fax: (312)440-3525
E-mail: info@dentalboards.org
URL: http://dentalboards.org

Description: Represents present and past members of state dental examining boards and board administrators. Assists member agencies with problems related to state dental board examinations and licensure, and enforcement of the state dental practice act. Conducts research; compiles statistics.

3498 ■ American College of Prosthodontists
211 E Chicago Ave., Ste. 1000
Chicago, IL 60611
Ph: (312)573-1260
Fax: (312)573-1257
URL: http://www.prosthodontics.org

Membership includes more than 3,300 prosthodontists, dental technicians, dental students and other dental professionals contributing to the specialty. Committed to the esthetic restoration of teeth, including bridges, crowns/caps, dental implants, dentures, partial dentures, whitening and veneers. Membership includes free subscriptions to the Journal of Prosthodontics, the Messenger, and e-blasts.

3499 ■ American Dental Association (ADA)
211 E Chicago Ave.
Chicago, IL 60611-2678
Ph: (312)440-2500

Fax: (312)440-2800
E-mail: membership@ada.org
URL: http://www.ada.org

Description: Professional society of dentists. Encourages the improvement of the health of the public and promotes the art and science of dentistry in matters of legislation and regulations. Inspects and accredits dental schools and schools for dental hygienists, assistants, and laboratory technicians. Conducts research programs at ADA Foundation Research Institute. Produces dental health education material used in the U.S. Sponsors National Children's Dental Health Month and Give Kids a Smile Day. Compiles statistics on personnel, practice, and dental care needs and attitudes of patients with regard to dental health.

3500 ■ American Dental Education Association (ADEA)
1400 K St. NW, Ste. 1100
Washington, DC 20005
Ph: (202)289-7201
Fax: (202)289-7204
E-mail: valachovicr@adea.org
URL: http://www.adea.org

Description: Individuals interested in dental education; schools of dentistry, advanced dental and allied dental education in the U.S., Canada, and Puerto Rico; affiliated institutions of the federal government and corporations. Works to promote better teaching and education in dentistry and dental research and to facilitate exchange of ideas among dental educators. Sponsors meetings, conferences, and workshops; conducts surveys, studies, and special projects and publishes their results. Maintains 37 sections and 8 special interest groups representing many different aspects of dental education.

3501 ■ American Dental Hygienists' Association (ADHA)
444 N Michigan Ave., Ste. 3400
Chicago, IL 60611
Ph: (312)440-8900
Fax: (312)467-1806
Fr: 800-243-ADHA
E-mail: mail@adha.net
URL: http://www.adha.org

Description: Professional organization of licensed dental hygienists possessing a degree or certificate in dental hygiene granted by an accredited school of dental hygiene. Makes available scholarships, research grants, and continuing education programs. Maintains accrediting service through the American Dental Association's Commission on Dental Accreditation. Compiles statistics.

3502 ■ American Public Health Association (APHA)
800 I St. NW
Washington, DC 20001
Ph: (202)777-2742
Fax: (202)777-2534
E-mail: comments@apha.org
URL: http://www.apha.org

Description: Professional organization of physicians, nurses, educators, academicians, environmentalists, epidemiologists, new professionals, social workers, health administrators, optometrists, podiatrists, pharmacists, dentists, nutritionists, health planners, other community and mental health specialists, and interested consumers. Seeks to protect and promote personal, mental, and environmental health. Services include: promulgation of standards; establishment of uniform practices and procedures; development of the etiology of communicable diseases; research in public health; exploration of medical care programs and their relationships to public health. Sponsors job placement service.

3503 ■ American School Health Association (ASHA)
4340 East West Hwy., Ste. 403
Bethesda, MD 20814
Ph: (301)652-8072

Fax: (301)652-8077
Fr: 800-445-2742
E-mail: info@ashaweb.org
URL: http://www.ashaweb.org

Description: School physicians, school nurses, counselors, nutritionists, psychologists, social workers, administrators, school health coordinators, health educators, and physical educators working in schools, professional preparation programs, public health, and community-based organizations. Promotes coordinated school health programs that include health education, health services, a healthful school environment, physical education, nutrition services, and psycho-social health services offered in schools collaboratively with families and other members of the community. Offers professional reference materials and professional development opportunities. Conducts pilot programs that inform materials development, provides technical assistance to school professionals, advocates for school health.

3504 ■ Crown Council
975 Woodoak Ln., Ste. 200
Salt Lake City, UT 84117
Ph: (801)293-8522
Fax: (801)293-8524
Fr: 800-276-9658
E-mail: success@crowncouncil.com
URL: http://www.mycrowncouncil.com

Description: Seeks to improve independent dental practices. Promotes oral health and the fight against oral cancer. Provides patient care and offers state-of-the-art dental procedure facilities.

3505 ■ Holistic Dental Association (HDA)
1825 Ponce de Leon Blvd., No. 148
Coral Gables, FL 33134

Ph: (305)356-7338
Fax: (305)468-6359
E-mail: director@holisticdental.org
URL: http://www.holisticdental.org

Description: Represents dentists, chiropractors, dental hygienists, physical therapists, and medical doctors. Aims to provide a holistic approach to better dental care for patients, and to expand techniques, medications, and philosophies that pertain to extractions, anesthetics, fillings, crowns, and orthodontics. Encourages the use of homeopathic medications, acupuncture, cranial osteopathy, nutritional techniques, and physical therapy in treating patients in addition to conventional treatments. Sponsors training and educational seminars.

3506 ■ National Dental Hygienists' Association (NDHA)
PO Box 22463
Tampa, FL 33622
Fr: 800-234-1096
E-mail: forndha@aol.com
URL: http://ndhaonline.org

Description: Minority dental hygienists. Cultivates and promotes the art and science of dental hygiene and enhances the professional image of dental hygienists. Attempts to meet the needs of society through educational, political, and social activities while giving the minority dental hygienist a voice in shaping the profession. Encourages cooperation and mutual support among minority professionals. Seeks to increase opportunities for continuing education and employment in the field of dental hygiene. Works to improve individual and community dental health. Sponsors annual seminar, fundraising events, and scholarship programs; participates in career orientation programs; counsels and assists students applying for or enrolled in dental hygiene programs. Maintains liaison with American Dental Hygienists' Association.

3507 ■ National Rural Health Association (NRHA)
Administrative Office
521 E 63rd St.
Kansas City, MO 64110-3329
Ph: (816)756-3140
Fax: (816)756-3144
E-mail: mail@nrharural.org
URL: http://www.ruralhealthweb.org

Description: Administrators, physicians, nurses, physician assistants, health planners, academicians, and others interested or involved in rural health care. Creates a better understanding of health care problems unique to rural areas; utilizes a collective approach in finding positive solutions; articulates and represents the health care needs of rural America; supplies current information to rural health care providers; serves as a liaison between rural health care programs throughout the country. Offers continuing education credits for medical, dental, nursing, and management courses.

3508 ■ Special Care Dentistry Association
401 N Michigan Ave., Ste. 2200
Chicago, IL 60611
Ph: (312)527-6764
Fax: (312)673-6663
E-mail: scda@scdaonline.org
URL: http://www.scdonline.org

Description: Dentists, hygienists, and lay public interested in special care dentistry. Aims to improve oral health and well being of people with special needs. Provides a forum for an exchange of clinical ideas and patient management techniques among members.

SOURCES OF HELP-WANTED ADS

3509 ■ ACD News
American College of Dentists
839J Quince Orchard Blvd.
Gaithersburg, MD 20878-1614
Ph: (301)977-3223
Fax: (301)977-3330
E-mail: office@acd.org
URL: http://www.acd.org/publications.htm

Description: Tri-annual. Presents accounts of College meetings, as well as remarks from the College's president. Publishes notices of scheduled events, spotlights individuals recognized or given awards by the College, and profiles convocation speakers, and other dental organizations. Recurring features include reports of meetings.

3510 ■ American Academy of Implant Dentistry Newsletter
American Academy of Implant Dentistry
211 E Chicago Ave., Ste. 750
Chicago, IL 60611
Ph: (312)335-1550
Fax: (312)335-9090
Fr: 877-335-AAID
E-mail: info@aaid.com
URL: http://www.aaid-implant.org

Description: Quarterly. Covers current activities in the field of implant dentistry, particularly the educational programs of the Academy.

3511 ■ American Dental Hygienists' Association Access
American Dental Hygienists' Association
444 N Michigan Ave., Ste. 3400
Chicago, IL 60611
Ph: (312)440-8900
Fr: 800-243-ADHA
URL: http://www.adha.org/publications/index.html

$48.00/year for individuals; $85.00/year for two years; $120.00/year for individuals, for 3 years. Magazine covering current dental hygiene topics, regulatory and legislative developments, and association news.

3512 ■ Bulletin of Dental Education
American Dental Education Association
1400 K St., NW, Ste. 1100
Washington, DC 20005
Ph: (202)289-7201
Fax: (202)289-7204
E-mail: publications@adea.org
URL: http://www.adea.org

Description: Monthly. Contains news and information on dental education. Recurring features include a calendar of events, reports of meetings, news of educational opportunities, job listings, and notices of publications available.

3513 ■ CDS Review
Chicago Dental Society
401 N Michigan Ave., Ste. 200
Chicago, IL 60611
Ph: (312)836-7300
Fax: (312)836-7337
URL: http://www.cds.org/cds_review/

$25.00/year for individuals; $30.00/year for institutions, and schools in USA & Canada; $45.00/year for other countries; $5.00/year for single issue. Dental journal.

3514 ■ Dental Economics
PennWell Corp.
1421 S Sheridan Rd.
Tulsa, OK 74112
Ph: (918)835-3161
Fax: (918)831-9497
Fr: 800-331-4463
URL: http://www.dentaleconomics.com/index.html

Monthly. $132.00/year for individuals; $179.00/year for Canada and Mexico; $248.00/year for other countries; $211.00/year for two years; $312.00/year for Canada and Mexico; $428.00/year for other countries, two years; $65.00/year online. Magazine featuring business-related articles for dentists.

3515 ■ Dental Laboratory Association of Texas
PO Box 140769
Dallas, TX 75214
Ph: (214)321-5428
Fax: (214)321-9942
Fr: 877-689-8848
E-mail: aurex@swbell.net
URL: http://www.dlat.org

Allows individuals seeking employment as a dental laboratory technician to submit their service, contact information, and resume.

3516 ■ Dental Town
Dental Town
9633 S 48th St., Ste. 200
Phoenix, AZ 85044
Ph: (480)598-0001
Fax: (480)598-3450
URL: http://www.dentaltown.com/

Monthly. Free to qualified subscribers. Magazine that offers information on the dental industry and latest dental equipment.

3517 ■ Hawaii Dental Journal
Hawaii Medical Journal
1360 S Beretania St., Ste. 200
Honolulu, HI 96814
Ph: (808)536-7702
Fax: (808)536-2376
E-mail: hda@hawaiidentalassociation.net
URL: http://www.hawaiidentalassociation.net/index.html

Bimonthly. $55.00/year for individuals. Dental journal.

3518 ■ Illinois Dental News
Illinois State Dental Society
1010 S Second St.
Springfield, IL 62704
Ph: (217)525-1406
URL: http://www.isds.org/memberBenefits/publications/IllinoisDent

Monthly. $10.00/year for single issue, outside United States; $45.00/year for individuals; $90.00/year for other countries; $5.00/year for single issue. Dental magazine.

3519 ■ InterFace
American Society for Geriatric Dentistry
401 N Michigan Ave., Ste. 2200
Chicago, IL 60611
Ph: (312)527-6764
Fax: (312)673-6663
E-mail: scda@scdaonline.org
URL: http://www.scdonline.org/displaynewsletter.cfm

Description: Quarterly. Publishes news of geriatric dentistry as well as news of the Society, its members and activities. Recurring features include legislative updates, a calendar of events, news of members, book reviews, editorials, a message from the president, bibliographies, and biographies.

3520 ■ Journal of the California Dental Association
California Dental Association
1201 K St.
Sacramento, CA 95814
Fr: 800-232-7645
URL: http://www.cda.org/publications/journal_of_the_california_de

Monthly. $18.00/year for members; $40.00/year for members, domestic; $75.00/year for nonmembers, ADA; $80.00/year for other countries; $10.00/year for members, back issue. Professional magazine for dentists.

3521 ■ Journal of Dental Education
American Dental Education Association
1400 K St. NW, Ste. 1100
Washington, DC 20005
Ph: (202)289-7201
Fax: (202)289-7204
URL: http://www.adea.org/publications/jde/Pages/default.aspx

Monthly. $80.00/year for members, print, online is free; $160.00/year for nonmembers, U.S., print; $190.00/year for nonmembers, Canada, print; $220.00/year for nonmembers, other countries, print; $390.00/year for institutions, Tier 1; $515.00/year for institutions, Tier 2; $665.00/year for institutions, Tier 3; $885.00/year for institutions, Tier 4; $1,100.00/year for institutions, Tier 5. Peer-reviewed journal for scholarly research and reviews on dental education.

3522 ■ Journal of Dental Hygiene
American Dental Hygienists' Association
444 N Michigan Ave., Ste. 3400
Chicago, IL 60611
Ph: (312)440-8900
Fr: 800-243-ADHA
E-mail: communications@adha.net
URL: http://www.adha.org/publications/index.html

Quarterly. $45.00/year for individuals; $65.00/year for two years; $90.00/year for individuals, 3 years. Professional journal on dental hygiene.

3523 ■ Journal of Dental Research
Sage Publications Inc.
2455 Teller Rd.
Thousand Oaks, CA 91320-2218
Ph: (805)499-9774
Fax: (805)583-2665
Fr: 800-818-7243
URL: http://www.dentalresearch.org/i4a/pages/
    index.cfm?pageid=332

Monthly. $877.00/year for institutions, print & online; $427.00/year for individuals, print only; $789.00/year for institutions, online only; $859.00/year for institutions, print only. Peer-reviewed dental science journal.

3524 ■ Journal of Dental Technology
Bldg. L103
325 John Knox Rd.
Tallahassee, FL 32303
Fax: (850)222-0053
Fr: 800-950-1150
E-mail: jdt@nadl.org
URL: http://www.jdtunbound.com

Serves dental laboratory professionals through articles, industry and product news, classified advertising for laboratory technicians and more (8 issues/year).

3525 ■ Journal of Operative Dentistry
American Academy of Gold Foil Operators
c/o Dr. Robert C. Keene, Sec.-Treas.
1 Woods End Rd.
Etna, NH 03750-4318
URL: http://academyofoperativedentistry.com/
    journal.html

Bimonthly. $75.00/year for individuals, online only; $200.00/year for institutions, online or print; $110.00/year for individuals, online or print; $85.00/year for other countries, online only; $115.00/year for other countries, print only; $250.00/year for institutions, other countries. Peer-reviewed professional journal covering issues in dentistry.

3526 ■ The Journal of Prosthetic Dentistry
Mosby Inc.
11830 Westline Industrial Dr.
St. Louis, MO 63146-3326
Ph: (314)872-8370
Fax: (314)432-1380
Fr: 800-325-4177
URL: http://journals.elsevierhealth.com/periodicals/
    ympr/home

Monthly. $259.00/year for individuals; $128.00/year for students; $171.00/year for students, Canada; $342.00/year for Canada; $171.00/year for students, Mexico; $342.00/year for individuals, Mexico; $171.00/year for students, other countries; $342.00/year for other countries. Peer-reviewed journal emphasizing new techniques, evaluation of dental materials, pertinent basic science concepts, and patient psychology in restorative dentistry.

3527 ■ Maryland State Dental Association Newsletter
Maryland State Dental Association
6410F Dobbin Rd.
Columbia, MD 21045
Ph: (410)964-2880
Fax: (410)964-0583
E-mail: mddent@msda.com
URL: http://www.msda.com

Description: Monthly. Reports on health, legislative,

economic, and medical issues that are pertinent to dentistry. Recurring features include letters to the editor, interviews, news of research, a calendar of events, reports of meetings, news of educational opportunities, and job listings.

3528 ■ MDS Connection
Massachusetts Dental Society
Two Willow St., Ste. 200
Southborough, MA 01745-1027
Fax: (508)480-0002
Fr: 800-342-8747
URL: http://www.massdental.org/

Description: Bimonthly. Provides news on the Society's activities and articles on the dental profession. Recurring features include reports of meetings, news of educational opportunities, job listings, and notices of publications available.

3529 ■ Pediatric Dentistry Today
American Academy of Pediatric Dentistry
211 E Chicago Ave., Ste. 1700
Chicago, IL 60611-2637
Ph: (312)337-2169
Fax: (312)337-6329
E-mail: aapdinfo@aapd. org
URL: http://www.aapd.org

Description: Bimonthly. Reports on the activities of the Academy, which seeks to advance the specialty of pediatric dentistry through practice, education, and research. Recurring features include news of research, profiles of members, and legislative updates.

3530 ■ Pennsylvania Dental Journal
Pennsylvania Dental Association
3501 N Front St.
PO Box 3341
Harrisburg, PA 17105
Ph: (717)234-5941
Fax: (717)234-2186
URL: http://www.padental.org/AM/
    Template.cfm?Section=Publications

Bimonthly. Professional dentistry magazine containing treatment/procedure news, PDA activities information, continuing education courses, and legislation updates.

3531 ■ Washington State Dental Laboratory Association Newsletter
PO Box 385
Graham, WA 98338
Ph: (360)832-2471
Fax: (360)832-2471
Fr: 800-652-2212
E-mail: peg2@mashell.com
URL: http://www.wsdla.com

Association newsletter featuring articles of interest to dental laboratory technicians as well as classified advertising for technical positions available.

3532 ■ Westviews
Western Los Angeles Dental Society
14722 Hawthorne Blvd., Ste. B
Lawndale, CA 90260
Ph: (310)349-2199
Fax: (310)349-2175
E-mail: wlads@pacbell.net
URL: http://www.westernlads.org

Description: Six issues/year. Carries items relating to organized dentistry and the clinical aspects of dentistry. Covers local community events involving the organization or the profession; provides updates of states agency actions affecting dentistry.

EMPLOYER DIRECTORIES AND NETWORKING LISTS

3533 ■ Who's Who In Dental Technology
National Association of Dental Laboratories
325 John Knox Rd., No. L103
Tallahassee, FL 32303

Ph: (850)205-5626
Fax: (850)222-0053
Fr: 800-950-1150
E-mail: membership@nadl.org
URL: http://www.nadl.org/scr/dir/index.cfm

Directory includes lab owners, technicians, suppliers, education members and components.

HANDBOOKS AND MANUALS

3534 ■ Careers in Health Care
The McGraw-Hill Companies
PO Box 182604
Columbus, OH 43272
Fax: (614)759-3749
Fr: 877-883-5524
E-mail: customer.service@mcgraw-hill.com
URL: http://www.mhprofessional.com/
    product.php?isbn=0071466533

Barbara M. Swanson. Fifth edition, 2005. $19.95 (paper). 192 pages. Describes job duties, work settings, salaries, licensing and certification requirements, educational preparation, and future outlook. Gives ideas on how to secure a job.

3535 ■ Opportunities in Dental Care Careers
McGraw-Hill Professional
PO Box 182604
Columbus, OH 43272
Ph: 877-833-5524
Fax: (614)759-3749
E-mail: pbg.ecommerce_custserv@mcgraw-hill.com
URL: http://www.mhprofessional.com/
    product.php?isbn=0071388346

Bonnie Kendall. $12.95 (e-book). 160 pages. Provides a complete overview of the job possibilities in dental industry. Includes the skill and training requirements to current salary figures.

3536 ■ Opportunities in Health and Medical Careers
The McGraw-Hill Companies
PO Box 182604
Columbus, OH 43272
Fax: (614)759-3749
Fr: 877-883-5524
E-mail: customer.service@mcgraw-hill.com
URL: http://www.mhprofessional.com/
    product.php?isbn=0071437274

I. Donald Snook, Jr. and Leo D'Orazio. 2004. $14.95 (paper). 157 pages. Covers the full range of medical and health occupations. Illustrated.

3537 ■ Resumes for Health and Medical Careers
The McGraw-Hill Companies
PO Box 182604
Columbus, OH 43272
Fax: (614)759-3749
Fr: 877-883-5524
E-mail: customer.service@mcgraw-hill.com
URL: http://www.mhprofessional.com/
    product.php?isbn=0071545352

Third edition, 2008. $12.95 (paper). 144 pages.

EMPLOYMENT AGENCIES AND SEARCH FIRMS

3538 ■ DDS Resources
16020 Swingley Ridge Rd., Ste. 340
Chesterfield, MO 63017
Ph: (636)536-6656
Fax: (636)536-6667
Fr: 877-337-0563
E-mail: info@mdr-inc.com
URL: http://www.mdr-inc.com/dentists.aspx

Serves as a dental recruitment agency in the United States. Specializes in matching qualified dentists with dental employers.

3539 ■ DDS Staffing Resources, Inc.
9755 Dogwood Rd., Ste. 200
Roswell, GA 30075
Ph: (770)998-7779
Fax: (770)552-0176
Fr: 888-668-7779
URL: http://msrstaffing.com
Dental staffing agency.

ONLINE JOB SOURCES AND SERVICES

3540 ■ DentalCrossing.com
URL: http://www.dentalcrossing.com

Description: Provides employment opportunities for dentists, dental assistants, dental hygienists, and dental lab technicians.

3541 ■ DentalLaboratoryTechnician.com
URL: http://www.dentallaboratorytechnician.com

Description: Connects job seekers and potential employers. Facilitates searching and posting of available jobs for dental lab technicians.

3542 ■ DentalPortal.com
URL: http://www.dentalportal.com

Description: Search engine for finding dentists, orthodontists, oral surgeons, and other dental professionals.

3543 ■ DentalPost.net
URL: http://www.dentalpost.net

Description: Lists dental jobs including dentist jobs, dental hygienist jobs, dental assistant jobs, dental lab technician jobs, and dental front office jobs.

3544 ■ DentalWorkers.com
URL: http://www.dentalworkers.com/employment

Description: Serves as an online employment resource among dental professionals. Provides classified ads for dental jobs, and free resume posting for workers.

3545 ■ DentistJobsNow.com
URL: http://www.dentist-jobs-now.com

Description: Provides assistance to new and practicing dentists, hygienists, and dental assistants in finding employment.

3546 ■ HEALTHeCAREERS Network
Fr: 888-884-8242
E-mail: info@healthecareers.com
URL: http://www.healthecareers.com

Description: Career search site for jobs in all health care specialties; educational resources; visa and licensing information for relocation; interesting articles; relocation tools; links to professional organizations and general resources.

3547 ■ iHireDental
URL: http://www.ihiredental.com

Description: Features dental jobs in different specialty areas.

3548 ■ ProHealthJobs.com
Ph: (484)443-8545
Fax: (484)443-8549
E-mail: info@prohealthjobs.com
URL: http://prohealthjobs.com/jobboard

Description: Career resources site for the medical and health care field. Lists professional opportunities, product information, continuing education and open positions.

TRADESHOWS

3549 ■ Chicago Dental Society Midwinter Meeting
Chicago Dental Society
401 N. Michigan Ave., Ste. 200
Chicago, IL 60611

Ph: (312)836-7300
URL: http://www.cds.org

Annual. Primary Exhibits: Dental equipment, services, and related business services. Dates and Locations: 2012 Feb 23-25; Chicago, IL; McCormick Place West.

3550 ■ Fun'n Sun Weekend
PO Box 206
Elkin, NC 28621
Ph: (336)835-9251
Fax: (336)835-9243
E-mail: contactus@fun-n-sun-weekend.com
URL: http://www.fun-n-sun-weekend.com

Annual seminar sponsored by Louisiana Dental Laboratory Association Inc. and the Mississippi Dental Laboratory Association, offering programs and exhibits of interest to dental technicians.

3551 ■ NADL Vision 21
325 John Knox Rd., No. L-103
Tallahassee, FL 32303
Ph: (850)205-5626
Fax: (850)222-0053
Fr: 800-950-1150
E-mail: membership@nadl.org
URL: http://www.nadl.org/V21

Annual conference of the National Association of Dental Laboratories provides dental laboratory technicians, owners and managers with information on the technology, education, and tools required to address issues in the dental technology arena.

3552 ■ Southeastern Conference of Dental Laboratories
PO Box 206
Elkin, SC 28621
Ph: (336)835-9251
Fax: (336)835-9243
E-mail: contactus@scdl-online.org
URL: http://www.scdl-online.org

Annual conference promoting the profession of dental laboratory technician and industry.

3553 ■ Star of the North Meeting
Minnesota Dental Association
1335 Industrial Blvd., Ste. 200
Minneapolis, MN 55413-4801
Ph: (612)767-8400
Fax: (612)767-8500
Fr: 800-950-3368
E-mail: info@mndental.org
URL: http://www.mndental.org

Annual. Primary Exhibits: Dental equipment and supplies, dental laboratory equipment, office equipment, and service organizations. Dates and Locations: 2012 Apr 26-28; 2013 Apr 25-27; 2014 Apr 24-26; 2015 Apr 23-25.

3554 ■ Yankee Dental Congress
Massachusetts Dental Society
2 Willow St., No. 200
Southborough, MA 01745-1027
Ph: (508)480-9797
Fax: (508)480-0002
Fr: 800-342-8747
E-mail: madental@massdental.org
URL: http://www.massdental.org

Annual. Primary Exhibits: Dental products, equipment, and services. Dates and Locations: 2012 Jan 25-29; Boston, MA; Boston Convention & Exhibition Center.

OTHER SOURCES

3555 ■ American Academy of Cosmetic Dentistry
402 W Wilson St.
Madison, WI 53703
Ph: (608)222-8583
Fax: (608)222-9540

Fr: 800-543-9220
E-mail: info@aacd.com
URL: http://www.aacd.com

Members include more than 8,000 cosmetic and reconstructive dentists, dental laboratory technicians, dental auxiliaries, dental hygienists, educators, researchers and students. Membership benefits include AACD accreditation, registration to AACD's Annual Scientific Session, publications, online search directory, marketing materials, and more.

3556 ■ American Academy of Dental Group Practice (AADGP)
2525 E Arizona Biltmore Cir., Ste. 127
Phoenix, AZ 85016
Ph: (602)381-1185
Fax: (602)381-1093
E-mail: aadgp@aadgp.org
URL: http://www.aadgp.org

Description: Represents active dentists and dental group practices. Aims to improve the level of dental service provided by members through exchanging and expanding of ideas and techniques for patient treatment and practice administration. Promotes group practice and research; accumulates and disseminates information; seeks to achieve the proper recognition for the aims and goals of group practice. Helps support an accreditation program as a system of voluntary peer review.

3557 ■ American College of Prosthodontists
211 E Chicago Ave., Ste. 1000
Chicago, IL 60611
Ph: (312)573-1260
Fax: (312)573-1257
URL: http://www.prosthodontics.org

Membership includes more than 3,300 prosthodontists, dental technicians, dental students and other dental professionals contributing to the specialty. Committed to the esthetic restoration of teeth, including bridges, crowns/caps, dental implants, dentures, partial dentures, whitening and veneers. Membership includes free subscriptions to the Journal of Prosthodontics, the Messenger, and e-blasts.

3558 ■ American Dental Association (ADA)
211 E Chicago Ave.
Chicago, IL 60611-2678
Ph: (312)440-2500
Fax: (312)440-2800
E-mail: membership@ada.org
URL: http://www.ada.org

Description: Professional society of dentists. Encourages the improvement of the health of the public and promotes the art and science of dentistry in matters of legislation and regulations. Inspects and accredits dental schools and schools for dental hygienists, assistants, and laboratory technicians. Conducts research programs at ADA Foundation Research Institute. Produces dental health education material used in the U.S. Sponsors National Children's Dental Health Month and Give Kids a Smile Day. Compiles statistics on personnel, practice, and dental care needs and attitudes of patients with regard to dental health.

3559 ■ American Dental Education Association (ADEA)
1400 K St. NW, Ste. 1100
Washington, DC 20005
Ph: (202)289-7201
Fax: (202)289-7204
E-mail: valachovicr@adea.org
URL: http://www.adea.org

Description: Individuals interested in dental education; schools of dentistry, advanced dental and allied dental education in the U.S., Canada, and Puerto Rico; affiliated institutions of the federal government and corporations. Works to promote better teaching and education in dentistry and dental research and to facilitate exchange of ideas among dental educators. Sponsors meetings, conferences, and workshops; conducts surveys, studies, and special projects and publishes their results. Maintains 37 sections and 8 special interest groups representing many different aspects of dental education.

3560 ■ Crown Council
975 Woodoak Ln., Ste. 200
Salt Lake City, UT 84117
Ph: (801)293-8522
Fax: (801)293-8524
Fr: 800-276-9658
E-mail: success@crowncouncil.com
URL: http://www.mycrowncouncil.com

Description: Seeks to improve independent dental practices. Promotes oral health and the fight against oral cancer. Provides patient care and offers state-of-the-art dental procedure facilities.

3561 ■ Florida Dental Laboratory Association
325 John Knox Rd., No. L103
Tallahassee, FL 32303
Ph: (850)224-0711
Fax: (850)222-3019
E-mail: fdla@executiveoffice.org
URL: http://www.fdla.net

Represents operators and technicians of dental laboratories and to advance standards of service to the dental profession.

3562 ■ Holistic Dental Association (HDA)
1825 Ponce de Leon Blvd., No. 148
Coral Gables, FL 33134
Ph: (305)356-7338
Fax: (305)468-6359
E-mail: director@holisticdental.org
URL: http://www.holisticdental.org

Description: Represents dentists, chiropractors, dental hygienists, physical therapists, and medical doctors. Aims to provide a holistic approach to better dental care for patients, and to expand techniques, medications, and philosophies that pertain to extractions, anesthetics, fillings, crowns, and orthodontics. Encourages the use of homeopathic medications, acupuncture, cranial osteopathy, nutritional techniques, and physical therapy in treating patients in addition to conventional treatments. Sponsors training and educational seminars.

3563 ■ Louisiana Dental Laboratory Association Inc.
PO Box 206
Elkin, LA 28621
Ph: (336)835-9251
Fax: (336)835-9243
E-mail: contactus@ldla.org
URL: http://www.ldla.org

Serves dental laboratory technicians in Louisiana

and surrounding areas; sponsors a spring meeting annually.

3564 ■ Michigan Association of Commercial Dental Laboratories
22800 Stair Dr.
Clinton Township, MI 48036
Ph: (586)469-1121
Fax: (586)469-1147
URL: http://www.macdl.org

Serves 800 members; promotes the dental laboratory profession through excellence, education, integrity, ethics and standards.

3565 ■ Minnesota Dental Laboratory Association Inc.
2345 Rice St., Ste. 220
St. Paul, MN 55113
Ph: (651)317-8065
Fax: (651)317-8048
E-mail: info@mwdentallab.org
URL: http://www.mndentallab.org/
advertising4520.php

Description: Association website provides a link to online advertising for dental technician positions, both wanted and available.

3566 ■ National Association of Dental Laboratories (NADL)
325 John Knox Rd., No. L103
Tallahassee, FL 32303
Ph: (850)205-5626
Fax: (850)222-0053
Fr: 800-950-1150
E-mail: nadl@nadl.org
URL: http://www.nadl.org

Description: Represents 2,900 commercial dental laboratories, manufacturers/suppliers and educators serving the dental profession. Develops criteria for ethical dental laboratories. Offers business and personal insurance programs, Hazardous Materials Training Program, and an infectious disease prevention training program, business management and technical education programs. Compiles statistics; conducts educational and charitable programs.

3567 ■ National Board for Certification in Dental Laboratory Technology
325 John Knox Rd., No. L103
Tallahassee, FL 32303
Ph: (850)205-5627
Fax: (850)222-0053
Fr: 800-684-5310
E-mail: jessica@nbccert.org
URL: http://www.nbccert.org

Certification program that represents compliance with

industry standards and a personal commitment to quality and professionalism.

3568 ■ North Carolina Dental Laboratory Association Inc.
PO Box 206
Elkin, NC 28621
Ph: (336)835-9251
Fax: (336)835-9243
E-mail: contactus@ncdla.org
URL: http://www.ncdla.org

Represents dental laboratory technicians and offers two meetings per year to promote educational opportunities for members.

3569 ■ Oregon Association of Dental Laboratories
PO Box 355
Rockaway Beach, OR 97136
Ph: (503)842-4100
Fr: 800-952-2751
E-mail: carol.oadl@gmail.com
URL: http://www.oregondentallabs.com

Serves owners of dental laboratories and dental laboratory technicians; seeks to advance the professional status of those engaged in the field of dental laboratory technology.

3570 ■ South Carolina Dental Laboratory Association
PO Box 2721
Spartanburg, SC 29304
Ph: (864)809-5587
Fax: (864)576-1490
E-mail: tulare@charter.net
URL: http://www.scdla.org

Promotes the art and science of dental laboratory operations; seeks to further the interests of dental laboratory owners and technicians.

3571 ■ Special Care Dentistry Association
401 N Michigan Ave., Ste. 2200
Chicago, IL 60611
Ph: (312)527-6764
Fax: (312)673-6663
E-mail: scda@scdaonline.org
URL: http://www.scdonline.org

Description: Dentists, hygienists, and lay public interested in special care dentistry. Aims to improve oral health and well being of people with special needs. Provides a forum for an exchange of clinical ideas and patient management techniques among members.

SOURCES OF HELP-WANTED ADS

3572 ■ AAOMS Surgical Update
American Association of Oral and Maxillofacial
Surgeons (AAOMS)
9700 W Bryn Mawr Ave.
Rosemont, IL 60018-5701
Ph: (847)678-6200
Fax: (847)678-6286
Fr: 800-822-6637
E-mail: mhynes@aaoms.org
URL: http://www.aaoms.org

Description: 2/year. Provides the dental profession
and others with current information on the specialty
of oral and maxillofacial surgery and patient care.

3573 ■ ACD News
American College of Dentists
839J Quince Orchard Blvd.
Gaithersburg, MD 20878-1614
Ph: (301)977-3223
Fax: (301)977-3330
E-mail: office@acd.org
URL: http://www.acd.org/publications.htm

Description: Tri-annual. Presents accounts of College meetings, as well as remarks from the College's
president. Publishes notices of scheduled events,
spotlights individuals recognized or given awards by
the College, and profiles convocation speakers, and
other dental organizations. Recurring features include
reports of meetings.

3574 ■ ACP Messenger
American College of Prosthodontists
211 E Chicago Ave., Ste. 1000
Chicago, IL 60611
Ph: (312)573-1260
Fax: (312)573-1257
E-mail: acp@prosthodontics.org
URL: http://www.prosthodontics.org/products/
Messenger.asp

Quarterly newsletter featuring industry news as well
as classified advertising.

3575 ■ ADSA Pulse
American Dental Society of Anesthesiology
211 E Chicago Ave., Ste. 780
Chicago, IL 60611
Ph: (312)664-8270
Fax: (312)224-8624
Fr: 877-255-3742
E-mail: adsahome@mac.com
URL: http://www.adsahome.org/

Description: Bimonthly. Features articles on developments in dental anesthesiology. Includes news of
research, editorials, news of the Society and its
members, and a calendar of events.

3576 ■ AGD Impact
Academy of General Dentistry
211 E Chicago Ave., Ste. 900
Chicago, IL 60611-1999
Fax: (312)440-0559
Fr: 888-AGD-DENT
E-mail: impact@agd.org
URL: http://www.agd.org/publications/?pubID=4

Description: Monthly. Covers the issues and trends
that impact on general dentists and the profession.
Includes CDE course list and fact sheets for patients.

3577 ■ Alpha Omegan
Reed Elsevier
125 Park Ave., 23rd Fl.
New York, NY 10017
Ph: (212)309-8100
Fax: (212)309-8187
URL: http://www.ao.org/resources/
publicationscommunications-mainm

Semiannual. $75.00/year for individuals. Journal
covering scientific issues of interest to the fraternity
of dentist.

**3578 ■ American Academy of Implant
Dentistry Newsletter**
American Academy of Implant Dentistry
211 E Chicago Ave., Ste. 750
Chicago, IL 60611
Ph: (312)335-1550
Fax: (312)335-9090
Fr: 877-335-AAID
E-mail: info@aaid.com
URL: http://www.aaid-implant.org

Description: Quarterly. Covers current activities in
the field of implant dentistry, particularly the educational programs of the Academy.

**3579 ■ American Association of Women
Dentists Chronicle**
American Association of Women Dentists
216 W Jackson Blvd, Ste. 625
Chicago, IL 60606
Fax: (312)750-1203
Fr: 800-920-2293
E-mail: info@aawd.org
URL: http://www.aawd.org/

Description: Quarterly. Includes articles of interest
on dentistry, nutrition, research, education, and
federal services. Provides information on the association, the practice of dentistry, and women in dentistry.

**3580 ■ American Dental Hygienists'
Association Access**
American Dental Hygienists' Association
444 N Michigan Ave., Ste. 3400
Chicago, IL 60611
Ph: (312)440-8900
Fr: 800-243-ADHA
URL: http://www.adha.org/publications/index.html

$48.00/year for individuals; $85.00/year for two years;
$120.00/year for individuals, for 3 years. Magazine

covering current dental hygiene topics, regulatory
and legislative developments, and association news.

**3581 ■ American Journal of Orthodontics
and Dentofacial Orthopedics**
Mosby Inc.
11830 Westline Industrial Dr.
St. Louis, MO 63146-3326
Ph: (314)872-8370
Fax: (314)432-1380
Fr: 800-325-4177
URL: http://www2.us.elsevierhealth.com

Monthly. $272.00/year for individuals; $145.00/year
for students; $367.00/year for Canada and Mexico;
$181.00/year for students, Canada and Mexico.
Journal for orthodontists and dentists who include
orthodontics as a portion of their practice.

3582 ■ ASDA News
Alliance of the American Dental Association
211 E Chicago Ave., Ste. 730
Chicago, IL 60611
Fax: (312)440-2587
Fr: 800-621-8099
URL: http://www.allianceada.org

Description: Monthly. Covers dentistry and association news. Recurring features include letters to the
editor, news of research, a calendar of events,
columns, Q&As, and reports of meetings.

3583 ■ Bulletin of Dental Education
American Dental Education Association
1400 K St., NW, Ste. 1100
Washington, DC 20005
Ph: (202)289-7201
Fax: (202)289-7204
E-mail: publications@adea.org
URL: http://www.adea.org

Description: Monthly. Contains news and information on dental education. Recurring features include
a calendar of events, reports of meetings, news of
educational opportunities, job listings, and notices of
publications available.

3584 ■ CDS Review
Chicago Dental Society
401 N Michigan Ave., Ste. 200
Chicago, IL 60611
Ph: (312)836-7300
Fax: (312)836-7337
URL: http://www.cds.org/cds_review/

$25.00/year for individuals; $30.00/year for institutions, and schools in USA & Canada; $45.00/year for
other countries; $5.00/year for single issue. Dental
journal.

3585 ■ The Cranial Letter
The Cranial Academy
3535 E. 96th St., Ste. 101
Indianapolis, IN 46240
Ph: (317)594-0411

Fax: (317)594-9299
E-mail: info@cranialacademy.org
URL: http://www.cranialacademy.org

Description: Quarterly. Provides information about osteopathy in the cranio-sacral field for doctors of osteopathy, dentistry, and medicine. Carries news of reports, papers, seminars, courses offered by the Academy, and research projects. Recurring features include obituaries, a calendar of events, and columns titled President's Message, The Dental Corner, and Scientific Section.

3586 ■ Dental Economics
PennWell Corp.
1421 S Sheridan Rd.
Tulsa, OK 74112
Ph: (918)835-3161
Fax: (918)831-9497
Fr: 800-331-4463
URL: http://www.dentaleconomics.com/index.html

Monthly. $132.00/year for individuals; $179.00/year for Canada and Mexico; $248.00/year for other countries; $211.00/year for two years; $312.00/year for Canada and Mexico; $428.00/year for other countries, two years; $65.00/year online. Magazine featuring business-related articles for dentists.

3587 ■ Dental Implantology Update
American Health Consultants Inc.
PO Box 740056
Atlanta, GA 30374
Ph: (404)262-5476
Fax: (404)814-0759
Fr: 800-688-2421
E-mail: editorial_questions@ahcmedia.com
URL: http://www.ahcmedia.com/public/pages/Dental-Implantology-Update.html#top

Description: Monthly. $599/year. Monitors clinical techniques and technologies in dental implants and treating patients.

3588 ■ Dental Town
Dental Town
9633 S 48th St., Ste. 200
Phoenix, AZ 85044
Ph: (480)598-0001
Fax: (480)598-3450
URL: http://www.dentaltown.com/

Monthly. Free to qualified subscribers. Magazine that offers information on the dental industry and latest dental equipment.

3589 ■ Dentistry in South Dakota
South Dakota Dental Association
804 N Euclid Ave., Ste. 103
PO Box 1194
Pierre, SD 57501
Ph: (605)224-9133
Fax: (605)224-9168
URL: http://www.sddental.org/communications_sdda_newsletter.htm

Description: Quarterly. Provides updates on dental profession issues, small business, employer/employee relations, nutrition, and safe workplace practices. Recurring features include letters to the editor, a calendar of events, reports of meetings, news of educational opportunities, and a column titled President's Corner.

3590 ■ Facets
San Diego County Dental Society
1275 W Morena Blvd., Ste. B
San Diego, CA 92110-1562
Ph: (619)275-0244
Fr: 800-201-0244
E-mail: lauren@sdcds.org
URL: http://www.sdcds.org

Description: Ten issues/year. Reports inhouse information on the Society. Recurring features include a calendar of events and columns titled New Applicants, New Members, Classified Advertising, and Continuing Education.

3591 ■ Hawaii Dental Journal
Hawaii Medical Journal
1360 S Beretania St., Ste. 200
Honolulu, HI 96814
Ph: (808)536-7702
Fax: (808)536-2376
E-mail: hda@hawaiidentalassociation.net
URL: http://www.hawaiidentalassociation.net/index.html

Bimonthly. $55.00/year for individuals. Dental journal.

3592 ■ HDA News & Reports
Hispanic Dental Association
3085 Stevenson Dr., Ste. 200
Springfield, IL 62703
Ph: (217)529-6517
Fax: (217)529-9120
Fr: 800-852-7921
E-mail: hispanicdental@hdassoc.org
URL: http://www.hdassoc.org

Quarterly. Provides information on HDA chapters, scholarship programs, and activities. Contains a classified advertising section, as well as previews of the annual meeting and reports of the immediate past meeting.

3593 ■ Illinois Dental News
Illinois State Dental Society
1010 S Second St.
Springfield, IL 62704
Ph: (217)525-1406
URL: http://www.isds.org/memberBenefits/publications/IllinoisDent

Monthly. $10.00/year for single issue, outside United States; $45.00/year for individuals; $90.00/year for other countries; $5.00/year for single issue. Dental magazine.

3594 ■ InterFace
American Society for Geriatric Dentistry
401 N Michigan Ave., Ste. 2200
Chicago, IL 60611
Ph: (312)527-6764
Fax: (312)673-6663
E-mail: scda@scdaonline.org
URL: http://www.scdonline.org/displaynewsletter.cfm

Description: Quarterly. Publishes news of geriatric dentistry as well as news of the Society, its members and activities. Recurring features include legislative updates, a calendar of events, news of members, book reviews, editorials, a message from the president, bibliographies, and biographies.

3595 ■ ISRN Dentistry
Hindawi Publishing Corporation
410 Park Ave., 15th Fl.
287 PMB
New York, NY 10022
E-mail: dentistry@isrn.com
URL: http://www.isrn.com/journals/dentistry

Peer-reviewed journal publishing original research articles, review articles, case reports, and clinical studies in all areas of dentistry.

3596 ■ Journal of the American Dental Association
ADA Publishing
211 E Chicago Ave.
Chicago, IL 60611-2678
Ph: (312)440-2500
URL: http://jada.ada.org/

Monthly. $128.00/year for individuals, U.S. and Mexico; $161.00/year for institutions, U.S. and Mexico; $16.00/year for single issue, U.S. and Mexico; $141.00/year for Canada, U.S. and Mexico; $183.00/year for institutions, Canada, plus airmail; $24.00/year for single issue, Canada, plus airmail; $161.00/year for individuals, Canada, plus airmail; $204.00/year for institutions, Canada, plus airmail; $24.00/year; $22.00/year for single issue, Canada, plus airmail. Trade journal for the dental profession.

3597 ■ Journal of the California Dental Association
California Dental Association
1201 K St.
Sacramento, CA 95814
Fr: 800-232-7645
URL: http://www.cda.org/publications/journal_of_the_california_de

Monthly. $18.00/year for members; $40.00/year for members, domestic; $75.00/year for nonmembers, ADA; $80.00/year for other countries; $10.00/year for members, back issue. Professional magazine for dentists.

3598 ■ Journal of Dental Education
American Dental Education Association
1400 K St. NW, Ste. 1100
Washington, DC 20005
Ph: (202)289-7201
Fax: (202)289-7204
URL: http://www.adea.org/publications/jde/Pages/default.aspx

Monthly. $80.00/year for members, print, online is free; $160.00/year for nonmembers, U.S., print; $190.00/year for nonmembers, Canada, print; $220.00/year for nonmembers, other countries, print; $390.00/year for institutions, Tier 1; $515.00/year for institutions, Tier 2; $665.00/year for institutions, Tier 3; $885.00/year for institutions, Tier 4; $1,100.00/year for institutions, Tier 5. Peer-reviewed journal for scholarly research and reviews on dental education.

3599 ■ Journal of Dental Hygiene
American Dental Hygienists' Association
444 N Michigan Ave., Ste. 3400
Chicago, IL 60611
Ph: (312)440-8900
Fr: 800-243-ADHA
E-mail: communications@adha.net
URL: http://www.adha.org/publications/index.html

Quarterly. $45.00/year for individuals; $65.00/year for two years; $90.00/year for individuals, 3 years. Professional journal on dental hygiene.

3600 ■ Journal of Dental Research
Sage Publications Inc.
2455 Teller Rd.
Thousand Oaks, CA 91320-2218
Ph: (805)499-9774
Fax: (805)583-2665
Fr: 800-818-7243
URL: http://www.dentalresearch.org/i4a/pages/index.cfm?pageid=332

Monthly. $877.00/year for institutions, print & online; $427.00/year for individuals, print only; $789.00/year for institutions, online only; $859.00/year for institutions, print only. Peer-reviewed dental science journal.

3601 ■ Journal of Operative Dentistry
American Academy of Gold Foil Operators
c/o Dr. Robert C. Keene, Sec.-Treas.
1 Woods End Rd.
Etna, NH 03750-4318
URL: http://academyofoperativedentistry.com/journal.html

Bimonthly. $75.00/year for individuals, online only; $200.00/year for institutions, online or print; $110.00/year for individuals, online or print; $85.00/year for other countries, online only; $115.00/year for other countries, print only; $250.00/year for institutions, other countries. Peer-reviewed professional journal covering issues in dentistry.

3602 ■ The Journal of Prosthetic Dentistry
Mosby Inc.
11830 Westline Industrial Dr.
St. Louis, MO 63146-3326
Ph: (314)872-8370
Fax: (314)432-1380
Fr: 800-325-4177
URL: http://journals.elsevierhealth.com/periodicals/ympr/home

Monthly. $259.00/year for individuals; $128.00/year

for students; $171.00/year for students, Canada; $342.00/year for Canada; $171.00/year for students, Mexico; $342.00/year for individuals, Mexico; $171.00/year for students, other countries; $342.00/year for other countries. Peer-reviewed journal emphasizing new techniques, evaluation of dental materials, pertinent basic science concepts, and patient psychology in restorative dentistry.

3603 ■ Keynotes
The USA Section of the International College of Dentists
51 Monroe St., Ste. 1400
Rockville, MD 20850-2408
Ph: (301)251-8861
Fax: (240)499-8975
E-mail: reg-sg@icd.org
URL: http://www.usa-icd.org/information/publications.htm

Description: Semiannual. Contains news of the activities and projects of the organization, which provides networking and educational opportunities for professionals in the dental field. Recurring features include a calendar of events, reports of meetings, news of educational opportunities, and a column titled the History Corner.

3604 ■ Maryland State Dental Association Newsletter
Maryland State Dental Association
6410F Dobbin Rd.
Columbia, MD 21045
Ph: (410)964-2880
Fax: (410)964-0583
E-mail: mddent@msda.com
URL: http://www.msda.com

Description: Monthly. Reports on health, legislative, economic, and medical issues that are pertinent to dentistry. Recurring features include letters to the editor, interviews, news of research, a calendar of events, reports of meetings, news of educational opportunities, and job listings.

3605 ■ MDS Connection
Massachusetts Dental Society
Two Willow St., Ste. 200
Southborough, MA 01745-1027
Fax: (508)480-0002
Fr: 800-342-8747
URL: http://www.massdental.org/

Description: Bimonthly. Provides news on the Society's activities and articles on the dental profession. Recurring features include reports of meetings, news of educational opportunities, job listings, and notices of publications available.

3606 ■ Momentum
Eastman Institute for Oral Health
601 Elmwood Ave.
Rochester, NY 14620
Ph: (585)275-5051
URL: http://www.urmc.rochester.edu/dentistry/newsletters.cfm

Description: Quarterly. Contains news of interest to Center alumni and friends. Recurring features include interviews, news of research, a calendar of events, and a message from the director.

3607 ■ News From The NIDCR
National Institute of Dental and Craniofacial Research
National Institutes of Health
Bethesda, MD 20892-2190
Fax: (301)480-4098
E-mail: nidcrinfo@mail.nih.gov
URL: http://www.nidcr.nih.gov

Description: Bimonthly. Includes the latest news about funding opportunities, training and career development opportunities, NIDCR and NIH news, and science advances.

3608 ■ Oral & Craniofacial Tissue Engineering
Quintessence Publishing Company Inc.
4350 Chandler Dr.
Hanover Park, IL 60133-6763
Ph: (630)736-3600
Fax: (630)736-3633
Fr: 800-621-0387
URL: http://www.quintpub.com/journals/octe/gp.php?journal_name=OC

Quarterly. Journal covering multiple disciplinary lines involving specialties of both dentistry and medicine.

3609 ■ Pediatric Dentistry Today
American Academy of Pediatric Dentistry
211 E Chicago Ave., Ste. 1700
Chicago, IL 60611-2637
Ph: (312)337-2169
Fax: (312)337-6329
E-mail: aapdinfo@aapd. org
URL: http://www.aapd.org

Description: Bimonthly. Reports on the activities of the Academy, which seeks to advance the specialty of pediatric dentistry through practice, education, and research. Recurring features include news of research, profiles of members, and legislative updates.

3610 ■ Pennsylvania Dental Journal
Pennsylvania Dental Association
3501 N Front St.
PO Box 3341
Harrisburg, PA 17105
Ph: (717)234-5941
Fax: (717)234-2186
URL: http://www.padental.org/AM/Template.cfm?Section=Publications

Bimonthly. Professional dentistry magazine containing treatment/procedure news, PDA activities information, continuing education courses, and legislation updates.

3611 ■ RDH
PennWell Publishing Co.
1421 S Sheridan Rd.
Tulsa, OK 74112
Ph: (918)835-3161
Fr: 800-331-4463
URL: http://www.rdhmag.com/index.html

Monthly. $79.00/year for individuals; $112.00/year for Canada; $141.00/year for other countries; $40.00/year for U.S. and other countries, digital. Magazine for dental hygiene professionals covering practice management, patient motivation, practice options, financial planning, personal development, preventive oral health care and treatment, home care instruction, radiology, anesthesia, nutrition, and new products.

3612 ■ Washington State Dental Laboratory Association Newsletter
PO Box 385
Graham, WA 98338
Ph: (360)832-2471
Fax: (360)832-2471
Fr: 800-652-2212
E-mail: peg2@mashell.com
URL: http://www.wsdla.com

Association newsletter featuring articles of interest to dental laboratory technicians as well as classified advertising for technical positions available.

3613 ■ Westviews
Western Los Angeles Dental Society
14722 Hawthorne Blvd., Ste. B
Lawndale, CA 90260
Ph: (310)349-2199
Fax: (310)349-2175
E-mail: wlads@pacbell.net
URL: http://www.westernlads.org

Description: Six issues/year. Carries items relating to organized dentistry and the clinical aspects of dentistry. Covers local community events involving

the organization or the profession; provides updates of states agency actions affecting dentistry.

3614 ■ WSDA News
Washington State Dental Association (WSDA)
126 NW Canal St.
Seattle, WA 98107
Ph: (206)448-1914
Fax: (206)443-9266
Fr: 800-448-3368
E-mail: info@wsda.org
URL: http://www.wsda.org/news

Description: Monthly. $67 per year. Contains information of interest to dentists on legislation, regulations, state boards and government, and business of the association. Recurring features include letters to the editor, editorial and op-ed columns, President's message, obituaries, practice opportunities, news of educational opportunities, and job listings.

EMPLOYER DIRECTORIES AND NETWORKING LISTS

3615 ■ American Academy of Pediatric Dentistry—Membership Directory
American Academy of Pediatric Dentistry
211 E Chicago Ave., Ste. 1700
Chicago, IL 60611-2663
Ph: (312)337-2169
Fax: (312)337-6329
URL: http://www.aapd.org

Annual, November. Covers: 5,600 pediatric dentists and several dentists in practice, teaching, and research. Entries include: Name, address, phone. Arrangement: Alphabetical. Indexes: Geographical.

3616 ■ International Association for Orthodontics—Membership Directory
International Association for Orthodontics
750 N Lincoln Memorial Dr., Ste. 422
Milwaukee, WI 53202
Ph: (414)272-2757
Fax: (414)272-2754
URL: http://www.iaortho.org

Annual, June. Covers: 2,500 general and children's dentists who also work to correct facial and jaw irregularities. Entries include: Name, office address and phone, orthodontic techniques practiced. Arrangement: Geographical. Indexes: Personal name.

3617 ■ Washington Physicians Directory
The Washington Physicians Directory
13912 Overton Ln.
PO Box 4436
Silver Spring, MD 20904
Ph: (301)384-1506
Fax: (301)384-6854
E-mail: wpd@wpdnetwork.com
URL: http://www.wpdnetwork.com

Annual, Latest edition 50th Anniversary Edition; 2012. Covers: 9,800 physicians in private practice or on full-time staff at hospitals in the Washington, D.C., metropolitan area. Entries include: Name, medical school and year of graduation; up to four office addresses with phone numbers for each; up to four medical specialties (indicating board certifications), Unique Physician Identification Numbers (UPIN), and e-mail. Arrangement: Alphabetical. Indexes: Geographical (within medical specialty); foreign language.

3618 ■ Worldwide Online Search Directory
402 W Wilson St.
Madison, WI 53703
Ph: (608)222-8583
Fax: (608)222-9540
Fr: 800-543-9220
E-mail: info@aacd.com
URL: http://www.aacd.com/professional/membershipbenefits.asp#4

Provides a worldwide listing of members of the American Academy of Cosmetic Dentistry.

HANDBOOKS AND MANUALS

3619 ■ Barron's Guide to Medical and Dental Schools
Barron's Educational Series, Inc.
250 Wireless Blvd.
Hauppauge, NY 11788-3917
Ph: (631)434-3311
Fax: (631)434-3723
Fr: 800-645-3476
E-mail: fbrown@barronseduc.com
URL: http://barronseduc.com

Sol Wischnitzer and Edith Wischnitzer. Twelve edition, 2009. $17.09. 768 pages. Updated with the latest facts and figures, this school directory and guidance manual presents profiles of all accredited medical, dental, and osteopathic schools in the United States and Canada.

3620 ■ Opportunities in Dental Care Careers
McGraw-Hill Professional
PO Box 182604
Columbus, OH 43272
Ph: 877-833-5524
Fax: (614)759-3749
E-mail: pbg.ecommerce_custserv@mcgraw-hill.com
URL: http://www.mhprofessional.com/
  product.php?isbn=0071388346

Bonnie Kendall. $12.95 (e-book). 160 pages. Provides a complete overview of the job possibilities in dental industry. Includes the skill and training requirements to current salary figures.

3621 ■ Opportunities in Health and Medical Careers
The McGraw-Hill Companies
PO Box 182604
Columbus, OH 43272
Fax: (614)759-3749
Fr: 877-883-5524
E-mail: customer.service@mcgraw-hill.com
URL: http://www.mhprofessional.com/
  product.php?isbn=0071437274

I. Donald Snook, Jr. and Leo D'Orazio. 2004. $14.95 (paper). 157 pages. Covers the full range of medical and health occupations. Illustrated.

3622 ■ Resumes for Health and Medical Careers
The McGraw-Hill Companies
PO Box 182604
Columbus, OH 43272
Fax: (614)759-3749
Fr: 877-883-5524
E-mail: customer.service@mcgraw-hill.com
URL: http://www.mhprofessional.com/
  product.php?isbn=0071545352

Third edition, 2008. $12.95 (paper). 144 pages.

3623 ■ Senior Dentist
National Learning Corporation
212 Michael Dr.
Syosset, NY 11791
Fr: 800-632-8888
URL: http://www.passbooks.com

2009. $69.95 (paper). Serves as an exam preparation guide for senior dentists.

EMPLOYMENT AGENCIES AND SEARCH FIRMS

3624 ■ Actuary Resources
115 N Castle Heights Ave., Ste. 202
Lebanon, TN 37087-2768
Ph: (615)360-5171
Fax: (615)360-5173
E-mail: info@actuaryresources.org
URL: http://www.actuaryresources.org

Provides staffing services to several different types of industries. Offers a free screening service to clients.

3625 ■ Career Advocates International
1539 Ave. A
Katy, TX 77493
Ph: (281)395-9848
Fax: (281)574-3949
URL: http://www.careeradvocates.org

Provides permanent placement and temporary staffing for executive and staff level positions. Specializes in multiple niches including: sales and marketing, accounting and financial services, banking, communications, human resources, chemicals, oil and gas, medical and dental, legal, information technology, energy, technology, engineering, manufacturing, construction, and light industrial.

3626 ■ DDS Resources
16020 Swingley Ridge Rd., Ste. 340
Chesterfield, MO 63017
Ph: (636)536-6656
Fax: (636)536-6667
Fr: 877-337-0563
E-mail: info@mdr-inc.com
URL: http://www.mdr-inc.com/dentists.aspx

Serves as a dental recruitment agency in the United States. Specializes in matching qualified dentists with dental employers.

3627 ■ DDS Staffing Resources, Inc.
9755 Dogwood Rd., Ste. 200
Roswell, GA 30075
Ph: (770)998-7779
Fax: (770)552-0176
Fr: 888-668-7779
URL: http://msrstaffing.com

Dental staffing agency.

3628 ■ Team Placement Service, Inc.
1414 Prince St., Ste. 202
Alexandria, VA 22314
Ph: (703)820-8618
Fax: (703)820-3368
Fr: 800-495-6767
E-mail: 4jobs@teamplace.com
URL: http://www.teamplace.com

Full-service personnel consultants provide placement for healthcare staff, physician and dentist, private practice, and hospitals. Conduct interviews, tests, and reference checks to select the top 20% of applicants. Survey applicants' skill levels, provide backup information on each candidate, select compatible candidates for consideration, and insure the hiring process minimizes potential legal liability. Industries served: healthcare and government agencies providing medical, dental, biotech, laboratory, hospitals, and physician search.

ONLINE JOB SOURCES AND SERVICES

3629 ■ CareersInDental.com
URL: http://www.careersindental.com

Description: Serves as a job board for the dental industry. Features listings of employment opportunities and job openings in the field.

3630 ■ CareerVitals.com
URL: http://www.careervitals.com

Description: Serves as a job board for healthcare professionals in different specializations.

3631 ■ DentalCrossing.com
URL: http://www.dentalcrossing.com

Description: Provides employment opportunities for dentists, dental assistants, dental hygienists, and dental lab technicians.

3632 ■ DentalJobsBoard.net
URL: http://www.dentaljobsboard.net

Description: Features dentist jobs, dental hygiene

jobs, dental assistant jobs, and jobs for dental lab technicians.

3633 ■ DentalPortal.com
URL: http://www.dentalportal.com

Description: Search engine for finding dentists, orthodontists, oral surgeons, and other dental professionals.

3634 ■ DentalPost.net
URL: http://www.dentalpost.net

Description: Lists dental jobs including dentist jobs, dental hygienist jobs, dental assistant jobs, dental lab technician jobs, and dental front office jobs.

3635 ■ DentalWorkers.com
URL: http://www.dentalworkers.com/employment

Description: Serves as an online employment resource among dental professionals. Provides classified ads for dental jobs, and free resume posting for workers.

3636 ■ Dentist Job Cafe
URL: http://www.dentistjobcafe.com

Description: Features dental job listings. Provides employment services for dentists, dental hygienists, and dental assistants.

3637 ■ DentistInfo.com
URL: http://www.dentistinfo.com

Description: Provides information on dental practice sales, dental seminars, dental jobs, and free listings and home page creation service.

3638 ■ DentistJobsNow.com
URL: http://www.dentist-jobs-now.com

Description: Provides assistance to new and practicing dentists, hygienists, and dental assistants in finding employment.

3639 ■ DentistryJob.com
URL: http://www.dentistryjob.com

Description: Serves as a job board for dentistry professionals.

3640 ■ HEALTHeCAREERS Network
Fr: 888-884-8242
E-mail: info@healthecareers.com
URL: http://www.healthecareers.com

Description: Career search site for jobs in all health care specialties; educational resources; visa and licensing information for relocation; interesting articles; relocation tools; links to professional organizations and general resources.

3641 ■ iHireDental
URL: http://www.ihiredental.com

Description: Features dental jobs in different specialty areas.

3642 ■ Medzilla.com
URL: http://www.medzilla.com

Description: General medical website which matches employers and job hunters to their ideal employees and jobs through search capabilities. Main files include: Post Jobs, Search Resumes, Post Resumes, Search Jobs, Head Hunters, Articles, Salary Survey.

3643 ■ Monster Healthcare
URL: http://healthcare.monster.com

Description: Delivers nationwide access to healthcare recruiting. Employers can post job listings or ads. Job seekers can post and code resumes, and search over 150,000 healthcare job listings, healthcare career advice columns, career resources information, and member employer profiles and services.

3644 ■ ProHealthJobs.com
Ph: (484)443-8545
Fax: (484)443-8549
E-mail: info@prohealthjobs.com
URL: http://prohealthjobs.com/jobboard
Description: Career resources site for the medical and health care field. Lists professional opportunities, product information, continuing education and open positions.

3645 ■ SmileJobs.com
URL: http://www.smilejobs.com
Description: Features job opportunities, resume search and postings for dental professionals.

TRADESHOWS

3646 ■ Academy of General Dentistry Annual Meeting
Academy of General Dentistry
211 E. Chicago Ave., Ste. 900
Chicago, IL 60611-1999
Fax: (312)440-0559
Fr: 888-243-3368
E-mail: agdmeet@agd.org
URL: http://www.agd.org
Annual. Primary Exhibits: Dental products and services. Dates and Locations: 2012 Jun 21-24; Philadelphia, PA; Philadelphia Marriott Downtown.

3647 ■ Alabama Dental Association Annual Session
Alabama Dental Association
836 Washington Ave.
Montgomery, AL 36104
Ph: (334)265-1684
Fax: (334)262-6218
E-mail: waren@aldaonline.org
URL: http://www.aldaonline.org
Annual. Primary Exhibits: Dental equipment, sundry dental supplies, computer software, and pharmaceutical and dental instruments. Dates and Locations: 2012 Jun 12-17.

3648 ■ American Academy of Esthetic Dentistry Annual Meeting
303 W Madison St., Ste. 2650
Chicago, IL 60611
Ph: (312)981-6770
Fax: (312)981-6787
E-mail: info@estheticacademy.org
URL: http://www.estheticacademy.org
Annual. Features lectures, sessions and discussions regarding controversies in the industry as well as scientific updates in the field of esthetic dentistry. 2012 August 7-10; Naples, FL; The Ritz-Carlton.

3649 ■ American Academy of Implant Dentistry Annual Meeting
American Academy of Implant Dentistry
211 E. Chicago Ave., Ste. 750
Chicago, IL 60611
Ph: (312)335-1550
Fax: (312)335-9090
Fr: 877-335-2243
E-mail: info@aaid.com
URL: http://www.aaid-implant.org
Annual. Primary Exhibits: Dental equipment, supplies, and services. Dates and Locations: 2012 Oct 03-06; Washington, DC; Hilton Washington; 2013 Oct 23-26; Phoenix, AZ; JW Marriott Desert Ridge Resort.

3650 ■ American Academy of Pediatric Dentistry Annual Session
American Academy of Pediatric Dentistry
211 E. Chicago Ave., Ste. 1700
Chicago, IL 60611-2637
Ph: (312)337-2169
Fax: (312)337-6329
URL: http://www.aapd.org
Annual. Primary Exhibits: Dental products and

publications. Dates and Locations: 2012 May 24-27; San Diego, CA; San Diego Marriott Hotel & Marina; 2013 May 23-26; Orlando, FL; Walt Disney World Swan Dolphin Resort; 2014 May 22-25; Boston, MA; Hynes Convention Center.

3651 ■ American Association of Dental Schools Annual Session and Exposition
American Dental Education Association
1400 K St. N.W., Ste. 1100
Washington, DC 20005
Ph: (202)289-7201
Fax: (202)289-7204
URL: http://www.adea.org/Pages/default.aspx
Annual. Primary Exhibits: Dental equipment and supplies, publications, video equipment, and computers. Dates and Locations: 2012 Mar 17-21; Orlando, FL; Hilton Bonnet Creek; 2013 Mar 16-19; Seattle, WA; Sheraton Seattle Hotel and Washington State Convention & Tra.

3652 ■ American Association of Endodontists Annual Convention and Trade Show
American Association of Endodontists
211 E. Chicago Ave., Ste. 1100
Chicago, IL 60611-2691
Ph: (312)266-7255
Fax: (312)266-9867
Fr: 800-872-3636
E-mail: info@aae.org
URL: http://www.aae.org/
Annual. Primary Exhibits: Industry-related equipment, supplies, and services. Dates and Locations: 2012 Apr 18-21; Boston, MA; Hynes Convention Center; 2013 Apr 17-20; Honolulu, HI; Hawaii Convention Center.

3653 ■ American Association of Orthodontists Trade Show and Scientific Session
American Association of Orthodontists
401 N. Lindbergh Blvd.
St. Louis, MO 63141-7816
Ph: (314)993-1700
Fax: (314)997-1745
Fr: 800-424-2841
E-mail: info@aaortho.org
URL: http://www.aaomembers.org/
Annual. Primary Exhibits: Orthodontic equipment and materials. Dates and Locations: 2012 May 04-08; Honolulu, HI; 2013 May 03-07; Philadelphia, PA; 2014 Apr 25-29; New Orleans, LA; 2015 May 15-19; San Francisco, CA; 2016 Apr 29 - May 02; Orlando, FL.

3654 ■ Annual Scientific Sessions
402 W Wilson St.
Madison, WI 53718
Ph: (608)222-8583
Fax: (608)222-9540
Fr: 800-543-9220
E-mail: info@aacd.com
URL: http://www.aacd.com
Annual conference allowing members to exchange new ideas and network on the latest in clinical procedures, cosmetic practice development and self-enrichment.

3655 ■ Chicago Dental Society Midwinter Meeting
Chicago Dental Society
401 N. Michigan Ave., Ste. 200
Chicago, IL 60611
Ph: (312)836-7300
URL: http://www.cds.org
Annual. Primary Exhibits: Dental equipment, services, and related business services. Dates and Locations: 2012 Feb 23-25; Chicago, IL; McCormick Place West.

3656 ■ Detroit Dental Review
Detroit District Dental Society
3011 W. Grand Blvd., Ste. 460
Detroit, MI 48202

Ph: (313)871-3500
Fax: (313)871-3503
E-mail: centraloffice@detroitdentalsociety.com
URL: http://detroitdentalsociety.org
Annual. Primary Exhibits: Dental equipment, supplies, and services, including office systems.

3657 ■ General Session and Exhibition of the IADR
International Association for Dental Research
1619 Duke St.
Alexandria, VA 22314-3406
Ph: (703)548-0066
Fax: (703)548-1883
URL: http://www.dentalresearch.org
Annual. Primary Exhibits: Dentistry equipment, supplies, and services. Dates and Locations: 2012 Jun 20-23; Rio de Janeiro, Brazil; 2013 Mar 20-23; Seattle, WA; 2014 Mar 19-22; Cape Town, Republic of South Africa; 2015 Mar 11-14; Boston, MA.

3658 ■ Greater New York Dental Meeting
Greater New York Dental Meeting
570 7th Ave., Ste. 800
New York, NY 10018
Ph: (212)398-6922
Fax: (212)398-6934
E-mail: info@gnydm.com
URL: http://www.gnydm.com
Annual. Primary Exhibits: Dental products and services. Dates and Locations: 2012 Nov 23-28; New York, NY; Jacob K. Javits Convention Center; 2013 Nov 29 - Dec 04; New York, NY; Jacob K. Javits Convention Center.

3659 ■ Hispanic Dental Association Annual Meeting
Hispanic Dental Association
3085 Stevenson Dr., Ste. 200
Springfield, IL 62703
Ph: (217)529-6517
Fax: (217)529-9120
Fr: 800-852-7921
E-mail: hispanicdental@hdassoc.org
URL: http://www.hdassoc.org
Annual. Discusses a wide variety of clinical and practice management issues of interest to Hispanic dental professionals and those who work within the Hispanic dental community. Offers an array of educational sessions geared for allied dental professionals.

3660 ■ Jewel of the Great Lakes—Wisconsin Dental Meeting
Wisconsin Dental Association
6737 W. Washington St., Ste. 2360
West Allis, WI 53214
Ph: (414)276-4520
Fax: (414)276-8431
URL: http://www.wda.org
Annual. Primary Exhibits: Dental equipment and supplies, office supplies, publications, and data processing. Dates and Locations: 2012 May 10-12; Madison, WI; Monona Terrace.

3661 ■ Michigan Dental Association Annual Session
Michigan Dental Association
Public Relations Dept.
3657 Okemos Rd., Ste. 200
Okemos, MI 48864
Ph: (517)372-9070
Fax: (517)372-0008
Fr: 800-589-2632
URL: http://www.smilemichigan.com
Annual. Primary Exhibits: Dental equipment, materials, and instruments; computers; software; uniforms; and estate planners. Dates and Locations: 2012 Apr 08-21; Lansing, MI; Lansing Center.

3662 ■ Mid-Continent Dental Congress
Greater St. Louis Dental Society
11457 Olde Cabin Rd., Ste. 300
St. Louis, MO 63141
Ph: (314)569-0444
Fax: (314)569-0448
E-mail: gslds@gslds.org
URL: http://www.gslds.org

Annual. Primary Exhibits: Dental equipment, supplies, and services.

3663 ■ National Dental Association Annual Convention
National Dental Association, Inc.
3517 16th St., N.W.
Washington, DC 20010
Ph: (202)588-1697
Fax: (202)588-1244
E-mail: admin@ndaonline.org
URL: http://www.ndaonline.org

Annual. Primary Exhibits: Dental and Pharmaceutical equipment, supplies, and services. Dates and Locations: 2012 Jul 20-24.

3664 ■ Nation's Capital Dental Meeting
District of Columbia Dental Society
502 C St., N.E.
Washington, DC 20002-5810
Ph: (202)547-7613
Fax: (202)546-1482
E-mail: info@dcdental.org
URL: http://www.dcdental.org

Annual. Primary Exhibits: Equipment, clothing, dental supplies, office management systems, and publications. Dates and Locations: 2012 Mar 29-31; Washington, DC; Washington Convention Center.

3665 ■ Ohio Dental Association Annual Session
Ohio Dental Association
1370 Dublin Rd.
Columbus, OH 43215-1098
Ph: (614)486-2700
Fax: (614)486-0381
E-mail: dentist@oda.org
URL: http://www.oda.org

Annual. Primary Exhibits: Dental equipment, supplies, and services, computers, and insurance. Dates and Locations: 2012 Sep 13-16; 2013 Sep 19-22.

3666 ■ Pacific Northwest Dental Conference
Washington State Dental Association
126 N.W. Canal St.
Seattle, WA 98107
Ph: (206)448-1914
Fax: (206)443-9266
Fr: 800-448-3368
E-mail: info@wsda.org
URL: http://www.wsda.org

Annual. Primary Exhibits: Dental supplies, instruments, and equipment. Dates and Locations: 2012 Jun 14-15; Seattle, WA; 2013 Jun 13-14; Bellevue, WA; 2014 Jun 12-13; Bellevue, WA.

3667 ■ Star of the North Meeting
Minnesota Dental Association
1335 Industrial Blvd., Ste. 200
Minneapolis, MN 55413-4801
Ph: (612)767-8400
Fax: (612)767-8500
Fr: 800-950-3368
E-mail: info@mndental.org
URL: http://www.mndental.org

Annual. Primary Exhibits: Dental equipment and supplies, dental laboratory equipment, office equipment, and service organizations. Dates and Locations: 2012 Apr 26-28; 2013 Apr 25-27; 2014 Apr 24-26; 2015 Apr 23-25.

3668 ■ Star of the South Dental Meeting
Greater Houston Dental Society
1 Greenway Plz., Ste. 110
Houston, TX 77046
Ph: (713)961-4337
Fax: (713)961-3617
URL: http://www.ghds.org

Annual. Primary Exhibits: Dental equipment, supplies, and dental office amenities. Dates and Locations: 2012 Mar 29-31; Houston, TX; George R. Brown Convention Center.

3669 ■ Thomas P. Hinman Dental Meeting & Exhibits
Thomas P. Hinman Dental Society of Atlanta
33 Lenox Pte.
Atlanta, GA 30324-3172
Ph: (404)231-1663
Fax: (404)231-9638
URL: http://www.hinman.org

Annual. Primary Exhibits: Dental equipment, supplies, and services. Dates and Locations: 2012 Mar 22-24; 2013 Mar 21-23.

3670 ■ Three Rivers Dental Conference
Dental Society of Western Pennsylvania
900 Cedar Ave.
Pittsburgh, PA 15212
Ph: (412)321-5810
Fax: (412)321-7719
URL: http://www.dswp.org

Annual. Primary Exhibits: Dental products and equipment, computers, office equipment, and insurance.

3671 ■ Western Regional Dental Convention
Arizona State Dental Association
3193 N. Drinkwater Blvd.
Scottsdale, AZ 85251-6491
Ph: (480)344-5777
Fax: (480)344-1442
Fr: 800-866-2732
URL: http://www.azdaservices.com/

Annual. Primary Exhibits: Dental supplies and services. Dates and Locations: 2012 Mar 29-31.

3672 ■ Yankee Dental Congress
Massachusetts Dental Society
2 Willow St., No. 200
Southborough, MA 01745-1027
Ph: (508)480-9797
Fax: (508)480-0002
Fr: 800-342-8747
E-mail: madental@massdental.org
URL: http://www.massdental.org

Annual. Primary Exhibits: Dental products, equipment, and services. Dates and Locations: 2012 Jan 25-29; Boston, MA; Boston Convention & Exhibition Center.

OTHER SOURCES

3673 ■ Academy of General Dentistry (AGD)
211 E Chicago Ave., Ste. 900
Chicago, IL 60611-1999
Fax: (312)440-0559
Fr: 888-243-3368
E-mail: membership@agd.org
URL: http://www.agd.org

Description: Seeks to serve the needs and represent the interest of general dentists. Fosters their dentists' continued proficiency through quality continuing dental education to better serves the public.

3674 ■ Academy of Operative Dentistry (AOD)
PO Box 34425
Los Angeles, CA 90034
Ph: (310)794-4387
Fax: (310)825-2536
Fr: 888-232-5011
E-mail: memberservices@academyofoperativedentistry.com
URL: http://www.academyofoperativedentistry.com

Description: Dentists and persons in allied industries. Seeks to ensure quality in all of operative dentistry, teaching, service and research.

3675 ■ American Academy of Cosmetic Dentistry
402 W Wilson St.
Madison, WI 53703
Ph: (608)222-8583
Fax: (608)222-9540
Fr: 800-543-9220
E-mail: info@aacd.com
URL: http://www.aacd.com

Members include more than 8,000 cosmetic and reconstructive dentists, dental laboratory technicians, dental auxiliaries, dental hygienists, educators, researchers and students. Membership benefits include AACD accreditation, registration to AACD's Annual Scientific Session, publications, online search directory, marketing materials, and more.

3676 ■ American Academy of Dental Group Practice (AADGP)
2525 E Arizona Biltmore Cir., Ste. 127
Phoenix, AZ 85016
Ph: (602)381-1185
Fax: (602)381-1093
E-mail: aadgp@aadgp.org
URL: http://www.aadgp.org

Description: Represents active dentists and dental group practices. Aims to improve the level of dental service provided by members through exchanging and expanding of ideas and techniques for patient treatment and practice administration. Promotes group practice and research; accumulates and disseminates information; seeks to achieve the proper recognition for the aims and goals of group practice. Helps support an accreditation program as a system of voluntary peer review.

3677 ■ American Association of Dental Boards
211 E Chicago Ave., Ste. 760
Chicago, IL 60611
Ph: (312)440-7464
Fax: (312)440-3525
E-mail: info@dentalboards.org
URL: http://dentalboards.org

Description: Represents present and past members of state dental examining boards and board administrators. Assists member agencies with problems related to state dental board examinations and licensure, and enforcement of the state dental practice act. Conducts research; compiles statistics.

3678 ■ American Association of Public Health Dentistry
3085 Stevenson Dr., Ste. 200
Springfield, IL 62703
Ph: (217)529-6941
Fax: (217)529-9120
E-mail: natoff@aaphd.org
URL: http://www.aaphd.org

Description: Represents individuals concerned with improving the public's oral health. Seeks to find ways to meet the challenge of improving oral health. Commits to the expansion of the knowledge base of dental public health and to fostering competency in its practice.

3679 ■ American Association of Women Dentists (AAWD)
216 W Jackson Blvd., Ste. 625
Chicago, IL 60606
Fax: (312)750-1203
Fr: 800-920-2293
E-mail: info@aawd.org
URL: http://www.aawd.org

Description: Represents dental students or dentists who are interested in dentistry and advancing women in dentistry. Dedicates itself to enhancing and promoting unique participation and leadership for women in organized dentistry.

3680 ■ American College of Dentists (ACD)
839J Quince Orchard Blvd.
Gaithersburg, MD 20878-1614
Ph: (301)977-3223
Fax: (301)977-3330
E-mail: office@acd.org
URL: http://acd.org

Description: Dentists and others serving in capacities related to the dental profession. Seeks to advance the standards of the profession of dentistry. Conducts educational and research programs. Maintains speakers' bureau and charitable programs.

3681 ■ American College of Prosthodontists
211 E Chicago Ave., Ste. 1000
Chicago, IL 60611
Ph: (312)573-1260
Fax: (312)573-1257
URL: http://www.prosthodontics.org

Membership includes more than 3,300 prosthodontists, dental technicians, dental students and other dental professionals contributing to the specialty. Committed to the esthetic restoration of teeth, including bridges, crowns/caps, dental implants, dentures, partial dentures, whitening and veneers. Membership includes free subscriptions to the Journal of Prosthodontics, the Messenger, and e-blasts.

3682 ■ American Dental Association (ADA)
211 E Chicago Ave.
Chicago, IL 60611-2678
Ph: (312)440-2500
Fax: (312)440-2800
E-mail: membership@ada.org
URL: http://www.ada.org

Description: Professional society of dentists. Encourages the improvement of the health of the public and promotes the art and science of dentistry in matters of legislation and regulations. Inspects and accredits dental schools and schools for dental hygienists, assistants, and laboratory technicians. Conducts research programs at ADA Foundation Research Institute. Produces dental health education material used in the U.S. Sponsors National Children's Dental Health Month and Give Kids a Smile Day. Compiles statistics on personnel, practice, and dental care needs and attitudes of patients with regard to dental health.

3683 ■ American Dental Education Association (ADEA)
1400 K St. NW, Ste. 1100
Washington, DC 20005
Ph: (202)289-7201
Fax: (202)289-7204
E-mail: valachovicr@adea.org
URL: http://www.adea.org

Description: Individuals interested in dental education; schools of dentistry, advanced dental and allied dental education in the U.S., Canada, and Puerto Rico; affiliated institutions of the federal government and corporations. Works to promote better teaching and education in dentistry and dental research and to facilitate exchange of ideas among dental educators. Sponsors meetings, conferences, and workshops; conducts surveys, studies, and special projects and publishes their results. Maintains 37 sections and 8 special interest groups representing many different aspects of dental education.

3684 ■ American Public Health Association (APHA)
800 I St. NW
Washington, DC 20001
Ph: (202)777-2742
Fax: (202)777-2534
E-mail: comments@apha.org
URL: http://www.apha.org

Description: Professional organization of physicians, nurses, educators, academicians, environmentalists, epidemiologists, new professionals, social workers, health administrators, optometrists, podiatrists, pharmacists, dentists, nutritionists, health planners, other community and mental health specialists, and interested consumers. Seeks to protect and promote personal, mental, and environmental health. Services include: promulgation of standards; establishment of uniform practices and procedures; development of the etiology of communicable diseases; research in public health; exploration of medical care programs and their relationships to public health. Sponsors job placement service.

3685 ■ American School Health Association (ASHA)
4340 East West Hwy., Ste. 403
Bethesda, MD 20814
Ph: (301)652-8072
Fax: (301)652-8077
Fr: 800-445-2742
E-mail: info@ashaweb.org
URL: http://www.ashaweb.org

Description: School physicians, school nurses, counselors, nutritionists, psychologists, social workers, administrators, school health coordinators, health educators, and physical educators working in schools, professional preparation programs, public health, and community-based organizations. Promotes coordinated school health programs that include health education, health services, a healthful school environment, physical education, nutrition services, and psycho-social health services offered in schools collaboratively with families and other members of the community. Offers professional reference materials and professional development opportunities. Conducts pilot programs that inform materials development, provides technical assistance to school professionals, advocates for school health.

3686 ■ American Society of Dentist Anesthesiologists
c/o Amy L. Brown, Exec. Dir.
304 Patrick St.
Vienna, VA 22180
Ph: (703)462-9196
Fax: (703)462-9333
E-mail: asda@asdahq.org
URL: http://www.asdahq.org

Description: Represents dentists who have completed a minimum of two years of full-time postdoctoral training in anesthesiology. Supports and encourages the clinical practice of anesthesia by dentists. Promotes the acquisition and dissemination of scientific knowledge associated therewith.

3687 ■ American Student Dental Association (ASDA)
211 E Chicago Ave., Ste. 700
Chicago, IL 60611-2687
Ph: (312)440-2795
Fax: (312)440-2820
Fr: 800-621-8099
E-mail: nancy@asdanet.org
URL: http://www.asdanet.org

Description: Predoctoral and postdoctoral dental students organized to improve the quality of dental education and to promote the accessibility of oral health care; additional membership categories include predental, postdoctoral, international and associate. Represents dental students before legislative bodies, organizations, and associations that affect dental students. Disseminates information to dental students. Sponsors advocacy program and "externships" including Washington National Health Policy, Chicago Administrative, State Government Affairs, and Research.

3688 ■ Crown Council
975 Woodoak Ln., Ste. 200
Salt Lake City, UT 84117
Ph: (801)293-8522
Fax: (801)293-8524
Fr: 800-276-9658
E-mail: success@crowncouncil.com
URL: http://www.mycrowncouncil.com

Description: Seeks to improve independent dental practices. Promotes oral health and the fight against oral cancer. Provides patient care and offers state-of-the-art dental procedure facilities.

3689 ■ Hispanic Dental Association
3085 Stevenson Dr., Ste. 200
Springfield, IL 62703
Ph: (217)529-6517
Fax: (217)529-9120
Fr: 800-852-7921
E-mail: hispanicdental@hdassoc.org
URL: http://www.hdassoc.org

Description: Works to promote the oral health of the Hispanic community through improved prevention, treatment and education. Disseminates information to both Hispanic dental professionals and the community at large. Provides a worldwide source of continuing education for oral health professionals serving the Hispanic community.

3690 ■ Holistic Dental Association (HDA)
1825 Ponce de Leon Blvd., No. 148
Coral Gables, FL 33134
Ph: (305)356-7338
Fax: (305)468-6359
E-mail: director@holisticdental.org
URL: http://www.holisticdental.org

Description: Represents dentists, chiropractors, dental hygienists, physical therapists, and medical doctors. Aims to provide a holistic approach to better dental care for patients, and to expand techniques, medications, and philosophies that pertain to extractions, anesthetics, fillings, crowns, and orthodontics. Encourages the use of homeopathic medications, acupuncture, cranial osteopathy, nutritional techniques, and physical therapy in treating patients in addition to conventional treatments. Sponsors training and educational seminars.

3691 ■ International Congress of Oral Implantologists (ICOI)
248 Lorraine Ave.
Upper Montclair, NJ 07043
Ph: (973)783-6300
Fax: (973)783-1175
Fr: 800-442-0525
E-mail: icoi@dentalimplants.com
URL: http://www.icoi.org

Description: Dentists and oral surgeons dedicated to the teaching of and research in oral implantology (branch of dentistry dealing with dental implants placed into or on top of the jaw bone). Offers fellowship, mastership, and diplomate certification programs. Compiles statistics and maintains registry of current research in the field. Sponsors classes, seminars, and workshops at universities, hospitals, and societies worldwide. Provides consultation and patient information/referral services.

3692 ■ National Dental Association (NDA)
3517 16th St. NW
Washington, DC 20010
Ph: (202)588-1697
Fax: (202)588-1244
Fr: 877-628-3368
E-mail: rsjohns@ndaonline.org
URL: http://www.ndaonline.org

Description: Professional society for dentists. Aims to provide quality dental care to the unserved and underserved public and promote knowledge of the art and science of dentistry. Advocates the inclusion of dental care services in health care programs on local, state, and national levels. Fosters the integration of minority dental health care providers in the profession, and promotes dentistry as a viable career for minorities through support programs. Conducts research programs. Group is distinct from the former name of the American Dental Association.

3693 ■ National Rural Health Association (NRHA)
Administrative Office
521 E 63rd St.
Kansas City, MO 64110-3329
Ph: (816)756-3140

Fax: (816)756-3144
E-mail: mail@nrharural.org
URL: http://www.ruralhealthweb.org

Description: Administrators, physicians, nurses, physician assistants, health planners, academicians, and others interested or involved in rural health care. Creates a better understanding of health care problems unique to rural areas; utilizes a collective approach in finding positive solutions; articulates and represents the health care needs of rural America; supplies current information to rural health care providers; serves as a liaison between rural health care programs throughout the country. Offers continuing education credits for medical, dental, nursing, and management courses.

3694 ■ North American Sikh Medical and Dental Association (NASMDA)
4104 Old Vestal Rd., Ste. 108
Vestal, NY 13850
Ph: (607)729-0726
Fax: (607)729-1341
E-mail: nasmda@gmail.com
URL: http://nasmda.org

Description: Promotes the interests of Sikh physicians and dentists in the United States, Canada and elsewhere. Supports Sikh physicians, dentists and other Sikh professionals pursuing their careers in those fields or any other fields. Assists Sikh medical and dental graduates to establish practices and help them obtain adequate post-graduate training. Seeks to improve the medical education and delivery of medical care in the parent homeland. Compiles a comprehensive directory of Sikh physicians and dentists residing in North America.

3695 ■ Society for Executive Leadership in Academic Medicine International (SELAM)
100 N 20th St., 4th Fl.
Philadelphia, PA 19103-1443
Ph: (215)564-3484
Fax: (215)564-2175
E-mail: selam@selaminternational.org
URL: http://www.selaminternational.org

Description: Advocates for the advancement and promotion of women to executive positions in academic health professions. Supports programs designed for individuals interested in careers in academic medicine and dentistry. Promotes collaborations and networking among members and other organizations that share common goals.

3696 ■ Special Care Dentistry Association
401 N Michigan Ave., Ste. 2200
Chicago, IL 60611
Ph: (312)527-6764
Fax: (312)673-6663
E-mail: scda@scdaonline.org
URL: http://www.scdonline.org

Description: Dentists, hygienists, and lay public interested in special care dentistry. Aims to improve oral health and well being of people with special needs. Provides a forum for an exchange of clinical ideas and patient management techniques among members.

3697 ■ Ukrainian Medical Association of North America (UMANA)
2247 W Chicago Ave.
Chicago, IL 60622
Fax: (773)278-6962
Fr: 888-RXU-MANA
E-mail: umana@umana.org
URL: http://www.umana.org

Description: Physicians, surgeons, dentists, and persons in related professions who are of Ukrainian descent. Provides assistance to members; sponsors lectures. Maintains placement service, museum, biographical and medical archives.

SOURCES OF HELP-WANTED ADS

3698 ■ *Appliance DESIGN Magazine*
BNP Media
2401 W Big Beaver Rd., Ste. 700
Troy, MI 48084
Ph: (248)362-3700
Fax: (248)362-0317
E-mail: ad@halldata.com
URL: http://www.appliancedesign.com

Monthly. Provides solutions for design and engineering teams in the global, commercial and medical appliance/durable goods industry. Includes current industry news and a variety of technical articles on technologies, components, materials and services used in the design and development of new products.

3699 ■ *Builder*
Hanley-Wood L.L.C.
1 Thomas Cir. NW, Ste. 600
Washington, DC 20005-5803
Ph: (202)452-0800
Fax: (202)785-1974
E-mail: builder@omeda.com
URL: http://www.hanleywood.com/
   default.aspx?page=magazines

$29.95/year for U.S. and Canada; $54.95/year for U.S. and Canada, 2 years; $192.00/year for other countries. Magazine covering housing and construction industry.

3700 ■ *Design News*
Reed Business Information
360 Park Ave. S
New York, NY 10010-1710
Ph: (646)746-6400
URL: http://www.designnews.com

Monthly. Magazine covering design engineering.

3701 ■ *Design Perspectives*
Industrial Designers Society of America
45195 Business Ct., Ste. 250
Dulles, VA 20166-6717
Ph: (703)707-6000
Fax: (703)787-8501
E-mail: donnap@idsa.org
URL: http://www.idsa.org

Description: Ten issues/year. The largest newsletter examining the news and trends of industrial design. Recurring features include: new and cutting-edge products, news of people and events in industrial design, resource section, reports of chapter and national activities of IDSA, and a calendar of events.

3702 ■ *ENR: Engineering News-Record*
McGraw-Hill Inc.
PO Box 182604
Columbus, OH 43218
Ph: (614)430-4000
Fax: (614)759-3749

Fr: 877-833-5524
URL: http://enr.construction.com/Default.asp

Weekly. $49.00/year for individuals, print; $89.00/year for Canada, print; $125.00/year for other countries, print. Magazine focusing on engineering and construction.

3703 ■ *Fabric Architecture*
Industrial Fabrics Association International
1801 County Rd. B W
Roseville, MN 55113
Ph: (651)222-2508
Fax: (651)631-9334
Fr: 800-225-4324
URL: http://fabricarchitecturemag.com/

Bimonthly. $39.00/year for two years; $49.00/year for two years, Canada and Mexico; $69.00/year for two years, international. Magazine specializing in interior and exterior design ideas and technical information for architectural fabric applications in architecture and the landscape.

3704 ■ *HOW Magazine*
F+W Media, Inc.
PO Box 420235
Palm Coast, FL 32142-0235
Ph: (386)246-3365
E-mail: fwclient@emailcustomerservice.com
URL: http://www.howdesign.com

Bimonthly. Focuses on helping designers, whether they work for a design firm, for an in-house design department or for themselves, run successful, creative, profitable studios.

3705 ■ *Hydraulics & Pneumatics*
Penton Media Inc.
249 W 17th St.
New York, NY 10011
Ph: (212)204-4200
URL: http://www.hydraulicspneumatics.com/
   default.aspx

Monthly. $63.00/year for individuals; $90.00/year for two years. Magazine of hydraulic and pneumatic systems and engineering.

3706 ■ *Live Design*
Penton Media Inc.
9800 Metcalf Ave.
Overland Park, KS 66212
Ph: (913)341-1300
Fax: (913)967-1898
URL: http://livedesignonline.com

The business of entertainment technology and design.

3707 ■ *Masonry Magazine*
Mason Contractors Association of America
1481 Merchant Dr.
Algonquin, IL 60102
Ph: (224)678-9709
Fax: (224)678-9714

Fr: 800-536-2225
URL: http://www.masoncontractors.org

Monthly. $43.00/2 years; $29.00/year. Covers every aspect of the mason contractor profession, from equipment and techniques to building codes and standards, training the future masonry labor force, business planning, promoting business, job interviewing, negotiation and legal issues.

3708 ■ *Producers Masterguide*
Producers Masterguide
60 E 8th St., 34th Fl.
New York, NY 10003-6514
Ph: (212)777-4002
Fax: (212)777-4101
URL: http://www.producers.masterguide.com/
   cover.html

Annual. $185.00/year for U.S.; $175.00/year for Canada; $205.00/year for other countries. An international film and TV production directory and guide for the professional motion picture, broadcast television, feature film, TV commercial, cable/satellite, digital and videotape industries in the U.S., Canada, the UK, the Caribbean Islands, Mexico, Australia, New Zealand, Europe, Israel, Morocco, the Far East, and South America.

3709 ■ *Professional Builder*
SGC Horizon LLC
3030 W Salt Creek Ln., Ste. 201
Arlington Heights, IL 60005
Ph: (847)391-1000
Fax: (847)390-0408
URL: http://www.housingzone.com/pb/pubhome/

Monthly. Free. The integrated engineering magazine of the building construction industry.

3710 ■ *Society for Environmental Graphic Design-Messages*
Society for Environmental Graphic Design
1000 Vermont Ave., NW. Ste. 400
Washington, DC 20005
Ph: (202)638-5555
Fax: (202)478-2286
E-mail: segd@segd.org
URL: http://www.segd.org/publications/
   messages.html

Description: Monthly. Reports on Society program news, member services, resources, and product news.

3711 ■ *Trace*
American Institute of Graphic Arts
164 5th Ave.
New York, NY 10010
Ph: (212)807-1990
Fax: (212)807-1799
Fr: 800-548-1634

Triennial. $13.00/year for individuals, quantity available: 1. Journal of design and visual culture.

3712 ■ Visual Merchandising and Store Design
ST Media Group International Inc.
11262 Cornell Park Dr.
Cincinnati, OH 45242
Ph: (513)421-2050
Fax: (513)421-5144
Fr: 800-421-1321
URL: http://www.stmediagroup.com/index.php3?d=pubs&p=vm

Monthly. $42.00/year for individuals, U.S.; $66.00/year for individuals, 2 years, U.S.; $62.00/year for individuals, Canada (surface); $100.00/year for individuals, 2 years, Canada (surface); $65.00/year for individuals, Mexico/Foreign (surface); $105.00/year for individuals, 2 years, Mexico/Foreign (surface); $100.00/year for individuals, Mexico, 1st Class; $175.00/year for individuals, 2 years, Mexico 1st Class; $115.00/year for individuals, Central/South America; $205.00/year for individuals, 2 years, Central/South America. The leading magazine of the retail design industry covering the latest trends in retail design, store planning, and merchandise presentation.

3713 ■ Wire & Cable Technology International
Initial Publications Inc.
3869 Darrow Rd., Ste. 109
Stow, OH 44224
Ph: (330)686-9544
Fax: (330)686-9563
E-mail: info@wiretech.com
URL: http://www.wiretech.com/

Bimonthly. Magazine for manufacturers of ferrous, nonferrous, bare, and insulated wire.

PLACEMENT AND JOB REFERRAL SERVICES

3714 ■ Aquent.com
711 Boylston St.
Boston, MA 02116
Ph: (617)535-6000
Fax: (617)535-6001
E-mail: questions@aquent.com
URL: http://aquent.us

Description: Aquent finds contract, project-based, and permanent work for a broad range of creative and information technology professionals. Applicants submit their applications, which are reviewed by an Aquent agent and, if qualifications match job opportunities, they will be called in for an interview and skills assessment. If skills and experience are appropriate, then will then be assigned an Aquent agent who will get to work finding contract or permanent jobs. Also offers free career resources.

EMPLOYER DIRECTORIES AND NETWORKING LISTS

3715 ■ Black Book Photography
Black Book Marketing Group
740 Broadway, Ste. 202
New York, NY 10003
Ph: (212)979-6700
Fax: (212)673-4321
Fr: 800-841-1246
URL: http://www.BlackBook.com

Annual, Latest edition 2008. $60.00 for individuals. Publication includes: Over 19,000 art directors, creative directors, photographers and photographic services, design firms, advertising agencies, and other firms whose products or services are used in advertising.

3716 ■ Career Opportunities in the Fashion Industry
Facts On File Inc.
132 W 31st St., 17th Fl.
New York, NY 10001

Ph: (212)967-8800
Fax: 800-678-3633
Fr: 800-322-8755
URL: http://factsonfile.infobasepublishing.com/

Latest edition 2nd; Published September, 2007. $49.50 for individuals. Publication includes: Lists of Internet resources, educational institutions, organizations, and associations related to the fashion industry. Principal content of publication is information on careers in the fashion world. Indexes: Alphabetical.

3717 ■ Careers in Focus—Design
Facts On File Inc.
132 W 31st St., 17th Fl.
New York, NY 10001
Ph: (212)967-8800
Fax: 800-678-3633
Fr: 800-322-8755
URL: http://www.infobasepublishing.com

Latest edition 3rd; Published November, 2010. $32.95 for individuals. Covers: An overview of design, followed by a selection of jobs profiled in detail, including the nature of the job, earnings, prospects for employment, what kind of training and skills it requires, and sources for further information.

3718 ■ ENR—Top 500 Design Firms Issue
McGraw-Hill Inc.
PO Box 182604
Columbus, OH 43218
Ph: (614)430-4000
Fax: (614)759-3749
Fr: 877-833-5524
URL: http://enr.construction.com/toplists/sourcebooks/2010/design

Annual, latest edition 2010. $82.00 for individuals. Publication includes: List of 500 leading architectural, engineering, and specialty design firms selected on basis of annual billings. Entries include: Company name, headquarters location, type of firm, current and prior year rank in billings, types of services, countries in which operated in preceding year. Arrangement: Ranked by billings.

HANDBOOKS AND MANUALS

3719 ■ 50 Designers/50 Costumes: Concept to Character
University of California Press/Journals
2120 Berkeley Way
Berkeley, CA 94704-1012
Ph: (510)642-4247
Fax: (510)643-7127
E-mail: permissions@ucpress.edu
URL: http://www.ucpress.edu

Jeffrey Kurland, Deborah Nadoolman Landis, and Academy of Motion Picture Arts and Sciences. 2005. $27.95. 124 pages. Costume designers discuss the challenges involved in creating designs for motion pictures.

3720 ■ 100 Habits of Successful Graphic Designers: Insider Secrets from the World's Top Talent
Rockport Publishers
100 Cummings Center, Ste., 406-L
Beverly, MA 01915
Ph: (978)282-9590
Fax: (978)283-2742
URL: http://www.rockpub.com/

Josh Berger and Sarah Dougher. 2005. $18.75. Illustrated. 192 pages.

3721 ■ 365 Habits of Successful Graphic Designers
Rockport Publishers
100 Cummings Ctr., 406-L
Beverly, MA 01915
Ph: (978)282-9590
Fax: (978)283-2742
URL: http://www.qbookshop.com

Laurel Saville, Joshua Berger, Steve Gordon Jr., and

Sarah Dougher. 2011. $40.00 (paper). 496 pages. Offers information from freelance designers whose years of experience have helped them find solutions for their clients' design needs.

3722 ■ An A-Z of Type Designers
Yale University Press
PO Box 209040
New Haven, CT 06520
Ph: (203)432-0960
Fax: (203)432-0948
URL: http://yalepress.yale.edu/home.asp

Neil Macmillan. 2006. $35.00. 208 pages.

3723 ■ Careers for Color Connoisseurs and Other Visual Types
The McGraw-Hill Companies
PO Box 182604
Columbus, OH 43272
Fax: (614)759-3749
Fr: 877-883-5524
E-mail: customer.service@mcgraw-hill.com
URL: http://www.mhprofessional.com/product.php?isbn=0071465197

Jan Goldberg. Second edition, 2005. $19.95 (paper). 176 pages.

3724 ■ Careers for Crafty People and Other Dexterous Types
The McGraw-Hill Companies
PO Box 182604
Columbus, OH 43272
Fax: (614)759-3749
Fr: 877-883-5524
E-mail: customer.service@mcgraw-hill.com
URL: http://www.mhprofessional.com/product.php?isbn=0071487263

Mark Rowh. Third edition, 2006. $13.95 (paper). 160 pages.

3725 ■ Careers for Fashion Plates and Other Trendsetters
The McGraw-Hill Companies
PO Box 182604
Columbus, OH 43272
Fax: (614)759-3749
Fr: 877-883-5524
E-mail: customer.service@mcgraw-hill.com
URL: http://www.mhprofessional.com/product.php?isbn=0071642005

Lucia Mauro. 2008. $14.95 (paper). 176 pages. Describes career opportunities in fashion, entertainment, retail, and promotion, with advice from fashion professionals.

3726 ■ Creating a Successful Fashion Collection: Everything You Need to Develop a Great Line and Portfolio
Barron's Educational Series, Inc.
250 Wireless Blvd.
Hauppauge, NY 11788
Fax: (631)434-3723
Fr: 800-645-3476
E-mail: barrons@barronseduc.com
URL: http://barronseduc.com

Steven Faerm. 2012. $22.99 (paperback). 160 pages. Shows fashion design beginners how to craft a winning portfolio and stand out from the competition. Includes sections on the job search process, creating resumes and cover letters, making a good impression during job interviews, and seeking out internships.

3727 ■ The Creative Business Guide to Running a Graphic Design Business
W. W. Norton & Company, Incorporated
500 Fifth Ave.
New York, NY 10110-0017
Ph: (212)354-5500
Fax: (212)869-0856

Fr: 800-233-4830
URL: http://books.wwnorton.com/books/
detail.aspx?ID=9939
Cameron Foote. 2009. $35.00. 416 pages.

**3728 ■ Design Secrets: Products 2: 50
Real-Life Projects Uncovered**
Rockport Publishers
100 Cummings Center. Ste. 406-L
Beverly, MA 01915
Ph: (978)282-9590
Fax: (978)283-2742
URL: http://www.rockpub.com

Cheryl Dangel Cullen and Lynn Haller. 2006. $30.00.
Fifty design projects are presented from conception
to completion.

**3729 ■ The Fashion Careers Guidebook: A
Guide to Every Career in the Fashion
Industry and How to Get In**
Barron's Educational Series, Inc.
250 Wireless Blvd.
Hauppauge, NY 11788
Fax: (631)434-3723
Fr: 800-645-3476
E-mail: barrons@barronseduc.com
URL: http://barronseduc.com

Julia Yates and Donna Gustavsen. 2011. $18.99
(flexibound). 192 pages. Offers detailed descriptions
of a variety of career opportunities in fashion.
Provides tips on: preparing resumes and portfolios;
dealing with job interviews; finding opportunities and
following up on job applications; and networking.

**3730 ■ Fashion Designer Survival Guide:
Start and Run Your Own Fashion Business**
Kaplan Publishing
1 Liberty Plz., 24th Fl.
New York, NY 10006
Fax: 800-943-9831
Fr: 800-223-2336
URL: http://www.kaplanpublishing.com

Mary Gehlar. 2005. $22.95. Advice is given to help
designers create their own fashion line.

3731 ■ Fashion Now, Volume 2
Taschen America, LLC
6671 Sunset Blvd., Ste. 1508
Los Angeles, CA 90028
Ph: (323)463-4441
Fax: (323)463-4442
E-mail: contact-us@taschen.com
URL: http://www.taschen.com

Terry Jones and Susie Rushton. Encyclopedia of
fashion personalities as well as a guide to the
contemporary fashion industry.

**3732 ■ Field Guide: How to be a Fashion
Designer**
Rockport Publishers
100 Cummings Ctr., 406-L
Beverly, MA 01915
Ph: (978)282-9590
Fax: (978)283-2742
URL: http://www.qbookshop.com

Marcarena San Martin. 2009. $30.00 (paper). 192
pages. Serves as a basic guide for aspiring fashion
designers. Covers fundamental concepts surrounding
the business of fashion design from both a creative
and marketing perspective. Includes a listing of major
fashion schools around the world.

**3733 ■ Field Guide: How to be a Graphic
Designer**
Rockport Publishers
100 Cummings Ctr., 406-L
Beverly, MA 01915
Ph: (978)282-9590
Fax: (978)283-2742
URL: http://www.qbookshop.com

Ana Labudovic and Nenad Vukusic. 2009. $30.00
(paper). 192 pages. Provides readers with practical
tips on how to make it in the world of graphic design.

Includes a complete reference of all the best design
schools around the world.

**3734 ■ Freelance Fashion Designer's
Handbook**
Wiley-Blackwell
111 River St.
Hoboken, NJ 07030-5774
Ph: (201)748-6000
Fax: (201)748-6088
E-mail: info@wiley.com
URL: http://www.wiley.com

Paula Keech. 2012. $46.99 (paper). 192 pages.
Serves as an essential guide on how to work as a
freelance fashion designer. Covers topics on how to
become a freelance fashion designer and the technical aspects of being a designer. Includes case
studies.

3735 ■ Fresh Dialogue 6: Friendly Fire
Princeton Architectural Press
37 E 7th St.
New York, NY 10003
Ph: (212)995-9620
Fax: (212)995-9454
Fr: 800-759-0190
E-mail: sales@papress.com
URL: http://www.papress.com

American Institute of Graphic Arts Staff. 2006.
$16.95. 112 pages.

3736 ■ Great Jobs for Theater Majors
The McGraw-Hill Companies
PO Box 182604
Columbus, OH 43272
Fax: (614)759-3749
Fr: 877-883-5524
E-mail: customer.service@mcgraw-hill.com
URL: http://www.mhprofessional.com/
product.php?isbn=007143853X

Jan Goldberg and Julie DeGalan. 2005. $15.95
(paper). 192 pages.

**3737 ■ How to Be a Graphic Designer
without Losing Your Soul**
Princeton Architectural Press
37 E 7th St.
New York, NY 10003
Ph: (212)995-9620
Fax: (212)995-9454
Fr: 800-759-0190
E-mail: sales@papress.com
URL: http://www.papress.com

Adrian Shaughnessy. 2010. $24.95 (paper). 176
pages. Contains practical advice with philosophical
guidance to help young professionals embark on their
careers. Offers guidance and strategies for setting
up, running, and promoting a studio; finding work;
and collaborating with clients. Includes interviews
with leading designers.

**3738 ■ Opportunities in Arts and Crafts
Careers**
The McGraw-Hill Companies
PO Box 182604
Columbus, OH 43272
Fax: (614)759-3749
Fr: 877-883-5524
E-mail: customer.service@mcgraw-hill.com
URL: http://www.mhprofessional.com/
product.php?isbn=0071448497

Elizabeth Gardner. 2005. $13.95 (paper). 211 pages.

3739 ■ Opportunities in Museum Careers
The McGraw-Hill Companies
PO Box 182604
Columbus, OH 43272
Fax: (614)759-3749
Fr: 877-883-5524
E-mail: customer.service@mcgraw-hill.com
URL: http://www.mhprofessional.com/
product.php?isbn=0071467696

Blythe Camenson. 2006. $13.95 (paper). 160 pages.

3740 ■ Opportunities in Visual Arts Careers
The McGraw-Hill Companies
PO Box 182604
Columbus, OH 43272
Fax: (614)759-3749
Fr: 877-883-5524
E-mail: customer.service@mcgraw-hill.com
URL: http://www.mhprofessional.com/
product.php?isbn=0071545298

Mark Salmon. 2008. $14.95 (paper). 160 pages.
Points the way to a career in the visual arts, examining opportunities for designers, painters, sculptors, illustrators, animators, photographers, art therapists,
educators, and others. Offers a view of the pros and
cons of working for an art or design company or on
your own.

3741 ■ Savvy Designers Guide to Success
F & W Publications Inc.
4700 E Galbraith Rd.
Cincinnati, OH 45236
Ph: (513)531-2690
Fax: (513)531-4082
Fr: 800-289-0963
URL: http://www.fwbookstore.com

Jeff Fisher. December 2004. $22.99. 192 pages.

**3742 ■ Talent Is Not Enough: Business
Secrets for Designers**
Peachpit Press
1249 8th St.
Berkeley, CA 94710-1413
Fr: 800-428-5331
URL: http://www.peachpit.com/store/
product.aspx?isbn=0321278798

Shel Perkins. 2006. $35.99. 392 pages. Guide for
any designer whether working for someone else to
becoming an independent design firm.

3743 ■ What Designers Know
Architectural Press
30 Corporate Dr., Ste. 400
Burlington, MA 01803
Ph: (781)313-4700
Fax: (781)313-4880
E-mail: usbkinfo@elsevier.com
URL: http://www.elsevier.com

Bryan Lawson. 2004. $40.95. 144 pages. Design
skills, knowledge and understanding are explored,
with each chapter focusing on a different technique.

**3744 ■ Winning Portfolios for Graphic
Designers: Create Your Own Graphic
Design Portfolio Online and in Print**
Barron's Educational Series, Inc.
250 Wireless Blvd.
Hauppauge, NY 11788
Fax: (631)434-3723
Fr: 800-645-3476
E-mail: barrons@barronseduc.com
URL: http://barronseduc.com

Cath Cadwell. 2010. $21.99 (paperback). 144 pages.
Serves as guidebook for aspiring graphic designers
in crafting portfolios online or in print. Features
demonstrative color illustrations, lists of dos and
don'ts, and design element examples. Includes tips
on making the best impression at a job interview, and
explains how working professionals in the field make
their sales pitch to get commissions.

Employment Agencies and Search Firms

3745 ■ Access Staffing
360 Lexington Ave., 8th Fl.
New York, NY 10017
Ph: (212)687-5440
Fax: (212)557-2544
URL: http://www.accessstaffingco.com

Serves as a staffing firm covering accounting/
financial, advertising, bilingual Japanese, creative,

event planning, fashion/retail, healthcare/ human services, human resources, information technology, insurance, legal, light industrial and office support.

3746 ■ Adkins & Associates
PO Box 16062
Greensboro, NC 27416
Ph: (336)378-1261
Fax: (336)274-7433
URL: http://www.adkinsassociates.com

Description: Exists as an executive search firm for the fashion industry.

3747 ■ Artisan Creative
1830 Stoner Ave., No. 6
Los Angeles, CA 90025
Ph: (310)312-2062
Fax: (310)312-0670
E-mail: lainfo@artisancreative.com
URL: http://www.artisancreative.com

Description: Serves as a network of designers, developers, account managers and production people providing companies with temporary staffing, full-time recruitment and project management solutions. Provides clients with the top creative resources to complete creative projects. Provides creative talent with opportunities to work for a variety of clients, in a number of roles, at locations around the country.

3748 ■ Artisan for Hire, Inc.
216 S Jefferson, Ste. 202
Chicago, IL 60661
Ph: (312)382-0200
Fr: 800-216-0600
E-mail: chicago@artisantalent.com
URL: http://www.artisantalent.com

Description: Provides listings for jobs within the creative industry.

3749 ■ The Aspire Group
711 Boylston St.
Boston, MA 02116-2616
Fax: (617)500-7284
Fr: 800-487-2967
URL: http://www.bmanet.com/Aspire/index.html
Employment agency.

3750 ■ Claremont-Branan, Inc.
1298 Rockbridge Rd., Ste. B
Stone Mountain, GA 30087
Fr: 800-875-1292
URL: http://cbisearch.com
Employment agency. Executive search firm.

3751 ■ Creative Placement
13 N Main St.
Norwalk, CT 06854-2702
Ph: (203)838-7772
Fr: 800-521-4616
E-mail: kheine@creativeplacement.com
URL: http://www.creativeplacement.com

Description: Serves as an executive search firm for the creative industry. Provides placement for web, design, branding, packaging, advertising, and promotion.

3752 ■ FILTER, LLC
1505 Fifth Ave., Ste. 600
Seattle, WA 98101
Ph: (206)682-6005
Fax: (206)682-5830
Fr: 800-336-0809
URL: http://www.filterdigital.com

Serves as creative resources company that provides talent in web, marketing, and creative professions. Represents virtually every discipline: designers, copywriters, web architects, icon artists, illustrators, animators, and other specialized artistic and technological talents.

3753 ■ Gene Kaufman Associates Ltd.
450 7th Ave., Ste. 913
New York, NY 10123-0101

Ph: (212)643-0625
Fax: (212)643-8598

Personnel consultant specializing in recruiting on all levels for the apparel industry in the areas of design, sales, merchandising, production, operations and administration.

3754 ■ PrintLink
620 Park Ave.
Rochester, NY 14607
Ph: (716)856-5054
Fax: (716)856-8500
Fr: 800-867-3463
E-mail: usjobs@printlink.com
URL: http://www.printlink.com

Description: Serves as a professional placement firm specializing in the graphic communications industry. Offers discreet, confidential permanent placement for all printing, publishing, packaging and document management positions.

3755 ■ Profiles
217 N Charles St., 4th Fl.
Baltimore, MD 21201
Ph: (410)244-6400
Fax: (410)244-6406
URL: http://careerprofiles.com

Recruits professionals for freelance, temporary, and direct hire opportunities specializing in marketing, advertising, creative, web design, graphic design and communications.

3756 ■ Randolph Associates, Inc.
950 Massachusetts Ave., Ste. 105
Cambridge, MA 02139-3174
Ph: (617)441-8777
Fax: (617)441-8778
E-mail: jobs@greatjobs.com
URL: http://www.greatjobs.com

Employment agency. Provides regular or temporary placement of staff.

3757 ■ RitaSue Siegel Resources, Inc.
PO Box 845
New York, NY 10150
Ph: (917)725-1603
E-mail: contact@ritasue.com
URL: http://www.ritasue.com

Executive search firm specializing in industrial and product design.

3758 ■ Semper, LLC
607 Bolyston St., 3rd Fl.
Boston, MA 02116
Fax: 888-836-9703
Fr: 800-954-4993
E-mail: dhresumes1@semperllc.com
URL: http://www.semperllc.com

Description: Serves as a placement firm in the graphic arts and printing industry. Specializes in the print, copy and digital industries. Offers several staffing options such as flexible, permanent, flex-to-hire and direct. Offers outplacement service that provides professional career management assistance and counseling to employees who are facing a career change.

3759 ■ Starpoint Solutions, LLC
22 Cortlandt St., Fl. 14
New York, NY 10007
Ph: (212)962-1550
Fax: (212)962-7175
URL: http://www.starpoint.com

Description: Serves as a staffing agency that places candidates in both freelance and full-time positions at Chicago and New York's advertising agencies, interactive agencies, and design firms.

3760 ■ TECHEAD
111 N 17th St.
Richmond, VA 23219
Ph: (804)782-6971
Fax: (804)782-2033

Fr: 877-TEC-HEAD
E-mail: info@techead.com
URL: http://www.techead.com

Description: Offers creative and IT staffing services for both job seekers and employers. Provides graphics support and desktop publishing services to local clients. Provides creative talent and information technology staffing services, ADOBE product software training, and creative web development solutions to clients.

ONLINE JOB SOURCES AND SERVICES

3761 ■ ArtBistro.com
URL: http://artbistro.monster.com

Description: Serves as a social network for artists and designers allowing them to advance their careers, share portfolios, make new connections, and read the latest art and design news.

3762 ■ Bright Green Talent - Green Jobs
URL: http://www.brightgreentalent.com/green-jobs

Description: Serves as online tool that offers green jobs listing and career advice to candidates interested and engaged in environmental career.

3763 ■ CasinoGigs.net
URL: http://www.casinogigs.net

Description: Serves as a career community for the gambling industry. Features job openings for casino workers, research into the arts, entertainment & gaming employment market, and a career articles section written and frequented by industry professionals.

3764 ■ Coroflot.com
URL: http://www.coroflot.com

Description: Provides networking and promotional tools, and an employer directory for the design industry.

3765 ■ CreativePublic.com
URL: http://www.creativepublic.com

Description: Offers graphic designers and web designers resources and information. Shows designers what to do and what not to do in the graphic design business world. Gives graphic designers resources for starting their own business or expanding into a freelance role.

3766 ■ Design Engineer Jobzone
URL: http://designengineerjobzone.com/site/2791/about.htm

Description: Database of job openings for design engineers. Lists the latest jobs from top companies in the field.

3767 ■ Designer Today
URL: http://designertoday.com/Home.aspx

Bimonthly. Online graphic design magazine for graphic designers. Features graphic design and related tutorials, graphic design software and hardware product reviews, resources for graphic design training, graphic design jobs as well as the latest in graphic design news.

3768 ■ FashionCareerCenter.com
URL: http://www.fashioncareercenter.com

Description: Collects and maintains job seeker and company information through voluntary posting of information. Features fashion schools and colleges, fashion jobs, and career advices.

3769 ■ FashionCrossing.com
URL: http://www.fashioncrossing.com

Description: Provides job listings and other resources related to fashion employment opportunities.

3770 ■ Graphic Design Freelance Jobs
URL: http://www.graphicdesignfreelancejobs.com

Description: Features listings for freelance graphic design employment.

3771 ■ GraphicArtistDesigner.com
URL: http://www.graphicartistdesigner.com

Description: Connects business professionals with the information and professional contacts needed to advance a career in graphic design. Provides access to books, magazines, articles and continuing education.

3772 ■ Guru.com
5001 Baum Blvd., Ste. 760
Pittsburgh, PA 15213
Fax: (412)687-4466
Fr: 888-687-1316
URL: http://www.guru.com

Description: Job board specializing in contract jobs for creative and information technology professionals. Also provides online incorporation and educational opportunities for independent contractors along with articles and advice.

3773 ■ StyleCareers.com
E-mail: info@stylecareers.com
URL: http://www.stylecareers.com

Description: Provides a job board for people in the fashion industry.

3774 ■ Talent Zoo
E-mail: support@talentzoo.com
URL: http://www.talentzoo.com

Description: Serves as a resource for advertising, marketing, digital and creative jobs.

3775 ■ You the Designer
URL: http://www.youthedesigner.com

Description: Serves as an online career resource that contains a graphic design blog, graphic design tips and graphic design job openings.

TRADESHOWS

3776 ■ American Textile Machinery Exhibition International
Textile Hall Corp.
PO Box 5823
Greenville, SC 29606
Ph: (864)233-2562
Fax: (864)233-0619
E-mail: atmei@textilehall.com

Monthly. Primary Exhibits: Machinery and supplies for yarn, fiber, and nonwoven manufacturing, weaving, knitting and finishing, and plant maintenance. Dates and Locations: 2012 Apr 24-26; Atlanta, GA; Georgia World Congress Center.

3777 ■ Society for News Design Annual Workshop & Exhibition
Society for News Design
424 E Central Blvd., Ste. 406
Orlando, FL 32801
Ph: (407)420-7748
Fax: (407)420-7697
E-mail: snd@snd.org
URL: http://www.snd.org

Annual. Gathers visual journalists from around the world for workshops and general sessions. 2012 October 11-13; Cleveland, OH; The Plain Dealer.

OTHER SOURCES

3778 ■ American Design Drafting Association (ADDA)
105 E Main St.
Newbern, TN 38059
Ph: (731)627-0802

Fax: (731)627-9321
E-mail: corporate@adda.org
URL: http://www.adda.org

Description: Designers, drafters, drafting managers, chief drafters, supervisors, administrators, instructors, and students of design and drafting. Encourages a continued program of education for self-improvement and professionalism in design and drafting and computer-aided design/drafting. Informs members of effective techniques and materials used in drawings and other graphic presentations. Evaluates curriculum of educational institutions through certification program; sponsors drafter certification program.

3779 ■ American Society of Furniture Designers (ASFD)
144 Woodland Dr.
New London, NC 28127
Ph: (910)576-1273
Fax: (910)576-1573
E-mail: info@asfd.com
URL: http://www.asfd.com

Description: Represents professional furniture designers, teachers, students, corporate suppliers of products and services; others who supply products and services related to furniture design. Seeks to promote the profession of furniture design. Conducts and cooperates in educational courses and seminars for furniture designers and persons planning to enter the field. Maintains placement service.

3780 ■ Association of AE Business Leaders (AEBL)
948 Capp St.
San Francisco, CA 94110-3911
Ph: (415)713-5379
E-mail: kathrynsprankle@aebl.org
URL: http://www.aebl.org

Description: Individuals responsible for any or all aspects of business management in a professional design firm. Aims to improve the effectiveness of professional design firms through the growth and development of business management skills. Seeks to: provide a forum for the exchange of ideas and information and discussion and resolution of common problems and issues; establish guidelines for approaches to common management concerns; initiate and maintain professional relationships among members; improve recognition and practice of management as a science in professional design firms; advance and improve reputable service to clients; offer a variety of comprehensive educational programs and opportunities. Maintains speakers' bureau and placement service. Holds seminars. Conducts surveys and research programs. Compiles statistics.

3781 ■ Association of Women Industrial Designers
PO Box 468
New York, NY 10011
E-mail: info@awidweb.com
URL: http://www.awidweb.com

Description: Serves as a resource that facilitates access to design talent, networking and social interaction in the design community. Advocates projects that enrich the growing public awareness of the work of women industrial designers. Provides a forum for publicizing the work of members and for the dissemination of current design news and information.

3782 ■ Fusion Architecture
PO Box 66853
Phoenix, AZ 85082-6853
E-mail: info@fusionarchitecture.org
URL: http://www.fusionarchitecture.org

Description: Represents the interests of architecture, urban design, graphic design, engineering and cultural practitioners. Encourages young designers to create design solutions to socio-cultural issues. Promotes the use of graphic and information design tools to reach out and produce projects that have

influence on the economics, politics, cultural and social structure facing urban communities.

3783 ■ Industrial Designers Society of America (IDSA)
45195 Business Ct., Ste. 250
Dulles, VA 20166-6717
Ph: (703)707-6000
Fax: (703)787-8501
E-mail: idsa@idsa.org
URL: http://www.idsa.org

Description: Professional society of industrial designers. Represents the profession in its relations with business, education, government, and international designers; promotes the industrial design profession. Conducts research, educational, and charitable programs. Compiles statistics.

3784 ■ Organization of Women Architects and Design Professionals
PO Box 10078
Berkeley, CA 94709
E-mail: info@owa-usa.org
URL: http://owa-usa.org

Description: Comprised of architects, interior designers, landscape architects, planners, lighting designers, graphic designers, photographers, artists, writers, educators and students. Strives to improve the professional standing of women in architecture and design-related fields. Advocates young women and students entering design related fields through mentoring, education, and employment opportunities.

3785 ■ Society for Design and Process Science (SDPS)
3824 Cedar Springs Rd., Ste. 368
Dallas, TX 75219-4136
Ph: (214)253-9025
Fax: (214)520-0227
E-mail: admin@sdpsnet.org
URL: http://sdpsnet.org/sdps

Description: Promotes the development of design and process science. Encourages and fosters research to advance the discipline of design and process science. Provides leadership and resources to foster cooperation among organizations in establishing international standards. Supports continuing education activities and develops international cooperation and understanding among members.

3786 ■ Society for News Design
424 E Central Blvd., Ste. 406
Orlando, FL 32801
Ph: (407)420-7748
Fax: (407)420-7697
E-mail: snd@snd.org
URL: http://www.snd.org

Description: Comprised of editors, designers, graphic artists, publishers, illustrators, art directors, photographers, advertising artists, website designers, students and faculty. Encourages high standards of journalism through design. Serves as a forum and resource for all those interested in news design.

3787 ■ Specialty Graphic Imaging Association
10015 Main St.
Fairfax, VA 22031-3489
Ph: (703)385-1335
Fax: (703)273-0456
E-mail: sgia@sgia.org
URL: http://www.sgia.org

Description: Serves as a group of graphic printers and suppliers. Provides primary imaging technologies services in screen printing, digital printing, embroidery, sublimation and pad printing to create products or add value to existing products. Provides a listing of employment opportunities.

3788 ■ University and College Designers Association (UCDA)
199 W Enon Spring Rd., Ste. 300
Smyrna, TN 37167

Ph: (615)459-4559
Fax: (615)459-5229
E-mail: info@ucda.com
URL: http://www.ucda.com

Description: Represents colleges, universities, junior colleges, or technical institutions that have an interest in visual communication design; individuals who are involved in the active production of such communication design or as teachers or students of these related disciplines. Improves members' skills and techniques in communication and design areas such as graphics, photography, signage, films, and other related fields of communication design. Aids and assists members in their efforts to be professionals in their respective fields through programs of education and information. Maintains placement service.

SOURCES OF HELP-WANTED ADS

3789 ■ ACM Transactions on Internet Technology
Association for Computing Machinery
PO Box 30777
New York, NY 10087
Ph: (212)626-0500
Fax: (212)944-1318
Fr: 800-342-6626
URL: http://toit.acm.org

Quarterly. $190.00/year for nonmembers, print only; $152.00/year for nonmembers, online only; $228.00/year for nonmembers, online and print. Publication of the Association for Computing Machinery. Brings together many computing disciplines including computer software engineering, computer programming languages, middleware, database management, security, knowledge discovery and data mining, networking and distributed systems, communications, performance and scalability, and more. Covers the results and roles of the individual disciplines and the relationships among them.

3790 ■ AVIOS Journal
Applied Voice Input/Output Society
PO Box 20817
San Jose, CA 95160
Ph: (408)323-1783
Fax: (408)323-1782
URL: http://www.avios.com/

Annual. Journal covering issues in computer science.

3791 ■ Computers and Composition
Elsevier Science Inc.
360 Park Ave. S
New York, NY 10010-1710
Ph: (212)989-5800
Fax: (212)633-3990
Fr: 888-437-4636
URL: http://www.elsevier.com/wps/find/journaldescription.cws_home

$454.00/year for institutions, all countries except Europe, Japan and Iran; $405.00/year for institutions, European countries and Iran; $53,500.00/year for institutions, Japan; $82.00/year for individuals, all countries except Europe, Japan and Iran; $62.00/year for individuals, European countries and Iran; $8,900.00/year for individuals, Japan. Journal covering computers in writing classes, programs, and research.

3792 ■ Computers Programs/PC World
IDG Communications Inc.
3 Speen St.
Framingham, MA 01701
Ph: (508)875-5000
URL: http://www.idg.com

Magazine devoted to IT specialists, covering practical questions of computing including purchase and usage of the computer technology, software, computer components and peripherals.

3793 ■ Computerworld/Correio Informatico
IDG Communications Inc.
3 Speen St.
Framingham, MA 01701
Ph: (508)875-5000
URL: http://www.idg.com/www/IDGProducts.nsf/0/B1E40F5ABD0169AB852

Weekly. Magazine providing news on latest developments in computer industry.

3794 ■ Computerworld Top 100
IDG Communications Inc.
3 Speen St.
Framingham, MA 01701
Ph: (508)875-5000
URL: http://www.idg.com/www/IDGProducts.nsf/0/E7EDD4EC98463F2C852

Annual. Magazine for analyzing trends and events of information technology business.

3795 ■ Computing SA
IDG Communications Inc.
3 Speen St.
Framingham, MA 01701
Ph: (508)875-5000
URL: http://www.idg.com/www/IDGProducts.nsf/0/12C44C74D05A07DF852

Monthly. Newspaper focusing computer hardware, software, networking, telecommunications, channel management and online computing.

3796 ■ CXO
IDG Communications Inc.
3 Speen St.
Framingham, MA 01701
Ph: (508)875-5000
URL: http://www.idg.com/www/IDGProducts.nsf/0/022796185EED5984852

Monthly. Magazine providing technology information for chief officers and managers.

3797 ■ Eclipse Review
BZ Media L.L.C.
7 High St., Ste. 407
Huntington, NY 11743
Ph: (631)421-4158
Fax: (631)421-4130
URL: http://www.eclipsesource.com/contact.htm

Magazine for IT professionals.

3798 ■ Foundations and Trends in Networking
Now Publishers
PO Box 1024
Hanover, MA 02339-1001
Ph: (781)871-0245
URL: http://www.nowpublishers.com/product.aspx?product=NET

$390.00/year for individuals, online only; $450.00/year for individuals, print and online; $390.00/year for other countries, online only; $450.00/year for other countries, print and online. Academic journal publishing new research in computer networking.

3799 ■ Government Computer News
PostNewsweek Tech Media
10 G St. NE, Ste. 500
Washington, DC 20002-4228
Ph: (202)772-2500
Fax: (202)772-2511
Fr: (866)447-6864
URL: http://gcn.com/

Semimonthly. Magazine for professionals interested in government IT.

3800 ■ IBPA Independent
Independent Book Publishers Association
1020 Manhattan Beach Blvd., Ste. 204
Manhattan Beach, CA 90266
Ph: (310)546-1818
Fax: (310)546-3939
E-mail: info@ibpa-online.org
URL: http://www.ibpa-online.org

Description: Monthly. Informs member entrepreneurial book publishers about upcoming marketing programs and other Association activities aimed at helping independent publishers succeed. Also carries articles on topics such as desktop publishing and typesetting systems. Recurring features include member, committee, and research news, notices of educational and cooperative marketing opportunities, a calendar of events, and columns titled News from the "Net" and From the Director's Desk.

3801 ■ IEEE Security & Privacy Magazine
IEEE Computer Society
10662 Los Vaqueros Cir.
PO Box 3014
Los Alamitos, CA 90720-1314
Ph: (714)821-8380
Fax: (714)821-4010
Fr: 800-272-6657
URL: http://www.computer.org/portal/site/security/

Bimonthly. $735.00/year for individuals, online; $770.00/year for individuals, print; $965.00/year for individuals, print and online. Journal that aims to explore role and importance of networked infrastructure and developing lasting security solutions.

3802 ■ Independent Publisher Online
Jenkins group Inc.
1129 Woodmere Ave., Ste. B
Traverse City, MI 49686
Ph: (231)933-0445
Fax: (231)933-0448
Fr: 800-706-4636
URL: http://www.independentpublisher.com/

Monthly. Free. Online magazine containing book reviews and articles about independent publishing.

3803 ■ Information Security
TechTarget
117 Kendrick St., Ste. 800
Needham, MA 02494
Ph: (781)657-1000
Fax: (781)657-1100
Fr: 888-274-4111
URL: http://searchsecurity.techtarget.com/

Monthly. Free to qualified subscribers. Magazine covering information security topics.

3804 ■ IT Solutions Guide
SYS-CON Media
577 Chestnut Ridge Rd.
Woodcliff Lake, NJ 07677
Ph: (201)802-3000
Fax: (201)782-9601
URL: http://itsolutions.sys-con.com/

Quarterly. Magazine for IT professionals.

3805 ■ Journal of Computer Science
Science Publications
Vails Gate Heights Dr.
PO Box 879
Vails Gate, NY 12584-0879
URL: http://thescipub.com/jcs.toc

Scholarly journal covering many areas of computer science, including: concurrent, parallel and distributed processing; artificial intelligence; image and voice processing; quality software and metrics; computer-aided education; wireless communication; real time processing; evaluative computation; and data bases and information recovery and neural networks.

3806 ■ Monitor
Capital PC User Group
19209 Mt. Airey Rd.
Brookeville, MD 20833
Ph: (301)560-6442
Fax: (301)760-3303
E-mail: editor@cpcug.org
URL: http://monitor.cpcug.org/index.html

Quarterly. Magazine covering computer hardware and software reviews, special interest user group news, advertisers and author/subject index, and calendar of events.

3807 ■ Queue
Association for Computing Machinery
PO Box 30777
New York, NY 10087
Ph: (212)626-0500
Fax: (212)944-1318
Fr: 800-342-6626
E-mail: queue@acm.org
URL: http://queue.acm.org/

Monthly. Free, U.S./Canadian residents and all members. Online magazine aimed at the computer professional. Magazine editorial does not provide solutions for the "here-and-now", but instead helps decision-makers plan future projects by examining the challenges and problems they are most likely to face.

3808 ■ Revenue
Montgomery Media International
55 New Montgomery St., Ste. 617
San Francisco, CA 94105
Ph: (415)371-8800
URL: http://www.revenuetoday.com/

Free to qualified subscribers. Magazine covering internet marketing strategies.

3809 ■ WITI FastTrack
United business Media L.L.C
240 W 35th St.
New York, NY 10001
Ph: (516)562-5000
URL: http://www.witi.com/corporate/fasttrack.php

Semiannual. Semiannual publication featuring in-depth content on the issues facing today's women professionals in technology.

PLACEMENT AND JOB REFERRAL SERVICES

3810 ■ Online News Association
c/o Jane McDonnell, Exec. Dir.
PO Box 65741
Washington, DC 20035
Ph: (646)290-7900
E-mail: director@journalists.org
URL: http://journalists.org

Description: Consists of news writers, producers, designers, editors, photographers, technologists and others who produce news for the Internet or other digital delivery systems, as well as academic members and others interested in the development of online journalism. Acts as a resource for journalists seeking guidance and growth. Provides conferences, training, awards and community outreach.

EMPLOYER DIRECTORIES AND NETWORKING LISTS

3811 ■ The Information Professional's Guide to Career Development Online
Information Today Inc.
143 Old Marlton Pike
Medford, NJ 08055-8750
Ph: (609)654-6266
Fax: (609)654-4309
Fr: 800-300-9868
URL: http://www.infotoday.com

$29.50 for individuals. Covers: Web sites, professional associations, and conferences for the career development of information professionals. Indexes: Alphabetical.

HANDBOOKS AND MANUALS

3812 ■ The Complete Help Book for Authors and Publishers
Hannacroix Creek Books, Incorporated
1127 High Ridge Rd., No. 110B
Stamford, CT 06905-1203
Ph: (203)321-8674
Fax: (203)968-0193
E-mail: hannacroix@aol.com
URL: http://www.hannacroixcreekbooks.com/

Jan Yeager. 2007. $29.95. Explores self-publishing for authors.

ONLINE JOB SOURCES AND SERVICES

3813 ■ GetDesktopPublishingJobs.com
URL: http://www.getdesktoppublishingjobs.com

Description: Provides resources for finding and filling desktop publishing positions. Offers job postings and employment opportunities worldwide.

3814 ■ Graphic Artists Guild
32 Broadway, Ste. 1114
New York, NY 10004
Ph: (212)791-3400
Fax: (212)791-0333
E-mail: membership@gag.org
URL: http://www.graphicartistsguild.org

Description: JOBLine News section of Guild Resources page contains weekly e-mail newsletter of job listings. Fee: Must subscribe to e-mail newsletter non-member six-month rates start at $80. Visitors may download a free sample.

3815 ■ Guru.com
5001 Baum Blvd., Ste. 760
Pittsburgh, PA 15213
Fax: (412)687-4466

Fr: 888-687-1316
URL: http://www.guru.com

Description: Job board specializing in contract jobs for creative and information technology professionals. Also provides online incorporation and educational opportunities for independent contractors along with articles and advice.

3816 ■ Publish.com
Ziff Davis Enterprise
28 E 28th St.
New York, NY 10016
Ph: (212)503-5900
E-mail: customerservice@ziffdavisenterprise.com
URL: http://www.publish.com

Description: Offers a variety of resources for desktop publishers.

3817 ■ PublishingMVP.com
URL: http://www.publishingmvp.com

Description: Provides job opportunities in the publishing arena of the marketing industry.

TRADESHOWS

3818 ■ Association of Alternative Newsmedia Web Publishing Conference
Association of Alternative Newsmedia
1156 15th St. NW, Ste. 905
Washington, DC 20005
Ph: (202)289-8484
Fax: (202)289-2004
E-mail: web@aan.org
URL: http://www.altweeklies.com/aan/web-publishing-conference/Page

Biennial. Provides assistance to AAN publishers and editors in strategizing online presence and adapting new electronic-publishing formats and technologies.

3819 ■ National Federation of Press Women Conference
National Federation of Press Women
PO Box 5556
Arlington, VA 22205
Fax: (703)237-9808
Fr: 800-780-2715
E-mail: presswomen@aol.com
URL: http://www.nfpw.org

Annual. Features speakers as well as other activities, workshops, resources, and networking opportunities.

3820 ■ Online News Association Annual Conference
Online News Association
c/o Jane McDonnell, Exec. Dir.
PO Box 65741
Washington, DC 20035
Ph: (646)290-7900
E-mail: director@journalists.org
URL: http://journalists.org

Annual. Includes activities such as pre-conference workshops, job fair, online journalism awards banquet and more. 2012 September 20-22; San Francisco, CA; Hyatt Regency San Francisco.

3821 ■ Society for News Design Annual Workshop & Exhibition
Society for News Design
424 E Central Blvd., Ste. 406
Orlando, FL 32801
Ph: (407)420-7748
Fax: (407)420-7697
E-mail: snd@snd.org
URL: http://www.snd.org

Annual. Gathers visual journalists from around the world for workshops and general sessions. 2012 October 11-13; Cleveland, OH; The Plain Dealer.

OTHER SOURCES

3822 ■ Association for Women in Computing (AWC)
PO Box 2768
Oakland, CA 94602
E-mail: info@awc-hq.org
URL: http://www.awc-hq.org

Description: Individuals interested in promoting the education, professional development, and advancement of women in computing.

3823 ■ National Association of Photoshop Professionals
333 Douglas Rd., E
Oldsmar, FL 34677

Ph: (813)433-5005
Fax: (813)433-5015
Fr: 800-738-8513
URL: http://www.photoshopuser.com

Description: Association website includes member job bank where visitors can search for available jobs or post their resumes for employer review, along with other career-related resources. Fee: Must be member of association to access; dues are $99 for a one-year membership.

3824 ■ National Federation of Press Women
PO Box 5556
Arlington, VA 22205
Fax: (703)237-9808
Fr: 800-780-2715
E-mail: presswomen@aol.com
URL: http://www.nfpw.org

Description: Serves as a group of professional women and men pursuing careers across the communications spectrum.

3825 ■ Society for News Design
424 E Central Blvd., Ste. 406
Orlando, FL 32801
Ph: (407)420-7748
Fax: (407)420-7697
E-mail: snd@snd.org
URL: http://www.snd.org

Description: Comprised of editors, designers, graphic artists, publishers, illustrators, art directors, photographers, advertising artists, website designers, students and faculty. Encourages high standards of journalism through design. Serves as a forum and resource for all those interested in news design.

SOURCES OF HELP-WANTED ADS

3826 ■ Health Focus
Nautilus Publishing Company
PO Box 40
Taylor, MS 38673
Ph: (662)513-0159
URL: http://www.nautiluspublishing.com/publishing/

Bimonthly. Health magazine featuring the latest health-related news and information.

3827 ■ SOBeFit
MPG Publishing
1201 Brickell Ave., Ste. 320
Miami, FL 33131
Ph: (305)375-9595
Fax: (305)375-9596
URL: http://www.sobefitmagazine.com

Bimonthly. Magazine focusing on fitness, nutrition, health, and sports.

3828 ■ Today's Dietitian
3801 Schuylkill Rd.
Spring City, PA 19475
Ph: (610)948-9500
Fax: (610)948-7202
Fr: 800-278-4400
URL: http://www.todaysdietitian.com

Monthly. Provides career development resources for nutrition professionals. Features articles on nutrition including culinary trends, long-term care issues, new products and technologies, clinical concerns, career strategies, and research updates.

EMPLOYER DIRECTORIES AND NETWORKING LISTS

3829 ■ Crain's List—Chicago's Largest Hospitals
Crain Communications Inc.
360 N Michigan Ave.
Chicago, IL 60601
Ph: (312)649-5200
URL: http://www.chicagobusiness.com/section/lists

Published November, 2010. $25.00 for individuals; $45.00 for individuals. Covers: 25 hospitals in Chicago area ranked by net patient revenues. Entries include: Name, address, phone number, fax, web address, corporate e-mail, hospital administrator, network affiliation, 2009 net patient revenue, percentage change from 2008, 2009 net profits, percentage change from 2008, inpatient days, available beds, daily occupancy rate, number of hospital employees as of December 31, 2009, fiscal year end, Chairman, President, CEO, Chief Financial Officer, Human Resources Manager, Media Relations/Public Relations Director, and Hospital Administrator.

HANDBOOKS AND MANUALS

3830 ■ Careers in Nutrition
Rosen Publishing Group
29 E 21st St.
New York, NY 10010
Fax: 888-436-4643
Fr: 800-237-9932
URL: http://www.rosenpublishing.com
Linda Bickerstaff. 2008. $33.25 (list price). 144 pages. Includes up-to-date information about job opportunities in the nutrition and dietetic fields, including coursework, training programs, and United States Department of Labor statistics on employment and salary ranges.

3831 ■ The Clinical Dietitian's Essential Pocket Guide
Lippincott Williams & Wilkins
Two Commerce Sq.
2001 Market St.
Philadelphia, PA 19103
Fr: 800-638-3030
URL: http://www.lww.com
Mary Width and Tonia Reinhard. 2008. $37.95. 512 pages. Covers nutritional assessment, life stage management, and nutrition support. Includes chapters on the major nutritionally relevant cases.

3832 ■ Counselling Skills for Dietitians, 2nd Edition
Wiley
111 River St.
Hoboken, NJ 07030
Ph: (201)748-6000
Fax: (201)748-6088
E-mail: info@wiley.com
URL: http://www.wiley.com
Judy Gable. 2007. $66.99 (paper). 272 pages. Demonstrates how a practitioner can develop a counselling approach and employ appropriate counselling skills to overcome the communication difficulties encountered by dietitians and those engaged in helping clients change their eating behavior.

3833 ■ Dietetic Technician, Registered Exam Secrets Study Guide
Mometrix Media LLC
3827 Phelan Blvd., No. 179
Beaumont, TX 77707
Fax: (866)235-0173
Fr: 800-673-8175
E-mail: support@mometrix.com
URL: http://www.mo-media.com
2009. Provides guidance on passing the dietetic technician examinations.

3834 ■ International Dietetics and Nutrition Terminology (IDNT) Reference Manual: Standardized Language for the Nutrition Care Process, 3rd Edition
American Dietetic Association
120 S Riverside Plaza, Ste. 2000
Chicago, IL 60606
URL: http://www.eatright.org

$45.00 for members; 95.00 for non-members. Serves as a guide for implementing the nutrition care process.

ONLINE JOB SOURCES AND SERVICES

3835 ■ CareerVitals.com
URL: http://www.careervitals.com

Description: Serves as a job board for healthcare professionals in different specializations.

3836 ■ DietaryAideJob.com
URL: http://www.indeed.com/q-Dietary-Aide-jobs.html

Description: Provides dietary aide job listings and career opportunities. Features other employment opportunities such as job qualification guides and job descriptions.

3837 ■ DietaryJobs.com
URL: http://www.dietaryjobs.com

Description: Offers dietary employment opportunities. Features dietary jobs across the United States.

3838 ■ DietaryJobs.org
URL: http://dietaryjobs.org

Description: Offers dietary job listings and employment opportunities. Enables job searching in specific locations and specific areas in the dietary field.

3839 ■ Dietetics.com
URL: http://www.dietetics.com

Description: Provides dietetic professionals with information including internet links on topics that affect careers and the profession in general. Contains employment opportunities for dietetic professionals.

3840 ■ DieticianJobs.com
URL: http://www.dieticianjobs.com

Description: Provides dietician job listings and career opportunities. Also lists salary information.

3841 ■ DieticianNutritionist.com
URL: http://www.dieticiannutritionist.com

Description: Serves as a job board for dieticians, nutritionists, and dietetic professionals. Provides access to books, magazines, articles, and continuing education. Provides help in finding new jobs, posting resumes, and accessing career resources.

3842 ■ Jobs In Dietetics
E-mail: info@jobsindietetics.com
URL: http://www.jobsindietetics.com

Description: Provides nationwide career support for nutritionists as well as dietetics and food service professionals. Offers a subscription job listing service.

3843 ■ RDLink.com
URL: http://www.rdlink.com

Description: Provides links to dietetic technicians, dietitians, and nutritionists on the web. Features job listings.

3844 ■ RegisteredDieticiansJobs.com
URL: http://www.registereddieticianjobs.com

Description: Offers career resources for diet and nutrition professionals. Provides jobs searching, resume posting, and career tools for job seekers.

OTHER SOURCES

3845 ■ American Society for Nutrition
9650 Rockville Pike
Bethesda, MD 20814
Ph: (301)634-7050
Fax: (301)634-7892
E-mail: info@nutrition.org
URL: http://www.nutrition.org

Description: Serves as the professional society of nutrition research scientists from universities, government, and industry. Seeks to advance the knowledge and application of nutrition for the sake of humans and animals.

3846 ■ Genetic Metabolic Dietitians International
PO Box 33985
Fort Worth, TX 76162
E-mail: info@gmdi.org
URL: http://www.gmdi.org

Description: Represents the interests of nutritionists and other health care practitioners. Enhances and supports the practice of genetic metabolic nutrition. Provides leadership in nutrition therapy for genetic metabolic disorders through clinical practice, education, advocacy, and research.

SOURCES OF HELP-WANTED ADS

3847 ■ *American Journal of Clinical Nutrition*
American Society for Nutrition
9650 Rockville Pike
Bethesda, MD 20814
Ph: (301)634-7050
Fax: (301)634-7892
E-mail: ajcn@nutrition.org
URL: http://www.nutrition.org/publications/the-american-journal-o

Monthly. $555.00/year for institutions, print and online U.S.; $515.00/year for institutions, online U.S.; $215.00/year for individuals, print and online U.S.; $180.00/year for individuals, online U.S.; $585.00/year for institutions, Canada and Mexico, print and online; $515.00/year for institutions, Canada and Mexico, online only; $610.00/year for other countries, print and online; $515.00/year for other countries, online only. Peer-reviewed journal publishing basic and clinical studies relevant to human nutrition.

3848 ■ *Bountiful Health*
JNE Publishing, Inc.
PO Box 5647
Huntsville, AL 35814
Ph: (256)837-3035
Fr: 800-313-7751
URL: http://www.jnepublishing.com/bountifulhealth.php?page=public

Magazine focusing on complementary and alternative medicine, exercise, vitamins and supplements, healthy eating, and green living.

3849 ■ *Chef*
Talcott Communication Corp.
233 N Michigan Ave., Ste. 1780
Chicago, IL 60601
Ph: (312)849-2220
Fax: (312)849-2174
E-mail: chef@talcott.com
URL: http://www.chefmagazine.com

$32.00/year for individuals; $47.00/year for two years; $64.00/year for individuals, 3 years; $43.00/year for Canada; $96.00/year for other countries. Food information for chefs.

3850 ■ *Dietary Manager Magazine*
Dietary Managers Association
406 Surrey Woods Dr.
St. Charles, IL 60174
Ph: (630)587-6336
Fax: (630)587-6308
Fr: 800-323-1908
URL: http://www.dmaonline.org/Publications/Dietary_Manager.shtml

Monthly. $40.00/year for individuals. Professional magazine focusing on nutrition and management issues encountered by dietary managers in noncommercial food service.

3851 ■ *Field & Feast*
Field & Feast
PO Box 205
Four Lakes, WA 99014
URL: http://www.fieldandfeast.net

Quarterly. $19.00/year for individuals. Magazine that offers information on organic food cultivation and its health benefits.

3852 ■ *Food Management*
Penton Media Inc.
249 W 17th St.
New York, NY 10011
Ph: (212)204-4200
URL: http://food-management.com/

Monthly. Magazine for foodservice professionals in the onsite 'noncommercial' market.

3853 ■ *Food and Nutrition Sciences*
Scientific Research Publishing
PO Box 54821
Irvine, CA 92619-4821
E-mail: fns@scirp.org
URL: http://www.scirp.org/journal/fns/

$390.00/year for individuals. Peer-reviewed journal publishing articles on the latest advancements in food and nutrition science and technology.

3854 ■ *FoodService Director*
Ideal Media L.L.C.
200 E Randolph St., 70th Fl.
Chicago, IL 60601
Ph: (312)456-2822
Fax: (312)240-0742
URL: http://www.fsdmag.com

Monthly. $79.00/year for individuals; $99.00/year for Canada; $235.00/year for out of country. Tabloid newspaper of the noncommercial foodservice market.

3855 ■ *Foodservice East*
The Newbury Street Group Inc.
93 Massachusetts Ave., Ste. 306
Boston, MA 02115
Ph: (617)267-2224
Fax: (617)267-5554
URL: http://www.foodserviceeast.com/

Bimonthly. $30.00/year for individuals. Compact Tabloid covering trends and analysis of the foodservice industry in the Northeast. A business-to-business publication featuring news, analysis and trends for the Northeast food service professional.

3856 ■ *Genes and Nutrition*
New Century Health Publishers L.L.C.
PO Box 175
Coppell, TX 75019
Fax: (940)565-8148
URL: http://www.newcenturyhealthpublishers.com/genes_and_nutritio

Quarterly. $428.00/year for institutions; $228.00/year for individuals. International, interdisciplinary peer reviewed scientific journal for critical evaluation of research on the relationship between genetics & nutrition with the goal of improving human health.

3857 ■ *Herbs for Health*
Echo Media
900 Cir. 75 Pky., Ste. 1600
Atlanta, GA 30339-6014
Ph: (770)955-3535
Fax: (770)955-3599
URL: http://www.echo-media.com

Bimonthly. Magazine covering topics ranging from recent scientific research to consumer guides, medicinal recipes, and legislative updates.

3858 ■ *The IHS Primary Care Provider*
Indian Health Service
The Reyes Bldg.
801 Thompson Ave., Ste. 400
Rockville, MD 20852-1627
Ph: (301)443-1011
URL: http://www.ihs.gov/provider

Monthly. Journal for health care professionals, physicians, nurses, pharmacists, dentists, and dietitians.

3859 ■ *Journal of the American College of Nutrition*
American College of Nutrition
300 S Duncan Ave., Ste. 225
Clearwater, FL 33755
Ph: (727)446-6086
Fax: (727)446-6202
URL: http://www.jacn.org

Bimonthly. $45.00/year for members; $85.00/year for other countries, members; $90.00/year for nonmembers; $130.00/year for other countries; $235.00/year for institutions; $275.00/year for institutions, other countries. Journal on nutrition.

3860 ■ *Journal of Diabetes Mellitus*
Scientific Research Publishing
PO Box 54821
Irvine, CA 92619-4821
E-mail: jdm@scirp.org
URL: http://www.scirp.org/journal/jdm/

Quarterly. $156.00/year for individuals. Peer-reviewed journal publishing research on diabetes mellitus.

3861 ■ *Journal of Parenteral and Enteral Nutrition*
SAGE Publications
2455 Teller Rd.
Newbury Park, CA 91320
Fax: 800-583-2665
Fr: 800-818-7243
E-mail: journals@sagepub.com
URL: http://www.sagepub.com

Bimonthly. $400/year for institutions; $190/year for individuals. Serves as a scientific journal of nutrition and metabolic support. Publishes original, peer-reviewed studies that discuss basic and clinical research in the field. Explores the science of optimizing the care of patients receiving enteral or IV therapies. Includes reviews, techniques, brief reports, case reports, abstracts, and advertising.

3862 ■ Nutrition Notes
American Society for Nutrition
9650 Rockville Pike
Bethesda, MD 20814
Ph: (301)634-7050
Fax: (301)634-7892
E-mail: ameyers@nutrition.org
URL: http://www.nutrition.org

Description: Quarterly. $30/year. Contains updates on nutrition legislation, public affairs, and public information policies. Reviews the results of nutritional research conducted by members of the Institute, which is comprised of nutrition scientists from universities, government, and industry. Recurring features include news of members, letters to the editor, job listings, notices of publications available, information on awards and fellowships, and news of scientific meetings.

3863 ■ Nutritional Outlook
Canon Communications L.L.C.
11444 W Olympic Blvd., Ste. 900
Los Angeles, CA 90064
Ph: (310)445-4200
Fax: (310)445-4299
E-mail: info@nutritionaloutlook.com
URL: http://www.nutritionaloutlook.com/

Magazine for manufacturer's resource for dietary supplements and healthy foods and beverages.

3864 ■ Real Food
Greenspring Media Group
600 US Trust Bldg.
730 2nd Ave. S
Minneapolis, MN 55402
Ph: (612)371-5800
Fax: (612)371-5801
Fr: 800-933-4398
URL: http://www.realfoodmag.com/

Quarterly. Magazine featuring food choices.

3865 ■ Southeast Food Service News
Southeast Publishing Company Inc.
5672 Peachtree Pky., Ste. E
Norcross, GA 30092
Ph: (770)499-9800
Fax: (770)499-9802
URL: http://www.sfsn.com

Monthly. $36.00/year for individuals; $5.00/year for single issue; $59.00/year for individuals, directory issue. Magazine (tabloid) serving the food industry.

3866 ■ Sunbelt Foodservice
Shelby Publishing Company Inc.
517 Green St. NW
Gainesville, GA 30501
Ph: (770)534-8380
Fax: (678)343-2197
URL: http://www.shelbypublishing.com/
    index.php?option=com_content

Monthly. $36.00/year for individuals; $60.00/year for two years. Trade newspaper (tabloid) covering the food industry geared toward restaurant operators.

3867 ■ Today's Dietitian
3801 Schuylkill Rd.
Spring City, PA 19475
Ph: (610)948-9500
Fax: (610)948-7202
Fr: 800-278-4400
URL: http://www.todaysdietitian.com

Monthly. Provides career development resources for nutrition professionals. Features articles on nutrition including culinary trends, long-term care issues, new products and technologies, clinical concerns, career strategies, and research updates.

3868 ■ Vegetarian Times
Active Interest Media
300 Continental Blvd., Ste. 650
El Segundo, CA 90245-5067
Ph: (310)356-4100
Fax: (310)356-4110
E-mail: editor@vegetariantimes.com
URL: http://www.vegetariantimes.com/

$14.95/year for individuals; $26.95/year for Canada, 9 issues; $47.95/year for Canada, 18 issues; $38.95/year for other countries, 9 issues; $71.95/year for other countries, 18 issues. Magazine devoted to plant-based foods and related topics such as health, fitness, and the environment.

EMPLOYER DIRECTORIES AND NETWORKING LISTS

3869 ■ Crain's List—Chicago's Largest Hospitals
Crain Communications Inc.
360 N Michigan Ave.
Chicago, IL 60601
Ph: (312)649-5200
URL: http://www.chicagobusiness.com/section/lists

Published November, 2010. $25.00 for individuals; $45.00 for individuals. Covers: 25 hospitals in Chicago area ranked by net patient revenues. Entries include: Name, address, phone number, fax, web address, corporate e-mail, hospital administrator, network affiliation, 2009 net patient revenue, percentage change from 2008, 2009 net profits, percentage change from 2008, inpatient days, available beds, daily occupancy rate, number of hospital employees as of December 31, 2009, fiscal year end, Chairman, President, CEO, Chief Financial Officer, Human Resources Manager, Media Relations/Public Relations Director, and Hospital Administrator.

3870 ■ Directory of Hospital Personnel
Grey House Publishing
4919 Rte. 22
PO Box 56
Amenia, NY 12501
Ph: (518)789-8700
Fax: (518)789-0556
Fr: 800-562-2139
URL: http://www.greyhouse.com/hospital_
    personnel.htm

Annual, Latest edition 2011. $325.00 for individuals. Covers: 200,000 executives at 6,000 U.S. Hospitals. Entries include: Name of hospital, address, phone, number of beds, type and JCAHO status of hospital, names and titles of key department heads and staff, medical and nursing school affiliations; number of residents, interns, and nursing students. Arrangement: Geographical. Indexes: Hospital name, personnel, hospital size.

3871 ■ Directory of the National Association of Advisors for the Health Professions
National Association of Advisors for the Health Professions
PO Box 1518
Champaign, IL 61824-1518
Ph: (217)355-0063
Fax: (217)355-1287
E-mail: naahpja@aol.com
URL: http://www.naahp.org

Annual, Latest edition 2011. $25.00. Covers: College and university faculty who advise and counsel students on health careers.

3872 ■ Discovering Careers for Your Future—Health
Facts On File Inc.
132 W 31st St., 17th Fl.
New York, NY 10001
Ph: (212)967-8800
Fax: 800-678-3633
Fr: 800-322-8755
URL: http://factsonfile.infobasepublishing.com

Latest edition 2nd, 2004. $21.95 for individuals. Covers: Dietitians and nutritionists, fitness experts, massage therapists, nurses, occupational therapists, pharmacists, and sports trainers; links career education to curriculum, helping children investigate the subjects they are interested in, and the careers those subjects might lead to.

3873 ■ Hospital Blue Book
Billian Publishing Inc. and Trans World Publishing Inc.
2100 River Edge Pky.
Atlanta, GA 30328
Ph: (770)955-5656
Fax: (770)952-0669
Fr: 800-800-5668
E-mail: blu-book@billian.com
URL: http://www.billianshealthdata.com/Products/
    bluebook.html

Annual, Latest edition 2010. $575.00 for individuals; $575.00 for individuals. Covers: More than 6,500 hospitals; some listings also appear in a separate southern edition of this publication. Entries include: Name of hospital, accreditation, mailing address, phone, fax, number of beds, type of facility (nonprofit, general, state, etc.); list of administrative personnel and chiefs of medical services, with specific titles. Arrangement: Geographical.

3874 ■ Medical and Health Information Directory
Gale
PO Box 6904
Florence, KY 41022-6904
Fr: 800-354-9706
URL: http://www.gale.cengage.com

Annual, Latest edition April 2011. $1190.00 for individuals; $501.00 for individuals. Covers: In volume 1, more than 33,000 medical and health oriented associations, organizations, institutions, and government agencies, including health maintenance organizations (HMOs), preferred provider organizations (PPOs), insurance companies, pharmaceutical companies, research centers, and medical and allied health schools. In Volume 2, over 20,000 medical book publishers; medical periodicals, directories, audiovisual producers and services, medical libraries and information centers, electronic resources, and health-related internet search engines. In Volume 3, more than 40,500 clinics, treatment centers, care programs, and counseling/diagnostic services for 34 subject areas. Entries include: Institution, service, or firm name, address, phone, fax, email and URL; many include names of key personnel and, when pertinent, descriptive annotation. Volume 3 was formerly listed separately as Health Services Directory. Arrangement: Classified by organization activity, service, etc. Indexes: Each volume has a complete alphabetical name and keyword index.

HANDBOOKS AND MANUALS

3875 ■ Ask the Nutritionists
AuthorHouse
1663 Liberty Dr.
Bloomington, IN 47403
Fr: 888-519-5121
E-mail: authorsupport@authorhouse.com
URL: http://www.authorhouse.com

Kathy Thames and George Rapitis. 2005. $12.95.

3876 ■ Career Opportunities in the Food and Beverage Industry
Facts on File, Inc.
132 W 31st St., 17th Fl.
New York, NY 10001-2006
Ph: (212)967-8800
Fax: 800-678-3633
Fr: 800-322-8755
E-mail: custserv@factsonfile.com
URL: http://www.infobasepublishing.com

Barbara Sims-Bell. 2010. $18.95 (paper). 223 pages.

Provides the job seeker with information about locating and landing 80 skilled and unskilled jobs in the industry. Includes detailed job descriptions for many specific positions and lists trade associations, recruiting organizations, and major agencies. Contains index and bibliography.

3877 ■ *Careers in Health Care*
The McGraw-Hill Companies
PO Box 182604
Columbus, OH 43272
Fax: (614)759-3749
Fr: 877-883-5524
E-mail: customer.service@mcgraw-hill.com
URL: http://www.mhprofessional.com/
     product.php?isbn=0071466533

Barbara M. Swanson. Fifth edition, 2005. $19.95 (paper). 192 pages. Describes job duties, work settings, salaries, licensing and certification requirements, educational preparation, and future outlook. Gives ideas on how to secure a job.

3878 ■ *Careers in Nutrition*
Rosen Publishing Group
29 E 21st St.
New York, NY 10010
Fax: 888-436-4643
Fr: 800-237-9932
URL: http://www.rosenpublishing.com

Linda Bickerstaff. 2008. $33.25 (list price). 144 pages. Includes up-to-date information about job opportunities in the nutrition and dietetic fields, including coursework, training programs, and United States Department of Labor statistics on employment and salary ranges.

3879 ■ *Careers in Social and Rehabilitation Services*
The McGraw-Hill Companies
PO Box 182604
Columbus, OH 43272
Fax: (614)759-3749
Fr: 877-883-5524
E-mail: customer.service@mcgraw-hill.com
URL: http://www.mhprofessional.com/
     product.php?isbn=0071641955

Geraldine O. Garner. 2008. $16.95. 192 pages.

3880 ■ *Counselling Skills for Dietitians, 2nd Edition*
Wiley
111 River St.
Hoboken, NJ 07030
Ph: (201)748-6000
Fax: (201)748-6088
E-mail: info@wiley.com
URL: http://www.wiley.com

Judy Gable. 2007. $66.99 (paper). 272 pages. Demonstrates how a practitioner can develop a counselling approach and employ appropriate counselling skills to overcome the communication difficulties encountered by dietitians and those engaged in helping clients change their eating behavior.

3881 ■ *Opportunities in Health and Medical Careers*
The McGraw-Hill Companies
PO Box 182604
Columbus, OH 43272
Fax: (614)759-3749
Fr: 877-883-5524
E-mail: customer.service@mcgraw-hill.com
URL: http://www.mhprofessional.com/
     product.php?isbn=0071437274

I. Donald Snook, Jr. and Leo D'Orazio. 2004. $14.95 (paper). 157 pages. Covers the full range of medical and health occupations. Illustrated.

3882 ■ *Opportunities in Nutrition Careers*
McGraw-Hill Professional
PO Box 182604
Columbus, OH 43272
Ph: 877-833-5524

Fax: (614)759-3749
E-mail: pbg.ecommerce_custserv@mcgraw-hill.com
URL: http://www.mhprofessional.com/
     product.php?isbn=0071438467

Carol Coles Caldwell. 2005. $13.95 (paperback). 160 pages. Offers the latest information on nutrition, training and education requirements needed, salary statistics, up-to-date professional and internet resources, and much more.

3883 ■ *The Profession of Dietetics: A Team Approach*
Jones & Bartlett Learning
5 Wall St.
Burlington, MA 01803
Ph: (978)443-5000
Fax: (978)443-8000
Fr: 800-832-0034
E-mail: info@jblearning.com
URL: http://www.jblearning.com

June R. Payne-Palacio and Deborah D. Canter. 2010. $60.95 (paper). 235 pages. Reviews the history of dietetics and contains an overview of the profession. Features a practical and personal approach to successfully maneuvering the often complicated and competitive steps to success in the nutrition profession.

3884 ■ *Resumes for Health and Medical Careers*
The McGraw-Hill Companies
PO Box 182604
Columbus, OH 43272
Fax: (614)759-3749
Fr: 877-883-5524
E-mail: customer.service@mcgraw-hill.com
URL: http://www.mhprofessional.com/
     product.php?isbn=0071545352

Third edition, 2008. $12.95 (paper). 144 pages.

EMPLOYMENT AGENCIES AND SEARCH FIRMS

3885 ■ Harper Associates
31000 NW Hwy., Ste. 240
Farmington Hills, MI 48334
Ph: (248)932-1170
Fax: (248)932-1214
E-mail: info@harperjobs.com
URL: http://www.harperjobs.com

Executive search firm and employment agency.

3886 ■ Professional Placement Associates, Inc.
287 Bowman Ave.
Purchase, NY 10577-2517
Ph: (914)251-1000
Fax: (914)251-1055
E-mail: careers@ppasearch.com
URL: http://www.ppasearch.com

Executive search firm specializing in the health and medical field.

ONLINE JOB SOURCES AND SERVICES

3887 ■ CareerVitals.com
URL: http://www.careervitals.com

Description: Serves as a job board for healthcare professionals in different specializations.

3888 ■ CNMJobs.com
URL: http://www.cnmjobs.com

Description: Helps registered dietitians and clinical nutritionists to search for jobs and identify companies that are interested in a diverse workforce.

3889 ■ DietaryJobs.com
URL: http://www.dietaryjobs.com

Description: Offers dietary employment opportunities. Features dietary jobs across the United States.

3890 ■ DietaryJobs.org
URL: http://dietaryjobs.org

Description: Offers dietary job listings and employment opportunities. Enables job searching in specific locations and specific areas in the dietary field.

3891 ■ DieticianJobs.com
URL: http://www.dieticianjobs.com

Description: Provides dietician job listings and career opportunities. Also lists salary information.

3892 ■ DieticianNutritionist.com
URL: http://www.dieticiannutritionist.com

Description: Serves as a job board for dieticians, nutritionists, and dietetic professionals. Provides access to books, magazines, articles, and continuing education. Provides help in finding new jobs, posting resumes, and accessing career resources.

3893 ■ DietitianCentral.com
URL: http://www.dietitiancentral.com

Description: Provides information on nutrition jobs, dietician jobs, dietician directory, and jobs in dietetics. Provides information on becoming a dietitian, current and projected national earning averages, job outlook and nature of work.

3894 ■ ExploreHealthCareers.org
E-mail: feedback@explorehealthcareers.org
URL: http://explorehealthcareers.org/en/home

Description: Provides employment information in health professions. Includes links to health-related education/training programs, financial aid resources, specialized learning opportunities, and current issues in health care.

3895 ■ Get Dietician Jobs
URL: http://www.getdieticianjobs.com

Description: Offers dietician job postings and employment opportunities.

3896 ■ HEALTHeCAREERS Network
Fr: 888-884-8242
E-mail: info@healthecareers.com
URL: http://www.healthecareers.com

Description: Career search site for jobs in all health care specialties; educational resources; visa and licensing information for relocation; interesting articles; relocation tools; links to professional organizations and general resources.

3897 ■ Institute of Food Technologists - IFT Career Center
525 W Van Buren, Ste. 1000
Chicago, IL 60607
Ph: (312)782-8424
Fax: (312)782-8348
Fr: 800-438-3663
E-mail: info@ift.org
URL: http://www.ift.org

Description: Offers job information and resources for those considering the Food Science and Technology field. Employers may post for full- or part-time positions and have the option of receiving a resume file of current job seekers. IFT members may register for a six-month confidential service to have their credentials reviewed by food industry employers. Job seekers who list credentials will receive the monthly Jobs Available bulletin. Main files include: Employment and Salary Information, How to Find Your First Job in the Food Sciences, Resources for Non-US Job Seekers, and more.

3898 ■ Jobs In Dietetics
E-mail: info@jobsindietetics.com
URL: http://www.jobsindietetics.com

Description: Provides nationwide career support for nutritionists as well as dietetics and food service professionals. Offers a subscription job listing service.

3899 ■ NutritionJobs.com
URL: http://www.nutritionjobs.com

Description: Advances the career opportunities for professionals in the fields of nutrition and dietetics. Allows searching or recruiting for jobs online, including timely access to opportunities.

3900 ■ ProHealthJobs.com
Ph: (484)443-8545
Fax: (484)443-8549
E-mail: info@prohealthjobs.com
URL: http://prohealthjobs.com/jobboard

Description: Career resources site for the medical and health care field. Lists professional opportunities, product information, continuing education and open positions.

3901 ■ RDLink.com
URL: http://www.rdlink.com

Description: Provides links to dietetic technicians, dietitians, and nutritionists on the web. Features job listings.

3902 ■ RegisteredDieticiansJobs.com
URL: http://www.registereddieticianjobs.com

Description: Offers career resources for diet and nutrition professionals. Provides jobs searching, resume posting, and career tools for job seekers.

TRADESHOWS

3903 ■ California Dietetic Association Meeting
California Dietetic Association
7740 Manchester Ave., Ste. 102
Playa Del Rey, CA 90293-8499
Ph: (310)822-0177
Fax: (310)823-0264
E-mail: patsmith@dietitian.org
URL: http://www.dietitian.org

Annual. Primary Exhibits: Food and nutrition services. Dates and Locations: 2012 Apr 26-28; Ontario, CA; The Ontario Convention Center.

3904 ■ Dietary Managers Association Meeting and Expo
Dietary Managers Association
406 Surrey Woods Dr.
St. Charles, IL 60174
Ph: (630)587-6336
Fax: (630)587-6308
E-mail: info@dmaonline.org
URL: http://www.dmaonline.org

Annual. Primary Exhibits: Dietary management equipment, supplies, and services. Dates and Locations: 2012 Jun 30 - Jul 03; San Diego, CA; Manchester Grand Hyatt.

3905 ■ IAACN Scientific Symposium
International and American Associations of Clinical Nutritionists
15280 Addison Rd., Ste. 130
Addison, TX 75001
Ph: (972)407-9089
Fax: (972)250-0233
E-mail: ddc@clinicalnutrition.com
URL: http://www.iaacn.org

Annual. Provides an opportunity for professional growth, networking, and exchange of ideas. 2012 August 8-11; San Antonio, TX; Marriott San Antonio Rivercenter.

OTHER SOURCES

3906 ■ American Association of Nutritional Consultants (AANC)
220 Parker St.
Warsaw, IN 46580

Ph: (574)269-6165
Fr: 888-828-2262
E-mail: registrar@aanc.net
URL: http://www.aanc.net

Description: Professional nutritional consultants. Seeks to create a forum for exchange of nutritional information. Offers benefits such as car rental and laboratory discounts.

3907 ■ American Dietetic Association (ADA)
120 S Riverside Plz., Ste. 2000
Chicago, IL 60606-6995
Ph: (312)899-0040
Fax: (312)899-4817
Fr: 800-877-1600
E-mail: pbabjak@eatright.org
URL: http://www.eatright.org

Description: Represents food and nutrition professionals. Promotes nutrition, health and well-being.

3908 ■ American Public Health Association (APHA)
800 I St. NW
Washington, DC 20001
Ph: (202)777-2742
Fax: (202)777-2534
E-mail: comments@apha.org
URL: http://www.apha.org

Description: Professional organization of physicians, nurses, educators, academicians, environmentalists, epidemiologists, new professionals, social workers, health administrators, optometrists, podiatrists, pharmacists, dentists, nutritionists, health planners, other community and mental health specialists, and interested consumers. Seeks to protect and promote personal, mental, and environmental health. Services include: promulgation of standards; establishment of uniform practices and procedures; development of the etiology of communicable diseases; research in public health; exploration of medical care programs and their relationships to public health. Sponsors job placement service.

3909 ■ American School Health Association (ASHA)
4340 East West Hwy., Ste. 403
Bethesda, MD 20814
Ph: (301)652-8072
Fax: (301)652-8077
Fr: 800-445-2742
E-mail: info@ashaweb.org
URL: http://www.ashaweb.org

Description: School physicians, school nurses, counselors, nutritionists, psychologists, social workers, administrators, school health coordinators, health educators, and physical educators working in schools, professional preparation programs, public health, and community-based organizations. Promotes coordinated school health programs that include health education, health services, a healthful school environment, physical education, nutrition services, and psycho-social health services offered in schools collaboratively with families and other members of the community. Offers professional reference materials and professional development opportunities. Conducts pilot programs that inform materials development, provides technical assistance to school professionals, advocates for school health.

3910 ■ American Society for Nutrition
9650 Rockville Pike
Bethesda, MD 20814
Ph: (301)634-7050
Fax: (301)634-7892
E-mail: info@nutrition.org
URL: http://www.nutrition.org

Description: Serves as the professional society of nutrition research scientists from universities, government, and industry. Seeks to advance the knowledge and application of nutrition for the sake of humans and animals.

3911 ■ American Society for Parenteral and Enteral Nutrition
8630 Fenton St., Ste. 412
Silver Spring, MD 20910
Ph: (301)587-6315
Fax: (301)587-2365
Fr: 800-727-4567
E-mail: aspen@nutr.org
URL: http://www.nutritioncare.org

Description: Seeks to improve patient care by advancing the science and practice of nutrition support therapy. Works closely with other health care organizations to advance a patient-centered approach to nutrition care and with government agencies to promote the optimal use of nutrition therapies.

3912 ■ Association for Healthcare Foodservice
455 S 4th St., Ste. 650
Louisville, KY 40202
Fax: (502)589-3602
Fr: 888-528-9552
E-mail: info@healthcarefoodservice.org
URL: http://www.healthcarefoodservice.org

Description: Represents professionals and suppliers in the self-operated healthcare foodservice industry. Advances healthcare foodservice professionals by ensuring that food and nutrition is a core competency. Provides education, advocacy, and management tools to support members.

3913 ■ Dietary Managers Association (DMA)
406 Surrey Woods Dr.
St. Charles, IL 60174
Ph: (630)587-6336
Fax: (630)587-6308
Fr: 800-323-1908
E-mail: info@dmaonline.org
URL: http://www.dmaonline.org

Description: Dietary managers united to maintain a high level of competency and quality in dietary departments through continuing education. Provides educational programs and placement service.

3914 ■ Genetic Metabolic Dietitians International
PO Box 33985
Fort Worth, TX 76162
E-mail: info@gmdi.org
URL: http://www.gmdi.org

Description: Represents the interests of nutritionists and other health care practitioners. Enhances and supports the practice of genetic metabolic nutrition. Provides leadership in nutrition therapy for genetic metabolic disorders through clinical practice, education, advocacy, and research.

3915 ■ IDEA Health and Fitness Association
10455 Pacific Center Ct.
San Diego, CA 92121
Ph: (858)535-8979
Fax: (858)535-8234
Fr: 800-999-IDEA
E-mail: contact@ideafit.com
URL: http://www.ideafit.com

Description: Provides continuing education for fitness professionals including; fitness instructors, personal trainers, program directors, and club/studio owners. Offers workshops for continuing education credits.

3916 ■ International and American Associations of Clinical Nutritionists
15280 Addison Rd., Ste. 130
Addison, TX 75001
Ph: (972)407-9089
Fax: (972)250-0233
E-mail: ddc@clinicalnutrition.com
URL: http://www.iaacn.org

Description: Serves as a professional association of practicing clinical nutritionists. Conducts and maintains standards for the field. Provides members with continuing education programs.

SOURCES OF HELP-WANTED ADS

3917 ■ Continuity Insights Magazine
Gardner Publications, Inc.
6915 Valley Ave.
Cincinnati, OH 45244
Ph: (513)527-8800
Fax: (513)527-8801
Fr: 800-950-8020
E-mail: info@continuityinsights.com
URL: http://www.gardnerweb.com

Bimonthly. Free for qualified subscribers within the United States and Canada; $96.00 for international subscriptions. Strives to provide readers with industry information and insights to continually improve their skills as business continuity professionals. Features business continuity resources, conferences and other materials dedicated to assure the integrity of business.

3918 ■ CSO Career
CSO - Security and Risk
PO Box 9208
Framingham, MA 01701-9208
Ph: (508)872-0080
Fax: (508)879-7784
E-mail: online@cxo.com
URL: http://www.csoonline.com

Biweekly. Newsletter of career and leadership-oriented news, articles, events and job postings.

3919 ■ CSO Online - Security and Risk
PO Box 9208
Framingham, MA 01701-9208
Ph: (508)872-0080
Fax: (508)879-7784
E-mail: online@cxo.com
URL: http://www.csoonline.com/security/jobs/1

Provides news, analysis and research on a broad range of security and risk management topics. Areas of focus include information security, physical security, business continuity, identity and access management and loss prevention.

3920 ■ Disaster Recovery Journal
1862 Old Lemay Ferry Rd.
Arnold, MO 63010
Ph: (636)282-5800
Fax: (636)282-5802
E-mail: drj@drj.com
URL: http://www.drj.com

Quarterly. Delivers in-depth knowledge and up-to-date information about business continuity planning.

3921 ■ SC Magazine
Haymarket Media, Inc.
114 W 26th St., 4th Fl.
New York, NY 10001
Ph: (646)638-6000
E-mail: custserv@haymarketmedia.com
URL: http://www.haymarket.com/sc_magazine/
    default.aspx

Description: Monthly. Provides IT security professionals with in-depth and unbiased information through timely news, comprehensive analysis, cutting-edge features, contributions from thought leaders and an extensive collection of product reviews in the business.

PLACEMENT AND JOB REFERRAL SERVICES

3922 ■ Acumin Consulting Ltd.
PO Box 114
Stockton, NJ 08559-0114
E-mail: careers@acuminconsulting.com
URL: http://www.acuminconsulting.com/JobSeekers/

Description: Provides both permanent and contract risk management staff at all levels to industries spanning all sectors from tier banks to global consultancies across EMEA and the U.S. Helps develop internal risk management teams within end users.

3923 ■ Alta Associates
8 Bartles Corner Rd.
Flemington, NJ 08822
Ph: (908)806-8442
Fax: (908)806-8443
E-mail: info@altaassociates.com
URL: http://www.altaassociates.com

Description: Executive recruitment firm specializing in Information Security, IT Audit, Business Resiliency, Risk Management and Privacy.

3924 ■ Andersen Steinberg Group
110 Wall St., 11th Fl.
New York, NY 10005-3817
Ph: (646)688-2375
E-mail: usa@andersensteinberg.com
URL: http://www.andersensteinberg.com

Description: Works with corporations across all industries to provide investment banking and financial services, consultancy and outsourcing. Provides organizations with a global head of business continuity, regional heads, national heads, team leads and members. Focuses on business continuity and resilience.

3925 ■ Artizen, Inc.
200 Main St., Ste. 21A
Redwood City, CA 94063
Ph: (650)261-9400
E-mail: info1110@artizen.com
URL: http://www.artizen.com

Provides project based, turnkey solutions. Specializes in business process re-engineering and information technology projects.

3926 ■ BC Management
17011 Beach Blvd., Ste. 1270
Huntington Beach, CA 92647
Ph: (714)960-7001
Fax: (714)369-8034
Fr: 888-250-7001
E-mail: info@bcmanagement.com
URL: http://www.bcmanagement.com

Serves as an executive search firm that specializes in identifying, recruiting, and placing professionals in business continuity, disaster recovery, crisis management, risk management, and information security careers. Renders placement services as an expert in both business continuity and recruiting. Serves both employers and job seekers through extensive industry knowledge, unmatched candidate contacts, and complete candidate screenings.

3927 ■ Data Center Assistance Group
78-17 164th St.
Flushing, NY 11366
Ph: (718)591-5553
Fax: (718)380-7322
E-mail: bronackt@dcag.com
URL: http://www.dcag.com

Serves as a full service data processing consulting and personnel placement firm that specializes in emergency management preparedness training, business resumption planning, systems management and workflow optimization. Provides services to clients that result in improved performance and increased productivity through enhanced operations and a safeguarded environment capable of recovering from a wide range of business interruptions. Develops systems that assist client firms in their efforts to optimize the quality of personnel performance and productivity of their firms.

3928 ■ Enterprise Solutions Inc.
14850 Quorum Dr., Ste. 410
Dallas, TX 75254
Ph: (972)732-7275
Fax: (972)732-7364
Fr: 800-889-4374
E-mail: info@esius.com
URL: http://www.esius.com

Seeks to service the specific IT requirements of customers in an expeditious manner. Provides clients with network centric consulting, contract based staffing and placement services.

3929 ■ Millennium Search Associates, LLC
Ph: (973)758-9200
E-mail: info@msasearch.net
URL: http://www.msasearch.net

Description: Provides career consultation for candidates in the Insurance Risk Management, Safety, Claims, Loss Control, Security Management and Business Continuity Planning professions.

3930 ■ Monarch Business Resiliency
125 Town Park Dr., Ste. 300
Kennesaw, GA 30144
Ph: (678)921-2574
Fax: (404)806-6422
E-mail: info@monarchresiliency.com
URL: http://www.monarchresiliency.com

Description: Staffing company that focuses on delivering value to clients by ensuring a more resilient business. Helps companies bring recovery capability in-house through its IT and BCP consultants.

3931 ■ Request Technology
200 E 5th Ave., Ste. 116
Naperville, IL 60563
Ph: (630)717-5865
Fax: (630)717-1109
E-mail: opportunity@requesttechnology.com
URL: http://www.requesttechnology.com

Description: Provides placement services for IT professionals throughout the world.

3932 ■ Robert Half Technology
2884 Sand Hill Rd.
Menlo Park, CA 94025
Fr: 800-793-5533
URL: http://www.roberthalftechnology.com

Provides IT professionals on a project and full-time basis. Specializes in initiatives ranging from web development and systems integration to network security and technical support. Offers flexible staffing solutions to premier organizations worldwide that require technical expertise on demand.

3933 ■ Robert Shields and Associates
16969 Texas Ave., Ste. 400
Webster, TX 77598
Ph: (281)488-7961
Fax: (281)486-1496
Fr: 800-423-5383
E-mail: info@rsacorp.com
URL: http://www.rsacorp.com

Description: Business technology services firm that solves business pains and helps companies grow through technology. Provides human resource search and staffing services for businesses and individuals.

3934 ■ SecurityRecruiter.com
PO Box 398
Woodland Park, CO 80866
Ph: (719)686-8810
Fr: 877-417-6830
E-mail: information@securityrecruiter.com
URL: http://www.securityrecruiter.com

Serves corporate clients, select security vendors and security focused professional services organizations. Placement service includes full-time and contract security jobs in the realm of Corporate Governance, Risk Management, Regulatory Compliance, Audit, Privacy, Information Security and Physical Security.

3935 ■ Tek Systems Inc.
7437 Race Rd.
Hanover, MD 21076
Fr: 888-519-0776
URL: http://www.teksystems.com/Careers

Maintains strong relationships with 82% of the Fortune 500 and multiple government agencies. Deploys technical professionals across the globe and matches the right talent and expertise with the right projects.

EMPLOYER DIRECTORIES AND NETWORKING LISTS

3936 ■ *Information Emergency Planning and Disaster Recovery Sourcebook*
Edwards Information LLC
PO Box 31
Ashton, MD 20861
Ph: (301)774-5414
Fax: (301)774-5416
Fr: 800-990-9936
URL: http://www.edwardsinformation.com

Provides a concise guide to disaster planning teams. Includes sections covering items from professional associations, training and conferences affiliated with DR functions, equipment and facilities vendors, clean-up services and software vendors.

HANDBOOKS AND MANUALS

3937 ■ *Business Continuity And Disaster Recovery Planning For IT Professionals*
Saunders
c/o Reed Elsevier
360 Park Ave., S
New York, NY 10010
Ph: (212)989-5800
Fax: (212)633-3990
URL: http://www.elsevier.com

$59.95. 456 pages. Contains updated information on risks from cyber attacks, rioting, protests, product tampering, bombs, explosions and terrorism. Provides extensive disaster planning and readiness checklists for IT infrastructure, enterprise applications, servers and desktops.

EMPLOYMENT AGENCIES AND SEARCH FIRMS

3938 ■ Abmax, Inc.
PO Box 35326
Tulsa, OK 74153
Ph: (918)627-8324
Fax: (918)628-1521
E-mail: business@abmax.net
URL: http://www.abmax.net

Provides consulting and staffing services within the information technology arena.

3939 ■ A.E. Feldman Associates, Inc.
445 Northern Blvd.
Great Neck, NY 10021
Ph: (516)719-7900
Fax: (516)719-7910
URL: http://www.aefeldman.com

Executive search and recruiting firm specializing in the financial, accounting, legal, infrastructure and technology industries.

3940 ■ Burke & Associates
1234 Summer St.
Stamford, CT 06905
Ph: (203)406-2300
E-mail: info@burkeandassociates.com
URL: http://burkeandassociates.com

Description: Provides services to clients including executive search, interim staffing and consulting services. Specializes in the areas of finance and accounting, human resources and IT.

3941 ■ DES Recruitment
1023 E Baltimore Pike, Ste. 215
Media, PA 19063
Ph: (484)442-8150
E-mail: hodge@desrecruitment.com
URL: http://www.desrecruitment.com

Staffing solutions and recruiting firm that focuses on SAP recruiting, sales and marketing, information security and diversity.

3942 ■ Kelly & Thomas Associates, Inc.
21 E 5th St.
Conshohocken, PA 19428
Ph: (610)825-3800
Fax: (610)825-6600
URL: http://www.kellythomas.net

Description: Provides services to clients including executive search, interim staffing and consulting

services. Specializes in the areas of engineering, manufacturing, information technology, pharmaceuticals, finance and accounting, construction and building technology, healthcare, food, sales and marketing.

3943 ■ Premier Staffing Partners
404 Ebenezer Rd.
Knoxville, TN 37923
Ph: (865)531-8588
URL: http://www.premierstaffingpartners.com

Description: Specializes in providing highly accomplished information technology professionals for short and long-term contract, contract to hire and direct placement positions.

ONLINE JOB SOURCES AND SERVICES

3944 ■ BankInfoSecurity.com
E-mail: advertising@bankinfosecurity.com
URL: http://www.bankinfosecurity.com

Description: Serves as a reference tool that promotes education on security issues. Reinforces the need for maintaining customer data confidentiality and integrity. Provides resources for individuals who want to work in the field such as interview tips, job postings, salary and hiring information and a resume center.

3945 ■ Blue Coat Systems Career Center
URL: http://www.bluecoat.com/company/careers

Description: Helps clients deliver the business-critical applications needed to enhance productivity, ensure a proactive line of defense and align network investments with business requirements.

3946 ■ GobsOfJobs.com
URL: http://www.gobsofjobs.com

Acts as an interactive career site devoted to the hardware, software and information technology industries. Functions as a career management tool for job candidates and employers.

3947 ■ InformationTechnologyCrossing.com
URL: http://www.informationtechnologycrossing.com

Description: Provides information on IT jobs.

3948 ■ ITworld
URL: http://www.itworld.com

Description: Participatory site that acts as a forum for IT professionals and technology vendors to discuss challenges and solutions in the IT world.

3949 ■ JustTechJobs.com
E-mail: support@justtechjobs.com
URL: http://www.justtechjobs.com

Description: Serves as a jobsite that provides employers with a technology specific focus and provides job seekers with job postings aimed at those specific tech jobs. Offers a community of 15 million tech professionals and also supports several technology websites.

3950 ■ Tech-Engine.com
URL: http://techengine.com

Description: Features employment listings concerning the IT and engineering fields. Features employers and recruiters information, resume posting and career resources.

TRADESHOWS

3951 ■ Business Continuity & Corporate Security Show and Conference
Flag Management Inc.
353 Lexington Ave.
New York, NY 10016
Ph: (212)286-0333

Fax: (212)286-0086
E-mail: flaggmgmt@msn.com
URL: http://www.flaggmgmt.com/bc/default.htm
Annual. Assembles 800 directors, global business continuity managers and corporate security executives from Wall Street, the New York business and medical and health care community.

3952 ■ Business Continuity & Safety Conference
Code Red Business Continuity Services LLC
911 Pontiac Ave.
Cranston, RI 02920
Ph: (401)785-4911
Fax: (401)785-9991
E-mail: info@coderedbcs.com
URL: http://www.coderedbcs.com

Annual. Features simulation exercises that utilize the disruption scenario that gradually increases in complexity and integrates across critical supply chain management. Helps participants in improving and recommending controls that they can use as business recovery professionals.

3953 ■ Digital ID World Conference
CSO Online - Security and Risk
PO Box 9208
Framingham, MA 01701-9208
Ph: (508)872-0080
Fax: (508)879-7784
URL: http://public.cxo.com/conferences/index.html?conferenceID=51
Annual. Helps participants to succeed in all phases of managing and protecting their organizational identities, as well as that of their employees and customers.

3954 ■ Enterprise Disaster Recovery/Business Continuity - Designing the Resilient Framework Conference
CAMP Conferences, Inc.
540 W Frontage Rd., Ste. 2205
Northfield, IL 60093
Ph: (312)527-2800
Fax: (847)881-0747
URL: http://campconferences.com/events/2010/disaster1.htm

Features strategies to help design, implement and manage disaster recovery and business continuity frameworks to protect an organization's core IT assets, people and processes.

3955 ■ InfoSec World Conference & Expo
MIS Training Institute
153 Cordaville Rd., Ste. 200
Southborough, MA 01772
Ph: (508)879-7999
Fax: (508)787-0033
E-mail: mis@misti.com
URL: http://www.misti.com

Annual. Provides education to all levels of information security professionals. Offers practical sessions that give participants the tools to strengthen their security without restricting their business.

3956 ■ Interop
UBM TechWeb
South Tower, Ste. 900, 9th Fl.
303 2nd St.
San Francisco, CA 94107
Ph: (415)947-6000
URL: http://www.interop.com

Annual. Provides opportunities for business and technology leaders to get the latest information on key technologies, learn about the latest trends and meet with leading vendors.

3957 ■ Next Generation Data Center Conference & Expo
International Data Group
1 Exeter Plz., 15th Fl.
Boston, MA 02116
Ph: (617)534-1200
URL: http://www.idg.com

Annual. Features sessions on advanced facilities management and planning, applications, introduction to facility infrastructure, security, storage information management, virtualization, networking services and data optimization.

3958 ■ Storage Networking World
Computerworld Inc.
492 Old Connecticut Path
Framingham, MA 01701
Ph: (508)879-0700
Fr: 800-355-0246
E-mail: snwreg@computerworld.com
URL: http://www.eiseverywhere.com/ehome/index.php?eventid=30283&

Annual. Focuses on technologies and solutions. Analyzes and discusses how user companies deploy their infrastructure management strategies in the enterprise.

OTHER SOURCES

3959 ■ Association of Contingency Planners - Alamo Chapter
BC Management
17011 Beach Blvd., Ste. 1270
Huntington Beach, CA 92647
Ph: (714)843-5470
Fr: 888-250-7001
E-mail: zboyles@bcmanagement.com
URL: http://alamo.acp-international.com

Description: Practitioners in the field of business continuity. Promotes the advancement of business continuity professionals. Provides networking opportunities to related risk management groups to gain extensive knowledge base of resources, valuable insights and partnerships, and enhance skills that prepare families, communities and the industry.

3960 ■ Association of Contingency Planners - Capital of Texas Chapter
PO Box 13371
Austin, TX 78711-3371
Ph: (469)348-6261
E-mail: president@capitaloftexas.acp-international.com
URL: http://www.acp-centraltexas.com

Description: Practitioners in the field of business continuity. Promotes the advancement of business continuity professionals. Provides a network for the development of business continuity professionals.

3961 ■ Association of Contingency Planners - Central Maryland Chapter
PO Box 1684
Owings Mills, MD 21117
Ph: (240)228-5777
E-mail: mary.lasky@jhuapl.edu
URL: http://centralmd.acp-international.com/jobs.html

Description: Practitioners in the field of business continuity. Promotes the advancement of business continuity professionals. Provides a network for the development of business continuity professionals.

3962 ■ Association of Contingency Planners - Northern Ohio Chapter
1220 W 6th St., Ste. 307
Cleveland, OH 44113
Ph: (330)321-8650
E-mail: brian.zawada@avalution.com
URL: http://www.acp-international.com/northohio/jobpostings.htm

Description: Practitioners in the field of business continuity. Promotes the advancement of business continuity professionals. Provides networking opportunities to related risk management groups to gain extensive knowledge base of resources, valuable insights and partnerships, and enhance skills that prepare families, communities and the industry.

3963 ■ Association of Contingency Planners - Sioux Empire Chapter
PO Box 884
Sioux Falls, SD 57101-0884
URL: http://www.acp-international.com/sioux

Description: Practitioners in the field of business continuity. Promotes the advancement of business continuity professionals. Provides networking opportunities to related risk management groups to gain extensive knowledge base of resources, valuable insights and partnerships, and enhance skills that prepare families, communities and the industry.

3964 ■ Association of Contingency Planners - The First State (Delaware) Chapter
801 Silver Lake Rd.
Dover, DE 19904
E-mail: firststateacp@comcast.net
URL: http://firststate.acp-international.com

Description: Practitioners in the field of business continuity. Promotes the advancement of business continuity professionals. Aims to foster continued professional growth and development in effective contingency and business resumption planning. Provides members with opportunities to set response and recovery trends while strengthening relationships through public and private partnerships.

3965 ■ Business Continuity Planners Association
PO Box 75930
St. Paul, MN 55175-0930
Ph: (651)998-9609
URL: http://www.bcpa.org

Description: Serves as a mutual benefit association of business professionals responsible for, or participating in, business recovery, crisis management, emergency management, contingency planning, disaster preparedness planning, or a related professional vocation. Provides a professional and educational environment for the exchange of experience, dissemination of information, professional growth, and for added value of mutual interest to the membership. Conducts meetings and disseminates information on the field of disaster recovery.

3966 ■ Business Recovery Managers Association
PO Box 2184
San Francisco, CA 94126
Ph: (925)355-8660
URL: http://www.brma.com

Description: Business continuity professionals and individuals interested in the fields of business recovery, disaster recovery, contingency and continuity planning, and emergency response management. Advances the theory and practice of business recovery, disaster recovery, contingency and continuity planning, and emergency response management. Provides latest trends and technologies available in the business continuity industry.

3967 ■ California Emergency Services Association
PO Box 630220
Simi Valley, CA 93063
Ph: (805)520-5854
Fax: (805)585-3227
URL: http://www.cesa.net

Composed of emergency managers and planners from all levels of government, hospital/medical professionals, education representatives, public service organizations, business/industry emergency planners, and other individuals interested in this field. Strives to improve emergency planning, training, and response techniques.

3968 ■ Central Arizona Association of Contingency Planners
PO Box 67434
Phoenix, AZ 85082
E-mail: president@azacp.org
URL: http://www.azacp.org

Description: Contingency planners, business continuity professionals, and emergency managers. Provides and facilitates an open environment for the exchange of experience and information. Identifies common planning needs and potential recovery response solutions as well as strengthens relationships through networking opportunities.

3969 ■ Contingency Planning Association of the Carolinas
PO Box 32492
Charlotte, NC 28232-2492
Ph: (704)733-5289
E-mail: chairman@cpaccarolinas.org
URL: http://www.cpaccarolinas.org

Description: Serves as a peer group of professionals/experts in disaster recovery or business continuity who share information, education, and resources in contingency planning in North and South Carolina. Supports proactive preparation for the resumption of business in the event of an unplanned interruption that adversely affects the operation of the organization. Provides a forum for the interchange of ideas, topics and information in the field of business continuity planning and disaster recovery.

3970 ■ DRI International
1115 Broadway, 12th Fl.
New York, NY 10010
Fr: (866)542-3744
URL: http://www.drii.org

Description: Serves professionals in the field of Business Continuity Management. Promotes advancement in the study, teaching and practice of disaster recovery and business continuity. Devises public and private infrastructure continuity plans and studies; sponsors professional development and other educational programs; conducts examinations and certifies business continuity professionals.

3971 ■ International Consortium for Organizational Resilience
PO Box 1171
Lombard, IL 60148
Ph: (630)705-0910
Fr: (866)765-8321
E-mail: info@theicor.org
URL: http://www.theicor.org

Description: Professionals with a demonstrated expertise in organizational resilience. Empowers professionals with skills that will allow them to embed the culture and systems of resilience within their organizations and communities. Provides thought-leadership, professional development and certification-enabling strategies for embedding the culture and systems of resilience within the organization.

3972 ■ Iowa Contingency Planners
PO Box 1365
Des Moines, IA 50305-1365
Ph: (515)376-6473
Fax: (515)376-9026
URL: http://www.icp-web.net

Serves as a professional group of individuals, companies, and government agencies in the field of contingency planning and emergency management. Provides contingency planning and disaster recovery educational and networking opportunities for members. Conducts meetings, conferences, and trainings in an attempt to completely cover the field of contingency planning and disaster recovery.

3973 ■ Mid-Atlantic Disaster Recovery Association, Inc.
PO Box 6145
Columbia, MD 21045
E-mail: contactus@madra.org
URL: http://www.madra.org

Serves as a group of volunteers, professionals, and individuals committed to ensuring that people and organizations are better prepared to manage any type of disaster or emergency event through information exchange and interaction. Strives to foster communications among individuals, groups, and the community working in the areas of Business Continuity Planning (BCP), Continuity of Operations Planning (COOP), and Disaster Recovery (DR) Planning. Provides a forum for the Mid-Atlantic's BCP/COOP/DR community to improve their skills through networking and education.

3974 ■ NCS Group
1941 Citrona Dr.
Fernandina Beach, FL 32034
Fax: 888-321-1504
Fr: 888-795-0050
URL: http://www.ncsjobs.com/home.asp

Description: Utilizes information technology as a tool to drive business results. Specializes in project based work as well as strategic staffing.

3975 ■ NorthEast Disaster Recovery Information X-Change
PO Box 52120
Boston, MA 02205-2120
E-mail: info@nedrix.com
URL: http://www.nedrix.com

Professionals in the fields of continuity/disaster planning and emergency management. Offers resources for continuity planning and crisis management professionals. Provides access to industry best practices and opportunities to meet and share ideas and experiences with peers through conferences, symposiums, and public/private sector services.

3976 ■ Storage Networking Industry Association
4410 ArrowsWest Dr.
Colorado Springs, CO 80907-3444
Ph: (719)694-1380
Fax: (719)694-1389
E-mail: tcinfo@snia.org
URL: http://www.snia.org

Description: IT professionals. Focuses on developing and promoting standards, technologies and educational services to empower organizations in the management of information. Enables members to develop solutions for storing and managing the massive volumes of information generated by today's businesses. Works to bring recognition on storage issues to the IT world, making storage less complicated for the end user.

3977 ■ Technology Executives Club
1580 S Milwaukee Ave., Ste. 305
Libertyville, IL 60048
Ph: (847)837-3900
Fax: (847)837-3901
E-mail: mtuthill@technologyexecutivesclub.com
URL: http://www.technologyexecutivesclub.com/classifiedads-jobs.php

Description: Provides seminars, webinars, whitepapers, on-demand webcasts and newsletters which help IT and business executives stay current and share best practices on information technology in the enterprise. Provides an IT directory, resource center, announcements, community events, classified ads and other tools pursuing business intelligence and efficiency through effective information management.

Disc Jockeys

SOURCES OF HELP-WANTED ADS

3978 ■ *AFTRA Magazine*
American Federation of Television and Radio Artists
260 Madison Ave.
New York, NY 10016-2401
Ph: (212)532-0800
Fax: (212)532-2242
URL: http://www.aftra.org/
Quarterly. $3.00/year for individuals. Membership magazine covering issues in television and radio broadcasting.

3979 ■ *Community Radio News*
National Federation of Community Broadcasters
1970 Broadway, Ste. 1000
Oakland, CA 94612
Ph: (510)451-8200
Fax: (510)451-8208
E-mail: newsletter@nfcb.org
URL: http://www.nfcb.org
Description: Monthly. Serves as a medium of communication for independent, community-licensed radio stations. Contains brief articles and news items on such topics as public broadcasting and programming, legislative developments, activities of the Federal Communications Commission, and local stations. Recurring features include notices of grants and awards, job openings, and a calendar of events/conferences for noncommercial broadcasters.

3980 ■ *Feminist Media Studies*
Routledge Journals
270 Madison Ave.
New York, NY 10016-0601
Ph: (212)216-7800
Fax: (212)563-2269
URL: http://www.tandf.co.uk/journals/titles/
    14680777.asp
Quarterly. $700.00/year for institutions, print + online; $129.00/year for individuals, print only; $630.00/year for institutions, online only. Journal covering media and communication studies.

3981 ■ *Radio and Records*
Nielsen Business Media
770 Broadway
New York, NY 10003-9595
E-mail: nbb@omeda.com
URL: http://www.radioandrecords.com
Weekly. $24.95/year for individuals, monthly, print & online; $299.00/year for individuals, print & online; $19.95/year for individuals, monthly, online. Magazine covering every format of music radio, regulatory developments, news radio, talk radio, and satellite radio.

HANDBOOKS AND MANUALS

3982 ■ *DJing For Dummies*
John Wiley & Sons, Inc.
111 River St.
Hoboken, NJ 07030
Ph: (201)748-6000
Fax: (201)748-6088
E-mail: info@wiley.com
URL: http://www.wiley.com
John Steventon. 2010. $19.99 (paperback). 424 pages. 2nd edition. Offers newcomers with technical information on starting a career as a disc jockey. Provides advice on creating a unique DJing style, expanding skills and fan base; plus tips on equipment essentials, mixing, and song structure. Includes updated information on the latest software and techniques, content on digital DJing and DJing over the Internet.

3983 ■ *Great Jobs for Music Majors*
The McGraw-Hill Companies
PO Box 182604
Columbus, OH 43272
Fax: (614)759-3749
Fr: 877-883-5524
E-mail: customer.service@mcgraw-hill.com
URL: http://www.mhprofessional.com/
    product.php?isbn=0071454616
Jan Goldberg. Second edition, 2004. $15.95 (paper). 180 pages.

3984 ■ *How to Be a DJ*
Course Technology, Inc.
20 Channel Center St.
Boston, MA 02210
Ph: (617)289-7700
Fax: (617)289-7844
Fr: 800-354-9706
URL: http://academic.cengage.com/
    coursetechnology/
    ?CFID=1051488&CFTOKEN=43747877
Chuck Fresh. 2005. 304 pages. Tips for working as a successful disc jockey in radio, bars and clubs, or private parties. Advice is given for choosing hardware and software equipment.

**3985 ■ *Opportunities in Broadcasting
Careers***
The McGraw-Hill Companies
PO Box 182604
Columbus, OH 43272
Fax: (614)759-3749
Fr: 877-883-5524
E-mail: customer.service@mcgraw-hill.com
URL: http://www.mhprofessional.com/
    product.php?isbn=0071454578
Elmo I. Ellis. 2004. $13.95. 176 pages. Discusses opportunities and job search techniques in broadcasting, television, and radio. Illustrated.

**3986 ■ *Starting Your Career in Broadcasting:
Working On and Off the Air in Radio and
Television***
Allworth Press
307 W 36th St., 11th Fl.
New York, NY 10018
Ph: (212)643-6816
Fax: (212)643-6819
URL: http://www.allworth.com
Chris Schneider. 2007. $19.95 (paper). 240 pages. Provides information on how to get into the communications business. Includes chapters on specific on-air and behind-the-scenes jobs, academic programs in broadcasting, what news and program directors seek in job candidates, how an aspiring broadcaster can buy time on the air, weathering the ups and downs of a competitive industry, and how professionals of all kinds can host their own talk shows.

**3987 ■ *What's Up Dawg: How to Become a
Superstar in the Music Business***
Hyperion Books
114 Fifth Ave.
New York, NY 10011
Ph: (917)661-2072
Fax: (917)661-6411
Fr: 800-242-7737
URL: http://www.hyperionbooks.com
Randy Jackson and K.C. Baker. 2004. $19.95 (paper). 208 pages.

ONLINE JOB SOURCES AND SERVICES

3988 ■ djjobs.us
URL: http://www.djjobs.us
Description: Helps job seekers find the best disc jockey career opportunities with the best companies. Assists employers and recruiters in their recruitment of qualified candidates to fill available positions.

OTHER SOURCES

**3989 ■ American Disc Jockey Association
(ADJA)**
20118 N 67th Ave., Ste. 300-605
Glendale, AZ 85308
Fr: 888-723-5776
E-mail: office@adja.org
URL: http://www.adja.org
Description: Mobile and night club disc jockeys. Seeks to promote the disc jockey as a professional form of entertainment; improves the industry by establishing standards, procedures, and benefits. Assists and trains members; provides forums for professional disc jockeys; conducts educational, charitable, and research programs.

3990 ■ American Optician
Opticians Association of America
4064 E Fir Hill Dr.
Lakeland, TN 38002
Ph: (901)388-2423
Fax: (901)388-2348
URL: http://www.oaa.org

Quarterly. Included in membership. Professional journal covering optometry.

3991 ■ EyeNet
American Academy of Ophthalmology
PO Box 7424
San Francisco, CA 94120-7424
Ph: (415)561-8500
Fax: (415)561-8533
E-mail: eyenet@aao.org
URL: http://www.eyenetmagazine.org

Monthly. $128.00/year for nonmembers, within U.S.; $180.00/year for nonmembers, outside US; $76.00/year for members, international; $20.00/year for individuals, inactive member. Professional magazine of the American Academy of Ophthalmology covering clinical, socioeconomic and political trends affecting their practice for members.

3992 ■ Investigative Ophthalmology & Visual Science
Association for Research in Vision and Ophthalmology
1801 Rockville Pike, Ste. 400
Rockville, MD 20852-1606
Ph: (240)221-2900
Fax: (240)221-0370
E-mail: iovs@arvo.org
URL: http://www.iovs.org

Monthly. $880.00/year for institutions, online only; $550.00/year for individuals, online only; $400.00/year for students, online only. Peer-reviewed journal dealing with all aspects of vision and ophthalmology.

3993 ■ Journal of Electronic Imaging
SPIE
1000 20th St.
PO Box 10
Bellingham, WA 98227-0010
Ph: (360)676-3290
Fax: (360)647-1445
Fr: 888-504-8171
URL: http://spie.org/x620.xml

Quarterly. $45.00/year for individuals, online; $70.00/year for individuals, print; $510.00/year for institutions, print and online; $550.00/year for institutions, other countries, print & online; $395.00/year for institutions, online. Journal covering issues in optical engineering.

3994 ■ Journal of Optical Communications and Networking
Optical Societyof America
2010 Massachusetts Ave. NW
Washington, DC 20036
Ph: (202)223-8130
Fax: (202)223-1096
E-mail: jocn@osa.org
URL: http://www.osa-jon.org/journal/jon/about.cfm

Monthly. $80.00/year for members, print & online; $56.00/year for members, online only; $180.00/year for other countries, members, print & online; $28.00/year for students, online only. Online journal covering for the optical networking community.

3995 ■ Ophthalmology
Mosby Inc.
11830 Westline Industrial Dr.
St. Louis, MO 63146-3326
Ph: (314)872-8370
Fax: (314)432-1380
Fr: 800-325-4177
URL: http://www.elsevier.com/wps/find/journaldescription.cws_home

Monthly. $385.00/year for individuals; $636.00/year for institutions; $385.00/year for Canada; $636.00/year for institutions, Canada. Journal publishing original, peer-reviewed reports of research in ophthalmology, including basic science investigations and clinical studies.

3996 ■ Optometry
American Optometric Association
243 N Lindbergh Blvd.
St. Louis, MO 63141
Ph: (314)983-4133
Fax: (314)991-4101
Fr: 800-365-2219
URL: http://www.optometryjaoa.com/

Monthly. $193.00/year for individuals; $95.00/year for students; $256.00/year for Canada; $153.00/year for students, other countries; $307.00/year for other countries; $153.00/year for students, other countries. Peer-reviewed clinical journal for members of the American Optometric Association.

3997 ■ Optometry and Vision Science
Lippincott Williams & Wilkins
351 W Camden St.
Baltimore, MD 21201
Ph: (410)528-4000
Fr: 800-638-3030
E-mail: ovs@osu.edu
URL: http://journals.lww.com/optvissci/pages/default.aspx

Monthly. $420.00/year for individuals; $619.00/year for institutions; $567.30/year for other countries; $841.30/year for institutions, other countries. Peer-reviewed journal providing the current developments and research in optometry, physiological optics, and vision science.

3998 ■ Review of Optometry
Jobson Professional Publications Group
11 Campus Blvd., Ste. 100
Newtown Square, PA 19073
Ph: (610)492-1000
Fax: (610)492-1039
URL: http://www.revoptom.com/
Monthly. Journal for the optometric profession and optical industry.

3999 ■ Careers in Health Care
The McGraw-Hill Companies
PO Box 182604
Columbus, OH 43272
Fax: (614)759-3749
Fr: 877-883-5524
E-mail: customer.service@mcgraw-hill.com
URL: http://www.mhprofessional.com/product.php?isbn=0071466533
Barbara M. Swanson. Fifth edition, 2005. $19.95 (paper). 192 pages. Describes job duties, work settings, salaries, licensing and certification requirements, educational preparation, and future outlook. Gives ideas on how to secure a job.

4000 ■ Opportunities in Health and Medical Careers
The McGraw-Hill Companies
PO Box 182604
Columbus, OH 43272
Fax: (614)759-3749
Fr: 877-883-5524
E-mail: customer.service@mcgraw-hill.com
URL: http://www.mhprofessional.com/product.php?isbn=0071437274
I. Donald Snook, Jr. and Leo D'Orazio. 2004. $14.95 (paper). 157 pages. Covers the full range of medical and health occupations. Illustrated.

4001 ■ Retail Recruiters
2189 Silas Deane Hwy.
Rocky Hill, CT 06067
Ph: (860)721-9550
Fax: (860)257-8813
E-mail: careers@retailrecruitersusa.com
URL: http://www.retailrecruitersusa.com
Employment agency. Affiliate offices in many locations across the country.

4002 ■ HEALTHeCAREERS Network
Fr: 888-884-8242
E-mail: info@healthecareers.com
URL: http://www.healthecareers.com

Description: Career search site for jobs in all health care specialties; educational resources; visa and licensing information for relocation; interesting articles; relocation tools; links to professional organizations and general resources.

4003 ■ ProHealthJobs.com
Ph: (484)443-8545
Fax: (484)443-8549
E-mail: info@prohealthjobs.com
URL: http://prohealthjobs.com/jobboard

Description: Career resources site for the medical and health care field. Lists professional opportunities, product information, continuing education and open positions.

TRADESHOWS

4004 ■ American Academy of Optometry
American Academy of Optometry
6110 Exec. Blvd., Ste. 506
Rockville, MD 20852
Ph: (301)984-1441
Fax: (301)984-4737
E-mail: aaoptom@aaoptom.org
URL: http://www.aaopt.org

Annual. Primary Exhibits: Exhibits focusing on the latest research and patient treatments relating to clinical practice standards, optometric education, and experimental research in visual problems. Dates and Locations: 2012 Oct 24-27; Phoenix, AZ; 2013 Oct 23-26; Seattle, WA; 2014 Nov 12-15; Denver, CO; 2015 Oct 14-17; New Orleans, LA.

4005 ■ International Vision Expo and Conference/East
Reed Exhibitions Contemporary Forums
11900 Silvergate Dr.
Dublin, CA 94568
Ph: (925)828-7100
Fax: 800-329-9923
E-mail: info@cforums.com
URL: http://www.contemporaryforums.com

Annual. Primary Exhibits: Equipment, supplies and services for the vision industry.

OTHER SOURCES

4006 ■ American Academy of Optometry (AAO)
6110 Executive Blvd., Ste. 506
Rockville, MD 20852
Ph: (301)984-1441
Fax: (301)984-4737
E-mail: aaoptom@aaoptom.org
URL: http://www.aaopt.org

Description: Represents optometrists, educators, and scientists interested in optometric education, and standards of care in visual problems. Conducts

continuing education for optometrists and visual scientists. Sponsors 4-day annual meeting.

4007 ■ American Board of Opticianry (ABO)
6506 Loisdale Rd., Ste. 209
Springfield, VA 22150
Ph: (703)719-5800
Fax: (703)719-9144
Fr: 800-296-1379
E-mail: mail@abo-ncle.org
URL: http://www.abo-ncle.org

Description: Provides uniform standards for dispensing opticians by administering the National Opticianry Competency Examination and by issuing the Certified Optician Certificate to those passing the exam. Administers the Master in Ophthalmic Optics Examination and issues certificates to opticians at the advanced level passing the exam. Maintains records of persons certified for competency in eyeglass dispensing. Adopts and enforces continuing education requirements; assists and encourages state licensing boards in the use of the National Opticianry Competency Examination for licensure purposes.

4008 ■ American Optometric Association (AOA)
243 N Lindbergh Blvd.
St. Louis, MO 63141
Ph: (314)991-4100
Fax: (314)991-4101
Fr: 800-365-2219
E-mail: dmcarlson@aoa.org
URL: http://www.aoa.org

Description: Professional association of optometrists, students of optometry, and paraoptometric assistants and technicians. Purposes are: to improve the quality, availability, and accessibility of eye and vision care; to represent the optometric profession; to help members conduct their practices; to promote the highest standards of patient care. Monitors and promotes legislation concerning the scope of optometric practice, alternate health care delivery systems, health care cost containment, Medicare, and other issues relevant to eye/vision care. Supports the International Library, Archives and Museum of Optometry which includes references on ophthalmic and related sciences with emphasis on the history and socioeconomic aspects of optometry. Operates Vision U.S.A. program, which provides free eye care to the working poor, and the InfantSEE program, which provides free vision assessments for infants between six and twelve months of age. Conducts specialized education programs; operates placement service; compiles statistics. Maintains museum. Conducts Seal of Acceptance Program.

4009 ■ Association of University Professors of Ophthalmology (AUPO)
PO Box 193030
San Francisco, CA 94119
Ph: (415)561-8548
Fax: (415)561-8531
E-mail: aupo@aao.org
URL: http://www.aupo.org

Description: Heads of departments or divisions of ophthalmology in accredited medical schools throughout the U.S. and Canada; directors of ophthalmology residency programs in institutions not connected to medical schools. Promotes medical education, research, and patient care relating to ophthalmology. Operates Ophthalmology Matching Program and faculty placement service, which aids ophthalmologists interested in being associated with university ophthalmology programs to locate such programs.

4010 ■ National Academy of Opticianry (NAO)
8401 Corporate Dr., Ste. 605
Landover, MD 20785
Fax: (301)577-3880
Fr: 800-229-4828
E-mail: info@nao.org
URL: http://www.nao.org

Description: Offers review courses for national certification and state licensure examinations to members. Maintains speakers' bureau and Career Progression Program.

4011 ■ National Contact Lens Examiners (NCLE)
6506 Loisdale Rd., Ste. 209
Springfield, VA 22150
Ph: (703)719-5800
Fax: (703)719-9144
E-mail: mail@abo-ncle.org
URL: http://www.abo.org

Description: Serves as National certifying agency promoting continued development of opticians and technicians as contact lens fitters by formulating standards and procedures for determination of entry-level competency. Assists in the continuation, development, administration, and monitoring of a national Contact Lens Registry Examination (CLRE), which verifies entry-level competency of contact lens fitters. Issues certificates. Activities include: maintaining records of those certified in contact lens fitting; encouraging state occupational licensing and credentialing agencies to use the CLRE for licensure purposes; identifying contact lens dispensing education needs as a result of findings of examination programs; disseminating information to sponsors of contact lens continuing education programs.

4012 ■ Opticians Association of America (OAA)
4064 E Fir Hill Dr.
Lakeland, TN 38002
Ph: (901)388-2423
Fax: (901)388-2348
E-mail: oaa@oaa.org
URL: http://www.oaa.org

Description: Retail dispensing opticians who fill prescriptions for glasses or contact lenses written by a vision care specialist. Works to advance the science of ophthalmic optics. Conducts research and educational programs. Maintains museum and speakers' bureau. Compiles statistics.

Sources of Help-Wanted Ads

4013 ■ Architectural Record
McGraw-Hill Inc.
PO Box 182604
Columbus, OH 43218
Ph: (614)430-4000
Fax: (614)759-3749
Fr: 877-833-5524
URL: http://archrecord.construction.com

Monthly. $49.00/year for individuals; $59.00/year for Canada; $109.00/year for other countries. Magazine focusing on architecture.

4014 ■ Builder
Hanley-Wood L.L.C.
1 Thomas Cir. NW, Ste. 600
Washington, DC 20005-5803
Ph: (202)452-0800
Fax: (202)785-1974
E-mail: builder@omeda.com
URL: http://www.hanleywood.com/
default.aspx?page=magazines

$29.95/year for U.S. and Canada; $54.95/year for U.S. and Canada, 2 years; $192.00/year for other countries. Magazine covering housing and construction industry.

4015 ■ Civil Engineering-ASCE
American Society of Civil Engineers (ASCE)
1801 Alexander Bell Dr.
Reston, VA 20191
Fr: 800-548-2723

Monthly. $230.00/year for institutions; $275.00/year for institutions, other countries; $230.00/year for individuals; $275.00/year for other countries; $30.00/year for members, domestic; $69.00/year for other countries, member; $30.00/year for students, member; domestic; $69.00/year for students, member; international. Professional magazine.

4016 ■ Constructor
Associated General Contractors of America
2300 Wilson Blvd., Ste. 400
Arlington, VA 22201
Ph: (703)548-3118
Fax: (703)548-3119
Fr: 800-242-1767
URL: http://constructor.agc.org/

Bimonthly. $95.00/year for individuals. Management magazine for the Construction Industry.

4017 ■ Design News
Reed Business Information
360 Park Ave. S
New York, NY 10010-1710
Ph: (646)746-6400
URL: http://www.designnews.com

Monthly. Magazine covering design engineering.

4018 ■ ENR: Engineering News-Record
McGraw-Hill Inc.
PO Box 182604
Columbus, OH 43218
Ph: (614)430-4000
Fax: (614)759-3749
Fr: 877-833-5524
URL: http://enr.construction.com/Default.asp

Weekly. $49.00/year for individuals, print; $89.00/year for Canada, print; $125.00/year for other countries, print. Magazine focusing on engineering and construction.

4019 ■ High Technology Careers Magazine
HTC
4701 Patrick Henry Dr., No. 1901
Santa Clara, CA 95054
Fax: (408)567-0242
URL: http://www.hightechcareers.com

Bimonthly. $29.00/year; $35.00/year for Canada; $85.00/year for out of country. Magazine (tabloid) containing employment opportunity information for the engineering and technical community.

4020 ■ NSBE Magazine
NSBE Publications
205 Daingerfield Rd.
Alexandria, VA 22314
Ph: (703)549-2207
Fax: (703)683-5312
URL: http://www.nsbe.org/News-Media/Magazines/
About-NSBE-Magazine

$20.00/year for individuals; $35.00/year for other countries; $15.00/year for students. Journal providing information on engineering careers, self-development, and cultural issues for recent graduates with technical majors.

4021 ■ Professional Builder
SGC Horizon LLC
3030 W Salt Creek Ln., Ste. 201
Arlington Heights, IL 60005
Ph: (847)391-1000
Fax: (847)390-0408
URL: http://www.housingzone.com/pb/pubhome/

Monthly. Free. The integrated engineering magazine of the building construction industry.

Employer Directories and Networking Lists

4022 ■ Directory of Contract Staffing Firms
C.E. Publications Inc.
PO Box 3006
Bothell, WA 98041-3006
Ph: (425)806-5200
Fax: (425)806-5585
URL: http://www.cjhunter.com/dcsf/overview.html

Annual. Covers: Nearly 1,300 contract firms actively engaged in the employment of engineering, IT/IS, and technical personnel for 'temporary' contract assignments throughout the world. Entries include: Company name, address, phone, name of contact, email, web address. Arrangement: Alphabetical. Indexes: Geographical.

4023 ■ ENR—Top 500 Design Firms Issue
McGraw-Hill Inc.
PO Box 182604
Columbus, OH 43218
Ph: (614)430-4000
Fax: (614)759-3749
Fr: 877-833-5524
URL: http://enr.construction.com/toplists/
sourcebooks/2010/design

Annual, latest edition 2010. $82.00 for individuals. Publication includes: List of 500 leading architectural, engineering, and specialty design firms selected on basis of annual billings. Entries include: Company name, headquarters location, type of firm, current and prior year rank in billings, types of services, countries in which operated in preceding year. Arrangement: Ranked by billings.

4024 ■ ProFile—The Architects Sourcebook
Reed Construction Data
30 Technology Pkwy. S, Ste. 100
Norcross, GA 30092
Ph: (770)417-4000
Fax: (770)417-4002
Fr: 800-424-3996
E-mail: profile@reedbusiness.com
URL: http://www.reedfirstsource.com

Annual. Covers: more than 27,000 architectural firms. Entries include: For firms—Firm name, address, phone, fax, year established, key staff and their primary responsibilities (for design, specification, etc.), number of staff personnel by discipline, types of work, geographical area served, projects. "ProFile" is an expanded version of, and replaces, the "Firm Directory." Arrangement: Firms are geographical. Indexes: Firm name, key individuals, specialization by category, consultants. Firm name, key individuals, specialization by category, consultants.

Handbooks and Manuals

4025 ■ Engineering, Mechanics, and Architecture
Ferguson Publishing
132 W 31st St., 17th Fl.
New York, NY 10001
Fax: 800-678-3633
Fr: 800-322-8755
E-mail: custserv@factsonfile.com
URL: http://www.infobasepublishing.com

Kelly Wiles. 2010. $39.95. 160 pages (hardcover). Serves as a guide for readers interested in switching jobs. Contains useful advice, career tips, interviews and self-asessment questions.

EMPLOYMENT AGENCIES AND SEARCH FIRMS

4026 ■ Agra Placements, Ltd.
8435 University Ave., Ste. 6
Des Moines, IA 50325
Ph: (515)225-6563
Fax: (515)225-7733
Fr: 888-696-5624
E-mail: careers@agrapl.com
URL: http://www.agraplacements.com

Executive search firm. Branch offices in Peru, IN, Lincoln, IL, and Andover, KS.

4027 ■ The Aspire Group
711 Boylston St.
Boston, MA 02116-2616
Fax: (617)500-7284
Fr: 800-487-2967
URL: http://www.bmanet.com/Aspire/index.html

Employment agency.

4028 ■ ENTEGEE
70 Blanchard Rd., Ste. 102
Burlington, MA 01803
Fr: 800-368-3433
E-mail: corporate@entegee.com
URL: http://www.entegee.com

Specializes in recruiting experienced professionals in the engineering and technical industries. Features a searchable database of employment opportunities in the engineering and technical fields.

4029 ■ Global Employment Solutions
10375 Park Meadows Dr., Ste. 375
Littleton, CO 80124
Ph: (303)216-9500
Fax: (303)216-9533
URL: http://www.gesnetwork.com
Employment agency.

4030 ■ International Staffing Consultants
31655 2nd Ave.
Laguna Beach, CA 92651
Ph: (949)255-5857
Fax: (949)767-5959
E-mail: iscinc@iscworld.com
URL: http://www.iscworld.com

Employment agency. Provides placement on regular or temporary basis. Affiliate office in London.

OTHER SOURCES

4031 ■ American Design Drafting Association (ADDA)
105 E Main St.
Newbern, TN 38059
Ph: (731)627-0802
Fax: (731)627-9321
E-mail: corporate@adda.org
URL: http://www.adda.org

Description: Designers, drafters, drafting managers, chief drafters, supervisors, administrators, instructors, and students of design and drafting. Encourages a continued program of education for self-improvement and professionalism in design and drafting and computer-aided design/drafting. Informs members of effective techniques and materials used in drawings and other graphic presentations. Evaluates curriculum of educational institutions through certification program; sponsors drafter certification program.

Sources of Help-Wanted Ads

4032 ■ *Brookings Papers on Economic Activity*
Brookings Institution Press
1775 Massachusetts Ave. NW
Washington, DC 20036
Ph: (202)797-6000
URL: http://www.brookings.edu/press/journals.htm#bpea

Semiannual. $55.00/year for individuals; $90.00/year for institutions; $69.00/year for other countries; $104.00/year for institutions, other countries. Publication covering economics and business.

4033 ■ *Bulletin of Economic Research*
John Wiley & Sons Inc.
350 Main St., Commerce Pl.
Malden, MA 02148-5089
Ph: (781)388-8200
Fax: (781)388-8210
URL: http://www.wiley.com/bw/journal.asp?ref=0307-3378&site=1

Quarterly. $84.00/year for individuals, print & online; $1,087.00/year for institutions, print & online; $945.00/year for institutions, print only; $945.00/year for institutions, online only; $50.00/year for individuals, print & online; $487.00/year for institutions, other countries, print & online; $423.00/year for institutions, other countries, print or online. Journal focusing on the entire field of economics, econometrics and economic history.

4034 ■ *Business Insurance*
Crain Communications Inc.
1155 Gratiot Ave.
Detroit, MI 48207-2997
Ph: (313)446-6000
URL: http://www.businessinsurance.com

Weekly. $399.00/year for individuals, print; $149.00/year for individuals, print & digital; $69.00/year for individuals, digital edition. International newsweekly reporting on corporate risk and employee benefit management news.

4035 ■ *Economic Journal*
John Wiley & Sons Inc.
350 Main St., Commerce Pl.
Malden, MA 02148-5089
Ph: (781)388-8200
Fax: (781)388-8210
URL: http://www.wiley.com/bw/journal.asp?ref=0013-0133

$768.00/year for institutions, print and online; $667.00/year for institutions, print or online; $482.00/year for institutions, other countries, print and online; $419.00/year for institutions, other countries, print or online; $612.00/year for institutions, print and online; $532.00/year for institutions, print or online. Journal focusing on economic issues.

4036 ■ *Economic Perspectives*
Federal Reserve Bank of Chicago
230 S LaSalle St.
Chicago, IL 60604-1413
Ph: (312)322-5322
Fax: (312)322-5515
URL: http://www.chicagofed.org/webpages/publications/economic_per

Quarterly. Publication covering the field of economics.

4037 ■ *Economic Policy*
John Wiley & Sons Inc.
350 Main St., Commerce Pl.
Malden, MA 02148-5089
Ph: (781)388-8200
Fax: (781)388-8210
URL: http://www.wiley.com/bw/journal.asp?ref=0266-4658

Quarterly. $84.00/year for individuals, print and online; $46.00/year for students, print and online; $680.00/year for institutions, print and online; $591.00/year for institutions, print or online; $450.00/year for institutions, other countries, print and online; $391.00/year for institutions, other countries, print or online; $55.00/year for individuals, print and online; $84.00/year for individuals, print and online. Journal publishing articles from economists and experts in the policy field all over the world.

4038 ■ *Economica*
John Wiley & Sons Inc.
350 Main St., Commerce Pl.
Malden, MA 02148-5089
Ph: (781)388-8200
Fax: (781)388-8210
URL: http://www.wiley.com/bw/journal.asp?ref=0013-0427

Quarterly. $70.00/year for individuals, print and online; $49.00/year for students, print and online; $474.00/year for institutions, print only; $431.00/year for institutions, online only; $274.00/year for institutions, other countries, print and online; $300.00/year for institutions, other countries, online only; $46.00/year for individuals, print and online; $58.00/year for individuals, print and online. Journal publishing research in all branches of economics.

4039 ■ *Economics Research International*
Hindawi Publishing Corp.
410 Park Ave., 15th Fl.
287 PMB
New York, NY 10022-4407
Fax: (215)893-4392
URL: http://www.hindawi.com/journals/econ

$295.00/year for individuals. Peer-reviewed journal publishing original research in all areas of economics.

4040 ■ *The Economists' Voice*
Berkeley Electronic Press
2809 Telegraph Ave., Ste. 202
Berkeley, CA 94705-1167

Ph: (510)665-1200
Fax: (510)665-1201
URL: http://www.bepress.com/ev/

Annual. $75.00/year for individuals; $300.00/year academic; $900.00/year corporate. Journal focusing on current economic issues. Its readership mainly comprises of economists of various hues, and from other professions such as lawyers, policy makers etc.

4041 ■ *Financial Management*
Financial Management Association International
4202 E Fowler Ave.
BSN 3331
Tampa, FL 33620-5500
Ph: (813)974-2084
Fax: (813)974-3318
E-mail: fma@coba.usf.edu
URL: http://www.fma.org/

Quarterly. $300.00/year for institutions, print + premium online; $95.00/year for institutions, premium online; $167.00/year for institutions, Europe, print + premium online; $158.00/year for institutions, Europe, premium online; $167.00/year for institutions, rest of world, print + premium online; $158.00/year for institutions, rest of world, premium online. Journal covering business, economics, finance and management.

4042 ■ *Journal of International Business and Economics*
International Academy of Business and Economics
PO Box 2536
Ceres, CA 95307
Ph: (702)560-0653
Fax: (702)508-9166
URL: http://www.iabe.eu/domains/iabeX/journal.aspx?journalid=9

Peer-reviewed journal publishing theoretical, conceptual, and applied research on topics related to research, practice and teaching in all areas of business, economics, e-commerce, and related subjects.

4043 ■ *Modern Economy*
Scientific Research Publishing
PO Box 54821
Irvine, CA 92619-4821
E-mail: me@scirp.org
URL: http://www.scirp.org/journal/me/

Quarterly. $156.00/year for individuals. Peer-reviewed journal publishing articles on all areas of international economics.

4044 ■ *OECD Observer*
Organisation for Economic Co-operation and Development
2001 L St. NW, Ste. 650
Washington, DC 20036-4922
Ph: (202)785-6323
Fax: (202)785-0350
Fr: 800-456-6323
E-mail: observer@oecd.org
URL: http://www.oecdobserver.org

$90.00/year for individuals, print + online; $70.00/year for individuals, print + online; $55.00/year for individuals, print + online; $9,800.00/year for individuals. Magazine on economic affairs, science, and technology.

4045 ■ Oxonomics
John Wiley & Sons Inc.
350 Main St., Commerce Pl.
Malden, MA 02148-5089
Ph: (781)388-8200
Fax: (781)388-8210
URL: http://www.wiley.com/bw/journal.asp?ref=1752-5195

Semiannual. $151.00/year for individuals, Americas (print only); $123.00/year for individuals, Europe (print only); $82.00/year for other countries, print only; $197.00/year for institutions, Americas (print only); $135.00/year for institutions, Europe (print only); $208.00/year for institutions, other countries, print only; $106.00/year for institutions, UK (print only). Peer-reviewed journal covering the field of economic studies.

4046 ■ The Review of Network Economics
CRA International
John Hancock Tower
200 Clarendon St., T-33
Boston, MA 02116-5092
Ph: (617)425-3000
Fax: (617)425-3132
URL: http://www.rnejournal.com/

Quarterly. $75.00/year for individuals. Journal covering new research in network economics and related subjects, including topics in the economics of networks, regulation, competition law, industrial organization etc.

4047 ■ Topics in Macroeconomics
Berkeley Electronic Press
2809 Telegraph Ave., Ste. 202
Berkeley, CA 94705-1167
Ph: (510)665-1200
Fax: (510)665-1201
URL: http://www.bepress.com/bejm/topics/

Irregular. $500.00/year for institutions. Academic journal covering macroeconomics.

EMPLOYER DIRECTORIES AND NETWORKING LISTS

4048 ■ The Bank Directory
Accuity Inc.
4709 Golf Rd.
Skokie, IL 60076
Ph: (847)676-9600
Fax: (847)933-8101
Fr: 800-321-3373
URL: http://store.accuitysolutions.com/order.html

Semiannual, June and December. $1,195.00 for individuals. Covers: In five volumes, about 11,000 banks and 50,000 branches of United States banks, and 60,000 foreign banks and branches engaged in foreign banking; Federal Reserve system and other United States government and state government banking agencies; 500 largest North American and International commercial banks; paper and automated clearinghouses. Volumes 1 and 2 contain North American listings; volumes 3 and 4, international listings (also cited as "M Thomson International Bank Directory"); volume 5, Worldwide Correspondents Guide containing key correspondent data to facilitate funds transfer. Entries include: For domestic banks—Bank name, address, phone, telex, cable, date established, routing number, charter type, bank holding company affiliation, memberships in Federal Reserve System and other banking organizations, principal officers by function performed, principal correspondent banks, and key financial data (deposits, etc.). For international banks—Bank name, address, phone, fax, telex, cable, SWIFT address, transit or sort codes within home country, ownership, financial data, names and titles of key personnel, branch locations. For branches—Bank name, address, phone, charter type, ownership and other details comparable to domestic bank listings. Arrangement: Geographical. Indexes: Alphabetical, geographical.

4049 ■ Business Economics—Membership Directory Issue
National Association for Business Economics
1233 20th St. NW, Ste. 505
Washington, DC 20036
Ph: (202)463-6223
Fax: (202)463-6239
URL: http://www.nabe.com

Annual, Latest edition 2008. $125.00; $150.00. Publication includes: List of about 3,000 members of the association, including students. Entries include: Name, address, phone, corporate affiliation, economic specialization, industries of research specialization, NABE activities, educational background, work experience. Arrangement: Alphabetical by member name, company, and roundtable affiliation. Indexes: Company, roundtable, and students.

4050 ■ National Association for Business Economics—Membership Directory
National Association for Business Economics
1233 20th St. NW, Ste. 505
Washington, DC 20036
Ph: (202)463-6223
Fax: (202)463-6239
URL: http://www.nabe.com

Annual, Latest edition 2008. Covers: About 3,600 members internationally. Entries include: Name, address, phone, company affiliation, educational background, prior employment history, areas of specialization and industries of research specialization, roundtable affiliation, Standard Industrial Classification (SIC) code. Arrangement: Alphabetical. Indexes: Company name, association roundtable affiliation.

4051 ■ National Economists Club—Membership Directory
National Economists Club
PO Box 19281
Washington, DC 20036
Ph: (703)493-8824
URL: http://www.national-economists.org

Biennial. Covers: Nearly 800 professional economists and others having an interest in economic subjects. Entries include: Name, address, phone. Arrangement: Alphabetical by organization.

4052 ■ North American Financial Institutions Directory
Accuity Inc.
4709 Golf Rd.
Skokie, IL 60076
Ph: (847)676-9600
Fax: (847)933-8101
Fr: 800-321-3373
URL: http://store.accuitysolutions.com/order.html

Semiannual, January and July. $955.00 for individuals. Covers: 15,000 banks and their branches; over 2,000 head offices, and 15,500 branches of savings and loan associations; over 5,500 credit unions with assets over $5 million; Federal Reserve System and other U.S. government and state government banking agencies; bank holding, commercial finance, and leasing companies; coverage includes the United States, Canada, Mexico, and Central America. Entries include: Bank name, address, phone, fax, telex, principal officers and directors, date established, financial data, association memberships, attorney or counsel, correspondent banks, out-of-town branch, holding company affiliation, ABA transit number and routing symbol, MICR number with check digit, credit card(s) issued, trust powers, current par value and dividend of common stock, kind of charter. Arrangement: Geographical. Indexes: Alphabetical.

4053 ■ Roster of Women Economists
Committee on the Status of Women in the Economics Profession
4901 Tower Ct.
Tallahassee, FL 32303

Ph: (850)562-1211
Fax: (850)562-3838
URL: http://www.cswep.org

Biennial, odd years. Covers: 6,000 women in economics. Entries include: Name, address, phone, title, affiliation, degrees, honors, specialty, number of articles and books published. e-mail, fax. Publisher is a standing committee of the American Economic Association. Arrangement: Alphabetical. Indexes: Geographical, employer, fields of specialization.

4054 ■ Top Careers for Economics Graduates
Facts On File Inc.
132 W 31st St., 17th Fl.
New York, NY 10001
Ph: (212)967-8800
Fax: 800-678-3633
Fr: 800-322-8755
URL: http://www.infobasepublishing.com

Published March, 2004. Covers: What it takes to transform the skills and experience gained from an economics degree into a great job.

4055 ■ Who's Who in Finance and Business
Marquis Who's Who L.L.C.
300 Connell Dr., Ste. 2000
Berkeley Heights, NJ 07922
Ph: (908)673-1000
Fax: (908)673-1189
Fr: 800-473-7020
E-mail: finance@marquiswhoswho.com
URL: http://www.marquiswhoswho.com

Biennial, latest edition 37th; 2009-2010. $349.00 for individuals. Covers: Over 24,000 individuals. Entries include: Name, home and office addresses, personal, career, and family data; civic and political activities; memberships, publications, awards. Arrangement: Alphabetical.

HANDBOOKS AND MANUALS

4056 ■ Associate Economist
National Learning Corporation
212 Michael Dr.
Syosset, NY 11791
Fr: 800-632-8888
URL: http://www.passbooks.com

2009. $39.95 (paper). Serves as an exam preparation guide for associate economists.

4057 ■ Opportunities in Social Science Careers
The McGraw-Hill Companies
PO Box 182604
Columbus, OH 43272
Fax: (614)759-3749
Fr: 877-883-5524
E-mail: customer.service@mcgraw-hill.com
URL: http://www.mcgraw-hill.com

Rosanne J. Marek. 2004. $13.95. 160 Pages. VGM Opportunities Series.

EMPLOYMENT AGENCIES AND SEARCH FIRMS

4058 ■ Choi & Burns LLC
156 W 56th St., 18th Fl.
New York, NY 10019
Ph: (212)755-7051
Fax: (212)335-2610
E-mail: info@choiburns.com
URL: http://www.choiburns.com

Executive search firm focuses on the financial industry.

4059 ■ Dussick Management Associates
White Birch Rd., Ste. 28
Madison, CT 06443

Ph: (203)245-9311
Fax: (203)245-1648
E-mail: vince@dussick.com
URL: http://www.dussick.com
Executive search firm.

4060 ■ Halbrecht & Co.
10195 Main St., Ste. L
PO Box 2601
Fairfax, VA 22031
Ph: (703)359-2880
Fax: (703)359-2933
E-mail: halbrechtandco@aol.com

Performs professional recruiting in data processing and operations research, economics, corporate planning, market research, telecommunications, and decision support systems.

4061 ■ International Staffing Consultants
31655 2nd Ave.
Laguna Beach, CA 92651
Ph: (949)255-5857
Fax: (949)767-5959
E-mail: iscinc@iscworld.com
URL: http://www.iscworld.com

Employment agency. Provides placement on regular or temporary basis. Affiliate office in London.

4062 ■ Sales Executives Inc.
33900 W 8 Mile Rd., Ste. 171
Farmington Hills, MI 48335
Ph: (248)615-0100
E-mail: dale@salesexecutives.com
URL: http://www.salesexecutives.com

Employment agency. Executive search firm.

ONLINE JOB SOURCES AND SERVICES

4063 ■ Econ-Jobs.com
URL: http://www.econ-jobs.com

Description: Serves as a job database for careers in economics, econometrics, and finance.

4064 ■ EconCareers.com
URL: http://www.econcareers.com

Description: Serves job seekers with backgrounds in economics, mathematics quantitative methods and econometrics.

OTHER SOURCES

4065 ■ African Studies Association (ASA)
Rutgers University, Livingston Campus
54 Joyce Kilmer Ave.
Piscataway, NJ 08854-8045
Ph: (848)445-8173
Fax: (732)445-1366
E-mail: karen.jenkins@africanstudies.org
URL: http://www.africanstudies.org

Description: Persons specializing in teaching, writing, or research on Africa including political scientists, historians, geographers, anthropologists, economists, librarians, linguists, and government officials; persons who are studying African subjects; institutional members are universities, libraries, government agencies, and others interested in receiving information about Africa. Seeks to foster communication and to stimulate research among scholars on Africa. Sponsors placement service; conducts panels and discussion groups; presents exhibits and films.

4066 ■ Agricultural and Applied Economics Association (AAEA)
555 E Wells St., Ste. 1100
Milwaukee, WI 53202
Ph: (414)918-3190

Fax: (414)276-3349
E-mail: info@aaea.org
URL: http://www.aaea.org

Description: Professional society of agricultural economists. Serves to enhance the skills, knowledge and professional contribution of those economists who serve society by solving problems related to agriculture, food, resources and economic development. Offers placement service.

4067 ■ American Economic Association (AEA)
2014 Broadway, Ste. 305
Nashville, TN 37203
Ph: (615)322-2595
Fax: (615)343-7590
E-mail: aeainfo@vanderbilt.edu
URL: http://www.vanderbilt.edu/AEA

Description: Educators, business executives, government administrators, journalists, lawyers, and others interested in economics and its application to present-day problems. Encourages historical and statistical research into actual conditions of industrial life and provides a nonpartisan forum for economic discussion.

4068 ■ Committee on the Status of Women in the Economics Profession (CSWEP)
PO Box 9300
Portland, ME 04104-9300
Ph: (207)228-8245
E-mail: cswep@usm.maine.edu
URL: http://www.aeaweb.org/committees/cswep

Description: A standing committee of American Economic Association. Women economists in the U.S. Aims to support and facilitate equality of opportunity for women economists. Disseminates information about job opportunities, research funding, and research related to the status of women in economics. Sponsors technical sessions.

4069 ■ Economic Policy Institute (EPI)
1333 H St. NW, Ste. 300
East Tower
Washington, DC 20005-4707
Ph: (202)775-8810
Fax: (202)775-0819
Fr: 800-374-4844
E-mail: epi@epi.org
URL: http://www.epi.org

Description: Conducts research and provides a forum for the exchange of information on economic policy issues. Promotes educational programs to encourage discussion of economic policy and economic issues, particularly the economics of poverty, unemployment, inflation, American industry, international competitiveness, and problems of economic adjustment as they affect the community and the individual. Sponsors seminars for economists and citizens.

4070 ■ Institute for Economic Analysis (IEA)
262 Harvard St., Apt. 12
Cambridge, MA 02139
Ph: (617)864-1903
E-mail: info@iea-macro-economics.org
URL: http://iea-macro-economics.org

Description: Purpose: Seeks to develop tools for macroeconomic analysis and policy that can maintain stable full employment growth, low inflation, low interest rates and equitable distribution of income and wealth. Integrates GDP and financial accounts for more systematic coordination of monetary and fiscal policy. Focuses on federal monetary policy, federal budget deficit/surplus, social security, consumer credit, and world economic recovery.

4071 ■ International Economic Alliance (IEA)
1 Mifflin Pl., Ste. 400
Cambridge, MA 02138
Ph: (617)418-1971

Fax: (617)812-0499
E-mail: van.mccormick@iealliance.org
URL: http://www.iealliance.org

Description: Aims to further global trade, economic development and advance business relations. Brings together the world's key players and decision-makers (business and government leaders, investors and leading intellectuals) for practical, open, bi-partisan and solution-oriented exchange of ideas. Serves as a source of knowledge, facilitator of relationships, and catalyst for new business opportunities.

4072 ■ International Studies Association (ISA)
University of Arizona
324 Social Sciences Bldg.
Tucson, AZ 85721
Ph: (520)621-7715
Fax: (520)621-5780
E-mail: isa@isanet.org
URL: http://www.isanet.org

Description: Social scientists and other scholars from a wide variety of disciplines who are specialists in international affairs and cross-cultural studies; academicians; government officials; officials in international organizations; business executives; students. Promotes research, improved teaching, and the orderly growth of knowledge in the field of international studies; emphasizes a multidisciplinary approach to problems. Conducts conventions, workshops and discussion groups.

4073 ■ National Association for Business Economics (NABE)
1233 20th St. NW, No. 505
Washington, DC 20036
Ph: (202)463-6223
Fax: (202)463-6239
E-mail: nabe@nabe.com
URL: http://www.nabe.com

Description: Professional society of institutions, businesses, and students with an active interest in business economics and individuals who are employed by academic, private, or governmental concerns in the area of business-related economic issues. Maintains placement service for members; conducts several seminars per year. Maintains speakers' bureau.

4074 ■ National Council on Economic Education (NCEE)
122 E 42nd St., Ste. 2600
New York, NY 10168
Ph: (212)730-7007
Fax: (212)730-1793
Fr: 800-338-1192
E-mail: customerservice@councilforeconed.org
URL: http://www.ncee.net

Description: Economists, educators, and representatives from business, labor, and finance dedicated to improving economic education by improving the quality and increasing the quantity of economics being taught in all levels of schools and colleges. Initiates curriculum development and research; experiments with new economics courses and ways to prepare teachers and students; provides updated teacher-pupil materials; coordinates national and local programs in economics education. Provides consulting services to educators; sponsors workshops; tests new methods in practical school situations.

4075 ■ Southern Economic Association (SEA)
University of Tennessee at Chattanooga
313 Fletcher Hall, Dept. 6106
615 McCallie Ave.
Chattanooga, TN 37403-2598
Ph: (423)425-4118
Fax: (423)425-5218
E-mail: ashley-harrison@utc.edu
URL: http://southerneconomic.org

Description: Professional economists in government, business, and academic institutions. Provides placement service for economists.

SOURCES OF HELP-WANTED ADS

4076 ■ ABHE Newsletter
Association for Biblical Higher Education
5850 T.G. Lee Blvd., Ste. 130
Orlando, FL 32822
Ph: (407)207-0808
Fax: (407)207-0840
E-mail: info@abhe.org
URL: http://www.abhe.org

Description: Five issues/year (always January, April, June, September, and November). Provides information on issues, events, and resources for Bible college administrators and others interested in Christian higher education. Recurring features include a calendar of events, reports of meetings, news of educational opportunities, book reviews, and notices of publications available.

4077 ■ About Campus
John Wiley & Sons Inc.
111 River St.
Hoboken, NJ 07030-5773
Ph: (201)748-6000
Fax: (201)748-6088
Fr: 800-825-7550
URL: http://onlinelibrary.wiley.com/journal/10.1002/
(ISSN)1536-06

Bimonthly. $207.00/year for institutions, print only; $267.00/year for institutions, Canada and Mexico, print only; $318.00/year for institutions, other countries, print only; $60.00/year for U.S., Canada, and Mexico, print only; $96.00/year for other countries, print only. Journal focused on the critical issues faced by both student affairs and academic affairs staff as they work on helping students learn.

4078 ■ American Academic
American Federation of Teachers
555 New Jersey Ave. NW
Washington, DC 20001
Ph: (202)879-4400
URL: http://www.aft.org/pubs-reports/american_
academic/index.htm

Higher education policy journal.

4079 ■ The American School Board Journal
American School Board Journal
1680 Duke St.
Alexandria, VA 22314
Ph: (703)838-6722
Fax: (703)549-6719
URL: http://www.asbj.com

Monthly. $47.00/year for individuals, print and online version; $36.00/year for individuals, online; $72.00/year for other countries; $53.00/year for individuals, Canada. Magazine serving school board members, superintendents, and other administrative officials.

4080 ■ American School & University
Penton Media Inc.
9800 Metcalf Ave.
Overland Park, KS 66212
Ph: (913)341-1300
Fax: (913)967-1898
URL: http://asumag.com/
Monthly. Trade magazine.

4081 ■ Annals of Medicine
Informa Healthcare
52 Vanderbilt Ave., 7th Fl.
New York, NY 10017-3846
Ph: (212)520-2777
URL: http://informahealthcare.com/ann

$595.00/year for institutions; $980.00/year for institutions; $780.00/year for institutions. Journal covering health science and medical education.

4082 ■ ASBSD-Bulletin
Associated School Boards of South Dakota
306 E Capitol Ave.
Pierre, SD 57501
Ph: (605)773-2500
Fax: (605)773-2501
E-mail: info@asbsd.org
URL: http://www.asbsd.org

Description: Monthly. Deals with policymaking, financing, and innovation in public education. Seeks to promote reorganization and adequate financing. Recurring features include letters to the editor, news of research, reports of meetings, news of educational opportunities, job listings, notices of publications available, and columns titled On the Line, Check This, and Board Policies.

4083 ■ Assessment & Evaluation in Higher Education
Routledge Journals
270 Madison Ave.
New York, NY 10016-0601
Ph: (212)216-7800
Fax: (212)563-2269
URL: http://www.tandf.co.uk/journals/titles/
02602938.asp

Bimonthly. $1,316.00/year for institutions, online only; $2,547.00/year for institutions, print + online; $1,462.00/year for individuals, print + online; $2,292.00/year for institutions, online only; $578.00/year for individuals, print only; $314.00/year for individuals, print only. Peer-reviewed journal focusing on publishing papers and reports on all aspects of assessment and evaluation within higher education.

4084 ■ Better
The Johns Hopkins University Press
2715 N Charles St.
Baltimore, MD 21218-4319
Ph: (410)516-6900
Fax: (410)516-6968
URL: http://www.press.jhu.edu/journals/better_
evidence_based_educ

$29.50/year for individuals, print and electronic; $80.00/year for institutions, print and electronic. Magazine for educators and policy makers interested in evidence-based education reform.

4085 ■ Brookings Papers on Education Policy
Brookings Institution Press
1775 Massachusetts Ave. NW
Washington, DC 20036
Ph: (202)797-6000
URL: http://www.brookings.edu/press/Journals/2007/
brookingspapers

$36.00/year for individuals. Journal dealing with all aspects of American education.

4086 ■ Change
Heldref Publications
325 Chestnut St., Ste. 800
Philadelphia, PA 19106
Ph: (215)625-8900
Fr: 800-354-1420
E-mail: ch@heldref.org
URL: http://www.heldref.org/change.php

Bimonthly. $52.00/year for individuals, print only; $39.00/year for institutions, print only; $64.00/year for individuals, print and online; $207.00/year for institutions, print and online. Magazine dealing with contemporary issues in higher learning.

4087 ■ The Chronicle of Higher Education
The Chronicle of Higher Education
1255 23rd St. NW, 7th Fl.
Washington, DC 20037-1125
Ph: (202)466-1000
Fax: (202)452-1033
Fr: 800-728-2803
URL: http://chronicle.com

Weekly. $82.50/year for individuals, 43 issues; $45.00/year for individuals, 21 issues; $140.00/year for individuals, 86 issues. Higher education magazine (tabloid).

4088 ■ Community Colleges Journal
American Association of Community Colleges
1 Dupont Cir. NW, Ste. 410
Washington, DC 20036-1145
Ph: (202)728-0200
Fax: (202)833-2467
URL: http://www.aacc.nche.edu/Publications/CCJ/
Pages/default.aspx

$34.00/year for nonmembers; $34.00/year for members; $39.00/year for nonmembers, International; $39.00/year for members, International; $24.00/year for single issue, non-member; $24.00/year for single issue, member. Educational magazine.

4089 ■ Creative Education
Scientific Research Publishing
PO Box 54821
Irvine, CA 92619-4821
E-mail: ce@scirp.org
URL: http://www.scirp.org/journal/ce/

$195.00/year for individuals. Peer-reviewed journal publishing articles on the latest advancements in creative education.

4090 ■ *Dean and Provost*

John Wiley & Sons Inc.
111 River St.
Hoboken, NJ 07030-5773
Ph: (201)748-6000
Fax: (201)748-6088
Fr: 800-825-7550
URL: http://onlinelibrary.wiley.com/journal/10.1002/ (ISSN)1943-75

Monthly. $222.00/year for U.S., Canada, and Mexico, individual (print only); $270.00/year for other countries, individual (print only); $2,870.00/year for institutions, print and online; $2,918.00/year for institutions, Canada and Mexico, print and online; $2,936.00/year for institutions, other countries, print and online; $2,495.00/year for institutions, print only; $2,543.00/year for institutions, Canada and Mexico, print only; $2,561.00/year for institutions, other countries, print only. Journal featuring innovative ways on how to manage all the challenges of leading an institution.

4091 ■ *The Department Chair*

John Wiley & Sons Inc.
111 River St.
Hoboken, NJ 07030-5773
Ph: (201)748-6000
Fax: (201)748-6088
Fr: 800-825-7550
URL: http://onlinelibrary.wiley.com/journal/10.1002/ (ISSN)1936-43

Quarterly. $99.00/year for individuals, print only; $1,020.00/year for institutions, print only; $1,060.00/year for institutions, Canada and Mexico, print only; $1,094.00/year for institutions, other countries, print only. Journal containing articles for chairs, deans, academic vice presidents, and other administrators.

4092 ■ *Education & Treatment of Children*

West Virginia University Press
139 Stansbury Hall
PO Box 6295
Morgantown, WV 26506
Ph: (304)293-8400
Fax: (304)293-6585
URL: http://www.educationandtreatmentofchildren.net

Quarterly. $85.00/year for institutions; $45.00/year for individuals; $100.00/year for institutions, elsewhere; $60.00/year for individuals, elsewhere. Periodical featuring information concerning the development of services for children and youth. Includes reports written for educators and other child care and mental health providers focused on teaching, training, and treatment effectiveness.

4093 ■ *Education Week*

Editorial Projects in Education Inc.
6935 Arlington Rd., Ste. 100
Bethesda, MD 20814-5287
Ph: (301)280-3100
Fax: (301)280-3200
Fr: 800-346-1834
E-mail: ew@epe.org
URL: http://www.edweek.org/ew

$90.00/year for individuals, print plus online. Professional newspaper for elementary and secondary school educators.

4094 ■ *Educational Research and Evaluation*

Routledge Journals
270 Madison Ave.
New York, NY 10016-0601
Ph: (212)216-7800
Fax: (212)563-2269
URL: http://www.tandf.co.uk/journals/titles/ 13803611.asp

Bimonthly. $428.00/year for institutions, print + online; $385.00/year for institutions, online only; $165.00/year for individuals, print only; $731.00/year for institutions, print + online; $658.00/year for institu-

tions, online only; $275.00/year for individuals, print only. Peer-reviewed journal on theory and practice.

4095 ■ *Educational Researcher*

American Educational Research Association
1430 K St. NW, Ste. 1200
Washington, DC 20005
Ph: (202)238-3200
Fax: (202)238-3250
URL: http://www.aera.net/publications/?id=317

Monthly. $48.00/year for individuals, plus foreign mailing charges; $150.00/year for institutions, plus foreign mailing charges. Educational research journal.

4096 ■ *Enrollment Management Report*

John Wiley & Sons Inc.
111 River St.
Hoboken, NJ 07030-5773
Ph: (201)748-6000
Fax: (201)748-6088
Fr: 800-825-7550
URL: http://onlinelibrary.wiley.com/journal/10.1002/ (ISSN)1945-62

Monthly. $225.00/year for U.S., Canada, and Mexico, individual (print only); $273.00/year for other countries, individual (print only); $2,909.00/year for institutions, print and online; $2,957.00/year for institutions, Canada and Mexico, print and online; $2,975.00/year for institutions, other countries, print and online; $2,525.00/year for institutions, print only; $2,573.00/year for institutions, Canada and Mexico, print only; $2,591.00/year for institutions, other countries, print only. Journal featuring practical guidance on all aspects of enrollment management including records, registration, recruitment, orientation, admissions, retention and more.

4097 ■ *Environmental Education Research*

Routledge Journals
270 Madison Ave.
New York, NY 10016-0601
Ph: (212)216-7800
Fax: (212)563-2269
URL: http://www.tandf.co.uk/journals/titles/ 13504622.asp

Bimonthly. $1,373.00/year for institutions, print + online; $1,236.00/year for institutions, online only; $364.00/year for individuals, print only. Journal covering all aspects of environmental education.

4098 ■ *Essays in Education*

University of South Carolina
471 University Pky.
Aiken, SC 29801
Ph: (803)648-6851
URL: http://www.usca.edu/essays/

Monthly. Journal covering issues that impact and influence education.

4099 ■ *Hematology*

American Society of Hematology
2021 L St. NW, Ste. 900
Washington, DC 20036
Ph: (202)776-0544
Fax: (202)776-0545
URL: http://asheducationbook.hematologylibrary.org

Annual. $75.00/year for members; $125.00/year for nonmembers. Journal providing continuing medical education for physicians.

4100 ■ *Higher Education FERPA Bulletin*

John Wiley & Sons Inc.
111 River St.
Hoboken, NJ 07030-5774
Ph: (201)748-6000
Fax: (201)748-6088

Journal covering all aspect of campus administration and life.

4101 ■ *Interdisciplinary Journal of Teaching and Learning*

Southern University at Baton Rouge
PO Box 9942
Baton Rouge, LA 70813
Ph: (225)711-4500
Fax: (225)771-4400
URL: http://www.subr.edu/CollegeofEducation/ COE%20ONLINE%20Journa

Online academic journal that publishes research and scholarly articles in the field of education and learning.

4102 ■ *The International Electronic Journal of Health Education*

American Alliance for Health, Physical Education, Recreation & Dance
1900 Association Dr.
Reston, VA 20191-1598
Ph: (703)476-3400
Fax: (703)476-9527
Fr: 800-213-7193
URL: http://www.aahperd.org/aahe/publications/iejhe/

Annual. Free, health education professionals and students. Journal promoting health through education and other systematic strategies.

4103 ■ *International Journal of Early Years Education*

Routledge Journals
270 Madison Ave.
New York, NY 10016-0601
Ph: (212)216-7800
Fax: (212)563-2269
URL: http://www.tandf.co.uk/journals/titles/ 09669760.asp

$705.00/year for institutions, online only; $783.00/year for institutions, print + online; $271.00/year for individuals, print only. Journal focusing on education world-wide.

4104 ■ *International Journal of Inclusive Education*

Routledge Journals
270 Madison Ave.
New York, NY 10016-0601
Ph: (212)216-7800
Fax: (212)563-2269
URL: http://www.tandf.co.uk/journals/titles/ 13603116.asp

$589.00/year for individuals, print only; $1,135.00/year for institutions, online only; $1,261.00/year for individuals, print + online; $355.00/year for individuals, print only; $694.00/year for institutions, online only; $771.00/year for institutions, print + online. Journal providing information on the nature of schools, universities and technical colleges for the educators and educational policy-makers.

4105 ■ *International Journal of Leadership in Education*

Routledge
711 3 Ave., 8 Fl.
New York, NY 10016
Ph: (212)216-7800
Fax: (212)563-2269
Fr: 800-634-7064
E-mail: ijle@txstate.edu
URL: http://www.tandf.co.uk/journals/tf/ 13603124.html

Quarterly. $240.00/year for individuals, print only; $612.00/year for institutions, print only; $680.00/year for institutions, print and online; $408.00/year for institutions, print and online; $367.00/year for institutions, online only; $142.00/year for individuals, print only. Journal dealing with leadership in education.

4106 ■ *International Journal of Progressive Education*

International Journal of Progressive Education
c/o Alex Jean-Charles, PhD, Asst. Mng. Ed.
320 Fitzelle Hall, Ravine Pky.
Oneonta, NY 13820
URL: http://www.inased.org/ijpe.htm

$35.00/year for members; $45.00/year for individuals; $140.00/year for institutions, library; $35.00/year for students; $25.00/year for single issue; $50.00/year for students, other countries. Peer-reviewed online journal that aims to create an open and continuing dialogue about current educational issues and future conceptions of educational theory.

4107 ■ International Journal of Whole Schooling
Whole Schooling Press
Wayne State University
217 Education
Detroit, MI 48202
URL: http://www.wholeschooling.net/Journal_of_Whole_Schooling/IJW

Free. International, refereed academic journal dedicated to exploring ways to improve learning and schooling for all children.

4108 ■ Journal of Academic Leadership
Academic Leadership
600 Park St.
Rarick Hall 219
Hays, KS 67601-4099
Ph: (785)628-4547
URL: http://www.academicleadership.org/

Journal focusing on the leadership issues in the academic world.

4109 ■ Journal of Cases in Educational Leadership
Sage Publications Inc.
2455 Teller Rd.
Thousand Oaks, CA 91320-2218
Ph: (805)499-9774
Fax: (805)583-2665
Fr: 800-818-7243
URL: http://jel.sagepub.com

Quarterly. $411.00/year for institutions, e-access; $94.00/year for individuals, e-access. Journal covering cases appropriate for use in programs that prepare educational leaders.

4110 ■ Journal of College Teaching & Learning
The Clute Institute for Academic Research
6901 S Pierce St., Ste. 239
Littleton, CO 80128
Ph: (303)904-4750
Fax: (303)259-2420
URL: http://www.cluteinstitute.com/journals/TLC.html

Monthly. $495.00/year for institutions, with airmail postage. Refereed academic journal covering all areas of college level teaching, learning and administration.

4111 ■ Journal of Curriculum and Supervision
Association for Supervision and Curriculum Development
1703 N Beauregard St.
Alexandria, VA 22311-1714
Ph: (703)578-9600
Fax: (703)575-5400
Fr: 800-933-2723
URL: http://www.ascd.org/publications/jcs/fall2002/On_Community.a

Scholarly journal focusing on curriculum and supervision.

4112 ■ Journal of Direct Instruction
Association for Direct Instruction
PO Box 10252
Eugene, OR 97440
Ph: (541)485-1293
Fax: (541)868-1397
Fr: 800-995-2464
URL: http://www.adihome.org/index.php?option=com_content&view=art

Quarterly. Included in membership. Journal covering education.

4113 ■ Journal of Diversity in Higher Education
American Psychological Association
750 1st St. NE
Washington, DC 20002-4242
Ph: (202)336-5500
Fax: (202)336-5549
Fr: 800-374-2721
URL: http://www.apa.org/pubs/journals/dhe/index.aspx

Quarterly. $65.00/year for members; $89.00/year for other countries, members; $415.00/year for institutions; $464.00/year for institutions, other countries; $65.00/year for students; $105.00/year for nonmembers; $134.00/year for other countries, nonmembers. Journal publishing research findings, theory and promising practices in higher education.

4114 ■ Journal of Higher Education Outreach and Engagement (JHEOE)
Institute of Higher Education (IHE)
Meigs Hall
Athens, GA 30602
Ph: (706)542-3464
Fax: (706)542-7588
URL: http://openjournals.libs.uga.edu/index.php/jheoe/

Semiannual. $60.00/year for individuals; $95.00/year for other countries; $30.00/year for students; $65.00/year for students, other countries; $100.00/year for institutions; $199.00/year for institutions, other countries. Journal covering higher education outreach and engagement for scholars, practitioners, and professionals.

4115 ■ Journal of Language, Identity, and Education
Routledge Journals
270 Madison Ave.
New York, NY 10016-0601
Ph: (212)216-7800
Fax: (212)563-2269
URL: http://www.tandf.co.uk/journals/titles/15348458.asp

$316.00/year for institutions, print + online; $284.00/year for institutions, online; $43.00/year for individuals, print + online; $527.00/year for institutions, print + online; $474.00/year for institutions, online; $71.00/year for individuals, print + online; $421.00/year for institutions, print + online; $379.00/year for institutions, online; $57.00/year for individuals, print + online. Scholarly, interdisciplinary journal covering issues in language, identity and education worldwide for academics, educators and policy specialists in a variety of disciplines, and others.

4116 ■ Journal of Latinos and Education
Routledge Journals
270 Madison Ave.
New York, NY 10016-0601
Ph: (212)216-7800
Fax: (212)563-2269
URL: http://www.tandf.co.uk/journals/titles/15348431.asp

Quarterly. $286.00/year for institutions, print + online; $257.00/year for institutions, online; $38.00/year for individuals, print + online; $480.00/year for institutions, print + online; $432.00/year for institutions, online; $63.00/year for individuals, print + online; $331.00/year for institutions, print + online; $343.00/year for institutions, online; $51.00/year for individuals, print + online. Scholarly, multidisciplinary journal covering educational issues that impact Latinos for researchers, teaching professionals, academics, scholars, institutions, and others.

4117 ■ Journal of STEM Education
Auburn University
9088 Haley Ctr.
Auburn, AL 36849
Ph: (334)844-9088
Fax: (334)844-9027
URL: http://ojs.jstem.org/index.php?journal=JSTEM

Semiannual. Journal for educators in Science, Technology, Engineering, and Mathematics (STEM) education.

4118 ■ Leadership and Policy in Schools
Routledge Journals
270 Madison Ave.
New York, NY 10016-0601
Ph: (212)216-7800
Fax: (212)563-2269
URL: http://www.tandf.co.uk/journals/titles/15700763.asp

Quarterly. $567.00/year for institutions, print and online; $260.00/year for individuals, print only; $510.00/year for institutions, online only. Journal providing information about leadership and policy in primary and secondary education.

4119 ■ NACE Journal
National Association of Colleges and Employers
62 Highland Ave.
Bethlehem, PA 18017-9085
Ph: (610)868-1421
Fax: (610)868-0208
Fr: 800-544-5272
URL: http://www.naceweb.org/KnowledgeCenter.aspx

Quarterly. $70.00/year for individuals, print; $20.00/year for single issue; $25.00/year for other countries, airmail postage; $12.50/year for individuals, additional copies. Journal on career planning, and recruitment of the college educated work force.

4120 ■ NJEA Review
New Jersey Education Association
180 W State St.
PO Box 1211
Trenton, NJ 08607-1211
Ph: (609)599-4561
Fax: (609)392-6321
E-mail: njeareview@njea.org
URL: http://www.njea.org/page.aspx?z=1094&pz=8

Monthly. $250.00/year for nonmembers. Educational journal for public school employees.

4121 ■ Oxford Review of Education
Routledge Journals
270 Madison Ave.
New York, NY 10016-0601
Ph: (212)216-7800
Fax: (212)563-2269
URL: http://www.tandf.co.uk/journals/titles/03054985.asp

$709.00/year for institutions, print + online; $1,224.00/year for institutions, print + online; $249.00/year for individuals, print only; $454.00/year for individuals, print only. Journal covering advance study of education.

4122 ■ The Physics Teacher
American Association of Physics Teachers
1 Physics Ellipse
College Park, MD 20740-3845
Ph: (301)209-3311
Fax: (301)209-0845
URL: http://tpt.aapt.org

; $434.00/year for nonmembers, domestic; $469.00/year for nonmembers, international. Scientific education magazine.

4123 ■ School and Community
Missouri State Teachers Association
407 S Sixth St.
PO Box 458
Columbia, MO 65205
Ph: (573)442-3127
Fax: (573)443-5079
Fr: 800-392-0532
URL: http://www.msta.org/resources/publications/snc/

Quarterly. Education magazine.

4124 ■ School Effectiveness and School Improvement
Routledge
711 3 Ave., 8 Fl.
New York, NY 10016
Ph: (212)216-7800
Fax: (212)563-2269
Fr: 800-634-7064
URL: http://www.tandf.co.uk/journals/titles/
09243453.asp

Quarterly. $387.00/year for institutions, print and on-line; $348.00/year for institutions, online only; $186.00/year for individuals, print only; $660.00/year for institutions, print and online; $594.00/year for institutions, online only; $312.00/year for individuals, print only. Journal focusing on educational progress of all students.

4125 ■ Teaching and Learning in Nursing
Elsevier Science Inc.
360 Park Ave. S
New York, NY 10010-1710
Ph: (212)989-5800
Fax: (212)633-3990
Fr: 888-437-4636
URL: http://www.elsevier.com/wps/find/
journaldescription.cws_home

Quarterly. $232.00/year for institutions, other countries; $134.00/year for other countries; $160.00/year for institutions; $91.00/year for individuals. Journal devoted to associate degree nursing education and practice.

4126 ■ Tech Directions
Prakken Publications Inc.
832 Phoenix Dr.
Ann Arbor, MI 48108
Ph: (734)975-2800
Fax: (734)975-2787
Fr: 800-530-9673
E-mail: tdedit@techdirections.com
URL: http://www.techdirections.com

Monthly. $30.00/year for individuals, U.S.; $47.00/year for institutions; $50.00/year for other countries; $100.00/year for individuals, domestic. Magazine covering issues, programs, and projects in industrial education, technology education, trade and industry, and vocational-technical career education. Articles are geared for teacher and administrator use and reference from elementary school through postsecondary levels.

4127 ■ Theory and Research in Education
Sage Publications Inc.
2455 Teller Rd.
Thousand Oaks, CA 91320-2218
Ph: (805)499-9774
Fax: (805)583-2665
Fr: 800-818-7243
URL: http://www.sagepub.com/
journalsProdDesc.nav?prodId=Journal20

$546.00/year for institutions, print and e-access; $491.00/year for institutions, e-access; $535.00/year for institutions, print; $85.00/year for individuals, print; $196.00/year for single issue, institutional; $37.00/year for single issue, individual. Interdisciplinary journal covering normative and theoretical issues concerning education including multi-faceted philosophical analysis of moral, social, political and epistemological problems and issues arising from educational practice.

4128 ■ Women in Higher Education
Wenniger Co.
5376 Farmco Dr.
Madison, WI 53704
Ph: (608)251-3232
Fax: (608)284-0601
E-mail: career@wihe.com
URL: http://www.wihe.com/

Description: Monthly. Focuses on leadership, career strategies, gender equity, and harassment of women administrators. Recurring features include interviews, news of research, reports of meetings and presenta-

tions, news of educational opportunities, job listings, book reviews, notices of publications available, columns titled Profile, Research Briefs, Newswatch, What Should She Do?, Moveable Type, and The Last Laugh.

EMPLOYER DIRECTORIES AND NETWORKING LISTS

4129 ■ Accredited Institutions of Postsecondary Education
Oryx Press
88 Post Rd. W
PO Box 5007
Westport, CT 06881
Fax: (203)222-1502
URL: http://www.greenwood.com/catalog/
OXAIPE05.aspx

Annual, latest edition 2006. $89.95 for individuals; $49.95 for individuals. Covers: More than 7,000 accredited institutions and programs of postsecondary education in the United States and U.S. -chartered schools in 14 countries. Entries include: Institution name, address, phone, whether public or private, any religious affiliation, type of institution and student body, branch campuses or affiliated institutions, date of first accreditation and latest reaffirmation of accrediting body, accredited programs in professional fields, level of degrees offered, name of chief executive officer, size and composition of enrollment, type of academic calendar. Arrangement: Geographical. Indexes: Institution.

4130 ■ Boarding Schools Directory
The Association of Boarding Schools
9 SW Pack Sq., Ste. 201
Asheville, NC 28801-3526
Ph: (828)258-5354
Fax: (828)258-6428
URL: http://www.schools.com

Annual, Latest edition 2007-2008. for U.S. and Canada. Covers: Boarding schools that are members of the Association of Boarding Schools. Entries include: School name, address, phone, e-mail and url's, grades for which boarding students are accepted, enrollment, brief description. Arrangement: Classified by type of school. Indexes: Geographical; program; Alphabetical.

4131 ■ Career Ideas for Teens in Education and Training
Facts On File Inc.
132 W 31st St., 17th Fl.
New York, NY 10001
Ph: (212)967-8800
Fax: 800-678-3633
Fr: 800-322-8755
URL: http://factsonfile.infobasepublishing.com

Published 2005. $40.00 for individuals. Covers: A multitude of career possibilities based on a teenager's specific interests and skills and links his/her talents to a wide variety of actual professions.

4132 ■ Christian Schools International—Directory
Christian Schools International
3350 E Paris Ave. SE
Grand Rapids, MI 49512-2907
Ph: (616)957-1070
Fax: (616)957-5022
Fr: 800-635-8288
URL: http://www.store.csionline.org/index.php?main_
page=index&cPath=

Annual, Latest edition 2007-2008. $15.00 for members. Covers: Nearly 450 Reformed Christian elementary and secondary schools; related associations; societies without schools. Entries include: For schools—School name, address, phone; name, title, and address of officers; names of faculty members. Arrangement: Geographical.

4133 ■ College and University Professional Association—Membership Directory
College and University Professional Association for Human Resources
1811 Commons Point Dr.
Knoxville, TN 37932
Ph: (865)637-7673
Fax: (865)637-7674
Fr: 877-287-2474
E-mail: memberservice@cupahr.org
URL: http://www.cupahr.org

Online continually updated; access restricted to members. Covers: More than 7,000 members interested in college and university human resource administration; over 1,700 institutions. Entries include: For members—Personal name, title, affiliation, address, fax, e-mail, phone. For institutions—Organization name, address, phone, and names/titles of representatives. Arrangement: Members are alphabetical; institutions are geographical.

4134 ■ Directory of Public School Systems in the U.S.
American Association for Employment in Education
3040 Riverside Dr., Ste. 117
Columbus, OH 43221
Ph: (614)485-1111
Fax: (360)244-7802
E-mail: office@aaee.org
URL: http://www.aaee.org/

Annual, Winter; latest edition 2004-2005 edition. $55.00 for members; $80.00 for nonmembers. Covers: About 14,000 public school systems in the United States and their administrative personnel. Entries include: System name, address, phone, website address, name and title of personnel administrator, levels taught and approx. Student population. Arrangement: Geographical by state.

4135 ■ Ganley's Catholic Schools in America—Elementary/Secondary/College & University
Fisher Publishing Co.
PO Box 5729
Sun City West, AZ 85376
Ph: (623)328-8326
URL: http://www.ganleyscatholicschools.com

Annual, summer; Latest edition 38th, 2010. $67.00 for individuals. Covers: over 8,400 Catholic K-12 Schools. Arrangement: Geographical by state, then alphabetical by Diocese name.

4136 ■ Handbook of Private Schools
Porter Sargent Publishers Inc.
11 Beacon St., Ste. 1400
Boston, MA 02108-3099
Ph: (617)523-1670
Fax: (617)523-1021
Fr: 800-342-7470
URL: http://www.portersargent.com

Annual, latest edition 92nd, 2011-2012. $99.00 for individuals. Covers: More than 1,700 elementary and secondary boarding and day schools in the United States. Entries include: School name, address, phone, fax, E-mail, URL, type of school (boarding or day), sex and age range, names and titles of administrators, grades offered, academic orientation, curriculum, new admissions yearly, tests required for admission, enrollment and faculty, graduate record, number of alumni, tuition and scholarship figures, summer session, plant evaluation and endowment, date of establishment, calendar, association membership, description of school's offerings and history, test score averages, uniform requirements, geographical, and demographic date. Arrangement: Geographical. Indexes: Alphabetical by school name, cross indexed by state, region, grade range, sexes accepted, school features and enrollment.

4137 ■ Independent Schools Association of the Southwest—Membership List
Independent Schools Association of the Southwest
Energy Sq., 505 N Big Spring St., Ste. 406
Midland, TX 79701

Ph: (432)684-9550
Fax: (432)684-9401
Fr: 800-688-5007
URL: http://www.isasw.org

Annual, August. Covers: Over 84 schools located in Arizona, Kansas, Louisiana, Mexico, New Mexico, Oklahoma, and Texas enrolling over 38,000 students. Entries include: School name, address, phone, chief administrative officer, structure, and enrollment. Arrangement: Geographical. Indexes: Alphabetical.

4138 ■ MDR's School Directories
Market Data Retrieval
6 Armstrong Rd., Ste. 301
Shelton, CT 06484-4722
Ph: (203)926-4800
Fax: (203)926-1826
Fr: 800-333-8802
URL: http://www.schooldata.com/mdrdir.asp

Annual, Latest edition 2008-2009. Covers: Over 90,000 public, 8,000 Catholic, and 15,000 other private schools (grades K-12) in the United States; over 15,000 school district offices, and 76,000 school librarians; and 27,000 media specialists, 33,000 technology coordinators. Includes names of over 165,000 school district administrators and staff members in county and state education administration. Entries include: District name and address; telephone and fax number; number of schools; number of teachers in the district; district enrollment; special Ed students; limited-English proficient students; minority percentage by race, college bound students; expenditures per student for instructional materials; poverty level; title 1 dollars; site-based management; district open/close dates; construction indicator; technologies and quantities; district-level administrators, new superintendents shaded; school name and address—new public shaded; telephone and fax number; principal new principal shaded; librarian, media specialist and technology coordinator; grade span; special programs and school type; student enrollment; technologies and quantities (instructional computer brand noting predominant brand); Multi-Media Computers; Internet connection or access; Tech Sophistication Index. Arrangement: Geographical. Indexes: District County; District Personnel; Principal; New Public Schools and Key Personnel; District and School Telephone; District URLs.

4139 ■ National Association of College and University Business Officers—Membership Directory
National Association of College and University Business Officers
1110 Vermont St. NW, Ste. 800
Washington, DC 20005
Ph: (202)861-2500
Fax: (202)861-2583
Fr: 800-462-4916
URL: http://www.nacubo.org

Annual, latest edition 2006. Number of listings: 2,800 institutions; 22,00 people. Entries include: Name of institution, address, names of primary representatives. Arrangement: Alphabetical and regional.

4140 ■ National Directory for Employment in Education
American Association for Employment in Education
3040 Riverside Dr., Ste. 117
Columbus, OH 43221
Ph: (614)485-1111
Fax: (360)244-7802
URL: http://www.aaee.org/

Annual, winter; latest edition 2008-2009. $20.00 for nonmembers; $10.00 for members. Covers: about 600 placement offices maintained by teacher-training institutions and 300 school district personnel officers and/or superintendents responsible for hiring professional staff. Entries include: Institution name, address, phone, contact name, email address, and website. Arrangement: Geographical. Indexes: Personal name, subject-field of teacher training,

institutions which provide vacancy bulletins and placement services to non-enrolled students.

4141 ■ National School Public Relations Association—Directory
National School Public Relations Association
15948 Derwood Rd.
Rockville, MD 20855-2123
Ph: (301)519-0496
Fax: (301)519-0494
URL: http://www.nspra.org

Annual, January. Covers: Approximately 2,000 school system public relations directors, school administrators, principals, and others who are members of the National School Public Relations Association. Entries include: Name, affiliation, address, phone. Arrangement: Geographical.

4142 ■ Patterson's American Education
Educational Directories Inc.
1025 W Wise Rd., Ste. 101
PO Box 68097
Schaumburg, IL 60168-0097
Ph: (847)891-1250
Fax: (847)891-0945
Fr: 800-357-6183
URL: http://www.ediusa.com

Annual, Latest edition 2012, vol. 108. $97.00 for individuals. Covers: Over 11,000 school districts in the United States; more than 34,000 public, private, and Catholic high schools, middle schools, and junior high schools; Approximately 300 parochial superintendents; 400 state department of education personnel. Entries include: For school districts and schools—District and superintendent Name, address, phone, fax, grade ranges, enrollment, school names, addresses, phone numbers, grade ranges, enrollment, names of principals. For postsecondary schools—School name, address, phone number, URL, e-mail, names of administrator or director of admissions. For private and Catholic high schools—name, address, phone, fax, enrollment, grades offered, name of principal. Postsecondary institutions are covered in 'Patterson's Schools Classified'. Arrangement: Geographical by state, then alphabetical by city.

4143 ■ Patterson's Schools Classified
Educational Directories Inc.
1025 W Wise Rd., Ste. 101
PO Box 68097
Schaumburg, IL 60168-0097
Ph: (847)891-1250
Fax: (847)891-0945
Fr: 800-357-6183
URL: http://www.ediusa.com

Annual, Latest edition 2010, volume 60. $23.00 for individuals. Covers: Over 6,000 accredited colleges, universities, community colleges, junior colleges, career schools and teaching hospitals. Entries include: School name, address, phone, URL, e-mail, name of administrator or admissions officer, description, professional accreditation (where applicable). Updated from previous year's edition of 'Patterson's American Education'. Arrangement: Classified by area of study, then geographical by state. Indexes: Alphabetical by name.

4144 ■ Private Independent Schools
Bunting and Lyon Inc.
615 Broad Swamp Rd.
Cheshire, CT 06410
Ph: (203)668-1811
Fax: (203)269-8908
URL: http://www.buntingandlyon.com

Annual, Latest edition 2010. $115.00 for individuals. Covers: 1,200 English-speaking elementary and secondary private schools and summer programs in North America and abroad. Entries include: School name, address, phone, fax, e-mail, website, enrollment, tuition and other fees, financial aid information, administrator's name and educational background, director of admission, regional accreditation, description of programs, curriculum, activities, learning dif-

ferences grid. Arrangement: Geographical. Indexes: School name; geographical. Summer programs, general classification grid, learning differences reference grid.

4145 ■ Requirements for Certification of Teachers, Counselors, Librarians, Administrators for Elementary and Secondary Schools
University of Chicago Press
Journals Division
1427 E 60th St.
Chicago, IL 60637-2954
Ph: (773)702-7636
Fax: (773)702-9756
URL: http://www.press.uchicago.edu

Annual, Latest edition 74th. $53.00. Publication includes: List of state and local departments of education. Entries include: Office name, address, phone. Principal content of publication is summaries of each state's teaching and administrative certification requirements. Arrangement: Geographical.

4146 ■ School Guide
School Guide Publications
210 North Ave.
New Rochelle, NY 10801-6402
Ph: (914)632-7771
Fax: (914)632-3412
Fr: 800-433-7771
URL: http://distance.schoolguides.com

Annual, Latest edition 2008. Covers: Over 3,000 colleges, vocational schools, and nursing schools in the United States. Entries include: Institution name, address, phone, courses offered, degrees awarded. Arrangement: Classified by type of institution, then geographical. Indexes: Subject.

HANDBOOKS AND MANUALS

4147 ■ Ferguson Career Coach: Managing Your Career in Education
Facts On File
132 W 31st St., 17th Fl.
New York, NY 10001
Fax: 800-678-3633
Fr: 800-322-8755
E-mail: custserv@factsonfile.com
URL: http://factsonfile.infobasepublishing.com

Shelly Field. 2008. $39.95 (hardcover). 272 pages. Contains tips on achieving career success in the field of education. Provides students with advice on making contacts, interviewing, and career strategies.

4148 ■ From Mandate to Achievement: 5 Steps to a Curriculum System That Works!
Corwin Press, Inc.
2455 Teller Rd.
Thousand Oaks, CA 91320
Ph: (805)499-9734
Fax: (805)499-5323
Fr: 800-233-9936
E-mail: order@corwin.com
URL: http://www.corwin.com

Elaine Makas. 2009. $38.95 (paperback); $85.95 (hardcover). 248 pages. Guides principals, district administrators, curriculum facilitators and teachers in establishing a consistent and accurate curriculum process that increases academic achievement and drives continuous school improvement.

4149 ■ Getting Serious About the System
Corwin Press, Inc.
2455 Teller Rd.
Thousand Oaks, CA 91320
Ph: (805)499-9734
Fax: (805)499-5323
Fr: 800-233-9936
E-mail: order@corwin.com
URL: http://www.corwin.com

D'Ette Cowan, Stacey Joyner and Shirley Beckwith. 2012. $31.95 (paperback). 120 pages. Provides teachers, administrators and leaders with a comprehensive resource in aligning curriculum, instruction and assessment. Presents a step-by-step, research-based approach to district and school transformation.

4150 ■ *Leading Curriculum Improvement*
Rowman & Littlefield Education
c/o Rowman & Littlefield Publishing Group
4501 Forbes Blvd., Ste. 200
Lanham, MD 20706
Ph: (301)459-3366
Fax: (301)429-5748
E-mail: customercare@rowman.com
URL: http://rowman.com

Marilyn Tallerico. 2011. $40.00 (hardback); $19.95 (paper). 136 pages. Offers guidance and curriculum leadership fundamentals to teacher leaders, instructional coordinators, central office personnel for facilitating curriculum improvement at the building level.

4151 ■ *The Principal's Guide to Curriculum Leadership*
Corwin
2455 Teller Rd.
Thousand Oaks, CA 91320
Ph: (805)499-9734
Fax: (805)499-5323
Fr: 800-233-9936
E-mail: order@corwin.com
URL: http://www.corwin.com

Richard D. Sorenson, Lloyd Milton Goldsmith, Zulma Y. Mendez, and Karen Taylor Maxwell. 2011. $41.95 (paper). 320 pages. Provides practical guidance for principal and other school administrators in initiating curriculum development and change. Features discussion questions, case studies, activities, specialized curriculum models, resources, and references.

Employment Agencies and Search Firms

4152 ■ Auerbach Associates Inc.
385 Concord Ave., Ste. 103
Belmont, MA 02478
Ph: (617)451-0095
Fax: (617)489-9111
E-mail: info@auerbach-assc.com
URL: http://auerbach-assc.com

Executive search firm focused on non-profit and higher education industries.

4153 ■ Hazard, Young, Attea and Associates
5600 N River Rd., Ste. 180
Rosemont, IL 60018
Ph: (847)724-8465
Fax: (847)724-8467
E-mail: office@hyasearch.com
URL: http://www.hyasupersearches.com

Executive search firm serving public school districts. Provides recruiting for school boards throughout the United States.

4154 ■ Institutional Advantage L.L.C.
340 Lothrop Rd.
Grosse Pointe Farms, MI 48236
Ph: (313)886-6349
Fax: (313)557-1331
E-mail: kts@ia-llc.com
URL: http://www.ia-llc.com

Retained executive search for higher education and not-for-profit clients.

4155 ■ King & King Consulting
10287 Grayfox Dr.
San Diego, CA 92131
Ph: (858)566-8985
Fax: (858)566-8985

Offers services in the following areas: needs assessment, career development, writing skills and communication, organizational development, manage-

ment development, employee development, team building, office management skills, and mid-life crisis management. Industries served: aviation, education, and scientific.

4156 ■ Perez-Arton Consultants Inc.
23 Spring St., Ste. 204B
Ossining, NY 10562
Ph: (914)762-2103
Fax: (914)762-7834
E-mail: perezart@bestweb.net

Provides executive searches for major academic and administrative units. Conducts institutional evaluations and executive staff assessments. Firm works for colleges, universities and education-related non-profits only.

4157 ■ Spelman & Johnson Group
3 Chapman Ave.
Easthampton, MA 01027
Ph: (413)529-2895
Fax: (413)527-6881
Fr: 800-827-6208
E-mail: info@spelmanandjohnson.com
URL: http://www.spelmanandjohnson.com

Description: Serves as a search firm specializing in filling positions for administrative positions within higher education.

Online Job Sources and Services

4158 ■ ABCTeachingJobs.com
URL: http://www.abcteachingjobs.com

Description: Serves as a source of teacher job postings and recruitment. Offers jobs for K-12 teachers and administrators.

4159 ■ Education Administration Jobs
URL: http://www.educationadministrationjobs.com

Description: Serves as an online recruiting resource for education administration employees.

4160 ■ Education America Networks
URL: http://www.educationamerica.net

Description: Education employment network for the United States. Provides information and employment opportunities specifically related to the education industry.

4161 ■ National Educators Employment Review
URL: http://www.thereview.com

Description: Matches qualified educators with employment for teachers, specialists, and administrators from kindergarten through college.

4162 ■ School-Jobs.net
URL: http://www.school-jobs.net/jobs

Description: Matches teachers, administrators, support staff, and other school employees to related jobs across the country. Features jobs by salary, location, and area of expertise.

4163 ■ SchoolSpring.com
E-mail: contact@schoolspring.com
URL: http://www.schoolspring.com

Description: Serves as an employment source for educators. Offers teaching jobs and other education job listings including complete archiving of all necessary documents and certifications, as well as access to all education jobs in a specific area.

4164 ■ UniversityJobs.com
E-mail: staff@universityjobs.com
URL: http://www.universityjobs.com

Description: Provides an online recruitment solution for colleges and universities to hire new faculty and administrators or staff.

4165 ■ WantToTeach.com
URL: http://www.wanttoteach.com

Description: Serves as an education website to search for administrative, instructional and support openings throughout the United States. Features job openings and job fairs and allows access to various education resources.

Tradeshows

4166 ■ American Association of School Personnel Administrators Annual Conference
American Association of School Personnel Administrators
11863 W 112th St., Ste. 100
Overland Park, KS 66210
Ph: (913)327-1222
Fax: (913)327-1223
E-mail: aaspa@aaspa.org
URL: http://www.aaspa.org

Annual. Provides school personnel professionals with knowledge and professional development opportunities. 2012 October 31-November 2; Chicago, IL; Palmer House.

4167 ■ Association for Biblical Higher Education Annual Meeting
Association for Biblical Higher Education
5850 T.G. Lee Blvd., Ste. 130
Orlando, FL 32822
Ph: (407)207-0808
Fax: (407)207-0840
E-mail: info@abhe.org
URL: http://www.abhe.org/

Annual. Primary Exhibits: Publications, office equipment, travel information, educational resources, fundraising services, computers, Bible literature, films, and related material for educational institutions. Dates and Locations: 2012 Feb 22-25; Orlando, FL; Doubletree Hotel; 2013 Feb 13-16; Orlando, FL; Hilton Orlando; 2014 Feb 19-22; Orlando, FL; Hilton Orlando.

4168 ■ Association of International Education Administrators Conference
Association of International Education Administrators
Duke University
Campus Box 20404
Durham, NC 27708
Ph: (919)668-1928
Fax: (919)684-8749
E-mail: aiea@duke.edu
URL: http://www.aieaworld.org

Annual. Provides practical strategies and solutions to several issues on campus administration. Offers networking opportunities.

4169 ■ CoSN Annual Conference
Consortium for School Networking
1025 Vermont Ave., Ste. 1010
Washington, DC 20005
Ph: (202)861-2676
Fax: (202)393-2011
Fr: (866)267-8747
E-mail: info@cosn.org
URL: http://www.cosn.org

Annual. Works to open a worldwide dialogue about the issues of technology and school networking. Brings together key education and policy leaders from the U.S. and other nations to examine global responses to the effective use of Information and Communication Technology (ICT) in education.

4170 ■ NASFAA National Conference
National Association of Student Financial Aid Administrators
1101 Connecticut Ave. NW, Ste. 1100
Washington, DC 20036
Ph: (202)785-0453

Fax: (202)785-1487
E-mail: web@nasfaa.org
URL: http://www.nasfaa.org

Annual. Offers professional advice, expert guidance from policymakers, and networking opportunities. 2012 July 22-25; Chicago, IL; Hyatt Regency Chicago.

4171 ■ National Association for Bilingual Education Conference

National Association for Bilingual Education
8701 Georgia Ave., Ste. 611
Silver Spring, MD 20910
Ph: (240)450-3700
Fax: (240)450-3799
E-mail: nabe@nabe.org
URL: http://www.nabe.org

Annual. Features speakers, sessions, product exhibits, and job fair.

4172 ■ National Association for Developmental Education Conference

National Association for Developmental Education
PMB 412
500 N Estrella Pkwy.
Goodyear, AZ 85338
Fax: (623)792-5747
Fr: 877-233-9455
E-mail: office@nade.net
URL: http://www.nade.net

Annual. Offers an opportunity for personal and professional growth. Includes job fair. 2013 February 27-March 2; Denver, CO; Sheraton Denver Hotel. 2014 March 5-8; Dallas, TX; Hilton Anatole.

4173 ■ National Association of Elementary School Principals Annual Convention and Exposition

National Association of Elementary School Principals
1615 Duke St.
Alexandria, VA 22314
Ph: (703)684-3345
Fax: (703)518-6281
Fr: 800-386-2877
E-mail: naesp@naesp.org
URL: http://www.naesp.org

Annual. Primary Exhibits: Textbooks publishers, classroom supplies and equipment; playground equipment; incentive/fundraising programs; curriculum; technology; professional/staff development. Dates and Locations: 2012 Apr 22-24; Seattle, WA.

4174 ■ National Association of Independent Schools Annual Conference

National Association of Independent Schools
1620 L St. NW, Ste. 1100
Washington, DC 20036-5695
Ph: (202)973-9700
Fax: (202)973-9790
E-mail: info@nais.org
URL: http://www.nais.org

Annual. Gathering of independent school community, serving school heads and leadership teams. Offers networking opportunities and professional development on critical leadership and educational issues.

4175 ■ National Association of Secondary School Principals Annual Convention

National Association of Secondary School Principals
1904 Association Dr.
Reston, VA 20191-1537
Ph: (703)860-0200
Fax: (703)476-5490
Fr: 800-253-1746
URL: http://www.nassp.org

Annual. Primary Exhibits: School furnishings, supplies and equipment; fund raising, school jewelry, awards, yearbooks; textbooks. Dates and Locations: 2012 Mar 08-10; Tampa, FL.

4176 ■ Southwestern Federation of Administrative Disciplines Convention

Southwestern Federation of Administrative Disciplines
2700 Bay Area Blvd.
Houston, TX 77058

Annual. Primary Exhibits: Educational materials and services.

4177 ■ UCEA Convention

University Council for Educational Administration
Curry School of Education
The University of Virginia
PO Box 400287
Charlottesville, VA 22904
Ph: (434)243-1041
Fax: (434)924-1384
URL: http://www.ucea.org

Annual. Primary Exhibits: Publications related to educational administration in universities. Dates and Locations: 2012 Nov 15-18; Denver, CO; Denver Marriott City Center; 2013 Nov 07-10; Indianapolis, IN; Hyatt Regency Indianapolis.

OTHER SOURCES

4178 ■ American Association of Christian Schools (AACS)

602 Belvoir Ave.
East Ridge, TN 37412
Ph: (423)629-4280
Fax: (423)622-7461
E-mail: info@aacs.org
URL: http://www.aacs.org

Description: Maintains teacher/administrator certification program and placement service. Participates in school accreditation program. Sponsors National Academic Tournament. Maintains American Christian Honor Society. Compiles statistics; maintains speakers' bureau and placement service.

4179 ■ American Association of Collegiate Registrars and Admissions Officers (AACRAO)

1 Dupont Cir. NW, Ste. 520
Washington, DC 20036
Ph: (202)293-9161
Fax: (202)872-8857
E-mail: membership@aacrao.org
URL: http://www.aacrao.org

Description: Degree-granting postsecondary institutions, government agencies, and higher education coordinating boards, private educational organizations, and education-oriented businesses. Promotes higher education and furthers the professional development of members working in admissions, enrollment management, institutional research, records, and registration.

4180 ■ American Association of School Administrators (AASA)

801 N Quincy St., Ste. 700
Arlington, VA 22203
Ph: (703)528-0700
Fax: (703)841-1543
E-mail: info@aasa.org
URL: http://www.aasa.org

Description: Professional association of administrators and executives of school systems and educational service agencies; school district superintendents; central, building, and service unit administrators; presidents of colleges, deans, and professors of educational administration; placement officers; executive directors and administrators of education associations. Sponsors numerous professional development conferences annually.

4181 ■ American Association of School Personnel Administrators

11863 W 112th St., Ste. 100
Overland Park, KS 66210
Ph: (913)327-1222

Fax: (913)327-1223
E-mail: aaspa@aaspa.org
URL: http://www.aaspa.org

Description: Represents school personnel professionals. Provides leadership in promoting effective human resources practices within education through professional development activities and a broad-based resource network.

4182 ■ American Association for Women in Community Colleges (AAWCC)

PO Box 30808
Salt Lake City, UT 84130-0808
Ph: (801)975-4225
Fax: (801)957-4440
E-mail: aawccsupport@gmail.com
URL: http://www.aawccnatl.org

Description: Women faculty members, administrators, staff members, students, and trustees of community colleges. Objectives are to: develop communication and disseminate information among women in community, junior, and technical colleges; encourage educational program development; obtain grants for educational projects for community college women. Disseminates information on women's issues and programs. Conducts regional and state professional development workshops and forums. Recognizes model programs that assist women in community colleges. An affiliate council of the American Association of Community Colleges.

4183 ■ American College Personnel Association (ACPA)

1 Dupont Cir. NW, Ste. 300
Washington, DC 20036-1188
Ph: (202)835-2272
Fax: (202)296-3286
E-mail: info@acpa.nche.edu
URL: http://www.acpa.nche.edu

Description: Represents individuals employed in higher education and involved in student personnel work, including administration, counseling, research, and teaching. Fosters student development in higher education in areas of service, advocacy, and standards by offering professional programs for educators committed to the overall development of postsecondary students. Sponsors professional and educational activities in cooperation with other organizations. Offers placement services.

4184 ■ American Council on Education, Fellows Program

1 Dupont Cir. NW
Washington, DC 20036-1193
Ph: (202)939-9300
E-mail: fellows@acenet.edu
URL: http://www.acenet.edu/AM/
    Template.cfm?Section=Fellows_Program1

Description: Service arm of the American Council on Education to strengthen leadership in American postsecondary education by identifying and preparing individuals who have shown promise for responsible positions in higher education administration. Purpose: Objectives are: to encourage and prepare individuals making higher education administration their professional career; to provide opportunities for planned observation and experience in decision-making; to identify and develop potential leaders. Arranges internships whereby senior faculty and administrators are given the opportunity to study higher education leadership as an intern at a host institution. The stipulations are that the fellow will do certain assigned reading in higher education administration, focus on a strategic learning project and serve at the home institution for the academic year following the internship. Provides services for alumni of the program.

4185 ■ American Federation of School Administrators (AFSA)

1101 17th St. NW, Ste. 408
Washington, DC 20036
Ph: (202)986-4209

Fax: (202)986-4211
E-mail: afsa@afsaadmin.org
URL: http://web.admin.org/sites/main/index.cfm

Description: Principals, vice-principals, directors, supervisors, and administrators involved in pedagogical education. Purposes are to: achieve the highest goals in education; maintain and improve standards, benefits, and conditions for personnel without regard to color, race, sex, background, or national origin; obtain job security; protect seniority and merit; cooperate with all responsible organizations in education; promote understanding, participation, and support of the public, communities, and agencies; be alert to resist attacks and campaigns that would create or entrench a spoils system; promote democratic society by supporting full educational opportunities for every child and student in the nation.

4186 ■ Association of Christian Schools International (ACSI)

PO Box 65130
Colorado Springs, CO 80962-5130
Fax: (719)531-0631
Fr: 800-367-0798
E-mail: acsi_email@acsi.org
URL: http://www.acsi.org

Description: Seeks to enable Christian educators and schools worldwide to effectively prepare students for life.

4187 ■ Association of College and University Housing Officers International (ACUHO-I)

941 Chatham Ln., Ste. 318
Columbus, OH 43221-2416
Ph: (614)292-0099
Fax: (614)292-3205
E-mail: office@acuho-i.org
URL: http://www.acuho-i.org

Description: Officials of educational institutions in 13 countries concerned with all aspects of student housing and food service operation. Supports and conducts research. Organizes seminars and workshops. Offers internships. Maintains biographical archives; offers placement service. Compiles statistics.

4188 ■ Association of Departments of English (ADE)

26 Broadway, 3rd Fl.
New York, NY 10004-1789
Ph: (646)576-5130
Fax: (646)835-4056
E-mail: dlaurence@mla.org
URL: http://www.ade.org

Description: Administrators of college and university departments of English, humanities, rhetoric, and communications. Works to improve the teaching of English and the administration of English departments. Conducts studies and surveys of literature and writing courses. Sponsors sessions at major English conventions and conferences nationwide. Sponsored by Modern Language Association of America.

4189 ■ Association for Education Finance and Policy (AEFP)

524 Ceras, 520 Galvez Mall
Stanford, CA 94305
Ph: (650)736-1258
E-mail: info@aefpweb.org
URL: http://www.aefpweb.org

Description: State and national teacher organizations, university personnel, school administrators, state educational agency personnel, legislators and legislative staff, federal agency personnel, and interested foundations and students. Facilitates communication among groups and individuals in the field of educational finance including academicians, researchers, and policymakers. Main interests include traditional school finance concepts, public policy issues, and the review and debate of emerging issues of educational finance. Conducts workshop. Compiles statistics. Maintains placement service.

4190 ■ Association on Higher Education and Disability (AHEAD)

107 Commerce Center Dr., Ste. 204
Huntersville, NC 28078
Ph: (704)947-7779
Fax: (704)948-7779
E-mail: ahead@ahead.org
URL: http://www.ahead.org

Description: Individuals interested in promoting the equal rights and opportunities of disabled postsecondary students, staff, faculty, and graduates. Provides an exchange of communication for those professionally involved with disabled students; collects, evaluates, and disseminates information; encourages and supports legislation for the benefit of disabled students. Conducts surveys on issues pertinent to college students with disabilities; offers resource referral system and employment exchange for positions in disability student services. Conducts research programs; compiles statistics.

4191 ■ Association for Humanistic Counseling

PO Box 791006
Baltimore, MD 21279-1006
Ph: (703)823-9800
Fax: 800-473-2329
Fr: 800-347-6647
E-mail: cmalchiodi@insightbb.com
URL: http://www.c-ahead.com

Description: A division of the American Counseling Association. Teachers, educational administrators, community agency workers, counselors, school social workers, and psychologists; others interested in the area of human development. Aims to assist individuals in improving their quality of life. Provides forum for the exchange of information about humanistically-oriented administrative and instructional practices. Supports humanistic practices and research on instructional and organizational methods for facilitating humanistic education; encourages cooperation among related professional groups.

4192 ■ Association of Independent School Admission Professionals (AISAP)

PO Box 709
Madison, CT 06443
Ph: (203)421-7051
E-mail: info@aisap.org
URL: http://www.aisap.org

Description: Supports the advancement of independent school professionals involved in all aspects of admission and enrollment management. Promotes the value of independent school education. Facilitates training and collaborative dialogue among professionals involved and responsible for enrollment management.

4193 ■ Association of Latino Administrators and Superintendents (ALAS)

65 W Boston Post Rd., Ste. 200
Marlborough, MA 01752
Ph: (508)486-4536
Fax: (508)624-6565
E-mail: hsalameh@alasedu.net
URL: http://www.alasedu.net

Description: Represents the interests of Latino superintendents and administrators. Provides professional development programs to strengthen the skills of superintendents, principals and other administrators. Advocates for policies to ensure the quality of the public education system.

4194 ■ Association for the Study of Higher Education (ASHE)

4505 S Maryland Pkwy.
UNLV Box 453068
Las Vegas, NV 89154
Ph: (702)895-2737
Fax: (702)895-4269
E-mail: ashe@unlv.edu
URL: http://www.ashe.ws

Description: Professors, researchers, administrators, policy analysts, graduate students, and others concerned with the study of higher education. Aims to advance the study of higher education and facilitate and encourage discussion of priority issues for research in the study of higher education.

4195 ■ College Media Advisers (CMA)

University of Memphis
Department of Journalism
3711 Veterans Ave., Rm. 300
Memphis, TN 38152-6661
Ph: (901)678-2403
Fax: (901)678-4798
E-mail: rsplbrgr@memphis.edu
URL: http://www.collegemedia.org

Description: Professional association serving advisers, directors, and chairmen of boards of college student media (newspapers, yearbooks, magazines, handbooks, directories, and radio and television stations); heads of schools and departments of journalism; and others interested in junior college, college, and university student media. Serves as a clearinghouse for student media; acts as consultant on student theses and dissertations on publications. Encourages high school journalism and examines its relationships to college and professional journalism. Conducts national survey of student media in rotation each year by type: newspapers, magazines, and yearbooks; radio and television stations. Compiles statistics. Maintains placement service and speakers' bureau.

4196 ■ Council of Educational Facility Planners International (CEFPI)

9180 E Desert Cove Dr., Ste. 104
Scottsdale, AZ 85260-6231
Ph: (480)391-0840
Fax: (480)391-0940
E-mail: michelle@cefpi.org
URL: http://www.cefpi.org

Description: Individuals and firms who are responsible for planning, designing, creating, maintaining, and equipping the physical environment of education. Sponsors an exchange of information, professional experiences, best practices research results, and other investigative techniques concerning educational facility planning. Activities include publication and review of current and emerging practices in educational facility planning; identification and execution of needed research; development of professional training programs; strengthening of planning services on various levels of government and in institutions of higher learning; leadership in the development of higher standards for facility design and the physical environment of education. Operates speakers' bureau; sponsors placement service; compiles statistics.

4197 ■ Friends Council on Education (FCE)

1507 Cherry St.
Philadelphia, PA 19102
Ph: (215)241-7245
Fax: (215)241-7299
E-mail: info@friendscouncil.org
URL: http://www.friendscouncil.org

Description: Representatives appointed by Friends Yearly Meetings; heads of Quaker secondary and elementary schools and colleges; members-at-large. Acts as a clearinghouse for information on Quaker schools and colleges. Holds meetings and conferences on education and provides in-service training for teachers, administrators and trustees in Friends schools.

4198 ■ International Association of Baptist Colleges and Universities (IABCU)

8120 Sawyer Brown Rd., Ste. 108
Nashville, TN 37221-1410
Ph: (615)673-1896
Fax: (615)662-1396
E-mail: marrington@baptistschools.org
URL: http://www.baptistschools.org

Description: Southern Baptist senior colleges, universities, junior colleges, academies, and Bible schools. Promotes Christian education through literature, faculty workshops, student recruitment, teacher placement, trustee orientation, statistical information, and other assistance to members.

4199 ■ The International Educator (TIE)

PO Box 513
Cummaquid, MA 02637
Ph: (508)790-1990
Fax: (508)790-1922
Fr: 877-375-6668
E-mail: tie@tieonline.com
URL: http://www.tieonline.com

Description: Facilitates the placement of teachers and administrators in American, British, and international schools. Seeks to create a network that provides for professional development opportunities and improved financial security of members. Offers advice and information on international school news, recent educational developments, job placement, and investment, consumer, and professional development opportunities. Makes available insurance and travel benefits. Operates International Schools Internship Program.

4200 ■ Jesuit Association of Student Personnel Administrators (JASPA)

2500 California Plz.
Omaha, NE 68178
Ph: (402)280-2717
Fax: (402)280-1275
E-mail: waynejr@creighton.edu
URL: http://jaspa.creighton.edu

Description: Represents administrators of student personnel programs in 28 Jesuit colleges and universities in the United States. Sponsors institutes and seminars for personnel in Jesuit colleges. Cooperates with Catholic and non-Catholic educational associations in various projects. Maintains placement service and conducts workshops. Operates organizational archives and compiles statistics.

4201 ■ Jewish Educators Assembly (JEA)

PO Box 413
Cedarhurst, NY 11516
Ph: (516)569-2537
Fax: (516)295-9039
E-mail: jewisheducators@jewisheducators.org
URL: http://www.jewisheducators.org

Description: Educational and supervisory personnel serving Jewish educational institutions. Seeks to: advance the development of Jewish education in the congregation on all levels in consonance with the philosophy of the Conservative Movement; cooperate with the United Synagogue of America Commission on Jewish Education as the policy-making body of the educational enterprise; join in cooperative effort with other Jewish educational institutions and organizations; establish and maintain professional standards for Jewish educators; serve as a forum for the exchange of ideas; promote the values of Jewish education as a basis for the creative continuity of the Jewish people. Maintains placement service and speaker's bureau.

4202 ■ NAFSA: Association of International Educators (NAFSA)

1307 New York Ave. NW, 8th Fl.
Washington, DC 20005-4701
Ph: (202)737-3699
Fax: (202)737-3657
E-mail: inbox@nafsa.org
URL: http://www.nafsa.org

Description: Individuals, organizations, and institutions dealing with international educational exchange, including foreign student advisers, overseas educational advisers, credentials and admissions officers, administrators and teachers of English as a second language, community support personnel, study-abroad administrators, and embassy cultural or educational personnel. Promotes self-regulation standards and responsibilities in international educational exchange; offers professional development opportunities primarily through publications, workshops, grants, and regional and national conferences.

Advocates for increased awareness and support of international education and exchange on campuses, in government, and in communities. Offers services including: a job registry for employers and professionals involved with international education; a consultant referral service. Sponsors joint liaison activities with a variety of other educational and government organizations to conduct a census of foreign student enrollment in the U.S.; conducts workshops about specific subjects and countries.

4203 ■ NASPA - Student Affairs Administrators in Higher Education

111 K St. NE, 10th Fl.
Washington, DC 20002
Ph: (202)265-7500
Fax: (202)898-5737
E-mail: office@naspa.org
URL: http://www.naspa.org

Description: Representatives of degree-granting institutions of higher education which have been fully accredited. Works to enrich the educational experience of all students. Serves colleges and universities by providing leadership and professional growth opportunities for the senior student affairs officer and other professionals who consider higher education and student affairs issues from an institutional perspective. Provides professional development; improves information and research; acts as an advocate for students in higher education. Maintains career service and conducts the Richard F. Stevens Institute. Supports minority undergraduate fellows program.

4204 ■ National Academic Advising Association (NACADA)

Kansas State University
2323 Anderson Ave., Ste. 225
Manhattan, KS 66502-2912
Ph: (785)532-5717
Fax: (785)532-7732
E-mail: nacada@ksu.edu
URL: http://www.nacada.ksu.edu

Description: Academic program advisors, faculty, administrators, counselors, and others concerned with the intellectual, personal, and career development of students in all types of postsecondary educational institutions. Works to support and promotes professional growth of academic advising and academic advisers. Provides a forum for discussion, debate, and exchange of ideas regarding academic advising. Serves as advocate for standards and quality programs in academic advising. Operates consultants' bureau to assist advising services on college campuses. Maintains placement service, speakers' bureau, and information clearinghouse.

4205 ■ National Alliance of Black School Educators (NABSE)

310 Pennsylvania Ave. SE
Washington, DC 20003
Ph: (202)608-6310
Fax: (202)608-6319
Fr: 800-221-2654
E-mail: info@nabse.org
URL: http://www.nabse.org

Description: Black educators from all levels; others indirectly involved in the education of black youth. Promotes awareness, professional expertise, and commitment among black educators. Goals are to: eliminate and rectify the results of racism in education; work with state, local, and national leaders to raise the academic achievement level of all black students; increase members' involvement in legislative activities; facilitate the introduction of a curriculum that more completely embraces black America; improve the ability of black educators to promote problem resolution; create a meaningful and effective network of strength, talent, and professional support. Sponsors workshops, commission meetings, and special projects. Encourages research, especially as it relates to blacks, and the presentation of papers during national conferences. Plans to establish a

National Black Educators Data Bank and offer placement service.

4206 ■ National Association for Bilingual Education

8701 Georgia Ave., Ste. 611
Silver Spring, MD 20910
Ph: (240)450-3700
Fax: (240)450-3799
E-mail: nabe@nabe.org
URL: http://www.nabe.org

Description: Comprised of bilingual and English language learner (ELL) teachers, parents, paraprofessionals, administrators, professors, advocates, researchers, and policy makers. Promotes English proficiency and respect for cultural and linguistic diversity. Creates and supports policies, programs, research, pedagogy, and professional development to achieve bilingualism and biliteracy.

4207 ■ National Association of College and University Business Officers (NACUBO)

1110 Vermont Ave. NW, Ste. 800
Washington, DC 20005
Ph: (202)861-2500
Fax: (202)861-2583
Fr: 800-462-4916
E-mail: john.walda@nacubo.org
URL: http://www.nacubo.org

Description: Colleges, universities, and companies that are members of a regional association. Develops and maintains national interest in improving the principles and practices of business and financial administration in higher education. Sponsors workshops in fields such as cash management, grant and contract maintenance, accounting, investment, student loan administration, and costing. Conducts research and information exchange programs between college and university personnel; compiles statistics.

4208 ■ National Association for Developmental Education

PMB 412
500 N Estrella Pkwy.
Goodyear, AZ 85338
Fax: (623)792-5747
Fr: 877-233-9455
E-mail: office@nade.net
URL: http://www.nade.net

Description: Seeks to improve the theory and practice of developmental education. Enhances the professional capabilities of development educators. Facilitates communication among developmental education professionals.

4209 ■ National Association of Elementary School Principals (NAESP)

1615 Duke St.
Alexandria, VA 22314
Ph: (703)684-3345
Fax: (703)549-5568
Fr: 800-386-2377
E-mail: naesp@naesp.org
URL: http://www.naesp.org

Description: Professional association of principals, assistant or vice principals, and aspiring principals; persons engaged in educational research and in the professional education of elementary and middle school administrators. Sponsors National Distinguished Principals Program, President's Award for Educational Excellence, American Student Council Association. Offers annual national convention and exhibition, on-site and internet professional development workshops throughout the year. Recently expanded professional publications offered through the National Principals' Resource Center.

4210 ■ National Association of Episcopal Schools (NAES)

815 2nd Ave., Ste. 819
New York, NY 10017-4594
Ph: (212)716-6134
Fax: (212)286-9366

Fr: 800-334-7626
E-mail: info@episcopalschools.org
URL: http://www.episcopalschools.org

Description: Represents Episcopal day and boarding schools and preschools. Promotes the educational ministry of the Episcopal Church. Provides publications, consultation services and conference focusing on Episcopal identity of schools, worship, religious education, spirituality, leadership development and governance for heads/directors, administrators, chaplains and teachers of religion, trustees, rectors and other church and school leaders.

4211 ■ National Association of Independent Schools (NAIS)

1620 L St. NW, Ste. 1100
Washington, DC 20036-5695
Ph: (202)973-9700
Fax: (202)973-9790
Fr: 800-793-6701
E-mail: bassett@nais.org
URL: http://www.nais.org

Description: Independent elementary and secondary school members; regional associations of independent schools and related associations. Provides curricular and administrative research and services. Conducts educational programs; compiles statistics.

4212 ■ National Association of Secondary School Principals (NASSP)

1904 Association Dr.
Reston, VA 20191-1537
Ph: (703)860-0200
Fax: (703)860-3422
Fr: 800-253-7746
E-mail: membership@principals.org
URL: http://www.nassp.org

Description: Middle level and high school principals, assistant principals, and aspiring school leaders, others engaged in secondary school administration and/or supervision; college professors teaching courses in secondary education. Administers the National Association of Student Councils (NASC), National Honor Society (NHS), National Junior Honor Society (NJHS), and the National Elementary Honor Society (NEHS).

4213 ■ National Association of Student Affairs Professionals

Fort Valley State University
1005 State University
Fort Valley, GA 31030
Ph: (478)825-6291
URL: http://www.nasap.net

Description: Promotes excellence in the area of student affairs. Provides programs and events to address the issues and needs of student affairs professionals.

4214 ■ National Association of Student Financial Aid Administrators

1101 Connecticut Ave. NW, Ste. 1100
Washington, DC 20036
Ph: (202)785-0453
Fax: (202)785-1487
E-mail: web@nasfaa.org
URL: http://www.nasfaa.org

Description: Represents financial aid professionals in colleges, universities, and career schools in the United States. Promotes the administration of student financial aid and facilitates communication among professionals. Encourages and promotes programs that remove financial barriers to ensure student access to postsecondary education.

4215 ■ National Association of Temple Educators (NATE)

633 3rd Ave.
New York, NY 10017-6778
Ph: (212)452-6510
Fax: (212)452-6512
E-mail: sschickler@natenet.org
URL: http://www.natenet.org

Description: Directors of education in Reform Jewish religious schools, principals, heads of departments, supervisors, educational consultants, students, and authors. Purposes are to: assist in the growth and development of Jewish religious education consistent with the aims of Reform Judaism; stimulate communal interest in Jewish religious education; represent and encourage the profession of temple educator. Conducts surveys on personnel practices, confirmation practices, religious school organization and administration, curricular practices, and other aspects of religious education. Sponsors institutes for principals and educational directors; maintains placement service.

4216 ■ National Community Education Association (NCEA)

3929 Old Lee Hwy., No. 91-A
Fairfax, VA 22030-2401
Ph: (703)359-8973
Fax: (703)359-0972
E-mail: ncea@ncea.com
URL: http://www.ncea.com

Description: Community school directors, principals, superintendents, professors, teachers, students, and laypeople. Promotes and establishes community schools as an integral part of the educational plan of every community. Emphasizes community and parent involvement in the schools, lifelong learning, and enrichment of K-12 and adult education. Serves as a clearinghouse for the exchange of ideas and information, and the sharing of efforts. Offers leadership training.

4217 ■ National Council for Accreditation of Teacher Education (NCATE)

2010 Massachusetts Ave. NW, Ste. 500
Washington, DC 20036
Ph: (202)466-7496
Fax: (202)296-6620
E-mail: ncate@ncate.org
URL: http://www.ncate.org

Description: Representatives from constituent colleges and universities, state departments of education, school boards, teacher, and other professional groups. Voluntary accrediting body devoted exclusively to: evaluation and accreditation of institutions for preparation of elementary and secondary school teachers; preparation of school service personnel, including school principals, supervisors, superintendents, school psychologists, instructional technolo-

gists, and other specialists for school-oriented positions.

4218 ■ *Overseas Employment Opportunities for Educators: Department of Defense Dependents Schools*

DIANE Publishing Co.
PO Box 617
Darby, PA 19023-0617
Fr: 800-782-3833
URL: http://www.dianepublishing.net

Barry Leonard, editor. $20.00. 52 pages. An introduction to teachings positions in the Dept. of Defense Dependents Schools (DoDDS), a worldwide school system, operated by the DoD in 14 countries.

4219 ■ Schechter Day School Network

820 2nd Ave.
New York, NY 10017
Ph: (212)533-7800
E-mail: cohen@uscj.org
URL: http://www.ssdsa.org

Description: A division of the United Synagogue of Conservative Judaism Commission on Jewish Education. Jewish elementary day schools and high schools with a total of over 21,500 students. Named for Solomon Schecter (1850-1915), scholar of Talmud and rabbinical literature at Cambridge and founder of the United Synagogue of America and the Jewish Theological Seminary. Provides visitations and consultations regarding education, governance and administration; publication of advisories and position papers, biennial conferences for lay leaders, annual conferences of the principals council, Shibboley Schechter newsletter, listserves for presidents, School heads, Business managers, and development directors. Also provides dissemination of demographics and statistics, chartering and accreditation of schools, seminars and board training for lay leaders, Schechter website, SHAR"R, 7th and 8th grade trips to Israel, placement service, MaToK-TaNaKH curriculum development project for Solomon Schecter Day schools, residency fellowship program to prepare professional leadership (SREL) and a listing of consultants.

4220 ■ University Council for Educational Administration (UCEA)

University of Virginia
Curry School of Education
405 Emmett St.
Charlottesville, VA 22904-0265
Ph: (434)243-1041
Fax: (434)924-1384
E-mail: ucea@virginia.edu
URL: http://www.ucea.org

Description: Consortium of universities with educational leadership and policy programs. Develops, promotes and disseminates information on the improvement of preparation, professional development and practice of school and higher education leaders. Conducts research, policy work and program development in educational leadership through inter-university cooperation. Operates placement service.

4221 ■ ADVANCE for Respiratory Care Practitioners
Merion Publications Inc.
2900 Horizon Dr.
PO Box 61556
King of Prussia, PA 19406-0956
Ph: (610)278-1400
Fr: 800-355-5627
URL: http://www.advanceweb.com/
  publications.asp?pub=RC

Biweekly. Free to qualified subscribers. Magazine for RRT's, CRTT's, and cardiopulmonary technologists across the country.

Employer Directories and Networking Lists

4222 ■ Crain's List—Chicago's Largest Hospitals
Crain Communications Inc.
360 N Michigan Ave.
Chicago, IL 60601
Ph: (312)649-5200
URL: http://www.chicagobusiness.com/section/lists

Published November, 2010. $25.00 for individuals; $45.00 for individuals. Covers: 25 hospitals in Chicago area ranked by net patient revenues. Entries include: Name, address, phone number, fax, web address, corporate e-mail, hospital administrator, network affiliation, 2009 net patient revenue, percentage change from 2008, 2009 net profits, percentage change from 2008, inpatient days, available beds, daily occupancy rate, number of hospital employees as of December 31, 2009, fiscal year end, Chairman, President, CEO, Chief Financial Officer, Human Resources Manager, Media Relations/Public Relations Director, and Hospital Administrator.

4223 ■ Directory of Hospital Personnel
Grey House Publishing
4919 Rte. 22
PO Box 56
Amenia, NY 12501
Ph: (518)789-8700
Fax: (518)789-0556
Fr: 800-562-2139
URL: http://www.greyhouse.com/hospital_
  personnel.htm

Annual, Latest edition 2011. $325.00 for individuals. Covers: 200,000 executives at 6,000 U.S. Hospitals. Entries include: Name of hospital, address, phone, number of beds, type and JCAHO status of hospital, names and titles of key department heads and staff, medical and nursing school affiliations; number of residents, interns, and nursing students. Arrangement: Geographical. Indexes: Hospital name, personnel, hospital size.

4224 ■ Hospital Blue Book
Billian Publishing Inc. and Trans World Publishing Inc.
2100 River Edge Pky.
Atlanta, GA 30328
Ph: (770)955-5656
Fax: (770)952-0669
Fr: 800-800-5668
E-mail: blu-book@billian.com
URL: http://www.billianshealthdata.com/Products/
  bluebook.html

Annual, Latest edition 2010. $575.00 for individuals; $575.00 for individuals. Covers: More than 6,500 hospitals; some listings also appear in a separate southern edition of this publication. Entries include: Name of hospital, accreditation, mailing address, phone, fax, number of beds, type of facility (nonprofit, general, state, etc.); list of administrative personnel and chiefs of medical services, with specific titles. Arrangement: Geographical.

4225 ■ Medical and Health Information Directory
Gale
PO Box 6904
Florence, KY 41022-6904
Fr: 800-354-9706
URL: http://www.gale.cengage.com

Annual, Latest edition April 2011. $1190.00 for individuals; $501.00 for individuals. Covers: In volume 1, more than 33,000 medical and health oriented associations, organizations, institutions, and government agencies, including health maintenance organizations (HMOs), preferred provider organizations (PPOs), insurance companies, pharmaceutical companies, research centers, and medical and allied health schools. In Volume 2, over 20,000 medical book publishers; medical periodicals, directories, audiovisual producers and services, medical libraries and information centers, electronic resources, and health-related internet search engines. In Volume 3, more than 40,500 clinics, treatment centers, care programs, and counseling/diagnostic services for 34 subject areas. Entries include: Institution, service, or firm name, address, phone, fax, email and URL; many include names of key personnel and, when pertinent, descriptive annotation. Volume 3 was formerly listed separately as Health Services Directory. Arrangement: Classified by organization activity, service, etc. Indexes: Each volume has a complete alphabetical name and keyword index.

Handbooks and Manuals

4226 ■ Careers in Health Care
The McGraw-Hill Companies
PO Box 182604
Columbus, OH 43272
Fax: (614)759-3749
Fr: 877-883-5524
E-mail: customer.service@mcgraw-hill.com
URL: http://www.mhprofessional.com/
  product.php?isbn=0071466533

Barbara M. Swanson. Fifth edition, 2005. $19.95 (paper). 192 pages. Describes job duties, work settings, salaries, licensing and certification requirements, educational preparation, and future outlook. Gives ideas on how to secure a job.

4227 ■ Exploring Health Care Careers, Second Edition
JIST Publishing
875 Montreal Way
St. Paul, MN 55102
Fax: 800-547-8329
Fr: 800-648-5478
E-mail: info@jist.com
URL: http://www.jist.com

2006. $125.00. 992 pages. Information about careers in the health industry, including education and certification requirements, earnings, and job outlook.

4228 ■ Opportunities in Health and Medical Careers
The McGraw-Hill Companies
PO Box 182604
Columbus, OH 43272
Fax: (614)759-3749
Fr: 877-883-5524
E-mail: customer.service@mcgraw-hill.com
URL: http://www.mhprofessional.com/
  product.php?isbn=0071437274

I. Donald Snook, Jr. and Leo D'Orazio. 2004. $14.95 (paper). 157 pages. Covers the full range of medical and health occupations. Illustrated.

4229 ■ Opportunities in Medical Imaging Careers
The McGraw-Hill Companies
PO Box 182604
Columbus, OH 43272
Fax: (614)759-3749
Fr: 877-883-5524
E-mail: customer.service@mcgraw-hill.com
URL: http://www.mhprofessional.com/
  product.php?isbn=0071458719

Clifford J. Sherry. 2006. $13.95. 160 pages.

4230 ■ Resumes for Health and Medical Careers
The McGraw-Hill Companies
PO Box 182604
Columbus, OH 43272
Fax: (614)759-3749
Fr: 877-883-5524
E-mail: customer.service@mcgraw-hill.com
URL: http://www.mhprofessional.com/
  product.php?isbn=0071545352

Third edition, 2008. $12.95 (paper). 144 pages.

Online Job Sources and Services

4231 ■ HEALTHeCAREERS Network
Fr: 888-884-8242
E-mail: info@healthecareers.com
URL: http://www.healthecareers.com

Description: Career search site for jobs in all health care specialties; educational resources; visa and licensing information for relocation; interesting articles; relocation tools; links to professional organizations and general resources.

4232 ■ ProHealthJobs.com
Ph: (484)443-8545
Fax: (484)443-8549
E-mail: info@prohealthjobs.com
URL: http://prohealthjobs.com/jobboard

Description: Career resources site for the medical and health care field. Lists professional opportunities, product information, continuing education and open positions.

TRADESHOWS

4233 ■ American Association of Neuromuscular and Electrodiagnostic Medicine Annual Scientific Meeting
American Association of Neuromuscular and Electrodiagnostic Medicine AANEM
2621 Superior Dr. N.W.
Rochester, MN 55901
Ph: (507)288-0100
Fax: (507)288-1225
E-mail: aanem@aanem.org
URL: http://www.aanem.org

Annual. Primary Exhibits: Electromyographic and electrodiagnostic equipment and accessories, pharmaceutical companies, and publishers. Dates and Locations: 2012 Oct 03-06; Orlando, FL; Grande Lakes Orlando; 2013 Oct 16-19; San Antonio, TX; JW Marriott San Antonio Hill Country Resort & Spa; 2014 Sep 17-20; Montreal, QC, Canada; Montreal Convention Centre; 2015 Oct 28-31; Honolulu, HI; Hawaii Convention Center and Hilton Hawaiian Village; 2016 Sep 14-17; New Orleans, LA; Hilton New Orleans.

4234 ■ American Clinical Neurophysiology Society Annual Meeting
American Clinical Neurophysiology Society
1 Regency Dr.
PO Box 30
Bloomfield, CT 06002
Ph: (860)243-3977
Fax: (860)286-0787
E-mail: info@acns.org
URL: http://www.acns.org

Annual. Primary Exhibits: Electroencephalographic and neurophysiology equipment, supplies, and services. Dates and Locations: 2012 Feb 07-12; San Antonio, TX; Marriott Rivercenter.

OTHER SOURCES

4235 ■ American Board of Registration of EEG and EP Technologists
2509 W Iles Ave., Ste. 102
Springfield, IL 62704
Ph: (217)726-7980

Fax: (217)726-7989
E-mail: abreteo@att.net
URL: http://abret.org

Description: Serves the electroneurodiagnostic community and patients. Offers credentialing exams to evaluate the skills and knowledge of technologists.

4236 ■ American Society of Electroneurodiagnostic Technologists (ASET)
402 E Bannister Rd., Ste. A
Kansas City, MO 64131-3019
Ph: (816)931-1120
Fax: (816)931-1145
E-mail: info@aset.org
URL: http://www.aset.org

Description: Persons engaged in clinical electroencephalographic (EEG) technology, evoked potential responses, nerve conduction studies, and polysomnography (sleep studies). Works for the advancement of electroneurodiagnostic technology education and practice standards.

SOURCES OF HELP-WANTED ADS

4237 ■ American Heart Journal
Mosby
1600 John F. Kennedy Blvd., Ste. 1800
Philadelphia, PA 19103-2899
Ph: (215)239-3275
Fax: (215)239-3286
URL: http://www.ahjonline.com/

Monthly. $298.00/year for individuals; $142.00/year for students; $395.00/year for other countries; $188.00/year for students, other countries. Medical journal serving practicing cardiologists, university-affiliated clinicians, and physicians keeping abreast of developments in the diagnosis and management of cardiovascular disease.

4238 ■ The American Journal of Cardiology
Excerpta Medica Inc.
685 US-202
Bridgewater, NJ 08807
Ph: (908)547-2100
Fax: (908)547-2200
URL: http://www.ajconline.org/

Semimonthly. $162.00/year for U.S. and Canada; $414.00/year for other countries; $88.00/year for students; $94.00/year for students, other countries. Peer-reviewed journal publishing information on cardiovascular disease.

4239 ■ Clinical Cardiology
Wiley InterScience
111 River St.
Hoboken, NJ 07030-5774
Ph: (201)748-6000
Fax: (201)748-6088
E-mail: clinicalcardiology@fams.org
URL: http://onlinelibrary.wiley.com/journal/10.1002/
(ISSN)1932-87

Monthly. $128.00/year for individuals; $128.00/year for Canada and Mexico; $128.00/year for other countries. Peer-reviewed indexed medical journal.

4240 ■ Heart and Lung
Mosby
1600 John F. Kennedy Blvd., Ste. 1800
Philadelphia, PA 19103-2899
Ph: (215)239-3275
Fax: (215)239-3286
URL: http://www.elsevier.com/wps/find/
journaldescription.cws_home

Bimonthly. $103.00/year for individuals; $445.00/year for institutions; $524.00/year for institutions, other countries; $153.00/year for other countries. Journal offering articles prepared by nurse and physician members of the critical care team, recognizing the nurse's role in the care and management of major organ-system conditions in critically ill patients.

4241 ■ Journal of the American Society of Echocardiography
Mosby
1600 John F. Kennedy Blvd., Ste. 1800
Philadelphia, PA 19103-2899
Ph: (215)239-3275
Fax: (215)239-3286
URL: http://www.elsevier.com/wps/find/
journalbibliographicinfo.cw

$408.00/year for other countries, print; $613.00/year for institutions, other countries, print; $298.00/year for individuals, print; $499.00/year for institutions, print; $196.00/year for students, other countries; $143.00/year for students. Official journal of the American Society of Echocardiography serving as a source of information on the technical basis and clinical application of echocardiography. Peer-reviewed publication featuring research, reviews, and case studies.

4242 ■ Journal of Cardiopulmonary Rehabilitation (JCR)
Lippincott Williams & Wilkins
530 Walnut St.
Philadelphia, PA 19106-3619
Ph: (215)521-8300
Fax: (215)521-8902
Fr: 800-638-3030
E-mail: jcr@sba.com
URL: http://journals.lww.com/jcrjournal/pages/
default.aspx

$134.00/year for individuals; $410.00/year for institutions; $262.00/year for other countries; $558.00/year for institutions, other countries; $65.49/year for individuals, in-training. Medical journal.

EMPLOYER DIRECTORIES AND NETWORKING LISTS

4243 ■ Crain's List—Chicago's Largest Hospitals
Crain Communications Inc.
360 N Michigan Ave.
Chicago, IL 60601
Ph: (312)649-5200
URL: http://www.chicagobusiness.com/section/lists

Published November, 2010. $25.00 for individuals; $45.00 for individuals. Covers: 25 hospitals in Chicago area ranked by net patient revenues. Entries include: Name, address, phone number, fax, web address, corporate e-mail, hospital administrator, network affiliation, 2009 net patient revenue, percentage change from 2008, 2009 net profits, percentage change from 2008, inpatient days, available beds, daily occupancy rate, number of hospital employees as of December 31, 2009, fiscal year end, Chairman, President, CEO, Chief Financial Officer, Human Resources Manager, Media Relations/Public Relations Director, and Hospital Administrator.

4244 ■ Directory of Hospital Personnel
Grey House Publishing
4919 Rte. 22
PO Box 56
Amenia, NY 12501
Ph: (518)789-8700
Fax: (518)789-0556
Fr: 800-562-2139
URL: http://www.greyhouse.com/hospital_
personnel.htm

Annual, Latest edition 2011. $325.00 for individuals. Covers: 200,000 executives at 6,000 U.S. Hospitals. Entries include: Name of hospital, address, phone, number of beds, type and JCAHO status of hospital, names and titles of key department heads and staff, medical and nursing school affiliations; number of residents, interns, and nursing students. Arrangement: Geographical. Indexes: Hospital name, personnel, hospital size.

4245 ■ Hospital Blue Book
Billian Publishing Inc. and Trans World Publishing Inc.
2100 River Edge Pky.
Atlanta, GA 30328
Ph: (770)955-5656
Fax: (770)952-0669
Fr: 800-800-5668
E-mail: blu-book@billian.com
URL: http://www.billianshealthdata.com/Products/
bluebook.html

Annual, Latest edition 2010. $575.00 for individuals; $575.00 for individuals. Covers: More than 6,500 hospitals; some listings also appear in a separate southern edition of this publication. Entries include: Name of hospital, accreditation, mailing address, phone, fax, number of beds, type of facility (nonprofit, general, state, etc.); list of administrative personnel and chiefs of medical services, with specific titles. Arrangement: Geographical.

4246 ■ Medical and Health Information Directory
Gale
PO Box 6904
Florence, KY 41022-6904
Fr: 800-354-9706
URL: http://www.gale.cengage.com

Annual, Latest edition April 2011. $1190.00 for individuals; $501.00 for individuals. Covers: In volume 1, more than 33,000 medical and health oriented associations, organizations, institutions, and government agencies, including health maintenance organizations (HMOs), preferred provider organizations (PPOs), insurance companies, pharmaceutical companies, research centers, and medical and allied health schools. In Volume 2, over 20,000 medical book publishers; medical periodicals, directories, audiovisual producers and services, medical libraries and information centers, electronic resources, and health-related internet search engines. In Volume 3, more than 40,500 clinics, treatment centers, care programs, and counseling/diagnostic services for 34 subject areas. Entries include: Institution, service, or firm name, address, phone, fax, email and URL; many include names of key personnel and, when pertinent, descriptive annotation. Volume 3 was formerly listed separately as Health Services Directory. Arrangement: Classified by organization activity, service, etc. Indexes: Each volume has a complete alphabetical name and keyword index.

HANDBOOKS AND MANUALS

4247 ■ Careers in Health Care
The McGraw-Hill Companies
PO Box 182604
Columbus, OH 43272
Fax: (614)759-3749
Fr: 877-883-5524
E-mail: customer.service@mcgraw-hill.com
URL: http://www.mhprofessional.com/ product.php?isbn=0071466533

Barbara M. Swanson. Fifth edition, 2005. $19.95 (paper). 192 pages. Describes job duties, work settings, salaries, licensing and certification requirements, educational preparation, and future outlook. Gives ideas on how to secure a job.

4248 ■ Exploring Health Care Careers, Second Edition
JIST Publishing
875 Montreal Way
St. Paul, MN 55102
Fax: 800-547-8329
Fr: 800-648-5478
E-mail: info@jist.com
URL: http://www.jist.com

2006. $125.00. 992 pages. Information about careers in the health industry, including education and certification requirements, earnings, and job outlook.

4249 ■ The Only EKG Book You'll Ever Need
Lippincott Williams & Wilkins
530 Walnut St.
Philadelphia, PA 19106
Ph: (215)521-8300
Fax: (215)521-8902
Fr: 800-638-3030
URL: http://www.lww.com/product/?978-1-60547-140-2

Malcolm S Thaler. Sixth edition, 2009. $61.95. 336 pages.

4250 ■ Opportunities in Health and Medical Careers
The McGraw-Hill Companies
PO Box 182604
Columbus, OH 43272
Fax: (614)759-3749
Fr: 877-883-5524
E-mail: customer.service@mcgraw-hill.com
URL: http://www.mhprofessional.com/ product.php?isbn=0071437274

I. Donald Snook, Jr. and Leo D'Orazio. 2004. $14.95 (paper). 157 pages. Covers the full range of medical and health occupations. Illustrated.

4251 ■ Opportunities in Medical Imaging Careers
The McGraw-Hill Companies
PO Box 182604
Columbus, OH 43272
Fax: (614)759-3749

Fr: 877-883-5524
E-mail: customer.service@mcgraw-hill.com
URL: http://www.mhprofessional.com/ product.php?isbn=0071458719

Clifford J. Sherry. 2006. $13.95. 160 pages.

4252 ■ Resumes for Health and Medical Careers
The McGraw-Hill Companies
PO Box 182604
Columbus, OH 43272
Fax: (614)759-3749
Fr: 877-883-5524
E-mail: customer.service@mcgraw-hill.com
URL: http://www.mhprofessional.com/ product.php?isbn=0071545352

Third edition, 2008. $12.95 (paper). 144 pages.

EMPLOYMENT AGENCIES AND SEARCH FIRMS

4253 ■ Team Placement Service, Inc.
1414 Prince St., Ste. 202
Alexandria, VA 22314
Ph: (703)820-8618
Fax: (703)820-3368
Fr: 800-495-6767
E-mail: 4jobs@teamplace.com
URL: http://www.teamplace.com

Full-service personnel consultants provide placement for healthcare staff, physician and dentist, private practice, and hospitals. Conduct interviews, tests, and reference checks to select the top 20% of applicants. Survey applicants' skill levels, provide backup information on each candidate, select compatible candidates for consideration, and insure the hiring process minimizes potential legal liability. Industries served: healthcare and government agencies providing medical, dental, biotech, laboratory, hospitals, and physician search.

ONLINE JOB SOURCES AND SERVICES

4254 ■ HEALTHeCAREERS Network
Fr: 888-884-8242
E-mail: info@healthecareers.com
URL: http://www.healthecareers.com

Description: Career search site for jobs in all health care specialties; educational resources; visa and licensing information for relocation; interesting articles; relocation tools; links to professional organizations and general resources.

4255 ■ Hospital Jobs OnLine
E-mail: support@hospitaljobsonline.com
URL: http://www.hospitaljobsonline.com

Description: Serves as a niche healthcare job board designed exclusively for hospitals, healthcare companies, and healthcare job seekers.

4256 ■ ProHealthJobs.com
Ph: (484)443-8545
Fax: (484)443-8549
E-mail: info@prohealthjobs.com
URL: http://prohealthjobs.com/jobboard

Description: Career resources site for the medical and health care field. Lists professional opportunities, product information, continuing education and open positions.

TRADESHOWS

4257 ■ American Association of Neuromuscular and Electrodiagnostic Medicine Annual Scientific Meeting
American Association of Neuromuscular and Electrodiagnostic Medicine AANEM
2621 Superior Dr. N.W.
Rochester, MN 55901
Ph: (507)288-0100
Fax: (507)288-1225
E-mail: aanem@aanem.org
URL: http://www.aanem.org

Annual. Primary Exhibits: Electromyographic and electrodiagnostic equipment and accessories, pharmaceutical companies, and publishers. Dates and Locations: 2012 Oct 03-06; Orlando, FL; Grande Lakes Orlando; 2013 Oct 16-19; San Antonio, TX; JW Marriott San Antonio Hill Country Resort & Spa; 2014 Sep 17-20; Montreal, QC, Canada; Montreal Convention Centre; 2015 Oct 28-31; Honolulu, HI; Hawaii Convention Center and Hilton Hawaiian Village; 2016 Sep 14-17; New Orleans, LA; Hilton New Orleans.

4258 ■ American Clinical Neurophysiology Society Annual Meeting
American Clinical Neurophysiology Society
1 Regency Dr.
PO Box 30
Bloomfield, CT 06002
Ph: (860)243-3977
Fax: (860)286-0787
E-mail: info@acns.org
URL: http://www.acns.org

Annual. Primary Exhibits: Electroencephalographic and neurophysiology equipment, supplies, and services. Dates and Locations: 2012 Feb 07-12; San Antonio, TX; Marriott Rivercenter.

4259 ■ American College of Cardiology Annual Scientific Session
American College of Cardiology
Heart House
2400 N. St. N.W.
Washington, DC 20037
Ph: (202)375-6000
Fax: (202)375-7000
URL: http://www.acc.org

Annual. Primary Exhibits: Products and services related to cardiovascular medicine.

OTHER SOURCES

4260 ■ Alliance of Cardiovascular Professionals (ACVP)
PO Box 2007
Midlothian, VA 23113
Ph: (804)632-0078
Fax: (804)639-9212
E-mail: peggymcelgunn@comcast.net
URL: http://www.acp-online.org

Description: Strives to meet educational needs. Develops programs to meet those needs. Provides a structure to offer the cardiovascular and pulmonary technology professional a key to the future as a valuable member of the medical team. Seeks advancement for members through communication and education. Provides coordinated programs to orient the newer professional to his field and continuing educational opportunities for technologist personnel; has established guidelines for educational programs in the hospital and university setting. Works with educators and physicians to provide basic, advanced, and in-service programs for technologists. Sponsors registration and certification programs which provide technology professionals with further opportunity to clarify their level of expertise. Compiles statistics.

SOURCES OF HELP-WANTED ADS

4261 ■ *Appliance Service News*
Gamit Enterprises Inc.
PO Box 809
St. Charles, IL 60174
Ph: (630)845-9481
Fax: (630)845-9483
Fr: 877-747-1625
URL: http://asnews.com

Monthly. $79.95/year for individuals, domestic; $96.95/year for individuals, domestic, first class delivery; $101.95/year for Canada, first class delivery; $125.95/year for other countries, first class delivery; $39.95/year for individuals, online. Magazine for appliance technicians.

4262 ■ *Electric Light & Power*
PennWell Corp.
1421 S Sheridan Rd.
Tulsa, OK 74112
Ph: (918)835-3161
Fax: (918)831-9497
Fr: 800-331-4463
URL: http://www.elp.com/index.html

Bimonthly. $85.00/year for Canada; $145.00/year for Canada, two years; $94.00/year for individuals, Mexico; $160.00/year for individuals, 2 years, Mexico; $225.00/year for other countries; $403.00/year for other countries, 2 years; free to qualified subscribers. Provides broad view of electric utility industry with in-depth analysis of key business issues for executives and management.

4263 ■ *Electronic Markets*
Springer-Verlag New York Inc.
233 Spring St.
New York, NY 10013-1578
Ph: (212)460-1500
Fax: (212)460-1575
Fr: 800-777-4643
URL: http://www.springer.com/business/
    business+information+system

$618.00/year for institutions, print or online; $742.00/year for institutions, print & enchanced access. Journal covering all system concepts of electronic commerce.

4264 ■ *Engineering Economist*
Taylor & Francis Group
270 Madison Ave.
New York, NY 10016
Fax: (212)244-4561
URL: http://www.tandf.co.uk/journals/titles/
    0013791x.asp

Quarterly. $89.00/year for individuals, print; $153.00/year for institutions, online only; $170.00/year for institutions, print & online. Publication covering business issues in the energy, petroleum and mining industries.

4265 ■ *The High-Tech News*
ETA International
5 Depot St.
Greencastle, IN 46135
Ph: (765)653-8262
Fax: (765)653-4287
Fr: 800-288-3824
E-mail: eta@eta-i.org
URL: http://www.eta-i.org

Description: Bimonthly. Serves member technicians with news of the Association and the electronics industry, including items on service, education, employment, management, and events. Contains information on membership, management, telecommunications, and business and technical training programs. Recurring features include editorials, news of research, letters to the editor, book reviews, and a calendar of events.

4266 ■ *Journal of Active and Passive Electronic Devices*
Old City Publishing
628 N 2nd St.
Philadelphia, PA 19123-3002
Ph: (215)925-4390
Fax: (215)925-4371
URL: http://www.oldcitypublishing.com/JAPED/
    JAPED.html

Quarterly. $766.00/year for institutions, print and online; $157.00/year for individuals, print only; $635.00/year for institutions, print and online; $148.00/year for individuals, print only; $76,372.00/year for institutions, print and online; $19,859.00/year for individuals, print only. International journal devoted to the science and technology of all types of electronic components.

4267 ■ *Journal of Vacuum Science and Technology A & B*
American Institute of Physics
1 Physics Ellipse
College Park, MD 20740-3843
Ph: (301)209-3100
Fax: (301)209-0843
E-mail: jvst@mcnc.org
URL: http://www.virtualjournals.org/

Monthly. $1,840.00/year for individuals, print & online; $1,980.00/year for other countries, print & online (surface); $2,040.00/year for individuals, print & online (air). Journal containing research review articles in all areas of vacuum science.

4268 ■ *Machine Design*
Penton Media Inc.
249 W 17th St.
New York, NY 10011
Ph: (212)204-4200
URL: http://machinedesign.com/

Magazine on design engineering function.

4269 ■ *Security Sales & Integration*
Bobit Business Media
3520 Challenger St.
Torrance, CA 90503
Ph: (310)533-2400
E-mail: secsales@bobit.com
URL: http://www.securitysales.com

Monthly. Free. Magazine covering the security industry.

EMPLOYER DIRECTORIES AND NETWORKING LISTS

4270 ■ *American Electronics Association—Member Directory*
AeA
601 Pennsylvania Ave. NW, North Bldg., Ste. 600
Washington, DC 20004
Ph: (202)682-9110
Fax: (202)682-9111
Fr: 800-284-4232
URL: http://www.aea.net/memberdirectory.asp

Covers: Over 3,000 member electronics and high-technology companies and 500 associate member firms including financial institutions, law firms, and accounting firms. Entries include: Company name, address, phone, World Wide Web addresses, cable address, fax, names of executives, number of employees, list of products or services, date founded, whether a public or private company, stock market where traded, ticker symbol. Arrangement: Alphabetical. Indexes: Geographical, product.

4271 ■ *Appliance Design—Buyers Guide*
Business News Publishing Co.
2401 W Big Weaver Rd., Ste. 700
Troy, MI 48084
Ph: (248)362-3700
E-mail: directories@bnpmedia.com
URL: http://www.appliancedesign.com/buyersguide

Annual, Latest edition 2010. Publication includes: Directory of manufacturers and suppliers of equipment, material, and components to the appliance industry; trade association.

HANDBOOKS AND MANUALS

4272 ■ *Careers in Focus: Electronics*
Ferguson Publishing
132 W 31st St., 17th Fl.
New York, NY 10001
Fax: 800-678-3633
Fr: 800-322-8755
E-mail: custserv@factsonfile.com
URL: http://ferguson.infobasepublishing.com

2009. $32.95 (hardcover). 200 pages. Profiles careers in electronics for young professionals.

4273 ■ *Opportunities in Electronics Careers*
The McGraw-Hill Companies
PO Box 182604
Columbus, OH 43272
Fax: (614)759-3749
Fr: 877-883-5524
E-mail: customer.service@mcgraw-hill.com
URL: http://www.mhprofessional.com/
    product.php?isbn=0071476075

Mark Rowh. 2007. $13.95 (paper). 221 pages. Discusses career opportunities in commercial and industrial electronics equipment repair, electronics home entertainment repair, electronics engineering, and engineering technology. Includes job outlook and how to get off to a good start on the job.

4274 ■ *Troubleshooting Electrical/Electronic Systems*
American Technical Publishers, Inc.
1155 W 175th St.
Homewood, IL 60430
Ph: (708)957-1100
Fax: (708)957-1101
Fr: 800-323-3471
URL: http://www.go2atp.com/Troubleshooting_
    Electrical_P14.cfm

Glen A. Mazur and Thomas E. Proctor. Third edition. $78.00. 631 pages. Step-by-step applications show how to troubleshoot electrical and electronic systems.

4275 ■ *Troubleshooting and Repairing Major Appliances*
McGraw-Hill Companies
PO Box 182604
Columbus, OH 43272
Fax: (614)759-3749
Fr: 877-883-5524
E-mail: pbg.ecommerce_custserv@mcgraw-hill.com
URL: http://www.mhprofessional.com/
    product.php?cat=113&isbn=0071481486

Eric Kleinert. 2007. $59.95. 744 pages.

EMPLOYMENT AGENCIES AND SEARCH FIRMS

4276 ■ Electronic Search, Inc.
5105 Tollview Dr., Ste. 245
Rolling Meadows, IL 60008
Ph: (847)506-0700
Fax: (847)506-9999
E-mail: email@electronicsearch.com
URL: http://www.electronicsearch.com

Description: Staffing solutions firm, specializing in filling highly technical requirements in the wireless, telecommunications, and public safety technology industries; includes job listings with contact person, location, job description, qualifications, and compensation.

4277 ■ Omni Recruiting Group, Inc.
227 Sandy Springs Pl., Ste D-370
Atlanta, GA 30328
Ph: (404)256-1575
Fax: (404)256-1585
E-mail: info@omnirecruiting.com
URL: http://www.omnirecruiting.com

Executive search firm specializing in sales.

4278 ■ S.D. Kelly and Associates, Inc.
130 S Washington St.
North Attleboro, MA 02760
Ph: (508)809-6496
Fax: (508)809-6495
E-mail: info@sdkelly.com
URL: http://www.sdkelly.com

Employment agency.

TRADESHOWS

4279 ■ Electronic Entertainment Expo
IDG Expo Management Co.
PO Box 620
Medfield, MA 02052-0620
URL: http://www.idgexpos.com

Annual. Primary Exhibits: Interactive entertainment equipment, supplies, and services.

4280 ■ International CES
Consumer Electronics Association CEA
2500 Wilson Blvd.
Arlington, VA 22201-3834
Ph: (703)907-7600
Fax: (703)907-7675
Fr: (866)233-7968
E-mail: cea@ce.org
URL: http://www.cesweb.org

Annual. Primary Exhibits: Electronic equipment, supplies, and services. Dates and Locations: 2013 Jan 06-09; Las Vegas, NV; 2014 Jan 09-12; Las Vegas, NV.

4281 ■ National Utility Contractors Association Convention
Nielsen Business Media
770 Broadway
New York, NY 10003-9595
Ph: (646)654-4500
E-mail: bmcomm@nielsen.com
URL: http://www.nielsenbusinessmedia.com/

Annual. Primary Exhibits: Equipment, supplies, and services for the construction of utility lines (pipes for storm and sanitary sewers and drainage, water lines, cables, ducts, conduits, and other utility work).

4282 ■ POWER-GEN International
PennWell Conferences and Exhibitions (Tulsa, Oklahoma)
1421 S. Sheridan Rd.
Tulsa, OK 74112
Ph: (918)835-3161

Fax: (918)831-9497
Fr: 800-331-4463
URL: http://www.pennwell.com
Annual. Primary Exhibits: Equipment and services for power generation industries.

OTHER SOURCES

4283 ■ Electronics Technicians Association International (ETA)
5 Depot St.
Greencastle, IN 46135
Ph: (765)653-8262
Fax: (765)653-4287
Fr: 800-288-3824
E-mail: eta@eta-i.org
URL: http://www.eta-i.org

Description: Skilled electronics technicians. Provides placement service; offers certification examinations for electronics technicians and satellite, fiber optics, and data cabling installers. Compiles wage and manpower statistics. Administers FCC Commercial License examinations and certification of computer network systems technicians and web and internet specialists.

4284 ■ International Society of Certified Electronics Technicians (ISCET)
3608 Pershing Ave.
Fort Worth, TX 76107-4527
Ph: (817)921-9101
Fax: (817)921-3741
Fr: 800-946-0201
E-mail: info@iscet.org
URL: http://www.iscet.org

Description: Technicians in 50 countries who have been certified by the society. Seeks to provide a fraternal bond among certified electronics technicians, raise their public image and improve the effectiveness of industry education programs for technicians. Offers training programs in new electronics information. Maintains library of service literature for consumer electronic equipment, including manuals and schematics for out-of-date equipment. Offers all FCC licenses. Sponsors testing program for certification of electronics technicians in the fields of audio, communications, computer, consumer, industrial, medical electronics, radar, radio-television and video.

4285 ■ National Electronics Service Dealers Association (NESDA)
3608 Pershing Ave.
Fort Worth, TX 76107-4527
Ph: (817)921-9061
Fax: (817)921-3741
Fr: 800-797-9197
E-mail: info@nesda.com
URL: http://www.nesda.com

Description: Local and state electronic service associations and companies. Supplies technical service information on business management training to electronic service dealers. Offers certification and training programs through International Society of Certified Electronics Technicians. Conducts technical service and business management seminars.

Electrical and Electronics Engineers

4286 ■ Circuits Assembly
UP Media Group Inc.
PO Box 470
Canton, GA 30169
Ph: (678)817-1286
URL: http://www.circuitsassembly.com

Monthly. Serves the PCB assembly marketplace.

4287 ■ Circuits and Systems
Scientific Research Publishing
PO Box 54821
Irvine, CA 92619-4821
E-mail: cs@scirp.org
URL: http://www.scirp.org/journal/cs/

Quarterly. $156.00/year for individuals. Peer-reviewed journal publishing articles on the latest advancement of theories, methods and applications in electronics, circuits and systems.

4288 ■ Communications of the ACM
Association for Computing Machinery
PO Box 30777
New York, NY 10087
Ph: (212)626-0500
Fax: (212)944-1318
Fr: 800-342-6626
URL: http://cacm.acm.org

Monthly. $99.00/year for members, professional. Computing news magazine.

4289 ■ Community Radio News
National Federation of Community Broadcasters
1970 Broadway, Ste. 1000
Oakland, CA 94612
Ph: (510)451-8200
Fax: (510)451-8208
E-mail: newsletter@nfcb.org
URL: http://www.nfcb.org

Description: Monthly. Serves as a medium of communication for independent, community-licensed radio stations. Contains brief articles and news items on such topics as public broadcasting and programming, legislative developments, activities of the Federal Communications Commission, and local stations. Recurring features include notices of grants and awards, job openings, and a calendar of events/conferences for noncommercial broadcasters.

4290 ■ Consulting-Specifying Engineer
CFE Media LLC
1111 W 22nd St., Ste. 250
Oak Brook, IL 60523
Ph: (630)571-4070
Fax: (630)214-4504
URL: http://www.csemag.com

The integrated engineering magazine of the building construction industry.

4291 ■ EE Evaluation Engineering
Nelson Publishing Inc.
2500 Tamiami Trl. N
Nokomis, FL 34275
Ph: (941)966-9521
Fax: (941)966-2590
URL: http://www.evaluationengineering.com/

Monthly. Free. Trade magazine covering electronic engineering, evaluation and test.

4292 ■ Electric Light & Power
PennWell Corp.
1421 S Sheridan Rd.
Tulsa, OK 74112
Ph: (918)835-3161
Fax: (918)831-9497
Fr: 800-331-4463
URL: http://www.elp.com/index.html

Bimonthly. $85.00/year for Canada; $145.00/year for Canada, two years; $94.00/year for individuals, Mexico; $160.00/year for individuals, 2 years, Mexico; $225.00/year for other countries; $403.00/year for other countries, 2 years; free to qualified subscribers. Provides broad view of electric utility industry with in-depth analysis of key business issues for executives and management.

4293 ■ The Electrochemical Society Interface
Electrochemical Society Inc.
65 S Main St., Bldg. D
Pennington, NJ 08534-2839
Ph: (609)737-1902
Fax: (609)737-2743
E-mail: interface@electrochem.org
URL: http://www.electrochem.org/dl/interface/

Quarterly. $64.00/year for individuals, tier 1, print & online; $82.00/year for other countries, tier 1, print & online. Publication featuring news and articles of interest to members of the Electrochemical Society.

4294 ■ Electronic Component News (ECN)
Advantage Business Media
100 Enterprise Dr., Ste. 600
Box 912
Rockaway, NJ 07866-0912
Ph: (973)920-7000
URL: http://www.ecnmag.com/

Free to members; $93.00/year for individuals; $112.00/year for individuals; $175.00/year for other countries. Magazine (tabloid) for electronics design engineers and engineering management.

4295 ■ Electronic Engineering Times
United business Media L.L.C
240 W 35th St.
New York, NY 10001
Ph: (516)562-5000
URL: http://www.cmp.com/products/pr_det_elecengtimesasia.jhtml

Semimonthly. Weekly trade newspaper.

4296 ■ Electronic Markets
Springer-Verlag New York Inc.
233 Spring St.
New York, NY 10013-1578
Ph: (212)460-1500
Fax: (212)460-1575
Fr: 800-777-4643
URL: http://www.springer.com/business/business+information+system

$618.00/year for institutions, print or online; $742.00/year for institutions, print & enchanced access. Journal covering all system concepts of electronic commerce.

4297 ■ Electronic Products
Hearst Business Communications/Electronics Group
50 Charles Lindbergh Blvd., Ste. 100
Uniondale, NY 11553
Ph: (516)227-1383
E-mail: lens@electronicproducts.com
URL: http://www.electronicproducts.com

Monthly. $12.00/year for individuals. Magazine for electronic design engineers and management.

4298 ■ Energy and Power Engineering
Scientific Research Publishing
PO Box 54821
Irvine, CA 92619-4821
E-mail: epe@scirp.org
URL: http://www.scirp.org/journal/epe/

$295.00/year for individuals. Journal publishing information on all important aspects of electric power engineering.

4299 ■ Engineering
Scientific Research Publishing
PO Box 54821
Irvine, CA 92619-4821
E-mail: eng@scirp.org
URL: http://www.scirp.org/journal/eng/

Monthly. $708.00/year for individuals. Peer-reviewed journal publishing articles on the latest advancements in engineering.

4300 ■ Engineering
Scientific Research Publishing
PO Box 54821
Irvine, CA 92619-4821
E-mail: eng@scirp.org
URL: http://www.scirp.org/journal/eng/

Monthly. $708.00/year for individuals. Peer-reviewed journal publishing articles on the latest advancements in engineering.

4301 ■ Engineering Economist
Taylor & Francis Group
270 Madison Ave.
New York, NY 10016
Fax: (212)244-4561
URL: http://www.tandf.co.uk/journals/titles/0013791x.asp

Quarterly. $89.00/year for individuals, print; $153.00/year for institutions, online only; $170.00/year for institutions, print & online. Publication covering business issues in the energy, petroleum and mining industries.

4302 ■ *ENR: Engineering News-Record*
McGraw-Hill Inc.
PO Box 182604
Columbus, OH 43218
Ph: (614)430-4000
Fax: (614)759-3749
Fr: 877-833-5524
URL: http://enr.construction.com/Default.asp

Weekly. $49.00/year for individuals, print; $89.00/year for Canada, print; $125.00/year for other countries, print. Magazine focusing on engineering and construction.

4303 ■ *Graduating Engineer & Computer Careers*
Career Recruitment Media
2 LAN Dr., Ste. 100
Westford, MA 01886
Ph: (978)692-5092
Fax: (978)692-4174
URL: http://www.graduatingengineer.com

Quarterly. $16.95/year for individuals. Magazine focusing on employment, education, and career development for entry-level engineers and computer scientists.

4304 ■ *The High-Tech News*
ETA International
5 Depot St.
Greencastle, IN 46135
Ph: (765)653-8262
Fax: (765)653-4287
Fr: 800-288-3824
E-mail: eta@eta-i.org
URL: http://www.eta-i.org

Description: Bimonthly. Serves member technicians with news of the Association and the electronics industry, including items on service, education, employment, management, and events. Contains information on membership, management, telecommunications, and business and technical training programs. Recurring features include editorials, news of research, letters to the editor, book reviews, and a calendar of events.

4305 ■ *High Technology Careers Magazine*
HTC
4701 Patrick Henry Dr., No. 1901
Santa Clara, CA 95054
Fax: (408)567-0242
URL: http://www.hightechcareers.com

Bimonthly. $29.00/year; $35.00/year for Canada; $85.00/year for out of country. Magazine (tabloid) containing employment opportunity information for the engineering and technical community.

4306 ■ *IEEE Spectrum*
Institute of Electrical and Electronics Engineers Inc.
3 Park Ave., 17th Fl.
New York, NY 10016-5997
Ph: (212)419-7900
Fax: (212)705-8999
URL: http://www.spectrum.ieee.org/mc_online

Monthly. $29.95/year for U.S. and Canada; $99.95/year for other countries. Magazine for the scientific and engineering professional. Provides information on developments and trends in engineering, physics, mathematics, chemistry, medicine/biology, and the nuclear sciences.

4307 ■ *IEEE Transactions on Electron Devices*
IEEE Electron Devices Society
445 Hoes Ln.
Piscataway, NJ 08854-4141
Ph: (732)562-3926

Fax: (732)235-1626
URL: http://ieeexplore.ieee.org/xpl/RecentIssue.jsp?punumber=16

Monthly. Included in membership, online. Journal covering theory, design, performance and reliability of electron devices.

4308 ■ *IEEE Transactions on Terahertz Science and Technology*
IEEE Microwave Theory and Techniques Society
c/o Edward C. Niehenke
Niehenke Consulting
5829 Bellanca Dr.
Elkridge, MD 21075
Ph: (410)796-5866
Fax: (410)796-5829
E-mail: thz.editors@ieee.org
URL: http://www.mtt.org/publications/118-terahertz.html

Peer-reviewed journal covering terahertz science and applications.

4309 ■ *IEEJ Transactions on Electrical and Electronic Engineering*
John Wiley & Sons Inc.
111 River St.
Hoboken, NJ 07030-5773
Ph: (201)748-6000
Fax: (201)748-6088
Fr: 800-825-7550
URL: http://onlinelibrary.wiley.com/journal/10.1002/(ISSN)1931-49

Bimonthly. Peer-reviewed journal covering the areas of electrical and electronic engineering and in related disciplines.

4310 ■ *ISRN Signal Processing*
Hindawi Publishing Corporation
410 Park Ave., 15th Fl.
287 PMB
New York, NY 10022
E-mail: sp@isrn.com
URL: http://www.isrn.com/journals/sp

Peer-reviewed journal publishing information in all areas of signal processing.

4311 ■ *Journal of Active and Passive Electronic Devices*
Old City Publishing
628 N 2nd St.
Philadelphia, PA 19123-3002
Ph: (215)925-4390
Fax: (215)925-4371
URL: http://www.oldcitypublishing.com/JAPED/JAPED.html

Quarterly. $766.00/year for institutions, print and online; $157.00/year for individuals, print only; $635.00/year for institutions, print and online; $148.00/year for individuals, print only; $76,372.00/year for institutions, print and online; $19,859.00/year for individuals, print only. International journal devoted to the science and technology of all types of electronic components.

4312 ■ *Journal of Signal and Information Processing*
Scientific Research Publishing
PO Box 54821
Irvine, CA 92619-4821
E-mail: jsip@scirp.org
URL: http://www.scirp.org/journal/jsip/

Quarterly. $156.00/year for individuals. Peer-reviewed journal publishing articles on the latest advancements in signal and information processing.

4313 ■ *Journal of Women and Minorities in Science and Engineering*
Begell House Inc.
50 Cross Hwy.
Redding, CT 06896
Ph: (203)938-1300

Fax: (203)938-1304
URL: http://www.begellhouse.com/journals/00551c876cc2f027

$248.00/year for institutions. Peer-reviewed journal featuring innovative ideas and programs for classroom teachers, scientific studies, and formulation of concepts related to the education, recruitment, and retention of under-represented groups in science and engineering.

4314 ■ *Journal of Women and Minorities in Science and Engineering*
Begell House Inc.
50 Cross Hwy.
Redding, CT 06896
Ph: (203)938-1300
Fax: (203)938-1304
URL: http://www.begellhouse.com/journals/00551c876cc2f027

$248.00/year for institutions. Peer-reviewed journal featuring innovative ideas and programs for classroom teachers, scientific studies, and formulation of concepts related to the education, recruitment, and retention of under-represented groups in science and engineering.

4315 ■ *Machine Design*
Penton Media Inc.
249 W 17th St.
New York, NY 10011
Ph: (212)204-4200
URL: http://machinedesign.com/

Magazine on design engineering function.

4316 ■ *Microwave Journal*
Horizon House Publications Inc.
685 Canton St.
Norwood, MA 02062
Ph: (781)769-9750
Fax: (781)769-5037
Fr: 800-966-8526
E-mail: mwj@mwjournal.com
URL: http://www.mwjournal.com

Monthly. Electronic engineering magazine.

4317 ■ *NSBE Magazine*
NSBE Publications
205 Daingerfield Rd.
Alexandria, VA 22314
Ph: (703)549-2207
Fax: (703)683-5312
URL: http://www.nsbe.org/News-Media/Magazines/About-NSBE-Magazine

$20.00/year for individuals; $35.00/year for other countries; $15.00/year for students. Journal providing information on engineering careers, self-development, and cultural issues for recent graduates with technical majors.

4318 ■ *PE*
National Society of Professional Engineers
1420 King St.
Alexandria, VA 22314
Ph: (703)684-2800
Fax: (703)684-4875
URL: http://www.nspe.org/PEmagazine/index.html

Monthly. Magazine (tabloid) covering professional, legislative, and techology issues for an engineering audience.

4319 ■ *PE & RS Photogrammetric Engineering & Remote Sensing*
The Imaging and Geospatial Information Society
5410 Grosvenor Ln., Ste. 210
Bethesda, MD 20814-2160
Ph: (301)493-0290
Fax: (301)493-0208
URL: http://www.asprs.org/PE-RS-Journal/

Monthly. $410.00/year for individuals, first class mail; $426.00/year for Canada, airmail; $420.00/year for other countries, air standard. Peer-reviewed journal covering photogrammetry, remote sensing, geographic information systems, cartography, and surveying, global positioning systems, digital photogrammetry.

4320 ■ *Printed Circuit Design & Manufacture*
UP Media Group Inc.
PO Box 470
Canton, GA 30169
Ph: (678)817-1286
URL: http://pcdandf.com/cms/

Monthly. Magazine for engineers and designers of PCBs and related technologies.

4321 ■ *Radio Physics and Radio Astronomy*
Begell House Inc.
50 Cross Hwy.
Redding, CT 06896
Ph: (203)938-1300
Fax: (203)938-1304
URL: http://www.begellhouse.com/journals/
6fd1549c0e2c05da

$708.00/year for institutions. Journal publishing articles on investigations in present-day radio physics and electronic engineering, radio astronomy and astrophysics.

4322 ■ *RF Design*
Penton Media Inc.
9800 Metcalf Ave.
Overland Park, KS 66212
Ph: (913)341-1300
Fax: (913)967-1898
URL: http://www.rfdesign.com/

Monthly. Free. Magazine covering the R.F. engineering field.

4323 ■ *SMT*
PennWell Corp.
1421 S Sheridan Rd.
Tulsa, OK 74112
Ph: (918)835-3161
Fax: (918)831-9497
Fr: 800-331-4463
URL: http://www.ems007.com/pages/ems007.cgi

Monthly. $115.00/year for U.S. and Canada; $215.00/year for other countries. Trade magazine for professional engineers involved in surface mount technology circuit design and board assembly.

4324 ■ *Solid State Technology*
PennWell Corp.
98 Spit Brook Rd.
Nashua, NH 03062-5737
Ph: (603)891-0123
Fax: (603)891-9294
Fr: 800-225-0556
URL: http://www.electroiq.com/index/
Semiconductors.html

Monthly. $258.00/year for individuals; $360.00/year for Canada, print; $434.00/year for other countries, print. Magazine containing electronic and semiconductor engineering news and information.

4325 ■ *SWE, Magazine of the Society of Women Engineers*
Society of Women Engineers
120 S La Salle St., Ste. 1515
Chicago, IL 60603
Ph: (312)596-5223
Fr: 877-793-4636
URL: http://societyofwomenengineers.swe.org/
index.php

Quarterly. $30.00/year for nonmembers. Magazine for engineering students and for women and men working in the engineering and technology fields. Covers career guidance, continuing development and topical issues.

4326 ■ *Telecommunications and Radio Engineering*
Begell House Inc.
50 Cross Hwy.
Redding, CT 06896
Ph: (203)938-1300

Fax: (203)938-1304
URL: http://www.begellhouse.com/journals/
0632a9d54950b268

$4,518.00/year for institutions. Journal covering telecommunications and radio engineering.

4327 ■ *Test & Measurement World*
Canon Communications L.L.C.
11444 W Olympic Blvd., Ste. 900
Los Angeles, CA 90064
Ph: (310)445-4200
Fax: (310)445-4299
E-mail: tmw@reedbusiness.com
URL: http://www.tmworld.com

Monthly. Free. Electronic engineering magazine specializing in test, measurement and inspection of electronic products.

4328 ■ *Transmission and Distribution World*
Penton Media Inc.
9800 Metcalf Ave.
Overland Park, KS 66212
Ph: (913)341-1300
Fax: (913)967-1898
URL: http://www.tdworld.com

Monthly. Magazine about powerline construction, transmission, and distribution.

4329 ■ *WEPANEWS*
Women in Engineering Programs & Advocates Network
1901 E Asbury Ave., Ste. 220
Denver, CO 80208
Ph: (303)871-4643
Fax: (303)871-4628
E-mail: dmatt@wepan.org
URL: http://www.wepan.org

Description: 2/year. Seeks to provide greater access for women to careers in engineering. Includes news of graduate, undergraduate, freshmen, pre-college, and re-entry engineering programs for women. Recurring features include job listings, faculty, grant, and conference news, international engineering program news, action group news, notices of publications available, and a column titled Kudos.

4330 ■ *Wireless Engineering and Technology*
Scientific Research Publishing
PO Box 54821
Irvine, CA 92619-4821
E-mail: wet@scirp.org
URL: http://www.scirp.org/journal/wet/

Quarterly. $156.00/year for individuals. Peer-reviewed journal publishing articles on wireless engineering and technology.

4331 ■ *Woman Engineer*
Equal Opportunity Publications, Inc.
445 Broadhollow Rd., Ste. 425
Melville, NY 11747
Ph: (631)421-9421
Fax: (631)421-1352
E-mail: info@eop.com
URL: http://www.eop.com

Annual. Magazine that is offered at no charge to qualified female engineering, computer-science, and information-technology students and professionals seeking to find employment and advancement in their careers.

EMPLOYER DIRECTORIES AND NETWORKING LISTS

4332 ■ *American Electronics Association—Member Directory*
AeA
601 Pennsylvania Ave. NW, North Bldg., Ste. 600
Washington, DC 20004
Ph: (202)682-9110

Fax: (202)682-9111
Fr: 800-284-4232
URL: http://www.aea.net/memberdirectory.asp

Covers: Over 3,000 member electronics and high-technology companies and 500 associate member firms including financial institutions, law firms, and accounting firms. Entries include: Company name, address, phone, World Wide Web addresses, cable address, fax, names of executives, number of employees, list of products or services, date founded, whether a public or private company, stock market where traded, ticker symbol. Arrangement: Alphabetical. Indexes: Geographical, product.

4333 ■ *American Men and Women of Science*
Gale
PO Box 6904
Florence, KY 41022-6904
Fr: 800-354-9706
URL: http://www.gale.cengage.com

Biennial, even years; New edition expected 29th, June 2011. $1,368.00 for individuals. Covers: Over 135,000 U.S. and Canadian scientists active in the physical, biological, mathematical, computer science, and engineering fields; includes references to previous edition for deceased scientists and nonrespondents. Entries include: Name, address, education, personal and career data, memberships, honors and awards, research interest. Arrangement: Alphabetical. Indexes: Discipline (in separate volume).

4334 ■ *Careers in Focus—Engineering*
Facts On File Inc.
132 W 31st St., 17th Fl.
New York, NY 10001
Ph: (212)967-8800
Fax: 800-678-3633
Fr: 800-322-8755
URL: http://www.infobasepublishing.com

Latest edition 3rd; Published July, 2007. $32.95 for individuals. Covers: An overview of engineering, followed by a selection of jobs profiled in detail, including the nature of the job, earnings, prospects for employment, what kind of training and skills it requires, and sources for further information.

4335 ■ *Design News OEM Directory*
Reed Business Information
360 Park Ave. S
New York, NY 10010-1710
Ph: (646)746-6400
E-mail: dn@cahners.com
URL: http://www.reedbusiness.com

Annual, November. Covers: About 5,000 manufacturers and suppliers of power transmission products, fluid power products, and electrical/electronic components to the OEM (original equipment manufacturer) market in SIC groups 34-39. Entries include: Company name, address, phone, fax, URL, e-mail. Arrangement: Alphabetical. Indexes: Product locator, Trade Name, supplier locator.

4336 ■ *Directory of Contract Staffing Firms*
C.E. Publications Inc.
PO Box 3006
Bothell, WA 98041-3006
Ph: (425)806-5200
Fax: (425)806-5585
URL: http://www.cjhunter.com/dcsf/overview.html

Annual. Covers: Nearly 1,300 contract firms actively engaged in the employment of engineering, IT/IS, and technical personnel for 'temporary' contract assignments throughout the world. Entries include: Company name, address, phone, name of contact, email, web address. Arrangement: Alphabetical. Indexes: Geographical.

4337 ■ *Indiana Society of Professional Engineers—Directory*
Indiana Society of Professional Engineers
PO Box 20806
Indianapolis, IN 46220

Ph: (317)255-2267
Fax: (317)255-2530
URL: http://www.indspe.org

Annual, fall. Covers: Member registered engineers, land surveyors, engineering students, and engineers in training. Entries include: Member name, address, phone, type of membership, business information, specialty. Arrangement: Alpha by chapter area.

4338 ■ International Association of Electrical Inspectors—Membership Directory
International Association of Electrical Inspectors
901 Waterfall Way, Ste. 602
Richardson, TX 75080-7702
Ph: (972)235-1455
Fax: (972)235-6858
URL: http://www.iaei.org

Annual, April. Covers: 26,000 state and federal government, industrial, utility, and insurance electrical inspectors, and, as associate members, electricians, manufacturers, engineers, architects, and wiremen. Entries include: Name, title, type of member, address, company affiliation. Arrangement: Geographical, then by division, chapter, or section, and type of membership, then alphabetical. Indexes: Committees; personal name.

HANDBOOKS AND MANUALS

4339 ■ Careers in Focus: Electronics
Ferguson Publishing
132 W 31st St., 17th Fl.
New York, NY 10001
Fax: 800-678-3633
Fr: 800-322-8755
E-mail: custserv@factsonfile.com
URL: http://ferguson.infobasepublishing.com

2009. $32.95 (hardcover). 200 pages. Profiles careers in electronics for young professionals.

4340 ■ Careers in Focus: Telecommunications
Ferguson Publishing
132 W 31st St., 17th Fl.
New York, NY 10001
Fr: 800-322-8755
E-mail: custserv@factsonfile.com
URL: http://factsonfile.infobasepublishing.com

2009. $32.95. Covers job profiles in telecommunications. Includes descriptions of certification, education, special skills, and trainings required.

4341 ■ Expert Resumes for Engineers
JIST Publishing
875 Montreal Way
St. Paul, MN 55102
Fr: 800-648-5478
E-mail: educate@emcp.com
URL: http://www.jist.com

Louise M. Kursmark and Wendy S. Enelow. 2009. $16.95 (softcover). 272 pages. Features a collection of written resume samples for all types of engineers including civil, mechanical, industrial, electrical, electronics, computer, and more. Contains tips and strategies for writing engineering resumes and finding the best jobs.

4342 ■ Opportunities in Electronics Careers
The McGraw-Hill Companies
PO Box 182604
Columbus, OH 43272
Fax: (614)759-3749
Fr: 877-883-5524
E-mail: customer.service@mcgraw-hill.com
URL: http://www.mhprofessional.com/
    product.php?isbn=0071476075

Mark Rowh. 2007. $13.95 (paper). 221 pages. Discusses career opportunities in commercial and industrial electronics equipment repair, electronics home entertainment repair, electronics engineering, and engineering technology. Includes job outlook and how to get off to a good start on the job.

4343 ■ Resumes for Scientific and Technical Careers
The McGraw-Hill Companies
PO Box 182604
Columbus, OH 43272
Fax: (614)759-3749
Fr: 877-883-5524
E-mail: customer.service@mcgraw-hill.com
URL: http://www.mhprofessional.com/
    product.php?isbn=0071482199

Third edition, 2007. $12.95 (paper). 144 pages. Provides resume advice for individuals interested in working in scientific and technical careers. Includes sample resumes and cover letters.

EMPLOYMENT AGENCIES AND SEARCH FIRMS

4344 ■ Apple and Associates
PO Box 996
Chapin, SC 29036
Ph: (803)932-2000
E-mail: info@appleassoc.com
URL: http://www.appleassoc.com

Provides staffing services to medical device, plastics, pharmaceutical and performance materials industries.

4345 ■ The Aspire Group
711 Boylston St.
Boston, MA 02116-2616
Fax: (617)500-7284
Fr: 800-487-2967
URL: http://www.bmanet.com/Aspire/index.html

Employment agency.

4346 ■ ATR Engineering
1230 Oakmead Pkwy.
Sunnyvale, CA 94085
Ph: (408)328-8000
Fax: (408)328-8001
Fr: 877-412-1100
E-mail: corporate@atr1.com
URL: http://www.atr-engineering.com

Description: Serves as an executive search firm specializing in the placement of engineering professionals in contract, contract-to-hire and full-time basis across all disciplines including design engineering, manufacturing engineering, hardware engineering, design engineering, electrical engineering and mechanical engineering.

4347 ■ The Bedford Group
3343 Peachtree Rd. NE, Ste. 333
Atlanta, GA 30326
Ph: (404)237-7471
Fax: (404)846-2172
E-mail: info@bedfordgroupconsulting.com
URL: http://www.bedfordgroupconsulting.com

Executive search firm.

4348 ■ Bell Oaks Co.
115 Perimeter Center Pl., Ste. 400
Atlanta, GA 30346
Ph: (678)287-2000
Fax: (678)287-2002
E-mail: info@belloaks.com
URL: http://www.belloaks.com

Personnel service firm.

4349 ■ Claremont-Branan, Inc.
1298 Rockbridge Rd., Ste. B
Stone Mountain, GA 30087
Fr: 800-875-1292
URL: http://cbisearch.com

Employment agency. Executive search firm.

4350 ■ Electronic Careers
21355 Pacific Coast Hwy., Ste. 100
Malibu, CA 90265

Ph: (310)317-6113
E-mail: e-careers@electroniccareers.com
URL: http://www.electroniccareers.com

Executive search firm.

4351 ■ Electronic Search, Inc.
5105 Tollview Dr., Ste. 245
Rolling Meadows, IL 60008
Ph: (847)506-0700
Fax: (847)506-9999
E-mail: email@electronicsearch.com
URL: http://www.electronicsearch.com

Description: Staffing solutions firm, specializing in filling highly technical requirements in the wireless, telecommunications, and public safety technology industries; includes job listings with contact person, location, job description, qualifications, and compensation.

4352 ■ Engineer One, Inc.
PO Box 23037
Knoxville, TN 37933
Fax: (865)691-0110
E-mail: engineerone@engineerone.com
URL: http://www.engineerone.com

Engineering employment service specializing in engineering and management in the chemical process, power utilities, manufacturing, mechanical, electrical, and electronic industries. Maintains an Information Technology Division that works nationwide across all industries. Also provides systems analysis consulting services specializing in VAX based systems.

4353 ■ ENTEGEE
70 Blanchard Rd., Ste. 102
Burlington, MA 01803
Fr: 800-368-3433
E-mail: corporate@entegee.com
URL: http://www.entegee.com

Specializes in recruiting experienced professionals in the engineering and technical industries. Features a searchable database of employment opportunities in the engineering and technical fields.

4354 ■ Essential Solutions
20863 Stevens Creek Blvd., Ste. 480
Cupertino, CA 95014
Ph: (408)850-2500
Fax: (408)985-1700
E-mail: info@esiweb.com
URL: http://www.esiweb.com

Description: Serves as an executive search firm specializing in the placement of leaders for venture capital firms and companies focused on wireless, communications/networking, semiconductor, web, software, cleantech, or related technologies.

4355 ■ Executive Recruiters Agency
PO Box 21810
Little Rock, AR 72211
Ph: (501)224-7000
Fax: (501)224-8534
E-mail: jobs@execrecruit.com
URL: http://www.execrecruit.com

Personnel service firm.

4356 ■ Global Employment Solutions
10375 Park Meadows Dr., Ste. 375
Littleton, CO 80124
Ph: (303)216-9500
Fax: (303)216-9533
URL: http://www.gesnetwork.com

Employment agency.

4357 ■ Kimmel & Associates
25 Page Ave.
Asheville, NC 28801
Ph: (828)251-9900
Fax: (828)251-9955
E-mail: kimmel@kimmel.com
URL: http://www.kimmel.com

Specializes in the construction, waste, architecture, engineering, logistics and supply chain industries.

4358 ■ ManpowerGroup
100 Manpower Pl.
Milwaukee, WI 53212
Ph: (414)961-1000
Fax: (414)906-7822
URL: http://us.manpower.com

Specializes in a wide range of employment services including permanent placement, recruitment process outsourcing, managed service programs, outplacement and human resources consulting. Provides companies with workforce solutions that help them increase productivity and improve efficiency.

4359 ■ SPECTRA Associates
PO Box 688
Stevensville, MT 59870
Ph: (406)369-1188
E-mail: engineering@spectra-assoc.com
URL: http://www.spectra-assoc.com

Description: Serves as an executive search firm specializing in recruitment for engineering markets including companies involved with manufacturing, production and engineering.

4360 ■ Technical Talent Locators Ltd.
5570 Sterrett Pl., Ste. 208
Columbia, MD 21044
Ph: (410)740-0091
E-mail: steve@ttlgroup.com
URL: http://www.ttlgroup.com

Permanent employment agency working within the following fields: software and database engineering; computer, communication, and telecommunication system engineering; and other computer-related disciplines.

4361 ■ Trambley The Recruiter
5325 Wyoming Blvd. NE, Ste. 200
Albuquerque, NM 87109-3132
Ph: (505)821-5440
Fax: (505)821-8509

Personnel consultancy firm recruits and places engineering professionals in specific areas of off-road equipment design and manufacturing. Industries served: construction, agricultural, lawn and garden, oil exploration and mining equipment manufacturing.

4362 ■ TRS Staffing Solutions USA
3 Polaris Way
Aliso Viejo, CA 92656
Ph: (949)349-3630
Fax: (949)349-7196
Fr: 800-248-8774
E-mail: info-av@trsstaffing.com
URL: http://www.trsstaffing.com/us

Specializes in engineering recruitment. Maintains a pool of experienced technical, engineering and professional services personnel.

4363 ■ TSS Consulting Ltd.
Arizona Biltmore Pavilion, 2525 E Arizona Biltmore Cir., Ste
Phoenix, AZ 85016
Ph: (602)795-1047
Fax: (602)795-0590
Fr: 800-489-2425
E-mail: john@tss-consulting.com
URL: http://www.tss-consulting.com

A technical executive search and consulting firm as a boutique executive search firm, specializes in technical contributor and management or executive level electrical engineer searches for venture-backed startups.

ONLINE JOB SOURCES AND SERVICES

4364 ■ ConstructionJobs.com
URL: http://www.constructionjobs.com/index_eng.cfm
Description: Serves as an employment job board

and resume database built exclusively for the construction, design, and building industries. Provides targeted candidate searches by geographic region, specific industries, job titles, education, and experience.

4365 ■ ElectricalEngineer.com
E-mail: info@careermarketplace.com
URL: http://www.electricalengineer.com

Description: Provides job listings, employment information and products for civil engineers.

4366 ■ ElectricalEngineerJobs.com
URL: http://www.electricalengineerjobs.com

Description: Lists electrical engineer jobs from all over the U.S. Allows users to post resumes and career profiles and search jobs by location. Provides information about degree programs, resume writing, interview tips and salaries.

4367 ■ ElectronicsEngineer.com
URL: http://www.electronicsengineer.com

Description: Serves as job board for electronics engineering employers showcasing open jobs and products to electronics engineers and to the EE community.

4368 ■ EnergyAuditorJobs.com
URL: http://www.energyauditorjobs.com

Description: Serves as a clearinghouse for energy auditor jobs. Contains salary information and surveys, resume postings, educational programs, and other related career resources.

4369 ■ EngineerJobs.com
URL: http://www.engineerjobs.com

Description: Provides job opportunities for engineering professionals in the following disciplines: aerospace, agricultural, biomedical, chemical, civil, electrical, environmental, industrial, manufacturing, marine, materials, mechanical, mining, nuclear, petroleum, process, project, quality, sales, software, solar, systems, and structural.

4370 ■ MEP Jobs
URL: http://www.mepjobs.com

Description: Serves as a job board and resume bank for professionals in the mechanical, electrical, and plumbing industries.

4371 ■ PowerPlantPro.com
E-mail: support@powerplantpro.com
URL: http://www.powerplantpro.com/main/sendform/4/18/3472

Description: Dedicated to professionals in the power and energy industry. Features career advice and employer listings.

4372 ■ Spherion
2050 Spectrum Blvd.
Fort Lauderdale, FL 33309
Ph: (954)308-7600
Fr: 800-774-3746
E-mail: help@spherion.com
URL: http://www.spherion.com

Description: Recruitment firm specializing in accounting and finance, sales and marketing, interim executives, technology, engineering, retail and human resources.

4373 ■ ThinkEnergyGroup.com
E-mail: resumes@thinkjobs.com
URL: http://www.thinkenergygroup.com

Description: Serves as a job board for professionals looking for positions in engineering, power plant, energy, and technical fields. Contains advice and tips on interviews, job searching, resume writing, hiring, and management. Provides choices of work location, pay rates in the field of expertise and contract, temp-to-hire, and direct hiring options.

TRADESHOWS

4374 ■ American Society for Engineering Education Annual Conference and Exposition
American Society for Engineering Education
1818 N. St. N.W., Ste. 600
Washington, DC 20036-2479
Ph: (202)331-3500
Fax: (202)265-8504
E-mail: conferences@asee.org
URL: http://www.asee.org

Annual. Primary Exhibits: Publications, engineering supplies and equipment, computers, software, and research companies all products and services related to engineering education. Dates and Locations: 2012 Jun 10-13; San Antonio, TX.

4375 ■ Electronic Imaging International - part of Photonics East
International Society for Optical Engineering SPIE
PO Box 10
Bellingham, WA 98227-0010
Ph: (360)676-3290
Fax: (360)647-1445
Fr: 888-504-8171
E-mail: customerservice@spie.org
URL: http://www.spie.org

Annual. Primary Exhibits: Equipment, supplies, and services for image processing computer graphics, fiber optics, high definition television, electronic printing and publishing, military electronics, medical tomography industries, and electronic imaging products.

4376 ■ PCB Design Conference West
CMP Media LLC (San Mateo, California)
2800 Campus Dr.
San Mateo, CA 94403
Ph: (650)513-4300
E-mail: cmp@cmp.com
URL: http://www.cmp.com

Annual. Primary Exhibits: To provide circuit board designers education and information about the industry, including tools and techniques.

OTHER SOURCES

4377 ■ Acoustical Society of America
2 Huntington Quadrangle, Ste. 1NO1
Melville, NY 11747-4502
Ph: (516)576-2360
Fax: (516)576-2377
E-mail: asa@aip.org
URL: http://acousticalsociety.org

Description: Represents members from various fields related to sound including physics, electrical, mechanical and aeronautical engineering, oceanography, biology, physiology, psychology, architecture, speech, noise and noise control, and music. Aims to increase and diffuse the knowledge of acoustics and its practical applications. Organizes meetings, provides reprints of out-of-print classic texts in acoustics, and translation books.

4378 ■ Aircraft Electronics Association (AEA)
3570 NE Ralph Powell Rd.
Lee's Summit, MO 64064
Ph: (816)347-8400
Fax: (816)347-8405
E-mail: info@aea.net
URL: http://www.aea.net

Description: Companies engaged in the sales, engineering, installation, and service of electronic aviation equipment and systems. Seeks to: advance the science of aircraft electronics; promote uniform and stable regulations and uniform standards of performance; establish and maintain a code of ethics; gather and disseminate technical data; advance the education of members and the public in the science of aircraft electronics. Offers supplement type certificates, test equipment licensing, temporary FCC licensing for new installations, spare parts availability and pricing, audiovisual technician training, equipment and spare parts loan, profitable installation, and service facility operation. Provides employment information, equipment exchange information and service assistance on member installations anywhere in the world.

4379 ■ American Association of Engineering Societies (AAES)
1801 Alexander Bell Dr.
Reston, VA 20191
Ph: (202)296-2237
Fax: (202)296-1151
Fr: 888-400-2237
E-mail: dbateson@aaes.org
URL: http://www.aaes.org

Description: Coordinates the efforts of the member societies in the provision of reliable and objective information to the general public concerning issues which affect the engineering profession and the field of engineering as a whole; collects, analyzes, documents, and disseminates data which will inform the general public of the relationship between engineering and the national welfare; provides a forum for the engineering societies to exchange and discuss their views on matters of common interest; and represents the U.S. engineering community abroad through representation in WFEO and UPADI.

4380 ■ American Indian Science and Engineering Society (AISES)
PO Box 9828
Albuquerque, NM 87119-9828
Ph: (505)765-1052
Fax: (505)765-5608
E-mail: info@aises.org
URL: http://www.aises.org

Description: Represents American Indian and non-Indian students and professionals in science, technology, and engineering fields; corporations representing energy, mining, aerospace, electronic, and computer fields. Seeks to motivate and encourage students to pursue undergraduate and graduate studies in science, engineering, and technology. Sponsors science fairs in grade schools, teacher training workshops, summer math/science sessions for 8th-12th graders, professional chapters, and student chapters in colleges. Offers scholarships. Adult members serve as role models, advisers, and mentors for students. Operates placement service.

4381 ■ American Society of Test Engineers (ASTE)
PO Box 389
Nutting Lake, MA 01865-0389
E-mail: aste@earthlink.net
URL: http://www.astetest.org

Description: Companies involved in the electronic testing industry and instrumentation are corporate members; engineers who work in test engineering related fields are regular members. Seeks to foster improved communication among individuals and companies in the testing industry. Offers job referral service.

4382 ■ ASPRS - The Imaging and Geospatial Information Society
5410 Grosvenor Ln., Ste. 210
Bethesda, MD 20814-2160
Ph: (301)493-0290
Fax: (301)493-0208
E-mail: asprs@asprs.org
URL: http://www.asprs.org

Description: Firms, individuals, government employees and academicians engaged in photogrammetry, photointerpretation, remote sensing, and geographic information systems and their application to such fields as archaeology, geographic information systems, military reconnaissance, urban planning, engineering, traffic surveys, meteorological observa-

tions, medicine, geology, forestry, agriculture, construction and topographic mapping. Seeks to advance knowledge and improve understanding of these sciences and promote responsible applications. Offers voluntary certification program open to persons associated with one or more functional area of photogrammetry, remote sensing and GIS. Surveys the profession of private firms in photogrammetry and remote sensing in the areas of products and services.

4383 ■ Association for the Advancement of Medical Instrumentation (AAMI)
4301 N Fairfax Dr., Ste. 301
Arlington, VA 22203-1633
Ph: (703)525-4890
Fax: (703)276-0793
Fr: 800-332-2264
E-mail: mlogan@aami.org
URL: http://www.aami.org

Description: Clinical engineers, biomedical equipment technicians, physicians, hospital administrators, consultants, engineers, manufacturers of medical devices, nurses, researchers and others interested in medical instrumentation. Works to improve the quality of medical care through the application, development, and management of technology. Maintains placement service. Offers certification programs for biomedical equipment technicians and clinical engineers. Produces numerous standards and recommended practices on medical devices and procedures. Offers educational programs.

4384 ■ Association for International Practical Training (AIPT)
10400 Little Patuxent Pkwy., Ste. 250
Columbia, MD 21044-3519
Ph: (410)997-2200
Fax: (410)992-3924
E-mail: aipt@aipt.org
URL: http://www.aipt.org

Description: Providers worldwide of on-the-job training programs for students and professionals seeking international career development and life-changing experiences. Arranges workplace exchanges in hundreds of professional fields, bringing employers and trainees together from around the world. Client list ranges from small farming communities to Fortune 500 companies.

4385 ■ Engineering Society of Detroit (ESD)
20700 Civic Center Dr., Ste. 450
Southfield, MI 48076
Ph: (248)353-0735
Fax: (248)353-0736
E-mail: esd@esd.org
URL: http://ww2.esd.org/home.htm

Description: Engineers from all disciplines; scientists and technologists. Conducts technical programs and engineering refresher courses; sponsors conferences and expositions. Maintains speakers' bureau; offers placement services; although based in Detroit, MI, society membership is international.

4386 ■ Global Semiconductor Alliance
Churchill Tower
12400 Coit Rd., Ste. 650
Dallas, TX 75251
Ph: (972)866-7579
Fax: (972)239-2292
E-mail: jshelton@gsaglobal.org
URL: http://www.gsaglobal.org

Description: Represents semiconductor companies including fabless, fab-lite, and integrated device manufacturers. Aims to accelerate the growth and increase of return on invested capital in the global semiconductor industry by fostering a more effective fabless ecosystem through collaboration, integration, and innovation.

4387 ■ International Association for Computer and Information Science (ACIS)
735 Meadowbrook Dr.
Mount Pleasant, MI 48858
Ph: (989)774-1175

Fax: (989)774-1174
E-mail: acis@acisinternational.org
URL: http://www.acisinternational.org

Description: Represents individuals in the fields of computer and information science. Disseminates the latest developments in the fields of computer and information science. Provides a forum for researchers in education and computer and information science industries.

4388 ■ International Microelectronics and Packaging Society (IMAPS)
611 2nd St. NE
Washington, DC 20002-4909
Ph: (202)548-4001
Fax: (202)548-6115
E-mail: modonoghue@imaps.org
URL: http://www.imaps.org

Description: Electronics engineers and specialists in industry, business, and education. Encourages the exchange of information across boundaries of fields of specialization; supports close interactions between the complementary technologies of ceramics, thick and thin films, semiconductor packaging, discrete semiconductor devices, and monolithic circuits. Promotes and assists in the development and expansion of microelectronics instruction in schools and departments of electrical and electronic engineering. Conducts seminars at international, national, regional, and chapter levels.

4389 ■ International Society of Automation (ISA)
67 Alexander Dr.
PO Box 12277
Research Triangle Park, NC 27709
Ph: (919)549-8411
Fax: (919)549-8288
E-mail: info@isa.org
URL: http://www.isa.org

Description: Sets the standard for automation by helping over 30,000 worldwide members and other professionals solve difficult technical problems, while enhancing their leadership and personal career capabilities. Develops standards; certifies industry professionals; provides education and training; publishes books and technical articles; and hosts the largest conference and exhibition for automation professionals in the Western Hemisphere. Is the founding sponsor of The Automation Federation.

4390 ■ International Society for Quality Electronic Design (ISQED)
PO Box 607
Los Altos, CA 94023
Ph: (408)573-0100
Fax: (408)573-0200
E-mail: info@isqed.com
URL: http://www.isqed.com

Description: Promotes quality in the design of micro-electronic, nano-electronic and bio-electronic circuits and systems. Fosters research, development and application of design methods and processes. Provides a forum and educational program on quality electronic design.

4391 ■ Korean-American Scientists and Engineers Association (KSEA)
1952 Gallows Rd., Ste. 300
Vienna, VA 22182
Ph: (703)748-1221
Fax: (703)748-1331
E-mail: sejong@ksea.org
URL: http://www.ksea.org

Description: Represents scientists and engineers holding single or advanced degrees. Promotes friendship and mutuality among Korean and American scientists and engineers; contributes to Korea's scientific, technological, industrial, and economic developments; strengthens the scientific, technological, and cultural bonds between Korea and the U.S. Sponsors symposium. Maintains speakers' bureau, placement service, and biographical archives. Compiles statistics.

4392 ■ National Action Council for Minorities in Engineering (NACME)
440 Hamilton Ave., Ste. 302
White Plains, NY 10601-1813
Ph: (914)539-4010
Fax: (914)539-4032
E-mail: info@nacme.org
URL: http://www.nacme.org

Description: Leads the national effort to increase access to careers in engineering and other science-based disciplines. Conducts research and public policy analysis, develops and operates national demonstration programs at precollege and university levels, and disseminates information through publications, conferences and electronic media. Serves as a privately funded source of scholarships for minority students in engineering.

4393 ■ National Society of Professional Engineers (NSPE)
1420 King St.
Alexandria, VA 22314-2794
Ph: (703)684-2800
Fax: (703)836-4875
Fr: 888-285-6773
E-mail: memserv@nspe.org
URL: http://www.nspe.org

Description: Represents professional engineers and engineers-in-training in all fields registered in accordance with the laws of states or territories of the U.S. or provinces of Canada; qualified graduate engineers, student members, and registered land surveyors. Is concerned with social, professional, ethical, and economic considerations of engineering as a profession; encompasses programs in public relations, employment practices, ethical considerations, education, and career guidance. Monitors legislative and regulatory actions of interest to the engineering profession.

4394 ■ Society of Hispanic Professional Engineers (SHPE)
13181 Crossroads Pkwy. N, Ste. 450
City of Industry, CA 91746-3496
Ph: (323)725-3970
Fax: (323)725-0316
E-mail: shpenational@shpe.org
URL: http://oneshpe.shpe.org/wps/portal/national

Description: Represents engineers, student engineers, and scientists. Aims to increase the number of Hispanic engineers by providing motivation and support to students. Sponsors competitions and educational programs. Maintains placement service and speakers' bureau; compiles statistics.

4395 ■ Society of Women Engineers (SWE)
203 N La Salle St., Ste. 1675
Chicago, IL 60601
Ph: (312)596-5223
Fax: (312)596-5252
Fr: 877-SWE-INFO
E-mail: hq@swe.org
URL: http://societyofwomenengineers.swe.org

Description: Educational and service organization representing both students and professional women in engineering and technical fields.

4396 ■ SPIE
PO Box 10
Bellingham, WA 98227-0010
Ph: (360)676-3290
Fax: (360)647-1445
Fr: 888-504-8171
E-mail: customerservice@spie.org
URL: http://www.spie.org

Description: Advances scientific research and engineering applications of optical, photonic, imaging and optoelectronic technologies through meetings, education programs and publications.

Sources of Help-Wanted Ads

4397 ■ *Builder*
Hanley-Wood L.L.C.
1 Thomas Cir. NW, Ste. 600
Washington, DC 20005-5803
Ph: (202)452-0800
Fax: (202)785-1974
E-mail: builder@omeda.com
URL: http://www.hanleywood.com/
default.aspx?page=magazines
$29.95/year for U.S. and Canada; $54.95/year for U.S. and Canada, 2 years; $192.00/year for other countries. Magazine covering housing and construction industry.

4398 ■ *Constructor*
Associated General Contractors of America
2300 Wilson Blvd., Ste. 400
Arlington, VA 22201
Ph: (703)548-3118
Fax: (703)548-3119
Fr: 800-242-1767
URL: http://constructor.agc.org/
Bimonthly. $95.00/year for individuals. Management magazine for the Construction Industry.

4399 ■ *Electric Light & Power*
PennWell Corp.
1421 S Sheridan Rd.
Tulsa, OK 74112
Ph: (918)835-3161
Fax: (918)831-9497
Fr: 800-331-4463
URL: http://www.elp.com/index.html
Bimonthly. $85.00/year for Canada; $145.00/year for Canada, two years; $94.00/year for individuals, Mexico; $160.00/year for individuals, 2 years, Mexico; $225.00/year for other countries; $403.00/year for other countries, 2 years; free to qualified subscribers. Provides broad view of electric utility industry with in-depth analysis of key business issues for executives and management.

4400 ■ *Engineering Economist*
Taylor & Francis Group
270 Madison Ave.
New York, NY 10016
Fax: (212)244-4561
URL: http://www.tandf.co.uk/journals/titles/
0013791x.asp
Quarterly. $89.00/year for individuals, print; $153.00/year for institutions, online only; $170.00/year for institutions, print & online. Publication covering business issues in the energy, petroleum and mining industries.

4401 ■ *The High-Tech News*
ETA International
5 Depot St.
Greencastle, IN 46135
Ph: (765)653-8262
Fax: (765)653-4287
Fr: 800-288-3824
E-mail: eta@eta-i.org
URL: http://www.eta-i.org
Description: Bimonthly. Serves member technicians with news of the Association and the electronics industry, including items on service, education, employment, management, and events. Contains information on membership, management, telecommunications, and business and technical training programs. Recurring features include editorials, news of research, letters to the editor, book reviews, and a calendar of events.

4402 ■ *Professional Builder*
SGC Horizon LLC
3030 W Salt Creek Ln., Ste. 201
Arlington Heights, IL 60005
Ph: (847)391-1000
Fax: (847)390-0408
URL: http://www.housingzone.com/pb/pubhome/
Monthly. Free. The integrated engineering magazine of the building construction industry.

Employer Directories and Networking Lists

4403 ■ *ABC Today—Associated Builders and Contractors National Membership Directory Issue*
Associated Builders and Contractors Inc.
4250 N Fairfax Dr., 9th Fl.
Arlington, VA 22203-1607
Ph: (703)812-2000
Fax: (703)812-8235
URL: http://www.abc.org
Annual, December. $150.00. Publication includes: List of approximately 19,000 member construction contractors and suppliers.

4404 ■ *Buyer's Guide & Membership Directory*
Independent Electrical Contractors Inc.
4401 Ford Ave., Ste. 1100
Alexandria, VA 22302-1432
Ph: (703)549-7351
Fax: (703)549-7448
Fr: 800-456-4324
E-mail: communications@ieci.org
URL: http://www.ieci.org
Annual. Covers: Member electrical contracting firms, electrical manufacturers, and distributors. Entries include: Name of company, address, names of principals. Arrangement: Geographical.

4405 ■ *ENR—Top 400 Construction Contractors Issue*
McGraw-Hill Inc.
PO Box 182604
Columbus, OH 43218
Ph: (614)430-4000
Fax: (614)759-3749
Fr: 877-833-5524
URL: http://enr.construction.com/toplists/Contractors/
001-100.asp
Annual, Latest edition 2011. $35.00 for individuals. Publication includes: List of 400 United States contractors receiving largest dollar volumes of contracts in preceding calendar year. Separate lists of 50 largest design/construct management firms; 50 largest program and construction managers; 25 building contractors; 25 heavy contractors.

4406 ■ *International Association of Electrical Inspectors—Membership Directory*
International Association of Electrical Inspectors
901 Waterfall Way, Ste. 602
Richardson, TX 75080-7702
Ph: (972)235-1455
Fax: (972)235-6858
URL: http://www.iaei.org
Annual, April. Covers: 26,000 state and federal government, industrial, utility, and insurance electrical inspectors, and, as associate members, electricians, manufacturers, engineers, architects, and wiremen. Entries include: Name, title, type of member, address, company affiliation. Arrangement: Geographical, then by division, chapter, or section, and type of membership, then alphabetical. Indexes: Committees; personal name.

Handbooks and Manuals

4407 ■ *Electrician's Exam Preparation Guide*
Craftsman Book Co.
6058 Corte del Cedro
Carlsbad, CA 92011
Ph: (760)438-7828
Fax: (760)438-0398
Fr: 800-829-8123
URL: http://www.craftsman-book.com
John E. Traister, updated by Dale Brickner. 2008. $49.50 (paper). 352 pages. Covers every area of electrical installation: electrical drawings, services and systems, transformers, capacitors, distribution equipment, branch circuits, feeders, calculations, measuring and testing, and more. Updated to the 2008 NEC.

4408 ■ *Electricity for the Trades*
McGraw-Hill
PO Box 182604
Columbus, OH 43272
Fax: (614)759-3749
Fr: 877-833-5524
E-mail: pbg.ecommerce_custserv@mcgraw-hill.com
URL: http://www.mhprofessional.com/
product.php?search_crawl=true&isbn=007328159X
Frank D. Petruzella. 2006. $127. Resource for students in basic electricity trades.

EMPLOYMENT AGENCIES AND SEARCH FIRMS

4409 ■ American Man Power Services
3032 Fleetbrook Dr.
Memphis, TN 38116
Ph: (901)396-5998
Fax: (901)396-5984
URL: http://www.amps-electricians.com

Specializes in providing recruitment and staffing solutions to the electrical service industry. Offers career opportunities to qualified personnel.

ONLINE JOB SOURCES AND SERVICES

4410 ■ BackstageJobs.com
URL: http://www.backstagejobs.com

Description: Lists behind-the-scenes jobs in the live entertainment industry. Also features backstage related news and information.

4411 ■ ElectricalAgent.com
URL: http://www.electricalagent.com

Description: Lists job opportunities for electricians such as electrical jobs, apartment maintenance jobs, facilities maintenance jobs and other industry related positions.

4412 ■ GetElectricianJobs.com
URL: http://www.getelectricianjobs.com

Description: Offers electrician job postings and employment opportunities.

TRADESHOWS

4413 ■ Edison Electric Institute Convention and Expo
Edison Electric Institute
701 Pennsylvania Ave. N.W.
Washington, DC 20004-2696
Ph: (202)508-5000
E-mail: eblume@eei.org
URL: http://www.eei.org

Annual. Primary Exhibits: Exhibits directed to investor-owned electric utility companies operating in the U.S. and abroad. Dates and Locations: 2012 Jun 03-06; Orlando, FL; JW Marriott Grande Lakes.

4414 ■ Electric Expo
Comprehensive Show Management, Inc.
PO Box 297
Springfield, PA 19064
Ph: (610)544-5775
Fax: (610)544-9808
E-mail: sally.oshea@verizon.net

Biennial. Primary Exhibits: Electrical equipment, supplies, and services.

4415 ■ Electri...FYI - Upstate Electrical Show
Electrical Association of Rochester
PO Box 20219
Rochester, NY 14602-0219
Ph: (585)538-6350
Fax: (585)538-6166
E-mail: info@earoch.com
URL: http://www.earoch.com

Triennial. Primary Exhibits: Electrical supplies and services.

4416 ■ Independent Electrical Contractors Annual Convention and Expo
Independent Electrical Contractors' Association
4401 Ford Ave., Ste 1100
Alexandria, VA 22302
Ph: (703)549-7351
Fax: (703)549-7448

Fr: 800-456-4324
E-mail: info@ieci.org
URL: http://www.ieci.org

Annual. Primary Exhibits: Equipment, supplies, and services for independent electrical contractors.

4417 ■ Upper Midwest Electrical Expo
North Central Electrical League
2901 Metro Dr., Ste. 203
Bloomington, MN 55425-1556
Ph: (952)854-4405
Fax: (952)854-7076
Fr: 800-925-4985
E-mail: dale@ncel.org
URL: http://www.ncel.org

Biennial. Primary Exhibits: Electrical equipment, supplies, and services. Dates and Locations: 2012 Apr 18-19; Minneapolis, MN; Minneapolis Convention Center & Hilton Hotel.

OTHER SOURCES

4418 ■ Associated Builders and Contractors (ABC)
4250 N Fairfax Dr., 9th Fl.
Arlington, VA 22203-1607
Ph: (703)812-2000
Fax: (703)812-8201
E-mail: gotquestions@abc.org
URL: http://www.abc.org

Description: Construction contractors, subcontractors, suppliers and associates. Aims to foster and perpetuate the principles of rewarding construction workers and management on the basis of merit. Sponsors management education programs and craft training; also sponsors apprenticeship and skill training programs. Disseminates technological and labor relations information.

4419 ■ Associated General Contractors of America (AGC)
2300 Wilson Blvd., Ste. 400
Arlington, VA 22201
Ph: (703)548-3118
Fax: (703)548-3119
Fr: 800-242-1767
E-mail: info@agc.org
URL: http://www.agc.org

Description: General construction contractors; subcontractors; industry suppliers; service firms. Provides market services through its divisions. Conducts special conferences and seminars designed specifically for construction firms. Compiles statistics on job accidents reported by member firms. Maintains 65 committees, including joint cooperative committees with other associations and liaison committees with federal agencies.

4420 ■ Associated Specialty Contractors (ASC)
3 Bethesda Metro Ctr., Ste. 1100
Bethesda, MD 20814
E-mail: dgw@necanet.org
URL: http://www.assoc-spec-con.org

Description: Works to promote efficient management and productivity. Coordinates the work of specialized branches of the industry in management information, research, public information, government relations and construction relations. Serves as a liaison among specialty trade associations in the areas of public relations, government relations, and with other organizations. Seeks to avoid unnecessary duplication of effort and expense or conflicting programs among affiliates. Identifies areas of interest and problems shared by members, and develops positions and approaches on such problems.

4421 ■ Electrical Rebuilder's Association (ERA)
PO Box 906
Union, MO 63084
Ph: (636)584-7400

Fax: (636)584-7401
E-mail: office@electricalrebuilders.org
URL: http://www.electricalrebuilders.org

Description: Represents rebuilders, suppliers, and individuals involved in the automotive electrical parts rebuilding industry. Promotes the well-being and professionalism of the electrical rebuilding industry in North America through education and training. Serves as a forum for members to exchange information on all aspects of the industry.

4422 ■ Independent Electrical Contractors (IEC)
4401 Ford Ave., Ste. 1100
Alexandria, VA 22302-1432
Ph: (703)549-7351
Fax: (703)549-7448
Fr: 800-456-4324
E-mail: info@ieci.org
URL: http://www.ieci.org

Description: Independent electrical contractors, small and large, primarily oPEN shop. Promotes the interests of members; works to eliminate "unwise and unfair business practices" and to protect its members against "unfair or unjust taxes and legislative enactments." Sponsors electrical apprenticeship programs; conducts educational programs on cost control and personnel motivation. Represents independent electrical contractors to the National Electrical Code panel. Conducts surveys on volume of sales and purchases and on type of products used. Has formulated National Pattern Standards for Apprentice Training for Electricians.

4423 ■ National Association of Home Builders (NAHB)
1201 15th St. NW
Washington, DC 20005
Ph: (202)266-8200
Fax: (202)266-8400
Fr: 800-368-5242
E-mail: jhoward@nahb.com
URL: http://www.nahb.org

Description: Single and multifamily home builders, commercial builders, and others associated with the building industry. Lobbies on behalf of the housing industry and conducts public affairs activities to increase public understanding of housing and the economy. Collects and disseminates data on current developments in home building and home builders' plans through its Economics Department and nationwide Metropolitan Housing Forecast. Maintains NAHB Research Center, which functions as the research arm of the home building industry. Sponsors seminars and workshops on construction, mortgage credit, labor relations, cost reduction, land use, remodeling, and business management. Compiles statistics; offers charitable program, spokesman training, and placement service; maintains speakers' bureau, and Hall of Fame. Subsidiaries include the National Council of the Housing Industry. Maintains over 50 committees in many areas of construction; operates National Commercial Builders Council, National Council of the Multifamily Housing Industry, National Remodelers Council, and National Sales and Marketing Council.

4424 ■ National Association of Women in Construction (NAWIC)
327 S Adams St.
Fort Worth, TX 76104
Ph: (817)877-5551
Fax: (817)877-0324
Fr: 800-552-3506
E-mail: nawic@nawic.org
URL: http://www.nawic.org

Description: Seeks to enhance the success of women in the construction industry.

4425 ■ National Electrical Contractors Association (NECA)
3 Bethesda Metro Ctr., Ste. 1100
Bethesda, MD 20814
Ph: (301)657-3110

Fax: (301)215-4500
URL: http://www.necanet.org
Description: Contractors erecting, installing, repairing, servicing, and maintaining electric wiring, equip-

ment, and appliances. Provides management services and labor relations programs for electrical contractors; conducts seminars for contractor sales and training. Conducts research and educational

programs; compiles statistics. Sponsors honorary society, the Academy of Electrical Contracting.

SOURCES OF HELP-WANTED ADS

4426 ■ *American Journal of Emergency Medicine*
Mosby Inc.
11830 Westline Industrial Dr.
St. Louis, MO 63146-3326
Ph: (314)872-8370
Fax: (314)432-1380
Fr: 800-325-4177
URL: http://www.elsevier.com/wps/find/
journaldescription.cws_home

$340.00/year for individuals; $529.00/year for institutions; $159.00/year for students; $523.00/year for other countries; $711.00/year for institutions, other countries; $261.00/year for students, other countries. Journal reporting on emergency medicine.

4427 ■ *Annals of Medicine*
Informa Healthcare
52 Vanderbilt Ave., 7th Fl.
New York, NY 10017-3846
Ph: (212)520-2777
URL: http://informahealthcare.com/ann

$595.00/year for institutions; $980.00/year for institutions; $780.00/year for institutions. Journal covering health science and medical education.

4428 ■ *Clinical Medicine & Research*
Marshfield Clinic
1000 N Oak Ave.
Marshfield, WI 54449
Ph: (715)387-5511
Fax: (715)389-3808
Fr: 800-782-8581
E-mail: clinmedres@mcrf.mfldclin.edu
URL: http://www.clinmedres.org/

Quarterly. Free within the U.S. Peer-reviewed journal that publishes scientific medical research that is relevant to a broad audience of medical researchers and healthcare professionals.

4429 ■ *CME Supplement to Emergency Medicine Clinics of North America*
Elsevier Science Inc.
360 Park Ave. S
New York, NY 10010-1710
Ph: (212)989-5800
Fax: (212)633-3990
Fr: 888-437-4636
URL: http://www.elsevier.com/wps/find/
journaldescription.cws_home

$209.00/year for individuals. Journal covering emergency medicine clinics.

4430 ■ *Discovery Medicine*
Discovery Medicine
10 Gerard Ave., Ste. 201
Timonium, MD 21093
Ph: (410)773-9938

Fax: 888-833-0526
URL: http://www.discoverymedicine.com

Bimonthly. $599.00/year for institutions, digital edition; $99.95/year for individuals, digital edition. Online journal that publishes articles on diseases, biology, new diagnostics, and treatments for medical professionals.

4431 ■ *Emergency Medical Services*
Cygnus Business Media
1233 Janesville Ave.
Fort Atkinson, WI 53538
Ph: (920)563-6388
Fax: (920)563-1702
Fr: 800-547-7377
URL: http://www.emsworld.com

Monthly. Magazine covering emergency care, rescue and transportation.

4432 ■ *Hospitals & Health Networks*
Health Forum L.L.C.
155 N Wacker Dr., Ste. 400
Chicago, IL 60606
Ph: (312)893-6800
Fax: (312)422-4500
Fr: 800-821-2039
URL: http://www.hhnmag.com

Weekly. Free. Publication covering the health care industry.

4433 ■ *The IHS Primary Care Provider*
Indian Health Service
The Reyes Bldg.
801 Thompson Ave., Ste. 400
Rockville, MD 20852-1627
Ph: (301)443-1011
URL: http://www.ihs.gov/provider

Monthly. Journal for health care professionals, physicians, nurses, pharmacists, dentists, and dietitians.

4434 ■ *Injury*
Mosby Inc.
11830 Westline Industrial Dr.
St. Louis, MO 63146-3326
Ph: (314)872-8370
Fax: (314)432-1380
Fr: 800-325-4177
URL: http://www.elsevier.com/wps/find/
journaldescription.cws_home

Monthly. $200.00/year for individuals, European countries and Iran; $224.00/year for individuals, all countries except Europe, Japan and Iran; $26,500.00/year for individuals; $1,381.00/year for institutions, European countries and Iran; $1,543.00/year for institutions, all Countries except Europe, Japan and Iran; $183,200.00/year for institutions. Journal publishing articles and research related to the treatment of injuries such as trauma systems and management; surgical procedures; epidemiological studies; surgery (of all tissues); resuscitation; biomechanics; rehabilitation; anaesthesia; radiology and wound management.

4435 ■ *Intensive and Critical Care Nursing*
Mosby Inc.
11830 Westline Industrial Dr.
St. Louis, MO 63146-3326
Ph: (314)872-8370
Fax: (314)432-1380
Fr: 800-325-4177
URL: http://www.elsevier.com/wps/find/
journaldescription.cws_home

Bimonthly. $114.00/year for individuals, for all countries except Europe, Japan & Iran; $501.00/year for institutions, for all countries except Europe, Japan & Iran; $124.00/year for individuals, for European countries and Iran; $565.00/year for institutions, for European countries and Iran. Journal for nurses in intensive and critical care nursing.

4436 ■ *The Internet Journal of Emergency Medicine*
Internet Scientific Publications L.L.C.
23 Rippling Creek Dr.
Sugar Land, TX 77479
Ph: (832)443-1193
URL: http://www.ispub.com/ostia/
index.php?xmlFilePath=journals/ij

Free, online. Electronic journal for medical professionals focusing on the field of emergency medicine.

4437 ■ *Journal of the American Society of Podiatric Medical Assistants*
American Society of Podiatric Medical Assistants
1616 N 78th Ct.
Elmwood Park, IL 60707
Fr: 888-882-7762
URL: http://www.aspma.org

Quarterly. Included in membership. Professional journal covering issues in podiatry.

4438 ■ *Journal of Health and Life Sciences Law*
American Health Lawyers Association
1620 Eye St. NW, 6th Fl.
Washington, DC 20006-4010
Ph: (202)833-1100
Fax: (202)833-1105
URL: http://www.healthlawyers.org

Quarterly. $149.00/year for individuals. Professional journal covering healthcare issues and cases and their impact on the health care arena.

4439 ■ *Journal of Hospital Medicine*
John Wiley & Sons Inc.
111 River St.
Hoboken, NJ 07030-5773
Ph: (201)748-6000
Fax: (201)748-6088
Fr: 800-825-7550
URL: http://onlinelibrary.wiley.com/journal/10.1002/
(ISSN)1553-56

$827.00/year for U.S., Canada, and Mexico, print only; $827.00/year for institutions, other countries, print only. Journal on hospital medicine.

4440 ■ *The Municipality*
League of Wisconsin Municipalities
122 W Washington Ave., Ste. 300
Madison, WI 53703-2715
Ph: (608)267-2380
Fax: (608)267-0645
Fr: 800-991-5502
URL: http://www.lwm-info.org/

Monthly. Magazine for officials of Wisconsin's local municipal governments.

4441 ■ *NAFAC News*
National Association for Ambulatory Urgent Care
18870 Rutledge Rd.
Minneapolis, MN 55391
E-mail: info@nafac.com
URL: http://www.urgentcare.org

Description: Reports on issues current to the ambulatory urgent care industry, including government activity, national developments, and trends in health care. Recurring features include editorials, news of research, letters to the editor, and Association news. Available online only.

4442 ■ *Same-Day Surgery*
American Health Consultants Inc.
3525 Piedmont Rd. NE, Bldg. 6-400
Atlanta, GA 30305
Ph: (404)262-5476
Fax: (404)262-5560
Fr: 800-688-2421
E-mail: editorial_questions@ahcmedia.com
URL: http://www.ahcmedia.com/public

Description: Monthly. $499. Focuses on the management, structure, and legal and medical aspects of ambulatory surgery. Carries expert opinions and recommendations on policies and procedures.

4443 ■ *USA Body Psychotherapy Journal*
United States Association for Body Psychotherapy
8639 B 16th St., Ste. 119
Silver Spring, MD 20910
Ph: (202)466-1619
E-mail: admin@usabp.org
URL: http://www.usabp.org/
    displaycommon.cfm?an=4

Semiannual. Academic journal that seeks to support, promote and stimulate the exchange of ideas, scholarship and research within the field of body psychotherapy as well as an interdisciplinary exchange with related fields of clinical practice and inquiry.

4444 ■ *Year Book of Critical Care Medicine*
Elsevier Science Inc.
360 Park Ave. S
New York, NY 10010-1710
Ph: (212)989-5800
Fax: (212)633-3990
Fr: 888-437-4636
URL: http://www.elsevier.com/wps/find/
    journaldescription.cws_home

Annual. $271.00/year for institutions, other countries; $197.00/year for other countries; $103.00/year for students, other countries; $250.00/year for institutions; $167.00/year for individuals; $81.00/year for students. Journal focused on treatment of severe sepsis and septic shock, echocardiography in the evaluation of hemo-dynamically unstable patients & mechanical ventilation of acute respiratory distress syndrome.

EMPLOYER DIRECTORIES AND NETWORKING LISTS

4445 ■ *Crain's List—Chicago's Largest Hospitals*
Crain Communications Inc.
360 N Michigan Ave.
Chicago, IL 60601

Ph: (312)649-5200
URL: http://www.chicagobusiness.com/section/lists

Published November, 2010. $25.00 for individuals; $45.00 for individuals. Covers: 25 hospitals in Chicago area ranked by net patient revenues. Entries include: Name, address, phone number, fax, web address, corporate e-mail, hospital administrator, network affiliation, 2009 net patient revenue, percentage change from 2008, 2009 net profits, percentage change from 2008, inpatient days, available beds, daily occupancy rate, number of hospital employees as of December 31, 2009, fiscal year end, Chairman, President, CEO, Chief Financial Officer, Human Resources Manager, Media Relations/Public Relations Director, and Hospital Administrator.

4446 ■ *Directory of Hospital Personnel*
Grey House Publishing
4919 Rte. 22
PO Box 56
Amenia, NY 12501
Ph: (518)789-8700
Fax: (518)789-0556
Fr: 800-562-2139
URL: http://www.greyhouse.com/hospital_
    personnel.htm

Annual, Latest edition 2011. $325.00 for individuals. Covers: 200,000 executives at 6,000 U.S. Hospitals. Entries include: Name of hospital, address, phone, number of beds, type and JCAHO status of hospital, names and titles of key department heads and staff, medical and nursing school affiliations; number of residents, interns, and nursing students. Arrangement: Geographical. Indexes: Hospital name, personnel, hospital size.

4447 ■ *Hospital Blue Book*
Billian Publishing Inc. and Trans World Publishing Inc.
2100 River Edge Pky.
Atlanta, GA 30328
Ph: (770)955-5656
Fax: (770)952-0669
Fr: 800-800-5668
E-mail: blu-book@billian.com
URL: http://www.billianshealthdata.com/Products/
    bluebook.html

Annual, Latest edition 2010. $575.00 for individuals; $575.00 for individuals. Covers: More than 6,500 hospitals; some listings also appear in a separate southern edition of this publication. Entries include: Name of hospital, accreditation, mailing address, phone, fax, number of beds, type of facility (nonprofit, general, state, etc.); list of administrative personnel and chiefs of medical services, with specific titles. Arrangement: Geographical.

4448 ■ *Medical and Health Information Directory*
Gale
PO Box 6904
Florence, KY 41022-6904
Fr: 800-354-9706
URL: http://www.gale.cengage.com

Annual, Latest edition April 2011. $1190.00 for individuals; $501.00 for individuals. Covers: In volume 1, more than 33,000 medical and health oriented associations, organizations, institutions, and government agencies, including health maintenance organizations (HMOs), preferred provider organizations (PPOs), insurance companies, pharmaceutical companies, research centers, and medical and allied health schools. In Volume 2, over 20,000 medical book publishers; medical periodicals, directories, audiovisual producers and services, medical libraries and information centers, electronic resources, and health-related internet search engines. In Volume 3, more than 40,500 clinics, treatment centers, care programs, and counseling/diagnostic services for 34 subject areas. Entries include: Institution, service, or firm name, address, phone, fax, email and URL; many include names of key personnel and, when pertinent, descriptive annotation. Volume 3 was formerly listed separately as Health Services

Directory. Arrangement: Classified by organization activity, service, etc. Indexes: Each volume has a complete alphabetical name and keyword index.

4449 ■ *National Directory of Fire Chiefs & EMS Administrators*
National Public Safety Information Bureau
601 Main St.
PO Box 365
Stevens Point, WI 54481-2617
Ph: (715)345-2772
Fax: (715)345-7288
Fr: 800-647-7579
URL: http://www.safetysource.com

Annual, Latest edition 2012. $169.00 for individuals; $199.00. Covers: Over 37,000 fire and emergency departments in the U.S. Entries include: Department name, address, phone, fax, county, name of chief, type of department, financial structure. Arrangement: Geographical.

HANDBOOKS AND MANUALS

4450 ■ *Careers in Health Care*
The McGraw-Hill Companies
PO Box 182604
Columbus, OH 43272
Fax: (614)759-3749
Fr: 877-883-5524
E-mail: customer.service@mcgraw-hill.com
URL: http://www.mhprofessional.com/
    product.php?isbn=0071466533

Barbara M. Swanson. Fifth edition, 2005. $19.95 (paper). 192 pages. Describes job duties, work settings, salaries, licensing and certification requirements, educational preparation, and future outlook. Gives ideas on how to secure a job.

4451 ■ *Careers in Medicine*
The McGraw-Hill Companies
PO Box 182604
Columbus, OH 43272
Fax: (614)759-3749
Fr: 877-883-5524
E-mail: customer.service@mcgraw-hill.com
URL: http://www.mhprofessional.com/
    product.php?isbn=0071458743

Terence J. Sacks. Third edition, 2006. $15.95 (paper). 192 pages. Examines the many paths open to M.D.s, D.O.s, and M.D./Ph.D.s, including clinical private or group practice, hospitals, public health organizations, the armed forces, emergency rooms, research institutions, medical schools, pharmaceutical companies and private industry, and research/advocacy groups like the World Health Organization. A special chapter on osteopathy and chiropractic explores this branch of medicine.

4452 ■ *Exploring Health Care Careers, Second Edition*
JIST Publishing
875 Montreal Way
St. Paul, MN 55102
Fax: 800-547-8329
Fr: 800-648-5478
E-mail: info@jist.com
URL: http://www.jist.com

2006. $125.00. 992 pages. Information about careers in the health industry, including education and certification requirements, earnings, and job outlook.

4453 ■ *Introduction to the Health Professions*
Jones & Bartlett Learning, LLC
PO Box 417289
Boston, MA 02241-7289
Ph: (978)443-5000
Fax: (978)443-8000
Fr: 800-832-0034
E-mail: info@jblearning.com
URL: http://www.jblearning.com

Peggy S. Stanfield, Y. H. Hui and Nanna Cross. 2012.

$93.95. 502 pages. Sixth edition. Provides current coverage of all major health professions. Outlines health-related careers, a review of the U.S. healthcare delivery system, managed care, and impact of new technology on healthcare services.

4454 ■ *Master the EMT-Basic Certification Exam*
Peterson's Publishing
c/o Peterson's Nelnet LLC
2000 Lenox Dr., 2nd Fl., Ste. 203
Lawrenceville, NJ 08648
E-mail: onlinestore@petersons.com
URL: http://www.petersonsbooks.com

2010. $18.95. 240 pages. Prepares test takers for the emergency medical technician qualifying exam. Includes customized study plans, tips on mental and physical preparation, test-taking strategies, advice on managing time and test anxiety. Features an up-to-date list of state EMT agencies, latest training methods and tips for a successful job search.

4455 ■ *Opportunities in Health and Medical Careers*
The McGraw-Hill Companies
PO Box 182604
Columbus, OH 43272
Fax: (614)759-3749
Fr: 877-883-5524
E-mail: customer.service@mcgraw-hill.com
URL: http://www.mhprofessional.com/product.php?isbn=0071437274

I. Donald Snook, Jr. and Leo D'Orazio. 2004. $14.95 (paper). 157 pages. Covers the full range of medical and health occupations. Illustrated.

4456 ■ *The Paramedic Exam Review*
Cengage Learning
PO Box 6904
Florence, KY 41022
Fax: 800-487-8488
Fr: 800-354-9706
E-mail: esales@cengage.com
URL: http://www.cengage.com

Bob Elling and Kirsten Elling. 2012. $56.95. 464 pages.

4457 ■ *Paramedic Survival Guide*
McGraw-Hill Professional
1221 Avenue of the Americas, 45th Fl.
New York, NY 10020
E-mail: scott_grillo@mcgraw-hill.com
URL: http://www.mhprofessional.com

Peter DiPrima Jr. 2012. $25.00. 208 pages. Offers both novice and experienced paramedics case studies, testimonials and advice to help them succeed and advance in their careers. Includes tips on picking the correct EMT job, recruitment and interview process, and various career paths and options open to paramedics.

4458 ■ *Plunkett's Health Care Industry Almanac 2012*
Plunkett Research, Ltd.
PO Drawer 541737
Houston, TX 77254-1737
Ph: (713)932-0000
Fax: (713)932-7080
E-mail: customersupport@plunkettresearch.com
URL: http://www.plunkettresearch.com

Jack W. Plunkett. 2011. $299.99. 717 pages. Features in-depth profiles of leading companies, associations and professional societies in the healthcare field. Covers major issues and trends, market forecasts and industry statistics.

4459 ■ *Resumes for Health and Medical Careers*
The McGraw-Hill Companies
PO Box 182604
Columbus, OH 43272
Fax: (614)759-3749

Fr: 877-883-5524
E-mail: customer.service@mcgraw-hill.com
URL: http://www.mhprofessional.com/product.php?isbn=0071545352
Third edition, 2008. $12.95 (paper). 144 pages.

EMPLOYMENT AGENCIES AND SEARCH FIRMS

4460 ■ B. E. Smith
9777 Ridge Dr.
Lenexa, KS 66219
Fr: 800-467-9117
URL: http://www.besmith.com

Serves as an executive search to healthcare organizations across the nation. Offers permanent and interim placements.

4461 ■ JPM International
26034 Acero
Mission Viejo, CA 92691
Ph: (949)699-4300
Fax: (949)699-4333
Fr: 800-685-7856
E-mail: qtek37@yahoo.com
URL: http://www.jpmintl.com/pages/qss.html
Executive search firm and employment agency.

4462 ■ Keystone Healthcare Management
6075 Poplar Ave., Ste. 727
Memphis, TN 38119
Ph: (901)795-3600
Fax: (901)795-6060
Fr: (866)291-8600
E-mail: scross@keystonehealthcare.com
URL: http://www.keystonehealthcare.com

Specializes in the organization and management of emergency physician groups, offering support services in emergency department management, emergency medicine and physician placement.

ONLINE JOB SOURCES AND SERVICES

4463 ■ HEALTHeCAREERS Network
Fr: 888-884-8242
E-mail: info@healthecareers.com
URL: http://www.healthecareers.com

Description: Career search site for jobs in all health care specialties; educational resources; visa and licensing information for relocation; interesting articles; relocation tools; links to professional organizations and general resources.

4464 ■ Hospital Jobs OnLine
E-mail: support@hospitaljobsonline.com
URL: http://www.hospitaljobsonline.com

Description: Serves as a niche healthcare job board designed exclusively for hospitals, healthcare companies, and healthcare job seekers.

4465 ■ ProHealthJobs.com
Ph: (484)443-8545
Fax: (484)443-8549
E-mail: info@prohealthjobs.com
URL: http://prohealthjobs.com/jobboard

Description: Career resources site for the medical and health care field. Lists professional opportunities, product information, continuing education and open positions.

TRADESHOWS

4466 ■ Ambulatory Surgery Center Association - Annual Meeting
Ambulatory Surgery Center Association
1012 Cameron St.
Alexandria, VA 22314

Ph: (703)836-8808
Fax: (703)549-0976
E-mail: asc@ascassociation.org
URL: http://www.fasa.org

Annual. Primary Exhibits: Ambulatory equipment, supplies, and services. Dates and Locations: 2012 May 09-12; Dallas, TX; Gaylord Texan.

4467 ■ American College of Emergency Physicians Scientific Assembly
American College of Emergency Physicians
1125 Executive Cir.
PO Box 619911
Irving, TX 75038-2522
Ph: (972)550-0911
Fax: (214)580-2816
Fr: 800-798-1822
URL: http://www.acep.org

Annual. Primary Exhibits: Products and services related to emergency medicine. Dates and Locations: 2012 Oct 08-11; Denver, CO; 2013 Oct 14-17; Seattle, WA; 2014 Oct 27-30; Chicago, IL; 2015 Oct 26-29; Boston, MA.

4468 ■ EMS World Expo
Cygnus Business Media
801 Cliff Rd. E, No. 201
Burnsville, MN 55337
Fr: 800-827-8009
E-mail: scott.samuels@cygnusexpos.com
URL: http://publicsafetyevents.com

Annual. Brings all elements of the emergency medical services community together at one time and place. Offers an opportunity to update skills, learn about new developments and techniques, and network with thousands of fellow EMS providers from across the United States and around the world. 2012 October 29-November 2; New Orleans, LA.

4469 ■ Society for Academic Emergency Medicine Annual Meeting
Society for Academic Emergency Medicine
2340 S. River Rd., Ste. 200
Des Plaines, IL 60018
Ph: (847)813-9823
Fax: (847)813-5450
E-mail: saem@saem.org
URL: http://www.saem.org

Annual. Primary Exhibits: Emergency medicine equipment, supplies, and services. Dates and Locations: 2012 May 09-12; Chicago, IL.

OTHER SOURCES

4470 ■ Commission on Accreditation of Allied Health Education Programs (CAAHEP)
1361 Park St.
Clearwater, FL 33756
Ph: (727)210-2350
Fax: (727)210-2354
E-mail: megivern@caahep.org
URL: http://www.caahep.org

Description: Serves as a nationally recognized accrediting agency for allied health programs in 23 occupational areas.

4471 ■ National Association of Emergency Medical Technicians (NAEMT)
PO Box 1400
Clinton, MS 39060-1400
Ph: (601)924-7744
Fax: (601)924-7325
Fr: 800-34N-AEMT
E-mail: info@naemt.org
URL: http://www.naemt.org

Description: Represents and supports EMTS, paramedics and other professionals working in pre-hospital emergency medicine working in all sectors of EMS, including government third-service agencies, fire departments, hospital-based ambulance services, private companies, industrial, special operations settings, and in the military. Acts as a voice for EMS personnel in Washington, DC regarding decisions affecting EMS; speaks on behalf of all EMS providers; representatives sit on boards, associations, expert panels, and commissions to ensure that EMS is represented in decisions affecting health care and public safety; works on behalf of members in the areas of compensation and recognition, recruitment and retention, safety, and education and training.

4472 ■ National Association of EMS Physicians

PO Box 19570
Lenexa, KS 66285-5945
Ph: (913)895-4611
Fax: (913)895-4652
Fr: 800-228-3677
E-mail: info-naemsp@goamp.com
URL: http://www.naemsp.org

Description: Medical directors responsible for emergency medical services and other physicians and nonphysicians dedicated to out-of-hospital emergency care. Promotes career development, communication and cooperation among EMS professionals.

4473 ■ National Association of Female Paramedics (NAFP)

PO Box 1133
Orlando, FL 32802
Ph: (407)932-2839
E-mail: national-director@nafp.org
URL: http://www.nafp.org

Description: Represents women dedicated to providing Emergency Medical Services (EMS). Provides financial assistance through grants, loans, and other funding options to women who are in the field of EMS.

4474 ■ National Registry of Emergency Medical Technicians (NREMT)

Rocco V. Morando Bldg.
6610 Busch Blvd.
PO Box 29233
Columbus, OH 43229
Ph: (614)888-4484
Fax: (614)888-8920
URL: http://www.nremt.org

Description: Promotes the improved delivery of emergency medical services. Assists in the development and evaluation of educational programs to train emergency medical technicians; establishes qualifications for eligibility to apply for registration; prepares and conducts examinations designed to assure the competency of emergency medical technicians and paramedics; establishes a system for biennial registration; establishes procedures for revocation of certificates of registration for cause; maintains a directory of registered emergency medical technicians.

SOURCES OF HELP-WANTED ADS

4475 ■ Advances in Developing Human Resources
Sage Publications Inc.
2455 Teller Rd.
Thousand Oaks, CA 91320-2218
Ph: (805)499-9774
Fax: (805)583-2665
Fr: 800-818-7243
URL: http://www.sagepub.com/
    journalsProdDesc.nav?prodId=Journal20

Bimonthly. $637.00/year for institutions, print & e-access; $573.00/year for institutions, e-access; $624.00/year for institutions, print only; $110.00/year for individuals, print only; $172.00/year for institutions, single print issue; $36.00/year for individuals, single print issue. Journal for professionals working in the field of human resource development.

4476 ■ Consultants News
Kennedy Information Inc.
1 Phoenix Mill Ln., 3rd Fl.
Peterborough, NH 03458
Ph: (603)924-1006
Fax: (603)924-4460
Fr: 800-531-0007
E-mail: support@kennedyinfo.com
URL: http://www.kennedyinfo.com/rt/rectrends.html

Description: Bimonthly. Provides strategies and tactics for creating and maintaining a competitive work force.

4477 ■ International Journal of Selection and Assessment
John Wiley & Sons Inc.
350 Main St., Commerce Pl.
Malden, MA 02148-5089
Ph: (781)388-8200
Fax: (781)388-8210
URL: http://www.wiley.com/bw/journal.asp?ref=0965-075X

Quarterly. $122.00/year for individuals, print and online; $95.00/year for students, print and online; $1,003.00/year for institutions, print and online; $872.00/year for institutions, print or online; $597.00/year for institutions, other countries, print and online; $519.00/year for institutions, other countries, print or online; $111.00/year for individuals, print and online, Europe; $74.00/year for individuals, print and online. Journal publishing articles related to all aspects of personnel selection, staffing, and assessment in organizations.

4478 ■ Journal of Business and Psychology
Springer-Verlag New York Inc.
233 Spring St.
New York, NY 10013-1578
Ph: (212)460-1500
Fax: (212)460-1575

Fr: 800-777-4643
URL: http://www.springer.com/psychology/
    community+%26+environment

$904.00/year for institutions, print or online; $1,085.00/year for institutions, print & enchanced access. Journal covering all aspects of psychology that apply to the business segment. Includes topics such as personnel selection and training, organizational assessment and development, risk management and loss control, marketing and consumer behavior research.

4479 ■ Journal of Job Placement
National Rehabilitation Association
633 S Washington St.
Alexandria, VA 22314
Ph: (703)836-0850
Fax: (703)836-0848
Fr: 888-258-4295
E-mail: info@natioanlrehab.org
URL: http://www.nationalrehab.org

Periodic. Employment journal.

4480 ■ SI Review
Staffing Industry Analysts Inc.
1975 W El Camino Real, Ste. 304
Mountain View, CA 94040
Ph: (650)390-6200
URL: http://www.staffingindustry.com/site/Research-
    Publications/P

Monthly. $99.00/year for individuals; $129.00/year for Canada; $149.00/year for other countries. Online news publication covering news and developments in employment and staffing.

4481 ■ Staffing Industry Employment Bulletin
Staffing Industry Analysts Inc.
1975 W El Camino Real, Ste. 304
Mountain View, CA 94040
Ph: (650)390-6200
URL: http://www.staffingindustry.com/

Irregular. Online news publication covering key events in employment and staffing.

4482 ■ Staffing Industry News Bulletin
Staffing Industry Analysts Inc.
1975 W El Camino Real, Ste. 304
Mountain View, CA 94040
Ph: (650)390-6200
URL: http://www.staffingindustry.com/

Daily. $10.00/year for single issue. Online publication covering key events in all sectors of the staffing industry.

4483 ■ Workforce Management
Crain Communications, Inc.
1155 Gratiot Ave.
Detroit, MI 48207-2997
Ph: (313)446-6000
URL: http://www.workforceonline.com

Biweekly. $79.00/year for individuals; $129.00/year for Canada and Mexico; $199.00/year for other countries. A Business magazine for human resources management leaders.

EMPLOYER DIRECTORIES AND NETWORKING LISTS

4484 ■ National Directory of Personnel Service Firms
National Association of Personnel Services
131 Prominence Ct., Ste. 130
Dawsonville, GA 30534
Ph: (706)531-0060
Fax: (866)739-4750
URL: http://www.recruitinglife.com

Annual, spring. Covers: Over 1,100 member private (for-profit) personnel service firms and temporary service firms. Entries include: Firm name, address, phone, fax, contact, area of specialization. Arrangement: Same information given geographically by employment specialty.

HANDBOOKS AND MANUALS

4485 ■ The Human Resource Professional's Career Guide: Building a Position of Strength
John Wiley & Sons, Inc.
1 Wiley Dr.
Somerset, NJ 08873
Ph: (732)469-4400
Fax: (732)302-2300
Fr: 800-526-5368
E-mail: custserv@wiley.com
URL: http://www.wiley.com/WileyCDA/

Jeanne Palmer, Martha I. Finney. June 2004. $44.95. 264 pages.

4486 ■ Senior Employment Interviewer
National Learning Corporation
212 Michael Dr.
Syosset, NY 11791
Fr: 800-632-8888
URL: http://www.passbooks.com

2009. $34.95 (paper). Serves as an exam preparation guide for senior employment interviewers.

EMPLOYMENT AGENCIES AND SEARCH FIRMS

4487 ■ The Aspire Group
711 Boylston St.
Boston, MA 02116-2616
Fax: (617)500-7284

Fr: 800-487-2967
URL: http://www.bmanet.com/Aspire/index.html

Employment agency.

4488 ■ Campbell/Carlson LLC
PO Box 34323
Charlotte, NC 28234
Ph: (704)373-0234
E-mail: recruiting@campbellcarlson.com
URL: http://www.campbellcarlson.com

Executive search firm.

4489 ■ Dankowski and Associates, Inc.
13089 Root Rd.
The Woods, Ste. 200 SE
Columbia Station, OH 44028
Ph: (216)973-0556
E-mail: info@dankowskiassocites.com
URL: http://www.dankowskiassociates.com

Executive search firm.

4490 ■ The Enfield Company
3005 S Lamar Blvd., Ste. D109-172
Austin, TX 78704
Ph: (512)585-0876
URL: http://silverdevelopment.com

Executive search firm.

4491 ■ John J. Davis & Associates Inc.
30 Chatham Rd.
PO Box G
Short Hills, NJ 07078
Ph: (973)467-8339
Fax: (973)467-3706
E-mail: jack.davis@jdavisassoc.com
URL: http://www.johnjdavisandassoc.com

Executive search firm.

4492 ■ Protocol Agency Inc.
27001 Agoura Rd., Ste. 210
Calabasas, CA 91301
Fr: 877-371-0069
E-mail: corp@protocolexec.com
URL: http://www.protocolagency.com

Executive search firm focusing on a variety of placements.

4493 ■ Williams Executive Search Inc.
4200 Wells Fargo Ctr.
90 S 7th St.
Minneapolis, MN 55402
Ph: (612)339-2900
Fax: (612)305-5040
E-mail: resumes@williams-exec.com
URL: http://www.williams-exec.com

Executive search firm.

4494 ■ Willmott and Associates, Inc.
922 Waltham St., Ste. 103
Lexington, MA 02421
Ph: (781)863-5400
Fax: (781)863-8000
E-mail: info@willmott.com
URL: http://www.willmott.com

Executive search firm and permanent employment agency. Also fills some temporary placements.

ONLINE JOB SOURCES AND SERVICES

4495 ■ Spherion
2050 Spectrum Blvd.
Fort Lauderdale, FL 33309
Ph: (954)308-7600
Fr: 800-774-3746
E-mail: help@spherion.com
URL: http://www.spherion.com

Description: Recruitment firm specializing in accounting and finance, sales and marketing, interim executives, technology, engineering, retail and human resources.

OTHER SOURCES

4496 ■ American Staffing Association (ASA)
277 S Washington St., Ste. 200
Alexandria, VA 22314-3675
Ph: (703)253-2020
Fax: (703)253-2053
E-mail: asa@americanstaffing.net
URL: http://www.americanstaffing.net

Description: Promotes and represents the staffing industry through legal and legislative advocacy, public relations, education, and the establishment of high standards of ethical conduct.

4497 ■ Association of Career Firms North America (ACFI)
8509 Crown Crescent C., Ste. ACF
Charlotte, NC 28227
Ph: (704)849-2500
Fax: (704)845-2420
E-mail: bcrigger@oipartners.net
URL: http://www.acf-northamerica.com

Description: Represents firms providing displaced employees, who are sponsored by their organization, with counsel and assistance in job searching and the techniques and practices of choosing a career. Develops, improves and encourages the art and science of outplacement consulting and the professional standards of competence, objectivity, and integrity in the service of clients. Cooperates with other industrial,

technical, educational, professional, and governmental bodies in areas of mutual interest and concern.

4498 ■ Employment Support Center (ESC)
1556 Wisconsin Ave. NW
Washington, DC 20007
Ph: (202)628-2919
Fax: (202)628-2919
URL: http://www.angelfire.com/biz/jobclubs

Description: Trains individuals to facilitate support groups for job-seekers. Operates a job bank for employment assistance; helps people learn to network for job contacts; provides technical assistance to employment support self help groups. Maintains speakers' bureau. Provides job-search skills training.

4499 ■ HR Policy Association
1100 13th St. NW, Ste. 850
Washington, DC 20005
Ph: (202)789-8670
Fax: (202)789-0064
E-mail: info@hrpolicy.org
URL: http://www.hrpolicy.org

Description: Senior human resource executives of Fortune 500 companies. Conducts research and publishes findings on matters relating to federal human resources policy and its application and effects. Maintains task forces to study pending employment issues; conducts seminars, and offers a suite of labor relations and HR effectiveness training courses.

4500 ■ International Association of Workforce Professionals (IAWP)
1801 Louisville Rd.
Frankfort, KY 40601
Ph: (502)223-4459
Fax: (502)223-4127
Fr: 888-898-9960
E-mail: iawp@iawponline.org
URL: http://www.iawponline.org

Description: Officials and others engaged in job placement, unemployment compensation, and labor market information administration through municipal, state, provincial, and federal government employment agencies and unemployment compensation agencies. Conducts workshops and research. Offers professional development program of study guides and tests.

4501 ■ National Association of Personnel Services (NAPS)
131 Prominence Ct., Ste. 130
Dawsonville, GA 30534
Ph: (706)531-0060
Fax: (866)739-4750
E-mail: conrad.taylor@recruitinglife.com
URL: http://www.recruitinglife.com

Description: Private employment and temporary service firms. Compiles statistics on professional agency growth and development; conducts certification program and educational programs. Association is distinct from former name of National Association of Personnel Consultants.

ONLINE JOB SOURCES AND SERVICES

4502 ■ Energy Auditor Jobs
URL: http://www.energyauditorjobs.org
Description: Connects employers with potential candidates who are seeking energy auditor jobs.

4503 ■ Justmeans - CSR JOBS
URL: http://www.justmeans.com

Description: Serves as online resource that provides available career opportunities for the sustainable business industry.

TRADESHOWS

4504 ■ Green Manufacturing Expo
Canon Communications LLC
11444 W. Olympic Blvd., Ste. 900
Los Angeles, CA 90064-1549

Ph: (310)445-4200
Fax: (310)445-4299
E-mail: info@cancom.com
URL: http://www.cancom.com

Annual. Primary Exhibits: Exhibits relating to sustainability, clean energy, energy managment, recycling in packaging, energy efficiency in manufacturing, and renewable energies.

4505 ■ AIE Perspectives Newsmagazine
American Institute of Engineers
4630 Appian Way, Ste. 206
El Sobrante, CA 94803-1875
Ph: (510)758-6240
Fax: (510)758-6240
URL: http://www.members-aie.org

Monthly. Professional magazine covering engineering.

4506 ■ Chemical & Engineering News
American Chemical Society
1155 16th St. NW
Washington, DC 20036
Ph: (202)872-4600
Fr: 800-227-5558
URL: http://pubs.acs.org/cen/about.html

Weekly. Magazine on chemical and engineering news.

4507 ■ EE Evaluation Engineering
Nelson Publishing Inc.
2500 Tamiami Trl. N
Nokomis, FL 34275
Ph: (941)966-9521
Fax: (941)966-2590
URL: http://www.evaluationengineering.com/

Monthly. Free. Trade magazine covering electronic engineering, evaluation and test.

4508 ■ Electronic Engineering Times
United business Media L.L.C
240 W 35th St.
New York, NY 10001
Ph: (516)562-5000
URL: http://www.cmp.com/products/pr_det_
elecengtimesasia.jhtml

Semimonthly. Weekly trade newspaper.

4509 ■ Electronic Products
Hearst Business Communications/Electronics Group
50 Charles Lindbergh Blvd., Ste. 100
Uniondale, NY 11553
Ph: (516)227-1383
E-mail: lens@electronicproducts.com
URL: http://www.electronicproducts.com

Monthly. $12.00/year for individuals. Magazine for electronic design engineers and management.

4510 ■ Engineering
Scientific Research Publishing
PO Box 54821
Irvine, CA 92619-4821
E-mail: eng@scirp.org
URL: http://www.scirp.org/journal/eng/

Monthly. $708.00/year for individuals. Peer-reviewed journal publishing articles on the latest advancements in engineering.

4511 ■ Engineering Conferences International Symposium Series
Berkeley Electronic Press
2809 Telegraph Ave., Ste. 202
Berkeley, CA 94705-1167
Ph: (510)665-1200
Fax: (510)665-1201
URL: http://services.bepress.com/eci/

Journal focusing on advance engineering science.

4512 ■ ENR: Engineering News-Record
McGraw-Hill Inc.
PO Box 182604
Columbus, OH 43218
Ph: (614)430-4000
Fax: (614)759-3749
Fr: 877-833-5524
URL: http://enr.construction.com/Default.asp

Weekly. $49.00/year for individuals, print; $89.00/year for Canada, print; $125.00/year for other countries, print. Magazine focusing on engineering and construction.

4513 ■ High Technology Careers Magazine
HTC
4701 Patrick Henry Dr., No. 1901
Santa Clara, CA 95054
Fax: (408)567-0242
URL: http://www.hightechcareers.com

Bimonthly. $29.00/year; $35.00/year for Canada; $85.00/year for out of country. Magazine (tabloid) containing employment opportunity information for the engineering and technical community.

4514 ■ InterJournal
New England Complex Systems Institute
283 Main St., Ste. 319
Cambridge, MA 02142
Ph: (617)547-4100
Fax: (617)661-7711
URL: http://www.interjournal.org/

Journal covering the fields of science and engineering.

4515 ■ Journal of Engineering Education
American Society for Engineering Education
1818 N St. NW, Ste. 600
Washington, DC 20036-2479
Ph: (202)331-3500
Fax: (202)265-8504
URL: http://www.jee.org

Quarterly. $100.00/year for libraries, online; $160.00/year for other countries, library; $150.00/year for U.S., Canada, and Mexico, library; $160.00/year for other countries, library. Peer-reviewed journal covering scholarly research in engineering education.

4516 ■ Journal of Women and Minorities in Science and Engineering
Begell House Inc.
50 Cross Hwy.
Redding, CT 06896

Ph: (203)938-1300
Fax: (203)938-1304
URL: http://www.begellhouse.com/journals/
00551c876cc2f027

$248.00/year for institutions. Peer-reviewed journal featuring innovative ideas and programs for classroom teachers, scientific studies, and formulation of concepts related to the education, recruitment, and retention of under-represented groups in science and engineering.

4517 ■ Mechanical Engineering
American Society of Mechanical Engineers
3 Park Ave.
New York, NY 10016-5990
Ph: (973)882-1170
Fr: 800-843-2763
E-mail: memag@asme.org
URL: http://www.memagazine.org

Monthly. $25.00/year for single issue; $3.50/year for single issue, international surface. Mechanical Engineering featuring technical and industry related technological advancements and news.

4518 ■ Microwave Journal
Horizon House Publications Inc.
685 Canton St.
Norwood, MA 02062
Ph: (781)769-9750
Fax: (781)769-5037
Fr: 800-966-8526
E-mail: mwj@mwjournal.com
URL: http://www.mwjournal.com

Monthly. Electronic engineering magazine.

4519 ■ Modern Metals
Trend Publishing
625 N Michigan Ave., Ste. 1100
Chicago, IL 60611-3118
Ph: (312)654-2300
Fax: (312)654-2323
Fr: 800-278-7363
URL: http://www.modernmetals.com

Monthly. $180.00/year for individuals; $270.00/year for two years; $260.00/year for individuals, airmail; $430.00/year for two years, airmail. Metals fabrication magazine.

4520 ■ NSBE Magazine
NSBE Publications
205 Daingerfield Rd.
Alexandria, VA 22314
Ph: (703)549-2207
Fax: (703)683-5312
URL: http://www.nsbe.org/News-Media/Magazines/
About-NSBE-Magazine

$20.00/year for individuals; $35.00/year for other countries; $15.00/year for students. Journal providing information on engineering careers, self-development, and cultural issues for recent graduates with technical majors.

4521 ■ PE
National Society of Professional Engineers
1420 King St.
Alexandria, VA 22314
Ph: (703)684-2800
Fax: (703)684-4875
URL: http://www.nspe.org/PEmagazine/index.html

Monthly. Magazine (tabloid) covering professional, legislative, and techology issues for an engineering audience.

4522 ■ Printed Circuit Design & Manufacture
UP Media Group Inc.
PO Box 470
Canton, GA 30169
Ph: (678)817-1286
URL: http://pcdandf.com/cms/

Monthly. Magazine for engineers and designers of PCBs and related technologies.

4523 ■ SMT
PennWell Corp.
1421 S Sheridan Rd.
Tulsa, OK 74112
Ph: (918)835-3161
Fax: (918)831-9497
Fr: 800-331-4463
URL: http://www.ems007.com/pages/ems007.cgi

Monthly. $115.00/year for U.S. and Canada; $215.00/year for other countries. Trade magazine for professional engineers involved in surface mount technology circuit design and board assembly.

4524 ■ SPE Technical Journals
Society of Petroleum Engineers (SPE)
830 S. Greenville Ave.
Allen, TX 75002
Ph: (972)952-9393
Fax: (972)952-9435
Fr: 800-456-6863

$80.00/year for members, print or online. Journal devoted to engineers and scientists.

4525 ■ Structure Magazine
American Council of Engineering Companies
1015 15th St. NW, 8th Fl.
Washington, DC 20005-2605
Ph: (202)347-7474
Fax: (202)898-0068
URL: http://www.structuremag.org

Annual. $65.00/year for nonmembers, for U.S residents; $35.00/year for students; $90.00/year for Canada; $125.00/year for other countries. Magazine focused on providing tips, tools, techniques, and innovative concepts for structural engineers.

4526 ■ SWE, Magazine of the Society of Women Engineers
Society of Women Engineers
120 S La Salle St., Ste. 1515
Chicago, IL 60603
Ph: (312)596-5223
Fr: 877-793-4636
URL: http://societyofwomenengineers.swe.org/index.php

Quarterly. $30.00/year for nonmembers. Magazine for engineering students and for women and men working in the engineering and technology fields. Covers career guidance, continuing development and topical issues.

4527 ■ Technology Interface
Ball State University
2000 W University Ave.
Muncie, IN 47306
Ph: (765)289-1241
Fr: 800-382-8540
URL: http://web.bsu.edu/tti/Subscribe.htm

Journal for the engineering technology profession serving education and industry.

4528 ■ Test & Measurement World
Canon Communications L.L.C.
11444 W Olympic Blvd., Ste. 900
Los Angeles, CA 90064
Ph: (310)445-4200
Fax: (310)445-4299
E-mail: tmw@reedbusiness.com
URL: http://www.tmworld.com

Monthly. Free. Electronic engineering magazine specializing in test, measurement and inspection of electronic products.

4529 ■ Tooling & Production
Nelson Publishing Inc.
2500 Tamiami Trl. N
Nokomis, FL 34275
Ph: (941)966-9521
Fax: (941)966-2590
URL: http://www.manufacturingcenter.com

Monthly. Free. Magazine concerning metalworking.

4530 ■ Wireless Engineering and Technology
Scientific Research Publishing
PO Box 54821
Irvine, CA 92619-4821
E-mail: wet@scirp.org
URL: http://www.scirp.org/journal/wet/

Quarterly. $156.00/year for individuals. Peer-reviewed journal publishing articles on wireless engineering and technology.

EMPLOYER DIRECTORIES AND NETWORKING LISTS

4531 ■ Careers in Focus—Technicians
Facts On File Inc.
132 W 31st St., 17th Fl.
New York, NY 10001
Ph: (212)967-8800
Fax: 800-678-3633
Fr: 800-322-8755
URL: http://www.infobasepublishing.com

Latest edition 3rd; Published May, 2010. $32.95 for individuals. Covers: An overview of technicians, followed by a selection of jobs profiled in detail, including the nature of the job, earnings, prospects for employment, what kind of training and skills it requires, and sources for further information.

4532 ■ Directory of Contract Staffing Firms
C.E. Publications Inc.
PO Box 3006
Bothell, WA 98041-3006
Ph: (425)806-5200
Fax: (425)806-5585
URL: http://www.cjhunter.com/dcsf/overview.html

Annual. Covers: Nearly 1,300 contract firms actively engaged in the employment of engineering, IT/IS, and technical personnel for 'temporary' contract assignments throughout the world. Entries include: Company name, address, phone, name of contact, email, web address. Arrangement: Alphabetical. Indexes: Geographical.

4533 ■ ENR—Top 500 Design Firms Issue
McGraw-Hill Inc.
PO Box 182604
Columbus, OH 43218
Ph: (614)430-4000
Fax: (614)759-3749
Fr: 877-833-5524
URL: http://enr.construction.com/toplists/sourcebooks/2010/design

Annual, latest edition 2010. $82.00 for individuals. Publication includes: List of 500 leading architectural, engineering, and specialty design firms selected on basis of annual billings. Entries include: Company name, headquarters location, type of firm, current and prior year rank in billings, types of services,

countries in which operated in preceding year. Arrangement: Ranked by billings.

4534 ■ Profiles of Engineering and Engineering Technology Colleges
American Society for Engineering Education
1818 N St. NW, Ste. 600
Washington, DC 20036-2479
Ph: (202)331-3500
Fax: (202)265-8504
URL: http://www.asee.org

Latest edition 2010. $75.00 for nonmembers; $50.00 for members; $25.00 for students. Covers: U.S. and Canadian schools offering undergraduate and graduate engineering and engineering technology programs. Entries include: Name, address, phone, fax.

HANDBOOKS AND MANUALS

4535 ■ Associate Engineering Technician
National Learning Corporation
212 Michael Dr.
Syosset, NY 11791
Fr: 800-632-8888
URL: http://www.passbooks.com

2009. $34.95 (paper). Serves as an exam preparation guide for associate engineering technicians.

4536 ■ Engineering, Mechanics, and Architecture
Ferguson Publishing
132 W 31st St., 17th Fl.
New York, NY 10001
Fax: 800-678-3633
Fr: 800-322-8755
E-mail: custserv@factsonfile.com
URL: http://www.infobasepublishing.com

Kelly Wiles. 2010. $39.95. 160 pages (hardcover). Serves as a guide for readers interested in switching jobs. Contains useful advice, career tips, interviews and self-asessment questions.

4537 ■ Engineering Technician
National Learning Corporation
212 Michael Dr.
Syosset, NY 11791
Fr: 800-632-8888
URL: http://www.passbooks.com

2009. $29.95 (paper). Serves as an exam preparation guide for engineering technicians.

4538 ■ Opportunities in Electronics Careers
The McGraw-Hill Companies
PO Box 182604
Columbus, OH 43272
Fax: (614)759-3749
Fr: 877-883-5524
E-mail: customer.service@mcgraw-hill.com
URL: http://www.mhprofessional.com/product.php?isbn=0071476075

Mark Rowh. 2007. $13.95 (paper). 221 pages. Discusses career opportunities in commercial and industrial electronics equipment repair, electronics home entertainment repair, electronics engineering, and engineering technology. Includes job outlook and how to get off to a good start on the job.

4539 ■ Resumes for Scientific and Technical Careers
The McGraw-Hill Companies
PO Box 182604
Columbus, OH 43272
Fax: (614)759-3749
Fr: 877-883-5524
E-mail: customer.service@mcgraw-hill.com
URL: http://www.mhprofessional.com/product.php?isbn=0071482199

Third edition, 2007. $12.95 (paper). 144 pages. Provides resume advice for individuals interested in working in scientific and technical careers. Includes sample resumes and cover letters.

EMPLOYMENT AGENCIES AND SEARCH FIRMS

4540 ■ Andrew Associates Executive Search Inc.
4800 Meadows Rd., Ste. 300
PO Box 2029
Lake Oswego, OR 97035
Ph: (503)620-5222
E-mail: aaes@andysrch.com
URL: http://www.andysrch.com

Executive search firm.

4541 ■ The Aspire Group
711 Boylston St.
Boston, MA 02116-2616
Fax: (617)500-7284
Fr: 800-487-2967
URL: http://www.bmanet.com/Aspire/index.html

Employment agency.

4542 ■ Ethos Consulting LLC
3219 E Camelback Rd., Ste. 515
Phoenix, AZ 85018
Ph: (480)296-3801
Fax: (480)664-7270
E-mail: conrad@ethosconsulting.com
URL: http://www.ethosconsulting.com

Executive search firm. Second branch in Scottsdale, AZ.

4543 ■ Executive Directions Inc.
PO Box 5742
Sarasota, CA 34277
Ph: (941)922-9180
E-mail: info@execdir.com
URL: http://www.execdir.com

Executive search firm.

4544 ■ Global Employment Solutions
10375 Park Meadows Dr., Ste. 375
Littleton, CO 80124
Ph: (303)216-9500
Fax: (303)216-9533
URL: http://www.gesnetwork.com

Employment agency.

ONLINE JOB SOURCES AND SERVICES

4545 ■ PowerPlantPro.com
E-mail: support@powerplantpro.com
URL: http://www.powerplantpro.com/main/sendform/4/18/3472

Description: Dedicated to professionals in the power and energy industry. Features career advice and employer listings.

4546 ■ TechniciansNow.com
URL: http://www.techniciansnow.com

Description: Provides an avenue to showcase jobs and products vital to the mechanical and technical trade communities.

4547 ■ ThinkEnergyGroup.com
E-mail: resumes@thinkjobs.com
URL: http://www.thinkenergygroup.com

Description: Serves as a job board for professionals looking for positions in engineering, power plant, energy, and technical fields. Contains advice and tips on interviews, job searching, resume writing, hiring, and management. Provides choices of work location, pay rates in the field of expertise and contract, temp-to-hire, and direct hiring options.

OTHER SOURCES

4548 ■ Aircraft Electronics Association (AEA)
3570 NE Ralph Powell Rd.
Lee's Summit, MO 64064
Ph: (816)347-8400
Fax: (816)347-8405
E-mail: info@aea.net
URL: http://www.aea.net

Description: Companies engaged in the sales, engineering, installation, and service of electronic aviation equipment and systems. Seeks to: advance the science of aircraft electronics; promote uniform and stable regulations and uniform standards of performance; establish and maintain a code of ethics; gather and disseminate technical data; advance the education of members and the public in the science of aircraft electronics. Offers supplement type certificates, test equipment licensing, temporary FCC licensing for new installations, spare parts availability and pricing, audiovisual technician training, equipment and spare parts loan, profitable installation, and service facility operation. Provides employment information, equipment exchange information and service assistance on member installations anywhere in the world.

4549 ■ American Association of Engineering Societies (AAES)
1801 Alexander Bell Dr.
Reston, VA 20191
Ph: (202)296-2237
Fax: (202)296-1151
Fr: 888-400-2237
E-mail: dbateson@aaes.org
URL: http://www.aaes.org

Description: Coordinates the efforts of the member societies in the provision of reliable and objective information to the general public concerning issues which affect the engineering profession and the field of engineering as a whole; collects, analyzes, documents, and disseminates data which will inform the general public of the relationship between engineering and the national welfare; provides a forum for the engineering societies to exchange and discuss their views on matters of common interest; and represents the U.S. engineering community abroad through representation in WFEO and UPADI.

4550 ■ American Engineering Association (AEA)
533 Waterside Blvd.
Monroe Township, NJ 08831
Ph: (201)664-6954
E-mail: aea@aea.org
URL: http://www.aea.org

Description: Members consist of Engineers and engineering professionals. Purpose to advance the engineering profession and U.S. engineering capabilities. Issues of concern include age discrimination, immigration laws, displacement of U.S. Engineers by foreign workers, trade agreements, off shoring of U.S. Engineering and manufacturing jobs, loss of U.S. manufacturing and engineering capability, and recruitment of foreign students. Testifies before Congress. Holds local Chapter meetings.

4551 ■ American Indian Science and Engineering Society (AISES)
PO Box 9828
Albuquerque, NM 87119-9828
Ph: (505)765-1052
Fax: (505)765-5608
E-mail: info@aises.org
URL: http://www.aises.org

Description: Represents American Indian and non-Indian students and professionals in science, technology, and engineering fields; corporations representing energy, mining, aerospace, electronic, and computer fields. Seeks to motivate and encourage students to pursue undergraduate and graduate studies in science, engineering, and technology. Spon-

sors science fairs in grade schools, teacher training workshops, summer math/science sessions for 8th-12th graders, professional chapters, and student chapters in colleges. Offers scholarships. Adult members serve as role models, advisers, and mentors for students. Operates placement service.

4552 ■ American Society of Certified Engineering Technicians (ASCET)
PO Box 1536
Brandon, MS 39043
Ph: (601)824-8991
E-mail: russ-freier@ascet.org
URL: http://www.ascet.org

Description: Represents certified and non-certified engineering technicians and technologists. Works to obtain recognition of the contribution of engineering technicians and engineering technologists as an essential part of the engineering-scientific team. Cooperates with engineering and scientific societies. Improves the utilization of the engineering technician and technologist. Assists the educational, social, economic, and ethical development of the engineering technician and technologist. Conducts triennial survey among members to determine employer support, pay scales, and fringe benefits. Offers referral service.

4553 ■ Association for International Practical Training (AIPT)
10400 Little Patuxent Pkwy., Ste. 250
Columbia, MD 21044-3519
Ph: (410)997-2200
Fax: (410)992-3924
E-mail: aipt@aipt.org
URL: http://www.aipt.org

Description: Providers worldwide of on-the-job training programs for students and professionals seeking international career development and life-changing experiences. Arranges workplace exchanges in hundreds of professional fields, bringing employers and trainees together from around the world. Client list ranges from small farming communities to Fortune 500 companies.

4554 ■ Electronics Technicians Association International (ETA)
5 Depot St.
Greencastle, IN 46135
Ph: (765)653-8262
Fax: (765)653-4287
Fr: 800-288-3824
E-mail: eta@eta-i.org
URL: http://www.eta-i.org

Description: Skilled electronics technicians. Provides placement service; offers certification examinations for electronics technicians and satellite, fiber optics, and data cabling installers. Compiles wage and manpower statistics. Administers FCC Commercial License examinations and certification of computer network systems technicians and web and internet specialists.

4555 ■ Engineering Society of Detroit (ESD)
20700 Civic Center Dr., Ste. 450
Southfield, MI 48076
Ph: (248)353-0735
Fax: (248)353-0736
E-mail: esd@esd.org
URL: http://ww2.esd.org/home.htm

Description: Engineers from all disciplines; scientists and technologists. Conducts technical programs and engineering refresher courses; sponsors conferences and expositions. Maintains speakers' bureau; offers placement services; although based in Detroit, MI, society membership is international.

4556 ■ International Society of Automation (ISA)
67 Alexander Dr.
PO Box 12277
Research Triangle Park, NC 27709
Ph: (919)549-8411

Fax: (919)549-8288
E-mail: info@isa.org
URL: http://www.isa.org

Description: Sets the standard for automation by helping over 30,000 worldwide members and other professionals solve difficult technical problems, while enhancing their leadership and personal career capabilities. Develops standards; certifies industry professionals; provides education and training; publishes books and technical articles; and hosts the largest conference and exhibition for automation professionals in the Western Hemisphere. Is the founding sponsor of The Automation Federation.

4557 ■ International Society of Certified Electronics Technicians (ISCET)
3608 Pershing Ave.
Fort Worth, TX 76107-4527
Ph: (817)921-9101
Fax: (817)921-3741
Fr: 800-946-0201
E-mail: info@iscet.org
URL: http://www.iscet.org

Description: Technicians in 50 countries who have been certified by the society. Seeks to provide a fraternal bond among certified electronics technicians, raise their public image and improve the effectiveness of industry education programs for technicians. Offers training programs in new electronics information. Maintains library of service literature for consumer electronic equipment, including manuals and schematics for out-of-date equipment. Offers all FCC licenses. Sponsors testing program for certification of electronics technicians in the fields of audio, communications, computer, consumer, indus-

trial, medical electronics, radar, radio-television and video.

4558 ■ National Institute for Certification in Engineering Technologies (NICET)
1420 King St.
Alexandria, VA 22314-2794
Ph: (703)548-1518
Fax: (703)682-2756
Fr: 888-548-1518
E-mail: test@nicet.org
URL: http://www.nicet.org

Description: Grants and issues certificates to engineering technicians and technologists who voluntarily apply for certification and satisfy competency criteria through examinations and verification of work experience. Requirements for certification involve work experience in terms of job task proficiency and length of progressively more responsible experience. Levels of certification are Technician Trainee, Associate Engineering Technician, Engineering Technician, Senior Engineering Technician, Associate Engineering Technologist, and Certified Engineering Technologist.

4559 ■ Society of Hispanic Professional Engineers (SHPE)
13181 Crossroads Pkwy. N, Ste. 450
City of Industry, CA 91746-3496
Ph: (323)725-3970
Fax: (323)725-0316
E-mail: shpenational@shpe.org
URL: http://oneshpe.shpe.org/wps/portal/national

Description: Represents engineers, student engineers, and scientists. Aims to increase the number of Hispanic engineers by providing motivation and sup-

port to students. Sponsors competitions and educational programs. Maintains placement service and speakers' bureau; compiles statistics.

4560 ■ Society for Mining, Metallurgy, and Exploration (SME)
12999 E Adam Aircraft Cir.
Englewood, CO 80112
Ph: (303)948-4200
Fax: (303)973-3845
Fr: 800-763-3132
E-mail: cs@smenet.org
URL: http://www.smenet.org

Description: A member society of the American Institute of Mining, Metallurgical and Petroleum Engineers. Persons engaged in the finding, exploitation, treatment, and marketing of all classes of minerals (metal ores, industrial minerals, and solid fuels) except petroleum. Promotes the arts and sciences connected with the production of useful minerals and metals. Offers specialized education programs; compiles enrollment and graduation statistics from schools offering engineering degrees in mining, mineral, mineral processing/metallurgical, geological, geophysical, and mining technology. Provides placement service and sponsors charitable programs.

4561 ■ Society of Women Engineers (SWE)
203 N La Salle St., Ste. 1675
Chicago, IL 60601
Ph: (312)596-5223
Fax: (312)596-5252
Fr: 877-SWE-INFO
E-mail: hq@swe.org
URL: http://societyofwomenengineers.swe.org

Description: Educational and service organization representing both students and professional women in engineering and technical fields.

HANDBOOKS AND MANUALS

4562 ■ 97 Things Every Software Architect Should Know
O'Reilly Media, Inc.
1005 Gravenstein Highway N
Sebastopol, CA 95472
Ph: (707)827-7000
Fax: (707)824-8268
Fr: 800-998-9938
URL: http://oreilly.com

Richard Monson-Haefel. 2009. $34.99 (paper). 224 pages. Presents principles on key development issues that go beyond technology. Offers advice for communicating with stakeholders, eliminating complexity, empowering developers, and other practical lessons.

4563 ■ Enterprise Architecture: A Pocket Guide
IT Governance Publishing
25 N Philippi St.
Boise, ID 83706
Fr: 877-317-2454
E-mail: servicecentre@itgovernanceusa.com
URL: http://www.itgovernanceusa.com

Tom Graves. 2009. $14.95 (paper). 62 pages. Describes the purpose, role, and value of architecture in the enterprise, and the makeup and skillsets of the architecture team in different business contexts.

4564 ■ Enterprise Architecture: Creating Value by Informed Governance
Springer
233 Spring St.
New York, NY 10013
Ph: (212)460-1500
Fax: (212)460-1575
URL: http://www.springer.com

Martin Op't Land, Erik Proper, Maarten Waage, Jeroen Cloo, and Claudia Steghuis. 2009. $59.95. 146 pages. Provides an overview of enterprise architecture including the process of creating, applying and maintaining it, and taking into account the perspectives of CxOs, business managers, enterprise architects, solution architects, designers, and engineers.

4565 ■ Enterprise Architecture Good Practices Guide
Trafford Publishing
1663 Liberty Dr.
Bloomington, IN 47403
Fr: 888-232-4444
URL: http://www.trafford.com

Jaap Schekkerman. 2008. $73.12 (softcover). 388 pages. Provides guidance to organizations in initiating, developing, using, and maintaining their enterprise architecture practice.

4566 ■ Handbook of Enterprise Systems Architecture in Practice
Information Science Reference
701 E Chocolate Ave.
Hershey, PA 17033
Ph: (717)533-8845
Fax: (717)533-8661
Fr: (866)342-6657
E-mail: cust@igi-global.com
URL: http://www.igi-global.com

Pallab Saha. 2007. $165.00. 500 pages. Provides an overview of the practical aspects of enterprise architecture. Includes EA theory, concepts, strategies, implementation challenges, and case studies.

4567 ■ Handbook for Interns and Architects
National Council of Architectural Registration Boards
1801 K St. NW, Ste. 700K
Washington, DC 20006
Ph: (202)783-6500
Fax: (202)783-0290
URL: http://www.ncarb.org

2012. Free. Provides information on how to become a registered architect and after initial registration, how to seek NCARB certification and registration in other jurisdictions. Provides services to interns and architects such as educational development, developing training requirements, compilation and evaluation of an individual's record on internship activities, transmitting an intern's record to a jurisdiction in support of the intern's application for examination, and/or registration.

4568 ■ Handbook of Research on Enterprise Systems Volume 1
Information Science Reference
701 E Chocolate Ave.
Hershey, PA 17033
Ph: (717)533-8845
Fax: (717)533-8661
Fr: (866)342-6657
E-mail: cust@igi-global.com
URL: http://www.igi-global.com

Jatinder N. D. Gupta, Sushil K. Sharma, and Mohammad Abdur Rashid. 2009. $265.00. 460 pages. Addresses the field of enterprise systems and covers progressive technologies, leading theories, and advanced applications.

ONLINE JOB SOURCES AND SERVICES

4569 ■ Enterprise Architecture Center
URL: http://www.enterprisearchitecturecenter.com

Description: Builds enterprise architecture awareness and evangelizes enterprise architecture culture and thought leadership to business and technology professionals. Provides strategic enterprise architecture advisory services and assists in finding enterprise architecture careers and IT architect jobs.

4570 ■ Enterprise Architecture Forum
URL: http://enterprisearchitectureforum.com

Description: Serves as forum that connects architects allows them to share, discuss, and study enterprise architecture. Enables professionals to share their views on the use of EA ROI calculators, the workings of different EA tools, the value of service oriented architecture, and the concept of enterprise applications integration.

4571 ■ IT Architect Jobs
E-mail: info@itarchitectjobs.com
URL: http://itarchitectjobs.com

Description: Dedicated to enterprise and information technology architecture. Covers industry domains such as enterprise architecture, business architecture, applications architecture, information architecture, technology architecture, solution architecture, software architecture, hardware architecture, and process architecture.

4572 ■ SOA Hub
URL: http://www.soahub.com

Description: Serves as a portal for the advancement of service oriented architecture. Features enterprise architecture guides, white papers, tutorials, message boards, job listings, and employment opportunities.

TRADESHOWS

4573 ■ BrainStorm
SOAInstitute.org
45 Lyman St., Ste. 24
Westboro, MA 01581
Ph: (508)475-0475
Fax: (508)475-0466
E-mail: info@soainstitute.org
URL: http://www.soainstitute.org

Quarterly. Features case studies and best practices from internationally-recognized companies and agencies on the cutting edge of BPM, SOA, business architecture, business rules, and organizational performance.

4574 ■ Enterprise Architecture Practitioners Conference
Open Group
8 New England Executive Park, 2nd Fl.
Burlington, MA 01803
Ph: (781)564-9200
Fax: (781)564-9220
URL: http://www3.opengroup.org

Quarterly. Offers educational and networking opportunities for information executives and IT professionals.

4575 ■ Enterprise Search Summit
Information Today
143 Old Marlton Pike
Medford, NJ 08055

Ph: (609)654-6266
Fax: (609)654-4309
E-mail: custserv@infotoday.com
URL: http://www.infotoday.com

Covers how to develop, implement, and enhance internal search capabilities in an organization. Presents and examines the different ways to leverage search tools, information architecture, classification, and other strategies and technologies to deliver meaningful results.

4576 ■ IT Architect Regional Conference

International Association of Software Architects
11044 Research Blvd., Ste. B-400
Austin, TX 78759
Ph: (512)637-4272
Fax: (512)382-5327
Fr: (866)399-4272
E-mail: contactus@iasahome.org
URL: http://www.iasaglobal.org/iasa/default.asp

Addresses the needs of IT architects. Features seminars in enterprise, infrastructure, software, information, and fundamentals.

4577 ■ Object Management Group Technical Meeting

Object Management Group
140 Kendrick St., Bldg. A, Ste. 300
Needham, MA 02494
Ph: (781)444-0404
Fax: (781)444-0320
E-mail: info@omg.org
URL: http://www.omg.org

Provides IT architects, business analysts, government experts, vendors, and end-users with a neutral forum to discuss, develop, and adopt standards that enable software interoperability for a wide range of industries.

OTHER SOURCES

4578 ■ Association for Enterprise Integration

2111 Wilson Blvd., Ste. 400
Arlington, VA 22201
Ph: (703)247-2597
Fax: (703)522-3192
E-mail: dchesebrough@afei.org
URL: http://www.afei.org

Description: Represents corporate, government agencies, academic institutions, non-profit organizations, government employees, and individuals. Establishes opportunities for collaboration on enterprise information issues among government, business, and academia.

4579 ■ Business Architects Association

727 S Dearborn St., Ste. 710
Chicago, IL 60605
URL: http://www.businessarchitectsassociation.org

Description: Promotes and advances the business architect field through education, research, community involvement, and application of methodologies for the benefit of the business community at large. Partners with universities to train practitioners for the field. Facilitates the creation of business architecture groups.

4580 ■ DAMA International

19239 Dale Mabry Hwy. N, No. 132
Lutz, FL 33548
Ph: (813)778-5495
Fax: (813)464-7864
E-mail: info@dama.org
URL: http://www.dama.org

Description: Represents the interests of technical and business professionals dedicated to advancing the concepts and practices of information resource management and data resource management. Defines and clarifies the roles of information and data resource management. Educates corporate management by demonstrating how information and data asset management affects corporate performance. Conducts regional and international conferences and symposia. Establishes academic and professional certification programs for the DRM/IRM professional.

4581 ■ Enterprise Architecture Center of Excellence

10895 Lake Point Dr.
Pinckney, MI 48169
Ph: (810)231-6356
Fax: (810)231-6631
E-mail: info@eacoe.org
URL: http://www.eacoe.org

Description: Advances implementation and understanding of enterprise architecture. Provides information and promotes professional and career development among members. Offers practice-based certification, professional networking, and knowledge development opportunities.

4582 ■ Information Architecture Institute

100 Cummings Ctr., Ste. 111J
Beverly, MA 01915
E-mail: info@iainstitute.org
URL: http://iainstitute.org

Description: Supports individuals and organizations specializing in the design and construction of shared information environments. Advances the information architecture profession through education, advocacy, services, and social networking. Provides a framework for members to improve their skills and enhance their professional standing.

SOURCES OF HELP-WANTED ADS

4583 ■ AIE Perspectives Newsmagazine
American Institute of Engineers
4630 Appian Way, Ste. 206
El Sobrante, CA 94803-1875
Ph: (510)758-6240
Fax: (510)758-6240
URL: http://www.members-aie.org

Monthly. Professional magazine covering engineering.

4584 ■ AWWA Streamlines
American Water Works Association
6666 W Quincy Ave.
Denver, CO 80235
Ph: (303)794-7711
Fax: (303)347-0804
Fr: 800-926-7337
E-mail: streamlines@awwa.org
URL: http://www.awwa.org/publications/
streamlinescurrent.cfm

Description: Biweekly, online; print issue is quarterly. Carries news of the Association and features about the drinking water industry, including regulations, legislation, conservation, treatment, quality, distribution, management, and utility operations. Recurring features include letters to the editor, a calendar of events, reports of meetings, news of educational opportunities, notices of publications available, education and job opportunities in the industry and legislative news.

4585 ■ Building Industry Technology
National Technical Information Service
5301 Shawnee Rd.
Alexandria, VA 22312
Ph: (703)605-6585
Fax: (703)605-6900
Fr: 800-553-6847
E-mail: info@ntis.gov
URL: http://www.ntis.gov/products/alerts.aspx

Description: Biweekly. $255. Consists of abstracts of reports on architectural and environmental design, building standards, construction materials and equipment, and structural analyses. Recurring features include a form for ordering reports from NTIS. Also available via e-mail.

4586 ■ City Trees
Society of Municipal Arborists
c/o Jerri J. LaHaie, Exec. Dir.
PO Box 641
Watkinsville, GA 30677
Ph: (706)769-7412
Fax: (706)769-7307
E-mail: urbanforestry@prodigy.net
URL: http://www.urban-forestry.com

Description: Bimonthly. Addresses all aspects of municipal (urban) forestry. Contains technical articles on species of trees, pest control, conservation, plan-

ning, design, and equipment. Recurring features include lists of new publications, statistics, news of research, letters to the editor, announcements of meetings, and columns titled President's Column, Professor's Column, City of the Month, Park of the Month, Tree of the Month, and Editor's Column.

4587 ■ Climate Alert
The Climate Institute
900 17th St. NW, Ste. 700
Washington, DC 20006
Ph: (202)552-4723
Fax: (202)737-6410
E-mail: info@climate.org
URL: http://www.climate.org/publications/climate-alert.html

Description: Quarterly. Addresses global climate issues in terms of science and policy.

4588 ■ Drinking Water & Backflow Prevention
IAPMO
9878 Burke Pond Ct.
Burke, VA 22015
Ph: (703)934-0115
Fax: (703)934-0119
Fr: 888-367-3927
E-mail: curtis@iapmo.org
URL: http://www.iapmodwbp.org

Description: Monthly. $45. Presents articles directed toward individuals, companies, organizations, agencies, and municipalities with an interest in drinking water protection and backflow prevention. Contains information on safety standards, water system protection, training programs, cross-connection control, and all issues related to preventing the contamination of potable drinking water supplies with backflow prevention devices. Recurring features include case studies, letters to the editor, news of research, columns titled Test Your Investigative Skills and Backflow Prevention Device Repairs, and reports of meetings. Also carries news of educational opportunities, job listings, notices of publications available, and a calendar of events.

4589 ■ Engineering
Scientific Research Publishing
PO Box 54821
Irvine, CA 92619-4821
E-mail: eng@scirp.org
URL: http://www.scirp.org/journal/eng/

Monthly. $708.00/year for individuals. Peer-reviewed journal publishing articles on the latest advancements in engineering.

4590 ■ Engineering Conferences International Symposium Series
Berkeley Electronic Press
2809 Telegraph Ave., Ste. 202
Berkeley, CA 94705-1167
Ph: (510)665-1200

Fax: (510)665-1201
URL: http://services.bepress.com/eci/
Journal focusing on advance engineering science.

4591 ■ Environmental Building News
Building Green Inc.
122 Birge St., Ste. 30
Brattleboro, VT 05301-3206
Ph: (802)257-7300
Fax: (802)257-7304
Fr: 800-861-0954
E-mail: info@buildinggreen.com
URL: http://www.buildinggreen.com/landing/
ebnperformance1102.html

Description: Monthly. $99/year. Covers the building trade with an environmental slant. Covers nontoxic materials, better landscaping and water use, and resources for energy conservation in a technical manner.

4592 ■ Environmental Business Journal
Environmental Business International Inc.
4452 Park Blvd., Ste. 306
San Diego, CA 92116
URL: http://www.ebiusa.com

Description: Twelve issues/year. $995/year. Provides research and articles on various segments of the environmental business industry. Recurring features include news of research.

4593 ■ Environmental Education Research
Routledge Journals
270 Madison Ave.
New York, NY 10016-0601
Ph: (212)216-7800
Fax: (212)563-2269
URL: http://www.tandf.co.uk/journals/titles/
13504622.asp

Bimonthly. $1,373.00/year for institutions, print + online; $1,236.00/year for institutions, online only; $364.00/year for individuals, print only. Journal covering all aspects of environmental education.

4594 ■ Environmental Pollution
Elsevier Science Inc.
360 Park Ave. S
New York, NY 10010-1710
Ph: (212)989-5800
Fax: (212)633-3990
Fr: 888-437-4636
E-mail: environmentalpollution@mindspring.com
URL: http://www.elsevier.com/wps/find/
journaldescription.cws_home

Monthly. $5,698.00/year for institutions, other countries, for all countries except Europe, Japan and Iran; $162.00/year for other countries, for all countries except Europe, Japan and Iran; $5,091.00/year for institutions, European and Iran; $676,600.00/year for institutions, European and Iran; $143.00/year for individuals, European and Iran; $18,700.00/year for individuals. Journal covering issues relevant to chemical pollutants in air, soil and water.

4595 ■ *Environmental Progress & Sustainable Energy*
John Wiley & Sons Inc.
111 River St.
Hoboken, NJ 07030-5773
Ph: (201)748-6000
Fax: (201)748-6088
Fr: 800-825-7550
URL: http://onlinelibrary.wiley.com/journal/10.1002/(ISSN)1944-74

Quarterly. $795.00/year for institutions, print only; $851.00/year for institutions, Canada and Mexico, print only; $879.00/year for institutions, other countries, print only; $915.00/year for institutions, print with online; $971.00/year for institutions, Canada and Mexico, print with online; $999.00/year for institutions, other countries, print with online. Journal reporting technological advances vital to engineering professionals whose responsibility includes or is related to environmental issues.

4596 ■ *Graduating Engineer & Computer Careers*
Career Recruitment Media
2 LAN Dr., Ste. 100
Westford, MA 01886
Ph: (978)692-5092
Fax: (978)692-4174
URL: http://www.graduatingengineer.com

Quarterly. $16.95/year for individuals. Magazine focusing on employment, education, and career development for entry-level engineers and computer scientists.

4597 ■ *Green Career Journal*
Environmental Career Center
2 Eaton St., Ste. 711
Hampton, VA 23669
Ph: (757)727-7895
Fax: (757)727-7904
Fr: 800-745-0639
E-mail: eccinfo@environmentalcareer.com
URL: http://environmentalcareer.com

Monthly. Provides information, articles and insight on the environmental businesses and organizations and their current job openings.

4598 ■ *Hardwood Research Bulletin*
National Hardwood Lumber Association
6830 Raleigh La Grange Rd.
Memphis, TN 38134-0518
Ph: (901)377-1818
Fax: (901)382-6419
Fr: 800-933-0318
E-mail: info@nhla.com
URL: http://www.nhla.com

Description: Monthly. Provides abstracts and digests of current research information concerning hardwood forest management, silviculture, insects, diseases, resource utilization, product development, manufacturing technology, and economics. Lists upcoming events, workshops, short courses, and seminars of interest to members.

4599 ■ *High Technology Careers Magazine*
HTC
4701 Patrick Henry Dr., No. 1901
Santa Clara, CA 95054
Fax: (408)567-0242
URL: http://www.hightechcareers.com

Bimonthly. $29.00/year; $35.00/year for Canada; $85.00/year for out of country. Magazine (tabloid) containing employment opportunity information for the engineering and technical community.

4600 ■ *InterJournal*
New England Complex Systems Institute
283 Main St., Ste. 319
Cambridge, MA 02142
Ph: (617)547-4100
Fax: (617)661-7711
URL: http://www.interjournal.org/

Journal covering the fields of science and engineering.

4601 ■ *ISRN Ecology*
Hindawi Publishing Corporation
410 Park Ave., 15th Fl.
287 PMB
New York, NY 10022
E-mail: ecology@isrn.com
URL: http://www.isrn.com/journals/ecology

Peer-reviewed journal publishing research articles in all areas of ecology.

4602 ■ *The Job Seeker*
PO Box 451
Fruita, CO 81521
Fax: (267)295-2004
E-mail: sarah@thejobseeker.net
URL: http://www.thejobseeker.net

Description: Semimonthly. Specializes in environmental and natural resource vacancies nationwide. Lists current vacancies from federal, state, local, private, and non-profit employers. Also available via e-mail.

4603 ■ *Journal of the American Water Works Association*
American Water Works Association
6666 W Quincy Ave.
Denver, CO 80235-3098
Ph: (303)794-7711
Fax: (303)347-0804
Fr: 800-926-7337
URL: http://www.awwa.org

Monthly. Included in membership. Magazine dealing with water supply resources, treatment, and distribution.

4604 ■ *Journal of Engineering Education*
American Society for Engineering Education
1818 N St. NW, Ste. 600
Washington, DC 20036-2479
Ph: (202)331-3500
Fax: (202)265-8504
URL: http://www.jee.org

Quarterly. $100.00/year for libraries, online; $160.00/year for other countries, library; $150.00/year for U.S., Canada, and Mexico, library; $160.00/year for other countries, library. Peer-reviewed journal covering scholarly research in engineering education.

4605 ■ *Journal of Engineering for Sustainable Development*
College Publishing
12309 Lynwood Dr.
Glen Allen, VA 23059
Ph: (804)364-8410
Fax: (804)364-8408
Fr: 800-827-0723
URL: http://www.collegepublishing.us/jesdsubs.htm

Annual. $29.00/year for individuals, online only; $69.00/year for institutions, online only. Peer-reviewed journal focusing on sustainable engineering.

4606 ■ *Journal of Environmental Engineering*
American Society of Civil Engineers
1801 Alexander Bell Dr.
Reston, VA 20191-4400
Ph: (703)295-6300
Fax: (703)295-6333
Fr: 800-548-2723
URL: http://ascelibrary.org/eeo

Monthly. $1,296.00/year for institutions, print & online; $1,356.00/year for institutions, other countries, print & online; $1,141.00/year for institutions, print; $1,201.00/year for institutions, other countries, print; $1,037.00/year for U.S. and other countries, online; $324.00/year for members, print & online; $384.00/year for members, international; print & online; $285.00/year for members, print; $345.00/year for members, international; print; $259.00/year for U.S. and other countries, online only. Peer-reviewed

journal on the practice and status of research in environmental engineering science, systems engineering, and sanitation.

4607 ■ *Journal of Environmental Health*
National Environmental Health Association
720 S Colorado Blvd., Ste. 1000-N
Denver, CO 80246
Ph: (303)756-9090
Fax: (303)691-9490
Fr: (866)956-2258
URL: http://www.neha.org/JEH/

$135.00/year for individuals; $160.00/year for other countries; $250.00/year for two years; $300.00/year for two years, OTC. Journal presenting environmental health and protection issues.

4608 ■ *Journal of Environmental Protection*
Scientific Research Publishing
PO Box 54821
Irvine, CA 92619-4821
E-mail: jep@scirp.org
URL: http://www.scirp.org/journal/jep/

$390.00/year for individuals. Peer-reviewed journal publishing articles on the latest advancements in environmental protection.

4609 ■ *Journal of Freshwater Ecology*
Taylor & Francis Group Journals
325 Chestnut St., Ste. 800
Philadelphia, PA 19106-2608
Ph: (215)625-8900
Fax: (215)625-2940
Fr: 800-354-1420
URL: http://www.tandf.co.uk/journals/TJFE

Quarterly. $117.00/year for institutions, print and online; $193.00/year for institutions, print and online; $154.00/year for institutions, print and online; $42.00/year for individuals, print only; $69.00/year for individuals, print only; $55.00/year for individuals, print only. Peer-reviewed journal publishing a wide variety of original ecological studies, observations and techniques.

4610 ■ *Journal of Water Resource and Protection*
Scientific Research Publishing
PO Box 54821
Irvine, CA 92619-4821
E-mail: jwarp@scirp.org
URL: http://www.scirp.org/Journal/jwarp/

Monthly. $708.00/year for individuals. Peer-reviewed journal publishing articles on the latest advancements in water resources and protection.

4611 ■ *Journal of Women and Minorities in Science and Engineering*
Begell House Inc.
50 Cross Hwy.
Redding, CT 06896
Ph: (203)938-1300
Fax: (203)938-1304
URL: http://www.begellhouse.com/journals/00551c876cc2f027

$248.00/year for institutions. Peer-reviewed journal featuring innovative ideas and programs for classroom teachers, scientific studies, and formulation of concepts related to the education, recruitment, and retention of under-represented groups in science and engineering.

4612 ■ *Lakes & Reservoirs*
John Wiley & Sons Inc.
350 Main St., Commerce Pl.
Malden, MA 02148-5089
Ph: (781)388-8200
Fax: (781)388-8210
URL: http://www.wiley.com/bw/journal.asp?ref=1320-5331

Quarterly. $505.00/year for institutions, UK (print and online); $814.00/year for institutions, Americas (print and online); $990.00/year for institutions, other countries, print and online; $642.00/year for institutions, Europe (print and online); $439.00/year for institutions, UK (print or online only); $861.00/year for institutions, other countries, print or online only; $708.00/year for institutions, Americas (print or online only). Peer-reviewed journal covering the research on the management and conservation of lakes and reservoirs.

4613 ■ Minority Engineer Magazine
Employment Opportunity Publications
445 Broad Hollow Rd., Ste. 425
Melville, NY 11747
Ph: (631)421-9421
Fax: (631)421-1352
E-mail: info@eop.com
URL: http://www.eop.com/mags-ME.php

$18.00/year for non-minority engineering student or professional; $34.00/2 years for non-minority engineering student or professional; $49.00/3 years for non-minority engineering student or professional. Provides job listings, company profiles, and articles geared toward the engineering student and professional.

4614 ■ Natural Resources
Scientific Research Publishing
PO Box 54821
Irvine, CA 92619-4821
E-mail: nr@scirp.org
URL: http://www.scirp.org/journal/nr/

Quarterly. $156.00/year for individuals. Peer-reviewed journal publishing articles on the latest advancements in natural resources.

4615 ■ Seedling News
TreePeople
12601 Mulholland Dr.
Beverly Hills, CA 90210
Ph: (818)753-4600
Fax: (818)753-4635
E-mail: info@treepeople.org
URL: http://www.treepeople.org/seedling-news

Description: Quarterly. Covers environmental topics, such as urban forestry and sustainable communities. Recurring features include a collection and reports of meetings.

4616 ■ Smart Grid and Renewable Energy
Scientific Research Publishing
PO Box 54821
Irvine, CA 92619-4821
E-mail: sgre@scirp.org
URL: http://www.scirp.org/journal/sgre/

Quarterly. $156.00/year for individuals. Peer-reviewed journal publishing articles on the latest advancements in all aspects of smart grid and renewable energy.

4617 ■ SPE Technical Journals
Society of Petroleum Engineers (SPE)
830 S. Greenville Ave.
Allen, TX 75002
Ph: (972)952-9393
Fax: (972)952-9435
Fr: 800-456-6863

$80.00/year for members, print or online. Journal devoted to engineers and scientists.

4618 ■ Structure Magazine
American Council of Engineering Companies
1015 15th St. NW, 8th Fl.
Washington, DC 20005-2605
Ph: (202)347-7474
Fax: (202)898-0068
URL: http://www.structuremag.org

Annual. $65.00/year for nonmembers, for U.S residents; $35.00/year for students; $90.00/year for Canada; $125.00/year for other countries. Magazine focused on providing tips, tools, techniques, and innovative concepts for structural engineers.

4619 ■ SWE, Magazine of the Society of Women Engineers
Society of Women Engineers
120 S La Salle St., Ste. 1515
Chicago, IL 60603
Ph: (312)596-5223
Fr: 877-793-4636
URL: http://societyofwomenengineers.swe.org/index.php

Quarterly. $30.00/year for nonmembers. Magazine for engineering students and for women and men working in the engineering and technology fields. Covers career guidance, continuing development and topical issues.

4620 ■ Water Environment Research
Water Environment Federation
601 Wythe St.
Alexandria, VA 22314-1994
Ph: (703)684-2400
Fax: (703)684-2492
Fr: 800-666-0206
URL: http://www.wef.org/Publications/page_detail.aspx?id=796

Monthly. $125.00/year for individuals, WEF Member, print plus online; $350.00/year for individuals, print plus online; $850.00/year for institutions, print plus online; $200.00/year for other countries, WEF Member, print plus online; $350.00/year for other countries, print plus online; $905.00/year for institutions, other countries, print plus online; $100.00/year for members, print only; $324.00/year for individuals, print only; $770.00/year for institutions, print only; $125.00/year for other countries, members, print only. Technical journal covering municipal and industrial water pollution control, water quality, and hazardous wastes.

4621 ■ WEPANEWS
Women in Engineering Programs & Advocates Network
1901 E Asbury Ave., Ste. 220
Denver, CO 80208
Ph: (303)871-4643
Fax: (303)871-4628
E-mail: dmatt@wepan.org
URL: http://www.wepan.org

Description: 2/year. Seeks to provide greater access for women to careers in engineering. Includes news of graduate, undergraduate, freshmen, pre-college, and re-entry engineering programs for women. Recurring features include job listings, faculty, grant, and conference news, international engineering program news, action group news, notices of publications available, and a column titled Kudos.

4622 ■ The Wildlifer
The Wildlife Society Inc.
5410 Grosvenor Ln., Ste. 200
Bethesda, MD 20814-2144
Ph: (301)897-9770
Fax: (301)530-2471
E-mail: yanin@wildlife.org
URL: http://joomla.wildlife.org

Description: Monthly. Serves as the Society's official publication of record. Contains items on section and chapter activities, meetings of interest, career notes, job opportunities, and timely articles on significant developments in conservation issues. Recurring features include editorials, news of members, letters to the editor, a calendar of events, and a column titled Call for Papers.

4623 ■ Woman Engineer
Equal Opportunity Publications, Inc.
445 Broadhollow Rd., Ste. 425
Melville, NY 11747
Ph: (631)421-9421
Fax: (631)421-1352
E-mail: info@eop.com
URL: http://www.eop.com

Annual. Magazine that is offered at no charge to qualified female engineering, computer-science, and information-technology students and professionals

seeking to find employment and advancement in their careers.

PLACEMENT AND JOB REFERRAL SERVICES

4624 ■ ASA-CSSA-SSSA Career Placement Center
5585 Guilford Rd.
Madison, WI 53711
Ph: (608)273-8080
Fax: (608)273-2021
URL: http://www.careerplacement.org

Serves as a clearinghouse for resumes and personnel listings. Promotes and encourages career opportunities in the agronomic, crop, soil, and environmental sciences.

EMPLOYER DIRECTORIES AND NETWORKING LISTS

4625 ■ American Men and Women of Science
Gale
PO Box 6904
Florence, KY 41022-6904
Fr: 800-354-9706
URL: http://www.gale.cengage.com

Biennial, even years; New edition expected 29th, June 2011. $1,368.00 for individuals. Covers: Over 135,000 U.S. and Canadian scientists active in the physical, biological, mathematical, computer science, and engineering fields; includes references to previous edition for deceased scientists and nonrespondents. Entries include: Name, address, education, personal and career data, memberships, honors and awards, research interest. Arrangement: Alphabetical. Indexes: Discipline (in separate volume).

4626 ■ Association of Conservation Engineers—Membership Directory
Association of Conservation Engineers
Missouri Department of Conservation
PO Box 180
Jefferson City, MO 65102-0180
Ph: (573)522-4115
Fax: (573)522-2324
URL: http://conservationengineers.org

Annual, June. Covers: 280 persons with administrative or engineering background in conservation. Entries include: Member name, address, phone, company or institution name. Arrangement: Alphabetical.

4627 ■ Careers in Focus—Environment
Facts On File Inc.
132 W 31st St., 17th Fl.
New York, NY 10001
Ph: (212)967-8800
Fax: 800-678-3633
Fr: 800-322-8755
URL: http://www.infobasepublishing.com

Latest edition 4th; Published May, 2010. $32.95 for individuals. Covers: An overview of environmental jobs, followed by a selection of jobs profiled in detail, including the nature of the job, earnings, prospects for employment, what kind of training and skills it requires, and sources for further information.

4628 ■ Directory of Contract Staffing Firms
C.E. Publications Inc.
PO Box 3006
Bothell, WA 98041-3006
Ph: (425)806-5200
Fax: (425)806-5585
URL: http://www.cjhunter.com/dcsf/overview.html

Annual. Covers: Nearly 1,300 contract firms actively engaged in the employment of engineering, IT/IS, and technical personnel for 'temporary' contract assignments throughout the world. Entries include: Company name, address, phone, name of contact, email, web address. Arrangement: Alphabetical. Indexes: Geographical.

4629 ■ Indiana Society of Professional Engineers—Directory
Indiana Society of Professional Engineers
PO Box 20806
Indianapolis, IN 46220
Ph: (317)255-2267
Fax: (317)255-2530
URL: http://www.indspe.org

Annual, fall. Covers: Member registered engineers, land surveyors, engineering students, and engineers in training. Entries include: Member name, address, phone, type of membership, business information, specialty. Arrangement: Alpha by chapter area.

4630 ■ Who's Who in Environmental Engineering
American Academy of Environmental Engineers
130 Holiday Ct., Ste. 100
Annapolis, MD 21401
Ph: (410)266-3311
Fax: (410)266-7653
URL: http://www.aaee.net/Website/WhosWho.htm

Annual, Latest edition 2011. $75.00 for individuals. Covers: About 2,400 licensed professional environmental engineers that have been certified by examination in one or more of seven specialties: air pollution control, general environmental engineering, industrial hygiene, hazardous waste management, radiation protection, solid waste management, water supply and wastewater. Entries include: Name, affiliation, address, phone, area of specialization, biographical data. Arrangement: Alphabetical, geographical, area of specialization.

HANDBOOKS AND MANUALS

4631 ■ Building Green Places: Careers in Planning, Designing, and Building (Green-Collar Careers)
Crabtree Publishing Company
350 5th Ave., 59th Fl.
PMB 59051
New York, NY 10118
Ph: (212)496-5040
Fax: 800-355-7166
Fr: 800-387-7650
URL: http://www.crabtreebooks.com

Ruth Owen. 2010. $31.93. 64 pages (hardcover). Features environmental careers related to planning, designing, and building facilities.

4632 ■ Career Opportunities in Conservation and the Environment
Facts On File Inc.
132 W 31st St., 17th Fl.
New York, NY 10001
Fr: 800-322-8755
E-mail: custserv@factsonfile.com
URL: http://factsonfile.infobasepublishing.com

2007. $49.50. 304 pages. Covers job profiles on conservation and the environment, followed by the descriptions of certification, education, special skills, and training required.

4633 ■ Careers in the Environment
The McGraw-Hill Companies
PO Box 182604
Columbus, OH 43272
Fax: (614)759-3749
Fr: 877-883-5524
E-mail: customer.service@mcgraw-hill.com
URL: http://www.mhprofessional.com/
    product.php?cat=106&isbn=0071476113

Michael Fasulo and Paul Walker. 2007. $15.95 (paper). 192 pages. Comprehensive information on

the diverse career opportunities available in environmental services.

4634 ■ Expert Resumes for Engineers
JIST Publishing
875 Montreal Way
St. Paul, MN 55102
Fr: 800-648-5478
E-mail: educate@emcp.com
URL: http://www.jist.com

Louise M. Kursmark and Wendy S. Enelow. 2009. $16.95 (softcover). 272 pages. Features a collection of written resume samples for all types of engineers including civil, mechanical, industrial, electrical, electronics, computer, and more. Contains tips and strategies for writing engineering resumes and finding the best jobs.

4635 ■ Great Jobs for Engineering Majors
The McGraw-Hill Companies
PO Box 182604
Columbus, OH 43272
Fax: (614)759-3749
Fr: 877-883-5524
E-mail: customer.service@mcgraw-hill.com
URL: http://www.mhprofessional.com/
    product.php?isbn=0071641963

Geraldine O. Garner. Second edition, 2008. $16.95. 192 pages. Covers all the career options open to students majoring in engineering.

4636 ■ Jobs in Environmental Cleanup and Emergency Hazmat Response
Rosen Publishing Group
29 E 21st St.
New York, NY 10010
Fax: 888-436-4643
Fr: 800-237-9932
URL: http://www.rosenpublishing.com

Daniel E. Harmon. 2010. $31.95 (library bound). 80 pages. Features jobs in environmental cleanup and emergency hazmat response. Explores numerous career paths for different environmental jobs that require special training or four-year and/or postgraduate degrees. Includes job profiles for professionals such as environmental engineers, geologists, microbiologists, science technicians, conservationists, foresters, park rangers, soil scientists, air control technicians, toxicologists, dredge operators, ecologists, hazardous waste managers, and zoologists.

4637 ■ Resumes for Scientific and Technical Careers
The McGraw-Hill Companies
PO Box 182604
Columbus, OH 43272
Fax: (614)759-3749
Fr: 877-883-5524
E-mail: customer.service@mcgraw-hill.com
URL: http://www.mhprofessional.com/
    product.php?isbn=0071482199

Third edition, 2007. $12.95 (paper). 144 pages. Provides resume advice for individuals interested in working in scientific and technical careers. Includes sample resumes and cover letters.

4638 ■ Sustainable Development in Practice: Case Studies for Engineers and Scientists
John Wiley & Sons, Inc.
111 River St.
Hoboken, NJ 07030-5774
Ph: (201)748-6000
Fax: (201)748-6088
E-mail: info@wiley.com
URL: http://www.wiley.com

Adisa Azapagic and Slobodan Perdan. 2011. $139.95 (hardcover). 536 pages. 2nd edition. Covers a wide range of sustainability issues in both developed and developing countries. Includes case studies. Serves as reading guide for engineers and scientists concerned with sustainable development.

4639 ■ Transport Modeling for Environmental Engineers and Scientists
John Wiley & Sons, Inc.
111 River St.
Hoboken, NJ 07030-5774
Ph: (201)748-6000
Fax: (201)748-6088
E-mail: info@wiley.com
URL: http://www.wiley.com

Mark M. Clark. 2009. $132.00 (hardcover). 664 pages. 2nd edition. Covers fundamentals of mass and momentum transport process emphasizing on aerosol and colloidal systems. Presents environmental focus on sedimentation, coagulation, adsorption and other key topics. Includes worked examples and end-of-chapter exercises.

EMPLOYMENT AGENCIES AND SEARCH FIRMS

4640 ■ Amtec Human Capital
2749 Saturn St.
Brea, CA 92821
Ph: (714)993-1900
Fax: (714)993-2419
E-mail: info@amtechc.com
URL: http://www.amtechc.com
Employment agency.

4641 ■ The Angus Group Ltd.
5080 Wooster Rd., Ste. 300
Cincinnati, OH 45226
Ph: (513)961-5575
Fax: (513)961-5616
E-mail: angus@angusgroup.com
URL: http://www.angusgroup.com
Executive search firm.

4642 ■ Bell Oaks Co.
115 Perimeter Center Pl., Ste. 400
Atlanta, GA 30346
Ph: (678)287-2000
Fax: (678)287-2002
E-mail: info@belloaks.com
URL: http://www.belloaks.com
Personnel service firm.

4643 ■ Bright Blue Alliance, LLC
4032 N Farwell Ave.
Milwaukee, WI 53211-2109
Ph: (414)377-4677
E-mail: connect@brightbluealliance.com
URL: http://brightbluealliance.com
Serves as executive search and recruitment firm for qualified candidates who are looking for a career in any significant water industry.

4644 ■ Career Center, Inc.
2184 Morris Ave.
Union, NJ 07083
Ph: (908)687-1812
Fr: 800-227-3379
E-mail: career@careercenterinc.com
URL: http://www.careercenterinc.com
Employment agency.

4645 ■ The Elliot Company
Ph: (843)388-0900
E-mail: suppt.staff@elliottco.net
URL: http://www.elliottco.net
Executive search firm.

4646 ■ Executive Recruiters Agency
PO Box 21810
Little Rock, AR 72211
Ph: (501)224-7000
Fax: (501)224-8534
E-mail: jobs@execrecruit.com
URL: http://www.execrecruit.com
Personnel service firm.

4647 ■ JPM International
26034 Acero
Mission Viejo, CA 92691
Ph: (949)699-4300
Fax: (949)699-4333
Fr: 800-685-7856
E-mail: qtek37@yahoo.com
URL: http://www.jpmintl.com/pages/qss.html
Executive search firm and employment agency.

4648 ■ ManpowerGroup
100 Manpower Pl.
Milwaukee, WI 53212
Ph: (414)961-1000
Fax: (414)906-7822
URL: http://us.manpower.com

Specializes in a wide range of employment services including permanent placement, recruitment process outsourcing, managed service programs, outplacement and human resources consulting. Provides companies with workforce solutions that help them increase productivity and improve efficiency.

4649 ■ McNichol Associates
8419 Germantown Ave.
Philadelphia, PA 19118
Ph: (215)922-4142
Fax: (215)922-0178
E-mail: mailbox@mcnicholassoc.com

Performs executive search for middle and senior-level management, marketing, and technical personnel for professional design firms; construction, management, and general contractors; engineering-construction organizations; environmental firms, and others needing technical management personnel.

4650 ■ Metzner Group
10130 Harmony Rd.
Myersville, MD 21773
Ph: (301)293-4206
URL: http://www.themetznergroup.com

Specializes in the recruitment of architects, civil engineers, environmental engineers and planners for the A/E/P communities.

4651 ■ Randolph Associates, Inc.
950 Massachusetts Ave., Ste. 105
Cambridge, MA 02139-3174
Ph: (617)441-8777
Fax: (617)441-8778
E-mail: jobs@greatjobs.com
URL: http://www.greatjobs.com

Employment agency. Provides regular or temporary placement of staff.

4652 ■ Roberson & Co.
10751 Parfet St.
Broomfield, CO 80021
Ph: (303)410-6510
E-mail: roberson@recruiterpro.com
URL: http://www.recruiterpro.com

Professional and executive recruiting firm working the national and international marketplace. Specializes in accounting, finance, data processing and information services, health care, environmental and mining, engineering, manufacturing, human resources, and sales and marketing.

4653 ■ Search North America Inc.
PO Box 3577
Sunriver, OR 97707-0577
Ph: (503)222-6461
Fax: (503)227-2804
E-mail: mylinda@searchna.com
URL: http://www.searchna.com

An executive search and recruiting firm whose focus is placing engineers, operations and maintenance managers, sales and marketing management, financial and general management executives (both domestic and international). Industries served: forest products, pulp and paper, waste to energy, environmental services, consulting and equipment suppliers for above related industries.

ONLINE JOB SOURCES AND SERVICES

4654 ■ AEJob.com
E-mail: customerservice@aejob.com
URL: http://aejob.com

Description: Provides lists of architectural jobs, engineering jobs and environmental consulting jobs nationwide.

4655 ■ Bright Green Talent - Green Jobs
URL: http://www.brightgreentalent.com/green-jobs

Description: Serves as online tool that offers green jobs listing and career advice to candidates interested and engaged in environmental career.

4656 ■ Conservation Job Board
URL: http://www.conservationjobboard.com

Description: Provides job seekers with a one-stop place for finding the latest job openings related to conservation. Assists employers to find the ideal candidates for their job openings, internships, graduate assistantships, and other volunteer opportunities.

4657 ■ Cyber-Sierra.com
E-mail: mtnplanner@cyber-sierra.com
URL: http://www.cyber-sierra.com

Description: Offers employment listings in natural resource occupations, ecology and environmental disciples.

4658 ■ Diversity Environmental Jobs
URL: http://www.diversityenvironmentaljobs.com

Description: Serves as a niche job board that provides diverse environmental career opportunities.

4659 ■ EnergyCentralJobs.com
E-mail: service@energycentral.com
URL: http://www.energycentraljobs.com

Description: Serves as an on-line job resource for candidates and power companies worldwide. Maintains a job search database dedicated to the power, nuclear, oil and gas career fields.

4660 ■ EngineerJobs.com
URL: http://www.engineerjobs.com

Description: Provides job opportunities for engineering professionals in the following disciplines: aerospace, agricultural, biomedical, chemical, civil, electrical, environmental, industrial, manufacturing, marine, materials, mechanical, mining, nuclear, petroleum, process, project, quality, sales, software, solar, systems, and structural.

4661 ■ Environmental Career Opportunities
URL: http://www.ecojobs.com

Description: Lists environmental jobs in conservation, education, policy, science and engineering.

4662 ■ Environmental Engineering Jobs
URL: http://www.jobsenvironmentalengineering.com

Description: Serves as a job site network that lists environmental engineering jobs from job postings, internet job boards, newspapers and classified ads.

4663 ■ Environmental Expert
URL: http://www.environmental-expert.com

Description: Connects environmental industry professionals from around the globe to companies that provide the products, services and information they need to do their job successfully.

4664 ■ Environmental Jobs
URL: http://environmental.jobs4.org

Description: Offers a searchable database of environmental job opportunities available throughout the United States.

4665 ■ EnvironmentalCrossing.com
URL: http://www.environmentalcrossing.com

Description: Provides a collection of environmental job listings. Includes lists of employer career pages, job websites, association websites, newspaper classifieds and recruitment sites.

4666 ■ EnvironmentalEngineer.com
URL: http://www.environmentalengineer.com

Description: Provides environmental engineering job listings and products to environmental engineers.

4667 ■ EnvironmentalJobs.com
URL: http://environmentaljobs.com

Description: Serves as online tool that provides current listings of environmental jobs.

4668 ■ Great Green Careers
URL: http://www.greatgreencareers.com

Description: Serves as online resource that connects employers and job seekers in the green jobs industries.

4669 ■ Greenopolis Green Job Listings
URL: http://jobs.greenopolis.com

Description: Provides an online searchable listing of diverse green jobs across the United States.

4670 ■ iHireEnvironmental
URL: http://www.ihireenvironmental.com

Description: Provides listings and services pertaining to environmental employment opportunities.

4671 ■ Justmeans - CSR JOBS
URL: http://www.justmeans.com

Description: Serves as online resource that provides available career opportunities for the sustainable business industry.

4672 ■ Spherion
2050 Spectrum Blvd.
Fort Lauderdale, FL 33309
Ph: (954)308-7600
Fr: 800-774-3746
E-mail: help@spherion.com
URL: http://www.spherion.com

Description: Recruitment firm specializing in accounting and finance, sales and marketing, interim executives, technology, engineering, retail and human resources.

4673 ■ ThinkEnergyGroup.com
E-mail: resumes@thinkjobs.com
URL: http://www.thinkenergygroup.com

Description: Serves as a job board for professionals looking for positions in engineering, power plant, energy, and technical fields. Contains advice and tips on interviews, job searching, resume writing, hiring, and management. Provides choices of work location, pay rates in the field of expertise and contract, temp-to-hire, and direct hiring options.

4674 ■ WorldwideWorker.com
URL: http://www.worldwideworker.com

Description: Features energy jobs for engineers and professionals covering all types of energy sectors, including oil and gas, renewables, mining, nuclear, power, marine, and railway. Provides any individual, engineer or professional, graduate or with an extensive experience list of jobs that can be browsed by location, job category, or company name, or can be directly found with search functionality.

TRADESHOWS

4675 ■ Air and Waste Management Association Annual Conference and Exhibition
Air and Waste Management Association
One Gateway Ctr., 3rd Fl.
420 Ft. Duquesne Blvd.
Pittsburgh, PA 15222-1435

Ph: (412)232-3444
Fax: (412)232-3450
Fr: 800-270-3444
E-mail: info@awma.org
URL: http://www.awma.org

Annual. Primary Exhibits: Instrumentation, environmental control products, and services. Dates and Locations: 2012 Jun 19-22; San Antonio, TX.

4676 ■ American Society for Engineering Education Annual Conference and Exposition

American Society for Engineering Education
1818 N. St. N.W., Ste. 600
Washington, DC 20036-2479
Ph: (202)331-3500
Fax: (202)265-8504
E-mail: conferences@asee.org
URL: http://www.asee.org

Annual. Primary Exhibits: Publications, engineering supplies and equipment, computers, software, and research companies all products and services related to engineering education. Dates and Locations: 2012 Jun 10-13; San Antonio, TX.

4677 ■ NGWA Annual Convention/Exposition

National Ground Water Association
601 Dempsey Rd.
Westerville, OH 43081-8978
Ph: (614)898-7791
Fax: (614)898-7786
Fr: 800-551-7379
E-mail: ngwa@ngwa.org
URL: http://www.ngwa.org

Annual. Primary Exhibits: Equipment, products and technology for the ground water industry.

4678 ■ Texas Ground Water Association Trade Show and Convention

Texas Ground Water Association TGWA
221 E. 9th St., Ste. 206
San Jacinto Bldg.
Austin, TX 78701
Ph: (512)472-7437
Fax: (512)472-0537
E-mail: goodson@twca.org
URL: http://www.tgwa.org

Annual. Primary Exhibits: Water well equipment, including drills. Dates and Locations: 2012 Jan 25-27; San Marcos, TX; San Marcos Hotel & Conference Center.

4679 ■ WEFTEC

Water Environment Federation
601 Wythe St.
Alexandria, VA 22314-1994
Ph: (703)684-2452
Fax: (703)684-2492
Fr: 800-666-0206
E-mail: csc@wef.org
URL: http://www.wef.org

Annual. Primary Exhibits: Water treatment equipment, supplies, and services.

OTHER SOURCES

4680 ■ Air and Waste Management Association (A&WMA)

1 Gateway Ctr., 3rd Fl.
420 Ft. Duquesne Blvd.
Pittsburgh, PA 15222-1435
Ph: (412)232-3444
Fax: (412)232-3450
Fr: 800-270-3444
E-mail: info@awma.org
URL: http://www.awma.org

Description: Serves as environmental, educational, and technical organization. Purpose: Seeks to provide a neutral forum for the exchange of technical

information on a wide variety of environmental topics.

4681 ■ American Academy of Environmental Engineers (AAEE)

130 Holiday Ct., Ste. 100
Annapolis, MD 21401
Ph: (410)266-3311
Fax: (410)266-7653
E-mail: info@aaee.net
URL: http://www.aaee.net

Description: Environmentally oriented registered professional engineers certified by examination as Diplomates of the Academy. Seeks to improve the standards of environmental engineering. Certifies those with special knowledge of environmental engineering. Furnishes lists of those certified to the public. Maintains speakers' bureau. Recognizes areas of specialization: Air Pollution Control; General Environmental; Hazardous Waste Management; Industrial Hygiene; Radiation Protection; Solid Waste Management; Water Supply and Wastewater. Requires written and oral examinations for certification. Works with other professional organizations on environmentally oriented activities. Identifies potential employment candidates through Talent Search Service.

4682 ■ American Association of Engineering Societies (AAES)

1801 Alexander Bell Dr.
Reston, VA 20191
Ph: (202)296-2237
Fax: (202)296-1151
Fr: 888-400-2237
E-mail: dbateson@aaes.org
URL: http://www.aaes.org

Description: Coordinates the efforts of the member societies in the provision of reliable and objective information to the general public concerning issues which affect the engineering profession and the field of engineering as a whole; collects, analyzes, documents, and disseminates data which will inform the general public of the relationship between engineering and the national welfare; provides a forum for the engineering societies to exchange and discuss their views on matters of common interest; and represents the U.S. engineering community abroad through representation in WFEO and UPADI.

4683 ■ American Association of Environmental Technicians (AAET)

PO Box 20434
West Palm Beach, FL 33416
Ph: (561)644-1208
Fax: (561)753-6651
E-mail: mahmood7438@bellsouth.net
URL: http://www.aaetonline.org

Description: Promotes ethical practices, technical competency and professional standards in the environmental fields. Fosters teamwork and cooperation in understanding of environmental techniques. Provides a forum for the environmental technicians and other environmental professionals.

4684 ■ American Engineering Association (AEA)

533 Waterside Blvd.
Monroe Township, NJ 08831
Ph: (201)664-6954
E-mail: aea@aea.org
URL: http://www.aea.org

Description: Members consist of Engineers and engineering professionals. Purpose to advance the engineering profession and U.S. engineering capabilities. Issues of concern include age discrimination, immigration laws, displacement of U.S. Engineers by foreign workers, trade agreements, off shoring of U.S. Engineering and manufacturing jobs, loss of U.S. manufacturing and engineering capability, and recruitment of foreign students. Testifies before Congress. Holds local Chapter meetings.

4685 ■ American Indian Science and Engineering Society (AISES)

PO Box 9828
Albuquerque, NM 87119-9828
Ph: (505)765-1052
Fax: (505)765-5608
E-mail: info@aises.org
URL: http://www.aises.org

Description: Represents American Indian and non-Indian students and professionals in science, technology, and engineering fields; corporations representing energy, mining, aerospace, electronic, and computer fields. Seeks to motivate and encourage students to pursue undergraduate and graduate studies in science, engineering, and technology. Sponsors science fairs in grade schools, teacher training workshops, summer math/science sessions for 8th-12th graders, professional chapters, and student chapters in colleges. Offers scholarships. Adult members serve as role models, advisers, and mentors for students. Operates placement service.

4686 ■ Defense of Place (DOP)

187 E Blithedale Ave.
Mill Valley, CA 94941
Ph: (415)928-3774
Fax: (415)373-6978
E-mail: info@rri.org
URL: http://www.rri.org/defenseofplace.php

Description: Aims to preserve the world's natural resources. Works to create awareness on wildlife conservation. Promotes environmental protection.

4687 ■ Engineering Society of Detroit (ESD)

20700 Civic Center Dr., Ste. 450
Southfield, MI 48076
Ph: (248)353-0735
Fax: (248)353-0736
E-mail: esd@esd.org
URL: http://ww2.esd.org/home.htm

Description: Engineers from all disciplines; scientists and technologists. Conducts technical programs and engineering refresher courses; sponsors conferences and expositions. Maintains speakers' bureau; offers placement services; although based in Detroit, MI, society membership is international.

4688 ■ Environmental Industry Associations (EIA)

4301 Connecticut Ave. NW, Ste. 300
Washington, DC 20008-2304
Ph: (202)244-4700
Fax: (202)966-4824
Fr: 800-424-2869
E-mail: membership@envasns.org
URL: http://www.environmentalistseveryday.org

Description: Compiles statistics; conducts research and educational programs.

4689 ■ Friends of the Osa (FOO)

1822 R St. NW, 4th Fl.
Washington, DC 20009
Ph: (202)234-2356
E-mail: info@osaconservation.org
URL: http://www.osaconservation.org

Description: Aims to maintain a largely forested landscape surrounded by an intact coastal zone that protects the Osa's biodiversity while supporting sustainable human livelihoods. Works with local, regional and international partners to protect the region's globally significant biodiversity. Encourages regional and local participation in conservation efforts. Facilitates the exchange of scientific and research expertise.

4690 ■ Indo-Pacific Conservation Alliance (IPCA)

1525 Bernice St.
Honolulu, HI 96817
Ph: (808)848-4124
Fax: (808)847-8252
E-mail: info@indopacific.org
URL: http://www.indopacific.org

Description: Focuses on the study and conservation of the native ecosystems of the tropical Indo-Pacific region. Supports traditional peoples in the stewardship of globally significant natural resources. Works as facilitators to local communities who request help in conserving their natural resources. Provides information, training, equipment and other support to local stakeholders to help conserve and manage natural resources.

4691 ■ Instream Flow Council (IFC)
645 Hatchery Rd.
Marion, NC 28752
Ph: (828)652-4360
Fax: (828)652-3279
E-mail: chris.goudreau@ncwildlife.org
URL: http://www.instreamflowcouncil.org

Description: Represents the interests of state and provincial fish and wildlife management agencies. Increases public awareness and understanding of instream flow issues and stewardship responsibilities. Helps to establish, maintain and administer programs for the quantification, protection and restoration of instream flows for aquatic resources.

4692 ■ Intelligent Transportation Society of America
1100 17th St. NW, Ste. 1200
Washington, DC 20036
Ph: (202)484-4847
Fr: 800-374-8472
E-mail: info@itsa.org
URL: http://www.itsa.org

Description: Includes private corporations, public agencies, and academic institutions involved in the research, development, and design of intelligent transportation systems technologies that enhance safety, increase mobility, and sustain the environment.

4693 ■ National Action Council for Minorities in Engineering (NACME)
440 Hamilton Ave., Ste. 302
White Plains, NY 10601-1813
Ph: (914)539-4010
Fax: (914)539-4032
E-mail: info@nacme.org
URL: http://www.nacme.org

Description: Leads the national effort to increase access to careers in engineering and other science-based disciplines. Conducts research and public policy analysis, develops and operates national demonstration programs at precollege and university levels, and disseminates information through publications, conferences and electronic media. Serves as a privately funded source of scholarships for minority students in engineering.

4694 ■ National Society of Professional Engineers (NSPE)
1420 King St.
Alexandria, VA 22314-2794

Ph: (703)684-2800
Fax: (703)836-4875
Fr: 888-285-6773
E-mail: memserv@nspe.org
URL: http://www.nspe.org

Description: Represents professional engineers and engineers-in-training in all fields registered in accordance with the laws of states or territories of the U.S. or provinces of Canada; qualified graduate engineers, student members, and registered land surveyors. Is concerned with social, professional, ethical, and economic considerations of engineering as a profession; encompasses programs in public relations, employment practices, ethical considerations, education, and career guidance. Monitors legislative and regulatory actions of interest to the engineering profession.

4695 ■ Ocean Conservation Research
PO Box 559
Lagunitas, CA 94938
Ph: (415)488-0553
E-mail: info@ocr.org
URL: http://ocr.org

Description: Represents scientists, engineers and ocean advocates devoted to improve the environmental health of the sea. Seeks to understand and explore solutions to the growing problem of human generated noise pollution and its impact on marine animals. Promotes the recovery and long term viability of the sea through research focusing on conservation priorities and practices.

4696 ■ Orion Grassroots Network
187 Main St.
Great Barrington, MA 01230
Ph: (413)528-4422
URL: http://www.oriongrassroots.org

Description: Consists of grassroots organizations across the United States. Provides job listing for future green leaders. Offers job posting service on a fee basis.

4697 ■ OurEarth.org
PO Box 212
Painted Post, NY 14870
Ph: (410)878-6485
URL: http://www.ourearth.org

Description: Represents graduate and medical students as well as environmental experts and leaders from around the country. Promotes the importance of natural resources energy savings and pollutant reductions. Conducts environmental programs, activities, initiatives, ideas and grassroots efforts across the country.

4698 ■ Rising Tide North America (RTNA)
PO Box 3928
Oakland, CA 94609

Ph: (503)438-4697
E-mail: contact@risingtidenorthamerica.org
URL: http://www.risingtidenorthamerica.org

Description: Fosters community-based solutions to the climate crisis. Aims to prevent catastrophic global warming by determining the root causes of climate change. Works to support direct action and encourages individuals and organizations to carry out autonomous actions that are in line with these principles.

4699 ■ Rivers Without Borders (RWB)
PO Box 154
Clinton, WA 98236
Ph: (360)341-1976
E-mail: admin@riverswithoutborders.org
URL: http://riverswithoutborders.org

Description: Represents individuals and groups coordinating to protect the diversity of the river. Aims to maintain the abundance of fish and wildlife species in transboundary watersheds. Provides information on how to conserve the river system.

4700 ■ Save Yemen's Flora and Fauna (SYFF)
1523 River Terrace Dr.
East Lansing, MI 48823
E-mail: jzindani@syff.org
URL: http://www.syff.org

Description: Represents individuals with an interest in environmental protection and wildlife conservation. Works to protect natural resources and wildlife habitats through efforts directed against pollution and violation of environmental laws. Conducts research and educational programs.

4701 ■ Society of Hispanic Professional Engineers (SHPE)
13181 Crossroads Pkwy. N, Ste. 450
City of Industry, CA 91746-3496
Ph: (323)725-3970
Fax: (323)725-0316
E-mail: shpenational@shpe.org
URL: http://oneshpe.shpe.org/wps/portal/national

Description: Represents engineers, student engineers, and scientists. Aims to increase the number of Hispanic engineers by providing motivation and support to students. Sponsors competitions and educational programs. Maintains placement service and speakers' bureau; compiles statistics.

4702 ■ Society of Women Engineers (SWE)
203 N La Salle St., Ste. 1675
Chicago, IL 60601
Ph: (312)596-5223
Fax: (312)596-5252
Fr: 877-SWE-INFO
E-mail: hq@swe.org
URL: http://societyofwomenengineers.swe.org

Description: Educational and service organization representing both students and professional women in engineering and technical fields.

SOURCES OF HELP-WANTED ADS

4703 ■ *Green and Sustainable Chemistry*
Scientific Research Publishing
PO Box 54821
Irvine, CA 92619-4821
E-mail: gsc@scirp.org
URL: http://www.scirp.org/journal/gsc/

Quarterly. $156.00/year for individuals. Peer-reviewed journal publishing articles related to reducing the environmental impact of chemicals and fuels.

4704 ■ *ISRN Ecology*
Hindawi Publishing Corporation
410 Park Ave., 15th Fl.
287 PMB
New York, NY 10022
E-mail: ecology@isrn.com
URL: http://www.isrn.com/journals/ecology

Peer-reviewed journal publishing research articles in all areas of ecology.

4705 ■ *Journal of Engineering for Sustainable Development*
College Publishing
12309 Lynwood Dr.
Glen Allen, VA 23059
Ph: (804)364-8410
Fax: (804)364-8408
Fr: 800-827-0723
URL: http://www.collegepublishing.us/jesdsubs.htm

Annual. $29.00/year for individuals, online only; $69.00/year for institutions, online only. Peer-reviewed journal focusing on sustainable engineering.

4706 ■ *Journal of Environmental Protection*
Scientific Research Publishing
PO Box 54821
Irvine, CA 92619-4821
E-mail: jep@scirp.org
URL: http://www.scirp.org/journal/jep/

$390.00/year for individuals. Peer-reviewed journal publishing articles on the latest advancements in environmental protection.

4707 ■ *Journal of Freshwater Ecology*
Taylor & Francis Group Journals
325 Chestnut St., Ste. 800
Philadelphia, PA 19106-2608
Ph: (215)625-8900
Fax: (215)625-2940
Fr: 800-354-1420
URL: http://www.tandf.co.uk/journals/TJFE

Quarterly. $117.00/year for institutions, print and online; $193.00/year for institutions, print and online; $154.00/year for institutions, print and online; $42.00/year for individuals, print only; $69.00/year for individuals, print only; $55.00/year for individuals, print only. Peer-reviewed journal publishing a wide variety of original ecological studies, observations and techniques.

4708 ■ *Journal of Water Resource and Protection*
Scientific Research Publishing
PO Box 54821
Irvine, CA 92619-4821
E-mail: jwarp@scirp.org
URL: http://www.scirp.org/Journal/jwarp/

Monthly. $708.00/year for individuals. Peer-reviewed journal publishing articles on the latest advancements in water resources and protection.

4709 ■ *Journal of Women and Minorities in Science and Engineering*
Begell House Inc.
50 Cross Hwy.
Redding, CT 06896
Ph: (203)938-1300
Fax: (203)938-1304
URL: http://www.begellhouse.com/journals/00551c876cc2f027

$248.00/year for institutions. Peer-reviewed journal featuring innovative ideas and programs for classroom teachers, scientific studies, and formulation of concepts related to the education, recruitment, and retention of under-represented groups in science and engineering.

4710 ■ *Natural Resources*
Scientific Research Publishing
PO Box 54821
Irvine, CA 92619-4821
E-mail: nr@scirp.org
URL: http://www.scirp.org/journal/nr/

Quarterly. $156.00/year for individuals. Peer-reviewed journal publishing articles on the latest advancements in natural resources.

4711 ■ *Pesticides, People and Nature*
Begell House Inc.
50 Cross Hwy.
Redding, CT 06896
Ph: (203)938-1300
Fax: (203)938-1304
URL: http://www.begellhouse.com/journals/33b67499180f0876

$180.00/year for institutions. Journal covering the impact of pesticides on people and the environment.

4712 ■ *Smart Grid and Renewable Energy*
Scientific Research Publishing
PO Box 54821
Irvine, CA 92619-4821
E-mail: sgre@scirp.org
URL: http://www.scirp.org/journal/sgre/

Quarterly. $156.00/year for individuals. Peer-reviewed journal publishing articles on the latest advancements in all aspects of smart grid and renewable energy.

HANDBOOKS AND MANUALS

4713 ■ *Associate Environmental Analyst*
National Learning Corporation
212 Michael Dr.
Syosset, NY 11791
Ph: (516)921-8888
Fr: 800-632-8888
URL: http://www.passbooks.com

2009. $34.95 (paper). Serves as a study guide to assist candidates in preparing for the associate environmental analyst examination.

4714 ■ *Environmental Control Specialist*
National Learning Corporation
212 Michael Dr.
Syosset, NY 11791
Ph: (516)921-8888
Fr: 800-632-8888
URL: http://www.passbooks.com

2009. $29.95 (paper). Serves as a study guide to assist candidates in preparing for the environmental control specialist examination.

4715 ■ *Environmental Enforcement Specialist*
National Learning Corporation
212 Michael Dr.
Syosset, NY 11791
Ph: (516)921-8888
Fr: 800-632-8888
URL: http://www.passbooks.com

2009. $29.95 (paper). Serves as a study guide to assist candidates in preparing for the environmental enforcement specialist examination.

4716 ■ *Environmental Impact Assessment: A Guide to Best Professional Practices*
CRC Press
6000 Broken Sound Pkwy. NW, Ste. 300
Boca Raton, FL 33487
Ph: (561)361-6000
URL: http://www.crcpress.com

Charles H. Eccleston. 2011. $119.95 (hardback). 290 pages. Covers all aspects of environmental impact assessment (EIA). Helps practitioners apply best professional practices in the development of EIAs.

4717 ■ *Environmental Science Experiments*
Chelsea House Publications
c/o Infobase Publishing
132 W 31st St., 17th Fl.
New York, NY 10001
Fax: 800-678-3633
Fr: 800-322-8755
E-mail: custserv@factsonfile.com
URL: http://www.infobasepublishing.com

Aviva Ebner. 2011. $35.00 (hardcover). 160 pages. Raises awareness on the challenges in balancing the use of resources with maintaining a healthy environment. Inspires students to pursue an education and career related to environmental studies.

4718 ■ *Green Jobs for a New Economy: The Career Guide to Emerging Opportunities*
Peterson's Publishing
2000 Lenox Dr.
Lawrenceville, NJ 08648
Ph: (609)896-1800
URL: http://www.petersonspublishing.com

2009. $21.95 (softcover). 400 pages. Provides a blueprint for students and career changers, and includes information about career trends, earning potentials, training and licensure requirements, and job search resources in the green economy.

4719 ■ *Jobs in Environmental Cleanup and Emergency Hazmat Response*
Rosen Publishing Group
29 E 21st St.
New York, NY 10010
Fax: 888-436-4643
Fr: 800-237-9932
URL: http://www.rosenpublishing.com

Daniel E. Harmon. 2010. $31.95 (library bound). 80 pages. Features jobs in environmental cleanup and emergency hazmat response. Explores numerous career paths for different environmental jobs that require special training or four-year and/or postgraduate degrees. Includes job profiles for professionals such as environmental engineers, geologists, microbiologists, science technicians, conservationists, foresters, park rangers, soil scientists, air control technicians, toxicologists, dredge operators, ecologists, hazardous waste managers, and zoologists.

4720 ■ *Principal Environmental Analyst*
National Learning Corporation
212 Michael Dr.
Syosset, NY 11791
Ph: (516)921-8888
Fr: 800-632-8888
URL: http://www.passbooks.com

2009. $39.95 (paper). Serves as a study guide to assist candidates in preparing for the principal environmental analyst examination.

4721 ■ *Re-Greening the Environment: Careers in Clean-up, Remediation and Restoration (Green-Collar Careers)*
Crabtree Publishing Company
350 5th Ave., 59th Fl.
PMB 59051
New York, NY 10018
Ph: (212)496-5040
Fax: 800-355-7166
Fr: 800-387-7650
URL: http://www.crabtreebooks.com

Suzy Gazlay. 2012. $10.95 (paperback). 64 pages. Features careers in environmental clean-up, remediation, and renewal, including jobs associated with preventing and correcting disasters.

4722 ■ *Routledge International Handbook of Green Criminology*
Routledge
711 3rd Ave., 8th Fl.
New York, NY 10017
Ph: (212)216-7800
Fax: (212)563-2269
URL: http://www.routledge.com

Nigel South and Avi Brisman. 2012. $199.00 (hardcover). 496 pages. Examines a wide range of issues in environmental crimes, harms and threats, including environmental legislation and regulation.

4723 ■ *Statistics for Earth and Environmental Scientists*
John Wiley & Sons, Inc.
111 River St.
Hoboken, NJ 07030-5774
Ph: (201)748-6000

Fax: (201)748-6088
E-mail: info@wiley.com
URL: http://www.wiley.com

John Schuenemeyer and Larry Drew. 2011. $110.00 (hardcover). 407 pages. Serves as reference for earth scientists, geologists, hydrologists, and environmental statisticians. Provides treatment of statistical applications for solving real-world environmental problems.

4724 ■ *Sustainable Development in Practice: Case Studies for Engineers and Scientists*
John Wiley & Sons, Inc.
111 River St.
Hoboken, NJ 07030-5774
Ph: (201)748-6000
Fax: (201)748-6088
E-mail: info@wiley.com
URL: http://www.wiley.com

Adisa Azapagic and Slobodan Perdan. 2011. $139.95 (hardcover). 536 pages. 2nd edition. Covers a wide range of sustainability issues in both developed and developing countries. Includes case studies. Serves as reading guide for engineers and scientists concerned with sustainable development.

4725 ■ *Transport Modeling for Environmental Engineers and Scientists*
John Wiley & Sons, Inc.
111 River St.
Hoboken, NJ 07030-5774
Ph: (201)748-6000
Fax: (201)748-6088
E-mail: info@wiley.com
URL: http://www.wiley.com

Mark M. Clark. 2009. $132.00 (hardcover). 664 pages. 2nd edition. Covers fundamentals of mass and momentum transport process emphasizing on aerosol and colloidal systems. Presents environmental focus on sedimentation, coagulation, adsorption and other key topics. Includes worked examples and end-of-chapter exercises.

EMPLOYMENT AGENCIES AND SEARCH FIRMS

4726 ■ Bright Blue Alliance, LLC
4032 N Farwell Ave.
Milwaukee, WI 53211-2109
Ph: (414)377-4677
E-mail: connect@brightbluealliance.com
URL: http://brightbluealliance.com

Serves as executive search and recruitment firm for qualified candidates who are looking for a career in any significant water industry.

4727 ■ Meticulum, LLC
PO Box 451
Vinalhaven, ME 04863-0451
Ph: (207)470-0447
Fax: 877-773-0447
E-mail: meticulum@meticulum.com
URL: http://www.meticulum.com

Specializes in the identification, recruitment and strategic placement of professionals within the environmental health, biotechnology and pharmaceutical industries.

4728 ■ On Demand Environmental
12770 Merit Dr., Ste. 900
Dallas, TX 75251
Ph: (972)419-5691
Fax: (214)615-5159
Fr: (866)862-1399
E-mail: pdelamater@ondemandenv.com
URL: http://www.ondemandenv.com

Specializes in matching high quality environmental, health and safety (EH&S) and corporate social responsibility (CSR) professionals with career advancement opportunities.

ONLINE JOB SOURCES AND SERVICES

4729 ■ Bright Green Talent - Green Jobs
URL: http://www.brightgreentalent.com/green-jobs

Description: Serves as online tool that offers green jobs listing and career advice to candidates interested and engaged in environmental career.

4730 ■ Conservation Job Board
URL: http://www.conservationjobboard.com

Description: Provides job seekers with a one-stop place for finding the latest job openings related to conservation. Assists employers to find the ideal candidates for their job openings, internships, graduate assistantships, and other volunteer opportunities.

4731 ■ Diversity Environmental Jobs
URL: http://www.diversityenvironmentaljobs.com

Description: Serves as a niche job board that provides diverse environmental career opportunities.

4732 ■ EHSJobs.org
E-mail: infol@ehsjobs.org
URL: http://ehsjobs.org

Description: Assists Environmental Health and Safety (EHS) professionals and specialists to find jobs and explore related occupations.

4733 ■ Environmental Health Specialist Jobs
URL: http://
www.environmentalhealthspecialistjobs.com

Description: Serves as a niche job board that focuses entirely on environmental health specialist employment opportunities and candidate recruiting.

4734 ■ Environmental Jobs
URL: http://environmental.jobs4.org

Description: Offers a searchable database of environmental job opportunities available throughout the United States.

4735 ■ Environmental Jobsite.com
URL: http://www.environmentaljobsite.com

Description: Provides job openings for environmental specialists.

4736 ■ Environmental Scientist Jobs
URL: http://www.environmentalscientistjobs.org

Description: Provides a niche job board that focuses entirely on environmental scientist employment opportunities and candidate recruiting.

4737 ■ EnvironmentalJobResource.com
URL: http://www.environmentaljobresource.com

Description: Provides job listings and other resources for students and professionals engaged in environmental field work.

4738 ■ EnvironmentalJobs.com
URL: http://environmentaljobs.com

Description: Serves as online tool that provides current listings of environmental jobs.

4739 ■ EnvironmentalSafetyHealthCrossing.com
URL: http://
www.environmentalsafetyhealthcrossing.com

Description: Provides job consolidation service in the employment industry for safety health jobs from every safety health employer, website, company, and organization.

4740 ■ EnvironmentalSpecialistJobs.com
URL: http://www.environmentalspecialistjobs.com

Description: Features environmental specialist jobs, environmental jobs, energy jobs, green jobs, green job seekers and green employers.

4741 ■ Get Environmental Scientist Jobs
URL: http://www.getenvironmentalscientistjobs.com
Description: Offers a one-stop resource for finding and filling environmental scientist positions. Features free environmental scientist job postings and career opportunities.

4742 ■ Great Green Careers
URL: http://www.greatgreencareers.com
Description: Serves as online resource that connects employers and job seekers in the green jobs industries.

4743 ■ Greenopolis Green Job Listings
URL: http://jobs.greenopolis.com
Description: Provides an online searchable listing of diverse green jobs across the United States.

4744 ■ iHireEnvironmental
URL: http://www.ihireenvironmental.com
Description: Provides listings and services pertaining to environmental employment opportunities.

4745 ■ Justmeans - CSR JOBS
URL: http://www.justmeans.com
Description: Serves as online resource that provides available career opportunities for the sustainable business industry.

4746 ■ ScientistCrossing.com
URL: http://www.scientistcrossing.com
Description: Provides job listings and other resources related to scientist employment opportunities.

OTHER SOURCES

4747 ■ Association of Environmental Health Academic Programs
8620 Roosevelt Way NE, Ste. A
Seattle, WA 98115
Ph: (206)522-5272
E-mail: info@aehap.org
URL: http://www.careersenvhealth.com
Description: Provides useful information for students interested in exploring career options in environmental health. Seeks to increase trained professionals in the field of environmental health.

4748 ■ Campus Safety, Health, and Environmental Management Association - Career Center
c/o Jack Voorhees
One City Centre, Ste. 204
120 W Seventh St.
Bloomington, IN 47404-3839
Ph: (812)245-8084
Fax: (812)245-0588
E-mail: info@cshema.org
URL: http://www.cshema.org
Description: Provides information and career opportunities available to people who are interested or enagaged in environmental health and safety.

4749 ■ Climate, Community and Biodiversity Alliance (CCBA)
2011 Crystal Dr., Ste. 500
Arlington, VA 22202
Ph: (703)341-2748
E-mail: info@climate-standards.org
URL: http://www.climate-standards.org
Description: Represents international non-governmental organizations (NGOs) and research institutes that promote integrated solutions to land management. Promotes responsible land management activities that will benefit local communities, minimize climate change and conserve biodiversity.

4750 ■ Ecological Research and Development Group (ERDG)
190 Main St.
Dover, DE 19901
Ph: (302)236-5383
E-mail: erdg@horseshoecrab.org
URL: http://www.horseshoecrab.org
Description: Promotes the conservation of horseshoe crab species. Provides educational programs to create an atmosphere of learning to inspire and nurture curiosity about the horseshoe crabs species and their habitat. Seeks solutions that prevent the extinction of the horseshoe crab species through scientific research and development.

4751 ■ MarineBio Conservation Society
PO Box 235273
Encinitas, CA 92023
Ph: (713)248-2576
E-mail: info@marinebio.org
URL: http://marinebio.org
Description: Works to protect marine life and the ocean for future generations. Creates an awareness of marine conservation issues and their solutions. Supports marine conservation scientists and students involved in the marine life sciences.

4752 ■ National Oceanic Society (NOS)
17300 Red Hill Ave., Ste. 280
Irvine, CA 92614
Ph: (949)500-5451
Fax: (949)675-1366
URL: http://nationaloceanic.org
Description: Promotes the fundamental concepts of marine conservation and preservation. Supports the education, research and scientific study of marine environment. Assists governmental agencies in the monitoring and detection of activities that are hazardous and harmful to marine environment.

4753 ■ Network of Conservation Educators and Practitioners (NCEP)
American Museum of Natural History
Center for Biodiversity and Conservation
Central Park West, 79th St.
New York, NY 10024
Ph: (212)769-5742
Fax: (212)769-5292
E-mail: ncep@amnh.org
URL: http://ncep.amnh.org
Description: Aims to improve the practice of biodiversity conservation. Promotes educational resources on managing and sustaining biological and cultural diversity. Provides opportunities for communication and interaction among conservation educators and practitioners.

4754 ■ Ocean Conservation Research
PO Box 559
Lagunitas, CA 94938
Ph: (415)488-0553
E-mail: info@ocr.org
URL: http://ocr.org
Description: Represents scientists, engineers and ocean advocates devoted to improve the environmental health of the sea. Seeks to understand and explore solutions to the growing problem of human generated noise pollution and its impact on marine animals. Promotes the recovery and long term viability of the sea through research focusing on conservation priorities and practices.

4755 ■ Orion Grassroots Network
187 Main St.
Great Barrington, MA 01230
Ph: (413)528-4422
URL: http://www.oriongrassroots.org
Description: Consists of grassroots organizations across the United States. Provides job listing for future green leaders. Offers job posting service on a fee basis.

4756 ■ Tropical Forest Group
1125 Ft. Stockton Dr.
San Diego, CA 92103
E-mail: info@tropicalforestgroup.org
URL: http://tropicalforestgroup.org
Description: Promotes the conservation and restoration of the planet's remaining tropical forests. Supports research and development of policies that help maintain the planet's most vital biome. Provides assistance to projects that restore and conserve tropical forests.

4757 ■ Advances in Internet of Things
Scientific Research Publishing
PO Box 54821
Irvine, CA 92619-4821
E-mail: ait@scirp.org
URL: http://www.scirp.org/journal/ait/

Peer-reviewed journal discussing issues on the impact of internet to society.

4758 ■ American Journal of Epidemiology
Oxford University Press
2001 Evans Rd.
Cary, NC 27513-2009
Ph: (919)677-0977
Fax: (919)677-1714
Fr: 800-852-7323
URL: http://aje.oupjournals.org

Semimonthly. $508.00/year for institutions, print & online; $762.00/year for institutions, print & online; $762.00/year for institutions, print & online; $237.00/year for individuals, online; $355.00/year for individuals, online; $355.00/year for individuals, online; $483.00/year for institutions, print; $724.00/year for institutions, print; $724.00/year for institutions, print. Science research and medical journal.

4759 ■ Annals of Medicine
Informa Healthcare
52 Vanderbilt Ave., 7th Fl.
New York, NY 10017-3846
Ph: (212)520-2777
URL: http://informahealthcare.com/ann

$595.00/year for institutions; $980.00/year for institutions; $780.00/year for institutions. Journal covering health science and medical education.

4760 ■ Atmospheric and Climate Sciences
Scientific Research Publishing
PO Box 54821
Irvine, CA 92619-4821
E-mail: acs@scirp.org
URL: http://www.scirp.org/journal/acs/

Quarterly. $156.00/year for individuals. Journal publishing articles on climate atmospheric science.

4761 ■ Clinical Medicine & Research
Marshfield Clinic
1000 N Oak Ave.
Marshfield, WI 54449
Ph: (715)387-5511
Fax: (715)389-3808
Fr: 800-782-8581
E-mail: clinmedres@mcrf.mfldclin.edu
URL: http://www.clinmedres.org

Quarterly. Free within the U.S. Peer-reviewed journal that publishes scientific medical research that is relevant to a broad audience of medical researchers and healthcare professionals.

4762 ■ CME Supplement to Emergency Medicine Clinics of North America
Elsevier Science Inc.
360 Park Ave. S
New York, NY 10010-1710
Ph: (212)989-5800
Fax: (212)633-3990
Fr: 888-437-4636
URL: http://www.elsevier.com/wps/find/journaldescription.cws_home

$209.00/year for individuals. Journal covering emergency medicine clinics.

4763 ■ Discovery Medicine
Discovery Medicine
10 Gerard Ave., Ste. 201
Timonium, MD 21093
Ph: (410)773-9938
Fax: 888-833-0526
URL: http://www.discoverymedicine.com

Bimonthly. $599.00/year for institutions, digital edition; $99.95/year for individuals, digital edition. Online journal that publishes articles on diseases, biology, new diagnostics, and treatments for medical professionals.

4764 ■ Education & Treatment of Children
West Virginia University Press
139 Stansbury Hall
PO Box 6295
Morgantown, WV 26506
Ph: (304)293-8400
Fax: (304)293-6585
URL: http://www.educationandtreatmentofchildren.net

Quarterly. $85.00/year for institutions; $45.00/year for individuals; $100.00/year for institutions, elsewhere; $60.00/year for individuals, elsewhere. Periodical featuring information concerning the development of services for children and youth. Includes reports written for educators and other child care and mental health providers focused on teaching, training, and treatment effectiveness.

4765 ■ Epidemiology
Lippincott Williams & Wilkins
530 Walnut St.
Philadelphia, PA 19106-3619
Ph: (215)521-8300
Fax: (215)521-8902
Fr: 800-638-3030
URL: http://journals.lww.com/epidem/pages/default.aspx

Bimonthly. $337.00/year for individuals; $835.00/year for institutions; $175.00/year for individuals, in-training; $427.10/year for other countries; $888.10/year for institutions, other countries; $187.10/year for other countries, in-training. Professional medical journal for epidemiologists and related disciplines.

4766 ■ Genetic Epidemiology
John Wiley & Sons Inc.
111 River St.
Hoboken, NJ 07030-5773

Ph: (201)748-6000
Fax: (201)748-6088
Fr: 800-825-7550
URL: http://onlinelibrary.wiley.com/journal/10.1002/(ISSN)1098-22

$3,610.00/year for institutions, print or online; $3,722.00/year for institutions, Canada and Mexico, print only; $3,778.00/year for institutions, other countries, print only; $4,152.00/year for institutions, print & online; $4,264.00/year for institutions, Canada and Mexico, print & online; $4,320.00/year for institutions, other countries, print & online. Peer-reviewed journal for discussion of research on the genetic causes of the distribution of human traits in families and populations.

4767 ■ Global Change, Peace & Security
Routledge
711 3 Ave., 8 Fl.
New York, NY 10016
Ph: (212)216-7800
Fax: (212)563-2269
Fr: 800-634-7064
URL: http://www.tandfonline.com/toc/cpar20/current

$160.00/year for individuals, print; $602.00/year for individuals, online only; $669.00/year for individuals, print & online. Journal promoting physical therapy and integration.

4768 ■ Green and Sustainable Chemistry
Scientific Research Publishing
PO Box 54821
Irvine, CA 92619-4821
E-mail: gsc@scirp.org
URL: http://www.scirp.org/journal/gsc/

Quarterly. $156.00/year for individuals. Peer-reviewed journal publishing articles related to reducing the environmental impact of chemicals and fuels.

4769 ■ iBusiness
Scientific Research Publishing
PO Box 54821
Irvine, CA 92619-4821
E-mail: ib@scirp.org
URL: http://www.scirp.org/journal/ib/

Quarterly. $236.00/year for individuals. Peer-reviewed journal publishing articles on the latest advancements in internet and business, and the intersection of economics with business applications.

4770 ■ The IHS Primary Care Provider
Indian Health Service
The Reyes Bldg.
801 Thompson Ave., Ste. 400
Rockville, MD 20852-1627
Ph: (301)443-1011
URL: http://www.ihs.gov/provider

Monthly. Journal for health care professionals, physicians, nurses, pharmacists, dentists, and dietitians.

4771 ■ Infection Control and Hospital Epidemiology
University of Chicago Press
1427 E 60th St.
Chicago, IL 60637-2954
Ph: (773)702-7600
Fax: (773)702-0694
E-mail: iche@press.uchicago.edu
URL: http://www.press.uchicago.edu/index.html

Monthly. $413.00/year for libraries, print & electronic; $332.00/year for libraries, electronic; $413.00/year for institutions, print only; $185.00/year for individuals, print & electronic; $103.00/year for other countries, electronic only; $93.00/year for individuals, fellow. Peer-reviewed medical journal that covers all areas of infection control and epidemiology for hospital or healthcare facility.

4772 ■ Infection Control Today
Virgo Publishing
3300 N Central Ave., Ste. 300
Phoenix, AZ 85012
Ph: (480)990-1101
Fax: (602)567-6852
E-mail: kpyrek@vpico.com
URL: http://www.infectioncontroltoday.com

Monthly. Online publication listing job opportunities in the field of epidemiology.

4773 ■ Infectious Diseases in Children
SLACK Incorporated
6900 Grove Rd.
Thorofare, NJ 08086-9447
Ph: (856)848-1000
Fax: (856)848-6091
E-mail: idc@slackinc.com
URL: http://www.idinchildren.com

Monthly. $299.00/year for individuals; $598.00/year for individuals, two years; $897.00/year for individuals, three years; $479.00/year for institutions; $958.00/year for institutions, two years; $1,437.00/year for institutions, three years; $149.00/year for individuals, resident; $39.00/year for single issue; $65.00/year for other countries. Newspapers for physician.

4774 ■ Injury
Mosby Inc.
11830 Westline Industrial Dr.
St. Louis, MO 63146-3326
Ph: (314)872-8370
Fax: (314)432-1380
Fr: 800-325-4177
URL: http://www.elsevier.com/wps/find/journaldescription.cws_home

Monthly. $200.00/year for individuals, European countries and Iran; $224.00/year for individuals, all countries except Europe, Japan and Iran; $26,500.00/year for institutions; $1,381.00/year for institutions, European countries and Iran; $1,543.00/year for institutions, all Countries except Europe, Japan and Iran; $183,200.00/year for institutions. Journal publishing articles and research related to the treatment of injuries such as trauma systems and management; surgical procedures; epidemiological studies; surgery (of all tissues); resuscitation; biomechanics; rehabilitation; anaesthesia; radiology and wound management.

4775 ■ ISRN Ecology
Hindawi Publishing Corporation
410 Park Ave., 15th Fl.
287 PMB
New York, NY 10022
E-mail: ecology@isrn.com
URL: http://www.isrn.com/journals/ecology

Peer-reviewed journal publishing research articles in all areas of ecology.

4776 ■ Journal of Diabetes Mellitus
Scientific Research Publishing
PO Box 54821
Irvine, CA 92619-4821
E-mail: jdm@scirp.org
URL: http://www.scirp.org/journal/jdm/

Quarterly. $156.00/year for individuals. Peer-reviewed journal publishing research on diabetes mellitus.

4777 ■ Journal of Environmental Pathology, Toxicology and Oncology
Begell House Inc.
50 Cross Hwy.
Redding, CT 06896
Ph: (203)938-1300
Fax: (203)938-1304
URL: http://www.begellhouse.com/journals/0ff459a57a4c08d0

$940.00/year for institutions. Journal covering research and reviews of factors and conditions that affect human and animal carcinogenesis.

4778 ■ Journal of Freshwater Ecology
Taylor & Francis Group Journals
325 Chestnut St., Ste. 800
Philadelphia, PA 19106-2608
Ph: (215)625-8900
Fax: (215)625-2940
Fr: 800-354-1420
URL: http://www.tandf.co.uk/journals/TJFE

Quarterly. $117.00/year for institutions, print and online; $193.00/year for institutions, print and online; $154.00/year for institutions, print and online; $42.00/year for individuals, print only; $69.00/year for individuals, print only; $55.00/year for individuals, print only. Peer-reviewed journal publishing a wide variety of original ecological studies, observations and techniques.

4779 ■ Journal of Hospital Medicine
John Wiley & Sons Inc.
111 River St.
Hoboken, NJ 07030-5773
Ph: (201)748-6000
Fax: (201)748-6088
Fr: 800-825-7550
URL: http://onlinelibrary.wiley.com/journal/10.1002/(ISSN)1553-56

$827.00/year for U.S., Canada, and Mexico, print only; $827.00/year for institutions, other countries, print only. Journal on hospital medicine.

4780 ■ Journal of Skin Cancer
Hindawi Publishing Corp.
410 Park Ave., 15th Fl.
287 PMB
New York, NY 10022-4407
Fax: (215)893-4392
E-mail: jsc@hindawi.com
URL: http://www.hindawi.com/journals/jsc/

$195.00/year for individuals. Peer-reviewed journal publishing original research and review articles, case reports and clinical studies related to all aspects of skin cancer.

4781 ■ Pesticides, People and Nature
Begell House Inc.
50 Cross Hwy.
Redding, CT 06896
Ph: (203)938-1300
Fax: (203)938-1304
URL: http://www.begellhouse.com/journals/33b67499180f0876

$180.00/year for institutions. Journal covering the impact of pesticides on people and the environment.

4782 ■ Psychology of Violence
American Psychological Association
750 1st St. NE
Washington, DC 20002-4242
Ph: (202)336-5500
Fax: (202)336-5549
Fr: 800-374-2721
URL: http://www.apa.org/pubs/journals/vio/index.aspx

Quarterly. $65.00/year for members; $89.00/year for other countries, members; $65.00/year for students; $110.00/year for nonmembers; $139.00/year for other countries, nonmembers; $441.00/year for institutions; $490.00/year for institutions, other countries. Multi-

disciplinary research journal concerning topics on the psychology of violence and extreme aggression.

4783 ■ Public Health Jobs Worldwide
Carlyle Corp.
PO Box 6729
Charlottesville, VA 22906-6729
Ph: (434)985-4924
URL: http://www.jobspublichealth.com

Weekly. Electronic newspaper with current public health job openings in the United States and worldwide.

4784 ■ PublicHealthJobs.net
Association of Schools of Public Health
1900 M St., NW, Ste. 710
Washington, DC 20036
Ph: (202)296-1099
Fax: (202)296-1252
E-mail: publichealthjobs@asph.org
URL: http://www.publichealthjobs.net

Online service that provides links to epidemiology job postings in the private sector, not-for-profit sector, and the federal government.

4785 ■ USA Body Psychotherapy Journal
United States Association for Body Psychotherapy
8639 B 16th St., Ste. 119
Silver Spring, MD 20910
Ph: (202)466-1619
E-mail: admin@usabp.org
URL: http://www.usabp.org/displaycommon.cfm?an=4

Semiannual. Academic journal that seeks to support, promote and stimulate the exchange of ideas, scholarship and research within the field of body psychotherapy as well as an interdisciplinary exchange with related fields of clinical practice and inquiry.

4786 ■ World Journal of AIDS
Scientific Research Publishing
PO Box 54821
Irvine, CA 92619-4821
E-mail: wja@scirp.org
URL: http://www.scirp.org/journal/wja/

Quarterly. $156.00/year for individuals. Peer-reviewed journal publishing articles on research data and education in all aspects of HIV and AIDS.

4787 ■ Year Book of Critical Care Medicine
Elsevier Science Inc.
360 Park Ave. S
New York, NY 10010-1710
Ph: (212)989-5800
Fax: (212)633-3990
Fr: 888-437-4636
URL: http://www.elsevier.com/wps/find/journaldescription.cws_home

Annual. $271.00/year for institutions, other countries; $197.00/year for other countries; $103.00/year for students, other countries; $250.00/year for institutions; $167.00/year for individuals; $81.00/year for students. Journal focused on treatment of severe sepsis and septic shock, echocardiography in the evaluation of hemo-dynamically unstable patients & mechanical ventilation of acute respiratory distress syndrome.

HANDBOOKS AND MANUALS

4788 ■ Managerial Epidemiology and Theory and Practice
Jones & Bartlett Publishers Inc.
40 Tall Pine Dr.
Sudbury, MA 01776
Ph: (978)443-5000
Fax: (978)443-8000

Fr: 800-832-0034
E-mail: info@jbpub.com
URL: http://www.jbpub.com/catalog/9780763731656
G.E. Alan Dever. 2006. $128.95. 598 pages.

ONLINE JOB SOURCES AND SERVICES

4789 ■ Epidemiologist.com
URL: http://www.epidemiologist.com

Description: Serves as an online source of information for professional epidemiologists, including job listings in the field.

4790 ■ EpidemiologistJobs.org
URL: http://epidemiologistjobs.org

Description: Features job sites, company career pages and associations for epidemiologist jobs.

4791 ■ EpidemiologyCareers.com
URL: http://epidemiologycareers.com

Description: Provides a database of epidemiology jobs and resources for job seekers. Includes job title, company, location, job type, salaries, employer and recruiters.

4792 ■ GetEpidemiologistJobs.com
URL: http://www.getepidemiologistjobs.com

Description: Provides a resource for finding and filling epidemiologist positions.

TRADESHOWS

4793 ■ Society for Epidemiologic Research Conference
Society for Epidemiologic Research
PO Box 990
Clearfield, UT 84089
Ph: (801)525-0231
Fax: (801)525-6549
E-mail: membership@epiresearch.org
URL: http://www.epiresearch.org

Annual. Primary Exhibits: Epidemiology equipment, supplies, and services.

OTHER SOURCES

4794 ■ American College of Epidemiology
1500 Sunday Dr., Ste. 102
Raleigh, NC 27607
Ph: (919)861-5573

Fax: (919)787-4916
E-mail: info@acepidemiology.org
URL: http://acepidemiology.org

Members: Professional epidemiologists. **Purpose:** Promotes the professional development of epidemiologists through educational initiatives; advocates for policies and actions that enhance the science and practice of epidemiology; recognizes excellence in epidemiology; and develops and maintains an active membership representing all aspects of epidemiology. **Activities:** Provides job-listing services for epidemiologists.

4795 ■ Association for Professionals in Infection Control and Epidemiology
1275 K St. NW, Ste. 1000
Washington, DC 20005-4006
Ph: (202)789-1890
Fax: (202)789-1899
E-mail: apicinfo@apic.org
URL: http://www.apic.org

Members: Professionals working in the field of infection control and epidemiology. **Purpose:** Promotes excellence in the prevention and control of infections and related adverse outcomes. **Activities:** Provides a forum for members to network, offers educational opportunities, produces publications, and serves as an advocate in governmental policymaking.

4796 ■ Council of State and Territorial Epidemiologists (CSTE)
2872 Woodcock Blvd., Ste. 303
Atlanta, GA 30341
Ph: (770)458-3811
Fax: (770)458-8516
E-mail: pmcconnon@cste.org
URL: http://www.cste.org/dnn

Description: State epidemiologists. Works to establish closer working relationships among members; consults with and advises appropriate disciplines in other health agencies; provides technical advice and assistance to the Association of State and Territorial Health Officials; works closely with Centers for Disease Control on epidemiology, surveillance, and prevention activities.

4797 ■ Emergency Management Institute
16825 S Seton Ave.
Emmitsburg, MD 21727
Ph: (301)447-1000
Fax: (301)447-1201
URL: http://training.fema.gov

Description: Offers access to listed employment opportunities in emergency management, including epidemiology, via the website.

4798 ■ International Society for Environmental Epidemiology
44 Farnsworth St.
Boston, MA 02210
Ph: (617)482-9485
Fax: (617)482-0617
E-mail: iseepi@jsi.org
URL: http://www.iseepi.org

Members: Environmental epidemiologists and scientists worldwide. **Purpose:** Provides a forum for the discussion of problems unique to the study of health and the environment. **Activities:** Holds meetings and workshops, publishes newsletter, acts as liaison with academic, governmental, inter-governmental, non-profit, and business institutions. Serves as a forum for networking among its members.

4799 ■ Society for Epidemiologic Research (SER)
PO Box 990
Clearfield, UT 84089
Ph: (801)525-0231
Fax: (801)525-6549
E-mail: membership@epiresearch.org
URL: http://www.epiresearch.org

Description: Epidemiologists, researchers, public health administrators, educators, mathematicians, statisticians, and others interested in epidemiological research. Stimulates scientific interest in and promotes the exchange of information about epidemiological research.

4800 ■ Society for Healthcare Epidemiology of America
1300 Wilson Blvd., Ste. 300
Arlington, VA 22209
Ph: (703)684-1006
Fax: (703)684-1009
E-mail: info@shea-online.org
URL: http://www.shea-online.org

Members: Professionals in all branches of medicine, public health, and healthcare epidemiology. **Purpose:** Advances the application of the science of healthcare epidemiology and works to maintain the quality of patient care and healthcare worker safety in all healthcare settings. **Activities:** Hosts meetings and provides a forum for networking among its members.

4801 ■ Society for Pediatric and Perinatal Epidemiologic Research
125 Paterson St.
New Brunswick, NJ 08901
Ph: (732)235-7940
URL: http://www.sper.org

Members: Professionals interested in the epidemiology of pregnancy, infancy, and childhood. **Purpose:** Fosters pediatric and perinatal epidemiologic research. **Activities:** Produces a newsletter and offers opportunities for networking among its members.

Sources of Help-Wanted Ads

4802 ■ Association News
Schneider Publishing Company Inc.
11835 W Olympic Blvd., 12th Fl.
Los Angeles, CA 90064
Ph: (310)577-3700
Fax: (310)577-3715
URL: http://www.associationnews.com/
Monthly. Free. Magazine containing management and meeting plan information for association executives and meeting planners.

4803 ■ Event Management
Cognizant Communications Corp.
3 Hartsdale Rd.
Elmsford, NY 10523-3701
Ph: (914)592-7720
Fax: (914)592-8981
URL: http://www.cognizantcommunication.com/
journal-titles/event-
Quarterly. $445.00/year for institutions, online only; $525.00/year for institutions, online & hard copy; $52.00/year for individuals, professional; $50.00/year for members, online & hard copy; $65.00/year for single issue. Peer-reviewed journal covering research and analytic needs of a rapidly growing profession focused on events.

4804 ■ Meeting News
Nielsen Business Media
770 Broadway
New York, NY 10003-9595
URL: http://www.mimegasite.com/mimegasite/
index.jsp
$89.00/year for individuals; $99.00/year for Canada; $205.00/year for other countries, by airmail. The newspaper for conventions, meetings, incentive travel and trade show professionals.

4805 ■ Special Events
Penton Media
249 W 17th St.
New York, NY 10011-5390
Ph: (212)204-4200
URL: http://specialevents.com
Monthly. $59.00/year, for free to qualified subscribers; $110.00/year for Canada; $106.00/year for other countries; $200.00/year for Canada, two years; $200.00/year for other countries, two years. Magazine for special event professionals.

Employer Directories and Networking Lists

4806 ■ Meeting Professionals International Membership Directory
Meeting Professionals International
3030 LBJ Fwy., Ste. 1700
Dallas, TX 75234-2759
Ph: (972)702-3000
Fax: (972)702-3070
Annual. Free. Covers: Profiles of the members of Meeting Professionals International.

Handbooks and Manuals

4807 ■ Association Meeting and Event Planners
Douglas Publications, Inc.
2807 N Parham Rd., Ste. 200
Richmond, VA 23294
Ph: (804)762-9600
Fax: (804)217-8999
Fr: 800-223-1797
E-mail: info@douglaspublications.com
URL: http://www.douglaspublications.com/Tsg/sub_
meeting.html
Patrick Snyder. 2010. $649.

4808 ■ FabJob Guide to Become an Event Planner
FabJob Inc.
4616 - 25th Ave. NE, No. 224
Seattle, WA 98105
Ph: (403)949-4980
Fr: 888-322-5621
URL: http://www.fabjob.com
Jan Riddell et al. $29.97 (e-book). 273 pages. Offers information on how to plan events, how to get an event planning job, how to start an event planning business, and more. Covers information on where to get creative ideas for events, how to develop the skills needed as an event planner, how to be certified as a professional event planner and more.

4809 ■ How to Start a Home-Based Event Planning Business
Globe Pequot Press
246 Goose Ln.
Guilford, CT 06437
Ph: (203)458-4500
Fr: 800-820-2329
E-mail: info@globepequot.com
URL: http://www.globepequot.com
Jill Moran. 2010. $18.95. 240 pages. This insider's handbook reveals how to start a successful business planning a wide variety of events from home.

4810 ■ Time Management for Event Planners
John Wiley & Sons, Inc.
111 River St.
Hoboken, NJ 07030
Ph: (201)748-6000
Fax: (201)748-6088
E-mail: info@wiley.com
URL: http://www.wiley.com/WileyCDA
Judy Allen. 2005. $39.95. 256 pages. Time management skills to help event planners balance personal and professional lives.

Employment Agencies and Search Firms

4811 ■ Access Staffing
360 Lexington Ave., 8th Fl.
New York, NY 10017
Ph: (212)687-5440
Fax: (212)557-2544
URL: http://www.accessstaffingco.com
Serves as a staffing firm covering accounting/ financial, advertising, bilingual Japanese, creative, event planning, fashion/retail, healthcare/ human services, human resources, information technology, insurance, legal, light industrial and office support.

Online Job Sources and Services

4812 ■ Event-jobs.net
URL: http://www.event-jobs.net
Description: Serves as a job site dedicated to the event industry. Offers job openings and careers from the event industry including event planning jobs.

4813 ■ Event Planner Directory 123
Fr: 800-379-4626
URL: http://www.eventplannerdirectory123.com
Description: Directory of various vendor resources.

4814 ■ ProductionHub.com
URL: http://www.productionhub.com
Description: Serves as an online resource and industry directory for film, television, video, live event and digital media production. Features job opportunities, events, directory and other resources for the production industry.

Tradeshows

4815 ■ IAVM Annual Conference and Trade Show
International Association of Venue Managers
635 Fritz Dr., Ste. 100
Coppell, TX 75019
Ph: (972)906-7441
Fax: (972)906-7418
URL: http://www.iavm.org
Annual. Presents exhibits to leaders who represent the entertainment, sports, conventions, trade, hospitality and tourism, movie theatres, and park and recreation departments. 2012 July 21-22; Fort Lauderdale, FL; Broward County Convention Center.

Other Sources

4816 ■ Association of Collegiate Conference and Events Directors International (ACCED-I)
419 Canyon Ave., Ste. 311
Fort Collins, CO 80521
Ph: (970)449-4960

Fax: (970)449-4965
Fr: 877-50-ACCED
E-mail: deborah@acced-i.org
URL: http://www.acced-i.org

Description: University conference and special events directors; professionals who design, coordinate, and market conferences and special events on college and university campuses. Dedicated to the professional development of the members; promotes the growth and distinction of the profession by uniting personnel and encouraging camaraderie. Promotes high standards of business and ethical conduct; works to foster communication, cooperation, and information sharing. Conducts research programs; collaborates with sister associations. Provides leadership opportunities through committee and board participation. Acts as an information clearinghouse; compiles statistics.

4817 ■ Association for Convention Operations Management (ACOM)
191 Clarksville Rd.
Princeton Junction, NJ 08550
Ph: (609)799-3712
Fax: (609)799-7032
E-mail: info@acomonline.org
URL: http://www.acomonline.org

Description: Convention service directors and managers of hotels, convention centers, and convention bureaus. Works to increase the effectiveness, productivity and quality of meetings, conventions and exhibitions. Works to establish high ethical standards, improve professional management techniques and increase awareness of client, employer and provider needs. Maintains speakers' bureau, resource center, and placement service; compiles statistics. Conducts research and educational programs.

4818 ■ Connected International Meeting Professionals Association (CIMPA)
9200 Bayard Pl.
Fairfax, VA 22032
Ph: (512)684-0889
Fax: (267)390-5193
E-mail: susan@cimpa.org
URL: http://www.cimpa.org

Description: Meeting planners, incentive organizers, travel agents, tour operators, and seminar organizers in 42 countries. Works to improve the skills of professional conference and convention planners. Serves as a clearinghouse of information on new travel destinations and planning technologies, techniques, and strategies. Facilitates exchange of information among Internet professionals. Produces a television program on travel and meetings. Conducts educational courses and awards Certified Internet Meeting Professional designation. Conducts research programs and placement service. Sponsors training courses on the Internet.

4819 ■ Exhibition Services and Contractors Association
5068 W Plano Pkwy., Ste. 300
Plano, TX 75093
Ph: (972)447-8212
Fax: (972)447-8212
Fr: 877-792-3722
E-mail: askus@esca.org
URL: http://www.esca.org

Description: Works for the advancement of the exhibition, meeting and special events industries. Serves as a clearinghouse for the exchange of information between members and all other entities of the meetings, exhibition, and convention industries.

4820 ■ GCG Event Partners
125 Main St., Ste. H
Stoneham, MA 02180-1600
Ph: (781)279-9887
Fr: (866)424-3836
E-mail: info@gcgeventpartners.com
URL: http://www.gcgeventpartners.com

Description: Network of event planning professionals.

4821 ■ Golf Tournament Association of America (GTAA)
PO Box 47405
Phoenix, AZ 85068
Ph: (602)524-7034
Fax: (602)569-0680
Fr: 888-810-4822
E-mail: info@gtaaweb.org
URL: http://www.gtaaweb.org

Description: Represents the interests of golf tournament planners and coordinators. Provides golf tournament planning tips, education and resources to golf tournament planners and coordinators. Conducts golf tournament planning seminars across the country.

4822 ■ International Association of Corporate Entertainment Producers (IACEP)
PO Box 9826
Wilmington, DE 19809
Ph: (302)765-3945
Fax: (302)241-2177
E-mail: mtannen@iacep.com
URL: http://www.iacep.com

Description: Aims to improve the lives and careers of professionals involved in the corporate entertainment industry. Strives to uphold the professional and ethical standards of the corporate entertainment industry. Provides education, networking, and leadership opportunities for its members.

4823 ■ International Association of Fairs and Expositions
PO Box 985
Springfield, MO 65801
Ph: (417)862-5771
Fax: (417)862-0156
Fr: 800-516-0313
E-mail: iafe@fairsandexpos.com
URL: http://www.fairsandexpos.com

Description: Individuals, corporations, and organizations involved with the planning and management of fairs, expositions.

4824 ■ International Association of Venue Managers
635 Fritz Dr., Ste. 100
Coppell, TX 75019
Ph: (972)906-7441
Fax: (972)906-7418
URL: http://www.iavm.org

Description: Represents managers and senior executives from auditoriums, arenas, convention centers, exhibit halls, stadiums, performing arts theaters, amphitheaters, and allied companies. Focuses on the needs of facility managers and the companies that serve public assembly facilities. Provides leadership, innovation, education, advocacy, opportunities for networking, and connections to other venue professionals worldwide.

4825 ■ International Festivals and Events Association
2603 W Eastover Terr.
Boise, ID 83706
Ph: (208)433-0950
Fax: (208)433-9812
URL: http://www.ifea.com

Description: Provides professional development opportunities and fundraising ideas for individuals involved in the special events industry.

4826 ■ International Society of Meeting Planners (ISMP)
810 N Farrell Dr.
Palm Springs, CA 92262
Ph: (760)327-5284
Fax: (760)327-5631
Fr: 877-743-6802
E-mail: support@assoc-hdqts.org
URL: http://ismp-assoc.org

Description: Meeting planners and related industries. Works to improve professionalism and competency in the industry as well as create new business op-

portunities for members. Provides networking opportunities. Offers professional designations: the RMP - Registered Meeting Planner, CDS Certified Destination Specialist, ITS - Incentive Travel Specialist, and CEP - Certified Event Planner.

4827 ■ International Special Events Society
401 N Michigan Ave., Ste. 2200
Chicago, IL 60611-4267
Ph: (312)321-6853
Fax: (312)673-6953
Fr: 800-688-4737
E-mail: info@ises.com
URL: http://www.ises.com

Description: Fosters performance through education. Represents special event producers.

4828 ■ Meeting Professionals International (MPI)
3030 Lyndon B. Johnson Fwy., Ste. 1700
Dallas, TX 75234-2759
Ph: (972)702-3000
Fax: (972)702-3070
E-mail: feedback@mpiweb.org
URL: http://www.mpiweb.org

Description: Meeting planners, full meeting consultants, and suppliers of goods and services. Works to improve meeting method education; create an "oPEN platform" for research and experimentation. Provides survey results, statistics, supply sources, and technical information; offers members assistance with specific problems; encourages information and idea exchange. Maintains professional code; standardizes terminology; monitors legislation affecting the industry. Maintains resource center. Conducts educational, charitable, and research programs.

4829 ■ National Coalition of Black Meeting Planners (NCBMP)
4401 Huntchase Dr.
Bowie, MD 20720
Ph: (301)860-0200
Fax: (301)860-0500
E-mail: ncbmp.hq@verizon.net
URL: http://www.ncbmp.com

Description: Black meeting planners. Purposes are to: act as liaison with hotels, airlines, convention centers and bureaus in an effort to assess the impact of minorities in these fields; assess the needs of the convention industry and how best to meet these needs; enhance members' sophistication in planning meetings; maximize employment of minorities in the convention industry. Maintains speakers' bureau. Conducts educational and research programs and compiles statistics on demographic employment of minorities in the convention industry. Maintains placement service.

4830 ■ Professional Convention Management Association (PCMA)
35 E Wacker Dr., Ste. 500
Chicago, IL 60601-2105
Ph: (312)423-7262
Fax: (312)423-7222
Fr: 877-827-7262
E-mail: president@pcma.org
URL: http://www.pcma.org

Description: Represents the interests of meeting management executives from associations, non-profit organizations, corporations, independent meeting planning companies, and multi-management firms who recognize the importance of meetings to their organization. Provides education, research and advocacy to advance the meetings and hospitality industry. Empowers members with the tools they need to succeed as meeting professionals and to promote the value of the industry to their organizations and the general public.

4831 ■ Religious Conference Management Association (RCMA)
7702 Woodland Dr., Ste. 120
Indianapolis, IN 46278
Ph: (317)632-1888

Fax: (317)632-7909
E-mail: rcma@rcmaweb.org
URL: http://www.rcmaweb.org

Description: Represents persons responsible for planning and/or managing religious conventions, meetings, and assemblies; associate members are individuals who directly support the logistics of religious meetings. Promotes professional excellence through exchange of ideas, techniques, and methods of management.

4832 ■ Society of Government Meeting Professionals (SGMP)
908 King St., Lower Level
Alexandria, VA 22314
Ph: (703)549-0892
Fax: (703)549-0708

Fr: 800-827-8916
E-mail: headquarters@sgmp.org
URL: http://www.sgmp.org

Description: Individuals involved in planning government meetings on a full- or part-time basis; suppliers of services to government planners. Provides education in basic and advanced areas of meeting planning and facilitates professional contact with other government planners and suppliers knowledgeable in government contracting. Maintains referral network of planning resources, information on latest techniques, and opportunities to inspect conference facilities.

4833 ■ Society of Independent Show Organizers
2601 Ocean Park Blvd., Ste 200
Santa Monica, CA 90405
Ph: (310)450-8831

Fax: (310)450-9305
Fr: 877-937-7476
E-mail: info@siso.org
URL: http://www.siso.org

Description: Represents independent show producers. Aims to meet the needs of CEOs and senior management of for-profit show producers in an environment where strategic and tactical decisions can be implemented to maximize profit potential. Provides peer networking opportunities, education, research, white papers, industry trends, and best practices in the events industry. Produces events globally including trade and consumer shows, industry and targeted conferences, and other face-to-face events.

Sources of Help-Wanted Ads

4834 ■ Beauty Launchpad
Creative Age Publications Inc.
7628 Densmore Ave.
Van Nuys, CA 91406-2042
Ph: (818)782-7328
Fax: (818)782-7450
Fr: 800-442-5667
URL: http://www.beautylaunchpad.com/index.php

Fashion magazine.

4835 ■ Clear
Clear Magazine
433 N Washington Ave.
Royal Oak, MI 48067
Ph: (248)544-2532
Fax: (248)544-0008
URL: http://www.clearmag.com

Bimonthly. $25.00/year for individuals; $55.00/year for Canada; $105.00/year for other countries. Contemporary fashion and design journal.

4836 ■ Daily Variety
Reed Business Information
360 Park Ave. S
New York, NY 10010-1710
Ph: (646)746-7764
Fax: (646)746-7583
URL: http://www.reedbusiness.com/
   index.asp?layout=theListProfile&

Daily. $329.99/year for individuals. Global entertainment newspaper (tabloid).

4837 ■ JQ
Adams Business Media
420 S Palm Canyon Dr., 2nd Fl.
Palm Springs, CA 92262
Ph: (760)318-7000
Fax: (760)323-4310
URL: http://www.jqintl.com/ME2/Default.asp

Bimonthly. $30.00/year for individuals; $50.00/year for two years; $45.00/year for Canada; $90.00/year for Canada, two years; $110.00/year for other countries, USA. Trade publication covering the fashion and retail industries.

4838 ■ New York Moves
New York Moves Magazine
4097 Lexington Ave.
New York, NY 10163
Ph: (212)396-2394
Fax: (212)202-7615
URL: http://www.newyorkmoves.com

$16.00/year for individuals. Fashion and lifestyle magazine for professional women in and around New York City.

Employer Directories and Networking Lists

4839 ■ Black Book Photography
Black Book Marketing Group
740 Broadway, Ste. 202
New York, NY 10003
Ph: (212)979-6700
Fax: (212)673-4321
Fr: 800-841-1246
URL: http://www.BlackBook.com

Annual, Latest edition 2008. $60.00 for individuals. Publication includes: Over 19,000 art directors, creative directors, photographers and photographic services, design firms, advertising agencies, and other firms whose products or services are used in advertising.

4840 ■ Careers in Focus—Fashion
Facts On File Inc.
132 W 31st St., 17th Fl.
New York, NY 10001
Ph: (212)967-8800
Fax: 800-678-3633
Fr: 800-322-8755
URL: http://www.infobasepublishing.com

Latest edition 3rd; Published September, 2006. $32.95 for individuals. Covers: An overview of fashion, followed by a selection of jobs profiled in detail, including the nature of the job, earnings, prospects for employment, what kind of training and skills it requires, and sources for further information.

4841 ■ Discovering Careers for Your Future—Fashion
Facts On File Inc.
132 W 31st St., 17th Fl.
New York, NY 10001
Ph: (212)967-8800
Fax: 800-678-3633
Fr: 800-322-8755
URL: http://factsonfile.infobasepublishing.com

Published 2004. $21.95 for individuals; $19.75 for libraries. Covers: Buyers, costume designers, fashion illustrators, fashion models, makeup artists, tailors and dressmakers, and textile manufacturing workers; links career education to curriculum, helping children investigate the subjects they are interested in, and the careers those subjects might lead to.

4842 ■ Model & Talent Directory
Peter Glenn Publications
235 SE 5th Ave., Ste. R
Delray Beach, FL 33483
Ph: (561)404-4685
Fax: (561)279-4672
Fr: 888-332-6700
URL: http://www.pgdirect.com

Annual, Latest edition 26th. $22.95 for individuals.

Covers: Over 1,954 listings of model and talent agencies worldwide. Arrangement: Geographical.

Handbooks and Manuals

4843 ■ Break into Modeling for Under $20
St. Martin's Griffin
175 Fifth Ave.
New York, NY 10010
Ph: (646)307-5151
E-mail: customerservice@mpsvirginia.com
URL: http://us.macmillan.com/
   breakintomodelingforunder20/JudyGoss

Judy Goss. 2008. $14.95. 224 pages. Focuses on dispelling the misconception that breaking into the modeling business requires expensive head shots and other costly investments. Discusses how one can actually launch a modeling career for $20 or less and gives tips on determining type of model, taking pictures at home in the right poses and clothes, preparing what to say and do at casting calls, avoiding costly scams, and much more.

4844 ■ Careers for Fashion Plates and Other Trendsetters
The McGraw-Hill Companies
PO Box 182604
Columbus, OH 43272
Fax: (614)759-3749
Fr: 877-883-5524
E-mail: customer.service@mcgraw-hill.com
URL: http://www.mhprofessional.com/
   product.php?isbn=0071642005

Lucia Mauro. 2008. $14.95 (paper). 176 pages. Describes career opportunities in fashion, entertainment, retail, and promotion, with advice from fashion professionals.

4845 ■ Opportunities in Beauty and Modeling Careers
The McGraw-Hill Companies
PO Box 182604
Columbus, OH 43272
Fax: (614)759-3749
Fr: 877-883-5524
E-mail: customer.service@mcgraw-hill.com
URL: http://www.mcgraw-hill.com

Susan Wood Gearhart. 2004. $13.95. 163 pages.

4846 ■ Your Modeling Career: You Don't Have to Be a Superstar to Succeed
Allworth Press
10 E 23rd St., Ste. 510
New York, NY 10010
Ph: (212)777-8395
Fax: (212)777-8261
Fr: 800-491-2808
URL: http://www.allworth.com

Debbie Press and Skip Press. Second edition, 2004. $24.95 (paper). 272 pages.

EMPLOYMENT AGENCIES AND SEARCH FIRMS

4847 ■ Forte Models
1231 Stationside Dr.
Oakland, FL 34787
Ph: (407)347-3810
E-mail: info@orlandomodelagent.com
URL: http://www.orlandomodelagent.com
Specializes in providing models to convention and trade show clients.

ONLINE JOB SOURCES AND SERVICES

4848 ■ FashionCrossing.com
URL: http://www.fashioncrossing.com

Description: Provides job listings and other resources related to fashion employment opportunities.

4849 ■ GetGigs.com
URL: http://www.getgigs.com

Description: Seeks to provide an on-line experience for creative types, performing artists, and musicians around the world by integrating internet technologies into a one-stop information resource. Also functions as a creative directory and talent network.

4850 ■ TalentNetworks.com
E-mail: info@talentnetworks.com
URL: http://www.talentnetworks.com/index.html

Description: A business-to-business portal for the fashion, arts, and entertainment industries. Online site contains industry listings, portfolios and news items.

4851 ■ Accounting for Banks
LexisNexis Group
1275 Broadway
Albany, NY 12204
Ph: (518)487-3000
Fr: 800-227-9597
URL: http://www.lexisnexis.com

Description: $393. Provides analysis and advice to accounting and banking professionals on day to day operations, internal accounting, investments, finances, assets, and more.

4852 ■ Accounting Horizons
American Accounting Association
5717 Bessie Dr.
Sarasota, FL 34233-2399
Ph: (941)921-7747
Fax: (941)923-4093
URL: http://aaahq.org/pubs/horizons.htm

Quarterly. $300.00/year for individuals, print only; $325.00/year for individuals, online, vol. 13 thru current issue; $375.00/year for individuals, online and print. Publication covering the banking, finance, and accounting industries.

4853 ■ American Banker
Banking Group
1 State Street Plz., 27th Fl.
New York, NY 10004-1483
Ph: (212)803-8200
Fax: (212)843-9600
Fr: 800-221-1809
URL: http://www.americanbanker.com

Daily. $995.00/year for individuals. Newspaper for senior executives in banking and other financial services industries. Coverage includes trends, analysis, and statistics of the legislative scene in Washington; finance; mortgages; technology; small business; and regional banking.

4854 ■ Bank Advisor
WiesnerMedia Financial Group
6160 S Syracuse, Ste. 300
Greenwood Village, CO 80111
Ph: (303)662-5200
URL: http://www.producersweb.com/r/baMag/d/main/

Bimonthly. Free. Magazine for advisors, consultants, and managers working with consumers in a sales capacity within the banking industry.

4855 ■ Bank Investment Consultant
Bank Investment Consultant
One State Street Plz., 27th Fl.
New York, NY 10004
Ph: (212)803-8200
URL: http://www.bankinvestmentconsultant.com/

Free to qualified subscribers. Magazine featuring news and analysis for financial advisers and senior sales management in bank investment programs.

4856 ■ Barron's
Dow Jones & Company Inc.
1 World Financial Ctr.
200 Liberty St.
New York, NY 10281
Ph: (212)416-2000
E-mail: editors@barrons.com
URL: http://online.barrons.com/public/main

Weekly (Mon.). $149.00/year for individuals, print & online; $99.00/year for individuals, print only; $79.00/year for individuals, online only. Business and finance magazine.

4857 ■ The Bond Buyer
SourceMedia Inc.
1 State St. Plz., 27th Fl.
New York, NY 10004-1561
Ph: (212)803-8200
Fax: (646)264-6828
URL: http://www.bondbuyer.com/

Daily. Newspaper focusing on municipal finance.

4858 ■ Boomer Market Advisor
Summit Business Media
5081 Olympic Blvd.
Erlanger, KY 41018
Ph: (859)692-2100
Fax: (859)692-2000
URL: http://www.advisorone.com

Monthly. Free to qualified subscribers; $120.00/year for Canada; $160.00/year for other countries. Magazine for financial planners who work with variable products.

4859 ■ Bulletin of Economic Research
John Wiley & Sons Inc.
350 Main St., Commerce Pl.
Malden, MA 02148-5089
Ph: (781)388-8200
Fax: (781)388-8210
URL: http://www.wiley.com/bw/journal.asp?ref=0307-3378&site=1

Quarterly. $84.00/year for individuals, print & online; $1,087.00/year for institutions, print & online; $945.00/year for institutions, online only; $50.00/year for individuals, print & online; $487.00/year for institutions, other countries, print & online; $423.00/year for institutions, other countries, print or online. Journal focusing on the entire field of economics, econometrics and economic history.

4860 ■ Business Credit
National Association of Credit Management
8840 Columbia 100 Pkwy.
Columbia, MD 21045-2158
Ph: (410)740-5560

Fax: (410)740-5574
URL: http://www.nacm.org/index.php?option=com_content&view=catego

$60.00/year for Canada; $65.00/year for other countries; $54.00/year for individuals; $48.00/year for libraries; $7.00/year for single issue. Magazine covering finance, business risk management, providing information for the extension of credit, maintenance of accounts receivable, and cash asset management.

4861 ■ Business Insurance
Crain Communications Inc.
1155 Gratiot Ave.
Detroit, MI 48207-2997
Ph: (313)446-6000
URL: http://www.businessinsurance.com

Weekly. $399.00/year for individuals, print; $149.00/year for individuals, print & digital; $69.00/year for individuals, digital edition. International newsweekly reporting on corporate risk and employee benefit management news.

4862 ■ CFO
CFO Publishing
6 W 48th St., 7th Fl.
New York, NY 10036
Ph: (212)459-3004
Fax: (212)459-3007
URL: http://www.cfo.com/magazine/index.cfm/about?f=aboutus_nav

Monthly. $120.00/year for other countries; free, U.S. Business magazine for small to mid-sized companies.

4863 ■ CFO Magazine
CFO Publishing Corporation
6 W 48th St., 7th Fl.
New York, NY 10036
Ph: (212)459-3004
Fax: (212)459-3007
URL: http://www3.cfo.com

Monthly. Free for U.S. residents; $120.00/year for subscribers outside U.S. Provides readers with news and trends, analyses of the accomplishments of finance executives facing complex problems, and research about economic issues.

4864 ■ FAO Today
Crossing Media
343 Thornall St., 5th Fl.
Edison, NJ 08837
Ph: (732)476-6160
Fax: (732)476-6155
URL: http://www.faotoday.com

$120.00/year for individuals. Business magazine featuring finance and accounting outsourcing.

4865 ■ Financial Management
Financial Management Association International
4202 E Fowler Ave.
BSN 3331
Tampa, FL 33620-5500
Ph: (813)974-2084

Fax: (813)974-3318
E-mail: fma@coba.usf.edu
URL: http://www.fma.org/

Quarterly. $300.00/year for institutions, print + premium online; $95.00/year for institutions, premium online; $167.00/year for institutions, Europe, print + premium online; $158.00/year for institutions, Europe, premium online; $167.00/year for institutions, rest of world, print + premium online; $158.00/year for institutions, rest of world, premium online. Journal covering business, economics, finance and management.

4866 ■ *Financial Week*
Crain Communications, Inc.
711 Third Ave.
New York, NY 10017
Ph: (212)210-0100
E-mail: fw_editor@financialweek.com
URL: http://www.financialweek.com/apps/pbcs.dll/
frontpage

$79.00/year for individuals; $149.00/year for Canada; $199.00/year for other countries. Newspaper focusing on the key decision-level financial officers within the 17,000 largest U.S.-based corporations regardless of business and industry.

4867 ■ *Forbes*
Forbes Magazine
60 5th Ave.
New York, NY 10011
Ph: (212)366-8900
Fr: 800-295-0893
URL: http://www.forbes.com

Biweekly. $19.99/year for individuals; $22.25/year for Canada. Magazine reporting on industry, business and finance management.

4868 ■ *Government Finance Officers Association Newsletter*
Government Finance Officers Association
203 N LaSalle St., Ste. 2700
Chicago, IL 60601-1210
Ph: (312)977-9700
Fax: (312)977-4806
URL: http://www.gfoa.org/

Description: Semimonthly. Provides updates on current events, innovations, and federal legislation affecting public finance management for state and local government finance officers. Covers cash management, budgeting, accounting, auditing, and financial reporting, public employee retirement administration, and related issues. Recurring features include news of research, news of members, a calendar of events, and columns titled Career Notes and Employment Opportunities. Subscription includes the bimonthly magazine Government Finance Review.

4869 ■ *Healthcare Finance News*
MedTech Media
71 Pineland Dr., Ste. 203
New Gloucester, ME 04260
Ph: (207)688-6270
Fax: (207)688-6273
URL: http://www.healthcarefinancenews.com/

Monthly. Newspaper delivering essential information, market data, and industry news.

4870 ■ *HFM Magazine*
Healthcare Financial Management Association
3 Westbrook Corporate Ctr., Ste. 600
Westchester, IL 60154
Ph: (708)531-9600
Fax: (708)531-0032
Fr: 800-252-4362
URL: http://www.hfma.org

Monthly. $250/year for individuals; $151/year for institutions; $240/year for non-US subscribers. Magazine whose primary audience is senior and mid-level healthcare financial managers including CFOs, VPs of finance, controllers, revenue cycle directors, patient financial services managers, business office

managers, and others responsible for healthcare financial management.

4871 ■ *Journal of Accountancy*
The American Institute of Certified Public Accountants
1211 Avenue of the Americas
New York, NY 10036-8775
Ph: (212)596-6200
Fax: (212)596-6213
URL: http://www.journalofaccountancy.com/

Monthly. $75.00/year for individuals; $60.00/year for members. Accounting journal.

4872 ■ *Journal of Financial and Quantitative Analysis*
Journal of Financial & Quantitative Analysis
University of Washington
Foster School of Business
115 Lewis Hall
PO Box 353200
Seattle, WA 98195-3200
Ph: (206)543-4598
Fax: (206)616-1894
E-mail: jfqa@u.washington.edu
URL: http://www.jfqa.org/

Quarterly. $85.00/year for individuals, print & online; $65.00/year for individuals, online only; $367.00/year for institutions, online only; $450.00/year for institutions, print & online. Journal on research in finance.

4873 ■ *Journal of International Business and Economics*
International Academy of Business and Economics
PO Box 2536
Ceres, CA 95307
Ph: (702)560-0653
Fax: (702)508-9166
URL: http://www.iabe.eu/domains/iabeX/
journal.aspx?journalid=9

Peer-reviewed journal publishing theoretical, conceptual, and applied research on topics related to research, practice and teaching in all areas of business, economics, e-commerce, and related subjects.

4874 ■ *The Journal of Taxation*
RIA Group
195 Broadway
New York, NY 10007-3100
Fr: 800-431-9025
URL: http://ria.thomson.com/estore/
detail.aspx?ID=JTAX

Monthly. $390.00/year for individuals, print; $565.00/year for individuals, online/print bundle; $440.00/year for individuals, online. Journal for sophisticated tax practitioners.

4875 ■ *Mortgage Banking Magazine*
Mortgage Bankers Association of America
1717 Rhode Island Ave., NW, Ste. 400
Washington, DC 20036
Ph: (202)557-2700
Fax: (202)721-0245
Fr: 800-793-MBAA
URL: http://www.mortgagebankingmagazine.com

Monthly. $65.00/year for members; $75.00/year for nonmembers; $90.00/year for other countries. Magazine of the real estate finance industry.

4876 ■ *National Mortgage News*
SourceMedia Inc.
1 State St. Plz., 27th Fl.
New York, NY 10004-1561
Ph: (212)803-8200
Fax: (646)264-6828
URL: http://www.nationalmortgagenews.com

Weekly. Newspaper for mortgage lenders and investment bankers.

4877 ■ *Northwestern Financial Review*
NFR Communications Inc.
7400 Metro Blvd., Ste. 217
Minneapolis, MN 55439

Ph: (952)835-2275
URL: http://www.northwesternfinancialreview.com

$99.00/year for individuals. Trade publication covering commercial banking.

4878 ■ *Pensions & Investments*
Crain Communications Inc.
1155 Gratiot Ave.
Detroit, MI 48207-2997
Ph: (313)446-6000
URL: http://www.pionline.com

Biweekly. $279.00/year for individuals, print; $995.00/year for individuals, daily email; $1,149.00/year for individuals, combo. Magazine containing news and features on investment management, pension management, corporate finance, and cash management.

4879 ■ *The Review of Asset Pricing Studies*
Oxford University Press
2001 Evans Rd., Ste. 12
Cary, NC 27513-2009
Ph: (919)677-0977
Fax: (919)677-1714
Fr: 800-852-7323
URL: http://raps.oxfordjournals.org/

Journal publishing articles on the study of financial institutions related to asset prices.

4880 ■ *The Review of Network Economics*
CRA International
John Hancock Tower
200 Clarendon St., T-33
Boston, MA 02116-5092
Ph: (617)425-3000
Fax: (617)425-3132
URL: http://www.rnejournal.com/

Quarterly. $75.00/year for individuals. Journal covering new research in network economics and related subjects, including topics in the economics of networks, regulation, competition law, industrial organization etc.

4881 ■ *Servicing Management*
Zackin Publications Inc.
PO Box 2180
Waterbury, CT 06722
Ph: (203)262-4670
Fax: (203)262-4680
Fr: 800-325-6745
URL: http://www.sm-online.com/sm

Monthly. $48.00/year for individuals; $72.00/year for two years. Trade magazine for mortgage professionals involved with mortgage loan servicing .

4882 ■ *Strategic Finance*
Institute of Management Accountants
10 Paragon Dr., Ste. 1
Montvale, NJ 07645-1718
Ph: (201)573-9000
Fax: (201)474-1600
Fr: 800-638-4427
URL: http://www.imanet.org/publications.asp

Monthly. $210.00/year for nonmembers; $48.00/year for members; $25.00/year for students; $18.00/year for single issue, back issue. Magazine reporting on corporate finance, accounting, cash management, and budgeting.

4883 ■ *U.S. Banker*
SourceMedia Inc.
1 State St. Plz., 27th Fl.
New York, NY 10004-1561
Ph: (212)803-8200
Fax: (646)264-6828
URL: http://www.americanbanker.com/usb.html

Monthly. $109.00/year for individuals; $139.00/year for individuals, Canada; $139.00/year for individuals, outside North America; $179.00/year for two years; $239.00/year for two years, Canada; $239.00/year for two years, outside North America. Magazine serving the financial services industry.

EMPLOYER DIRECTORIES AND NETWORKING LISTS

4884 ■ America's Corporate Finance Directory
LexisNexis Group
9443 Springboro Pike
Dayton, OH 45342
Fr: 888-285-3947
URL: http://www.lexisnexis.com/corpfinancedir
Annual, September. $1,399.00 for individuals. Covers: Financial personnel and outside financial services relationships of 5,000 leading United States corporations and their wholly-owned United States subsidiaries. Entries include: Company name, address, phone, fax, telex, e-mail addresses, stock exchange information, earnings, total assets, size of pension/profit-sharing fund portfolio, number of employees, description of business, wholly-owned U.S. Subsidiaries of parent company; name and title of key executives; outside suppliers of financial services. Arrangement: Alphabetical. Indexes: Financial responsibilities, Standard Industrial Classification (SIC) code, geographical, Personnel, private companies, company name.

4885 ■ Association for Investment Management & Research—Membership Directory
CFA Institute
560 Ray C. Hunt Dr.
PO Box 3668
Charlottesville, VA 22903
Ph: (434)951-5499
Fax: (434)951-5262
Fr: 800-247-8132
URL: http://www.cfainstitute.org
Annual, January. $150.00. Covers: 38,000 security and financial analysts who are practicing investment analysis. Entries include: Name, firm affiliation and address, phone, fax, e-mail. Arrangement: Alphabetical.

4886 ■ The Bank Directory
Accuity Inc.
4709 Golf Rd.
Skokie, IL 60076
Ph: (847)676-9600
Fax: (847)933-8101
Fr: 800-321-3373
URL: http://store.accuitysolutions.com/order.html
Semiannual, June and December. $1,195.00 for individuals. Covers: In five volumes, about 11,000 banks and 50,000 branches of United States banks, and 60,000 foreign banks and branches engaged in foreign banking; Federal Reserve system and other United States government and state government banking agencies; 500 largest North American and International commercial banks; paper and automated clearinghouses. Volumes 1 and 2 contain North American listings; volumes 3 and 4, international listings (also cited as "M Thomson International Bank Directory"); volume 5, Worldwide Correspondents Guide containing key correspondent data to facilitate funds transfer. Entries include: For domestic banks—Bank name, address, phone, telex, cable, date established, routing number, charter type, bank holding company affiliation, memberships in Federal Reserve System and other banking organizations, principal officers by function performed, principal correspondent banks, and key financial data (deposits, etc.). For international banks—Bank name, address, phone, fax, telex, cable, SWIFT address, transit or sort codes within home country, ownership, financial data, names and titles of key personnel, branch locations. For branches—Bank name, address, phone, charter type, ownership and other details comparable to domestic bank listings. Arrangement: Geographical. Indexes: Alphabetical, geographical.

4887 ■ Career Opportunities in Banking, Finance, and Insurance
Facts On File Inc.
132 W 31st St., 17th Fl.
New York, NY 10001

Ph: (212)967-8800
Fax: 800-678-3633
Fr: 800-322-8755
URL: http://factsonfile.infobasepublishing.com
Latest edition 2nd; Published February, 2007. $49.50 for individuals. Publication includes: Lists of colleges with programs supporting banking, finance, and industry; professional associations; professional certifications; regulatory agencies; and Internet resources for career planning. Principal content of publication is job descriptions for professions in the banking, finance, and insurance industries. Indexes: Alphabetical.

4888 ■ Corporate Finance Sourcebook
LexisNexis Group
9443 Springboro Pike
Dayton, OH 45342
Fr: 888-285-3947
E-mail: nrpsales@marquiswhoswho.com
URL: http://www.financesourcebook.com
Annual, Latest edition 2010. $695.00 for individuals; $556.00 for individuals. Covers: Securities research analysts; major private lenders; investment banking firms; commercial banks; United States-based foreign banks; commercial finance firms; leasing companies; foreign investment bankers in the United States; pension managers; banks that offer master trusts; cash managers; business insurance brokers; business real estate specialists; lists about 3,500 firms; 14,500 key financial experts. Entries include: All entries include firm name, address, phone, e-mail, and names and titles of officers, contacts, or specialists in corporate finance. Additional details are given as appropriate, including names of major clients, number of companies served, services, total assets, branch locations, years in business. Arrangement: Classified by line of business and then alphabetized within that line of business. Indexes: Firm name, personnel name, geographical.

4889 ■ Directory of Trust Banking
Firstmark Inc.
25 Vintinner Rd.
PO Box 1270
Campton, NH 03223-4669
Ph: (603)726-4800
Fax: (603)726-4840
Fr: 800-729-2600
URL: http://www.firstmark.com/fmkdirs/acc_trust.htm
$575.00 for individuals. Covers: 4,000 U.S. banks and trust companies. Entries include: Contact information, charter type, officer names and responsibilities, holding company and owners, and types of collective investment funds.

4890 ■ Directory of Venture Capital and Private Equity Firms
Grey House Publishing
PO Box 56
Amenia, NY 12501
Ph: (518)789-8700
Fax: (518)789-0556
Fr: 800-562-2139
E-mail: books@greyhouse.com
URL: http://www.greyhouse.com/venture.htm
2011. $685.00/regular; $450.00/library. 1,200 pages. Gives librarians, entrepreneurs and others interested in the venture capital and private equity fields information on the venture capital industry. Features up-to-date, comprehensive data on each firm including address, phone and fax numbers, e-mail and web site addresses for both the primary and branch locations. Contains details on the firm's mission statement, industry group preferences, geographic preferences, average and minimum investments, and investment criteria. Offers five indexes: the Geographic Index, Executive Name Index, Portfolio Company Index, Industry Preference Index, and College and University Index.

4891 ■ North American Financial Institutions Directory
Accuity Inc.
4709 Golf Rd.
Skokie, IL 60076

Ph: (847)676-9600
Fax: (847)933-8101
Fr: 800-321-3373
URL: http://store.accuitysolutions.com/order.html
Semiannual, January and July. $955.00 for individuals. Covers: 15,000 banks and their branches; over 2,000 head offices, and 15,500 branches of savings and loan associations; over 5,500 credit unions with assets over $5 million; Federal Reserve System and other U.S. government and state government banking agencies; bank holding, commercial finance, and leasing companies; coverage includes the United States, Canada, Mexico, and Central America. Entries include: Bank name, address, phone, fax, telex, principal officers and directors, date established, financial data, association memberships, attorney or counsel, correspondent banks, out-of-town branch, holding company affiliation, ABA transit number and routing symbol, MICR number with check digit, credit card(s) issued, trust powers, current par value and dividend of common stock, kind of charter. Arrangement: Geographical. Indexes: Alphabetical.

4892 ■ Who's Who in Finance and Business
Marquis Who's Who L.L.C.
300 Connell Dr., Ste. 2000
Berkeley Heights, NJ 07922
Ph: (908)673-1000
Fax: (908)673-1189
Fr: 800-473-7020
E-mail: finance@marquiswhoswho.com
URL: http://www.marquiswhoswho.com
Biennial, latest edition 37th; 2009-2010. $349.00 for individuals. Covers: Over 24,000 individuals. Entries include: Name, home and office addresses, personal, career, and family data; civic and political activities; memberships, publications, awards. Arrangement: Alphabetical.

4893 ■ Women in Insurance and Financial Services—Membership Directory
Women in Insurance and Financial Services
6748 Wauconda Dr.
Larkspur, CO 80118
Ph: (303)681-9777
Fr: (866)264-9437
URL: http://www.w-wifs.org

Covers: list of contact information of WIFS' members who are devoted to helping women succeed in both insurance and financial services.

HANDBOOKS AND MANUALS

4894 ■ Accountants' Handbook
John Wiley & Sons, Inc.
111 River St.
Hoboken, NJ 07030
Ph: (201)748-6000
Fax: (201)748-6088
E-mail: info@wiley.com
URL: http://as.wiley.com/WileyCDA
D.R. Carmichael and Lynford Graham. 2012. $119.95. 1056 pages. Series covering accounting and financial reporting of interest to accountants, auditors, financial analysts, and users of accounting information.

4895 ■ Careers for Financial Mavens and Other Money Movers
The McGraw-Hill Companies
PO Box 182604
Columbus, OH 43272
Fax: (614)759-3749
Fr: 877-883-5524
E-mail: customer.service@mcgraw-hill.com
URL: http://www.mhprofessional.com/
    product.php?cat=106&isbn=0071454551
Marjorie Eberts and Margaret Gisler. Second edition, 2004. $19.95 (paper). 153 pages.

4896 ■ Great Jobs for Business Majors
The McGraw-Hill Companies
PO Box 182604
Columbus, OH 43272
Fax: (614)759-3749
Fr: 877-883-5524
E-mail: customer.service@mcgraw-hill.com
URL: http://www.mhprofessional.com/
  product.php?isbn=0071544836

Stephen Lambert. Third edition, 2008. $16.95 (paper).
240 pages.

**4897 ■ The Million-Dollar Financial Services
  Practice: A Proven System for Becoming a
  Top Producer**
AMACOM Publishing
c/o American Management Association
1601 Broadway
New York, NY 10019-7434
Ph: (212)586-8100
Fax: (518)891-0368
Fr: 800-714-6395
E-mail: pubs_cust_serv@amanet.org
URL: http://www.amacombooks.org

David J. Mullen. 2007. $30.00 (hardback). 352 pages.
Features information on how to become a financial
advisor using the methods given in the book. Combines marketing, prospecting, sales, and time management techniques into a system that will help readers build a successful and lucrative practice.

4898 ■ Opportunities in Financial Careers
The McGraw-Hill Companies
PO Box 182604
Columbus, OH 43272
Fax: (614)759-3749
Fr: 877-883-5524
E-mail: customer.service@mcgraw-hill.com
URL: http://www.mhprofessional.com/
  product.php?isbn=0071442502

Michael Sumichrast and Martin A. Sumichrast. 2004.
$13.95 (paper). 160 pages. A guide to planning for
and seeking opportunities in this challenging field.

**4899 ■ Opportunities in Hospital
  Administration Careers**
The McGraw-Hill Companies
PO Box 182604
Columbus, OH 43272
Fax: (614)759-3749
Fr: 877-883-5524
E-mail: customer.service@mcgraw-hill.com
URL: http://www.mhprofessional.com/
  product.php?isbn=0071467688

I. Donald Snook. 2006. $13.95. 160 pages. Discusses
opportunities for administrators in a variety of
management settings: hospital, department, clinic,
group practice, HMO, mental health, and extended
care facilities.

**4900 ■ Reinventing the CFO: How Financial
  Managers Can Reinvent Their Roles and
  Add Greater Value**
Harvard Business School Press
60 Harvard Way
Boston, MA 02163
Ph: (617)783-7500
Fax: (617)783-7555
Fr: 800-988-0886
URL: http://www.hbsp.harvard.edu

Jeremy Hope. 2006. $29.95. Outlines seven critical
roles for CFOs to follow in order to streamline
processes and regulate risk.

**4901 ■ Your Successful Career as a
  Mortgage Broker**
AMACOM Publishing
c/o American Management Association
1601 Broadway
New York, NY 10019-7434
Ph: (212)586-8100
Fax: (518)891-0368

Fr: 800-714-6395
E-mail: pubs_cust_serv@amanet.org
URL: http://www.amacombooks.org

David Reed. 2007. $18.95 (paper/softback). 240
pages. Offers advice on licensing and educational
requirements as well as guidance on the different
career options available as a mortgage broker,
mortgage banker, correspondent mortgage banker,
and more. Provides tips on how to quote interest
rates; get approved by wholesale lenders; negotiate
the steps of the loan process; and market and
prospect successfully.

EMPLOYMENT AGENCIES AND SEARCH FIRMS

4902 ■ 20-20 Foresight Executive Search Inc.
150 N Michigan Ave., Ste. 2800
Chicago, IL 60601
Ph: (708)246-2100
E-mail: bcavoto@202-4.com
URL: http://www.2020-4.com

Executive search firm. Affiliate offices in California
and Washington DC.

4903 ■ A-L Associates Inc.
60 E 42nd St., Ste. 1534
New York, NY 10036
Ph: (212)878-9000
URL: http://www.alassociatesltd.com

Executive search firm.

4904 ■ AC Lordi Search
235 Montgomery St., Ste. 630
San Francisco, CA 94104
Ph: (415)781-8644
E-mail: info@aclordi.com
URL: http://www.aclordi.com

Executive search firm for finance and accounting.
Uses referral-based outsourcing, affinity networking,
and cold-calling to identify talented accounting
professionals.

4905 ■ Adams Inc. Financial Recruiting
17330 Wright St., Ste. 101
Omaha, NE 68130
Ph: (402)333-3009
Fax: (402)333-3448
Fr: 800-536-4933
E-mail: info@adams-inc.com
URL: http://www.adams-inc.com

Description: Provides recruitment and candidate
placement in the banking/financial, trust/investment,
and credit card industries.

4906 ■ Advantage Group
350 N Old Woodward Ave., Ste. 218
Birmingham, MI 48009
Ph: (248)540-0400
Fax: (248)540-0401
E-mail: info@advantage-grp.com
URL: http://advantage-grp.com

Specializes in the placement of accounting and
financial executives.

4907 ■ AKS Associates Ltd.
PO Box 2863
Duxbury, MA 02331
Ph: (781)934-5333
Fax: (781)934-6333
E-mail: sandy@akssearch.com
URL: http://www.akssearch.com

Senior search firm. Concentrates on the financial
industry.

4908 ■ Albion Accounting Staffing Solutions
2520 NW 97th Ave., Ste. 110
Miami, FL 33172
Ph: (305)406-1000

Fax: (305)406-1010
E-mail: resumes@albionstaffing.com
URL: http://www.albionaccounting.com

Description: Specializes in the placement of financial, accounting, bookkeeping, mortgage and banking
positions on a temporary, temp-to-hire or direct hire
basis. Offers full service recruiting and consulting
services.

4909 ■ Allard Institute Inc.
39811 Sharon Ave.
Davis, CA 95616
Ph: (530)297-0200
Fax: 800-526-7791
Fr: 800-291-5279
E-mail: resourcing@allardinstitute.com
URL: http://www.allardinstitute.com

The firm helps its client partners earn higher returns
on cumulative investments in intellectual capital, by
recruiting talent, coaching and developing leaders,
and accessing such scientifically-based productivity-
enhancing business tools as risk management, data
mining, advanced analytic solutions, automated
platforms, new payments infrastructures, customer
relationship management (CRM), rules-based engines, networks and knowledge exchanges, advanced fraud and anti-terrorism technologies, and
e-commerce.

4910 ■ Allen Evans Klein International
305 Madison Ave.
New York, NY 10165
Ph: (212)983-9300
Fax: (212)983-9272
E-mail: info@allenevans.com
URL: http://www.allenevans.com

Global Executive search firm.

4911 ■ Allerton Heneghan & O'Neill
1415 W 22nd St., Tower Fl.
Oak Brook, IL 60523
Ph: (630)645-2294
Fax: (630)645-2298
E-mail: info@ahosearch.com
URL: http://www.ahosearch.com

Executive search firm.

4912 ■ American Executive Management Inc.
30 Federal St.
Salem, MA 01970
E-mail: execsearch@americanexecutive.us
URL: http://www.americanexecutive.us

Executive search firm. Second location in Boston.

**4913 ■ American Human Resources
  Associates Ltd. (AHRA)**
PO Box 18269
Cleveland, OH 44118-0269
Ph: (440)317-0981
E-mail: ahra@ahrasearch.com
URL: http://www.ahrasearch.com

Executive search firm. Focused on real estate, banking and credit & collection.

4914 ■ The Angus Group Ltd.
5080 Wooster Rd., Ste. 300
Cincinnati, OH 45226
Ph: (513)961-5575
Fax: (513)961-5616
E-mail: angus@angusgroup.com
URL: http://www.angusgroup.com

Executive search firm.

4915 ■ Arlene Clapp Ltd.
4250 Park Glen Rd.
Minneapolis, MN 55416
Ph: (952)928-7474
E-mail: arlene@arleneclapp.com
URL: http://www.arleneclapp.com

Executive search firm.

4916 ■ The Bankers Register
1140 Avenue of the Americas
New York, NY 10036
Ph: (212)840-0800
Fax: (212)840-7039
E-mail: recruiter@spgbankingjobs.com

Specialists in the recruitment and placement of men and women in the banking community. Committed exclusively to: commercial banking, international banking, trust/investments, and thrift/mortgage banking.

4917 ■ Bartholdi Partners
12020 Sunrise Valley Dr.
Reston, VA 20191
Ph: (703)476-5519
Fax: (703)753-6217
E-mail: info@bartholdisearch.com
URL: http://www.bartholdisearch.com

Executive search firm. Affiliates in San Francisco; San Jose; Phoenix; Scottsdale; Parker, CO; and Framingham, MA.

4918 ■ Bialecki Inc.
780 3rd Ave., Ste. 4203
New York, NY 10017
Ph: (212)755-1090
Fax: (212)755-1130
E-mail: linda@bialecki.com
URL: http://www.bialecki.com

Senior executive search firm focused on the financial industry.

4919 ■ Brandjes & Associates
721 Cliveden Rd.
PO Box 5971
Pikesville, MD 21208-4715
Ph: (410)484-5423
Fax: (410)484-6140
Fr: 877-485-8193

Executive recruiting for the financial services industry.

4920 ■ The Burling Group Ltd.
600 N Kingsbury St., Ste. 1507
Chicago, IL 60614
Ph: (773)883-0888
E-mail: web@burlinggroup.com
URL: http://www.burlinggroup.com

Executive search firm.

4921 ■ Butterfass, Pepe & MacCallan Inc.
PO Box 179
Franklin Lakes, NJ 07417
Ph: (201)560-9500
Fax: (201)560-9506
E-mail: staff@bpmi.com
URL: http://www.bpmi.com

Executive search firm.

4922 ■ Buxbaum/Rink Consulting L.L.C.
1 Bradley Rd., Ste. 901
Woodbridge, CT 06525-2296
Ph: (203)389-5949
Fax: (203)397-0615

Personnel consulting firms offer contingency search, recruitment and placement of accounting and finance, as well as other business management positions. In addition to serving these two major career areas, also provides similar services to operations, marketing and human resources executives. Industries served: manufacturing, financial services, and service.

4923 ■ Canny, Bowen Inc.
400 Madison Ave., Rm. 11-D
New York, NY 10017
Ph: (212)949-6611
Fax: (212)949-5191
E-mail: main@cannybowen.com
URL: http://www.cannybowen.com

Executive search firm.

4924 ■ Career Advocates International
1539 Ave. A
Katy, TX 77493
Ph: (281)395-9848
Fax: (281)574-3949
URL: http://www.careeradvocates.org

Provides permanent placement and temporary staffing for executive and staff level positions. Specializes in multiple niches including: sales and marketing, accounting and financial services, banking, communications, human resources, chemicals, oil and gas, medical and dental, legal, information technology, energy, technology, engineering, manufacturing, construction, and light industrial.

4925 ■ Carrington & Carrington Ltd
39 S LaSalle St., Ste. 400
Chicago, IL 60603
Ph: (312)606-0015
Fax: (312)606-0501
E-mail: resume@carringtonandcarrington.com
URL: http://www.carringtonandcarrington.com

Executive search firm.

4926 ■ CarterBaldwin
200 Mansell Ct. E, Ste. 450
Roswell, GA 30076
Ph: (678)448-0000
Fr: (866)781-6844
E-mail: jdelikat@carterbaldwin.com
URL: http://www.carterbaldwin.com

Executive search firm.

4927 ■ Chanko-Ward Ltd.
2 W 45th St., Ste. 1201
New York, NY 10036
Ph: (212)869-4040
Fax: (212)869-0281
E-mail: info@chankoward.com
URL: http://www.chankoward.com

Primarily engaged in executive recruiting for individuals and corporations, where disciplines of accounting, planning, mergers and acquisitions, finance, or MIS required. In addition will function as the internal personnel department of a corporation, either to augment present staff or in a situation where there is no formal personnel department. Serves private industries as well as government agencies.

4928 ■ Charles Aris, Inc.
300 N Greene St., Ste. 1800
Greensboro, NC 27401
Ph: (336)378-1818
Fax: (336)378-0129
E-mail: info@charlesaris.com
URL: http://www.charlesaris.com

Provides executive search and placement services in the areas of consumer packaged goods, retail, strategy/business development, global life sciences, healthcare, chemicals, textiles/apparel, private equity, and business services.

4929 ■ Choi & Burns LLC
156 W 56th St., 18th Fl.
New York, NY 10019
Ph: (212)755-7051
Fax: (212)335-2610
E-mail: info@choiburns.com
URL: http://www.choiburns.com

Executive search firm focuses on the financial industry.

4930 ■ Christian & Timbers
28601 Chagrin Blvd., Ste. 600
Cleveland, OH 44122
Ph: (216)682-3200
Fax: (216)464-6172
E-mail: jsilver@ctnet.com
URL: http://www.ctnet.com

Executive search firm. Eight branches spanning the USA.

4931 ■ Coffou Partners Inc.
880 N Lake Shore Dr., No. 13CD
Chicago, IL 60611
Ph: (312)867-1781
E-mail: info@coffou.com
URL: http://www.coffou.com

Executive search firm.

4932 ■ Consultants to Executive Management Company Ltd.
20 S Clark St.
Chicago, IL 60603
Ph: (312)855-1500
Fax: (312)855-1510
Fr: 800-800-2362

National personnel consultancy specializes in executive search with focus on accounting and finance, management information systems, professional medical, and real estate fields. Industries served: All.

4933 ■ The Consulting Group
757 Third Ave., 23rd Fl.
New York, NY 10017
Ph: (212)751-8484
E-mail: research@consultinggroupny.com
URL: http://www.consultinggroupny.com

Executive search firm.

4934 ■ Cornell Global
PO Box 7113
Wilton, CT 06897
Ph: (203)762-0730
Fax: (203)761-9507
E-mail: info@cornellglobal.com
URL: http://www.cornellglobal.com

Executive search firm.

4935 ■ The Corporate Source Group Inc.
5420 Bay Center Dr., Ste. 105
Tampa, FL 33609
Ph: (813)286-4422
Fax: (978)475-6800
E-mail: inquiry@csg-search.com
URL: http://www.csg-search.com

Executive search firm branches in Boston, MA; Chicago, IL; Los Angeles, CA; New York, NY; Tampa, FL; Washington, DC.

4936 ■ Deerfield Associates
572 Washington St., Ste. 15
Wellesley, MA 02482
Ph: (781)237-2800
Fax: (781)237-5600
E-mail: jobs@deerfieldassociates.com
URL: http://www.deerfieldassociates.com

Executive search firm.

4937 ■ DGL Consultants
189 S Main St.
PO Box 450
Richford, VT 05476
Ph: (802)848-7764
Fax: (802)848-3117
E-mail: info@dglconsultants.com
URL: http://www.dglconsultants.com

Executive search firm.

4938 ■ DLG Associates Inc.
2210 Roswell Ave., No. 103
Charlotte, NC 28207
Ph: (704)372-2155
Fax: (704)372-2188
E-mail: dguilford@dlgassociates.com
URL: http://www.dlgassociates.com

Executive search firm.

4939 ■ Douglas-Allen Inc.
Tower Square, 24th Fl.
PO Box 15368
Springfield, MA 01115

Ph: (413)739-0900
E-mail: research@douglas-allen.com
URL: http://www.douglas-allen.com

Executive search firm.

4940 ■ Dowd Associates Inc.
777 Westchester Ave., Ste. 120
White Plains, NY 10604
Ph: (914)251-1515
Fax: (914)251-1321
E-mail: mail@dowdassociates.com
URL: http://www.dowdassociates.com

Specializes in the recruitment of senior level financial
professionals.

4941 ■ Eileen Finn & Associates Inc.
230 Park Ave., Fl. 10
New York, NY 10169
Ph: (212)687-1260
Fax: (212)551-1473
E-mail: eileen@eileenfinn.com
URL: http://www.eileenfinn.com

Executive search firm.

4942 ■ Epsen, Fuller & Associates LLC
1776 On The Green
67 Park Pl., E
Morristown, NJ 07960
Ph: (973)387-4900
Fax: (973)359-9928
E-mail: info@epsenfuller.com
URL: http://www.epsenfuller.com

Executive search firm.

4943 ■ Essex Consulting Group Inc.
PO Box 550
Essex, MA 01929
Ph: (978)337-6633
E-mail: brad@essexsearch.com
URL: http://www.essexsearch.com

Executive search firm.

4944 ■ Ethos Consulting LLC
3219 E Camelback Rd., Ste. 515
Phoenix, AZ 85018
Ph: (480)296-3801
Fax: (480)664-7270
E-mail: conrad@ethosconsulting.com
URL: http://www.ethosconsulting.com

Executive search firm. Second branch in Scottsdale,
AZ.

4945 ■ Executive Dimensions
5820 Main St., Ste. 403
Williamsville, NY 14221
Ph: (716)632-9034
Fax: (716)632-2889
E-mail: execsearch@executivedimensions.com
URL: http://www.executivedimensions.com

Executive search firm.

4946 ■ Executive Search Consultants Ltd.
3030 N Josey Ln., Ste. 101
Carrollton, TX 75007
Ph: (972)394-4131
Fax: (972)394-2111

Firm offers executive recruitment to the transportation, computer manufacturing, health and beauty aids,
consumer package goods, and financial service
industries.

4947 ■ The Executive Source Inc.
55 5th Ave., 19th Fl.
New York, NY 10003
Ph: (212)691-5505
Fax: (212)691-9839
E-mail: tes1@executivesource.com
URL: http://executivesource.com

Executive search firm.

4948 ■ Ferrari Search Group
200 East End Ave., Ste. 5N
New York, NY 10128
Ph: (212)289-5099
Fax: (716)386-2367
E-mail: contactus@ferrarisearchgroup.com
URL: http://www.ferrarisearchgroup.com

Executive search firm.

4949 ■ Financial Professionals
4100 Spring Valley Rd., Ste. 250
Dallas, TX 75244
Ph: (972)991-8999
Fax: (972)702-0776
E-mail: rita@fpstaff.net
URL: http://www.fpstaff.net

Executive search consultants with additional offices
in Forth Worth and Houston.

4950 ■ Financial Search Group, Ltd.
307 Fourth Ave., Ste. 810
Pittsburgh, PA 15222
Ph: (412)288-0505
Fax: (412)288-0699
E-mail: fsgltd@fsgltd.com
URL: http://www.fsgltd.com

Description: Provides staffing services on a wide
variety of companies from contingency or retainer
basis. Identifies the candidates that match each
employer's needs.

4951 ■ Foster McKay Group
30 Vreeland Rd.
Florham Park, NJ 07932
Ph: (973)966-0909
Fax: (973)966-6925
E-mail: careers@fostermckaynj.com
URL: http://www.fostermckay.com

Executive search firm that specializes in accounting
and finance. Specializes in placing financial, accounting, and tax professionals.

4952 ■ Frank Palma Associates
17 Beechwood Lane
Kinnelon, NJ 07405
Ph: (973)884-1498
Fax: (973)884-1499
E-mail: fpalma@fpassocs.com
URL: http://www.fpassocs.com

Executive search firm. Additional location in Duluth,
GA.

4953 ■ Gans, Gans and Associates
7445 Quail Meadow Rd.
Plant City, FL 33565-3314
Ph: (813)986-4441
Fax: (813)986-4775
E-mail: simone@gansgans.com
URL: http://www.gansgans.com

A human resources firm that specializes in executive
search, human resources, management consulting,
diversity consulting, and resume assessment. Takes
a personal approach in the development of tailored
programs that consider the corporate culture, history,
and objectives of client. Industries served: consulting,
financial services, legal, insurance, engineering,
healthcare, manufacturing, utilities, and the public
sector.

4954 ■ The Hanover Consulting Group
11707 Hunters Run Dr.
Hunt Valley, MD 21030
Ph: (410)785-1912
Fax: (410)785-1913
Fr: 800-785-1912
E-mail: info@thehanovergroup.net
URL: http://www.thehanovergroup.net

Specializes in finding, evaluating, and selecting top
talent for the banking and trust industries.

4955 ■ International Insurance Consultants Inc.
1191 E Newport Center Dr., Ste. 206
Deerfield Beach, FL 33442
Ph: (954)421-0122
Fax: (954)449-0497
E-mail: info@insurancerecruitersusa.com
URL: http://www.insurancerecruitersusa.com

Offers executive search to the insurance industry.
Clients include insurance companies, brokers,
consultants and investment banks. Industries served:
insurance and financial services industries.

4956 ■ Karen Dexter & Associates Inc.
2012 Chestnut Ave. N, Ste. 29
Wilmette, IL 60091-1512
Ph: (847)853-9500
Fax: (847)256-7108

Training and development consultant offering interpersonal skills training and one on one performance
counseling for employees of large organizations.
Industries served: advertising, banking and finance,
consumer products, entertainment, food and beverage, healthcare, legal profession, manufacturing,
government agencies, publishing and broadcasting.

4957 ■ KForce
Fr: 877-4KF-ORCE
URL: http://www.kforce.com

Executive search firm. More than 41 locations
throughout the United States and two in the
Philippines.

4958 ■ Milo Research
305 Madison Ave., Ste. 1762
New York, NY 10165-6227
Ph: (212)972-2780
Fax: (212)983-5854
E-mail: miloresearch@compuserve.com

Human resources firm helps executives find work in
the publishing, finance, telecommunications, direct
mail, and consumer products fields.

4959 ■ Neal Management Inc.
450 7th Ave., Ste. 923
New York, NY 10123-0101
Ph: (212)686-1686
Fax: (212)686-1590
E-mail: info@nealmanagement.com
URL: http://nealmanagement.com

An executive search firm dedicated to the placement
of financial professionals.

4960 ■ Oliver & Rozner Associates
598 Madison Ave., Ste. 11
New York, NY 10022
Ph: (212)688-1850

Performs executive search for top tiers of management including presidents, general management,
advertising account management, division management, group executive and vice presidential line positions in such areas as marketing, research, operations, sales, finance, human resources and others;
hard-to-find specialists including specific marketing/
advertising executives, research and development
expertise, computer/data processing knowledge,
scientific, physicians-product efficacy and occupational medicine and engineering. Industries served
include pharmaceutical, health care, hospital, advertising, consumer products and packaged goods,
house wares, direct selling, cosmetics/toiletries,
industrial products, high technology products, forest
products, engineering, construction, environment/
resource recovery, graphic arts, chemical and government agencies.

4961 ■ Pate Resources Group Inc.
505 Orleans St., Ste. 300
Beaumont, TX 77701
Ph: (409)833-4514
Fax: (409)833-4646

Fr: 800-669-4514
E-mail: opportunities@pateresourcesgroup.com
URL: http://www.pateresourcesgroup.com

Offers executive search and recruiting services to professionals who include physicians, healthcare administrators, engineers, accounting and financial disciplines, legal, outplacement, sales and marketing. Industries served: healthcare, petrochemicals, accounting, utility, legal, and municipalities.

4962 ■ Penn Hill Associates Inc.
14323 Ocean Hwy., Ste. 4131
PO Box 1367
Pawleys Island, SC 29585-4817
Ph: (843)237-8988
Fax: (843)237-9220
E-mail: janette@pennhillassociates.com
URL: http://www.pennhillassociates.com

Offers executive search services for consumer finance companies. Industries served: consumer finance, home equity, and auto financing.

4963 ■ Penn Search Inc.
1045 1st Ave., Ste. 110
PO Box 688
King of Prussia, PA 19406
Ph: (610)964-8820
Fax: (610)964-8916
E-mail: charlied@pennsearch.com
URL: http://www.pennsearch.com

Assists in recruiting and hiring accounting and financial professionals from staff accountant to chief financial officer. Industries served: all.

4964 ■ Princeton Executive Search
2667 Nottingham Way
Trenton, NJ 08619
Ph: (609)584-1100
Fax: (856)596-8866
E-mail: pes@bonifield.com

Provides search and placement for management level professions. Specializes in accounting, banking, engineering and human resources. Industries served: financial, research and development, insurance, manufacturing, banking, and government agencies.

4965 ■ Pro Advantage Executive Search
381 Park Ave. S, Ste. 1112
New York, NY 10016
Ph: (212)944-0222
Fax: (212)944-2666
E-mail: info@proadvantagejobs.com
URL: http://www.proadvantagejobs.com

Description: Executive recruiting and research firm specializes in financial services industries. Offers career opportunities in the field of accounting, internal auditing, finance, compliance, tax, operations, and marketing.

4966 ■ Quirk-Corporon and Associates Inc.
1229 N Jackson St., Ste. 205
Milwaukee, WI 53202-2655
Ph: (414)224-9399
Fax: (414)224-9472
E-mail: quirkrecruiters@sbcglobal.net
URL: http://www.quirkinsrecruiters.com

Employment agency specializing in all disciplines of the insurance and financial industries; insurance recruiters, is a contingency and retained recruiting and consulting firm specializing in the placement of permanent candidates; provides talented professional and technical employees, locally and nationally, who are skilled in property or casualty, life or health, employee benefits and managed care; provides a highly respected dimension of counseling skill to both clients and candidates in all areas of staffing and employee relations.

4967 ■ Raines International Inc.
250 Park Ave., 17th Fl.
New York, NY 10177
Ph: (212)997-1100

Fax: (212)997-0196
E-mail: contact@rainesinternational.com
URL: http://www.rainesinternational.com

International generalist firm specializing in middle to upper management executives. Concentrations include general management, finance and accounting, information technology, operations or procurement, strategic planning, investment banking, real estate or finance, human resources, insurance, and legal.

4968 ■ Raymond Alexander Associates
97 Lackawanna Ave., Ste. 102
Totowa, NJ 07512-2332
Ph: (973)256-1000
Fax: (973)256-5871
E-mail: raa@raymondalexander.com
URL: http://www.raymondalexander.com

Personnel consulting firm conducts executive search services in the specific areas of accounting, tax and finance. Industries served: manufacturing, financial services, and public accounting.

4969 ■ Real Estate Executive Search, Inc.
225 E Dania Beach Blvd. Ste., 200
Dania Beach, FL 33004
Ph: (954)927-6000
Fax: (954)927-6003
E-mail: reesearch954@aol.com
URL: http://reesearchinc.com

Executive search firm for the real estate and finance fields.

4970 ■ Roberson & Co.
10751 Parfet St.
Broomfield, CO 80021
Ph: (303)410-6510
E-mail: roberson@recruiterpro.com
URL: http://www.recruiterpro.com

Professional and executive recruiting firm working the national and international marketplace. Specializes in accounting, finance, data processing and information services, health care, environmental and mining, engineering, manufacturing, human resources, and sales and marketing.

4971 ■ Rocky Mountain Recruiters, Inc.
1776 S Jackson St., Ste. 320
Denver, CO 80210
Ph: (303)296-2000
E-mail: resumes@rmrecruiters.com
URL: http://www.rmrecruiters.com

Accounting, financial, and executive search firm.

4972 ■ Search North America Inc.
PO Box 3577
Sunriver, OR 97707-0577
Ph: (503)222-6461
Fax: (503)227-2804
E-mail: mylinda@searchna.com
URL: http://www.searchna.com

An executive search and recruiting firm whose focus is placing engineers, operations and maintenance managers, sales and marketing management, financial and general management executives (both domestic and international). Industries served: forest products, pulp and paper, waste to energy, environmental services, consulting and equipment suppliers for above related industries.

4973 ■ Sherpa LLC
1001 Morehead Square Dr., Ste. 600
Charlotte, NC 28203
Ph: (704)374-0001
E-mail: info@sherpallc.com
URL: http://www.sherpallc.com

Specializes in recruiting, staffing and consulting services for accounting/finance, information technology and project management in direct hire, temporary and project-based consulting positions.

4974 ■ Spectrum Group, LLC
1919 Gallows Rd., Ste. 600
Vienna, VA 22182
Ph: (703)738-1200
Fax: (703)761-9477
E-mail: web@spectrumcareers.com
URL: http://www.spectrumcareers.com

Description: Serves as executive search firm for accounting and finance, information technology and sales and marketing industries.

4975 ■ Techtronix Technical Search
4805 N 24th Pl.
PO Box 17713
Milwaukee, WI 53217-0173
Ph: (414)466-3100
Fax: (414)466-3598

Firm specializes in recruiting executives for the engineering, information systems, manufacturing, marketing, finance, and human resources industries. Industries include electronic, manufacturing and finance.

4976 ■ Terry Taylor & Associates
459 Bechman St.
Springdale, PA 15144-1170
Ph: (724)274-5627

An executive search consulting firm specializing in financial, litigation support, performance improvement and management information systems recruitment.

4977 ■ TRC Staffing Services Inc.
115 Perimeter Center Pl. NE, Ste. 855
Atlanta, GA 30346
Ph: (770)392-1411
Fax: (770)392-7926
E-mail: info@trcstaff.com
URL: http://www.trcstaff.com

A full-service executive search company with permanent placements encompassing engineering, industrial sales, financial and computer science positions. Screen, interview, and verify past employment for all candidates prior to referral. Also assist personnel staffs in the attainment of their EEO/AAP goals with the placement of talented individuals in positions which were underutilized with minorities and/or women. Industries served: all.

4978 ■ Val Executive Resources Group
100 Merrick Rd., East Twr., Ste. 302
Rockville Centre, NY 11570-4801
Ph: (516)764-9000
Fax: (516)764-9122
E-mail: info@val-group.com
URL: http://www.val-group.com

Personnel consultants recruiting on contingency and retained search basis specializing in Banking and Finance, to include: Corporate, Commercial and Consumer Banking, Private Banking, Trust, Investments, Human Resources, Marketing, focusing on lower, middle, and senior management positions. Industries served: banking, finance, brokerage, insurance.

ONLINE JOB SOURCES AND SERVICES

4979 ■ American Association of Finance and Accounting
URL: http://www.aafa.com

Description: AAFA is the largest and oldest alliance of executive search firms specializing in the recruitment and placement of finance and accounting professionals. Contains career opportunities site with job board for both job seekers and hiring employers. One does not have to be a member to search for jobs.

4980 ■ BankingCareers.com
URL: http://www.bankingcareers.com

Description: Provides lists of jobs and products to bankers in the banking and finance community.

4981 ■ BankJobs.com
URL: http://www.bankjobs.com

Description: Posts jobs and resumes for the banking and finance industry. Allows users to post, preview and search jobs for free.

4982 ■ CareerBank
URL: http://www.careerbank.com/home/ index.cfm?site_id=8162

Description: Provides jobs in finance, banking, mortgage, insurance, and accounting. Specializes in online job posting and job search, resume upload and resume database search, and career advice services.

4983 ■ The Digital Financier
URL: http://www.dfin.com

Description: Job postings from financial companies. Offers links to major job search websites. Has leads for further training and allows companies to post its own job links.

4984 ■ Financial Job Network
PO Box 55431
Sherman Oaks, CA 91403
Ph: (818)905-5272
E-mail: info@fjn.com
URL: http://www.fjn.com

Description: Contains information on international and national employment opportunities for those in the financial job market. Job listings may be submitted, as well as resumes. Main files include: Testimonials, Calendar, Corporate Listings, FJN Clients, more. Free to candidates.

4985 ■ Financial Management Jobs
URL: http://www.financialmanagementjobs.org

Description: Serves as a job board for financial management employment opportunities.

4986 ■ FinancialJobBank.com
URL: http://www.financialjobbank.com

Description: Works as a job engine that helps individual to find job openings in the areas of accounting, finance, taxation, banking, and mortgage.

4987 ■ FinancialJobs.com
URL: http://www.financialjobs.com

Description: Lists accounting and finance jobs for professionals at all levels of their careers. Features resume writing tips, relocation assistance, networking techniques, salary calculator, and other related links.

4988 ■ FinancialServicesCrossing.com
URL: http://www.financialservicescrossing.com

Description: Offers a collection of top financial services job openings carefully researched by analysts. Provides instant access to a comprehensive pool of listings in the industry of financial services.

4989 ■ InsuranceAgencyCareers.com
URL: http://www.insuranceagencycareers.com

Description: Online job search provides employment opportunities in the insurance industry.

4990 ■ Spherion
2050 Spectrum Blvd.
Fort Lauderdale, FL 33309
Ph: (954)308-7600
Fr: 800-774-3746
E-mail: help@spherion.com
URL: http://www.spherion.com

Description: Recruitment firm specializing in accounting and finance, sales and marketing, interim executives, technology, engineering, retail and human resources.

4991 ■ Transearch.com
E-mail: contact@transearch.com
URL: http://www.transearch.com

Description: International executive search firm concentrating in searches for executives in retail, real estate, information technology, industry, life sciences and financial services. Seekers may search job board and submit their resume for recruiter review.

4992 ■ Vault.com
132 W 31st St., 15th Fl.
New York, NY 10001
Ph: (212)366-4212
Fax: (212)366-6117
E-mail: publicity@vault.com
URL: http://www.vault.com

Description: Job board website with searches emphasizing jobs in legal, business, consulting and finance fields of practice. Contains online profile posting, resume review, company research, salary calculators and relocation tools.

TRADESHOWS

4993 ■ Alliance of Merger and Acquisition Advisors Conference
Alliance of Merger and Acquisition Advisors
200 E. Randolph St., 24th Fl.
Chicago, IL 60601
Ph: (312)856-9590
Fax: (312)729-9800
Fr: 877-844-2535
E-mail: info@amaaonline.org
URL: http://www.amaaonline.org

Semiannual. Primary Exhibits: Exhibits relating to financial services.

4994 ■ Bankers' Association for Finance and Trade Annual Meeting
Bankers' Association for Finance and Trade
1120 Connecticut Ave. NW, 5th Fl.
Washington, DC 20036
Ph: (202)663-7575
Fax: (202)663-5538
E-mail: baft@aba.com
URL: http://www.baft.org

Annual. Primary Exhibits: Exhibits relating to finance, trade, economic issues, enterprise risk management, supply chain finance, payments and remittances, regulatory compliance, and service.

4995 ■ Independent Community Bankers of America Annual Convention and Techworld
Independent Community Bankers of America
1615 L St. N.W., Ste. 900
Washington, DC 20036
Ph: (202)659-8111
Fax: (202)659-3604
Fr: 800-422-8439
E-mail: info@icba.org
URL: http://www.icba.org

Annual. Primary Exhibits: Exhibits relating to community banking. Dates and Locations: 2012 Mar 11-15; Nashville, TN; Gaylord Opryland Hotel.

4996 ■ National Association of Personal Financial Advisors National Conference
National Association of Personal Financial Advisors
3250 N Arlington Heights Rd., Ste. 109
Arlington Heights, IL 60004
Ph: (847)483-5400
Fax: (847)483-5415
E-mail: info@napfa.org
URL: http://www.napfa.org

Annual. Offers sessions in all areas of financial planning.

4997 ■ Pennsylvania Association of Community Bankers Convention
Pennsylvania Association of Community Bankers
2405 N. Front St.
Harrisburg, PA 17110
Ph: (717)231-7447
Fax: (717)231-7445

Fr: 800-443-5076
E-mail: pacb@pacb.org
URL: http://www.pacb.org

Annual. Primary Exhibits: Equipment, supplies, and services for community banks, thrifts, and associate firms.

4998 ■ Western Independent Bankers Conference for Bank Presidents, Senior Officers and Directors
Western Independent Bankers
601 Montgomery St., Ste. 1200
San Francisco, CA 94111
Ph: (415)352-2323
Fax: (415)352-2314
E-mail: info@wib.org
URL: http://www.wib.org

Annual. Primary Exhibits: Exhibits relating to banking, including industry trends, issues, and innovation.

OTHER SOURCES

4999 ■ American Bankers Association (ABA)
1120 Connecticut Ave. NW
Washington, DC 20036
Ph: (202)663-5564
Fax: (202)663-7543
Fr: 800-226-5377
E-mail: custserv@aba.com
URL: http://www.aba.com

Description: Members are principally commercial banks and trust companies; combined assets of members represent approximately 90% of the U.S. banking industry; approximately 94% of members are community banks with less than $500 million in assets. Seeks to enhance the role of commercial bankers as preeminent providers of financial services through communications, research, legal action, lobbying of federal legislative and regulatory bodies, and education and training programs. Serves as spokesperson for the banking industry; facilitates exchange of information among members. Maintains the American Institute of Banking, an industry-sponsored adult education program. Conducts educational and training programs for bank employees and officers through a wide range of banking schools and national conferences. Maintains liaison with federal bank regulators; lobbies Congress on issues affecting commercial banks; testifies before congressional committees; represents members in U.S. postal rate proceedings. Serves as secretariat of the International Monetary Conference and the Financial Institutions Committee for the American National Standards Institute. Files briefs and lawsuits in major court cases affecting the industry. Conducts teleconferences with state banking associations on such issues as regulatory compliance; works to build consensus and coordinate activities of leading bank and financial service trade groups. Provides services to members including: public advocacy; news media contact; insurance program providing directors and officers with liability coverage, financial institution bond, and trust errors and omissions coverage; research service operated through ABA Center for Banking Information; fingerprint set processing in conjunction with the Federal Bureau of Investigation; discounts on operational and income-producing projects through the Corporation for American Banking. Conducts conferences, forums, and workshops covering subjects such as small business, consumer credit, agricultural and community banking, trust management, bank operations, and automation. Sponsors ABA Educational Foundation and the Personal Economics Program, which educates schoolchildren and the community on banking, economics, and personal finance.

5000 ■ American Financial Services Association (AFSA)
919 18th St. NW, Ste. 300
Washington, DC 20006-5526
Ph: (202)296-5544

Fax: (202)223-0321
E-mail: susie@afsamail.org
URL: http://www.afsaonline.org

Description: Represents companies whose business is primarily direct credit lending to consumers and/or the purchase of sales finance paper on consumer goods. Has members that have insurance and retail subsidiaries; some are themselves subsidiaries of highly diversified parent corporations. Encourages the business of financing individuals and families for necessary and useful purposes at reasonable charges, including interest; promotes consumer understanding of basic money management principles as well as constructive uses of consumer credit. Includes educational services such as films, textbooks and study units for the classroom and budgeting guides for individuals and families. Compiles statistical reports; offers seminars.

5001 ■ Association of African American Financial Advisors (AAAA)
PO Box 4853
Capitol Heights, MD 20791-4853
Ph: (240)396-2530
Fax: 888-392-5702
E-mail: info@aaafa.com
URL: http://aaafainc.com

Description: Seeks to develop and foster professional relationships among African American professionals working in the financial advisory industry. Provides assistance and nurturing for those families that seek to improve their opportunities for participating and prospering financially in an economically progressive society. Strives to create support networks for minority financial professionals. Provides a forum for further education, training and visibility of its members.

5002 ■ Association of Divorce Financial Planners (ADFP)
514 Fourth St.
East Northport, NY 11731
Ph: (631)754-6125
Fr: 888-838-7773
E-mail: adfp@divorceandfinance.org
URL: http://www.divorceandfinance.org

Description: Aims to create awareness of the benefits of divorce financial planning. Provides members with continuing education. Promotes communication, networking and peer review.

5003 ■ Association for Financial Professionals (AFP)
4520 E West Hwy., Ste. 750
Bethesda, MD 20814
Ph: (301)907-2862
Fax: (301)907-2864
E-mail: afp@afponline.org
URL: http://www.afponline.org

Description: Seeks to establish a national forum for the exchange of concepts and techniques related to improving the management of treasury and the careers of professionals through research, education, publications and recognition of the treasury management profession through a certification program. Conducts educational programs. Operates career center.

5004 ■ Bank Administration Institute (BAI)
115 S LaSalle St., Ste. 3300
Chicago, IL 60603
Ph: (312)683-2464
Fax: (312)683-2373
Fr: 800-224-9889
E-mail: info@bai.org
URL: http://www.bai.org

Description: Works to improve the competitive position of banking companies through strategic research and educational offerings.

5005 ■ Commercial Finance Association (CFA)
370 7th Ave., Ste. 1801
New York, NY 10001-3979

Ph: (212)792-9390
Fax: (212)564-6053
E-mail: info@cfa.com
URL: http://www.cfa.com

Description: Organizations engaged in asset-based financial services including commercial financing and factoring and lending money on a secured basis to small- and medium-sized business firms. Acts as a forum for information and consideration about ideas, opportunities and legislation concerning asset-based financial services. Seeks to improve the industry's legal and operational procedures. Offers job placement and reference services for members. Sponsors School for Field Examiners and other educational programs. Compiles statistics; conducts seminars and surveys; maintains speakers' bureau and 21 committees.

5006 ■ Eastern Finance Association (EFA)
Auburn Montgomery
School of Business
PO Box 244023
Montgomery, AL 36124-4023
E-mail: membershipservices@
  blackwellpublishers.co.uk
URL: http://etnpconferences.net/efa

Description: College and university professors and financial officers; libraries. Provides a meeting place for persons interested in any aspect of finance, including financial management, investments, and banking. Sponsors research competitions.

5007 ■ Financial Executives International (FEI)
1250 Headquarters Plz., West Tower, 7th Fl.
Morristown, NJ 07960
Ph: (973)765-1000
Fax: (973)765-1018
E-mail: mhollein@financialexecutives.org
URL: http://www.financialexecutives.org

Description: Professional organization of corporate financial executives performing duties of chief financial officer, controller, treasurer, or vice-president-finance. Sponsors research activities through its affiliated Financial Executives Research Foundation. Maintains offices in Toronto, Canada, and Washington, DC.

5008 ■ Financial Management Association International (FMA)
University of South Florida
College of Business Administration
4202 E Fowler Ave., BSN 3331
Tampa, FL 33620-5500
Ph: (813)974-2084
Fax: (813)974-3318
E-mail: fma@coba.usf.edu
URL: http://www.fma.org

Description: Professors of financial management; corporate financial officers. Facilitates exchange of ideas among persons involved in financial management or the study thereof. Conducts workshops for comparison of current research projects and development of cooperative ventures in writing and research. Sponsors honorary society for superior students at 300 colleges and universities. Offers placement services.

5009 ■ Financial Managers Society (FMS)
100 W Monroe St., Ste. 1700
Chicago, IL 60603-1907
Ph: (312)578-1300
Fax: (312)578-1308
Fr: 800-275-4367
E-mail: info@fmsinc.org
URL: http://www.fmsinc.org

Description: Works for the needs of finance and accounting professionals from banks, thrifts and credit unions. Offers career-enhancing education, specialized publications, national leadership opportunities and worldwide connections with other industry professionals.

5010 ■ Financial Planning Association
7535 E Hampden Ave., Ste. 600
Denver, CO 80231
Ph: (303)759-4900
Fax: (303)759-0749
Fr: 800-322-4237
URL: http://www.fpanet.org

Description: Provides educational opportunities and industry specific resources. Includes information and tools connecting those who provide, support and benefit from professional financial planning.

5011 ■ Financial Women's Association of New York (FWA)
215 Park Ave. S, Ste. 1712
New York, NY 10003
Ph: (212)533-2141
Fax: (212)982-3008
E-mail: fwaoffice@fwa.org
URL: http://www.fwa.org

Description: Persons of professional status in the field of finance in the New York metropolitan area. Works to promote and maintain high professional standards in the financial and business communities; provide an opportunity for members to enhance one another's professional contacts; achieve recognition of the contribution of women to the financial and business communities; encourage other women to seek professional positions within the financial and business communities. Activities include educational trips to foreign countries; college internship program including foreign student exchange; high school mentorship program; Washington and international briefings; placement service for members. Maintains speakers' bureau.

5012 ■ International Association of Credit Portfolio Managers (IACPM)
360 Madison Ave., 17th Fl.
New York, NY 10017-7111
Ph: (646)289-5430
Fax: (646)289-5429
E-mail: dara@iacpm.org
URL: http://www.iacpm.org

Description: Represents financial institutions that manage portfolios of corporate loans, bonds, or similar credit sensitive financial instruments. Aims to advance the practice of credit exposure management. Conducts research on the credit portfolio management field. Works with other organizations in addressing issues of mutual interest relating to the measurement and management of portfolio risk.

5013 ■ International Association of Qualified Financial Planners (IAQFP)
PO Box 7007
Beverly Hills, CA 90212-7007
Fr: 877-346-3037
E-mail: info@iaqfp.org
URL: http://www.iaqfp.org

Description: Aims to unite the financial planning profession. Encourages research to advance the discipline, theory and practice of financial planning. Provides a medium for professional interchange and forum.

5014 ■ Media Financial Management Association (MFM)
550 W Frontage Rd., Ste. 3600
Northfield, IL 60093
Ph: (847)716-7000
Fax: (847)716-7004
E-mail: info@mediafinance.org
URL: http://www.mediafinance.org

Description: Controllers, chief accountants, auditors, business managers, treasurers, secretaries and related newspaper executives, educators, and public accountants. Conducts research projects on accounting methods and procedures for newspapers. Offers placement service; maintains speakers' bureau. Produces conferences and seminars.

5015 ■ National Association of Black Accountants (NABA)

7474 Greenway Center Dr., Ste. 1120
Greenbelt, MD 20770
Ph: (301)474-6222
Fax: (301)474-3114
Fr: 888-571-2939
E-mail: customerservice@nabainc.org
URL: http://www.nabainc.org

Description: Minority students and professionals currently working, or interested in the fields of accounting, finance, technology, consulting or general business. Seeks, promotes, develops, and represents the interests of current and future minority business professionals.

5016 ■ National Association of Corporate Treasurers (NACT)

12100 Sunset Hills Rd., Ste. 130
Reston, VA 20190
Ph: (703)437-4377
Fax: (703)435-4390
E-mail: nact@nact.org
URL: http://www.nact.org

Description: Serves as a forum for high-level finance executives who perform all or a substantial part of the duties of corporate treasurership. Seeks to produce and facilitate the exchange of information relevant to the management of corporate treasury operations. Sponsors general sessions on such topics as Cash Management Issues for the 90's, Corporate Finance, Data Processing/Electronic Services, International Liquidity Management. Offers job clearinghouse services.

5017 ■ National Association of Personal Financial Advisors

3250 N Arlington Heights Rd., Ste. 109
Arlington Heights, IL 60004
Ph: (847)483-5400
Fax: (847)483-5415
E-mail: info@napfa.org
URL: http://www.napfa.org

Description: Represents the interest of financial advisors for consumers and institutions. Promotes the public interest by advancing the financial planning profession and supporting its members. Advocates high standards for personal financial planning.

5018 ■ National Bankers Association (NBA)

1513 P St. NW
Washington, DC 20005
Ph: (202)588-5432

Fax: (202)588-5443
E-mail: mgrant@nationalbankers.org
URL: http://www.nationalbankers.org

Description: Minority banking institutions owned by minority individuals and institutions. Serves as an advocate for the minority banking industry. Organizes banking services, government relations, marketing, scholarship, and technical assistance programs. Offers placement services; compiles statistics.

5019 ■ National Investment Banking Association (NIBA)

PO Box 6625
Athens, GA 30604
Ph: (706)208-9620
Fax: (706)993-3342
E-mail: emily@nibanet.org
URL: http://www.nibanet.org

Description: Represents regional and independent brokerages, investment banking firms, and related capital market service providers. Provides a forum for small companies seeking access and exposure to underwriters and brokers/dealers in connection with their capital formation. Supports an enhanced capital formation environment for small companies.

5020 ■ National Money Transmitters Association (NMTA)

12 Welwyn Rd., Ste. C
Great Neck, NY 11021
Ph: (516)829-2742
Fax: (516)706-0203
E-mail: david@nmta.us
URL: http://www.nmta.us

Description: Represents the interests, upholds the image, and voices the concerns of U.S. licensed money transmitters, in all public and governmental matters. Aims to advance a regulatory landscape under which money transmitters can operate without biased impediments. Fosters good industry compliance with all state and federal laws. Addresses all issues concerning the money transmission industry.

5021 ■ Risk and Insurance Management Society (RIMS)

1065 Avenue of the Americas, 13th Fl.
New York, NY 10018
Ph: (212)286-9292
E-mail: membership@rims.org
URL: http://www.rims.org

Description: Business association serving corporate risk and insurance managers. Dedicated to advancing the practice of risk management, a discipline that protects physical, financial, and human resources.

5022 ■ Risk Management Association

1801 Market St., Ste. 300
Philadelphia, PA 19103-1628
Ph: (215)446-4000
Fax: (215)446-4101
Fr: 800-677-7621
E-mail: member@rmahq.org
URL: http://www.rmahq.org/RMA

Description: Commercial and savings banks, and savings and loan, and other financial services companies. Conducts research and professional development activities in areas of loan administration, asset management, and commercial lending and credit to increase professionalism.

5023 ■ Society of Cost Estimating and Analysis (SCEA)

527 Maple Ave. E, Ste. 301
Vienna, VA 22180
Ph: (703)938-5090
Fax: (703)938-5091
E-mail: scea@sceaonline.org
URL: http://www.sceaonline.net

Description: Works to improve cost estimating and analysis in government and industry and to enhance the professional competence and achievements of its members. Administers a professional certification program leading to the designation of Certified Cost Estimator/Analyst; offers extensive literature in the field through its Professional Development Program. Goals of the Society include enhancing the profession of cost estimating and analysis, fostering the professional growth of its members, enhancing the understanding and application of cost estimating, analysis and related disciplines throughout government and industry and providing forums and media through which current issues of interest to the profession can be addressed and advances in the state-of-the-art can be shared.

5024 ■ Society for Financial Education and Professional Development (SFEPD)

2120 Washington Blvd., Ste. 400
Arlington, VA 22204
Ph: (202)842-3807
Fax: (703)920-3807
E-mail: tdaniels@sfepd.org
URL: http://www.sfepd.org

Description: Aims to enhance the level of financial and economic literacy of individuals and households in the United States. Develops and presents customized financial education and professional development seminars and workshops. Works with organizations that support financial education and professional development programs.

SOURCES OF HELP-WANTED ADS

5025 ■ American City and County
Penton Media Inc.
9800 Metcalf Ave.
Overland Park, KS 66212
Ph: (913)341-1300
Fax: (913)967-1898
URL: http://americancityandcounty.com

Monthly. Municipal and county administration magazine.

5026 ■ Fire Chief
Penton Media Inc.
249 W 17th St.
New York, NY 10011
Ph: (212)204-4200
URL: http://firechief.com

Description: Features articles by fire officers from across the country and overseas covering a wide variety of areas that are important to today's fire chief.

5027 ■ Firehouse Magazine
Cygnus Business Media Inc.
3 Huntington Quadrangle, Ste. 301 N
Melville, NY 11747
Ph: (631)845-2700
Fax: (631)845-7109
Fr: 800-308-6397
URL: http://www.firehouse.com

Monthly. $24.95/year for individuals; $44.95/year for two years. Magazine focusing on fire protection.

5028 ■ IAFC On Scene
International Association of Fire Chiefs
4025 Fair Ridge Dr., Ste. 300
Fairfax, VA 22033-2868
Ph: (703)273-0911
Fax: (703)273-9363
E-mail: onscene@iafc.org
URL: http://www.iafc.org/MemberCenter/
OnSceneIssueList.cfm?navItemNumber=685

Description: Semimonthly. Covers management, technical, and legislative issues that affect fire fighting professionals, including volunteers. Recurring features include letters to the editor, interviews, news of research, reports of meetings, news of educational opportunities, job listings, notices of publications available, and columns titled Executive Director's Column, Comm Center, Announcements, Section News, President's Column, and Staying Out of Trouble-A Case Study.

5029 ■ International Fire Fighter
International Association of Fire Fighters
1750 New York Ave. NW, Ste. 300
Washington, DC 20006-5395
Ph: (202)737-8484
Fax: (202)737-8418
URL: http://www.iaff.org/comm/magazine/

Bimonthly. $18.00/year for individuals. Union tabloid.

5030 ■ The Municipality
League of Wisconsin Municipalities
122 W Washington Ave., Ste. 300
Madison, WI 53703-2715
Ph: (608)267-2380
Fax: (608)267-0645
Fr: 800-991-5502
URL: http://www.lwm-info.org/

Monthly. Magazine for officials of Wisconsin's local municipal governments.

5031 ■ NFPA Journal
National Fire Protection Association
1 Batterymarch Pk.
Quincy, MA 02169-7471
Ph: (617)770-3000
Fax: (617)770-0700
Fr: 800-344-3555
URL: http://www.nfpa.org/
journalPortal.asp?categoryID=187&src=NFP

Bimonthly. Magazine concerning fire protection, prevention.

5032 ■ Turn Out
International Fire Buff Associates Inc.
PO Box 242
Indianapolis, IN 46206
E-mail: indyturnout@gmail.com
URL: http://www.ifba.org/

Description: Semiannual. Concerned with the firefighting activities of fire departments across the nation. Includes historical accounts and news of association and member activities.

5033 ■ Western City
League of California Cities
1400 K St., 4th Fl.
Sacramento, CA 95814
Ph: (916)658-8200
Fax: (916)658-8240
Fr: 800-262-1801
URL: http://www.westerncity.com

Monthly. $39.00/year for individuals; $63.00/year for two years; $52.00/year for other countries; $26.50/year for students. Municipal interest magazine.

EMPLOYER DIRECTORIES AND NETWORKING LISTS

5034 ■ Fellowship of Christian Firefighters International—Directory
Fellowship of Christian Firefighters International
6887 Red Mountain Rd.
PO Box 901
Livermore, CO 80536-8921
Ph: (970)416-9076
Fr: 800-322-9848
URL: http://www.fellowshipofchristianfirefighters.com

Biennial, Odd years. Covers: about 2,000 member Christian firefighters. Entries include: Name, address, phone. Arrangement: Alphabetical. Indexes: Local chapter.

5035 ■ National Directory of Fire Chiefs & EMS Administrators
National Public Safety Information Bureau
601 Main St.
PO Box 365
Stevens Point, WI 54481-2617
Ph: (715)345-2772
Fax: (715)345-7288
Fr: 800-647-7579
URL: http://www.safetysource.com

Annual, Latest edition 2012. $169.00 for individuals; $199.00. Covers: Over 37,000 fire and emergency departments in the U.S. Entries include: Department name, address, phone, fax, county, name of chief, type of department, financial structure. Arrangement: Geographical.

5036 ■ What Can I Do Now—Public Safety
Facts On File Inc.
132 W 31st St., 17th Fl.
New York, NY 10001
Ph: (212)967-8800
Fax: 800-678-3633
Fr: 800-322-8755
URL: http://factsonfile.infobasepublishing.com

$22.95 for individuals; $20.65 for libraries. Covers: Border patrol officers, corrections officers, crime analysts, emergency medical technicians, FBI agents, firefighters, and police officers.

HANDBOOKS AND MANUALS

5037 ■ FabJob Guide to Become a Firefighter
FabJob Inc.
4616 - 25th Ave. NE, No. 224
Seattle, WA 98105
Ph: (403)949-4980
Fr: 888-322-5621
URL: http://www.fabjob.com/Firefighter.asp

Mark Armstrong. $14.97(e-book). 99 pages. Contains career advice from firefighting professionals.

5038 ■ Master the Firefighter Exam
Peterson's
Princeton Pike Corporate Center
2000 Lenox Dr.
Lawrenceville, NJ 08648
Ph: (609)896-1800
Fax: (609)896-4531
Fr: 800-338-3282
E-mail: custsvc@petersons.com
URL: http://www.petersons.com

2009. 432 pages. Provides information to help the individual pass local, state, and national written exams, including test-taking strategies, information on the firefighter screening process, expert oral interview and job search advice, and a review of the Candidate Physical Ability Test.

5039 ■ *Real-Resumes for Firefighting Jobs*
PREP Publishing
1110 1/2 Hay St., PMB 66
Fayetteville, NC 28305
Ph: (910)483-6611
Fax: (910)483-2439
Fr: 800-533-2814
URL: http://www.prep-pub.com

Anne McKinney. 2004. $16.95. Illustrated. 192 pages. Firefighting careers.

EMPLOYMENT AGENCIES AND SEARCH FIRMS

5040 ■ Fire Hire
PO Box 1822
Elk Grove, CA 95759-1822
Ph: (916)714-8734
Fax: (866)685-7305
Fr: 800-755-5891
E-mail: firehire@firehire.com
URL: http://www.firehire.com

Description: Exists as a fire service recruitment registry. Provides quality candidates for participating agencies and services.

ONLINE JOB SOURCES AND SERVICES

5041 ■ Fire Career Assistance
URL: http://www.firecareerassist.com

Description: Provides a wide range of career services for fire fighters through features that include job openings, fire fighter qualifications, physical fitness test, firefighter oral board questions, written exams, firefighter interviews and others.

5042 ■ Fire Service Employment
URL: http://www.fireserviceemployment.com

Description: Gives special focus on EMTs and firefighters. Provides free recruitment information, links to fire service websites, firefighter and EMS job posting for employers, firefighter testing and interview tips and fire service career advice.

5043 ■ Firefighter-Jobs.com
URL: http://www.firefighter-jobs.com

Description: Exists as an online job site that lists various city, state or federal firefighting or EMT jobs. Includes other important employment information for aspiring firefighters such as a guide for professional resume writing and preparing for an interview.

5044 ■ Firehouse.com
URL: http://www.firehouse.com

Description: Provides fire rescue professionals with career services through features that include job openings, forums, products, news, members information, images, trainings, and events. Features a job board that covers company information, position type, position title, requirements, and salary.

5045 ■ FireJobs.com
URL: http://www.firejobs.com

Description: Seeks to find new firefighter employment for recruit firefighters just out of the academy and those who are already firefighters and want to move to a different department.

5046 ■ FiremenJobs.com
URL: http://www.firemenjobs.com

Description: Exists as an online firefighter job search site that provide its members with a database of updated jobs. Includes preparation tips, exam books, list of fire departments and schools and other career services.

5047 ■ FireRescue1.com
URL: http://www.firerescue1.com

Description: Serves as an online career portal that provides firefighters with the information and resources that make them better able to protect their communities and stay safer on the job. Serves as a growing network where firefighting personnel and aspiring professionals can find relevant news, watch online videos, locate important training information and product purchases, and interact with each other.

5048 ■ WildlandFire.com
E-mail: abercrombie@wildlandfire.com
URL: http://www.wildlandfire.com

Description: Provides career services for fire fighters through features that includes issues, news, forum, and a classifieds page.

TRADESHOWS

5049 ■ Fire - Rescue International
International Association of Fire Chiefs
4025 Fair Ridge Dr.
Fairfax, VA 22033-2868
Ph: (703)273-0911
Fax: (703)273-9363
E-mail: cafc@igs.net
URL: http://www.iafc.org

Annual. Primary Exhibits: Fire safety and emergency medical service equipment, supplies, and services; related training and support materials.

OTHER SOURCES

5050 ■ International Association of Fire Chiefs (IAFC)
4025 Fair Ridge Dr., Ste. 300
Fairfax, VA 22033-2868
Ph: (703)273-0911
Fax: (703)273-9363
E-mail: mlight@iafc.org
URL: http://www.iafc.org

Description: Fire Department chief officers, emergency services administrators and emergency medical services directors/managers and supervisors, career, volunteer, municipal and private, who are interested in improving fire, rescue, and EMS coverage to the general public. Provides leadership to career and volunteer chiefs, chief fire officers and managers of emergency service organizations throughout the international community through vision, information, education, services and representation to enhance their professionalism and capabilities.

5051 ■ International Association of Women in Fire and Emergency Services
4025 Fair Ridge Dr., Ste. 300
Fairfax, VA 22033
Ph: (703)896-4858
Fax: (703)273-9363
E-mail: staff@i-women.org
URL: http://www.i-women.org

Description: Provides a proactive network that supports, mentors, and educates women in fire and emergency services. Promotes professional development of members in an effort to make women more effective firefighters.

SOURCES OF HELP-WANTED ADS

5052 ■ *AAHPERD UpdatePLUS*
American Alliance for Health, Physical Education, Recreation & Dance
1900 Association Dr.
Reston, VA 20191
Ph: (703)476-3400
Fax: (703)476-9527
Fr: 800-213-7193
E-mail: info@aahperd.org
URL: http://www.aahperd.org

Description: Six issues/year. Provides news and information on the Alliance. Discusses current issues and research in the areas of health, physical education, recreation, dances, fitness, and adapted physical education. Recurring features include a calendar of events, reports of meetings, news of educational opportunities, job listings, notices of publications available, and columns titled President's Message, Membership Corner, and From the EVP's Desk.

5053 ■ *ACE FitnessMatters*
American Council on Exercise
4851 Paramont Dr.
San Diego, CA 92123
Ph: (858)279-8227
Fax: (858)279-8064
Fr: 800-825-3636
URL: http://www.acefitness.org/acestore/p-515-fitness-matters.asp

Bimonthly. $19.95/year for individuals; $35.00/year for two years; $33.00/year for Canada and Mexico; $60.00/year for Canada and Mexico, 2 years. Consumer magazine covering health and fitness news.

5054 ■ *Bountiful Health*
JNE Publishing, Inc.
PO Box 5647
Huntsville, AL 35814
Ph: (256)837-3035
Fr: 800-313-7751
URL: http://www.jnepublishing.com/bountifulhealth.php?page=public

Magazine focusing on complementary and alternative medicine, exercise, vitamins and supplements, healthy eating, and green living.

5055 ■ *The IHS Primary Care Provider*
Indian Health Service
The Reyes Bldg.
801 Thompson Ave., Ste. 400
Rockville, MD 20852-1627
Ph: (301)443-1011
URL: http://www.ihs.gov/provider

Monthly. Journal for health care professionals, physicians, nurses, pharmacists, dentists, and dietitians.

5056 ■ *NSCA Bulletin*
National Strength & Conditioning Association
1885 Bob Johnson Dr.
Colorado Springs, CO 80906
Ph: (719)632-6722
Fax: (719)632-6367
Fr: 800-815-6826
E-mail: nsca@nsca-lift.org
URL: http://www.nsca-lift.org/Publications/journals/nonmember.asp

Description: Bimonthly. Tracks Association activities. Recurring features include interviews, a calendar of events, reports of meetings, news of educational opportunities, job listings, book reviews, and notices of publications available.

5057 ■ *Nutritional Outlook*
Canon Communications L.L.C.
11444 W Olympic Blvd., Ste. 900
Los Angeles, CA 90064
Ph: (310)445-4200
Fax: (310)445-4299
E-mail: info@nutritionaloutlook.com
URL: http://www.nutritionaloutlook.com/

Magazine for manufacturer's resource for dietary supplements and healthy foods and beverages.

HANDBOOKS AND MANUALS

5058 ■ *Advances in Functional Training*
On Target Publications
PO Box 1335
Aptos, CA 95001
Ph: (831)466-9182
Fax: (831)466-9183
URL: http://ontargetpublications.net

Dave Draper. 2010. $34.95 (paper). 315 pages. Presents modern and effective training strategies for coaches, personal trainers, and athletes. Discusses injury prevention, treatment, rehabilitation and training after injury.

5059 ■ *Careers in Fitness and Personal Training*
Rosen Publishing
29 E 21st St.
New York, NY 10010
Fax: 888-436-4643
Fr: 800-237-9932
URL: http://www.rosenpublishing.com

Randy Littlejohn. 2005. $31.95. 144 pages. Provides resources for individuals interested in fitness training careers.

5060 ■ *Careers for Health Nuts and Others Who Like to Stay Fit*
The McGraw-Hill Companies
PO Box 182604
Columbus, OH 43272
Fax: (614)759-3749

Fr: 877-883-5524
E-mail: customer.service@mcgraw-hill.com
URL: http://www.mhprofessional.com

Blythe Camenson. Second edition. $13.95 (paper). 208 pages.

5061 ■ *Fitness Professional's Guide to Strength Training Older Adults*
Human Kinetics
PO Box 5076
Champaign, IL 61825-5076
Fax: (217)351-1549
Fr: 800-747-4457
E-mail: info@hkusa.com
URL: http://www.humankinetics.com

Thomas R. Baechle and Wayne Westcott. 2010. $34.00 (paper). 344 pages. 2nd edition. Contains information and tools to educate, motivate and assist older adults in committing to and benefiting from individualized strength training programs. Includes updated information on: sport conditioning programs; program design and performance for special populations; and specific nutrition guidelines.

5062 ■ *Functional Testing in Human Performance*
Human Kinetics
PO Box 5076
Champaign, IL 61825-5076
Fax: (217)351-1549
Fr: 800-747-4457
E-mail: info@hkusa.com
URL: http://www.humankinetics.com

Michael Reiman and Robert Manske. 2009. $79.00 (DVD and cloth). 328 pages. Serves as resource for the accurate assessment of an individual's functional abilities. Offers clinicians the compilation of information on clinical and data-based functional testing for sport, exercise and occupational settings. Accompanying DVD features live-action demonstrations of 40 of the most advanced tests.

5063 ■ *NSCA-CPT Practice Exam*
Human Kinetics
PO Box 5076
Champaign, IL 61825-5076
Fax: (217)351-1549
Fr: 800-747-4457
E-mail: info@hkusa.com
URL: http://www.humankinetics.com

National Strength and Conditioning Association. 2011. $40.00 (DVD and book). Helps applicants prepare for the NSCA-Certified Personal Trainer examination. Covers the nature and scope of the NSCA-CPT, plus the level of difficulty of typical exam questions. Includes exam booklet and DVD.

5064 ■ *NSCA's Essentials of Personal Training*
Human Kinetics
PO Box 5076
Champaign, IL 61825-5076

Fax: (217)351-1549
Fr: 800-747-4457
E-mail: info@hkusa.com
URL: http://www.humankinetics.com

National Strength and Conditioning Association. 2012. $295.00. Serves as a tool for personal trainers, health and fitness instructors, and other fitness professionals in taking the NSCA-CPT exam.

ONLINE JOB SOURCES AND SERVICES

5065 ■ Athletic Jobs
URL: http://www.athleticjobs.org
Description: Serves as niche job board that provides listings on athletic jobs.

5066 ■ ExerciseCareers.com
URL: http://www.exercisecareers.com
Description: Provides an avenue for professionals to search and recruit for jobs in the health and fitness industry.

5067 ■ ExerciseJobs.com
URL: http://www.exercisejobs.com
Description: Offers career resources for exercise, fitness, kinesiology, and health professionals.

5068 ■ FitnessJobs.com
URL: http://www.fitnessjobs.com
Description: Serves as a job board that specializes in the health, fitness, recreation, and leisure industries. Offers job listings and employment opportunities.

5069 ■ Online Sports Career Center
Fr: 800-856-2638
E-mail: comments@atsonlinesports.com
URL: http://www.onlinesports.com/pages/careercenter.html
Description: Resource for sports-related career opportunities, as well as a resume bank for the perusal of potential employers within the sports and recreation industries. Main files include: Job Bank, Resume Bank, Newsletter, Work With Online Sports, Other Internet Resources.

5070 ■ Premier Health and Fitness Resources
URL: http://phfr.com
Description: Health and fitness professionals. Offers a broad spectrum of health promotion services, networking opportunities, and resource sharing materials. Features resources for finding quality fitness jobs, health promotion job postings, corporate wellness employment opportunities, or other fitness staff positions.

OTHER SOURCES

5071 ■ Aerobics and Fitness Association of America
15250 Ventura Blvd., Ste. 200
Sherman Oaks, CA 91403
Fr: 877-968-7263
URL: http://www.afaa.com
Description: Provides cognitive and practical education for fitness professionals. Upholds safe and effective fitness practice. Offers courses and certifications beneficial to and of interest for the fitness industry.

5072 ■ American College of Sports Medicine (ACSM)
401 W Michigan St.
Indianapolis, IN 46202-3233
Ph: (317)637-9200
Fax: (317)634-7817
E-mail: publicinfo@acsm.org
URL: http://www.acsm.org
Description: Promotes and integrates scientific research, education, and practical applications of sports medicine and exercise science to maintain and enhance physical performance, fitness, health, and quality of life. Certifies fitness leaders, fitness instructors, exercise test technologists, exercise specialists, health/fitness program directors, and U.S. military fitness personnel. Grants Continuing Medical Education (CME) and Continuing Education Credits (CEC). Operates more than 50 committees.

5073 ■ American Council on Exercise (ACE)
4851 Paramount Dr.
San Diego, CA 92123
Ph: (858)576-6500
Fax: (858)576-6564
Fr: 888-825-3636
E-mail: support@acefitness.org
URL: http://www.acefitness.org
Description: Promotes the benefits of physical activity and protects consumers against unsafe and ineffective fitness products and instruction. Sponsors university-based exercise science research and testing that targets fitness products and trends. Sets standards for fitness professionals.

5074 ■ American Senior Fitness Association (SFA)
PO Box 2575
New Smyrna Beach, FL 32170
Ph: (386)423-6634
Fax: 877-365-3048
Fr: 888-689-6791
E-mail: asfa@seniorfitness.net
URL: http://www.seniorfitness.net
Description: Promotes excellence in older adult fitness. Provides comprehensive training, recognized certification, professional resources and member support for fitness professionals who serve older adults. Offers senior fitness specialist courses for colleges and universities.

5075 ■ Exercise Safety Association (ESA)
PO Box 547916
Orlando, FL 32854-7916
Ph: (407)246-5090
E-mail: askesa@aol.com
URL: http://www.exercisesafety.com
Description: Fitness instructors, personal trainers, health spas, YMCAs, community recreation departments, and hospital wellness programs. Purposes are: to improve the qualifications of exercise instructors; to train instructors to develop safe exercise programs that will help people avoid injury while exercising; to prepare instructors for national certification. Offers training in aerobics and exercise and on the physiological aspects of exercise. Conducts exercise safety and research programs. Sponsors charitable program; maintains speakers' bureau. Offers instructor placement services.

5076 ■ IDEA Health and Fitness Association
10455 Pacific Center Ct.
San Diego, CA 92121
Ph: (858)535-8979
Fax: (858)535-8234
Fr: 800-999-IDEA
E-mail: contact@ideafit.com
URL: http://www.ideafit.com
Description: Provides continuing education for fitness professionals including; fitness instructors, personal trainers, program directors, and club/studio owners. Offers workshops for continuing education credits.

5077 ■ International Fitness Professionals Association (IFPA)
14509 University Point Pl.
Tampa, FL 33613
Ph: (813)979-1925
Fax: (813)979-1978
Fr: 800-785-1924
E-mail: info@ifpa-fitness.com
URL: http://www.ifpa-fitness.com
Description: Promotes the interests of fitness professionals. Fosters the learning experience and professional recognition of fitness instructors. Provides practical and scientifically based health and fitness information to members.

5078 ■ National Athletic Trainers' Association (NATA)
2952 Stemmons Fwy., No. 200
Dallas, TX 75247-6196
Ph: (214)637-6282
Fax: (214)637-2206
Fr: 800-879-6282
E-mail: marjea@nata.org
URL: http://www.nata.org
Description: Athletic trainers from universities, colleges, and junior colleges; professional football, baseball, basketball, and ice hockey; high schools, preparatory schools, military establishments, sports medicine clinics, and business/industrial health programs. Maintains hall of fame and placement service. Conducts research programs; compiles statistics.

5079 ■ National Federation of Professional Trainers (NFPT)
PO Box 4579
Lafayette, IN 47903-4579
Ph: (765)471-4514
Fax: (765)471-7369
Fr: 800-729-6378
E-mail: info@nfpt.com
URL: http://www.nfpt.com
Description: Offers affordable, convenient, comprehensive, and applicable information to those seeking personal fitness trainer certification. Offers organizational certification credentials for consumer recognition of competence; provides certified affiliates with ongoing education; establishes a network of support, and provides professional products and services to trainers and consumers; and facilitates and encourages the exchange of ideas, knowledge, business experiences, and financial opportunities between all fitness administrators internationally. Offers educational programs.

5080 ■ Natural Fitness Trainers Association (NFTA)
PO Box 49874
Athens, GA 30606-9998
Ph: (706)254-2798
URL: http://www.naturalfitnesstrainers.com
Description: Represents the interests of professional fitness trainers. Promotes the sports of natural bodybuilding and fitness. Provides ethical, legitimate, and fair certification standards. Advances the professional recognition of natural bodybuilding and fitness trainers.

SOURCES OF HELP-WANTED ADS

5081 ■ *Aviation Today*
Access Intelligence L.L.C.
4 Choke Cherry Rd., 2nd Fl.
Rockville, MD 20850
Ph: (301)354-2000
Fax: (301)309-3847
Fr: 800-777-5006
E-mail: info@accessintel.com
URL: http://www.accessintel.com

Description: Covers the commuter/regional airline industry, including airline management, marketing, labor, personnel changes, aircraft acquisitions, new products, and the financial and operational environment. Recurring features include interviews, news of research, a calendar of events, reports of meetings, job listings, and notices of publications available.

5082 ■ *Flying*
Hachette Filipacchi Media U.S. Inc.
1633 Broadway
New York, NY 10019-6708
Ph: (212)767-6000
URL: http://www.flyingmag.com

Monthly. $14.00/year for individuals, print; $22.00/ year for two years, print; $33.00/year for Canada, print; $33.00/year for other countries, print. General aviation magazine.

EMPLOYER DIRECTORIES AND NETWORKING LISTS

5083 ■ *National Air Transportation Association—Aviation Resource and Membership Directory*
National Air Transportation Association
4226 King St.
Alexandria, VA 22302
Ph: (703)845-9000
Fax: (703)845-8176
Fr: 800-808-6282
URL: http://www.nata.aero

Annual, Latest edition 2008. $50.00 for nonmembers; $25.00 for members. Covers: More than 1,000 regular, associate, and affiliate members; regular members include airport service organizations, air taxi operators, and commuter airlines. Entries include: Company name, address, phone, fax number, name and title of contact. Arrangement: Regular members are classified by service; associate and affiliate members are alphabetical in separate sections. Indexes: Geographical.

5084 ■ *World Aviation Directory & Aerospace Database (WAD&AD)*
McGraw-Hill, Inc.
1200 G St. NW, Ste. 200
Washington, DC 20005

Ph: (515)237-3682
Fax: 888-385-1428
Fr: 800-525-5003
E-mail: wad@mcgraw-hill.com
URL: http://a1.ecom01.com/aw_marketdatacenter?s_
id=7

Semiannual, Latest edition 2010. $269.00 for U.S.; $1,295.00 for U.S.; $595.00 for U.S.; $495.00 for U.S.; $149.00 for U.S. Database covers: 22,000 airlines, manufacturers, MRO stations, airports military/government and distributors/suppliers; 6,000 product/service categories and 166,000 listings; 69,000 aviation/aerospace professionals; 500,000 users across all 3 platforms/formats and, Commercial, Military & Business Aviation Fleet Data. Arrangement: Classified by major activity (manufacturers, airlines, etc.). Indexes: Company and organization, personnel, product, trade name.

HANDBOOKS AND MANUALS

5085 ■ *Careers in Travel, Tourism, and Hospitality*
The McGraw-Hill Companies
PO Box 182604
Columbus, OH 43272
Fax: (614)759-3749
Fr: 877-883-5524
E-mail: customer.service@mcgraw-hill.com
URL: http://www.mhprofessional.com

Marjorie Eberts, Linda Brothers, and Ann Gisler. Second edition, 2005. $15.95 (paper). 224 pages.

5086 ■ *FabJob Guide to Become a Flight Attendant*
FabJob Inc.
4616 - 25th Ave. NE, No. 224
Seattle, WA 98105
Ph: (403)949-4980
Fr: 888-322-5621
URL: http://www.fabjob.com

Julia Dean. $19.97(e-book). 270 pages. Provides information about careers in the airline industry, how to become a flight attendant and job opportunities with more than 70 airlines.

5087 ■ *Jobs for Travel Lovers: Opportunities at Home and Abroad*
Impact Publications
9104 Manassas Dr., Ste. N
Manassas Park, VA 20111-5211
Ph: (703)361-7300
Fax: (703)335-9486
URL: http://www.impactpublications.com

2006. $19.95. 320 pages. Covers job search strategies, with hundreds of jobs in business, government, and education, including the travel and hospital industry, non-profit organizations, international organizations, education institutions, and consulting. Includes opportunities involving airlines and cruise lines, international jobs, travel agencies and tour

operators, internships and volunteering, hotels and resorts, military and merchant marine, teaching abroad, travel writing, and short-term work experiences. Provides names, addresses, telephone/ fax numbers, e-mails, and websites for contacting potential employers.

5088 ■ *Welcome Aboard!: Your Career As a Flight Attendant*
Aviation Supplies & Academics, Inc.
7005 132nd Pl. SE
Newcastle, WA 98059
Ph: (425)235-1500
Fr: 800-272-2359
URL: http://www.asa2fly.com/index.aspx

Becky S. Bock. Third edition. $19.95 (paper). 136 pages.

EMPLOYMENT AGENCIES AND SEARCH FIRMS

5089 ■ *Jet Professionals*
114 Charles A. Lindbergh Dr.
Teterboro, NJ 07608
Ph: (201)393-6900
Fax: (201)462-4081
Fr: 800-441-6016
E-mail: jobs@jet-professionals.com
URL: http://www.jet-professionals.com

Provides staffing services to the aviation industry. Offers jobs for corporate aviation executives, chief pilots, flight attendants, maintenance professionals, dispatchers, schedulers and more.

ONLINE JOB SOURCES AND SERVICES

5090 ■ *AirJobsDaily.com*
E-mail: staff@airjobsdaily.com
URL: http://www.airjobsdaily.com

Description: Serves as a source of current aviation and aerospace job openings.

5091 ■ *AirlineCareer.com*
Ph: (978)615-3190
E-mail: jbelotti@airlinecareer.com
URL: http://www.airlinecareer.com

Web-based training center. Provides flight attendant job placement services.

5092 ■ *AirlineCareer.info*
URL: http://www.airlinecareer.info

Description: Provides jobs in the airline community covering airport careers, aircraft manufacturing, aerospace careers, and cabin crew careers.

5093 ■ AvCrew.com
URL: http://www.avcrew.com

Description: Provides service designed exclusively for career employment in the business aviation sector. Features flight crew jobs, conducts applicant screening, and assists selected flight departments with candidate searches.

5094 ■ AviaNation
URL: http://www.avianation.com

Description: Features aviation jobs, pilot jobs, flight attendant jobs, jobs for A&P mechanics, and other aviation job openings around the world.

5095 ■ The Aviation MD
E-mail: adrian@theaviationmd.com
URL: http://www.theaviationmd.com

Description: Serves as international aviation database for employers and jobseekers in the aviation industry.

5096 ■ AviationCrossing.com
URL: http://www.aviationcrossing.com

Provides aviation jobs for agents, managers, mechanics, operators, specialists, supervisors, technicians, engineers, maintenance, pilots and other related aviation professionals.

5097 ■ AvJobs.com
URL: http://www.avjobs.com

Description: Provides information on a number of different careers in the aviation and aerospace industry. Features aviation schools directory, affiliate programs, research and networking, employment resources, salaries and wages, aviation careers descriptions, aviation guide and other resources.

5098 ■ BestAviation.net
URL: http://www.bestaviation.net

Description: Provides source for information on flight school training, helicopter schools, aviation college programs, flight attendant careers, aircraft maintenance and pilot jobs.

5099 ■ CabinCrewJobs.com
URL: http://www.cabincrewjobs.com

Description: Offers detailed information about how to successfully launch a career in the airline industry. Includes career resources such as tips on resume writing, interviews, training, salaries, job benefits and more.

5100 ■ FlightAttendantFacts.com
URL: http://www.flightattendantfacts.com

Description: Serves as an online networking site for flight attendants. Features flight attendant job openings, salary information, and interview tips.

5101 ■ FlightAttendantJobsite.com
URL: http://www.flightattendantjobsite.com

Description: Serves as an online career resource for flight attendants. Allows job seekers to post their resumes and features other career resources such as job search and interviewing, self-assessment tools and more.

5102 ■ FlightLevelJobs.com
URL: http://www.flightleveljobs.com

Description: Serves as a source of aviation employment information. Features aviation and aerospace jobs and employment opportunities.

5103 ■ FlyContract.com
URL: http://www.flycontract.com

Description: Provides a directory to help corporate pilots and corporate flight attendants obtain jobs.

5104 ■ JetEmployment.com
URL: http://jetemployment.com

Description: Features employment opportunities for pilots and other workers in the airline, airport, and business aviation industry.

5105 ■ Locate Flight Attendant Jobs
URL: http://www.locateflightattendantjobs.com

Description: Provides a searchable database of employment opportunities for flight attendants.

5106 ■ PlaneJobs.com
E-mail: jobmaster@planejobs.com
URL: http://planejobs.com

Description: Serves as an employment, resume, career, and job search database for the aviation industry.

OTHER SOURCES

5107 ■ Association of Flight Attendants - CWA (AFA)
501 3rd St., NW
Washington, DC 20001
Ph: (202)434-1300
E-mail: info@afacwa.org
URL: http://www.afanet.org

Description: Labor union organized by flight attendants. AFA represents over 50,000 flight attendants at 22 airlines, serving as a voice for flight attendants at their workplace, in the industry, and in the media.

Sources of Help-Wanted Ads

5108 ■ Florists' Review
PO Box 4368
Topeka, KS 66604
Ph: (785)266-0888
Fax: (785)266-0333
Fr: 800-367-4708
E-mail: mail@floristsreview.com
URL: http://www.floristsreview.com

Monthly guidebook for operating a successful floral business.

5109 ■ Grower Talks
Ball Publishing
622 Town Rd.
PO Box 1660
West Chicago, IL 60186
Ph: (630)231-3675
Fax: (630)231-5254
Fr: 888-888-0013
URL: http://www.ballpublishing.com/GrowerTalks/
   default.aspx

Monthly. $35.00/year for U.S. and Canada; $99.00/year for other countries; free to qualified subscribers. Trade magazine covering issues for commercial greenhouse growers with a focus on North American production.

Employer Directories and Networking Lists

5110 ■ Michigan Florist—Membership Directory
Michigan Floral Association
1152 Haslett Rd.
Haslett, MI 48840
Ph: (517)575-0110
Fax: (517)575-0115
URL: http://www.michiganfloral.org

Annual, fall. Publication includes: List of about 1,100 member floral retailers and wholesalers, nurseries and garden centers, and individual members. Entries include: Company name, owner's name, address, phone, type of business. Arrangement: Separate geographical and alphabetical lists.

5111 ■ Professional Floral Communicators-International—Directory
Society of American Florists
1601 Duke St.
Alexandria, VA 22314
Ph: (703)836-8700
Fax: (703)836-8705
Fr: 800-336-4743
E-mail: keidam@safnow.org
URL: http://alliedfloristsofhouston.org/z-old/
   memberdirectory.htm

Covers: about 80 member floral presenters and educators. Entries include: Name, address, phone, professional affiliation, education, career data, interests, design and presentation techniques. Arrangement: Alphabetical/geographic/area of expertise.

5112 ■ Wholesale Florist & Florist Supplier Association—Membership Directory
Wholesale Florists & Florist Supplier Association
105 Eastern Ave., Ste. 104
Annapolis, MD 21403
Ph: (410)940-6580
Fax: (410)263-1659
Fr: 888-289-3372
URL: http://www.wffsa.org

Biennial, summer/winter. Number of listings: 1,275. Entries include: Company name, address, phone, names of executives, list of products or services. Arrangement: Geographical. Indexes: Alphabetical.

Handbooks and Manuals

5113 ■ Careers in Horticulture and Botany
The McGraw-Hill Companies
PO Box 182604
Columbus, OH 43272
Fax: (614)759-3749
Fr: 877-883-5524
E-mail: customer.service@mcgraw-hill.com
URL: http://www.mhprofessional.com/
   product.php?isbn=0071467734

Jerry Garner. 2006. 16.95 (paper). 192 pages. Includes bibliographical references.

5114 ■ Careers for Plant Lovers and Other Green Thumb Types
The McGraw-Hill Companies
PO Box 182604
Columbus, OH 43272
Fax: (614)759-3749
Fr: 877-883-5524
E-mail: customer.service@mcgraw-hill.com
URL: http://www.mhprofessional.com/
   product.php?isbn=0071442413

Blythe Camenson. Second edition, 2004. $13.95. 160 pages. Describes careers for people who love working with plants and flowers.

5115 ■ FabJob Guide to Become a Florist
FabJob.com
4616 25 Ave. NE, No. 224
Seattle, WA 98105
Ph: (403)873-1018
URL: http://www.fabjob.com

2004. $29.97. 267 pages. Offers a step-by-step guide to becoming a florist.

5116 ■ Florist
National Learning Corporation
212 Michael Dr.
Syosset, NY 11791
Fr: 800-632-8888
URL: http://www.passbooks.com

2009. $29.95 (paper). Serves as an exam preparation guide for florists.

Online Job Sources and Services

5117 ■ AllFloristJobs.com
URL: http://allfloristjobs.com

Description: Features job sites, company career pages and associations for florist jobs.

5118 ■ FloralJobs.org
URL: http://floraljobs.org

Description: Features job sites, company career pages and associations for floral jobs.

Tradeshows

5119 ■ American Institute of Floral Designers National Symposium
American Institute of Floral Designers
720 Light St.
Baltimore, MD 21230
Ph: (410)752-3318
E-mail: aifd@assnhqtrs.com
URL: http://www.aifd.org

Annual. Features programs and the latest trends in the floral design industry. Provides opportunities for attendees to meet colleagues and acquire new skills, ideas, and innovations.

Other Sources

5120 ■ American Institute of Floral Designers (AIFD)
720 Light St.
Baltimore, MD 21230
Ph: (410)752-3318
Fax: (410)752-8295
E-mail: aifd@assnhqtrs.com
URL: http://www.aifd.org

Description: Active floral designers, associates, retired floral designers and other individuals. Works to promote the profession and art of floral design. Maintains student chapter.

5121 ■ Holiday and Decorative Association (HDA)
PO Box 420244
Dallas, TX 75342-0244
Ph: (214)742-2747

Fax: (214)742-2648
E-mail: hda@hdanow.org
URL: http://www.hdanow.org
Description: Purpose: Strives to act as the national organization for importers, domestic manufacturers, wholesalers, retailers, overseas suppliers, manufacturers sales representatives, etc., of artificial, botanical, Christmas and floral products and accessories.

5122 ■ Society of American Florists (SAF)
1601 Duke St.
Alexandria, VA 22314-3406
Ph: (703)836-8700
Fax: (703)836-8705
Fr: 800-336-4743
E-mail: info@safnow.org
URL: http://www.safnow.org

Description: Growers, wholesalers, retailers, and allied tradesmen in the floral industry. Lobbies Congress on behalf of the industry; sponsors educational programs; promotes the floral industry; prepares materials for consumers and for high school and college students; provides business resources. Sponsors Floricultural Hall of Fame, American Academy of Floriculture, and Professional Floral Commentators International. Compiles statistics; sponsors competitions.

5123 ■ Wholesale Florist and Florist Supplier Association (WF&FSA)
147 Old Solomons Island Rd., Ste. 302
Annapolis, MD 21401
Ph: (410)573-0400

Fax: (410)573-5001
Fr: 888-289-3372
E-mail: info@wffsa.org
URL: http://www.wffsa.org

Description: Proprietorships, partnerships or corporations conducting wholesale businesses in fresh flowers, greens, or plants, or engaged in the manufacture and/or wholesaling of florist supplies; others actively engaged in the floral industry are associate members. Preserves and strengthens the wholesale florists' position in the floral industry. Provides a unified voice to promote the wholesalers' contributions to the industry.

Sources of Help-Wanted Ads

5124 ■ *AWIS Magazine*
Association for Women in Science
1321 Duke St., Ste. 210
Alexandria, VA 22314
Ph: (703)894-4490
Fax: (703)894-4489
Fr: (866)657-2947
URL: http://www.awis.org/
displaycommon.cfm?an=1&subarticlenbr=2

Quarterly. Included in membership. Professional magazine covering the status of women in science.

5125 ■ *Current Opinion in Pharmacology*
Elsevier Science Inc.
360 Park Ave. S
New York, NY 10010-1710
Ph: (212)989-5800
Fax: (212)633-3990
Fr: 888-437-4636
URL: http://www.elsevier.com/wps/find/
journaldescription.cws_home

$2,102.00/year for institutions, all countries except Europe, Japan and Iran; $260,800.00/year for institutions, Japan; $1,881.00/year for institutions, European countries and Iran; $386.00/year for individuals, all countries except Europe, Japan and Iran; $43,200.00/year for individuals, Japan; $355.00/year for individuals, European countries and Iran. Journal covering current advances in pharmacology.

5126 ■ *Forensic Science, Medicine and Pathology*
Humana Press Inc.
233 Spring St.
New York, NY 10013-1578
Ph: (973)256-1699
Fax: (973)256-8341
Fr: 800-777-4643
URL: http://www.springer.com/humana+press/
pathology+%26+laborator

$541.00/year for institutions, print and electronic; $649.00/year for institutions, print and enchanced access. Journal focusing on forensic science, medicine, and pathology.

5127 ■ *Harvard Science Review*
Harvard University Press
79 Garden St.
Cambridge, MA 02138
Ph: (401)531-2800
Fax: (401)531-2801
Fr: 800-405-1619
E-mail: hsr@hcs.harvard.edu
URL: http://www.hcs.harvard.edu/~hsr/

Semiannual. A science journal.

5128 ■ *InterJournal*
New England Complex Systems Institute
283 Main St., Ste. 319
Cambridge, MA 02142
Ph: (617)547-4100
Fax: (617)661-7711
URL: http://www.interjournal.org/

Journal covering the fields of science and engineering.

5129 ■ *The Internet Journal of Forensic Science*
Internet Scientific Publications L.L.C.
23 Rippling Creek Dr.
Sugar Land, TX 77479
Ph: (832)443-1193
URL: http://www.ispub.com/ostia/
index.php?xmlFilePath=journals/ij

Free, online. Electronic journal for medical professionals focusing on the field of forensic science.

5130 ■ *Journal of the American Society of Questioned Document Examiners*
American Society of Questioned Document Examiners
PO Box 18298
Long Beach, CA 90807
Ph: (562)901-3376
Fax: (562)901-3378
URL: http://www.asqde.org

Semiannual. $70.00/year for U.S. and Canada; $110.00/year for U.S. and Canada, agency; $85.00/year for other countries; $125.00/year for institutions, other countries, agency. Professional journal covering forensic sciences.

5131 ■ *Journal of Forensic Identification*
International Association for Identification
2131 Hollywood Blvd., Ste. 403
Hollywood, FL 33020
Ph: (954)589-0628
Fax: (954)589-0657
E-mail: iaisecty@theiai.org
URL: http://www.theiai.org

A scientific journal that provides over 115 pages of articles related to forensics. Also offers information regarding training and educational events, job postings and announcements. Yearly subscriptions: $175.00 for individuals, $205.00 for institutions and libraries.

5132 ■ *Journal of Women and Minorities in Science and Engineering*
Begell House Inc.
50 Cross Hwy.
Redding, CT 06896
Ph: (203)938-1300
Fax: (203)938-1304
URL: http://www.begellhouse.com/journals/
00551c876cc2f027

$248.00/year for institutions. Peer-reviewed journal featuring innovative ideas and programs for classroom teachers, scientific studies, and formulation of concepts related to the education, recruitment, and retention of under-represented groups in science and engineering.

5133 ■ *Oxymag*
Elsevier Science Inc.
360 Park Ave. S
New York, NY 10010-1710
Ph: (212)989-5800
Fax: (212)633-3990
Fr: 888-437-4636
URL: http://www.elsevier.com/wps/find/
journaldescription.cws_home

$124.39/year for institutions, for France; $23,700.00/year for individuals; $190.00/year for institutions, other countries; $155.00/year for institutions, European countries and Iran; $73.46/year for individuals, for France; $89.00/year for U.S. and other countries; $11,100.00/year for individuals; $75.00/year for individuals, European countries and Iran; $51.91/year for students, for France; $63.00/year for students, other countries. Journal related to the construction field covering information in the manufacture of commercial, industrial, spark proof and decorative terrazzo floors, flooring for railroad boxcars, industrial fireproof coatings, fire-resistant marine interior deckings and a variety of building units.

5134 ■ *Psychology Journal*
Psychological Publishing
PO Box 176
Natchitoches, LA 71458
E-mail: psychjournal@aol.com
URL: http://www.psychologicalpublishing.com/

Quarterly. $90.00/year for individuals; $175.00/year for institutions. Journal dedicated to all areas of the science and practice of counseling and clinical psychology.

5135 ■ *Science*
American Association for the Advancement of Science
1200 New York Ave., NW
Washington, DC 20005
Ph: (202)326-6550
URL: http://www.scienceonline.org

Weekly (Fri.). $146.00/year for members, professional, print & online; $119.00/year for individuals, NPA postdoctoral, print & online; $99.00/year for individuals, postdoctoral/resident, print & online; $75.00/year for students, print & online; $146.00/year for individuals, k-12 teacher, print & online; $310.00/year for individuals, patron, print & online; $115.00/year for individuals, emeritus, print & online; $211.05/year for Canada, professional members, print & online; $161.00/year for Canada, postdoctoral/resident, print & online; $136.50/year for students, Canada, print & online. Magazine devoted to science, scientific research, and public policy.

EMPLOYER DIRECTORIES AND NETWORKING LISTS

5136 ■ American Academy of Forensic Sciences—Membership Directory
American Academy of Forensic Sciences
410 N 21st St.
Colorado Springs, CO 80904
Ph: (719)636-1100
Fax: (719)636-1993
URL: http://www.aafs.org

Annual, May. Covers: 3,800 persons qualified in forensic sciences, including law, pathology, biology, odontology, physical anthropology, psychiatry, questioned documents, criminalistics, engineering, and toxicology. Entries include: Name, office address and phone, highest degree held, professional title, type of certification. Arrangement: Alphabetical. Indexes: Geographical, subject.

5137 ■ Career Opportunities in Science
Facts On File Inc.
132 W 31st St., 17th Fl.
New York, NY 10001
Ph: (212)967-8800
Fax: 800-678-3633
Fr: 800-322-8755
URL: http://factsonfile.infobasepublishing.com

Latest edition 2008. $49.50 for individuals. Covers: More than 80 jobs, such as biochemist, molecular biologist, bioinformatic specialist, pharmacologist, computer engineer, geographic information systems specialist, science teacher, forensic scientist, patent agent, as well as physicist, astronomer, chemist, zoologist, oceanographer, and geologist.

5138 ■ International Association for Identification—Membership Directory
International Association for Identification
2535 Pilot Knob Rd., Ste. 117
Mendota Heights, MN 55120-1120
Ph: (651)681-8566
Fax: (651)681-8443
URL: http://www.theiai.org

Annual, December. Covers: About 4,600 police officials, identification personnel, and others engaged in forensic identification, investigation, and scientific crime detection. Entries include: Name, preferred mailing address. Arrangement: Geographical. Indexes: Alphabetical.

5139 ■ Opportunities in Forensic Science
The McGraw-Hill Cos.
PO Box 182604
Columbus, OH 43272
Ph: (609)426-5793
Fax: (614)759-3749
Fr: 877-833-5524
URL: http://www.mcgraw-hill.com/

Latest edition 2008. $14.95 for individuals. Publication includes: a list of colleges and universities offering graduate programs and internships in the field of forensic science. Principal content of publication is is information on career opportunities in the forensic sciences, including educational requirements, qualifications needed, and salary. Publisher also offers a catalog card kit for this title.

HANDBOOKS AND MANUALS

5140 ■ Career Opportunities in Forensic Science
Facts On File Inc.
132 W 31st St., 17th Fl.
New York, NY 10001
Fr: 800-322-8755
E-mail: custserv@factsonfile.com
URL: http://factsonfile.infobasepublishing.com

2008. $49.50. 336 pages. Includes a total of 82 job profiles in the field of forensic science. Contains ap-

pendixes that include education and training resources, certification program listings and professional associations.

5141 ■ Careers in Focus: Forensics
Ferguson Publishing
132 W 31st St., 17th Fl.
New York, NY 10001
Fax: 800-678-3633
Fr: 800-322-8755
E-mail: custserv@factsonfile.com
URL: http://ferguson.infobasepublishing.com

2010. $32.95 (hardcover). 208 pages. Discusses the career opportunities for individuals who are interested in crime solving.

5142 ■ Forensic Science Handbook
Prentice Hall PTR
1 Lake St.
Upper Saddle River, NJ 07458
Ph: (201)236-7000
Fr: 800-922-0579
URL: http://www.pearsonhighered.com

Second edition, 2009. $177. 552 pages. Reference source for the field of criminalistics. Each chapter offers a review of a particular aspect of the field written by noted experts.

ONLINE JOB SOURCES AND SERVICES

5143 ■ ForensicScienceJobs.org
URL: http://forensicsciencejobs.org

Description: Serves as an online employment site for professionals in the forensic science industry.

5144 ■ ScientistCrossing.com
URL: http://www.scientistcrossing.com

Description: Provides job listings and other resources related to scientist employment opportunities.

TRADESHOWS

5145 ■ American Academy of Forensic Sciences Annual Scientific Meeting
American Academy of Forensic Sciences
410 N. 21st St.
Colorado Springs, CO 80904
Ph: (719)636-1100
Fax: (719)636-1993
URL: http://www.aafs.org

Annual. Primary Exhibits: Scientific instruments. Dates and Locations: 2012 Feb 20-25; Atlanta, GA; Marriott Marquis; 2013 Feb 18-23; Washington, DC; Marriott Wardman Park Hotel; 2014 Feb 17-22; Seattle, WA; Washington State Convention and Trade Center.

OTHER SOURCES

5146 ■ American Academy of Forensic Sciences (AAFS)
410 N 21st St.
Colorado Springs, CO 80904
Ph: (719)636-1100
Fax: (719)636-1993
E-mail: awarren@aafs.org
URL: http://www.aafs.org

Description: Represents criminalists, scientists, members of the bench and bar, pathologists, biologists, psychiatrists, examiners of questioned documents, toxicologists, odontologists, anthropologists, and engineers. Works to: encourage the study, improve the practice, elevate the standards, and advance the cause of the forensic sciences; improve the quality of scientific techniques, tests, and criteria; plan, organize, and administer meetings, reports, and other projects for the stimulation and advancement of these and related purposes. Maintains Forensic Sci-

ences Job Listing; conducts selected research for the government; offers forensic expert referral service.

5147 ■ American Board of Criminalistics (ABC)
PO Box 1358
Palmetto, FL 34220
E-mail: abcregistrar@verizon.net
URL: http://www.criminalistics.com

Description: Regional and national organizations of forensic scientists and criminalists. Offers certificates of Professional Competency in Criminalistics as well as in specialty disciplines of forensic biology, drug chemistry, fire debris analysis, and various areas of trace evidence examination. Works to establish professional standards and promote growth within the industry. Answers questions regarding the certification process.

5148 ■ American Board of Forensic Toxicology (ABFT)
410 N 21st St.
Colorado Springs, CO 80904
Ph: (719)636-1100
Fax: (719)636-1993
E-mail: mstajic@aol.com
URL: http://www.abft.org

Description: Works to establish, enhance, and revise as necessary, standards of qualification for those who practice forensic toxicology, and to certify as qualified specialists those applicants who comply with the requirements of the Board.

5149 ■ American College of Forensic Examiners International (ACFEI)
2750 E Sunshine St.
Springfield, MO 65804
Ph: (417)881-3818
Fax: (417)881-4702
Fr: 800-423-9737
E-mail: cao@acfei.com
URL: http://www.acfei.com

Description: Professionals in the field of forensic examination, including the following disciplines: accounting, accident reconstruction, criminology, crisis intervention, counselors, social work, nursing and law enforcement hypnosis, all medical fields, physics, psychiatry, psychology, and toxicology. Works to advance the profession of forensic examination through education, training, and certification.

5150 ■ American Society of Crime Laboratory Directors
139A Technology Dr.
Garner, NC 27529
Ph: (919)773-2044
Fax: (919)861-9930
URL: http://www.ascld.org

Description: Nonprofit professional society dedicated to providing excellence in forensic science analysis through leadership in the management of forensic science. The purpose of the organization is to foster professional interests; assist the development of laboratory management principles and techniques; acquire, preserve and disseminate forensic based information; maintain and improve communications among crime laboratory directors; and to promote, encourage and maintain the highest standards of practice in the field.

5151 ■ American Society of Criminology (ASC)
1314 Kinnear Rd., Ste. 212
Columbus, OH 43212-1156
Ph: (614)292-9207
Fax: (614)292-6767
E-mail: asc@asc41.com
URL: http://www.asc41.com

Description: Represents professional and academic criminologists, students of criminology in accredited universities, psychiatrists, psychologists, and sociologists. Develops criminology as a science and academic discipline. Aids in the construction of criminological curricula in accredited universities. Upgrades the practitioner in criminological fields (police, prisons, probation, parole, delinquency workers). Conducts research programs and sponsors three student paper competitions. Provides placement service at annual convention.

5152 ■ American Society of Digital Forensics and eDiscovery (ASDFED)
2451 Cumberland Pkwy., Ste. 3382
Atlanta, GA 30339-6157
Fr: (866)534-9734
E-mail: member_services@asdfed.org
URL: http://www.asdfed.com

Description: Represents digital forensic examiners, legal professionals, litigation support analysts and managers, law enforcement, and government investigators. Promotes digital forensics and electronic discovery through advocacy, education, research and information. Conducts conferences, training programs and workshops.

5153 ■ American Society of Forensic Podiatry (ASFP)
PO Box 549
Bandon, OR 97411
E-mail: asfpdpm@aol.com
URL: http://theasfp.org

Description: Aims to advance the cause of forensic podiatry. Promotes the use of podiatry in forensics cases. Develops and maintains the highest standards of practice through research, discussion, education, publications, and liaison with other organized agencies.

5154 ■ Association of Forensic Document Examiners (AFDE)
5432 E Karen Dr.
Scottsdale, AZ 85254-8205
E-mail: journal.jfde@gmail.com
URL: http://www.afde.org

Description: Represents forensic document examiners and students of document examination. Sponsors annual continuing education conferences and offers a certification program.

5155 ■ Evidence Photographers International Council (EPIC)
229 Peachtree St. NE, No. 2200
Atlanta, GA 30303
Fax: (404)614-6406
Fr: (866)868-3742
E-mail: cwerner@evidencephotographers.com
URL: http://www.epic-photo.org

Description: Law enforcement and civil evidence photographers; others in related fields. Objectives are to: aid in the worldwide advancement of forensic photography; assist in research and development of new techniques; enhance professional education; inform members of new procedures. Maintains speakers' bureau. Offers certification upon satisfactory completion of an oral or written examination by a three-member panel, receipt of a minimum of 30 prints for review, and a $150 application fee. Provides an honors program to recognize those who have shown expertise in the field of forensic photography,

and service to the Council. Sponsors the EPIC Witness Referral Service.

5156 ■ Forensic Sciences Foundation (FSF)
410 N 21st St.
Colorado Springs, CO 80904
Ph: (719)636-1100
Fax: (719)636-1993
E-mail: awarren@aafs.org
URL: http://www.forensicsciencesfoundation.org

Description: Purposes are to: conduct research in the procedures and standards utilized in the practice of forensic sciences; develop and implement useful educational and training programs and methods of benefit to forensic sciences; conduct programs of public education concerning issues of importance to the forensic sciences; engage in activities which will promote, encourage, and assist the development of the forensic sciences. Provides referral service for forensic scientists. Compiles statistics. Operates the Forensic Sciences Foundation Press.

5157 ■ International Association of Computer Investigative Specialists (IACIS)
PO Box 2411
Leesburg, VA 20177
Ph: (304)915-0555
Fr: 888-884-2247
E-mail: secretary@cops.org
URL: http://www.iacis.com

Description: Provides education and certification of law enforcement professionals in the field of computer forensic science. Creates and establishes procedures, trains personnel, and certifies forensic examiners in the recovery of evidence from computer systems. Offers professional training in the seizure and processing computer systems. Provides an opportunity to network with other law enforcement officers trained in computer forensics, and to share and learn from others.

5158 ■ International Association for Identification (IAI)
2131 Hollywood Blvd., Ste. 403
Hollywood, FL 33020
Ph: (954)589-0628
Fax: (954)589-0657
E-mail: iaisecty@theiai.org
URL: http://www.theiai.org

Description: Individuals engaged in forensic identification, investigation, and scientific crime detection. Strives to improve methods of scientific identification techniques used in criminal investigations.

5159 ■ Law Enforcement and Emergency Services Video Association (LEVA)
PO Box 547
Midlothian, TX 76065
Ph: (469)285-9435
Fax: (469)533-3659
E-mail: president@leva.org
URL: http://www.leva.org

Description: Serves as a key resource to the global public safety community by focusing on the needs of video production and forensic imaging disciplines. Provides opportunities for professional development through quality training and informational exchange.

Offers forensic video analysis training to law enforcement professionals.

5160 ■ National Forensic Center (NFC)
PO Box 270529
San Diego, CA 92198-2529
Fax: (858)487-7747
Fr: 800-735-6660
E-mail: info@national-experts.com
URL: http://www.national-experts.com

Description: Expert witnesses and litigation consultants who serve attorneys, insurance companies, and government agencies. Trains consultants to work with attorneys and to testify in court; trains individuals to serve as expert witnesses and litigation consultants. Makes speakers available upon request. Compiles statistics on experts' fees.

5161 ■ National Forensic Science Technology Center
7881 114th Ave., N
Largo, FL 33773
Ph: (727)549-6067
Fax: (727)549-6070
E-mail: info@nfstc.org
URL: http://www.nfstc.org

Description: Provides systems support, training and education to the forensic science community in the United States.

5162 ■ Professional Society of Forensic Mapping (PSFM)
4891 Independence St., Ste. 140
Wheat Ridge, CO 80033
E-mail: axidentrecon@aol.com
URL: http://www.psfm.org

Description: Promotes the field of forensic mapping through high professional and personal conduct of its members. Provides members with a forum for the exchange of information pertaining to skills and techniques for the electronic documentation of crash or crime scenes. Offers training to members of law enforcement, governmental, and quasi-governmental agencies, private consultants and other persons in the field of forensic mapping.

5163 ■ Society of Forensic Toxicologists (SOFT)
One MacDonald Center
1 N MacDonald St., Ste. 15
Mesa, AZ 85201
Ph: (480)839-9106
Fax: (480)839-9106
Fr: 888-866-7638
E-mail: office@soft-tox.org
URL: http://www.soft-tox.org

Description: Scientists who analyze tissue and body fluids for drugs and poisons and interpret the information for judicial purposes. Objectives are to establish uniform qualifications and requirements for certification of forensic toxicologists and promote support mechanisms for continued certification; to stimulate research and development; to provide review board for cases involving differences of professional opinion; to act on administrative and career problems affecting forensic toxicologists. Serves as clearinghouse; conducts proficiency testing programs; provides information on case histories and job opportunities. Sponsors American Board of Forensic Toxicology.

Foresters and Conservation Scientists

SOURCES OF HELP-WANTED ADS

5164 ■ *Atmospheric and Climate Sciences*
Scientific Research Publishing
PO Box 54821
Irvine, CA 92619-4821
E-mail: acs@scirp.org
URL: http://www.scirp.org/journal/acs/

Quarterly. $156.00/year for individuals. Journal publishing articles on climate atmospheric science.

5165 ■ *Capital Ideas*
Alabama Forest Owners' Association
c/o R. Lee Laechelt, Exec.VP
PO Box 361434
Birmingham, AL 35236
Ph: (205)987-8811
Fax: (205)987-9824
E-mail: rll@afoa.org
URL: http://www.afoa.org

Description: Monthly. Covers activities of Alabama Forest Owners' Association. Contains calendar of forestry events and forestry related news.

5166 ■ *Carolina Forestry Journal*
South Carolina Forestry Association
PO Box 21303
Columbia, SC 29221-1303
Ph: (803)798-4170
Fax: (803)798-2340
URL: http://www.scforestry.org

Bimonthly. Journal containing information for the forestry industry, including forest conservation and preservation.

5167 ■ *CINTRAFOR News*
Center for International Trade in Forest Products
College of Forest Resources
Box 352100
Seattle, WA 98195-2100
Ph: (206)543-8684
Fax: (206)685-0790
E-mail: eastin@u.washington.edu
URL: http://www.cintrafor.org

Description: Quarterly. Summarizes research and related activities in the area of forest products trade, including international symposiums, workshops, publications, and new technology trends sponsored by the Center.

5168 ■ *City Trees*
Society of Municipal Arborists
c/o Jerri J. LaHaie, Exec. Dir.
PO Box 641
Watkinsville, GA 30677
Ph: (706)769-7412
Fax: (706)769-7307
E-mail: urbanforestry@prodigy.net
URL: http://www.urban-forestry.com
Description: Bimonthly. Addresses all aspects of

municipal (urban) forestry. Contains technical articles on species of trees, pest control, conservation, planning, design, and equipment. Recurring features include lists of new publications, statistics, news of research, letters to the editor, announcements of meetings, and columns titled President's Column, Professor's Column, City of the Month, Park of the Month, Tree of the Month, and Editor's Column.

5169 ■ *Corporate Social Responsibility and Environmental Management*
John Wiley & Sons Inc.
111 River St.
Hoboken, NJ 07030-5773
Ph: (201)748-6000
Fax: (201)748-6088
Fr: 800-825-7550
URL: http://onlinelibrary.wiley.com/journal/10.1002/
   (ISSN)1535-39

Bimonthly. $1,355.00/year for institutions, other countries, print only; $874.00/year for institutions, other countries, print only; $692.00/year for institutions, print only; $1,006.00/year for institutions, other countries, print with online; $796.00/year for institutions, print with online; $1,559.00/year for institutions, other countries, print with online. Journal providing a resource for organizations concerned with social and environmental responsibilities in the context of sustainable development.

5170 ■ *Drinking Water & Backflow Prevention*
IAPMO
9878 Burke Pond Ct.
Burke, VA 22015
Ph: (703)934-0115
Fax: (703)934-0119
Fr: 888-367-3927
E-mail: curtis@iapmo.org
URL: http://www.iapmodwbp.org

Description: Monthly. $45. Presents articles directed toward individuals, companies, organizations, agencies, and municipalities with an interest in drinking water protection and backflow prevention. Contains information on safety standards, water system protection, training programs, cross-connection control, and all issues related to preventing the contamination of potable drinking water supplies with backflow prevention devices. Recurring features include case studies, letters to the editor, news of research, columns titled Test Your Investigative Skills and Backflow Prevention Device Repairs, and reports of meetings. Also carries news of educational opportunities, job listings, notices of publications available, and a calendar of events.

5171 ■ *Ecological Entomology*
John Wiley & Sons Inc.
350 Main St., Commerce Pl.
Malden, MA 02148-5089
Ph: (781)388-8200

Fax: (781)388-8210
URL: http://www.wiley.com/bw/journal.asp?ref=0307-
   6946
Bimonthly. $1,422.00/year for institutions, print & online; $2,070.00/year for institutions, print & online; $1,800.00/year for institutions, print or online; $1,236.00/year for institutions, print or online; $1,119.00/year for institutions, other countries, print & online; $973.00/year for institutions, print or online. Journal publishing articles on conversation issues.

5172 ■ *Environmental Business Journal*
Environmental Business International Inc.
4452 Park Blvd., Ste. 306
San Diego, CA 92116
URL: http://www.ebiusa.com

Description: Twelve issues/year. $995/year. Provides research and articles on various segments of the environmental business industry. Recurring features include news of research.

5173 ■ *Environmental Conservation*
Cambridge University Press
32 Avenue of the Americas
New York, NY 10013-2473
Ph: (212)924-3900
Fax: (212)691-3239
E-mail: envcons@ncl.ac.uk
URL: http://journals.cambridge.org/action/
   displayJournal?jid=ENC

Quarterly. $798.00/year for institutions, print & online; $614.00/year for institutions, online only; $220.00/year for individuals, print & online; $45.00/year for single issue, article; $155.00/year for individuals, online only. Peer-reviewed journal covering environmental policy, practice, and natural and social science of environmental concern at a global level. Topics covered include issues in human institutions, pollution and habitat degradation, resource exploitation, terrestrial biomes, atmospheric and oceanic processes, and coastal and land management.

5174 ■ *Environmental Education Research*
Routledge Journals
270 Madison Ave.
New York, NY 10016-0601
Ph: (212)216-7800
Fax: (212)563-2269
URL: http://www.tandf.co.uk/journals/titles/
   13504622.asp

Bimonthly. $1,373.00/year for institutions, print + online; $1,236.00/year for institutions, online only; $364.00/year for individuals, print only. Journal covering all aspects of environmental education.

5175 ■ *Fisheries*
American Fisheries Society
5410 Grosvenor Ln.
Bethesda, MD 20814-2144
Ph: (301)897-8616
Fax: (301)897-8096
URL: http://www.fisheries.org

Monthly. $441.00/year for individuals, online. Magazine covering fisheries management and aquatic resource issues.

5176 ■ Forest Pathology
John Wiley & Sons Inc.
350 Main St., Commerce Pl.
Malden, MA 02148-5089
Ph: (781)388-8200
Fax: (781)388-8210
URL: http://www.wiley.com/bw/journal.asp?ref=1437-4781&site=1

Bimonthly. $303.00/year for individuals, print & online; $1,356.00/year for institutions, print & online; $1,179.00/year for institutions, print or online; $188.00/year for other countries, print and online; $1,026.00/year for institutions, Europe, print and online; $892.00/year for institutions, Europe, online only; $281.00/year for individuals, Europe (Euro zone), print and online. Peer-reviewed journal covering forest pathological problems occurring in any part of the world.

5177 ■ Forests for Oregon
Oregon Department of Forestry
2600 State St.
Salem, OR 97310
Ph: (503)945-7200
Fax: (503)945-7212
Fr: 800-437-4490
E-mail: information@odf.state.or.us
URL: http://egov.oregon.gov/ODF/

Description: Quarterly. Discusses forestry issues on state and private lands, laws regarding forest management, and practices. Recurring features include interviews, news of research, report of meetings, and notices of publications available.

5178 ■ FRA Bulletin
Forest Resources Association
600 Jefferson Pl., Ste. 350
Rockville, MD 20852
Ph: (301)838-9385
Fax: (301)838-9481
E-mail: rl@forestresources.org
URL: http://www.forestresources.org

Description: Monthly. Electronic newsletter covering current events and policy in wood supply and forest management. Recurring features include a calendar of events, news of educational opportunities, job listings, and notices of publications available.

5179 ■ FYI
Washington Forest Protection Association
724 Columbia St. NW, Ste. 250
Olympia, WA 98501
Ph: (360)352-1500
Fax: (360)352-4621
E-mail: info@wfpa.org
URL: http://www.wfpa.org

Description: Quarterly. Covers activities of Washington Forest Protection Association. Contains research summary.

5180 ■ Hardwood Research Bulletin
National Hardwood Lumber Association
6830 Raleigh La Grange Rd.
Memphis, TN 38134-0518
Ph: (901)377-1818
Fax: (901)382-6419
Fr: 800-933-0318
E-mail: info@nhla.com
URL: http://www.nhla.com

Description: Monthly. Provides abstracts and digests of current research information concerning hardwood forest management, silviculture, insects, diseases, resource utilization, product development, manufacturing technology, and economics. Lists upcoming events, workshops, short courses, and seminars of interest to members.

5181 ■ ISTF News
International Society of Tropical Foresters Inc.
5400 Grosvenor Ln.
Bethesda, MD 20814-2161
Ph: (301)530-4514
Fax: (301)897-3690
E-mail: istf.bethesda@verizon.net
URL: http://www.istf-bethesda.org

Description: Quarterly. Covers developments in tropical forestry. Recurring features include book reviews, notices of upcoming meetings, lists of members, and notes on member activities.

5182 ■ The Job Seeker
PO Box 451
Fruita, CO 81521
Fax: (267)295-2004
E-mail: sarah@thejobseeker.net
URL: http://www.thejobseeker.net

Description: Semimonthly. Specializes in environmental and natural resource vacancies nationwide. Lists current vacancies from federal, state, local, private, and non-profit employers. Also available via e-mail.

5183 ■ Journal of Applied Ecology
John Wiley & Sons Inc.
350 Main St., Commerce Pl.
Malden, MA 02148-5089
Ph: (781)388-8200
Fax: (781)388-8210
URL: http://www.journalofappliedecology.org/view/0/index.html

Bimonthly. $1,582.00/year for institutions, U.S. print and online; $1,375.00/year for institutions, U.S. print or online; $856.00/year for institutions, print and online; $744.00/year for institutions, print or online. Journal focusing on ecological science and environmental management.

5184 ■ Journal of Environmental Protection
Scientific Research Publishing
PO Box 54821
Irvine, CA 92619-4821
E-mail: jep@scirp.org
URL: http://www.scirp.org/journal/jep/

$390.00/year for individuals. Peer-reviewed journal publishing articles on the latest advancements in environmental protection.

5185 ■ Journal of Forest Products Business Research
Forest Products Society
2801 Marshall Ct.
Madison, WI 53705-2295
Ph: (608)231-1361
Fax: (608)231-2152
URL: http://www.forestprod.org/jfpbr.html

Annual. $155.00/year for nonmembers; $165.00/year for Canada, non-members; $195.00/year for other countries, non-members. Peer-reviewed journal that publishes research manuscripts that focus on the forest industry.

5186 ■ Journal of Forestry
Society of American Foresters
5400 Grosvenor Ln.
Bethesda, MD 20814-2198
Ph: (301)897-3691
Fax: (301)897-3690
Fr: (866)897-8720
E-mail: journal@safnet.org
URL: http://www.safnet.org/publications/jof/index.cfm

$123.00/year for nonmembers, U.S./Canada, print only; $270.00/year for institutions, U.S./Canada, print only; $224.00/year for nonmembers, online only; $333.00/year for institutions, online only; $253.00/year for nonmembers, U.S./Canada, print and online; $386.00/year for institutions, U.S./Canada, print and online; $168.00/year for nonmembers, foreign, print only; $315.00/year for institutions, foreign, print only; $298.00/year for nonmembers, foreign, print and online; $431.00/year for institutions, other countries,

print and online. Peer-reviewed journal of forestry serves to advance the profession by keeping professionals informed about significant developments and ideas in forest science, natural resource management, and forest policy.

5187 ■ Journal of Water Resource and Protection
Scientific Research Publishing
PO Box 54821
Irvine, CA 92619-4821
E-mail: jwarp@scirp.org
URL: http://www.scirp.org/Journal/jwarp/

Monthly. $708.00/year for individuals. Peer-reviewed journal publishing articles on the latest advancements in water resources and protection.

5188 ■ Natural Resources
Scientific Research Publishing
PO Box 54821
Irvine, CA 92619-4821
E-mail: nr@scirp.org
URL: http://www.scirp.org/journal/nr/

Quarterly. $156.00/year for individuals. Peer-reviewed journal publishing articles on the latest advancements in natural resources.

5189 ■ Nature International Weekly Journal of Science
Nature Publishing Group
75 Varick St., 9th Fl.
New York, NY 10013-1917
Ph: (212)726-9200
Fax: (212)696-9006
Fr: 888-331-6288
E-mail: nature@natureny.com
URL: http://www.nature.com/nature/index.html

Weekly. $199.00/year for individuals, print and online; $338.00/year for two years, print and online. Magazine covering science and technology, including the fields of biology, biochemistry, genetics, medicine, earth sciences, physics, pharmacology, and behavioral sciences.

5190 ■ Northern Logger and Timber Processor
N.L. Publishing Inc.
3311 State Rte. 28
PO Box 69
Old Forge, NY 13420
Ph: (315)369-3078
Fax: (315)369-3736
Fr: 800-318-7561
URL: http://www.northernlogger.com/pages/northernLoggerMag/northe

Monthly. $18.00/year for individuals; $29.00/year for two years. Magazine for the logging and lumber industries.

5191 ■ Ornithological Newsletter
Ornithological Societies of North America
5400 Bosque Blvd., Ste. 680
Waco, TX 76710
Ph: (254)399-9636
Fax: (254)776-3767
E-mail: business@osnabirds.org
URL: http://www.osnabirds.org

Description: Bimonthly. Provides information of interest to ornithologists. Recurring features include listings of available grants and awards, news of members, a calendar of events, activities of sponsoring societies, and notices of publications available. Notices of employment opportunities are also available on the Web version.

5192 ■ P2
John Wiley & Sons Inc.
111 River St.
Hoboken, NJ 07030-5773
Ph: (201)748-6000
Fax: (201)748-6088

Fr: 800-825-7550
URL: http://as.wiley.com/WileyCDA/WileyTitle/
productCd-PPR.html

Quarterly. Journal discussing source reduction and waste minimization, and focusing on the tactics, techniques, and answers for solving pollution problems before they begin.

5193 ■ PALAIOS

SEPM Publications
4111 S Darlington, Ste. 100
Tulsa, OK 74135-6373
Ph: (918)610-3361
Fax: (918)621-1685
Fr: 800-865-9765
E-mail: palois@ku.edu
URL: http://palaios.ku.edu/

Monthly. $315.00/year for individuals, for U.S.; online version with CD-ROM; $415.00/year for individuals, for U.S.; print and online version with CD-ROM; $315.00/year for other countries, online version with CD-ROM; $425.00/year for other countries, print and online version with CD-ROM. Journal providing information on the impact of life on Earth history as recorded in the paleontological and sedimentological records. Covers areas such as biogeochemistry, ichnology, sedimentology, stratigraphy, paleoecology, paleoclimatology, and paleoceanography.

5194 ■ PE & RS Photogrammetric Engineering & Remote Sensing

The Imaging and Geospatial Information Society
5410 Grosvenor Ln., Ste. 210
Bethesda, MD 20814-2160
Ph: (301)493-0290
Fax: (301)493-0208
URL: http://www.asprs.org/PE-RS-Journal/

Monthly. $410.00/year for individuals, first class mail; $426.00/year for Canada, airmail; $420.00/year for other countries, air standard. Peer-reviewed journal covering photogrammetry, remote sensing, geographic information systems, cartography, and surveying, global positioning systems, digital photogrammetry.

5195 ■ Seedling News

TreePeople
12601 Mulholland Dr.
Beverly Hills, CA 90210
Ph: (818)753-4600
Fax: (818)753-4635
E-mail: info@treepeople.org
URL: http://www.treepeople.org/seedling-news

Description: Quarterly. Covers environmental topics, such as urban forestry and sustainable communities. Recurring features include a collection and reports of meetings.

5196 ■ SFPA Newsletter

Southern Forest Products Association
2900 Indiana Ave.
Kenner, LA 70065
Ph: (504)443-4464
Fax: (504)443-6612
E-mail: mail@sfpa.org
URL: http://sfpa.org

Description: Weekly. Covers activities of Southern Forest Products Association. Covers forest products, timber resources, market development activities, transportation, lumber manufacturing, and business and association news.

5197 ■ The Southeastern Naturalist

Humboldt Field Research Institute
59 Eagle Hill Rd.
PO Box 9
Steuben, ME 04680-0009
Ph: (207)546-2821
Fax: (207)546-3042
E-mail: office@eaglehill.us
URL: http://www.eaglehill.us/programs/journals/sena/
southeastern-

Quarterly. $50.00/year for individuals; $40.00/year for

students; $150.00/year for institutions, organization; $70.00/year for Canada; $90.00/year for other countries; $60.00/year for students, In Canada; $80.00/year for students, other countries; $170.00/year for institutions, in Canada; $190.00/year for institutions, other countries. Peer-reviewed interdisciplinary scientific journal covering field ecology, biology, behavior, biogeography, taxonomy, anatomy, physiology, geology and related fields in the southeastern United States.

5198 ■ Under the Canopy-Forestry & Forest Products Newsletter

Alaska Cooperative Extension
University of Alaska Fairbanks
PO Box 756180
Fairbanks, AK 99775-6180
Ph: (907)474-5211
Fax: (907)474-2631
E-mail: cesweb@uaf.edu
URL: http://www.uaf.edu/ces/newsltrs

Description: Three issues/year. Focuses on forestry in Alaska, including legislation, tree diseases, forest fires, wood use, and tree farms. Recurring features include news from the Board of Forestry, the 4-H Forestry Camp, and state forests in Alaska and a list of free publications from the Cooperative Extension Service.

5199 ■ Wetlands

Society of Wetland Scientists
1313 Dolley Madison Blvd., Ste. 402
Mc Lean, VA 22101
Ph: (703)790-1745
Fax: (703)790-2672
URL: http://www.sws.org/wetlands/index.mgi

Quarterly. $100.00/year for individuals; $35.00/year for students; $500.00/year for institutions; $200.00/year for libraries; $65.00/year for members, paper & electronic, from developing country. Scholarly journal covering all aspects of wetlands biology, ecology, hydrology, water chemistry, soil and sediment characteristics, management, and laws and regulations.

5200 ■ The Wildlifer

The Wildlife Society Inc.
5410 Grosvenor Ln., Ste. 200
Bethesda, MD 20814-2144
Ph: (301)897-9770
Fax: (301)530-2471
E-mail: yanin@wildlife.org
URL: http://joomla.wildlife.org

Description: Monthly. Serves as the Society's official publication of record. Contains items on section and chapter activities, meetings of interest, career notes, job opportunities, and timely articles on significant developments in conservation issues. Recurring features include editorials, news of members, letters to the editor, a calendar of events, and a column titled Call for Papers.

5201 ■ The Woodland Steward

Massachusetts Forest Landowners Association
PO Box 623
Leverett, MA 01054
Ph: (413)549-5900
Fax: (413)339-5526
E-mail: gcox@crocker.com
URL: http://www.massforests.org

Description: Five issues/year. Presents issues, facts, and events concerning Massachusetts forests, trees, and ecology. Advocates sustainable forest use. Recurring features include news of research, a calendar of events, and columns titled Forest Health, Practical Management, Tree Farm News, and Legislation & Policy.

EMPLOYER DIRECTORIES AND NETWORKING LISTS

5202 ■ American Men and Women of Science

Gale
PO Box 6904
Florence, KY 41022-6904

Fr: 800-354-9706
URL: http://www.gale.cengage.com

Biennial, even years; New edition expected 29th, June 2011. $1,368.00 for individuals. Covers: Over 135,000 U.S. and Canadian scientists active in the physical, biological, mathematical, computer science, and engineering fields; includes references to previous edition for deceased scientists and nonrespondents. Entries include: Name, address, education, personal and career data, memberships, honors and awards, research interest. Arrangement: Alphabetical. Indexes: Discipline (in separate volume).

5203 ■ Association of Consulting Foresters—Membership Specialization Directory

Association of Consulting Foresters
312 Montgomery St., Ste. 208
Alexandria, VA 22314
Ph: (703)548-0990
Fax: (703)548-6395
URL: http://www.acf-foresters.org

Annual, August. Free. Covers: Nearly 500 member forestry consulting firms and professional foresters who earn the largest part of their income from consulting. Entries include: Name, address, phone, specialties, background, career data, staff (if a consulting firm), geographic area served, capabilities, including equipment available and foreign language proficiency. Arrangement: Alphabetical. Indexes: Name, office location, language, international capability.

5204 ■ Conservation Directory

National Wildlife Federation
11100 Wildlife Center Dr.
Reston, VA 20190-5362
Ph: (703)638-6000
Fax: (703)438-6061
Fr: 800-822-9919
E-mail: admin@nwf.org
URL: http://www.nwf.org/conservationdirectory/

Annual, latest edition 2010. Covers: Over 4,258 organizations, agencies, colleges and universities with conservation programs and more than 18,000 officials concerned with environmental conservation, education, and natural resource use and management. Entries include: Agency name, address, branch or subsidiary office name and address, names and titles of key personnel, descriptions of program areas, size of membership (where appropriate), telephone, fax, e-mail and URL addresses. Arrangement: Classified by type of organization. Indexes: Personal name, keyword, geographic, organization.

HANDBOOKS AND MANUALS

5205 ■ Career Opportunities in Conservation and the Environment

Facts On File Inc.
132 W 31st St., 17th Fl.
New York, NY 10001
Fr: 800-322-8755
E-mail: custserv@factsonfile.com
URL: http://factsonfile.infobasepublishing.com

2007. $49.50. 304 pages. Covers job profiles on conservation and the environment, followed by the descriptions of certification, education, special skills, and training required.

5206 ■ Careers in the Environment

The McGraw-Hill Companies
PO Box 182604
Columbus, OH 43272
Fax: (614)759-3749
Fr: 877-883-5524
E-mail: customer.service@mcgraw-hill.com
URL: http://www.mhprofessional.com/
product.php?cat=106&isbn=0071476113

Michael Fasulo and Paul Walker. 2007. $15.95

(paper). 192 pages. Comprehensive information on the diverse career opportunities available in environmental services.

5207 ■ *Careers for Health Nuts and Others Who Like to Stay Fit*
The McGraw-Hill Companies
PO Box 182604
Columbus, OH 43272
Fax: (614)759-3749
Fr: 877-883-5524
E-mail: customer.service@mcgraw-hill.com
URL: http://www.mhprofessional.com

Blythe Camenson. Second edition. $13.95 (paper). 208 pages.

5208 ■ *Jobs in Environmental Cleanup and Emergency Hazmat Response*
Rosen Publishing Group
29 E 21st St.
New York, NY 10010
Fax: 888-436-4643
Fr: 800-237-9932
URL: http://www.rosenpublishing.com

Daniel E. Harmon. 2010. $31.95 (library bound). 80 pages. Features jobs in environmental cleanup and emergency hazmat response. Explores numerous career paths for different environmental jobs that require special training or four-year and/or postgraduate degrees. Includes job profiles for professionals such as environmental engineers, geologists, microbiologists, science technicians, conservationists, foresters, park rangers, soil scientists, air control technicians, toxicologists, dredge operators, ecologists, hazardous waste managers, and zoologists.

5209 ■ *Opportunities in Biological Science Careers*
The McGraw-Hill Companies
PO Box 182604
Columbus, OH 43272
Fax: (614)759-3749
Fr: 877-883-5524
E-mail: customer.service@mcgraw-hill.com
URL: http://www.mhprofessional.com/
   product.php?isbn=007143187X

Charles A. Winter. 2004. $13.95 (paper). 160 pages. Identifies employers and outlines opportunities in plant and animal biology, biological specialties, biomedical sciences, applied biology, and other areas. Illustrated.

5210 ■ *Resumes for Scientific and Technical Careers*
The McGraw-Hill Companies
PO Box 182604
Columbus, OH 43272
Fax: (614)759-3749
Fr: 877-883-5524
E-mail: customer.service@mcgraw-hill.com
URL: http://www.mhprofessional.com/
   product.php?isbn=0071482199

Third edition, 2007. $12.95 (paper). 144 pages. Provides resume advice for individuals interested in working in scientific and technical careers. Includes sample resumes and cover letters.

ONLINE JOB SOURCES AND SERVICES

5211 ■ Conservation Job Board
URL: http://www.conservationjobboard.com

Description: Provides job seekers with a one-stop place for finding the latest job openings related to conservation. Assists employers to find the ideal candidates for their job openings, internships, graduate assistantships, and other volunteer opportunities.

5212 ■ Environmental Career Opportunities
URL: http://www.ecojobs.com

Description: Lists environmental jobs in conservation, education, policy, science and engineering.

5213 ■ Environmental Expert
URL: http://www.environmental-expert.com

Description: Connects environmental industry professionals from around the globe to companies that provide the products, services and information they need to do their job successfully.

5214 ■ Environmental Jobs
URL: http://environmental.jobs4.org

Description: Offers a searchable database of environmental job opportunities available throughout the United States.

5215 ■ EnvironmentalJobs.com
URL: http://environmentaljobs.com

Description: Serves as online tool that provides current listings of environmental jobs.

5216 ■ ForestryUSA.com
URL: http://www.forestryusa.com

Description: Provides resources on forestry and the forest products industry in the United States. Lists job opportunities in the field.

TRADESHOWS

5217 ■ Forest Products Machinery & Equipment Exposition
Southern Forest Products Association
2900 Indiana Ave.
Kenner, LA 70065
Ph: (504)443-4464
Fax: (504)443-6612
E-mail: mail@sfpa.org
URL: http://www.sfpa.org

Biennial. Primary Exhibits: Equipment, supplies, and services for the forest products industry. Including lumber, panels, engineered wood products, plywood, secondary processing, forestry and land management.

5218 ■ Northeastern Forest Products Equipment Expo
Northeastern Loggers Association
PO Box 69
3311 St. Rte. 28
Old Forge, NY 13420-0069
Ph: (315)369-3078
Fax: (315)369-3736
E-mail: mona@northernlogger.com
URL: http://www.loggertraining.com

Annual. Primary Exhibits: Forest industry services, equipment, and associated products. Dates and Locations: 2012 May 11-12; Hamburg, NY.

5219 ■ Pacific Logging Congress
Pacific Logging Congress
PO Box 1281
Maple Valley, WA 98038
Ph: (425)413-2808
Fax: (425)413-1359
E-mail: pacificlogging@aol.com
URL: http://www.pacificloggingcongress.com

Annual. Primary Exhibits: Logging and allied industry equipment.

5220 ■ Redwood Region Logging Conference
Redwood Region Logging Conference
5601 S. Broadway
Eureka, CA 95503
Ph: (707)443-4091
Fax: (707)443-0926
E-mail: rrlc@rrlc.net
URL: http://www.rrlc.net

Annual. Primary Exhibits: Logging equipment supplies and services. Dates and Locations: 2012 Mar 15-17; Ukiah, CA; Redwood Empire Fairgrounds.

5221 ■ Society of American Foresters National Convention
Society of American Foresters
5400 Grosvenor Ln.
Bethesda, MD 20814-2198
Ph: (301)897-8720
Fax: (301)897-3690
E-mail: safweb@safnet.org
URL: http://www.safnet.org

Annual. Primary Exhibits: Forestry equipment, publications, hardware and software, chemicals, machinery, and geographic information systems.

5222 ■ Soil and Water Conservation Society International Conference
Soil and Water Conservation Society
945 SW Ankeny Rd.
Ankeny, IA 50023
Ph: (515)289-2331
Fax: (515)289-1227
E-mail: swcs@swcs.org
URL: http://www.swcs.org

Annual. Explores the current issues in conservation and environmental management science, technology, practice, programs, and policy. 2012 July 22-25; Fort Worth, TX.

OTHER SOURCES

5223 ■ Advanced Conservation Strategies
PO Box 1201
Midway, UT 84049
Ph: (435)200-3031
E-mail: acs@advancedconservation.org
URL: http://www.advancedconservation.org

Description: Aims to deliver innovative, self-sustaining and economically efficient solutions to environmental challenges. Builds cross-sector synergy and integrates biological, economic, technological and socio-political threats and opportunities to address environmental and sustainability issues.

5224 ■ Alliance for Global Conservation
PO Box 1200
Washington, DC 20013-1200
Ph: (202)739-8155
E-mail: jwise@pewtrusts.org
URL: http://www.actforconservation.org

Description: Aims to protect life on earth through conservation of wildlife, natural areas and human communities around the world. Supports global policies that will prevent the destruction of the world's remaining natural ecosystems for the species and human communities that depend on them.

5225 ■ Alliance for Water Efficiency (AWE)
300 W Adams St., Ste. 601
Chicago, IL 60606
Ph: (773)360-5100
Fax: (773)345-3636
Fr: (866)730-A4WE
E-mail: jeffrey@a4we.org
URL: http://www.a4we.org

Description: Promotes efficient and sustainable use of water. Serves as an advocate for water-efficient products and programs. Provides information and assistance on water conservation efforts.

5226 ■ American Forests
PO Box 2000
Washington, DC 20013
Ph: (202)737-1944
Fax: (202)737-2457
E-mail: info@amfor.org
URL: http://www.americanforests.org

Description: Works to advance the intelligent management and use of forests, soil, water, wildlife, and all other natural resources. Promotes public appreciation of natural resources, helps plant trees to restore areas damaged by wildfire.

5227 ■ American Reef Coalition (ARC)
PO Box 844
Kihei, HI 96753
Ph: (808)870-5817
E-mail: info@americanreef.org
URL: http://www.americanreef.org

Description: To protect coral reef ecosystems, ocean resources and wilderness through a variety of proven methods and by providing support to other nonprofit organizations and government agencies engaged in marine, wilderness and natural area research, conservation and education.

5228 ■ ASPRS - The Imaging and Geospatial Information Society
5410 Grosvenor Ln., Ste. 210
Bethesda, MD 20814-2160
Ph: (301)493-0290
Fax: (301)493-0208
E-mail: asprs@asprs.org
URL: http://www.asprs.org

Description: Firms, individuals, government employees and academicians engaged in photogrammetry, photointerpretation, remote sensing, and geographic information systems and their application to such fields as archaeology, geographic information systems, military reconnaissance, urban planning, engineering, traffic surveys, meteorological observations, medicine, geology, forestry, agriculture, construction and topographic mapping. Seeks to advance knowledge and improve understanding of these sciences and promote responsible applications. Offers voluntary certification program open to persons associated with one or more functional area of photogrammetry, remote sensing and GIS. Surveys the profession of private firms in photogrammetry and remote sensing in the areas of products and services.

5229 ■ Association of Consulting Foresters of America (ACF)
312 Montgomery St., Ste. 208
Alexandria, VA 22314
Ph: (703)548-0990
Fax: (703)548-6395
E-mail: director@acf-foresters.org
URL: http://www.acf-foresters.org

Description: Professional foresters in the field of applied forestry and forest utilization who work for private landowners or industry on a contract or contingency basis. Members must be graduates of an association-approved forestry school and have five years experience in forest administration and management. Provides client referral service. Compiles statistics.

5230 ■ Association for International Practical Training (AIPT)
10400 Little Patuxent Pkwy., Ste. 250
Columbia, MD 21044-3519
Ph: (410)997-2200
Fax: (410)992-3924
E-mail: aipt@aipt.org
URL: http://www.aipt.org

Description: Providers worldwide of on-the-job training programs for students and professionals seeking international career development and life-changing experiences. Arranges workplace exchanges in hundreds of professional fields, bringing employers and trainees together from around the world. Client list ranges from small farming communities to Fortune 500 companies.

5231 ■ Audubon International
46 Rarick Rd.
Selkirk, NY 12158
Ph: (518)767-9051
Fax: (518)767-9076
E-mail: kfletcher@auduboninternational.org
URL: http://www.auduboninternational.org

Description: Promotes sustainable communities through good stewardship of the natural environment where people live, work and recreate. Collaborates with nonprofits, governments, businesses and the public to ensure better environmental decision-making and improve the quality of human and natural communities. Provides people with the assistance needed to practice responsible management of land, water, wildlife and natural resources.

5232 ■ Climate, Community and Biodiversity Alliance (CCBA)
2011 Crystal Dr., Ste. 500
Arlington, VA 22202
Ph: (703)341-2748
E-mail: info@climate-standards.org
URL: http://www.climate-standards.org

Description: Represents international non-governmental organizations (NGOs) and research institutes that promote integrated solutions to land management. Promotes responsible land management activities that will benefit local communities, minimize climate change and conserve biodiversity.

5233 ■ Community Forestry International
1356 Mokelumne Dr.
Antioch, CA 94531
Ph: (925)706-2906
Fax: (925)706-2906
E-mail: k8smith@aol.com
URL: http://www.communityforestryinternational.org

Description: Assists rural communities to stabilize and regenerate forests. Creates a forum and encourages the exchange of views and ideas about sustainable community forest management. Draws tools and techniques that support and empower communities engaged in forest management.

5234 ■ Conservation through Poverty Alleviation International (CPALI)
221 Lincoln Rd.
Lincoln, MA 01773
E-mail: ccraig@cpali.org
URL: http://www.cpali.org/CPALI_Home.html

Description: Works to identify, develop and implement new means of income generation for poor farmers living in areas of high biodiversity or conservation value. Promotes natural resource conservation by developing integrated, small enterprise systems that link the livelihood of farm families and communities to the maintenance of natural ecosystems.

5235 ■ Defense of Place (DOP)
187 E Blithedale Ave.
Mill Valley, CA 94941
Ph: (415)928-3774
Fax: (415)373-6978
E-mail: info@rri.org
URL: http://www.rri.org/defenseofplace.php

Description: Aims to preserve the world's natural resources. Works to create awareness on wildlife conservation. Promotes environmental protection.

5236 ■ Ecological Research and Development Group (ERDG)
190 Main St.
Dover, DE 19901
Ph: (302)236-5383
E-mail: erdg@horseshoecrab.org
URL: http://www.horseshoecrab.org

Description: Promotes the conservation of horseshoe crab species. Provides educational programs to create an atmosphere of learning to inspire and nurture curiosity about the horseshoe crabs species and their habitat. Seeks solutions that prevent the extinction of the horseshoe crab species through scientific research and development.

5237 ■ Environmental Paper Network (EPN)
16 Eagle St., Ste. 200
Asheville, NC 28801
Ph: (828)251-8558
E-mail: info@environmentalpaper.org
URL: http://www.environmentalpaper.org

Description: Works to accelerate social and environmental transformation in the pulp and paper industry. Aims to protect the world's last endangered forests, to safeguard the global climate and ensure abundant, clean drinking water and respect for community and indigenous rights.

5238 ■ Forest Bird Society
10969 SW 47th Terr.
Miami, FL 33165
Ph: (305)223-2680
Fax: (305)223-2680
E-mail: forestbirdsoc@aol.com
URL: http://www.forestbirdsociety.org

Description: Aims to protect native plants, animals and wild places, on land and in oceans. Promotes environmental education and the preservtion of natural ecosystems. Supports projects to study and protect the habitats of forest birds.

5239 ■ Friends of the Osa (FOO)
1822 R St. NW, 4th Fl.
Washington, DC 20009
Ph: (202)234-2356
E-mail: info@osaconservation.org
URL: http://www.osaconservation.org

Description: Aims to maintain a largely forested landscape surrounded by an intact coastal zone that protects the Osa's biodiversity while supporting sustainable human livelihoods. Works with local, regional and international partners to protect the region's globally significant biodiversity. Encourages regional and local participation in conservation efforts. Facilitates the exchange of scientific and research expertise.

5240 ■ GAIA Movement USA
8918 S Green St.
Chicago, IL 60620
Ph: (773)651-7870
Fax: (773)651-7890
Fr: 877-651-7870
E-mail: eva@gaia-movement.org
URL: http://www.gaia-movement-usa.org

Description: Educates young and old people on environmental issues including recycling, renewable energy, conservation and wildlife preservation. Develops and preserves natural areas and virgin lands as nature reserves. Promotes the use of renewable energies such as solar, wind and geothermal.

5241 ■ Global Parks
3803 Sulgrave Dr.
Alexandria, VA 22309
Ph: (703)317-1669
E-mail: todd@globalparks.org
URL: http://globalparks.org

Description: Aims to support retired senior conservation professionals to help strengthen protected areas and national park systems around the world. Collaborates with partners to plan activities for parks and protected areas. Provides analysis, advice and assistance in developing, reviewing, and implementing various protected areas plans, strategies and issues.

5242 ■ Growing Planet
3133 Frontera Way, Ste. 113
Burlingame, CA 94010-5759
Fr: (866)476-9873
E-mail: info@growingplanet.org
URL: http://www.growingplanet.org

Description: Promotes planting and cultivating of trees to improve the quality of life. Engages in an effort to replenish the earth's forests and reduce greenhouse gases to protect the Earth's ozone layer. Replaces trees that have been logged for commercial purposes, destroyed by fire or cut down due to an increase in urban development.

5243 ■ Indo-Pacific Conservation Alliance (IPCA)
1525 Bernice St.
Honolulu, HI 96817
Ph: (808)848-4124

Fax: (808)847-8252
E-mail: info@indopacific.org
URL: http://www.indopacific.org

Description: Focuses on the study and conservation of the native ecosystems of the tropical Indo-Pacific region. Supports traditional peoples in the stewardship of globally significant natural resources. Works as facilitators to local communities who request help in conserving their natural resources. Provides information, training, equipment and other support to local stakeholders to help conserve and manage natural resources.

5244 ■ Instream Flow Council (IFC)
645 Hatchery Rd.
Marion, NC 28752
Ph: (828)652-4360
Fax: (828)652-3279
E-mail: chris.goudreau@ncwildlife.org
URL: http://www.instreamflowcouncil.org

Description: Represents the interests of state and provincial fish and wildlife management agencies. Increases public awareness and understanding of instream flow issues and stewardship responsibilities. Helps to establish, maintain and administer programs for the quantification, protection and restoration of instream flows for aquatic resources.

5245 ■ Korean-American Scientists and Engineers Association (KSEA)
1952 Gallows Rd., Ste. 300
Vienna, VA 22182
Ph: (703)748-1221
Fax: (703)748-1331
E-mail: sejong@ksea.org
URL: http://www.ksea.org

Description: Represents scientists and engineers holding single or advanced degrees. Promotes friendship and mutuality among Korean and American scientists and engineers; contributes to Korea's scientific, technological, industrial, and economic developments; strengthens the scientific, technological, and cultural bonds between Korea and the U.S. Sponsors symposium. Maintains speakers' bureau, placement service, and biographical archives. Compiles statistics.

5246 ■ MarineBio Conservation Society
PO Box 235273
Encinitas, CA 92023
Ph: (713)248-2576
E-mail: info@marinebio.org
URL: http://marinebio.org

Description: Works to protect marine life and the ocean for future generations. Creates an awareness of marine conservation issues and their solutions. Supports marine conservation scientists and students involved in the marine life sciences.

5247 ■ National Alliance of Forest Owners (NAFO)
122 C St. NW, Ste. 630
Washington, DC 20001
Ph: (202)747-0759
Fax: (202)824-0770
E-mail: info@nafoalliance.org
URL: http://www.nafoalliance.org

Description: Aims to protect and enhance the economic and environmental values of privately-owned forests through targeted policy advocacy at the national level. Focuses on issues for regulatory advocacy including climate change, renewable energy, environment, tax policy, land use, trade and market policy. Seeks public policies that shape environmental regulations, taxes, land use decisions, and timber and non-timber markets in ways that protect and grow forest values.

5248 ■ National Association of Conservation Districts (NACD)
509 Capitol Ct. NE
Washington, DC 20002-4937
Ph: (202)547-6223
Fax: (202)547-6450

Fr: 888-695-2433
E-mail: jeff-eisenberg@nacdnet.org
URL: http://www.nacdnet.org

Description: Soil and water conservation districts organized by the citizens of watersheds, counties, or communities under provisions of state laws. Directs and coordinates, through local self-government efforts, the conservation and development of soil, water, and related natural resources. Includes districts over 90% of the nation's privately owned land. Conducts educational programs and children's services.

5249 ■ National Association of State Foresters
444 N Capitol St. NW, Ste. 540
Washington, DC 20001
Ph: (202)624-5415
Fax: (202)624-5407
E-mail: nasf@stateforesters.org
URL: http://www.stateforesters.org

Description: Consists of directors of forestry agencies. Promotes cooperation in forestry matters among states and between states and the federal government. Acts on national legislation relating to forestry issues. Maintains history of state forestry agencies; conducts educational programs on forestry issues; compiles statistics.

5250 ■ National Oceanic Society (NOS)
17300 Red Hill Ave., Ste. 280
Irvine, CA 92614
Ph: (949)500-5451
Fax: (949)675-1366
URL: http://nationaloceanic.org

Description: Promotes the fundamental concepts of marine conservation and preservation. Supports the education, research and scientific study of marine environment. Assists governmental agencies in the monitoring and detection of activities that are hazardous and harmful to marine environment.

5251 ■ Nature's Voice Our Choice (NVOC)
1940 Duke St. Ste. 200
Alexandria, VA 22314
Ph: (202)360-8373
E-mail: brandy@nv-oc.org
URL: http://www.naturesvoice-ourchoice.org

Description: Aims to preserve, conserve and restore the world's water resources through education and public awareness. Empowers people to become stewards of their natural resources and implements projects that make environmental protection economically feasible. Supports ecologically engineered natural waste water treatment systems.

5252 ■ Neotropical Grassland Conservancy (NGC)
6274 Heathcliff Dr.
Carmichael, CA 95608
Ph: (916)967-3223
URL: http://www.conservegrassland.org

Description: Promotes the conservation of savannas, gallery forests, wetlands and associated ecosystems in Central and South America. Collaborates with North American, Central and South American scientists and institutions by providing shared scientific and educational opportunities. Offers equipment and grants to students and scientists from Central and South America working in grassland habitats.

5253 ■ Network of Conservation Educators and Practitioners (NCEP)
American Museum of Natural History
Center for Biodiversity and Conservation
Central Park West, 79th St.
New York, NY 10024
Ph: (212)769-5742
Fax: (212)769-5292
E-mail: ncep@amnh.org
URL: http://ncep.amnh.org

Description: Aims to improve the practice of biodiversity conservation. Promotes educational resources

on managing and sustaining biological and cultural diversity. Provides opportunities for communication and interaction among conservation educators and practitioners.

5254 ■ Ocean Conservation Research
PO Box 559
Lagunitas, CA 94938
Ph: (415)488-0553
E-mail: info@ocr.org
URL: http://ocr.org

Description: Represents scientists, engineers and ocean advocates devoted to improve the environmental health of the sea. Seeks to understand and explore solutions to the growing problem of human generated noise pollution and its impact on marine animals. Promotes the recovery and long term viability of the sea through research focusing on conservation priorities and practices.

5255 ■ Orion Grassroots Network
187 Main St.
Great Barrington, MA 01230
Ph: (413)528-4422
URL: http://www.oriongrassroots.org

Description: Consists of grassroots organizations across the United States. Provides job listing for future green leaders. Offers job posting service on a fee basis.

5256 ■ OurEarth.org
PO Box 212
Painted Post, NY 14870
Ph: (410)878-6485
URL: http://www.ourearth.org

Description: Represents graduate and medical students as well as environmental experts and leaders from around the country. Promotes the importance of natural resources energy savings and pollutant reductions. Conducts environmental programs, activities, initiatives, ideas and grassroots efforts across the country.

5257 ■ Rising Tide North America (RTNA)
PO Box 3928
Oakland, CA 94609
Ph: (503)438-4697
E-mail: contact@risingtidenorthamerica.org
URL: http://www.risingtidenorthamerica.org

Description: Fosters community-based solutions to the climate crisis. Aims to prevent catastrophic global warming by determining the root causes of climate change. Works to support direct action and encourages individuals and organizations to carry out autonomous actions that are in line with these principles.

5258 ■ Rivers Without Borders (RWB)
PO Box 154
Clinton, WA 98236
Ph: (360)341-1976
E-mail: admin@riverswithoutborders.org
URL: http://riverswithoutborders.org

Description: Represents individuals and groups coordinating to protect the diversity of the river. Aims to maintain the abundance of fish and wildlife species in transboundary watersheds. Provides information on how to conserve the river system.

5259 ■ Save Yemen's Flora and Fauna (SYFF)
1523 River Terrace Dr.
East Lansing, MI 48823
E-mail: jzindani@syff.org
URL: http://www.syff.org

Description: Represents individuals with an interest in environmental protection and wildlife conservation. Works to protect natural resources and wildlife habitats through efforts directed against pollution and violation of environmental laws. Conducts research and educational programs.

5260 ■ Society of American Foresters (SAF)
5400 Grosvenor Ln.
Bethesda, MD 20814-2198
Ph: (301)897-8720
Fax: (301)897-3690
Fr: (866)897-8720
E-mail: safweb@safnet.org
URL: http://www.safnet.org

Description: National scientific and educational organization representing forestry in the United States. Aims to advance the science, education, technology, and practice of forestry. Supports 28 subject-oriented working groups.

5261 ■ Society for Range Management (SRM)
10030 W 27th Ave.
Wheat Ridge, CO 80215-6601
Ph: (303)986-3309
Fax: (303)986-3892
E-mail: info@rangelands.org
URL: http://www.rangelands.org

Description: Professional international society of scientists, technicians, ranchers, administrators, teachers, and students interested in the study, use, and management of rangeland resources for livestock, wildlife, watershed, and recreation.

5262 ■ Soil and Water Conservation Society
945 SW Ankeny Rd.
Ankeny, IA 50023

Ph: (515)289-2331
Fax: (515)289-1227
E-mail: swcs@swcs.org
URL: http://www.swcs.org

Description: Advances the science and art of natural resource conservation. Enhances the capabilities of conservationists through training and professional development. Maintains standards and encourages the spirit of professionalism among conservationists through networking and mutual support.

5263 ■ Student Conservation Association (SCA)
PO Box 550
Charlestown, NH 03603-0550
Ph: (603)543-1700
Fax: (603)543-1828
E-mail: dfitzgerald@thesca.org
URL: http://www.thesca.org

Description: Works to build the next generation of conservation leaders and inspire lifelong stewardship of the environment and communities by engaging young people in hands-on service to the land. Provides conservation service opportunities, outdoor education and leadership development for young people. Offers college and graduate students, as well as older adults expense-paid conservation internships, these positions includes wildlife research, wilderness patrols and interpretive opportunities and provide participants with valuable hands-on career experience. Places 15-19 year old high school

students in four-week volunteer conservation crews in national parks forests and refuges across the country each summer to accomplish a range of trail building and habitat conservation projects. Offers year-round diversity conservation programs for young women and young persons of color in leading metropolitan areas of U.S.

5264 ■ Tropical Forest Group
1125 Ft. Stockton Dr.
San Diego, CA 92103
E-mail: info@tropicalforestgroup.org
URL: http://tropicalforestgroup.org

Description: Promotes the conservation and restoration of the planet's remaining tropical forests. Supports research and development of policies that help maintain the planet's most vital biome. Provides assistance to projects that restore and conserve tropical forests.

5265 ■ World Federation for Coral Reef Conservation
PO Box 942
Safety Harbor, FL 34695
E-mail: vic.ferguson@wfcrc.org
URL: http://wfcrc.org/default.aspx

Description: Works to stop the destruction of coral reefs by involving local citizens, scientists and recreational divers. Collaborates with like-minded organizations in implementing programs for coral reef decline management. Supports conservation efforts on coral reefs.

SOURCES OF HELP-WANTED ADS

5266 ■ *Advanced Fuel Cell Technology*
Seven Mountains Scientific Inc.
PO Box 650
913 Tressler St.
Boalsburg, PA 16827
Ph: (814)466-6559
Fax: (814)466-2777
E-mail: mike@7ms.com
URL: http://www.7ms.com

Monthly. Covers research on fuel cell technology and the people and companies involved with the development of such technology.

5267 ■ *AIE Perspectives Newsmagazine*
American Institute of Engineers
4630 Appian Way, Ste. 206
El Sobrante, CA 94803-1875
Ph: (510)758-6240
Fax: (510)758-6240
URL: http://www.members-aie.org

Monthly. Professional magazine covering engineering.

5268 ■ *Engineering Conferences International Symposium Series*
Berkeley Electronic Press
2809 Telegraph Ave., Ste. 202
Berkeley, CA 94705-1167
Ph: (510)665-1200
Fax: (510)665-1201
URL: http://services.bepress.com/eci/

Journal focusing on advance engineering science.

5269 ■ *ENR: Engineering News-Record*
McGraw-Hill Inc.
PO Box 182604
Columbus, OH 43218
Ph: (614)430-4000
Fax: (614)759-3749
Fr: 877-833-5524
URL: http://enr.construction.com/Default.asp

Weekly. $49.00/year for individuals, print; $89.00/year for Canada, print; $125.00/year for other countries, print. Magazine focusing on engineering and construction.

5270 ■ *High Technology Careers Magazine*
HTC
4701 Patrick Henry Dr., No. 1901
Santa Clara, CA 95054
Fax: (408)567-0242
URL: http://www.hightechcareers.com

Bimonthly. $29.00/year; $35.00/year for Canada; $85.00/year for out of country. Magazine (tabloid) containing employment opportunity information for the engineering and technical community.

5271 ■ *InterJournal*
New England Complex Systems Institute
283 Main St., Ste. 319
Cambridge, MA 02142
Ph: (617)547-4100
Fax: (617)661-7711
URL: http://www.interjournal.org/

Journal covering the fields of science and engineering.

5272 ■ *International Journal of Energetic Materials and Chemical Propulsion*
Begell House Inc.
50 Cross Hwy.
Redding, CT 06896
Ph: (203)938-1300
Fax: (203)938-1304
URL: http://www.begellhouse.com/journals/
17bbb47e377ce023

$1,240.00/year for institutions. Journal promoting scientific investigation, technical advancements and information exchange on energetic materials and chemical propulsion.

5273 ■ *National Fuel Cell Research Center Journal*
National Fuel Cell Research Center
University of California Irvine
221 Engineering Lab Facility, Bldg. 323
Irvine, CA 92697-3550
Ph: (949)824-1999
Fax: (949)824-7423
E-mail: ssr@nfcrc.uci.edu
URL: http://www.nfcrc.uci.edu

Quarterly. $60/year. Provides a forum for the discussion of information related to high efficiency, environmentally sensitive energy and power technologies.

5274 ■ *NSBE Magazine*
NSBE Publications
205 Daingerfield Rd.
Alexandria, VA 22314
Ph: (703)549-2207
Fax: (703)683-5312
URL: http://www.nsbe.org/News-Media/Magazines/
About-NSBE-Magazine

$20.00/year for individuals; $35.00/year for other countries; $15.00/year for students. Journal providing information on engineering careers, self-development, and cultural issues for recent graduates with technical majors.

5275 ■ *PE*
National Society of Professional Engineers
1420 King St.
Alexandria, VA 22314
Ph: (703)684-2800
Fax: (703)684-4875
URL: http://www.nspe.org/PEmagazine/index.html

Monthly. Magazine (tabloid) covering professional, legislative, and techology issues for an engineering audience.

5276 ■ *Sustainable Facility*
BNP Media
2401 W Big Beaver Rd., Ste. 700
Troy, MI 48084-3333
Ph: (847)763-9534
Fax: (847)763-9538
URL: http://www.sustainablefacility.com/

Monthly. Magazine reporting on the energy management market as it relates to commercial, industrial, and institutional facilities.

5277 ■ *SWE, Magazine of the Society of Women Engineers*
Society of Women Engineers
120 S La Salle St., Ste. 1515
Chicago, IL 60603
Ph: (312)596-5223
Fr: 877-793-4636
URL: http://societyofwomenengineers.swe.org/
index.php

Quarterly. $30.00/year for nonmembers. Magazine for engineering students and for women and men working in the engineering and technology fields. Covers career guidance, continuing development and topical issues.

5278 ■ *WEPANEWS*
Women in Engineering Programs & Advocates Network
1901 E Asbury Ave., Ste. 220
Denver, CO 80208
Ph: (303)871-4643
Fax: (303)871-4628
E-mail: dmatt@wepan.org
URL: http://www.wepan.org

Description: 2/year. Seeks to provide greater access for women to careers in engineering. Includes news of graduate, undergraduate, freshmen, precollege, and re-entry engineering programs for women. Recurring features include job listings, faculty, grant, and conference news, international engineering program news, action group news, notices of publications available, and a column titled Kudos.

5279 ■ *Woman Engineer*
Equal Opportunity Publications, Inc.
445 Broadhollow Rd., Ste. 425
Melville, NY 11747
Ph: (631)421-9421
Fax: (631)421-1352
E-mail: info@eop.com
URL: http://www.eop.com

Annual. Magazine that is offered at no charge to qualified female engineering, computer-science, and information-technology students and professionals seeking to find employment and advancement in their careers.

EMPLOYER DIRECTORIES AND NETWORKING LISTS

5280 ■ *Careers in Focus—Engineering*
Facts On File Inc.
132 W 31st St., 17th Fl.
New York, NY 10001

Ph: (212)967-8800
Fax: 800-678-3633
Fr: 800-322-8755
URL: http://www.infobasepublishing.com

Latest edition 3rd; Published July, 2007. $32.95 for individuals. Covers: An overview of engineering, followed by a selection of jobs profiled in detail, including the nature of the job, earnings, prospects for employment, what kind of training and skills it requires, and sources for further information.

HANDBOOKS AND MANUALS

5281 ■ *Great Jobs for Engineering Majors*
The McGraw-Hill Companies
PO Box 182604
Columbus, OH 43272
Fax: (614)759-3749
Fr: 877-883-5524
E-mail: customer.service@mcgraw-hill.com
URL: http://www.mhprofessional.com/
  product.php?isbn=0071641963

Geraldine O. Garner. Second edition, 2008. $16.95. 192 pages. Covers all the career options open to students majoring in engineering.

EMPLOYMENT AGENCIES AND SEARCH FIRMS

5282 ■ **Aureus Group**
C&A Plz., 13609 California St., Ste. 100
Omaha, NE 68154-3503
Ph: (402)891-6900
Fax: (402)891-1290
Fr: 888-239-5993
E-mail: omaha@aureusgroup.com
URL: http://www.aureusgroup.com

Provides human capital management services in a wide variety of industries. Executive search and recruiting consultants specializing in six areas: accounting and finance, data processing, aerospace, engineering, manufacturing and medical professionals. Industries served: hospitals, all mainframe computer shops and all areas of accounting.

ONLINE JOB SOURCES AND SERVICES

5283 ■ **BiofuelEngineerJobs.com**
URL: http://www.biofuelengineerjobs.com

Description: Features biofuel engineer jobs, salary information and surveys, resume postings, and other career resources.

5284 ■ **Fuel Cells 2000**
1100 H St. NW, Ste. 800
Washington, DC 20005
Ph: (202)785-4222
Fax: (202)785-4313
E-mail: jennifer@fuelcells.org
URL: http://www.fuelcells.org

Description: Provides news, educational resources, and job postings.

TRADESHOWS

5285 ■ **American Society for Engineering Education Annual Conference and Exposition**
American Society for Engineering Education
1818 N. St. N.W., Ste. 600
Washington, DC 20036-2479
Ph: (202)331-3500
Fax: (202)265-8504
E-mail: conferences@asee.org
URL: http://www.asee.org

Annual. Primary Exhibits: Publications, engineering supplies and equipment, computers, software, and research companies all products and services related to engineering education. Dates and Locations: 2012 Jun 10-13; San Antonio, TX.

OTHER SOURCES

5286 ■ **American Association of Blacks in Energy (AABE)**
1625 K St. NW, Ste. 405
Washington, DC 20006
Ph: (202)371-9530
Fax: (202)371-9218
Fr: 800-466-0204
E-mail: info@aabe.org
URL: http://www.aabe.org

Description: Seeks to increase the knowledge, understanding, and awareness of the minority community in energy issues by serving as an energy information source for policymakers, recommending blacks and other minorities to appropriate energy officials and executives, encouraging students to pursue professional careers in the energy industry, and advocating the participation of blacks and other minorities in energy programs and policymaking activities. Updates members on key legislation and regulations being developed by the Department of Energy, the Department of Interior, the Department of Commerce, the Small Business Administration, and other federal and state agencies.

5287 ■ **American Association of Engineering Societies (AAES)**
1801 Alexander Bell Dr.
Reston, VA 20191
Ph: (202)296-2237
Fax: (202)296-1151
Fr: 888-400-2237
E-mail: dbateson@aaes.org
URL: http://www.aaes.org

Description: Coordinates the efforts of the member societies in the provision of reliable and objective information to the general public concerning issues which affect the engineering profession and the field of engineering as a whole; collects, analyzes, documents, and disseminates data which will inform the general public of the relationship between engineering and the national welfare; provides a forum for the engineering societies to exchange and discuss their views on matters of common interest; and represents the U.S. engineering community abroad through representation in WFEO and UPADI.

5288 ■ **American Engineering Association (AEA)**
533 Waterside Blvd.
Monroe Township, NJ 08831
Ph: (201)664-6954
E-mail: aea@aea.org
URL: http://www.aea.org

Description: Members consist of Engineers and engineering professionals. Purpose to advance the engineering profession and U.S. engineering capabilities. Issues of concern include age discrimination, immigration laws, displacement of U.S. Engineers by foreign workers, trade agreements, off shoring of U.S. Engineering and manufacturing jobs, loss of U.S. manufacturing and engineering capability, and recruitment of foreign students. Testifies before Congress. Holds local Chapter meetings.

5289 ■ **American Hydrogen Association**
2350 W Shangri La
Phoenix, AZ 85029
Ph: (602)328-4238
URL: http://www.clean-air.org

Description: Seeks to stimulate interest and help establish the renewable hydrogen energy economy.

5290 ■ **American Institute of Engineers (AIE)**
4630 Appian Way, Ste. 206
El Sobrante, CA 94803-1875
Ph: (510)758-6240
Fax: (510)758-6240
E-mail: aie@aieonline.org
URL: http://www.members-aie.org

Description: Professional association for engineers, scientists, and mathematicians. Multi-disciplined, non-technical association who aims to improve the stature and image of engineers, scientists, and mathematicians. Provides endorsements, awards and opportunities for small business start-ups within the AIE Councils. Sponsors "LA Engineer", a comedy-drama television series; produces annual "Academy Hall of FAME (TV)".

5291 ■ **Association of Energy Engineers**
4025 Pleasantdale Rd., Ste. 420
Atlanta, GA 30340
Ph: (770)447-5083
Fax: (770)446-3969
E-mail: jennifer@aeecenter.org
URL: http://www.aeecenter.org

Description: Provides information on energy efficiency, utility deregulation, facility management, plant engineering, and environmental compliance. Offers resources such as seminars, tradeshows, and certification programs.

5292 ■ **California Fuel Cell Partnership**
3300 Industrial Blvd., Ste. 1000
West Sacramento, CA 95691
Ph: (916)371-2870
Fax: (916)375-2008
E-mail: info@cafcp.org
URL: http://cafcp.org

Description: Auto manufacturers, energy companies, fuel cell technology companies, and government agencies striving to advance new vehicle technology.

5293 ■ **Engineering Society of Detroit (ESD)**
20700 Civic Center Dr., Ste. 450
Southfield, MI 48076
Ph: (248)353-0735
Fax: (248)353-0736
E-mail: esd@esd.org
URL: http://ww2.esd.org/home.htm

Description: Engineers from all disciplines; scientists and technologists. Conducts technical programs and engineering refresher courses; sponsors conferences and expositions. Maintains speakers' bureau; offers placement services; although based in Detroit, MI, society membership is international.

5294 ■ **Engineering Workforce Commission (EWC)**
1801 Alexander Bell Dr.
Reston, VA 20191
Ph: (202)296-2237
Fax: (202)296-1151
Fr: 888-400-2237
E-mail: dbateson@aaes.org
URL: http://www.ewc-online.org

Description: Represents commissioners appointed by member societies of the American Association of Engineering Societies to engage in studies and analyses of the supply, demand, use and remuneration of engineering and technical personnel. Provides representation to government groups dealing with professional manpower policy; consults with industry. Gathers and disseminates information on the engineering profession. Conducts surveys of engineering school enrollments, degrees, and salaries; monitors federal labor statistics.

5295 ■ **International Federation of Professional and Technical Engineers (IFPTE)**
501 3rd St. NW, Ste. 701
Washington, DC 20001
Ph: (202)239-4880

Fax: (202)239-4881
E-mail: generalinfo@ifpte.org
URL: http://www.ifpte.org

Description: Represents engineers, scientists, architects and technicians.

5296 ■ National Action Council for Minorities in Engineering (NACME)
440 Hamilton Ave., Ste. 302
White Plains, NY 10601-1813
Ph: (914)539-4010
Fax: (914)539-4032
E-mail: info@nacme.org
URL: http://www.nacme.org

Description: Leads the national effort to increase access to careers in engineering and other science-based disciplines. Conducts research and public policy analysis, develops and operates national demonstration programs at precollege and university levels, and disseminates information through publications, conferences and electronic media. Serves as a privately funded source of scholarships for minority students in engineering.

5297 ■ National Society of Professional Engineers (NSPE)
1420 King St.
Alexandria, VA 22314-2794
Ph: (703)684-2800
Fax: (703)836-4875
Fr: 888-285-6773
E-mail: memserv@nspe.org
URL: http://www.nspe.org

Description: Represents professional engineers and engineers-in-training in all fields registered in accordance with the laws of states or territories of the U.S. or provinces of Canada; qualified graduate engineers, student members, and registered land surveyors. Is concerned with social, professional, ethical, and economic considerations of engineering

as a profession; encompasses programs in public relations, employment practices, ethical considerations, education, and career guidance. Monitors legislative and regulatory actions of interest to the engineering profession.

5298 ■ Society of Engineering Science (SES)
University of Illinois at Urbana-Champaign
Beckman Institute for Advanced Science and Technology
405 N Mathews Ave., Rm. 3361
Urbana, IL 61801
E-mail: swhite@uiuc.edu
URL: http://www.sesinc.org

Description: Individuals with at least a baccalaureate degree who are engaged in any aspect of engineering science or in other pursuits that contribute to the advancement of engineering science. Fosters and promotes the interchange of ideas and information among the various fields of engineering science and among engineering science and the fields of theoretical and applied physics, chemistry, and mathematics. Is dedicated to the advancement of interdisciplinary research and to the establishment of a bridge between science and engineering.

5299 ■ Society of Hispanic Professional Engineers (SHPE)
13181 Crossroads Pkwy. N, Ste. 450
City of Industry, CA 91746-3496
Ph: (323)725-3970
Fax: (323)725-0316
E-mail: shpenational@shpe.org
URL: http://oneshpe.shpe.org/wps/portal/national

Description: Represents engineers, student engineers, and scientists. Aims to increase the number of Hispanic engineers by providing motivation and support to students. Sponsors competitions and educational programs. Maintains placement service and speakers' bureau; compiles statistics.

5300 ■ Society of Women Engineers (SWE)
203 N La Salle St., Ste. 1675
Chicago, IL 60601
Ph: (312)596-5223
Fax: (312)596-5252
Fr: 877-SWE-INFO
E-mail: hq@swe.org
URL: http://societyofwomenengineers.swe.org

Description: Educational and service organization representing both students and professional women in engineering and technical fields.

5301 ■ United Engineering Foundation (UEF)
PO Box 70
Mount Vernon, VA 22121-0070
Ph: (973)244-2328
Fax: (973)882-5155
E-mail: engfnd@aol.com
URL: http://www.uefoundation.org

Description: Federation of 5 major national engineering societies: American Institute of Chemical Engineers; American Institute of Mining, Metallurgical and Petroleum Engineers; American Society of Civil Engineers; American Society of Mechanical Engineers; Institute of Electrical and Electronics Engineers. Supports research in engineering and advances the engineering arts and sciences through its conference program.

5302 ■ U.S. Fuel Cell Council
1211 Connecticut Ave. NW, Ste. 600
Washington, DC 20036
Ph: (202)261-1331
E-mail: brose@usfcc.com
URL: http://www.usfcc.com

Description: Dedicated to fostering the commercialization of fuel cells in the United States. Provides technical advice, collects information and issues reports on the industry, and raises public awareness of fuel cells and their potential.

Fund Raisers

Sources of Help-Wanted Ads

5303 ■ *The Chronicle of Philanthropy*
The Chronicle of Philanthropy
1255 23rd St. NW, Ste. 700
Washington, DC 20037
Ph: (202)466-1200
E-mail: editor@philanthropy.com
URL: http://philanthropy.com

$72.00/year for individuals; $125.00/year for two years; $72.00/year for individuals, online access only; $99.75/year for Canada; $72.00/year for Canada, on-line access only; $135.00/year for other countries; $72.00/year for other countries, online access only. Magazine covering fundraising, philanthropy, and non-profit organizations. Includes information on tax rulings, new grants, and statistics, reports on grant makers, and profiles of foundations.

5304 ■ *Community Radio News*
National Federation of Community Broadcasters
1970 Broadway, Ste. 1000
Oakland, CA 94612
Ph: (510)451-8200
Fax: (510)451-8208
E-mail: newsletter@nfcb.org
URL: http://www.nfcb.org

Description: Monthly. Serves as a medium of communication for independent, community-licensed radio stations. Contains brief articles and news items on such topics as public broadcasting and programming, legislative developments, activities of the Federal Communications Commission, and local stations. Recurring features include notices of grants and awards, job openings, and a calendar of events/conferences for noncommercial broadcasters.

5305 ■ *DM News*
DM News
114 W 26th St., 4th Fl.
New York, NY 10001
Ph: (646)638-6000
Fax: (646)638-6159
E-mail: inquiry@dmnews.com
URL: http://www.dmnews.com

Weekly. $148.00/year for individuals; $198.00/year for Canada; $228.00/year for other countries; $265.00/year for two years; $355.00/year for Canada, 2 years; $395.00/year for other countries, 2 years. Tabloid newspaper for publishers, fund raisers, financial marketers, catalogers, package goods advertisers and their agencies, and other marketers who use direct mail, mail order advertising, catalogs, or other direct response media to sell their products or services.

5306 ■ *The NonProfit Times*
NPT Publishing Group Inc.
201 Littleton Rd., 2nd Fl.
Morris Plains, NJ 07950
Ph: (973)401-0202

Fax: (973)401-0404
E-mail: ednchief@nptimes.com
URL: http://www.nptimes.com/

$49.95/year for individuals, print; $19.95/year for individuals, digital only; $59.95/year for individuals, digital & print. Trade journal serving nonprofit organizations.

Employer Directories and Networking Lists

5307 ■ *American Association of Fund-Raising Counsel Membership Directory*
American Association of Fund-Raising Counsel Inc.
4700 W Lake Ave.
Glenview, IL 60025
Ph: (847)375-4709
Fr: 800-462-2372
URL: http://www.aafrc.org/

Annual. Covers: Member fund-raising consulting firms. Entries include: Company name, address, phone, fax, geographical area served, types of clients, description of services. Arrangement: Alphabetical.

5308 ■ *National Directory of Nonprofit Organizations*
Taft Group
27500 Drake Rd.
Farmington Hills, MI 48331-3535
Ph: (248)699-4253
Fax: (248)699-8061
Fr: 800-877-4253
URL: http://www.gale.cengage.com

Annual, latest edition 27th; February 2012. $718.00 for individuals; $484.00 for individuals. Covers: Over 265,000 nonprofit organizations; volume 1 covers organizations with annual incomes of over $100,000; volume 2 covers organizations with incomes between $25,000 and $99,999. Entries include: Organization name, address, phone, annual income, IRS filing status, employer identification number, tax deductible status, activity description. Arrangement: Alphabetical. Indexes: Area of activity, geographical.

Handbooks and Manuals

5309 ■ *Careers for Good Samaritans and Other Humanitarian Types*
The McGraw-Hill Companies
PO Box 182604
Columbus, OH 43272
Fax: (614)759-3749
Fr: 877-883-5524
E-mail: customer.service@mcgraw-hill.com
URL: http://www.mhprofessional.com

Marjorie Eberts and Margaret Gisler. Third edition,

2006. $16.95 (paper). 160 pages. Contains hundreds of ideas for turning good work into paid work. Inventories opportunities in service organizations like the Red Cross, Goodwill, and the Salvation Army; religious groups, VISTA, the Peace Corps, and UNICEF; and agencies at all levels of the government. Part of Careers for You series.

5310 ■ *Fundraising As a Profession: Advancements and Challenges in the Field*
Jossey-Bass
989 Market St.
San Francisco, CA 94103
Ph: (415)433-1740
Fax: (415)433-0499
Fr: 800-255-5945
E-mail: custserv@wiley.com
URL: http://www.josseybass.com/WileyCDA/

Lilya D. Wagner and Patrick Ryan. May 2004. $29.00. 104 pages. Part of the J-B PF Single Issue Philanthropic Fundraising Series.

5311 ■ *Great Jobs for Liberal Arts Majors*
The McGraw-Hill Companies
PO Box 182604
Columbus, OH 43272
Fax: (614)759-3749
Fr: 877-883-5524
E-mail: customer.service@mcgraw-hill.com
URL: http://www.mhprofessional.com/
   product.php?isbn=0071482148

Blythe Camenson. Second edition, 2007. $16.95 (paper). 192 pages.

Employment Agencies and Search Firms

5312 ■ Thomas R. Moore Executive Search L.L.C.
2000 E Lamar Blvd., Ste. 600
Arlington, TX 76006
Ph: (817)548-8766
Fax: (817)588-3099
E-mail: trmsearch@msn.com

Search firm focusing on the recruitment of experienced fund raising professionals for institutions, organizations and firms associated with the not-for-profit industry.

Online Job Sources and Services

5313 ■ FundraisingCrossing.com
URL: http://www.fundraisingcrossing.com

Description: Provides a comprehensive collection of researched fundraising job openings. Provides instant access to listings based on particular area of focus. Includes ads from Fortune 500 and Fortune 1,000 companies.

5314 ■ FundraisingJobs.com
URL: http://www.fundraisingjobs.com

Description: Provides job postings. Also allows users to post resumes for potential employers.

5315 ■ Philanthropy.com
URL: http://philanthropy.com/section/Jobs/224

Description: Provides news and job listings to those in the nonprofit sector. Information from The Chronicle of Philanthropy is available through the website.

OTHER SOURCES

5316 ■ Association of Fundraising
Professionals
4300 Wilson Blvd., Ste. 300
Arlington, VA 22203
Ph: (703)684-0410
Fax: (703)684-0540

Fr: 800-666-3863
URL: http://www.afpnet.org

Description: Consists of fundraising executives who work for non-profit and philanthropic organizations. Fosters the development and growth of professional fundraising executives. Promotes high ethical standards in the fundraising profession. Supports philanthropy through advocacy, research, education and certification programs.

5317 ■ Association of Professional
Researchers for Advancement (APRA)
401 N Michigan Ave., Ste. 2200
Chicago, IL 60611
Ph: (312)321-5196
Fax: (312)673-6966
E-mail: info@aprahome.org
URL: http://www.aprahome.org

Description: Individuals involved in educational, medical, cultural, and religious organizations; fundraising consultants. Facilitates education and dissemination of information about prospect research; encourages professional development and cooperative relationships among members. Prospect research is aimed at securing gifts, grants, and charitable donations for nonprofit organizations.

5318 ■ Society for Nonprofit Organizations
(SNPO)
5820 Canton Center Rd., Ste. 165
Canton, MI 48187-2683
Ph: (734)451-3582
Fax: (734)451-5935
E-mail: info@snpo.org
URL: http://www.snpo.org

Description: Brings together those who serve in the nonprofit world in order to build a strong network of professionals throughout the country; provides a forum for the exchange of information, knowledge, and ideas on strengthening and increasing productivity within nonprofit organizations and among their leaders. Mission is accomplished through the publication of Nonprofit World magazine, educational programs offered by the Learning Institute, and other communications with its members.

SOURCES OF HELP-WANTED ADS

5319 ■ *Funeral Monitor*
Abbott & Hast Publications
2361 Horseshoe Dr.
West Bloomfield, MI 48322
Ph: (248)737-9294
Fax: (248)737-9296
Fr: 800-453-1199
E-mail: info@abbottandhast.com
URL: http://www.funeralmonitor.com

Description: Weekly. $239/year for domestic subscription; $265/year for foreign (U.S. funds). Provides information on the funeral industry.

5320 ■ *Funeral Service Insider*
United Communications Group
Two Washingtonian Center
9737 Washingtonian Blvd., Ste. 100
Gaithersburg, MD 20878-7364
Ph: (301)287-2700
Fax: (301)287-2039
URL: http://www.ucg.com

Description: Weekly. Covers the latest trends in funeral service education, legislation, franchising, marketing, and consumer purchasing. Recurring features include editorials, news of research, letters to the editor, and a calendar of events.

5321 ■ *NFDA Bulletin*
National Funeral Directors Association
13625 Bishop's Dr.
Brookfield, WI 53005-6607
Ph: (262)789-1880
Fax: (262)789-6977
Fr: 800-228-6332
E-mail: nfda@nfda.org
URL: http://www.nfda.org

Description: Monthly. Covers association activities and funeral business management topics. Reports on association news, government regulation, public relations issues, and local developments.

PLACEMENT AND JOB REFERRAL SERVICES

5322 ■ FuneralStaff
4430 Wade Green Rd., Ste. 180-138
Kennesaw, GA 30144
Ph: (770)966-8048
Fax: (770)966-8049
Fr: (866)386-7823
E-mail: funeralstaff@bellsouth.net
URL: http://www.funeralstaff.com

Full service staffing and consulting firm specializing in placing funeral service professionals, administrators and support staff.

HANDBOOKS AND MANUALS

5323 ■ *FabJob Guide to Become a Funeral Director*
FabJob Inc.
4616 - 25th Ave. NE, No. 224
Seattle, WA 98105
Ph: (403)949-4980
Fr: 888-322-5621
URL: http://www.fabjob.com/funeraldirector.asp

Kelly Boyer-Sagert. $19.97(e-book). 200 pages. Guide for anyone seeking a career in the funeral industry.

ONLINE JOB SOURCES AND SERVICES

5324 ■ FuneralJobs.com
URL: http://funeraljobs.com/go/jobs/Index

Description: Lists job postings around the country. Also provides interview and resume tips.

5325 ■ FuneralNet.com
Fr: 800-721-8166
E-mail: info@funeralnet.com
URL: http://www.funeralnet.com

Description: General mortuary science information site contains Funeral Careers section with information on continuing education and classifieds section with postings for internship and employment opportunities.

TRADESHOWS

5326 ■ National Funeral Directors Association Annual Convention & Expo
National Funeral Directors Association
13625 Bishop's Dr.
Brookfield, WI 53005-6607
Ph: (262)789-1880
Fax: (262)789-6977
Fr: 800-228-6332
E-mail: nfda@nfda.org
URL: http://www.nfda.org

Annual. Primary Exhibits: Equipment, supplies, and services for funeral directors and morticians. Dates and Locations: 2012 Oct 07-12; 2013 Oct 20-23.

5327 ■ New Jersey State Funeral Directors Association Convention
New Jersey State Funeral Directors Association
PO Box L
Manasquan, NJ 08736
Ph: (732)974-9444
Fax: (732)974-8144
E-mail: njsfda@njsfda.org
URL: http://www.njsfda.org

Annual. Primary Exhibits: Funeral industry equipment, supplies, and services.

5328 ■ South Dakota Funeral Directors Association Annual Convention
South Dakota Funeral Directors Association
25654 431st Ave.
Spencer, SD 57374
Ph: (605)226-9466
Fax: (605)226-2466
URL: http://www.sdfda.org

Annual. Primary Exhibits: Caskets, chemical supplies, publications, clothing, coaches, accounting services, computer services, vaults, funeral vehicles, and cemetery monument dealers.

OTHER SOURCES

5329 ■ American Board of Funeral Service Education
3414 Ashland Ave.
Ste. G
St. Joseph, MO 64506
Ph: (816)233-3747
Fax: (816)233-3793
E-mail: exdir@abfse.org
URL: http://www.abfse.org

Description: Serves as the national academic accreditation agency for college programs in Funeral Service and Mortuary Science Education.

5330 ■ Illinois Funeral Directors Association
215 S Grand Ave., W
Springfield, IL 62704-3838
Ph: (217)525-2000
Fax: (217)525-8342
Fr: 800-240-4332
E-mail: info@ifda.org
URL: http://www.ifda.org

Members: Funeral Directors seeking a common voice, a way to share information, ideas and methods, and to protect themselves and consumers through legislation. **Activities:** Offers services to members and the public, including a credit union, funeral financing, legislative lobbying, and a job location service.

5331 ■ National Funeral Directors Association
13625 Bishop's Dr.
Brookfield, WI 53005-6607
Ph: (262)789-1880
Fax: (262)789-6977
Fr: 800-228-6332
E-mail: nfda@nfda.org
URL: http://www.nfda.org

Description: Association web site contains employment classifieds and career resources such as licensing and educational requirements, continuing education credit opportunities and more for those interested in finding a position as a funeral director.

5332 ■ New York State Funeral Directors Association, Inc.
426 New Karner Rd.
Albany, NY 12205
Ph: (518)452-8230
Fax: (518)452-8667
Fr: 800-291-2629
E-mail: info@nysfda.org
URL: http://www.nysfda.org
Description: Aims to enhance the environment in which the members operate and to promote the highest standards of funeral service to the public.

EMPLOYER DIRECTORIES AND NETWORKING LISTS

5333 ■ *American Casino Guide*
Casino Vacations
PO Box 703
Dania, FL 33004
Ph: (954)989-2766
URL: http://www.americancasinoguide.com

Annual, Latest edition 2011. $18.95 for individuals; $11.75 for individuals. Covers: more than 700 casino/resorts, riverboat casinos, and Indian casinos in the U.S. Entries include: Casino name, address, phone, toll-free number, room rates, dining information, games offered, features, web site addresses. Arrangement: Geographical. Indexes: Name.

5334 ■ *Career Opportunities in Casinos and Casino Hotels*
Facts On File Inc.
132 W 31st St., 17th Fl.
New York, NY 10001
Ph: (212)967-8800
Fax: 800-678-3633
Fr: 800-322-8755
URL: http://factsonfile.infobasepublishing.com/

Irregular, Latest edition 2nd; Published May, 2009. $49.50 for individuals. Publication includes: A directory of casinos and cruise lines, gaming conferences and expos, seminars, workshops, and industry Web sites. Principal content of publication is 100 occupations in 10 employment sections on careers in gaming, administration, management, security, entertainment, hotel management, and food and beverage service in the casino industry.

5335 ■ *Casino Camping*
Roundabout Publications
PO Box 569
La Cygne, KS 66040
Fr: 800-455-2207
URL: http://www.travelbooksusa.com/shop/viewitem.php?productid=22

Annual, Latest edition 2010. $15.95 for individuals. Covers: 300 RV-friendly casinos in America. Entries include: Contact information, detailed description, available discounts, driving directions, and RV parking information.

5336 ■ *Casino Vendors Guide*
Casino City Press
95 Wells Ave.
Newton, MA 02459
Ph: (617)332-2850
Fax: (617)964-2280
Fr: 800-490-1715
URL: http://www.casinocitypress.com

Annual, Latest edition 2011. $49.95. Covers: 10,000 industry suppliers, manufacturers, and distributors, 1,000 gaming products and services, 1,500 gaming

properties around the world, gaming associations, analysts, attorneys, trade shows, and trade publications. Entries include: Company name, address, branch office locations, phone and fax numbers, email and website addresses, executive contacts and company description.

5337 ■ *Gaming Business Directory*
Casino City Press
95 Wells Ave.
Newton, MA 02459
Ph: (617)332-2850
Fax: (617)964-2280
Fr: 800-490-1715
URL: http://www.casinocitypress.com

Annual, Latest edition 2009-2010. $249.95; $399.95 for individuals; $449.95. Covers: Information on more than 4,500 casinos, card rooms, horse tracks, dog tracks, and casino cruises and cruise ships, around the world, 650 major gaming property owners, and 2,000 gaming properties owned and operated. Entries include: 26,000 executive contacts, names and titles by department, property name, location and mailing addresses, and phone and fax numbers. Indexes: Alphabetical by size; alphabetical by property type.

EMPLOYMENT AGENCIES AND SEARCH FIRMS

5338 ■ The IMC Group of Companies Ltd.
120 White Plains Rd., Ste. 405
Tarrytown, NY 10591
Ph: (914)468-7050
Fax: (914)468-7051
E-mail: herbert.regehly@the-imc.com
URL: http://www.the-imc.com

International executive recruiting and management consulting company providing leading-edge services for the hospitality, leisure, entertainment, gaming and new media industries throughout the United States, Europe, Africa, Asia Pacific and Latin America.

ONLINE JOB SOURCES AND SERVICES

5339 ■ Casino Careers Online
URL: http://www.casinocareers.com

Description: Serves as a job board that focuses on career opportunities for different levels and departments within the gaming industry.

5340 ■ CasinoGigs.net
URL: http://www.casinogigs.net

Description: Serves as a career community for the gambling industry. Features job openings for casino workers, research into the arts, entertainment & gaming employment market, and a career articles section written and frequented by industry professionals.

5341 ■ HCareers.com
E-mail: hospitalitydivision@hcareers.com
URL: http://www.hcareers.com

Description: Connects employers and candidates within the hospitality industry. Enables candidates to search for jobs within a specific industry or location.

TRADESHOWS

5342 ■ North American Association of State and Provincial Lotteries Conference and Trade Show
North American Association of State and Provincial Lotteries
6 N. Broadway
Geneva, OH 44041
Ph: (440)466-5630
Fax: (440)466-5649
E-mail: info@nasplhq.org
URL: http://www.naspl.org

Annual. Primary Exhibits: Lottery equipment, supplies, and services.

OTHER SOURCES

5343 ■ American Gaming Association
1299 Pennsylvania Ave. NW, Ste. 1175
Washington, DC 20004
Ph: (202)552-2675
Fax: (202)552-2676
E-mail: info@americangaming.org
URL: http://www.americangaming.org

Description: Represents the commercial casino entertainment industry by addressing federal legislative and regulatory issues affecting its members and their employees and customers, such as federal taxation, regulatory issues, and travel and tourism matters.

5344 ■ Gambling Portal Webmasters Association (GPWA)
95 Wells Ave.
Newton Centre, MA 02459
Ph: (617)332-2850
Fax: (617)964-2280
Fr: 800-490-1715
E-mail: sales@gpwa.org
URL: http://www.gpwa.org

Description: Helps members succeed in the online gaming industry. Strengthens relationships between affiliate program managers and portal webmasters. Provides members with opportunities to collaborate with other webmasters and online gaming affiliates.

5345 ■ Gaming Standards Association (GSA)
48377 Fremont Blvd., Ste. 117
Fremont, CA 94538
Ph: (510)492-4060

Fax: (510)492-4001
E-mail: sec@gamingstandards.com
URL: http://www.gamingstandards.com
Description: Gaming manufacturers, suppliers and operators. Promotes identification, definition, development, and implementation of open standards to facilitate innovation, education and communication for the gaming industry.

5346 ■ International Simulation and Gaming Association (ISAGA)
George Washington University
School of Business and Public Mgt.
Monroe Hall
Washington, DC 20052

Ph: (202)994-4930
E-mail: info@isaga.info
URL: http://www.isaga.info
Description: Individuals interested in any facet of simulation and gaming. Maintains resource lists; conducts specialized education; sponsors workshops, symposia, and research activities.

5347 ■ North American Gaming Regulators Association
1000 Westgate Dr., Ste. 252
St. Paul, MN 55114

Ph: (651)203-7244
Fax: (651)290-2266
E-mail: info@nagra.org
URL: http://www.nagra.org
Description: Brings together agencies that regulate gaming activities and provides a forum for the mutual exchange of regulatory information and techniques. Collects and disseminates regulatory and enforcement information, procedures, and experiences from all jurisdictions provided on-going gaming education and training for all members.

SOURCES OF HELP-WANTED ADS

5348 ■ *Academy of Management Journal*
Academy of Management
235 Elm Rd.
PO Box 3020
Briarcliff Manor, NY 10510-8020
Ph: (914)923-2607
Fax: (914)923-2615
URL: http://journals.aomonline.org/amj/
Bimonthly. Professional journal covering management.

5349 ■ *Academy of Management Learning & Education*
Academy of Management
235 Elm Rd.
PO Box 3020
Briarcliff Manor, NY 10510-8020
Ph: (914)923-2607
Fax: (914)923-2615
URL: http://journals.aomonline.org/amle
Quarterly. $85.00/year for individuals, print; $130.00/year for individuals, print & online; $125.00/year for libraries, print; $170.00/year for libraries, print and online; $105.00/year for other countries, print; $150.00/year for other countries, print & online; $195.00/year for other countries, print, corporate library; $235.00/year for other countries, print & online, corporate library. Journal covering management issues for professionals.

5350 ■ *AMI Bulletin*
Association for Management Information in Financial Services (AMI)
14247 Saffron Cir.
Carmel, IN 46032
Ph: (317)815-5857
Fax: (317)815-5877
E-mail: ami2@amifs.org
URL: http://www.amifs.org/
Description: Quarterly. Monitors events and profiles members and committees. Recurring features include reports of meetings and workshops and a calendar of events.

5351 ■ *Association News*
Schneider Publishing Company Inc.
11835 W Olympic Blvd., 12th Fl.
Los Angeles, CA 90064
Ph: (310)577-3700
Fax: (310)577-3715
URL: http://www.associationnews.com/
Monthly. Free. Magazine containing management and meeting plan information for association executives and meeting planners.

5352 ■ *Aviation Today*
Access Intelligence L.L.C.
4 Choke Cherry Rd., 2nd Fl.
Rockville, MD 20850

Ph: (301)354-2000
Fax: (301)309-3847
Fr: 800-777-5006
E-mail: info@accessintel.com
URL: http://www.accessintel.com
Description: Covers the commuter/regional airline industry, including airline management, marketing, labor, personnel changes, aircraft acquisitions, new products, and the financial and operational environment. Recurring features include interviews, news of research, a calendar of events, reports of meetings, job listings, and notices of publications available.

5353 ■ *Business Performance Management*
Penton Media Inc.
249 W 17th St.
New York, NY 10011
Ph: (212)204-4200
URL: http://www.bpmmag.net/
Free to qualified subscribers. Magazine for business managers. Covers organizing, automating, and analyzing of business methodologies and processes.

5354 ■ *CEO Update*
1990 M St. NW, 8th Fl.
Washington, DC 20036
Ph: (202)721-7656
E-mail: info@ceoupdate.com
URL: http://www.ceoupdate.com
Bimonthly. $395.00/year. Provides trend analysis and information on new and departing leaders. Offers senior-level openings in associations, professional societies, and nonprofits.

5355 ■ *CFO*
CFO Publishing
6 W 48th St., 7th Fl.
New York, NY 10036
Ph: (212)459-3004
Fax: (212)459-3007
URL: http://www.cfo.com/magazine/index.cfm/
    about?f=aboutus_nav
Monthly. $120.00/year for other countries; free, U.S. Business magazine for small to mid-sized companies.

5356 ■ *CXO*
IDG Communications Inc.
3 Speen St.
Framingham, MA 01701
Ph: (508)875-5000
URL: http://www.idg.com/www/IDGProducts.nsf/0/
    022796185EED5984852
Monthly. Magazine providing technology information for chief officers and managers.

5357 ■ *D CEO*
D Magazine
750 N Saint Paul St., Ste. 2100
Dallas, TX 75201
Ph: (214)939-3636

Fax: (214)748-4579
URL: http://www.dmagazine.com/Issues/D_CEO_
    APR_2009.aspx
Monthly. $27.00/year for individuals. Magazine for executives and business leaders.

5358 ■ *D & O Advisor*
American Lawyer Media L.P.
120 Broadway, 5th Fl.
New York, NY 10271
Ph: (212)457-9400
Fax: (646)417-7705
Fr: 800-603-6571
URL: http://www.alm.com
Quarterly. Magazine that offers advice and perspective on corporate oversight responsibilities for directors and officers.

5359 ■ *E Journal of Organizational Learning and Leadership*
WeLEAD Inc.
PO Box 202
Litchfield, OH 44253
Fr: 877-778-5494
URL: http://www.leadingtoday.org/weleadinlearning/
Semiannual. Free. Online academic journal about organizational leadership.

5360 ■ *Executive Leadership*
National Institute of Business Management
PO Box 9070
McLean, VA 22102
Fax: (703)905-8040
Fr: 800-543-2055
E-mail: customer@businessmanagementdaily.com
URL: http://www.businessmanagementdaily.com
Description: Monthly. $115/year. Shows the reader how to become a better leader. Contains information on taking charge in the workplace, enjoying a wider business perspective, leading organizations to more efficiency and greater success, and rising faster in the field of management.

5361 ■ *Executive Legal Adviser*
Incisive Media
120 Broadway, 5th Fl.
New York, NY 10271
Ph: (212)457-9400
Fax: (646)417-7705
URL: http://www.executivelegaladviser.com
Bimonthly. Free to qualified subscribers. Magazine that offers legal advice for corporate executives.

5362 ■ *Fleet Maintenance*
Cygnus Business Media Inc.
3 Huntington Quadrangle, Ste. 301 N
Melville, NY 11747
Ph: (631)845-2700
Fax: (631)845-7109
Fr: 800-308-6397
URL: http://www.fleetmag.com

Business tabloid magazine offering a chapterized curriculum of technical, regulatory and managerial information designed to help maintenance managers, directors and supervisors better perform their jobs and reduce their overall cost-per-mile.

5363 ■ Forbes
Forbes Magazine
60 5th Ave.
New York, NY 10011
Ph: (212)366-8900
Fr: 800-295-0893
URL: http://www.forbes.com

Biweekly. $19.99/year for individuals; $22.25/year for Canada. Magazine reporting on industry, business and finance management.

5364 ■ Forrester
Forrester Research Inc.
400 Technology Sq.
Cambridge, MA 02139
Ph: (617)613-5730
Fr: (866)367-7378
URL: http://www.forrester.com/mag

Free. Journal that aims to provide ideas and advice that is relevant to today's CEOs.

5365 ■ Franchising World
International Franchise Association
1501 K St. NW, Ste. 350
Washington, DC 20005
Ph: (202)628-8000
Fax: (202)628-0812
Fr: 800-543-1038
URL: http://www.franchise.org/

Monthly. $50.00/year for individuals. Trade magazine covering topics of interest to franchise company executives and the business world.

5366 ■ IndustryWeek
Penton Media Inc.
249 W 17th St.
New York, NY 10011
Ph: (212)204-4200
E-mail: iwinfo@industryweek.com
URL: http://www.industryweek.com

Monthly. Magazine containing articles to help industry executives sharpen their managerial skills and increase their effectiveness.

5367 ■ International Journal of Business Research
International Academy of Business and Economics
PO Box 2536
Ceres, CA 95307
Ph: (702)560-0653
Fax: (702)508-9166
URL: http://www.iabe.eu/domains/iabeX/
　journal.aspx?journalid=12

Peer-reviewed journal publishing theoretical, conceptual, and applied research on topics related to research, practice and teaching in all areas of business, management, and marketing.

5368 ■ Journal of Academic Leadership
Academic Leadership
600 Park St.
Rarick Hall 219
Hays, KS 67601-4099
Ph: (785)628-4547
URL: http://www.academicleadership.org/

Journal focusing on the leadership issues in the academic world.

5369 ■ Journal of Business and Psychology
Springer-Verlag New York Inc.
233 Spring St.
New York, NY 10013-1578
Ph: (212)460-1500
Fax: (212)460-1575
Fr: 800-777-4643
URL: http://www.springer.com/psychology/
　community+%26+environment

$904.00/year for institutions, print or online; $1,085.00/year for institutions, print & enchanced access. Journal covering all aspects of psychology that apply to the business segment. Includes topics such as personnel selection and training, organizational assessment and development, risk management and loss control, marketing and consumer behavior research.

5370 ■ Journal of International Business Strategy
International Academy of Business and Economics
PO Box 2536
Ceres, CA 95307
Ph: (702)560-0653
Fax: (702)508-9166
URL: http://www.iabe.eu/domains/iabeX/
　journal.aspx?journalid=7

Peer-reviewed journal publishing theoretical, conceptual, and applied research on topics related to strategy in international business.

5371 ■ The Los Angeles Business Journal
The Los Angeles Business Journal
5700 Wilshire, No. 170
Los Angeles, CA 90036
Ph: (213)549-5225
Fax: (213)549-5255
URL: http://www.labusinessjournal.com

Weekly (Mon.). $99.95/year for individuals; $179.95/year for two years. Newspaper (tabloid) covering local business news, business trends, executive profiles, and information for the Los Angeles area executive.

5372 ■ Management Research
M.E. Sharpe Inc.
80 Business Pk. Dr.
Armonk, NY 10504
Ph: (914)273-1800
Fax: (914)273-2106
Fr: 800-541-6563
URL: http://www.mesharpe.com/mall/
　results1.asp?ACR=JMR

$75.00/year for individuals; $399.00/year for institutions; $87.00/year for other countries; $441.00/year for institutions, other countries. International journal dedicated to advancing the understanding of management in private and public sector organizations through empirical investigation and theoretical analysis. Attempts to promote an international dialogue between researchers, improve the understanding of the nature of management in different settings, and achieve a reasonable transfer of research results to management practice in several contexts. Receptive to research across a broad range of management topics such as human resource management, organizational behavior, organizational theory, and strategic management. While not regional in nature, articles dealing with Iberoamerican issues are particularly welcomed.

5373 ■ Organization Management Journal
Eastern Academy of Management
c/o Vicki Fairbanks Taylor, VP
John I. Grove College of Business
45 Keefer Way
Mechanicsburg, PA 17011
Ph: (518)762-4651
Fax: (518)736-1716
E-mail: omj@palgrave.com
URL: http://www1.wnec.edu/omj

Free to qualified subscribers. Refereed, online journal focusing on organization management issues.

5374 ■ Public Performance and Management Review
M.E. Sharpe Inc.
80 Business Pk. Dr.
Armonk, NY 10504
Ph: (914)273-1800
Fax: (914)273-2106

Fr: 800-541-6563
URL: http://www.mesharpe.com/mall/
　results1.asp?ACR=pmr

Quarterly. $95.00/year for individuals; $528.00/year for institutions; $111.00/year for other countries; $560.00/year for institutions, other countries. Journal addressing a broad range of factors influencing the performance of public and nonprofit organizations and agencies. Aims to facilitate the development of innovative techniques and encourage a wider application of those already established; stimulate research and critical thinking about the relationship between public and private management theories; present integrated analyses of theories, concepts, strategies and techniques dealing with productivity, measurement and related questions of performance improvement; and provide a forum for practitioner-academic exchange. Continuing themes include managing for productivity, measuring and evaluating performance, improving budget strategies, managing human resources, building partnerships, and applying new technologies.

5375 ■ San Diego Business Journal
San Diego Business Journal
4909 Murphy Canyon Rd., Ste. 200
San Diego, CA 92123
Ph: (858)277-6359
Fax: (858)277-2149
URL: http://www.sdbj.com

Weekly (Mon.). $99.00/year for individuals; $180.00/year for two years. Metropolitan business newspaper specializing in investigative and enterprise reporting on San Diego County businesses and related issues.

5376 ■ San Diego Daily Transcript
San Diego Daily Transcript
2131 3rd Ave.
San Diego, CA 92101
Ph: (619)232-4381
Fax: (619)239-5716
Fr: 800-697-6397
URL: http://www.sddt.com

Daily (morn.). $229.30/year for individuals, print + online; $366.36/year for two years, print + online. Local business newspaper.

5377 ■ San Francisco Business Times
American City Business Journals Inc.
120 W Morehead St.
Charlotte, NC 28202
E-mail: sanfrancisco@bizjournals.com
URL: http://www.bizjournals.com/sanfrancisco

Weekly. $98.00/year for individuals; $176.00/year for two years; $198.00/year for individuals, three years. Local business newspaper (tabloid) serving the San Francisco Bay Area.

5378 ■ Supply Chain Management Review
Reed Business Information
360 Park Ave. S
New York, NY 10010-1710
Ph: (646)746-6400
URL: http://www.scmr.com

$199.00/year for individuals; $199.00/year for Canada; $337.00/year for other countries. Publication covering business and management.

EMPLOYER DIRECTORIES AND NETWORKING LISTS

5379 ■ Careers in Focus—Business
Facts On File Inc.
132 W 31st St., 17th Fl.
New York, NY 10001
Ph: (212)967-8800
Fax: 800-678-3633
Fr: 800-322-8755
URL: http://www.infobasepublishing.com

Latest edition 3rd; Published May, 2010. $32.95 for individuals. Covers: An overview of business, followed by a selection of jobs profiled in detail, including the nature of the job, earnings, prospects for employment, what kind of training and skills it requires, and sources for further information.

5380 ■ D & B Million Dollar Directory
Dun & Bradstreet Corp.
103 JFK Pky.
Short Hills, NJ 07078
Ph: (973)921-5500
Fr: 800-234-3867
URL: http://www.dnblearn.com/
  index.php?page=million-dollar-direct
Annual, Latest edition 2008. Covers: 1,600,000 public and private businesses with either a net worth of $500,000 or more, 250 or more employees at that location, or $25,000,000 or more in sales volume; includes industrial corporations, utilities, transportation companies, bank and trust companies, stock brokers, mutual and stock insurance companies, wholesalers, retailers, and domestic subsidiaries of foreign corporations. Entries include: Company name, address, phone, state of incorporation; annual sales; number of employees, company ticker symbol on stock exchange, Standard Industrial Classification (SIC) number, line of business; principal bank, accounting firm; parent company name, current ownership date, division names and functions, directors or trustees; names, titles, functions of principal executives, number of employees, import/export designation. Arrangement: Alphabetical, cross referenced geographically and by industry classification. Indexes: Geographical (with address and SIC), product by SIC (with address).

5381 ■ Financial Managers Society—Membership and Peer Consulting Directory
Financial Managers Society
100 W Monroe, Ste. 810
Chicago, IL 60603
Ph: (312)578-1300
Fax: (312)578-1308
Fr: 800-275-4367
URL: http://www.fmsinc.org
Annual. Covers: Executives and managers of financial institutions.

5382 ■ Forbes—Up-and-Comers 200
Forbes Magazine
60 5th Ave.
New York, NY 10011
Ph: (212)366-8900
Fr: 800-295-0893
URL: http://www.forbes.com
Weekly, Latest edition October, 2007. Publication includes: List of 200 small companies judged to be high quality and fast-growing on the basis of 5-year return on equity and other qualitative measurements. Also includes a list of the 100 best small companies outside the U.S. Note: Issue does not carry address or CEO information for the foreign companies.

5383 ■ Inc.—The Inc. 500 Issue
Gruner & Jahr USA Publishing
375 Lexington Ave., 42nd St.
New York, NY 10017-5514
Ph: (212)499-2000
Fax: (212)499-1629
URL: http://www.inc.com
Annual, Latest edition 2010. Publication includes: List of 500 fastest-growing privately held companies based on percentage increase in sales over the five year period prior to compilation of current year's list.

5384 ■ List of CEOs & Executives in Food Industry
Business Information Agency, Inc.
1300 S Arlington Ridge Rd., Ste. 502
Arlington, VA 22202
Ph: (703)685-2776
Fax: (703)685-1851
URL: http://www.planetinform.com/
  salesLeadsCard.aspx?prodID=3913

Covers: CEOs and executives from 500 food companies and sub-industries including meat, dairy, fruit, vegetables, flour, cereals, rice, dog and cat food, candies, chocolates and crackers, fats, oil, alcohol and softdrinks, fish and seafood, macaroni, spaghetti, vermicelli and food preparations.

5385 ■ Standard & Poor's Register of Corporations, Directors and Executives
Standard & Poor's
55 Water St.
New York, NY 10041-0004
Ph: (212)438-2000
Fr: 800-852-1641
URL: http://www2.standardandpoors.com
Annual, January; supplements in April, July, and October. Covers: over 55,000 public and privately held corporations in the United States, including names and titles of over 400,000 officials (Volume 1); 70,000 biographies of directors and executives (Volume 2). Entries include: For companies—Name, address, phone, names of principal executives and accountants; primary bank, primary law firm, number of employees, estimated annual sales, outside directors, Standard Industrial Classification (SIC) code, product or service provided. For directors and executives—Name, home and principal business addresses, date and place of birth, fraternal organization memberships, business affiliations. Arrangement: Alphabetical. Indexes: Volume 3 indexes companies geographically, by Standard Industrial Classification (SIC) code, and by corporate family groups.

5386 ■ Vault Guide to the Top Business Services Employers
Vault.com Inc.
150 W 22nd St., 5th Fl.
New York, NY 10011
Ph: (212)366-4212
Fax: (212)366-6117
Fr: 888-562-8285
URL: http://www.vault.com
Latest edition February, 2006. $19.95 for individuals; $19.95 for members. Covers: Top business service companies in United States. Entries include: Company name, contact person, location, address, phone and fax numbers, zip code, statistics, hiring process and email.

5387 ■ Vault Guide to the Top Private Equity Employers
Vault.com Inc.
150 W 22nd St., 5th Fl.
New York, NY 10011
Ph: (212)366-4212
Fax: (212)366-6117
Fr: 888-562-8285
URL: http://www.vault.com
Latest edition 2008. $29.95 for individuals; $29.95 for members. Covers: 2,700 private equity companies worldwide. Entries include: Company name, address, phone and fax numbers, statistics, contact person and email address. Arrangement: Alphabetical by company name.

HANDBOOKS AND MANUALS

5388 ■ Airport Report Today
American Association of Airport Executives
601 Madison St., Ste. 400
Alexandria, VA 22314
Ph: (703)824-0500
Fax: (703)820-1395
E-mail: member.services@aaae.org
URL: http://www.aaae.org/news_publications/airport_
  report_today/
Description: Bimonthly. Represents airport management personnel at public-use commercial and general aviation airports. Posts employment and business opportunities.

5389 ■ The Directory of Executive & Professional Recruiters
Kennedy Information Inc.
1 Phoenix Mill Lane, 3rd Fl.
Peterborough, NH 03458
Ph: (603)924-1006
Fax: (603)924-4460
Fr: 800-531-0007
E-mail: bookstore@kennedyinfo.com
URL: http://www.kennedyinfo.com
2011-2012. $ 69.95. 1200 pages. Contains detailed contact information for over 6,000 search firms located in the United States, Canada, and Mexico.

5390 ■ Expert Resumes for Managers and Executives
Jist Works
875 Montreal Way
St. Paul, MN 55102
Fr: 800-648-5478
E-mail: info@jist.com
URL: http://www.jist.com
Wendy S. Enelow, Louise M. Kursmark. 2012. $17.95. 274 pages.

EMPLOYMENT AGENCIES AND SEARCH FIRMS

5391 ■ A-L Associates Inc.
60 E 42nd St., Ste. 1534
New York, NY 10036
Ph: (212)878-9000
URL: http://www.alassociatesltd.com
Executive search firm.

5392 ■ Abbott Smith Associates, Inc.
11697 W Grand Ave.
Northlake, IL 60164
Ph: (708)223-1191
E-mail: contactus@abbottsmith.com
URL: http://www.abbottsmith.com
Human Resources executive search firm.

5393 ■ Abeln, Magy, Underberg & Associates
800 E Wayzata Blvd., Ste. 200
Wayzata, MN 55391
Ph: (952)476-4938
Fax: (952)404-7470
E-mail: info@abelnmagy.com
URL: http://www.abelnmagy.com
Executive search firm.

5394 ■ The Adkins Group Inc.
8700 Manchaca Rd., Ste. 504
Austin, TX 78704
Ph: (512)916-9600
Fax: (512)916-9665
Fr: (866)916-9600
E-mail: info@theadkinsgroup.com
URL: http://www.theadkinsgroup.com
Executive search firm.

5395 ■ Advantage Partners Inc.
29225 Chagrin Blvd., Ste. 300
Cleveland, OH 44122
Ph: (216)514-1212
Fax: (216)514-1213
E-mail: pamtaubert@advantagepartnersinc.com
URL: http://www.advantagepartnersinc.com
Executive search firm.

5396 ■ Aegis Group Search Consultants LLC
41451 W 11 Mile Rd.
Novi, MI 48375-1855
Ph: (248)344-1450
Fax: (248)347-2231
E-mail: resume@aegis-group.com
URL: http://www.aegis-group.com
Executive search and consultant firm. Focuses on the medical industry.

5397 ■ AGORA Consulting
1880 Office Club Pointe
Colorado Springs, CO 80920
Ph: (719)219-0360
Fax: (719)272-8361
E-mail: agora@agoraconsulting.com
URL: http://www.agoraconsulting.com

An executive search firm that recruits for senior-level management positions, primarily in the high-tech industry. Consultants research target companies and candidates, set up interviews, perform reference checks and assist with salary negotiations. Provides a range of other consulting services, including providing competitive intelligence and market research services as well as advising on staffing strategy and organizational design.

5398 ■ Ahern Search Partners
3982 Powell Rd., Ste. 205
Powell, OH 43065
Ph: (614)436-4126
Fax: (614)436-4125
E-mail: mollie@ahernsearch.com
URL: http://www.ahernsearch.com

Executive search firm. Concentrates on the healthcare market.

5399 ■ AKS Associates Ltd.
PO Box 2863
Duxbury, MA 02331
Ph: (781)934-5333
Fax: (781)934-6333
E-mail: sandy@akssearch.com
URL: http://www.akssearch.com

Senior search firm. Concentrates on the financial industry.

5400 ■ The Alexander Group
2700 Post Oak Blvd., Ste. 2400
Houston, TX 77056
Ph: (713)993-7900
URL: http://www.thealexandergroup.com

Executive search firm. Second location in San Francisco.

5401 ■ Alexander Ross & Company
100 Park Ave., 34th Fl.
New York, NY 10017
Ph: (212)889-9333
Fax: (212)864-5111
E-mail: info@alexanderross.com
URL: http://www.alexanderross.com

Executive search firm.

5402 ■ The Alfus Group Inc.
353 Lexington Ave.
New York, NY 10016
Ph: (212)599-1000
Fax: (212)599-1523
E-mail: mail@thealfusgroup.com
URL: http://www.thealfusgroup.com

Executive search firm. Specializes in the hospitality industry.

5403 ■ Allen Adell Executive Search and Consulting
7853 Gunn Hwy., No. 260
Tampa, FL 33626-1611
Ph: (813)920-8900
E-mail: info@allenadell.com
URL: http://www.allenadell.com

Functions as a retained executive search and human capital consulting firm that specializes in recruiting potential candidates for senior, mid-managerial and high-performing individual positions in the healthcare industry. Conducts talent assessment, competitive compensation surveys and objective and comprehensive exit interviews.

5404 ■ Allen Associates
3805 Edwards Rd., Ste. 550
Cincinnati, OH 45209
Ph: (513)563-3040
E-mail: feedback@allensearch.com
URL: http://www.allensearch.com

Executive senior-level search firm.

5405 ■ Allen Austin
4543 Post Oak Place Dr., Ste. 217
Houston, TX 77027
Ph: (713)355-1900
Fax: (713)355-1901
E-mail: randrews@allenaustinsearch.com
URL: http://www.allenaustinsearch.com

Executive search firm. Branches in North Carolina and Dallas.

5406 ■ Allen Evans Klein International
305 Madison Ave.
New York, NY 10165
Ph: (212)983-9300
Fax: (212)983-9272
E-mail: info@allenevans.com
URL: http://www.allenevans.com

Global Executive search firm.

5407 ■ Allerton Heneghan & O'Neill
1415 W 22nd St., Tower Fl.
Oak Brook, IL 60523
Ph: (630)645-2294
Fax: (630)645-2298
E-mail: info@ahosearch.com
URL: http://www.ahosearch.com

Executive search firm.

5408 ■ Alliance Search Management Inc.
594 Sawdust Rd., Ste. 194
The Woodlands, TX 77380
Ph: (281)419-5111
E-mail: kathy@alliancesearch.com
URL: http://www.alliancesearch.com

Employment agency.

5409 ■ American Executive Management Inc.
30 Federal St.
Salem, MA 01970
E-mail: execsearch@americanexecutive.us
URL: http://www.americanexecutive.us

Executive search firm. Second location in Boston.

5410 ■ American Incite
917 Hillfield Ct.
Oceanside, CA 92058
Ph: (760)754-2444
Fax: (760)754-2453
E-mail: talent@americanincite.com
URL: http://www.americanincite.com

Executive search firm.

5411 ■ Anderson & Associates
112 S Tryon St., Ste. 700
Charlotte, NC 28284
Ph: (704)347-0090
Fax: (704)347-0064
E-mail: info@andersonexecsearch.com
URL: http://www.andersonexecsearch.com

Executive search firm. Branch in Cumming, Georgia.

5412 ■ Andre David & Associates Inc.
PO Box 700967
Dallas, TX 75370
Ph: (972)250-1986
Fax: (972)250-2243
E-mail: info@andredavid.com
URL: http://www.andredavid.com

Executive search firm.

5413 ■ Andrew Associates Executive Search Inc.
4800 Meadows Rd., Ste. 300
PO Box 2029
Lake Oswego, OR 97035
Ph: (503)620-5222
E-mail: aaes@andysrch.com
URL: http://www.andysrch.com

Executive search firm.

5414 ■ The Angus Group Ltd.
5080 Wooster Rd., Ste. 300
Cincinnati, OH 45226
Ph: (513)961-5575
Fax: (513)961-5616
E-mail: angus@angusgroup.com
URL: http://www.angusgroup.com

Executive search firm.

5415 ■ APA Search Inc.
1 Byram Brook Pl., Ste. 104
Armonk, NY 10504
Ph: (914)273-6000
Fax: (914)273-8025
E-mail: info@apasearch.com
URL: http://www.apasearch.com

Employment agency specializing in the automotive, retail, and hardware industries.

5416 ■ Apple and Associates
PO Box 996
Chapin, SC 29036
Ph: (803)932-2000
E-mail: info@appleassoc.com
URL: http://www.appleassoc.com

Provides staffing services to medical device, plastics, pharmaceutical and performance materials industries.

5417 ■ Arthur Diamond Associates Inc.
4630 Montgomery Ave., Ste. 200
Bethesda, MD 20814-3436
Ph: (301)657-8866
Fax: (301)657-8876
E-mail: info@arthurdiamond.com
URL: http://www.arthurdiamond.com

Executive search firm.

5418 ■ Association Executive Resources Group
PO Box 3880
Gaithersburg, MD 20885-3880
Ph: (301)417-7045
Fax: (301)417-7049
URL: http://www.aerg.org

Executive search firm. Concentrates on non-profits.

5419 ■ Association Strategies
1111 N Fairfax St.
Alexandria, VA 22314
Ph: (703)683-0580
Fax: (703)683-1006
E-mail: info@assnstrategies.com
URL: http://www.assnstrategies.com

Employment agency.

5420 ■ Aster Search Group
555 Madison Ave.
New York, NY 10022
Ph: (212)888-6182
E-mail: ecohen@astersearch.com
URL: http://www.astersearch.com

Executive search firm focused on the healthcare industry.

5421 ■ Auguston and Associates Inc.
1010 S Ocean Blvd., Ste. 601
Pompano Beach, FL 33062
Ph: (954)943-0503
Fax: (954)784-1660
E-mail: g.auguston@augustonandassociates.com
URL: http://www.augustonandassociates.com/

Executive search firm focused on medical devices.

5422 ■ Avery Associates
3 1/2 N Santa Cruz Ave., Ste. A
Los Gatos, CA 95030

Ph: (408)399-4424
E-mail: jobs@averyassoc.net
URL: http://www.averyassoc.net
Administration search firm.

5423 ■ Avery James Inc.
6601 Center Dr. W, Ste. 500
Los Angeles, CA 90045
Ph: (310)342-8224
Fax: (310)348-8150
E-mail: resume@averyjames.com
URL: http://www.averyjames.com
Executive search firm.

5424 ■ The Ayers Group
101 Merritt 7, 1st Fl.
Norwalk, CT 06851
Ph: (203)354-7788
Fax: (203)354-6683
Fr: 888-786-7834
URL: http://www.ayers.com
Executive search firm.

5425 ■ The Baer Group
900 Ashwood Pkwy., Ste. 300
Atlanta, GA 30346
Ph: (770)557-4900
Fax: (770)557-3499
E-mail: info@baergroup.com
URL: http://www.baergroup.com
Executive search firm.

5426 ■ Baker Montgomery
One Magnificent Mile, Ste. 1815
980 N Michigan Ave.
Chicago, IL 60611
Ph: (312)397-8808
Fax: (312)397-9631
E-mail: contact@bakermontgomery.com
URL: http://www.bakermontgomery.com
Executive search firm.

5427 ■ Barone-O'Hara Associates Inc.
34 Fackler Rd.
Princeton, NJ 08540
Ph: (609)683-5566
Fax: (609)683-8077
E-mail: marialice@baroneohara.com
URL: http://www.baroneohara.com
Executive search firm focused on medical devices.

5428 ■ Barro Global Search Inc.
The Tower, Ste. 1600
10940 Wilshire Blvd.
Los Angeles, CA 90024
Ph: (310)443-4277
Fax: (310)441-5305
E-mail: drbarro@winwithoutcompeting.com
URL: http://www.barroglobal.com
Executive search firm focused on healthcare and hospitals.

5429 ■ Bartholdi Partners
12020 Sunrise Valley Dr.
Reston, VA 20191
Ph: (703)476-5519
Fax: (703)753-6217
E-mail: info@bartholdisearch.com
URL: http://www.bartholdisearch.com
Executive search firm. Affiliates in San Francisco; San Jose; Phoenix; Scottsdale; Parker, CO; and Framingham, MA.

5430 ■ Barton Associates Inc.
4314 Yoakum Blvd.
Houston, TX 77006
Ph: (713)961-9111
Fax: (713)403-5574
E-mail: info@bartona.com
URL: http://www.bartona.com
Executive search firm. Affiliate in Houston, TX.

5431 ■ Battalia Winston International
555 Madison Ave.
New York, NY 10022
Ph: (212)308-8080
URL: http://www.battaliawinston.com

Executive search firm. Branches in Los Angeles; Chicago; Wellesley Hills, MA; Edison, NJ.

5432 ■ The Bedford Group
3343 Peachtree Rd. NE, Ste. 333
Atlanta, GA 30326
Ph: (404)237-7471
Fax: (404)846-2172
E-mail: info@bedfordgroupconsulting.com
URL: http://www.bedfordgroupconsulting.com

Executive search firm.

5433 ■ Bert Davis Executive Search Inc.
425 Madison Ave.
New York, NY 10017
Ph: (212)838-4000
Fax: (212)935-3291
E-mail: info@bertdavis.com
URL: http://www.bertdavis.com
Executive search firm.

5434 ■ BFL Associates Ltd.
11 Greenway Plaza, Ste. 545
Houston, TX 77046
Ph: (713)965-2112
Fax: (713)965-2114
E-mail: bjorn@bflassociates.com
URL: http://www.bflassociates.com
Executive search firm.

5435 ■ Bialecki Inc.
780 3rd Ave., Ste. 4203
New York, NY 10017
Ph: (212)755-1090
Fax: (212)755-1130
E-mail: linda@bialecki.com
URL: http://www.bialecki.com
Senior executive search firm focused on the financial industry.

5436 ■ Bishop Partners
28 W 44th St., Ste. 2100A
New York, NY 10036
Ph: (212)986-3419
Fax: (212)575-1050
E-mail: info@bishoppartners.com
URL: http://www.bishoppartners.com

A retainer based executive search firm specializing in media and communications. This includes cable, broadcasting, publishing, Internet and interactive media, entertainment. Consulting closely with clients, finds the right person to fill a specific need or solve a specific business issue in functional areas which include CEO and COO, sales, marketing, finance, human resources, programming and production, and ecommerce.

5437 ■ Blumenthal-Hart LLC
195 N Harbor Dr., Ste. 2902
Chicago, IL 60604-3413
Ph: (312)318-1930
Fax: (312)946-1928
E-mail: resumes@blumenthal-hart.com
URL: http://www.blumenthal-hart.com
Executive search firm.

5438 ■ Bonnell Associates Ltd.
1499 Post Rd., 2nd Fl.
Fairfield, CT 06824
Ph: (203)319-7214
Fax: (203)319-7219
E-mail: wbonnell@bonnellassociates.com
URL: http://www.bonnellassociates.com
Executive search firm.

5439 ■ Boston Search Group Inc.
224 Clarendon St., Ste. 41
Boston, MA 02116-3729
Ph: (617)266-4333
Fax: (781)735-0562
E-mail: ralph@bsgtv.com
URL: http://www.bostonsearchgroup.com
Executive search firm.

5440 ■ The Boulware Group, Inc.
625 N Michigan Ave., Ste. 422
Chicago, IL 60611
Ph: (312)322-0088
Fax: (312)322-0092
E-mail: resume@boulwareinc.com
URL: http://www.boulwareinc.com
Executive search firm.

5441 ■ Boyle & Associates Retained Search Group
PO Box 16658
St. Paul, MN 55116
Ph: (651)223-5050
Fax: (651)699-5378
E-mail: paul@talenthunt.com
URL: http://www.talenthunt.com
Executive search firm.

5442 ■ The Bradbury Group Inc.
1200 E Cole St.
PO Box 667
Moundridge, KS 67107
Ph: (620)345-6394
Fax: (620)345-6381
Fr: 800-397-6394
URL: http://www.bradburygroup.net
Executive search firm.

5443 ■ Brandywine Consulting Group
1398 Morstein Rd.
West Chester, PA 19380
Ph: (610)696-5872
Fax: (610)429-1954
URL: http://www.brandywineconsulting.com
Executive search firm. An Affiliate of Brandywine Management Group in Berlin, MD.

5444 ■ Brennan and Brennan Executive Search
2483 Heritage Village, Ste. 16 No. 167
Snellville, GA 30078
E-mail: jb@brennanandbrennan.com
URL: http://www.brennanandbrennan.com

Exists as a recruitment firm that provides service in retained and contingency search. Delivers recruitment solutions in executive search as well as meeting targeted general staffing needs on a national and international level.

5445 ■ The Brentwood Group Inc.
170 Kinnelon Rd.
Kinnelon, NJ 07405
Ph: (973)283-1000
Fax: (973)850-6103
E-mail: officemanager@thebrentwoodgroup.com
URL: http://www.thebrentwoodgroup.com
Executive search firm.

5446 ■ BridgeGate LLC
17701 Cowan Ave., Ste. 240
Irvine, CA 92614
Ph: (949)553-9200
Fax: (949)660-1810
E-mail: info@bridgegate.com
URL: http://www.bridgegate.com
Executive search firm.

5447 ■ Brindisi Search
10020 Baltimore National Pike., Ste. 100
PO Box 6034
Ellicott City, MD 21042
Ph: (410)489-6699

Fax: (410)823-0146
E-mail: tbrindisi@aol.com
URL: http://www.brindisisearch.com

Specializes in contemporary human resource and select strategic leadership assignments, ranging from manager to senior vice president level.

5448 ■ Brown Venture Associates Inc.
5150 El Camino Real, Ste. B-30
Los Altos, CA 94022
Ph: (650)233-0205
E-mail: brown@bva.com
URL: http://www.bva.com

Executive search firm.

5449 ■ Brownson & Associates LP
2825 Wilcrest, Ste. 530
Houston, TX 77042
Ph: (713)626-4790
Fax: (713)877-1745
E-mail: brownsonassoc@brownson.com
URL: http://www.brownson.com

Executive search firm.

5450 ■ Buffkin & Associates LLC
730 Cool Springs Blvd., Ste. 120
Franklin, TN 37067
Ph: (615)778-2142
E-mail: info@thebuffkingroup.com
URL: http://www.buffkinassociates.com/www

Executive search firm.

5451 ■ The Burling Group Ltd.
600 N Kingsbury St., Ste. 1507
Chicago, IL 60614
Ph: (773)883-0888
E-mail: web@burlinggroup.com
URL: http://www.burlinggroup.com

Executive search firm.

5452 ■ Burton & Grove Executive Search.
1320 Tower Rd.
Schaumburg, IL 60173
Ph: (847)919-8880
E-mail: support@burtonandgrove.com
URL: http://www.burtonandgrove.com

Executive search firm.

5453 ■ Busch International
1000 Fremont Ave., Ste. 195
Los Altos, CA 94024
Ph: (650)949-6500
E-mail: olga@buschint.com
URL: http://www.buschint.com

Executive search firm focused solely on high-technology electronics.

5454 ■ Buxbaum/Rink Consulting L.L.C.
1 Bradley Rd., Ste. 901
Woodbridge, CT 06525-2296
Ph: (203)389-5949
Fax: (203)397-0615

Personnel consulting firms offer contingency search, recruitment and placement of accounting and finance, as well as other business management positions. In addition to serving these two major career areas, also provides similar services to operations, marketing and human resources executives. Industries served: manufacturing, financial services, and service.

5455 ■ Byron Leonard International
99 Long Ct., Ste. 201
Thousand Oaks, CA 91360
Ph: (805)373-7500
Fax: (805)373-5531
E-mail: bli@bli-inc.com
URL: http://www.bli-inc.com

Executive search firm.

5456 ■ CAA Search
5469 Sunbird Dr.
Loves Park, IL 61111
Ph: (815)654-8535
Fax: (815)654-0469
E-mail: info@caasearch.com
URL: http://www.caasearch.com

Executive search firm.

5457 ■ Cabot Consultants Inc.
1600 Tysons Blvd., 8th Fl.
McLean, VA 22102
Ph: (703)744-1081
Fax: (703)744-1001
Fr: (866)475-1984
E-mail: info@cabotinc.com
URL: http://www.cabotinc.com

A retained executive search firm specializing in filling senior-level positions.

5458 ■ The Caler Group
23337 Lago Mar Cir.
Boca Raton, FL 33433
Ph: (561)394-8045
Fax: (561)394-4645
URL: http://www.calergroup.com

Executive search firm.

5459 ■ Caliber Associates
6336 Greenwich Dr., Ste. C
San Diego, CA 92122
Ph: (858)551-7880
Fax: (858)551-7887
E-mail: info@caliberassociates.com
URL: http://www.caliberassociates.com

Executive search firm.

5460 ■ Callan Associates Ltd.
1211 W 22nd St., Ste. 821
Oak Brook, IL 60523
Ph: (630)574-9300
Fax: (630)574-3099
E-mail: info@callanassociates.com
URL: http://www.callanassociates.com

Executive search firm.

5461 ■ Calland & Company
2296 Henderson Mill Rd. NE, Ste. 222
Atlanta, GA 30345
Ph: (770)270-9100
Fax: (770)270-9300
E-mail: bob@callandcompany.com
URL: http://www.callandcompany.com

Executive search firm focused on senior management and healthcare.

5462 ■ Campbell/Carlson LLC
PO Box 34323
Charlotte, NC 28234
Ph: (704)373-0234
E-mail: recruiting@campbellcarlson.com
URL: http://www.campbellcarlson.com

Executive search firm.

5463 ■ Capodice & Associates
Midtown Plaza
1243 S Tamiami Trail
Sarasota, FL 34239
Ph: (941)906-1990
Fax: (941)906-1991
E-mail: peter@capodice.com
URL: http://www.capodice.com

Executive search firm. Branch in Carlisle, MA.

5464 ■ Caprio & Associates Inc.
1415 W 22nd St., Tower Level
Oak Brook, IL 60523
Ph: (630)705-9101
Fax: (630)705-9102
E-mail: jerry@caprioassociates.com
URL: http://www.caprioassociates.com

Executive search firm.

5465 ■ Capstone Consulting Inc.
723 S Dearborn St.
Chicago, IL 60605
Ph: (312)753-5701
E-mail: mark@capstoneconsulting.com
URL: http://www.capstoneconsulting.com

Executive search firm.

5466 ■ Capstone Inc.
971 Albany Shaker Rd.
Latham, NY 12110
Ph: (518)783-9300
Fax: (518)783-9328
E-mail: info@capstone-inc.com
URL: http://www.capstone-inc.com

Executive search firm.

5467 ■ Career Advocates International
1539 Ave. A
Katy, TX 77493
Ph: (281)395-9848
Fax: (281)574-3949
URL: http://www.careeradvocates.org

Provides permanent placement and temporary staffing for executive and staff level positions. Specializes in multiple niches including: sales and marketing, accounting and financial services, banking, communications, human resources, chemicals, oil and gas, medical and dental, legal, information technology, energy, technology, engineering, manufacturing, construction, and light industrial.

5468 ■ Carrington & Carrington Ltd
39 S LaSalle St., Ste. 400
Chicago, IL 60603
Ph: (312)606-0015
Fax: (312)606-0501
E-mail: resume@carringtonandcarrington.com
URL: http://www.carringtonandcarrington.com

Executive search firm.

5469 ■ CarterBaldwin
200 Mansell Ct. E, Ste. 450
Roswell, GA 30076
Ph: (678)448-0000
Fr: (866)781-6844
E-mail: jdelikat@carterbaldwin.com
URL: http://www.carterbaldwin.com

Executive search firm.

5470 ■ Caruso & Associates Inc.
990 Stinson Way, Ste. 201
West Palm Beach, FL 33411
Ph: (561)683-2336
E-mail: info@carusoassociates.com
URL: http://www.carusoassociates.com

Executive search firm.

5471 ■ Centennial, Inc.
8044 Montgomery Rd., Ste. 260
Cincinnati, OH 45236
Ph: (513)366-3760
Fax: (513)366-3761
E-mail: info@centennialinc.com
URL: http://www.centennialinc.com

Serves as an executive search firm specializing in the areas of executive and general management, accounting and finance, human resources, information technology, manufacturing, engineering, marketing and advertising, not-for-profit, sales and business development, and supply chain and logistics. Performs executive coaching as well as career coaching for clients.

5472 ■ Charles Aris, Inc.
300 N Greene St., Ste. 1800
Greensboro, NC 27401
Ph: (336)378-1818
Fax: (336)378-0129
E-mail: info@charlesaris.com
URL: http://www.charlesaris.com

Provides executive search and placement services in

the areas of consumer packaged goods, retail, strategy/business development, global life sciences, healthcare, chemicals, textiles/apparel, private equity, and business services.

5473 ■ The Cherbonnier Group Inc.
1 Riverway, Ste. 1700
Houston, TX 77056
Ph: (713)688-4701
E-mail: consult@thecherbonniergroup.com
URL: http://www.thecherbonniergroup.com
Executive search firm.

5474 ■ Cheryl Alexander & Associates
8588 Shadow Creek Dr.
Maple Grove, MN 55311
Ph: (763)416-4570
E-mail: cheryl@cherylalexander.com
URL: http://www.cherylalexander.com
Executive search firm.

5475 ■ Christian & Timbers
28601 Chagrin Blvd., Ste. 600
Cleveland, OH 44122
Ph: (216)682-3200
Fax: (216)464-6172
E-mail: jsilver@ctnet.com
URL: http://www.ctnet.com
Executive search firm. Eight branches spanning the USA.

5476 ■ Clarey Andrews & Klein Inc.
1347 Hillside Rd.
Northbrook, IL 60062
Ph: (847)498-2870
E-mail: cak@clarey-a-klein.com
URL: http://www.clarey-a-klein.com
Executive search firm.

5477 ■ Cole, Warren & Long Inc.
Two Penn Center Plaza, Ste. 312
Philadelphia, PA 19102
Ph: (215)563-0701
Fax: (215)563-2907
Fr: 800-394-8517
URL: http://www.cwl-inc.com
Executive search firm with international placement.

5478 ■ Coleman Lew & Associates Inc.
326 W 10th St.
Charlotte, NC 28202
Ph: (704)377-0362
Fax: (704)377-0424
Fr: 800-533-9523
E-mail: info@colemanlew.com
URL: http://www.colemanlew.com
Executive search firm.

5479 ■ Columbia Consulting Group
5525 Twin Knolls Rd., Ste. 331
Columbia, MD 21045
Ph: (443)276-2525
Fax: (410)276-2536
E-mail: info@ccgsearch.com
URL: http://www.ccgsearch.com
Executive search firm. Branch in New York, NY.

5480 ■ Conard Associates Inc.
74 Northeastern Blvd., Unit 22A
Nashua, NH 03062
Ph: (603)886-0600
Fax: (603)804-0421
URL: http://www.conardassociates.com
Executive search firm.

5481 ■ Cooper Staffing & Consulting, Inc.
730 Orchard Court
Atlanta, GA 30328
Ph: (770)522-8868
URL: http://www.cooperstaffing.com

Specializes in finding and placing sales, marketing, technical professionals and senior management for

companies in the pharmaceutical, biotech, medical, and advertising sectors.

5482 ■ Core Management Search LLC
PO Box 421042
Minneapolis, MN 55442
Ph: (763)559-0977
E-mail: jlentner@coremanage.com
URL: http://www.coremanage.com
Executive search firm.

5483 ■ Corporate Moves Inc.
PO Box 1638
Williamsville, NY 14231-1638
Ph: (716)633-0234
Fax: (716)626-9147
E-mail: info@cmisearch.com
URL: http://www.corporatemovesinc.com

Executive search and recruitment specialist firm with emphasis on Sales, Marketing and Senior Management generally in the $70,000 and above income levels. Industries served: medical, biotech, scientific, pharmaceutical, industrial, business products.

5484 ■ Courtright & Associates Inc.
PO Box 236
Scranton, PA 18504
E-mail: rjcx@comcast.net
URL: http://www.courtrightassoc.com
Executive search firm.

5485 ■ CraigSearch
1130 E Arapaho Rd., Ste. 180
Richardson, TX 75081
Ph: (972)644-3264
E-mail: search@craigsearch.com
URL: http://www.craigsearch.com
Executive search firm.

5486 ■ Creative-Leadership Inc.
1900 Polaris Pkwy., Ste. 450
Columbus, OH 43240
Ph: (614)410-6506
Fax: (614)760-0737
Fr: 800-875-5323
E-mail: info@clci.com
URL: http://www.clci.com
Executive search firm.

5487 ■ Crist/Kolder Associates
21 W 2nd St., 3rd Fl.
Hinsdale, IL 60521
Ph: (630)321-1110
Fax: (630)321-1112
URL: http://www.cristassociates.com
Executive search firm.

5488 ■ Cross Hill Partners LLC
845 Third Ave., 6th Fl.
New York, NY 10022
Ph: (646)405-7500
Fax: (866)927-4449
E-mail: info@crosshillpartners.com
URL: http://www.crosshillpartners.com
Executive search firm.

5489 ■ Crown Advisors Inc.
100 McKnight Park Dr., Ste. 110
Pittsburgh, PA 15212
Ph: (412)348-1540
E-mail: info@crownsearch.com
URL: http://www.crownsearch.com
Executive search firm.

5490 ■ CTR Group
11843-C Canon Blvd.
Newport News, CA 23606
Ph: (757)462-5900
Fax: (866)597-0055

Fr: 800-945-9095
E-mail: info@ctrc.com
URL: http://www.ctrc.com
Executive search firm.

5491 ■ Curran Partners Inc.
6 Landmark Sq., Ste. 400
Stamford, CT 06901
Ph: (203)359-5737
Fax: (203)363-5353
E-mail: research@curranpartners.com
URL: http://www.curranpartners.com
Executive search firm.

5492 ■ Dahl-Morrow International
1821 Michael Faraday Dr., Ste. 202
Reston, VA 20190
Ph: (703)787-8117
E-mail: info@dahl-morrowintl.com
URL: http://www.dahl-morrowintl.com
Executive search firm specializing in high technology.

5493 ■ DAL Partners
501 Kings Highway E, Ste. 101
Fairfield, CT 06825
Ph: (203)256-3777
Fax: (203)256-8294
E-mail: resumes@dalpartners.com
URL: http://www.dalpartners.com
Executive search firm.

5494 ■ Dalton Group, LLC
15954 Jackson Creek Pkwy., Ste. B-323
Monument, CO 80132
Ph: (719)495-7898
Fax: (719)344-2309
E-mail: info@daltongroupllc.com
URL: http://www.daltongroupllc.com

Retained, executive search firm that focuses on assisting for-profit companies and nonprofit organizations in identifying and selecting senior leaders.

5495 ■ Daly & Company Inc.
175 Federal St.
Boston, MA 02110-2210
Ph: (617)262-2800
Fax: (617)728-4477
E-mail: info@dalyco.com
URL: http://www.dalyco.com
Executive search firm.

5496 ■ Derba & Derba
7 Whispering Pines Dr.
Andover, MA 01810
Ph: (978)470-8270
Fax: (978)470-4592
E-mail: rderba@derbaandderba.com
URL: http://derbaandderba.com

Executive search firm focused on the hospitality industry.

5497 ■ Design Staffing, LLC
14024 Clopper Rd.
Boyds, MD 20841
Ph: (301)428-9673
URL: http://www.designstaffing.com

Description: Designs staffing programs tailored for individual clients. Assists companies with hard to fill positions that do not fit the traditional mold. Also provides a range of related staffing services such as staffing plan development, job description preparation, outplacement services, career counseling and resume development.

5498 ■ DHR International
10 S Riverside Plaza, Ste. 2220
Chicago, IL 60606
Ph: (312)782-1581
Fax: (312)782-2096
URL: http://www.dhrinternational.com

Executive search firm. International organization with a variety of affiliate offices.

5499 ■ Dieck Executive Search
30 Rough Lee Ct.
Madison, WI 53705
Ph: (608)238-1000
E-mail: dan@dieckexecutivesearch.com
URL: http://dieckexecutivesearch.com
Executive search firm focused on pulp, paper and
the packaging industries.

5500 ■ The Diestel Group
2180 S 1300 E, Ste. 350
Salt Lake City, UT 84106
Ph: (801)365-0400
Fax: (801)365-0401
E-mail: info@diestel.com
URL: http://www.diestel.com
Executive search firm.

5501 ■ Dinte Resources Inc.
8300 Greensboro Dr., Ste. 750
McLean, VA 22102
Ph: (703)448-3300
Fax: (703)448-0215
E-mail: pdinte@dinte.com
URL: http://www.dinte.com
Executive search firm.

5502 ■ DLB Associates
265 Industrial Way, W
Eatontown, NJ 07724
Ph: (732)774-2000
Fax: (732)774-5000
E-mail: info@dlbassociates.com
URL: http://www.dlbassociates.com
Executive search firm.

5503 ■ DNPitchon Associates
60 W Ridgewood Ave.
Ridgewood, NJ 07450
Ph: (201)612-8350
E-mail: info@dnpitchon.com
URL: http://www.dnpitchon.com
Executive search firm.

5504 ■ Donahue/Patterson Associates
8833 Elm Valley Rd.
Union Pier, MI 49129
Ph: (312)732-0999
E-mail: info@donahuepatterson.com
URL: http://www.donahuepatterson.com
Executive search firm.

5505 ■ Dowd Associates Inc.
777 Westchester Ave., Ste. 120
White Plains, NY 10604
Ph: (914)251-1515
Fax: (914)251-1321
E-mail: mail@dowdassociates.com
URL: http://www.dowdassociates.com
Specializes in the recruitment of senior level financial
professionals.

5506 ■ DSML Executive Search
120 N La Salle St., Ste. 2600
Chicago, IL 60602
Ph: (312)268-6166
E-mail: contact@dsmlexecutivesearch.com
URL: http://www.dsmlexecutivesearch.com
Provides recruiting services for European companies
doing business in the United States. Specializes in
the recruitment of qualified personnel for sales,
marketing and operational management positions.

5507 ■ DuVall & Associates
4203 Costa Salada
San Clemente, CA 92673
Ph: (949)488-8790
Fax: (949)488-8793
E-mail: karen@ducall.com
URL: http://www.duvall.com
Executive search firm specializing in management
team placement.

5508 ■ E/Search International
PO Box 408
West Suffield, CT 06093-0408
Ph: (860)668-5848
Fax: (860)668-5125
Fr: 800-300-0477
E-mail: bob@directcompetitor.com
URL: http://www.esearchinternational.net
Executive search firm for companies needing highly
successful, industry-specific executives. A database
of executives and sales people in sales, operations,
manufacturing, engineering, and supply chain
management.

5509 ■ EFL Associates
11440 Tomahawk Creek Pky.
Leawood, KS 66211
Ph: (913)234-1560
URL: http://www.cbiz.com/eflassociates
Executive search firm. Locations in Englewood, CO
and Lake Forest, IL.

5510 ■ Egan & Associates Inc.
White House Ctr.
1784 Barton Ave., Ste. 10
West Bend, WI 53095
Ph: (262)335-0707
Fax: (262)335-0625
E-mail: info@eganassociates.com
URL: http://www.eganassociates.com
Executive search firm.

5511 ■ The Elliot Company
Ph: (843)388-0900
E-mail: suppt.staff@elliottco.net
URL: http://www.elliottco.net
Executive search firm.

5512 ■ ET Search Inc.
PO Box 2389
La Jolla, CA 92038
Ph: (858)459-3443
Fax: (858)459-4147
E-mail: ets@etsearch.com
URL: http://www.etsearch.com
Executive search firm focused on the tax industry.

**5513 ■ Executive Resources International
LLC**
63 Atlantic Ave.
Boston, MA 02110-3722
Ph: (617)742-8970
E-mail: john@erisearch.net
URL: http://www.erisearch.net
Executive search firm.

5514 ■ Executive Search Advisors, Inc.
18501 Germain St.
Northridge, CA 91326
Ph: (818)396-6656
Fax: (818)484-2600
E-mail: ceo@execsa.com
URL: http://www.execsa.com
Serves as an executive search consultancy which
focuses on enhancing the ability of public and
privately-held corporations, private equity and venture
capital firms, and retained executive search firms to
become successful.

5515 ■ Executives Unlimited Inc.
5000 E Spring St., Ste. 395
Long Beach, CA 90815
Ph: (562)627-3800
Fax: (562)627-1092
Fr: (866)957-4466
URL: http://www.executivesunlimited.com
Executive search firm. Branches in Western Springs,
IL; Scotch Plains, NJ; Long Beach, CA.

5516 ■ Fahr Group
49 Oneda Ave.
Moorestown, NJ 08057

Fr: 888-461-2566
E-mail: info@thefahrgroup.com
URL: http://www.thefahrgroup.com
Commits to helping organizations grow and prosper
through the identification and selection of key execu-
tive management professionals.

5517 ■ The Ferneborg Group
1700 S El Camino Real, Ste. 375
San Mateo, CA 94402
Ph: (650)577-0100
Fax: (650)577-0122
E-mail: mailbox@execsearch.com
URL: http://www.execsearch.com
Executive search firm.

5518 ■ Fishpond Recruiting
PO Box 1448
Novato, CA 94948-1448
Ph: (415)898-5677
Fax: (415)898-9787
E-mail: jobs@fishpondrecruiting.com
URL: http://www.fishpondrecruiting.com
Description: Specializes in all levels of direct hire,
temporary and contract placement in a variety of
industries.

5519 ■ Fortis Partners
2400 Broadway Ave., Ste. D590
Santa Monica, CA 90404
Ph: (310)586-5555
E-mail: tnieman@fortispartners.com
URL: http://www.fortispartners.com
Retained executive search firm that specializes in
recruiting CEOs and vice presidents for a range of
technology companies - from venture capital-backed
startups to public entities.

5520 ■ Francis & Associates
6923 Vista Dr.
West Des Moines, IA 50266
Ph: (515)221-9800
Fax: (515)221-9806
E-mail: knovak@fa-search.com
URL: http://www.francisassociates.com
Executive search firm.

5521 ■ Freeman Philanthropic Services, LLC
1115 Broadway, Ste. 1200
New York, NY 10010
Ph: (212)924-3727
Fax: (646)375-2173
URL: http://www.glfreemanllc.com
Description: Specializes in recruitment for nonprofit
institutions and organizations. Provides management
training services that include interactive workshops,
planning and feasibility studies, analysis of staffing
needs, articulation and development of fundraising
tools and development audits.

5522 ■ Graystone Partners L.L.C.
62 Southfield Ave., Ste. 204
Stamford, CT 06902-7229
Ph: (203)323-0023
Fax: (203)353-9035
E-mail: contact@graystonepartners.com
URL: http://www.graystonepartners.com
A retainer-based, executive search firm providing
professional consulting services in the area of executive recruitment and management selection. Functional areas of expertise include senior level general
management, financial officers, technology officers,
marketing and human resource executives.

5523 ■ Hager Executive Search
1483 Sutter St., Ste. 1003
San Francisco, CA 94109
Ph: (415)441-2234
E-mail: connect@hagerexecutivesearch.com
URL: http://www.hagerexecutivesearch.com
Specializes in executive and C level talent searches

in marketing/branding, business development, sales and digital media across varied business sectors.

5524 ■ Hawthorne Executive Search
1319 Military Cutoff Rd., Ste. CC No. 147
Wilmington, NC 28405
Ph: (910)798-1800
Fax: (910)798-2811
E-mail: info@hawthornesearch.com
URL: http://hawthornesearch.com

Specializes in search assignments of executives that range from manager to vice president to C-level and board assignments.

5525 ■ Heidrick and Struggles, Inc.
233 S Wacker Dr., Ste. 4200
Sears Tower
Chicago, IL 60606-6303
Ph: (312)496-1200
URL: http://www.heidrick.com

Executive search firm. International organization with a variety of affiliate offices.

5526 ■ Herd Freed Hartz, Inc.
Two Union Square
601 Union St., Ste. 4610
Seattle, WA 98101
Ph: (206)525-9700
Fax: (206)374-3067
E-mail: jim@herdfreedhartz.com
URL: http://www.herdfreedhartz.com

Description: Serves as a nationwide executive recruiting firm covering technology, life science, and manufacturing.

5527 ■ Hunt Executive Search, Inc.
100 Park Ave.
New York, NY 10017
Ph: (212)861-2680
Fr: 800-486-8476
E-mail: info@hungroup.com
URL: http://www.huntsearch.com

Provides executive search services to consumer products, life sciences, retail, professional services and diversified industrial markets.

5528 ■ Integrated Search Solutions Group
33 Main St.
Port Washington, NY 11050
Ph: (516)767-3030
E-mail: info@issg.net
URL: http://www.issg.net

A retainer based executive search firm that has been successful in attracting top talent in the areas of outsourcing, consulting and traditional IT functions.

5529 ■ J H Dugan & Company
225 Crossroads Blvd., Ste. 415
Carmel, CA 93923
Fax: 888-530-5610
Fr: 800-254-3396
E-mail: plastic-recruiter@jhdugan.com
URL: http://www.jhdugan.com

Executive search firm.

5530 ■ James Drury Partners
875 N Michigan Ave., Ste. 3805
Chicago, IL 60611
Ph: (312)654-6708
Fax: (312)654-6710
E-mail: resume@jdrurypartners.com
URL: http://www.jdrurypartners.com

Executive search firm.

5531 ■ John J. Davis & Associates Inc.
30 Chatham Rd.
PO Box G
Short Hills, NJ 07078
Ph: (973)467-8339

Fax: (973)467-3706
E-mail: jack.davis@jdavisassoc.com
URL: http://www.johnjdavisandassoc.com

Executive search firm.

5532 ■ Joy Reed Belt Search Consultants Inc.
PO Box 54410
Oklahoma City, OK 73154
Ph: (405)842-5155
Fax: (405)842-6357
E-mail: executiverecruiter@joyreedbelt.com
URL: http://www.joyreedbeltsearch.com

Executive search firm. Branch in Tulsa, OK.

5533 ■ J.R. Bechtle & Company
67 S Bedford St., Ste. 400 W
Burlington, MA 01803-5177
Ph: (781)229-5804
Fax: (781)359-1829
E-mail: jrb.boston@jrbechtle.com
URL: http://www.jrbechtle.com

Executive search firm.

5534 ■ JT Brady & Associates
10900 Perry Hwy. No. 12203
Wexford, PA 15090
Fax: (724)935-8059
E-mail: jack@jtbrady.net
URL: http://www.jtbrady.net

Executive search firm.

5535 ■ Judith Cushman & Associates
15600 NE 8th St., Ste. B1
Bellevue, WA 98008
Ph: (425)392-8660
Fax: (425)644-9043
E-mail: jcushman@jc-a.com
URL: http://www.jc-a.com

Executive search firm.

5536 ■ Kimmel & Associates
25 Page Ave.
Asheville, NC 28801
Ph: (828)251-9900
Fax: (828)251-9955
E-mail: kimmel@kimmel.com
URL: http://www.kimmel.com

Specializes in the construction, waste, architecture, engineering, logistics and supply chain industries.

5537 ■ Kinser & Baillou L.L.C.
590 Madison Ave., Fl. 21
New York, NY 10022
Ph: (212)588-8801
Fax: (212)588-8802
E-mail: search@kinserbaillou.com
URL: http://www.kinserbaillou.com

Specializes in boards, management consulting and communications/marketing communications.

5538 ■ Korn/Ferry International
1900 Ave. of the Stars, Ste. 2600
Los Angeles, CA 90067
Ph: (310)552-1834
URL: http://www.kornferry.com

Executive search firm. International organization with a variety of affiliate offices.

5539 ■ Lancaster Associates
35 W High St.
Somerville, NJ 08876-2114
Ph: (908)526-5440
Fax: (908)526-1992
E-mail: rfl@lancasterinc.net
URL: http://www.lancasterassociates.net

Personnel consulting firm focuses recruitment on information systems, voice and data communications, managers, telecommunications, client server technology, data warehouse, project leaders, and systems programmers. Industries served: pharmaceutical,

consumer products, manufacturing, transportation, financial services and insurance.

5540 ■ Leadership Capital Group
606 Post Rd. E, Ste. 605
Westport, CT 06880
Ph: (203)682-1627
Fax: (203)841-1117
E-mail: info@lcgsearch.com
URL: http://www.lcgsearch.com

Executive search firm focused at the CEO and Board through the VP levels. Maintains a database of executives at the $200,000+ compensation level.

5541 ■ Lonergan Partners
203 Redwood Shore Pkwy., Ste. 600
Redwood City, CA 94065
Ph: (650)413-6000
Fax: (650)413-6009
E-mail: sjg@lonerganpartners.com
URL: http://www.lonerganpartners.com

Executive search firm that focuses on recruitment of top executives. Offers positions for CEO, Board of Directors, and senior executive management.

5542 ■ Lucas Group
3384 Peachtree Rd., Ste. 900
Atlanta, GA 30326
Ph: (404)239-5630
Fax: (404)260-7290
Fr: 800-515-0819
E-mail: info@lucasgroup.com
URL: http://www.lucasgroup.com

Specializes in accounting/finance, advertising/marketing, aerospace/defense, alternative energy, call center, capital markets, construction/real estate, consumer products, hospitality, human resources, industrial services, insurance, legal, manufacturing/engineering/supply chain/logistics, medical device/biotech/ pharmaceutical, military transition, oil/gas and technology.

5543 ■ Management Architects
6484 Washington St., Ste. B
Yountville, CA 94599
Ph: (707)945-1340
Fax: (707)945-1345
E-mail: doug@managementarchitects.net
URL: http://www.managementarchitects.net

Executive search firm. Focuses on networking industries.

5544 ■ Management Recruiters International, Inc.
1717 Arch St., 36th Fl.
Philadelphia, PA 19103
Ph: (866)836-9890
Fax: (215)751-1757
URL: http://www.mrinetwork.com

Executive search firm. More than 300 offices throughout the U.S.

5545 ■ MJS Executive Search
2 Overhill Rd., Ste. 400
Scarsdale, NY 10583
Ph: (914)631-1774
Fax: (914)631-0435
E-mail: info@mjsearch.com
URL: http://www.mjsearch.com

Serves as a retained executive recruiting firm specializing in placing professionals in consumer goods, entertainment, media, social media, sports, marketing services and other industries.

5546 ■ Neil Frank & Company
PO Box 3570
Redondo Beach, CA 90277-1570
Ph: (310)543-1611
E-mail: neilnick@aol.com
URL: http://www.neilfrank.com

Executive search firm.

5547 ■ New World Staffing
304 Park Ave. S, 11th Fl.
New York, NY 10010
Fr: 800-884-5157
E-mail: contact@newworldstaffing.org
URL: http://newworldstaffing.org

Description: Strives to match proven executives who are looking for career growth with successful companies across the United States.

5548 ■ Next Level Executive Search
24 Cathedral Pl., Ste. 500
St. Augustine, FL 32084
Ph: (904)810-5177
Fax: (904)810-6855
URL: http://www.nextlevelexecutive.com

Description: Serves as executive search and consulting firm specializing in the sports industry for interim and permanent middle management to senior level positions.

5549 ■ Norman Broadbent International
233 S Wacker Dr., Ste. 8000
Chicago, IL 60606
Ph: (312)876-3300
Fax: (312)876-3640
E-mail: info@nbisearch.com

Consultants specializing in the recruitment of management professionals.

5550 ■ Novo Group
1033 N Mayfair Rd., Ste. 310
Milwaukee, WI 53226
Ph: (414)727-8755
Fax: (414)727-4895
URL: http://www.thenovogroup.com

Description: Serves as a professional services firm focusing on finding executive, managerial, professional, sales, marketing and technical talent for organizations.

5551 ■ Oliver & Rozner Associates
598 Madison Ave., Ste. 11
New York, NY 10022
Ph: (212)688-1850

Performs executive search for top tiers of management including presidents, general management, advertising account management, division management, group executive and vice presidential line positions in such areas as marketing, research, operations, sales, finance, human resources and others; hard-to-find specialists including specific marketing/advertising executives, research and development expertise, computer/data processing knowledge, scientific, physicians-product efficacy and occupational medicine and engineering. Industries served include pharmaceutical, health care, hospital, advertising, consumer products and packaged goods, house wares, direct selling, cosmetics/toiletries, industrial products, high technology products, forest products, engineering, construction, environment/resource recovery, graphic arts, chemical and government agencies.

5552 ■ Onstott Group
55 Williams St.
Wellesley, MA 02481
Ph: (781)235-3050
Fax: (781)235-8653
E-mail: info@onstott.com
URL: http://www.onstott.com

Provides executive search services that focus on board level, chief executive, and other senior executive positions.

5553 ■ Paul Bodner & Associates Inc.
9217 Tudor Park Pl.
Las Vegas, NV 89145
Ph: (702)528-0780
E-mail: paul@paulbodnerassociates.com
URL: http://www.paulbodnerassociates.com/index.html

Executive search firm. Second branch in Denver, CO.

5554 ■ Phillip's Personnel/Phillip's Temps
1675 Broadway, Ste. 2410
Denver, CO 80204
Ph: (303)893-1850
Fax: (303)893-0639
E-mail: info@phillipspersonnel.com
URL: http://www.phillipspersonnel.com

Personnel recruiting and staffing consultants in: accounting and finance, MIS, sales and marketing, engineering, administration and general and executive management. Industries served: telecommunications, distribution, financial services and general business.

5555 ■ Polly Brown Associates Inc.
150 E 57th St., Ste. 25A
New York, NY 10022
E-mail: pbrown@pollybrownassociates.com
URL: http://www.pollybrownassociates.com

Executive search firm.

5556 ■ Primary Group
2180 W State Rd. 434, Ste. 4160
Longwood, FL 32791-6160
Ph: (407)869-4111
Fax: (407)682-3321
URL: http://www.theprimarygroup.com

Exists as an executive search firm that recruits professionals from the spectrum of sales, marketing, management, operations, or any executive level.

5557 ■ Princeton Executive Search
2667 Nottingham Way
Trenton, NJ 08619
Ph: (609)584-1100
Fax: (856)596-8866
E-mail: pes@bonifield.com

Provides search and placement for management level professions. Specializes in accounting, banking, engineering and human resources. Industries served: financial, research and development, insurance, manufacturing, banking, and government agencies.

5558 ■ Pro Staff
14300 Nicollet Ct., Ste. 208
Burnsville, MN 55306
Ph: (952)892-3240
Fax: (952)892-7304
Fr: 800-938-WORK
E-mail: burnsville@prostaff.com
URL: http://www.prostaff.com

Description: Strives to enhance the success and development of client-companies through cost-efficient, comprehensive workforce management solutions. Focuses on the employment market, labor trends, and best practices in administrative, finance and accounting, information technology, technical, and creative services.

5559 ■ R Gaines Baty Associates Inc.
6606 LBJ Freeway, Ste. 100
Dallas, TX 75240
Ph: (972)386-7900
Fax: (972)387-2224
E-mail: gbaty@rgba.com
URL: http://www.rgba.com

Executive search firm.

5560 ■ Raines International Inc.
250 Park Ave., 17th Fl.
New York, NY 10177
Ph: (212)997-1100
Fax: (212)997-0196
E-mail: contact@rainesinternational.com
URL: http://www.rainesinternational.com

International generalist firm specializing in middle to upper management executives. Concentrations include general management, finance and accounting, information technology, operations or procurement, strategic planning, investment banking, real estate or finance, human resources, insurance, and legal.

5561 ■ Recruiting Partners
3494 Camino Tassajara Rd., No. 404
Danville, CA 94506
Ph: (925)964-0249
E-mail: info@recruitingpartners.com
URL: http://www.recruitingpartners.com

Description: Serves as an executive and technical recruiting firm that specializes in accounting, legal, information technology, engineering, executive management and technical writing.

5562 ■ Rice Professional Search
363 N Sam Houston Pkwy. E, Ste. 1100
Houston, TX 77060
Ph: (281)931-6400
Fax: (281)931-0929
E-mail: info@riceprosearch.com
URL: http://www.riceprosearch.com

Serves as an executive job placement firm that provides professional search and staffing services.

5563 ■ Robert W. Dingman Company Inc.
650 Hampshire Rd., No. 116
Westlake Village, CA 91361
Ph: (805)778-1777
Fax: (805)778-9288
E-mail: info@dingman.com
URL: http://www.dingman.com

Executive search firm with a second office in Black Forest, CO.

5564 ■ Ropella Group
8100 Opportunity Dr.
Milton, FL 32583
Ph: (850)983-4777
Fax: (850)983-1627
E-mail: info@ropella.com
URL: http://www.ropella.com

Serves as an executive search and consulting firm specializing in the chemical, consumer products, energy, and other technology industries. Provides positions from senior executives to middle management in all areas of business covering executive level management, marketing, public relations and communications, strategic planning and commercial development, sales, business development and customer service, purchasing, logistics and supply chain, manufacturing and facilities maintenance, research and development, engineering, human resources, mergers, acquisitions and joint ventures, accounting and finance, real estate and asset management.

5565 ■ RSMR Global Resources
308 W Erie St.
Chicago, IL 60654
Ph: (312)957-0337
E-mail: info@rsmr.com
URL: http://www.rsmr.com

Serves as a retained executive search and human resources consulting firm dedicated to finding the right executives for companies. Specializes in placement in the areas of energy, real estate, architecture, engineering, construction, manufacturing and banking.

5566 ■ Russell Reynolds Associates, Inc.
200 Park Ave., Ste. 2300
New York, NY 10166-0002
Ph: (212)351-2000
E-mail: hcamericas@russellreynolds.com
URL: http://www.russellreynolds.com

Executive search firm. Affiliate offices across the country and abroad.

5567 ■ Sanford Rose Associates
1305 Mall of Georgia Blvd., Ste. 160
Akron, OH 44333-8369
Ph: (678)833-9305
Fax: (770)904-0359

Fr: 800-731-7724
E-mail: hq@sanfordrose.com
URL: http://www.sanfordrose.com

Executive search firm. Over 80 franchised office locations nationwide.

5568 ■ Scion Staffing
576 Sacramento St., 2nd Fl.
San Francisco, CA 94111
Ph: (415)392-7500
E-mail: info@scionstaffing.com
URL: http://scionstaffing.com

Serves as an executive search firm and temporary agency for professional candidates.

5569 ■ Search North America Inc.
PO Box 3577
Sunriver, OR 97707-0577
Ph: (503)222-6461
Fax: (503)227-2804
E-mail: mylinda@searchna.com
URL: http://www.searchna.com

An executive search and recruiting firm whose focus is placing engineers, operations and maintenance managers, sales and marketing management, financial and general management executives (both domestic and international). Industries served: forest products, pulp and paper, waste to energy, environmental services, consulting and equipment suppliers for above related industries.

5570 ■ SHS Careers Front Page
711 DeLasalle Ct.
Naperville, IL 60565
Ph: (630)718-1704
Fax: (630)718-1709
URL: http://www.shsinc.com

Executive search firm for pharmaceutical advertising, medical communications and education, healthcare public relations, and biotechnology industries.

5571 ■ Slayton Search Partners
311 S Wacker, Ste. 3200
Chicago, IL 60606
Ph: (312)456-0080
Fax: (312)456-0089
URL: http://www.slaytonsearch.com

Description: Serves as an executive search firm specializing in finding, attracting, and retaining executive management talents.

5572 ■ Sports Group International
7317 Spyglass Way, Ste. 400
Raleigh, NC 27615
Ph: (919)855-0226
Fax: (919)855-0793
E-mail: sgisearch@aol.com
URL: http://www.sgisearch.com

Serves as an executive search firm for the sporting goods and recreational products industries. Specializes in the recruitment of senior and middle level managers who excel in sales, marketing, product design and development, and general management.

5573 ■ S.R. Clarke
105 Huntercombe
Williamburg, VA 23188
Ph: (703)934-4200
Fax: (703)344-0259
URL: http://www.srclarke.com/index.html

Serves as an executive search and recruitment firm specializing in commercial construction, commercial real estate development, residential asset management, residential construction and development, subcontractor trades, finance, accounting, administration, heavy construction, architectural design and engineering design.

5574 ■ Stanton Chase International
5005 LBJ Fwy., Ste. 810
Dallas, TX 75244

Ph: (972)404-8411
E-mail: dallas@stantonchase.com
URL: http://www.stantonchase.com

Description: Serves as an executive search firm focusing on the recruitment of talent for top management positions.

5575 ■ Strategic Resource Services, Inc.
400 - 108th Ave. NE, Ste. 620
Bellevue, WA 98004
Ph: (425)688-1151
Fax: (425)732-2112
E-mail: corporate@strategicresources.com
URL: http://www.strategicresources.com

Description: Exists as an executive search firm that specializes in finding top-level executives and board members for U.S. companies. Develops job specifications, assembles a list of potential prospects, performs background checks, and assists with interviews and negotiating final offers.

5576 ■ TeamWork Consulting Inc.
22550 McCauley Rd.
Shaker Heights, OH 44122
Ph: (216)360-1790
Fax: (216)292-9265
E-mail: info@teamworkonline.com
URL: http://www.teamworkconsulting.com

A retained executive search firm to sports, live event management, location-based retail entertainment properties.

5577 ■ Valerie Fredrickson & Company
800 Menlo Ave., Ste. 220
Menlo Park, CA 94025
Ph: (650)614-0220
E-mail: recruiting@vfandco.com
URL: http://www.vfandco.com

Executive search firm.

5578 ■ William J. Christopher Associates Inc.
307 N Walnut St.
West Chester, PA 19380
Ph: (610)696-4397
Fax: (610)692-5177
E-mail: wjc@wjca.com
URL: http://www.wjca.com

Executive search firm.

5579 ■ Williams Executive Search Inc.
4200 Wells Fargo Ctr.
90 S 7th St.
Minneapolis, MN 55402
Ph: (612)339-2900
Fax: (612)305-5040
E-mail: resumes@williams-exec.com
URL: http://www.williams-exec.com

Executive search firm.

ONLINE JOB SOURCES AND SERVICES

5580 ■ 6Figurejobs.com
E-mail: info@6figurejobs.com
URL: http://www.6figurejobs.com

Description: Provides executives and experienced professionals with access to some of the most exclusive executive jobs, executive recruiters and career management tools available. Includes tools for both posting and viewing jobs, resume refinement, company research and more.

5581 ■ BankingCareers.com
URL: http://www.bankingcareers.com

Description: Provides lists of jobs and products to bankers in the banking and finance community.

5582 ■ Chief Executive Officer Jobs
URL: http://www.chiefexecutiveofficerjobs.org

Description: Serves as a niche job board for chief

executive officers. Offers updated job listings for candidates and job posting for employers.

5583 ■ ExecuNet.com
295 Westport Ave.
Norwalk, CT 06851
Fr: 800-637-3126
E-mail: member.services@execunet.com
URL: http://www.execunet.com

Description: Job site dedicated to the $150,000+ executive job seeker. Members may access job bank, recruiter and employer information, have their resumes reviewed, attend networking meetings, and access cutting-edge career information and references. Fee: Must become member to access services, cost is $219 for six-month membership.

5584 ■ ExecutivesOnly.com, Inc.
100 Jefferson Blvd.
3 Jefferson Pl., Ste. 310
Warwick, RI 02888
Fax: (401)921-6429
Fr: 877-804-5627
E-mail: support@executivesonly.com
URL: http://www.executivesonly.com

Description: Job site specializing in executive positions netting an annual salary of $100K or more. Members can view job bank and set up daily e-mail alerts. They may also choose to recruit the help of a senior adviser who can help review resumes and distribute them to recruiters. Fee: Must become member to access services.

5585 ■ HealthCareProfessional.com
URL: http://www.healthcareprofessional.com

Description: Provides jobs for directors, executives, managers, and supervisors in the health care industry.

5586 ■ Heidrick & Struggles Management Search
233 S Wacker Dr.
Willis Tower, Ste. 4200
Chicago, IL 60606-6303
Ph: (312)496-1200
URL: http://www.heidrick.com/pages/default.aspx

Description: Executive search firm that will distribute registered resumes to recruiters with suitable positions available.

5587 ■ JobMetaSeek.com
URL: http://www.jobmetaseek.com

Description: Seeks to address the career and job search needs of managers, professionals, executives, and other skilled and experienced job seekers in the United States and Canada. Features links to employment and career related sites, local and international sites, recruiters, education & training, resume sites, salary surveys, news, and others.

5588 ■ MBA Careers
3934 SW Corbett Ave.
Portland, OR 97239
Ph: (503)221-7779
Fax: (503)221-7780
E-mail: eric@careerexposure.com
URL: http://mbacareers.com

Description: Job site that provides resume posting, databank search and e-mail alert services to MBA and other advanced graduate degree holders.

5589 ■ NetShare.com
83 Hamilton Dr., Ste. 202
Novato, CA 94949
Fr: 800-241-5642
E-mail: netshare@netshare.com
URL: http://www.netshare.com

Description: Members-only resource for $100,000+ executives who are actively searching for new positions or passively tracking the job market. Listings that match posted profile will be e-mailed. Fee: Fees vary by level of service; annual basic level dues are $360.

5590 ■ Spherion
2050 Spectrum Blvd.
Fort Lauderdale, FL 33309
Ph: (954)308-7600
Fr: 800-774-3746
E-mail: help@spherion.com
URL: http://www.spherion.com

Description: Recruitment firm specializing in accounting and finance, sales and marketing, interim executives, technology, engineering, retail and human resources.

5591 ■ Transearch.com
E-mail: contact@transearch.com
URL: http://www.transearch.com

Description: International executive search firm concentrating in searches for executives in retail, real estate, information technology, industry, life sciences and financial services. Seekers may search job board and submit their resume for recruiter review.

5592 ■ WSA Executive Job Search Center
Ph: (251)895-2125
E-mail: info@wsacorp.com
URL: http://www.wsacorp.com

Description: A site intended for $50K-$700K range executives. Offers resume preparation, critiques and distribution, and interview preparation.

OTHER SOURCES

5593 ■ American Chamber of Commerce Executives (ACCE)
4875 Eisenhower Ave., Ste. 250
Alexandria, VA 22304
Ph: (703)998-0072
Fax: (703)212-9512
E-mail: mfleming@acce.org
URL: http://www.acce.org

Description: Professional society of chamber of commerce executives and staff members.

5594 ■ American Management Association (AMA)
1601 Broadway
New York, NY 10019-7420
Ph: (212)586-8100
Fax: (212)903-8168
Fr: 877-566-9441
E-mail: customerservice@amanet.org
URL: http://www.amanet.org

Description: Provides educational forums worldwide where members and their colleagues learn superior, practical business skills and explore best practices of world-class organizations through interaction with each other and expert faculty practitioners. **Purpose:** Maintains a publishing program providing tools individuals use to extend learning beyond the classroom in a process of life-long professional growth and development through education.

5595 ■ American Society of Association Executives (ASAE)
1575 I St. NW
Washington, DC 20005
Ph: (202)371-0940
Fax: (202)371-8315
Fr: 888-950-2723
E-mail: asaeservice@asaecenter.org
URL: http://www.asaecenter.org

Description: Professional society of paid executives of international, national, state, and local trade, professional, and philanthropic associations. Seeks to educate association executives on effective management, including: the proper objectives, functions, and activities of associations; the basic principles of association management; the legal aspects of association activity; policies relating to association management; efficient methods, procedures, and techniques of association management; the responsibilities and professional standards of association executives. Maintains information resource center. Conducts resume, guidance, and consultation services; compiles statistics in the form of reports, surveys, and studies; carries out research and education. Maintains ASAE Services Corporation to provide special services and ASAE Foundation to do future-oriented research and make grant awards. Offers executive search services and insurance programs. Provides CEO center for chief staff executives. Conducts Certified Association Executive (CAE) program.

5596 ■ Center for Creative Leadership (CCL)
PO Box 26300
Greensboro, NC 27438-6300
Ph: (336)545-2810
Fax: (336)282-3284
E-mail: info@ccl.org
URL: http://www.ccl.org

Description: Promotes behavioral science research and leadership education.

5597 ■ The International Alliance for Women (TIAW)
1760 Old Meadow Rd., Ste. 500
McLean, VA 22102
Fr: (866)533-8429
E-mail: info@tiaw.org
URL: http://www.tiaw.org

Description: Local networks comprising 50,000 professional and executive women in 12 countries; individual businesswomen without a network affiliation are alliance associates. Promotes recognition of the achievements of women in business. Encourages placement of women in senior executive positions. Maintains high standards of professional competence among members. Facilitates communication on an international scale among professional women's networks and their members. Represents members' interests before policymaking business and government. Sponsors programs that support equal opportunity and enhance members' business and professional skills. Operates appointments and directors service. Maintains speakers' bureau.

5598 ■ National Association of Corporate Directors (NACD)
Two Lafayette Ctr.
1133 21st St. NW, Ste. 700
Washington, DC 20036
Ph: (202)775-0509
Fax: (202)775-4857
E-mail: info@nacdonline.org
URL: http://www.nacdonline.org

Description: Corporate directors and boards of directors; chief executive officers, presidents, accountants, lawyers, consultants, and other executives are members. Conducts research, surveys, and seminars.

5599 ■ National Association for Female Executives
PO Box 3052
Langhorne, PA 19047
Fr: 800-927-6233
E-mail: carol.evans@workingmother.com
URL: http://www.nafe.com

Description: Represents women executives, business owners, and entrepreneurs. Provides networking opportunities for all members. Advocates for the advancement of women in the workplace.

5600 ■ National Association of Television Program Executives
5757 Wilshire Blvd., Penthouse 10
Los Angeles, CA 90036-3681
Ph: (310)453-4440
Fax: (310)453-5258
URL: http://www.natpe.org/natpe

Description: Comprised of television program professionals, exhibitors, buyers and faculty. Focuses on the creation, development and distribution of televised programming in all forms across all mature and emerging media platforms. Provides members with education, networking, professional enhancement and technological guidance through year-round activities and events, and directories.

5601 ■ National Black MBA Association (NBMBAA)
180 N Michigan Ave., Ste. 1400
Chicago, IL 60601
Ph: (312)236-2622
Fax: (312)236-0390
E-mail: mail@nbmbaa.org
URL: http://www.nbmbaa.org

Description: Business professionals, lawyers, accountants, and engineers concerned with the role of blacks who hold advanced management degrees. Works to create economic and intellectual wealth for the black community. Encourages blacks to pursue continuing business education; assists students preparing to enter the business world. Provides programs for minority youths, students, and professionals, and entrepreneurs including workshops, panel discussions, and Destination MBA seminar. Sponsors job fairs. Works with graduate schools. Operates job placement service.

5602 ■ National Management Association (NMA)
2210 Arbor Blvd.
Dayton, OH 45439
Ph: (937)294-0421
Fax: (937)294-2374
E-mail: nma@nma1.org
URL: http://www.nma1.org

Description: Business and industrial management personnel; membership comes from supervisory level, with the remainder from middle management and above. Seeks to develop and recognize management as a profession and to promote the free enterprise system. Prepares chapter programs on basic management, management policy and practice, communications, human behavior, industrial relations, economics, political education, and liberal education. Maintains speakers' bureau and hall of fame. Maintains educational, charitable, and research programs. Sponsors charitable programs.

5603 ■ National Society of Hispanic MBAs (NSHMBA)
1303 Walnut Hill Ln., Ste. 100
Irving, TX 75038
Ph: (214)596-9338
Fax: (214)596-9325
Fr: 877-467-4622
E-mail: saramos@nshmba.org
URL: http://www.nshmba.org

Description: Hispanic MBA professional business network dedicated to economic and philanthropic advancement.

5604 ■ Women in Management (WIM)
PO Box 1032
Dundee, IL 60118-7032
Ph: (708)386-0496
Fax: (847)683-3751
Fr: 877-946-6285
E-mail: nationalwim@wimonline.org
URL: http://www.wimonline.org

Description: Supports network of women in professional and management positions that facilitate the exchange of experience and ideas. Promotes self-growth in management; provides speakers who are successful in management; sponsors workshops and special interest groups to discuss problems and share job experiences.

Genetic Counselors

SOURCES OF HELP-WANTED ADS

5605 ■ The American Journal of Human Genetics
Elsevier
1600 John F. Kennedy Blvd., Ste. 1800
Philadelphia, PA 19103-2822
Ph: (215)239-3900
Fax: (215)238-7883
E-mail: ajhg@ajhg.net
URL: http://www.cell.com/AJHG

Monthly. $1,100.00/year for individuals, print and electronic; $990.00/year for individuals, electronic only; $990.00/year for individuals, print only; $1,100.00/year for institutions, print and electronic; $990.00/year for institutions, electronic only; $990.00/year for institutions, print only; $110.00/year for institutions, single copy; $1,190.00/year for institutions, Canada, print and electronic; $1,049.40/year for institutions, Canada, electronic only; $1,073.40/year for institutions, Canada, print only. Journal devoted to research and review on heredity in man and the application of genetic principles in medicine, psychology, anthropology, and social sciences.

5606 ■ Annals of Human Genetics
John Wiley & Sons Inc.
350 Main St., Commerce Pl.
Malden, MA 02148-5089
Ph: (781)388-8200
Fax: (781)388-8210
URL: http://www.blackwellpublishing.com/
    journal.asp?ref=0003-4800

Bimonthly. $324.00/year for individuals, print & online; $998.00/year for institutions, print & online. Journal focusing on research of human genetics and human inheritance.

5607 ■ Annual Review of Genetics
Annual Reviews Inc.
4139 El Camino Way
Palo Alto, CA 94306
Ph: (650)493-4400
Fax: (650)424-0910
Fr: 800-523-8635
URL: http://www.annualreviews.org/journal/genet

Annual. $86.00/year for individuals, print & online; $263.00/year for institutions, print & online; $219.00/year for institutions, online; $219.00/year for institutions, print. Periodical covering issues in genetics and the biological sciences.

5608 ■ Clinical Genetics
John Wiley & Sons Inc.
350 Main St., Commerce Pl.
Malden, MA 02148-5089
Ph: (781)388-8200
Fax: (781)388-8210
URL: http://www.wiley.com/bw/journal.asp?ref=0009-
    9163&site=1

Monthly. $493.00/year for individuals, print & online;

$444.00/year for individuals, online only; $1,713.00/year for institutions, print & online; $1,489.00/year for institutions, print or online; $318.00/year for members, print and online; $269.00/year for members, online only; $1,021.00/year for institutions, other countries, print & online; $887.00/year for institutions, other countries, print or online. Journal focusing on research related to molecular approaches to genetic disease and the translation of these advances for the practicing geneticist.

5609 ■ Genetic Alliance Community Job Postings
4301 Connecticut Ave. NW, Ste. 404
Washington, DC 20008
Ph: (202)966-5557
Fax: (202)966-8553
E-mail: network@geneticalliance.org
URL: http://www.geneticalliance.org/job.board

Presents job postings in the genetics community at no cost for non profit and not-for-profit organizations; for-profits companies can post want ads for $50/month.

5610 ■ Genetical Research
Cambridge University Press
32 Avenue of the Americas
New York, NY 10013-2473
Ph: (212)924-3900
Fax: (212)691-3239
E-mail: ad_sales@cambridge.org
URL: http://journals.cambridge.org/action/
    displayJournal?jid=GRH

$919.00/year for institutions, online only; $1,136.00/year for institutions, online and print. Science journal on all aspects of genetics.

5611 ■ Genetics
Genetics Society of America
9650 Rockville Pike
Bethesda, MD 20814-3998
Ph: (301)634-7300
Fax: (301)530-7079
Fr: (866)HUM-GENE
E-mail: genetics-gsa@andrew.cmu.edu
URL: http://www.genetics.org

Monthly. $800.00/year for nonmembers, online, institutions. Journal on genetics.

5612 ■ HelpWantedSanDiego.com
6465 Greenwood Plaza Blvd., Ste. 400
Centennial, CO 80111
Fax: 800-595-2929
Fr: 800-365-8630
URL: http://helpwantedsandiego.com/home/257.htm

Online job source for genetics professionals highlighting help wanted ads on the Internet and local radio stations. Resumes are sent to the advertiser's private online account.

5613 ■ Human Biology
Wayne State University Press
4809 Woodward Ave.
Detroit, MI 48201-1309
Ph: (313)577-6120
Fax: (313)577-6131
Fr: 800-978-7323
E-mail: human.biology@mnmh.fr
URL: http://digitalcommons.wayne.edu/humbiol

Bimonthly. $335.00/year for institutions; $130.00/year for individuals; $45.00/year for students, senior. Journal on population genetics, evolutionary and genetic demography, and behavioral genetics.

5614 ■ Job Line
Association of Genetic Technologists
PO Box 19193
Lenexa, KS 66285
Ph: (913)895-4605
Fax: (913)895-4652
E-mail: agt-info@goamp.com
URL: http://www.agt-info.org

Association Website offering classified job advertising for careers in genetics, posted by region.

5615 ■ Perspectives in Genetic Counseling Newsletter
National Society of Genetic Counselors
401 N Michigan Ave.
Chicago, IL 60611
Ph: (312)321-6834
Fax: (312)673-6972
E-mail: nsgc@nsgc.org
URL: http://archive.nsgc.org/resources/pgc_
    newsletter.cfm

Quarterly newsletter spotlighting new legislation regarding genetics issues and genetic counselors, marketing strategies for organizations, media reporting on medical genetics, meeting announcements and job listings in the field of genetics counseling.

5616 ■ PLoS Genetics
Public Library of Science
1160 Battery St.
San Francisco, CA 94111
Ph: (415)624-1200
Fax: (415)546-4090
E-mail: plosgenetics@plos.org
URL: http://www.plosgenetics.org/home.action

Weekly. Free, online. Open access, peer-reviewed journal that publishes research and case studies in the field of genetics.

EMPLOYER DIRECTORIES AND NETWORKING LISTS

5617 ■ American Board of Genetic Counseling—Membership Directory
American Board of Genetic Counseling
18000 W 105th St.
Olathe, KS 66061

Ph: (913)895-4617
Fax: (913)895-4652
URL: http://www.abgc.net

Covers: Individuals who have passed the Board examination and includes the ABGC, Genetics Society of America, American Society of Human Genetics, American College of Medical Genetics, and the American Board of Medical Genetics.

5618 ■ American Society of Human Genetics—Membership Directory

Genetics Society of America
9650 Rockville Pike
Bethesda, MD 20814-3998
Ph: (301)634-7300
Fax: (301)530-7079
Fr: (866)HUM-GENE
URL: http://www.genetics-gsa.org/cgi-bin/Search-GSA

Biennial, even years. Covers: about 10,000 teachers, physicians, researchers, genetic counselors, and others interested in human genetics. Lists members of the American Society of Human Genetics, the American Board of Medical Genetics, the Genetics Society of America, the American College of Medical Genetics, and the American Board of Genetic Counseling. Entries include: Name, degree(s), institution name, department name, address, phone; type of membership and society of which a member. Arrangement: Alphabetical. Indexes: Geographical, subspecialty (American Board of Medical Genetics Members and American Board of Genetic Counseling Members) and American College of Medical Genetics.

5619 ■ Genetic Disorders Sourcebook

Omnigraphics Inc.
PO Box 31-1640
Detroit, MI 48231
Fr: 800-234-1340
URL: http://www.omnigraphics.com

Irregular, latest edition 4th, Published 2010. $85.00 for individuals; $95.00 for individuals. Covers: Information about genetic disorders and related organizations. Entries include: Contact information. Indexes: General.

HANDBOOKS AND MANUALS

5620 ■ Careers in Medicine

The McGraw-Hill Companies
PO Box 182604
Columbus, OH 43272
Fax: (614)759-3749
Fr: 877-883-5524
E-mail: customer.service@mcgraw-hill.com
URL: http://www.mhprofessional.com/product.php?isbn=0071458743

Terence J. Sacks. Third edition, 2006. $15.95 (paper). 192 pages. Examines the many paths open to M.D.s, D.O.s, and M.D./Ph.D.s, including clinical private or group practice, hospitals, public health organizations, the armed forces, emergency rooms, research institutions, medical schools, pharmaceutical companies and private industry, and research/advocacy groups like the World Health Organization. A special chapter on osteopathy and chiropractic explores this branch of medicine.

5621 ■ Professional Status Survey

National Society of Genetic Counselors
401 N Michigan Ave.
Chicago, IL 60611
Ph: (312)321-6834
Fax: (312)673-6972
E-mail: nsgc@nsgc.org
URL: http://www.nsgc.org/Publications/ProfessionalStatusSurvey/tabid/142/Default.aspx

Bi-annual survey presenting an overview of genetics professions; includes information regarding salary ranges, work environments, faculty status, and job satisfaction.

EMPLOYMENT AGENCIES AND SEARCH FIRMS

5622 ■ DDS Resources

16020 Swingley Ridge Rd., Ste. 340
Chesterfield, MO 63017
Ph: (636)536-6656
Fax: (636)536-6667
Fr: 877-337-0563
E-mail: info@mdr-inc.com
URL: http://www.mdr-inc.com/dentists.aspx

Serves as a dental recruitment agency in the United States. Specializes in matching qualified dentists with dental employers.

ONLINE JOB SOURCES AND SERVICES

5623 ■ Employment Spot

URL: http://www.employmentspot.com

Help wanted advertisements for professional positions, including those in the genetics field. Users can search for positions by city, state or industry.

5624 ■ Get Genetic Counseling Jobs

URL: http://www.getgeneticcounselingjobs.com

Description: Features a searchable database of employment opportunities for genetic counselors.

5625 ■ National Society of Genetic Counselors E-Blast

E-mail: nsgc@nsgc.org
URL: http://www.nsgc.org

Allows members to email announcements and messages to the desktops of other members.

5626 ■ National Society of Genetic Counselors Job Connection Service

E-mail: nsgc@nsgc.org
URL: http://jobconnection.nsgc.org

Services include a three-month posting on the Society's website as well as a one-time posting on its Listserv, reaching more than 85 percent of the society's full and associated members. The Listserv allows users to target a select audience of members in the following specialties: cancer, prenatal, pediatric, cardiovascular, industry, psychiatric disorders, and general.

OTHER SOURCES

5627 ■ Alstrom Syndrome International (ASI)

14 Whitney Farm Rd.
Mount Desert, ME 04660
Fr: 800-371-3628
E-mail: jdm@jax.org
URL: http://www.alstrom.org

Description: Individuals with Alstrom's syndrome (a genetic disorder resulting in multiple organ failures) and their families; health care professionals with an interest in the syndrome and its diagnosis and treatment. Seeks to improve the quality of life of people with Alstrom's syndrome. Serves as a clearinghouse on the syndrome and its treatment; functions as a support group for people with Alstrom's syndrome and their families. Encourages and fosters genetic and clinical research on Alstrom Syndrome.

5628 ■ American Board of Genetic Counseling (ABGC)

PO Box 14216
Lenexa, KS 66285
Ph: (913)895-4617
Fax: (913)895-4652
E-mail: info@abgc.net
URL: http://www.abgc.net

Description: Comprised of individuals who have passed the certification examination. Certifies indi-

viduals for the delivery of genetic counseling services and accredits genetic counseling master's degree granting programs.

5629 ■ American Board of Medical Genetics (ABMG)

9650 Rockville Pike
Bethesda, MD 20814-3998
Ph: (301)634-7315
Fax: (301)634-7320
E-mail: abmg@abmg.org
URL: http://www.abmg.org

Description: Certifies MDs and PhDs and accredits post doctoral laboratory training fellowship programs in the field of human genetics.

5630 ■ American College of Medical Genetics (ACMG)

7220 Wisconsin Ave., Ste. 300
Bethesda, MD 20814
Ph: (301)718-9603
Fax: (301)718-9604
E-mail: acmg@acmg.net
URL: http://www.acmg.net

Description: Physicians and others with an interest in genetics and the delivery of medical genetics services to the public. Works to insure the availability of genetic services without regard to considerations of race, gender, sexual orientation, disability, or ability to pay. Promotes and supports genetics research. Establishes and maintains scientific and professional standards for medical genetics education, research, and practice. Lobbies for effective and fair health policies and legislation; provides information and technical assistance to government agencies engaged in health care regulation or policy formation. Makes available continuing professional education programs; represents members' interests. Conducts advocacy campaigns for people with genetic problems; sponsors public education programs.

5631 ■ American Genetic Association (AGA)

2030 SE Marine Science Dr.
Newport, OR 97365
Ph: (541)867-0334
E-mail: agajoh@oregonstate.edu
URL: http://www.theaga.org

Description: Represents biologists, zoologists, geneticists, botanists, and others engaged in basic and applied research in genetics. Explores transmission genetics of plants and animals.

5632 ■ American Society of Human Genetics (ASHG)

9650 Rockville Pike
Bethesda, MD 20814-3998
Ph: (301)634-7300
Fax: (301)634-7079
Fr: (866)HUM-GENE
E-mail: society@ashg.org
URL: http://www.ashg.org

Description: Professional society of physicians, researchers, genetic counselors, and others interested in human genetics.

5633 ■ Association of Genetic Technologists

PO Box 15945-288
Lenexa, KS 66285
Ph: (913)895-4605
Fax: (913)895-4652
E-mail: agt-info@goamp.com
URL: http://www.agt-info.org

Professional organization of 1,200 technologists, supervisors and laboratory directors dedicated to promoting these professionals engaged in classical cytogenetics and molecular and biochemical genetics; and to stimulate interest in genetics as a career.

5634 ■ Association of Professors of Human and Medical Genetics (APHMG)

University of Maryland School of Medicine
Department of Pediatrics, Division of Human Genetics
655 W Baltimore St., Rm. 11-037
Baltimore, MD 21201

Ph: (410)706-4065
Fax: (410)706-6105
E-mail: mblitzer@peds.umaryland.edu
URL: http://www.aphmg.org

Description: Promotes human and medical genetics educational programs in North American medical and graduate schools. Conducts academic activities and workshops that deal with medical genetics.

5635 ■ Behavior Genetics Association (BGA)
345 UCB
Dept. of Psychology
Boulder, CO 80309
E-mail: soo.rhee@colorado.edu
URL: http://www.bga.org

Description: Consists of individuals engaged in teaching or research in some area of behavior genetics. Seeks to promote the scientific study of the interrelationship of genetic mechanisms and human and animal behavior through sponsorship of scientific meetings, publications, and communications among and by members; to encourage and aid the education and training of research workers in the field of behavior genetics; to aid in public dissemination and interpretation of information concerning the interrelationship of genetics and behavior and its implications for health, human development, and education.

5636 ■ Genetic Counseling Foundation
401 N Michigan Ave., 22nd Fl.
Chicago, IL 60611
Ph: (312)321-6834
E-mail: nsgc@nsgc.org
URL: http://www.nsgc.org

Seeks to improve quality education and research in the field of genetic counseling and to enhance the value, availability and awareness of genetic information and counseling in the medical community as well as the general public.

5637 ■ Genetics Society of America (GSA)
9650 Rockville Pike
Bethesda, MD 20814-3998

Ph: (301)634-7300
Fax: (301)634-7079
Fr: (866)486-GENE
E-mail: pws@caltech.edu
URL: http://www.genetics-gsa.org

Description: Individuals and organizations interested in any field of genetics. Provides facilities for association and conferences of students in heredity; encourages communication among workers in genetics and those in related sciences.

5638 ■ International Society of Nurses in Genetics (ISONG)
461 Cochran Rd.
Box 246
Pittsburgh, PA 15228
Ph: (412)344-1414
Fax: (412)344-0599
E-mail: isonghq@msn.com
URL: http://www.isong.org

Description: Represents case managers, administrators, coordinators of public and private programs, educators in the field of nursing and/or genetics, genetic counselors, researchers. Committed to incorporating the knowledge of human genetics into nursing practice, education and research activities.

5639 ■ Mountain States Genetics Foundation (MostGene)
8129 W Fremont Ave.
Littleton, CO 80128
Ph: (303)978-0125
Fax: (303)948-1890
E-mail: jhooker@msgrcc.org
URL: http://www.mostgene.org

Description: Advocates and supports education, awareness and access to medical genetics information.

5640 ■ National Board for Certified Counselors and Affiliates (NBCC)
3 Terrace Way
Greensboro, NC 27403-3660

Ph: (336)547-0607
Fax: (336)547-0017
E-mail: nbcc@nbcc.org
URL: http://www.nbcc.org

Description: Purpose: Establishes and monitors professional credentialing standards for counselors. Identifies individuals who have obtained voluntary certification as a National Certified Counselor, one who assists persons with aging, vocational development, adolescence, family, and marital concerns, or a National Certified School Counselor, one who specializes in counseling within the school setting, or a Certified Clinical Mental Health Counselor, one who specializes in working in clinical settings, or a Master Addictions Counselor, one who specializes in addictions counseling. Maintains a database of nearly 37,000 certified counselors.

5641 ■ National Coalition for Health Professional Education in Genetics (NCHPEG)
2360 W Joppa Rd., Ste. 320
Lutherville, MD 21093
Ph: (410)583-0600
Fax: (410)583-0520
E-mail: jscott@nchpeg.org
URL: http://www.nchpeg.org

Description: Promotes advances in health professional education and access to human genetics information.

5642 ■ National Society of Genetic Counselors (NSGC)
401 N Michigan Ave.
Chicago, IL 60611
Ph: (312)321-6834
Fax: (312)673-6972
E-mail: nsgc@nsgc.org
URL: http://www.nsgc.org

Description: Promotes the genetic counseling profession as a recognized and integral part of health care delivery, education, research and public policy.

Sources of Help-Wanted Ads

5643 ■ AAG Newsletter
Association of American Geographers
1710 16th St. NW
Washington, DC 20009-3198
Ph: (202)234-1450
Fax: (202)234-2744
E-mail: newsletter@aag.org
URL: http://www.aag.org/cs/publications/aag_
newsletter/overview

Description: Monthly. Publishes items of interest to Association members and persons in related disciplines. Contains news of research, news of members, listings of publications, information on grant and employment opportunities, notices of field courses and seminars, calls for papers, and a calendar of events.

5644 ■ Base Line
Map and Geography Round Table
c/o Danielle M. Alderson
American Library Association
50 E Huron St.
Chicago, IL 60611-2788
Ph: (312)280-3213
Fax: (312)944-6131
E-mail: dponton@ala.org
URL: http://www.ala.org/magirt

Description: Bimonthly. Provides current information on cartographic materials, publications of interest to map and geography librarians, related government activities, and map librarianship. Recurring features include conference and meeting information, news of research, job listings, and columns by the Division chair and the editor.

5645 ■ Geographical Journal
John Wiley & Sons Inc.
350 Main St., Commerce Pl.
Malden, MA 02148-5089
Ph: (781)388-8200
Fax: (781)388-8210
URL: http://www.wiley.com/bw/journal.asp?ref=0016-
7398&site=1

Quarterly. $359.00/year for institutions, print and online; $312.00/year for institutions, print or online; $213.00/year for institutions, other countries, print and online; $185.00/year for institutions, other countries, print or online. Journal focusing on original research and scholarship in physical and human geography.

5646 ■ Geographical Research
John Wiley & Sons Inc.
350 Main St., Commerce Pl.
Malden, MA 02148-5089
Ph: (781)388-8200
Fax: (781)388-8210
URL: http://www.wiley.com/bw/journal.asp?ref=1745-
5863&site=1

Quarterly. $80.00/year for individuals, print and online, rest of the world; $39.00/year for members, print and online, Europe; $340.00/year for institutions, print and online, Australia & New Zealand; $310.00/year for institutions, print or online, Australia & New Zealand; $80.00/year for individuals, print and online; $55.00/year for members, print and online; $312.00/year for institutions, other countries, print and online; $271.00/year for institutions, print or online. Journal focusing on advancing geographical research across the discipline.

5647 ■ Journal of Geographic Information System
Scientific Research Publishing
PO Box 54821
Irvine, CA 92619-4821
URL: http://www.scirp.org/journal/jgis/

Peer-reviewed journal featuring the latest advancements in geographic information system.

5648 ■ Journal of Latin American Geography
University of Texas Press
2100 Comal
Austin, TX 78722
Ph: (512)471-7233
Fax: (512)232-7178
Fr: 800-252-3206
URL: http://www.utexas.edu/utpress/journals/jlag.html

Semiannual. $60.00/year for individuals; $70.00/year for Canada; $20.00/year for individuals, Latin America; $77.50/year for other countries; $15.00/year for students, retired; $25.00/year for students, Canada, retired; $32.50/year for students, other countries, retired; $120.00/year for institutions; $130.00/year for institutions, Canada; $20.00/year for institutions, Latin America. Journal of the Conference of Latin American Geographists containing articles of interest to professionals in the field.

5649 ■ PALAIOS
SEPM Publications
4111 S Darlington, Ste. 100
Tulsa, OK 74135-6373
Ph: (918)610-3361
Fax: (918)621-1685
Fr: 800-865-9765
E-mail: palois@ku.edu
URL: http://palaios.ku.edu/

Monthly. $315.00/year for individuals, for U.S.; online version with CD-ROM; $415.00/year for individuals, for U.S.; print and online version with CD-ROM; $315.00/year for other countries, online version with CD-ROM; $425.00/year for other countries, print and online version with CD-ROM. Journal providing information on the impact of life on Earth history as recorded in the paleontological and sedimentological records. Covers areas such as biogeochemistry, ichnology, sedimentology, stratigraphy, paleoecology, paleoclimatology, and paleoceanography.

5650 ■ PE & RS Photogrammetric Engineering & Remote Sensing
The Imaging and Geospatial Information Society
5410 Grosvenor Ln., Ste. 210
Bethesda, MD 20814-2160
Ph: (301)493-0290
Fax: (301)493-0208
URL: http://www.asprs.org/PE-RS-Journal/

Monthly. $410.00/year for individuals, first class mail; $426.00/year for Canada, airmail; $420.00/year for other countries, air standard. Peer-reviewed journal covering photogrammetry, remote sensing, geographic information systems, cartography, and surveying, global positioning systems, digital photogrammetry.

5651 ■ Population, Space and Place
John Wiley & Sons Inc.
111 River St.
Hoboken, NJ 07030-5773
Ph: (201)748-6000
Fax: (201)748-6088
Fr: 800-825-7550
URL: http://onlinelibrary.wiley.com/journal/10.1002/
(ISSN)1544-84

Bimonthly. $1,188.00/year for institutions, online only; $1,188.00/year for institutions, other countries, online only; $766.00/year for institutions, other countries, online only; $607.00/year for institutions, online only; $1,188.00/year for institutions, Canada and Mexico, online only. Journal focusing on research in the field of geographical population studies.

5652 ■ Positioning
Scientific Research Publishing
PO Box 54821
Irvine, CA 92619-4821
E-mail: pos@scirp.org
URL: http://www.scirp.org/journal/pos/

Quarterly. $156.00/year for individuals. Peer-reviewed journal publishing articles on different areas of navigation and positioning.

5653 ■ The Professional Geographer
San Diego State University
5500 Campanile Dr.
San Diego, CA 92182
Ph: (619)594-5200
URL: http://www.aag.org/cs/publications/the_
professional_geograph

Quarterly. Geographical journal.

Employer Directories and Networking Lists

5654 ■ Guide to Programs in Geography in the United States and Canada/AAG Handbook and Directory of Geographers
Association of American Geographers
1710 16th St. NW
Washington, DC 20009-3198

Ph: (202)234-1450
Fax: (202)234-2744
URL: http://www.aag.org
Annual, Latest edition 2008-2009. $60.00 for non-members; $25.00 for students; $35.00 for members. Covers: Institutions offering undergraduate and graduate geography programs; and government agencies, private firms and research institutions that employ geographers in the U.S., Canada and Mexico. Entries include: For institutions—Department, address, and phone, contact person, requirements, programs, facilities, financial aid, faculty, titles of dissertations and theses completed. For individuals—Name, address, birth date, degrees received, place of employment. Arrangement: Geographical. Indexes: Department specialty; ZIP code.

HANDBOOKS AND MANUALS

5655 ■ *Opportunities in Social Science Careers*
The McGraw-Hill Companies
PO Box 182604
Columbus, OH 43272
Fax: (614)759-3749
Fr: 877-883-5524
E-mail: customer.service@mcgraw-hill.com
URL: http://www.mcgraw-hill.com
Rosanne J. Marek. 2004. $13.95. 160 Pages. VGM Opportunities Series.

ONLINE JOB SOURCES AND SERVICES

5656 ■ GeoCommunity
URL: http://www.geocomm.com
Description: Serves as a clearinghouse for posting or browsing GIS, GPS, CAD, remote sensing, and earth sciences related announcements, resumes, and consultant listings.

5657 ■ Geographer Jobs
URL: http://www.geographerjobs.net
Description: Serves as a career resource and job search site for geographer employment opportunities.

TRADESHOWS

5658 ■ Association of American Geographers Annual Meeting
Association of American Geographers
1710 16th St. NW
Washington, DC 20009-3198

Ph: (202)234-1450
Fax: (202)234-2744
E-mail: gaia@aag.org
URL: http://www.aag.org/
Annual. Primary Exhibits: Publications, geographic information systems, and technical equipment.

OTHER SOURCES

5659 ■ African Studies Association (ASA)
Rutgers University, Livingston Campus
54 Joyce Kilmer Ave.
Piscataway, NJ 08854-8045
Ph: (848)445-8173
Fax: (732)445-1366
E-mail: karen.jenkins@africanstudies.org
URL: http://www.africanstudies.org
Description: Persons specializing in teaching, writing, or research on Africa including political scientists, historians, geographers, anthropologists, economists, librarians, linguists, and government officials; persons who are studying African subjects; institutional members are universities, libraries, government agencies, and others interested in receiving information about Africa. Seeks to foster communication and to stimulate research among scholars on Africa. Sponsors placement service; conducts panels and discussion groups; presents exhibits and films.

5660 ■ American Geographical Society
32 Court St., Ste. 201
Brooklyn, NY 11201-4404
Ph: (718)624-2212
Fax: (718)624-2239
E-mail: ags@amergeog.org
URL: http://www.amergeog.org
Description: Industry professionals and other interested individuals.

5661 ■ ASPRS - The Imaging and Geospatial Information Society
5410 Grosvenor Ln., Ste. 210
Bethesda, MD 20814-2160
Ph: (301)493-0290
Fax: (301)493-0208
E-mail: asprs@asprs.org
URL: http://www.asprs.org
Description: Firms, individuals, government employees and academicians engaged in photogrammetry, photointerpretation, remote sensing, and geographic information systems and their application to such fields as archaeology, geographic information systems, military reconnaissance, urban planning, engineering, traffic surveys, meteorological observa-

tions, medicine, geology, forestry, agriculture, construction and topographic mapping. Seeks to advance knowledge and improve understanding of these sciences and promote responsible applications. Offers voluntary certification program open to persons associated with one or more functional area of photogrammetry, remote sensing and GIS. Surveys the profession of private firms in photogrammetry and remote sensing in the areas of products and services.

5662 ■ Association of American Geographers (AAG)
1710 16th St. NW
Washington, DC 20009-3198
Ph: (202)234-1450
Fax: (202)234-2744
E-mail: membership@aag.org
URL: http://www.aag.org
Description: Professional society of educators and scientists in the field of geography. Seeks to further professional investigations in geography and to encourage the application of geographic research in education, government, and business. Conducts research; compiles statistics.

5663 ■ Geography Education National Implementation Project
Texas A & M University
College Station, TX 77843-3147
Ph: (979)845-1579
Fax: (979)862-4487
E-mail: s-bednarz@tamu.edu
URL: http://genip.tamu.edu
Description: Consortium of geographic associations committed to improving the status and quality of geography education.

5664 ■ National Council for Geographic Education (NCGE)
1145 17th St. NW, Rm. 7620
Washington, DC 20036
Ph: (202)857-7695
Fax: (202)618-6249
E-mail: ncge@ncge.org
URL: http://www.ncge.org
Description: Teachers of geography and social studies in elementary and secondary schools, colleges and universities; geographers in governmental agencies and private businesses. Encourages the training of teachers in geographic concepts, practices, teaching methods and techniques; works to develop effective geographic educational programs in schools and colleges and with adult groups; stimulates the production and use of accurate and understandable geographic teaching aids and materials.

5665 ■ *AAPG Bulletin*
American Association of Petroleum Geologists
1444 S Boulder
Tulsa, OK 74119
Ph: (918)584-2555
Fax: (918)560-2665
Fr: 800-364-2274
E-mail: bulletin@aapg.org
URL: http://www.aapg.org/bulletin

Monthly. Included in membership. Peer-reviewed journal on the application of geological and geophysical principles to exploration and production for the development of energy resources. Subjects include petroleum geology, oil shale, coal, uranium, and geothermal energy.

5666 ■ *AAPG Explorer*
American Association of Petroleum Geologists
1444 S Boulder
Tulsa, OK 74119
Ph: (918)584-2555
Fax: (918)560-2665
Fr: 800-364-2274
URL: http://www.aapg.org/explorer/

Monthly. $75.00/year for nonmembers; $147.00/year for individuals, airmail service; $55.00/year for members, airmail. Magazine containing articles about energy issues with an emphasis on exploration for hydrocarbons and energy minerals.

5667 ■ *AEG News*
Association of Environmental & Engineering Geologists
PO Box 460518
Denver, CO 80246
Ph: (303)757-2926
E-mail: aeg@aegweb.org
URL: http://www.aegweb.org

Description: Bimonthly. $40 per year for nonmember. Covers news of the engineering geology profession and the Association, whose members are engineering geologists and geological engineers worldwide. Recurring features include letters to the editor, a calendar of events, news of research, and short articles of technical interest.

5668 ■ *Computational Thermal Sciences*
Begell House Inc.
50 Cross Hwy.
Redding, CT 06896
Ph: (203)938-1300
Fax: (203)938-1304
URL: http://www.begellhouse.com/journals/
648192910890cd0e

$672.00/year for institutions. Journal focusing on the fundamental methods of thermodynamics, fluid mechanics, heat transfer and combustion.

5669 ■ *Earth*
American Geological Institute
4220 King St.
Alexandria, VA 22302
Ph: (703)379-2480
Fax: (703)379-7563
E-mail: earth@earthmagazine.org
URL: http://www.agiweb.org

Monthly. $36/year in United States; $51/year in Canada; $81/year in other countries. Covers the latest happenings in earth, energy, and the environment.

5670 ■ *Engineering and Mining Journal*
Mining Media Inc.
8751 E Hampden Ave., Ste. B-1
Denver, CO 80231
Ph: (303)283-0640
Fax: (303)283-0641
URL: http://www.mining-media.com/publications/emj/

Monthly. Provides professionals in metallic and nonmetallic ores and minerals industries with news and technical economic information.

5671 ■ *Geological Abstracts*
Elsevier Science Inc.
360 Park Ave. S
New York, NY 10010-1710
Ph: (212)989-5800
Fax: (212)633-3990
Fr: 888-437-4636
URL: http://www.elsevier.com/wps/find/
journaldescription.cws_home

$4,611.00/year for institutions, other countries; $4,119.00/year for institutions, European countries and Iran; $546,800.00/year for institutions, Japan. Journal relating to geological literature.

5672 ■ *Geology*
Geological Society of America Inc.
PO Box 9140
Boulder, CO 80301-9140
Ph: (303)357-1000
Fax: (303)357-1070
Fr: 888-443-4472
E-mail: pubs@geocociety.org
URL: http://geology.gsapubs.org/

Monthly. $85.00/year for members, print (includes online access); $90.00/year for members, international; print (includes online access); $45.00/year for students, members; print (includes online access); $45.00/year for students, other countries, members; print (includes online access); $875.00/year for institutions, & nonmembers; print & online; $800.00/year for institutions, & nonmembers; online only. Geology journal.

5673 ■ *Geophysical Journal International*
John Wiley & Sons Inc.
350 Main St., Commerce Pl.
Malden, MA 02148-5089
Ph: (781)388-8200

Fax: (781)388-8210
URL: http://www.wiley.com/bw/journal.asp?ref=0956-
540X&site=1

Monthly. $431.00/year for individuals, print and online; $394.00/year for individuals, online only; $209.00/year for members, print and online; $2,936.00/year for institutions, print & online; $2,553.00/year for institutions, print or online; $233.00/year for individuals, print and online; $1,383.00/year for institutions, other countries, print or online. Journal focusing on research in geophysics.

5674 ■ *ISEM Newsletter*
Institute for the Study of Earth and Man
N.L. Heroy Hall
PO Box 0274
Dallas, TX 75275-0274
Ph: (214)768-2425
E-mail: isem@mail.smu.edu
URL: http://www.smu.edu/isem

Description: Semiannual. Reports on research in the anthropological, geological, and statistical sciences. Includes notices of research funds, grants, and contracts awarded. Provides biographical sketches of new faculty members in the anthropological, geological, and statistical sciences departments at Southern Methodist University. Recurring features include news of research and news of members.

5675 ■ *Nature International Weekly Journal of Science*
Nature Publishing Group
75 Varick St., 9th Fl.
New York, NY 10013-1917
Ph: (212)726-9200
Fax: (212)696-9006
Fr: 888-331-6288
E-mail: nature@natureny.com
URL: http://www.nature.com/nature/index.html

Weekly. $199.00/year for individuals, print and online; $338.00/year for two years, print and online. Magazine covering science and technology, including the fields of biology, biochemistry, genetics, medicine, earth sciences, physics, pharmacology, and behavioral sciences.

5676 ■ *Oil & Gas Journal*
PennWell Publishing Co.
1455 W Loop S, Ste. 400
Houston, TX 77027
Ph: (713)621-9720
Fr: 800-736-6935
URL: http://www.ogj.com/index.html

Weekly. $69.00/year for individuals, print; $49.00/year for individuals, online; $73.00/year for other countries, Canada and Latin America; $108.00/year for other countries. Trade magazine serving engineers and managers in international petroleum operations.

5677 ■ *PALAIOS*
SEPM Publications
4111 S Darlington, Ste. 100
Tulsa, OK 74135-6373

Ph: (918)610-3361
Fax: (918)621-1685
Fr: 800-865-9765
E-mail: palois@ku.edu
URL: http://palaios.ku.edu/

Monthly. $315.00/year for individuals, for U.S.; online version with CD-ROM; $415.00/year for individuals, for U.S.; print and online version with CD-ROM; $315.00/year for other countries, online version with CD-ROM; $425.00/year for other countries, print and online version with CD-ROM. Journal providing information on the impact of life on Earth history as recorded in the paleontological and sedimentological records. Covers areas such as biogeochemistry, ichnology, sedimentology, stratigraphy, paleoecology, paleoclimatology, and paleoceanography.

5678 ■ PE & RS Photogrammetric Engineering & Remote Sensing
The Imaging and Geospatial Information Society
5410 Grosvenor Ln., Ste. 210
Bethesda, MD 20814-2160
Ph: (301)493-0290
Fax: (301)493-0208
URL: http://www.asprs.org/PE-RS-Journal/

Monthly. $410.00/year for individuals, first class mail; $426.00/year for Canada, airmail; $420.00/year for other countries, air standard. Peer-reviewed journal covering photogrammetry, remote sensing, geographic information systems, cartography, and surveying, global positioning systems, digital photogrammetry.

5679 ■ The Scientist
The Scientist Inc.
121 W 27th St., Ste. 604
New York, NY 10001
Ph: (212)461-4470
Fax: (347)626-2385
URL: http://www.the-scientist.com

Monthly. $39.95/year for individuals, print only; $49.95/year for individuals, print & online; $64.95/year for other countries, print only; $74.95/year for other countries, print & online. News journal (tabloid) for life scientists featuring news, opinions, research, and professional section.

EMPLOYER DIRECTORIES AND NETWORKING LISTS

5680 ■ American Men and Women of Science
Gale
PO Box 6904
Florence, KY 41022-6904
Fr: 800-354-9706
URL: http://www.gale.cengage.com

Biennial, even years; New edition expected 29th, June 2011. $1,368.00 for individuals. Covers: Over 135,000 U.S. and Canadian scientists active in the physical, biological, mathematical, computer science, and engineering fields; includes references to previous edition for deceased scientists and nonrespondents. Entries include: Name, address, education, personal and career data, memberships, honors and awards, research interest. Arrangement: Alphabetical. Indexes: Discipline (in separate volume).

5681 ■ Directory of Certified Petroleum Geologists
American Association of Petroleum Geologists
1444 S Boulder
Tulsa, OK 74119
Ph: (918)584-2555
Fax: (918)560-2665
Fr: 800-364-2274
URL: http://www.aapg.org/dpadirectory

Covers: About 3,400 members of the association. Entries include: Name, address; education and career

data; whether available for consulting. Arrangement: Alphabetical. Indexes: Geographical.

5682 ■ Directory of Physics, Astronomy, and Geophysics Staff
American Institute of Physics
1 Physics Ellipse
College Park, MD 20740-3843
Ph: (301)209-3100
Fax: (301)209-0843
URL: http://www.aip.org/pubs/books/dpags.html

Biennial, Latest edition 2006. $82.00 for individuals. Covers: 36,000 staff members at 2,600 colleges, universities, and laboratories throughout North America that employ physicists and astronomers; list of foreign organizations. Entries include: Name, address, phone, fax, electronic mail address. Arrangement: Separate alphabetical sections for individuals, academic institutions, and laboratories. Indexes: Academic institution location, type of laboratory.

5683 ■ The Geophysical Directory
Geophysical Directory Inc.
PO Box 130508
Houston, TX 77219
Ph: (713)529-8789
Fax: (713)529-3646
Fr: 800-929-2462
E-mail: info@geophysicaldirectory.com
URL: http://www.geophysicaldirectory.com

Annual, Latest edition 66th; 2011. $150.00 for individuals; $165.00 for individuals. Covers: About 4,581 companies that provide geophysical equipment, supplies, or services, and mining and petroleum companies that use geophysical techniques; international coverage. Entries include: Company name, address, phone, fax, names of principal executives, operations, and 9,719 key personnel; similar information for branch locations. Arrangement: Classified by product or service. Indexes: Company name, personal name.

5684 ■ Geophysicists
American Geophysical Union
2000 Florida Ave. NW
Washington, DC 20009-1277
Ph: (202)462-6900
Fax: (202)328-0566
Fr: 800-966-2481
URL: http://www.agu.org

Covers: 40,000 member geophysicists. Entries include: Name, address, office and home phone numbers, fax, electronic mail addresses, type of membership, year joined, and section affiliation. Arrangement: Alphabetical.

5685 ■ The Oil & Gas Directory
Geophysical Directory Inc.
PO Box 130508
Houston, TX 77219
Ph: (713)529-8789
Fax: (713)529-3646
Fr: 800-929-2462
URL: http://www.geophysicaldirectory.com

Annual, Latest edition 2011. $140.00 for individuals; $150.00 for individuals. Covers: About 12,904 companies worldwide involved in petroleum exploration, drilling, and production, and suppliers to the industry. Entries include: Company name, address, phone, fax, names of principal personnel, branch office addresses, phone numbers, and 22,675 key personnel. Arrangement: Classified by activity. Indexes: Company name, personal name and regional.

5686 ■ Society of Exploration Geophysicists—Yearbook
Society of Exploration Geophysicists
PO Box 702740
Tulsa, OK 74170
Ph: (918)497-5500
Fax: (918)497-5557
URL: http://www.seg.org

Annual, May. Publication includes: Membership roster of nearly 14,500 geophysicists, corporations, and

students. Entries include: Name, address, phone, fax, e-mail type of member; affiliation given for individuals. Arrangement: Alphabetical; geographical.

HANDBOOKS AND MANUALS

5687 ■ Great Jobs for Geology Majors
McGraw-Hill Professional
PO Box 182604
Columbus, OH 43272
Fax: (609)308-4480
Fr: 800-262-4729
E-mail: customer.service@mcgraw-hill.com
URL: http://www.mhprofessional.com

Blythe Camenson. 2006. $15.95. 224 pages. Offers a complete overview of job possibilities including volcanologist, soil scientist, economic geologist, geodynamicist, laboratory technician, oceanographer, architect, petroleum engineer, and surveyor. Provides salary figures, experience and training for geology majors.

5688 ■ Jobs in Environmental Cleanup and Emergency Hazmat Response
Rosen Publishing Group
29 E 21st St.
New York, NY 10010
Fax: 888-436-4643
Fr: 800-237-9932
URL: http://www.rosenpublishing.com

Daniel E. Harmon. 2010. $31.95 (library bound). 80 pages. Features jobs in environmental cleanup and emergency hazmat response. Explores numerous career paths for different environmental jobs that require special training or four-year and/or postgraduate degrees. Includes job profiles for professionals such as environmental engineers, geologists, microbiologists, science technicians, conservationists, foresters, park rangers, soil scientists, air control technicians, toxicologists, dredge operators, ecologists, hazardous waste managers, and zoologists.

5689 ■ Resumes for Scientific and Technical Careers
The McGraw-Hill Companies
PO Box 182604
Columbus, OH 43272
Fax: (614)759-3749
Fr: 877-883-5524
E-mail: customer.service@mcgraw-hill.com
URL: http://www.mhprofessional.com/product.php?isbn=0071482199

Third edition, 2007. $12.95 (paper). 144 pages. Provides resume advice for individuals interested in working in scientific and technical careers. Includes sample resumes and cover letters.

ONLINE JOB SOURCES AND SERVICES

5690 ■ Diversity Environmental Jobs
URL: http://www.diversityenvironmentaljobs.com

Description: Serves as a niche job board that provides diverse environmental career opportunities.

5691 ■ GeoCommunity
URL: http://www.geocomm.com

Description: Serves as a clearinghouse for posting or browsing GIS, GPS, CAD, remote sensing, and earth sciences related announcements, resumes, and consultant listings.

5692 ■ GeologistCareers.com
URL: http://www.geologistcareers.com

Description: Online job search that provides information and resources for geologists.

5693 ■ GeologistJobs.com
URL: http://www.geologistjobs.com

Description: Serves as a career community for the

geology industry. Provides information and lists job openings for geologists.

5694 ■ Get Geophysicist Jobs
URL: http://www.getgeophysicistjobs.com

Description: Serves as a source of employment and career opportunities for geophysicist job seekers and employers.

5695 ■ ScientistCrossing.com
URL: http://www.scientistcrossing.com

Description: Provides job listings and other resources related to scientist employment opportunities.

TRADESHOWS

5696 ■ Society of Exploration Geophysicists International Exposition and Annual Meeting
Society of Exploration Geophysicists
8801 S. Yale, Ste. 500
PO Box 702740
Tulsa, OK 74170-2740
Ph: (918)497-5500
Fax: (918)497-5557
URL: http://www.seg.org

Annual. Primary Exhibits: Geophysical products and services, computer hardware and software, data storage, visualization technology.

OTHER SOURCES

5697 ■ American Geological Institute (AGI)
4220 King St.
Alexandria, VA 22302-1502
Ph: (703)379-2480
Fax: (703)379-7563
E-mail: agi@agiweb.org
URL: http://www.agiweb.org

Description: Federation of national scientific and technical societies in the Earth sciences. Seeks to: stimulate public understanding of Geological sciences; improve teaching of the geological sciences in schools, colleges, and universities; maintain high standards of professional training and conduct; work for the general welfare of members. Provides career guidance program.

5698 ■ American Geophysical Union (AGU)
2000 Florida Ave. NW
Washington, DC 20009-1277
Ph: (202)462-6900
Fax: (202)328-0566
Fr: 800-966-2481
E-mail: service@agu.org
URL: http://www.agu.org

Description: Individuals professionally associated with the field of geophysics; supporting institutional members are companies and other organizations whose work involves geophysics. Promotes the study of problems concerned with the figure and physics of the earth; initiates and coordinates research that depends upon national and international cooperation and provides for scientific discussion of research results. Sponsors placement service at semiannual meeting.

5699 ■ American Institute of Professional Geologists (AIPG)
12000 Washington St., Ste. 285
Thornton, CO 80241
Ph: (303)412-6205
Fax: (303)253-9220
E-mail: aipg@aipg.org
URL: http://www.aipg.org

Description: Geologists. Provides certification to geologists attesting to their competence and integrity. Represents the geologic profession before government bodies and the public.

5700 ■ ASPRS - The Imaging and Geospatial Information Society
5410 Grosvenor Ln., Ste. 210
Bethesda, MD 20814-2160
Ph: (301)493-0290
Fax: (301)493-0208
E-mail: asprs@asprs.org
URL: http://www.asprs.org

Description: Firms, individuals, government employees and academicians engaged in photogrammetry, photointerpretation, remote sensing, and geographic information systems and their application to such fields as archaeology, geographic information systems, military reconnaissance, urban planning, engineering, traffic surveys, meteorological observations, medicine, geology, forestry, agriculture, construction and topographic mapping. Seeks to advance knowledge and improve understanding of these sciences and promote responsible applications. Offers voluntary certification program open to persons associated with one or more functional area of photogrammetry, remote sensing and GIS. Surveys the profession of private firms in photogrammetry and remote sensing in the areas of products and services.

5701 ■ Association of Environmental and Engineering Geologists (AEG)
PO Box 460518
Denver, CO 80246
Ph: (303)757-2926
Fax: (720)230-4846
E-mail: aeg@aegweb.org
URL: http://www.aegweb.org

Description: Represents graduate geologists and geological engineers; full members must have five years experience in the field of engineering geology. Promotes professional success by providing leadership, advocacy, and applied research in environmental and engineering geology. Seeks to provide a forum for the discussion and dissemination of technical and scientific information. Encourages the advancement of professional recognition, scientific research, and high ethical and professional standards. Compiles information on engineering geology curricula of colleges and universities. Promotes public understanding, health, safety and welfare, and acceptance of the engineering geology profession. Conducts technical sessions, symposia, abstracts, and short courses; cosponsors seminars and conferences with other professional and technical societies and organizations.

5702 ■ Association of Ground Water Scientists and Engineers (AGWSE)
National Ground Water Association
601 Dempsey Rd.
Westerville, OH 43081-8978
Ph: (614)898-7791
Fax: (614)898-7786
Fr: 800-551-7379
E-mail: tfreeman@ngwa.org
URL: http://www.ngwa.org/agwse/index.aspx

Description: A technical division of the National Ground Water Association. Hydrogeologists, geologists, hydrologists, civil and environmental engineers, geochemists, biologists, and scientists in related fields. Seeks to: provide leadership and guidance for scientific, economical, and beneficial groundwater development; promote the use, protection, and management of the world's groundwater resources. Conducts educational programs, seminars, short courses, symposia, and field research projects. Maintains speakers' bureau and museum; offers placement service; sponsors competitions; compiles statistics.

5703 ■ Association for International Practical Training (AIPT)
10400 Little Patuxent Pkwy., Ste. 250
Columbia, MD 21044-3519
Ph: (410)997-2200
Fax: (410)992-3924
E-mail: aipt@aipt.org
URL: http://www.aipt.org

Description: Providers worldwide of on-the-job training programs for students and professionals seeking international career development and life-changing experiences. Arranges workplace exchanges in hundreds of professional fields, bringing employers and trainees together from around the world. Client list ranges from small farming communities to Fortune 500 companies.

5704 ■ Association for Women Geoscientists (AWG)
12000 N Washington St., Ste. 285
Thornton, CO 80241
Ph: (303)412-6219
Fax: (303)253-9220
E-mail: office@awg.org
URL: http://www.awg.org

Description: Represents men and women geologists, geophysicists, petroleum engineers, geological engineers, hydrogeologists, paleontologists, geochemists, and other geoscientists. Aims to encourage the participation of women in the geosciences. Exchanges educational, technical, and professional information. Enhances the professional growth and advancement of women in the geosciences. Provides information through web site on opportunities and careers available to women in the geosciences. Sponsors educational booths and programs at geological society conventions. Operates charitable program. Maintains speaker's bureau, and Association for Women Geoscientists Foundation.

5705 ■ Geological Society of America (GSA)
PO Box 9140
Boulder, CO 80301-9140
Ph: (303)357-1000
Fax: (303)357-1070
Fr: 888-443-4472
E-mail: gsaservice@geosociety.org
URL: http://www.geosociety.org

Description: Serves as professional society of earth scientists. Promotes the science of geology. Maintains placement service.

5706 ■ Marine Technology Society (MTS)
5565 Sterrett Pl., Ste. 108
Columbia, MD 21044
Ph: (410)884-5330
Fax: (410)884-9060
E-mail: membership@mtsociety.org
URL: http://www.mtsociety.org

Description: Scientists, engineers, educators, and others with professional interest in the marine sciences or related fields; includes institutional and corporate members. Disseminates marine scientific and technical information, including institutional, environmental, physical, and biological aspects; fosters a deeper understanding of the world's seas and attendant technologies. Maintains 13 sections and 29 professional committees. Conducts tutorials.

5707 ■ National Association of Black Geologists and Geophysicists
4212 San Felipe, Ste. 420
Houston, TX 77027
E-mail: nabgg_us@hotmail.com
URL: http://www.nabgg.com

Description: Serves as a group dedicated to environmental concerns and the ethical development of natural resources. Works to inform students of career opportunities that exist in the field of geosciences and to encourage them to take advantage of scholarship programs, grant, loans, etc., that are established for minority students. Strives to assist in the development of professional standards and practices of members within their geoscience careers and entrepreneurial pursuits.

5708 ■ National Ground Water Association (NGWA)
601 Dempsey Rd.
Westerville, OH 43081-8978
Ph: (614)898-7791

Fax: (614)898-7786
Fr: 800-551-7379
E-mail: ngwa@ngwa.org
URL: http://www.ngwa.org

Description: Ground water drilling contractors; manufacturers and suppliers of drilling equipment; ground water scientists such as geologists, engineers, public health officials, and others interested in the problems of locating, developing, preserving, and using ground water supplies. Conducts seminars, and

continuing education programs. Encourages scientific education, research, and the development of standards; offers placement services; compiles market statistics. Offers charitable program. Maintains speakers' bureau.

5709 ■ Society of Exploration Geophysicists (SEG)
PO Box 702740
Tulsa, OK 74170-2740
Ph: (918)497-5500

Fax: (918)497-5557
E-mail: klaas.koster@apachecorp.com
URL: http://www.seg.org

Description: Promotes the science of geophysics and education. Fosters the expert and ethical practice of geophysics in the exploration and development of natural resources, in characterizing the near surface, and in mitigating Earth hazards. Fulfills its mission through its publications, conferences, forums, web sites, and educational opportunities.

SOURCES OF HELP-WANTED ADS

5710 ■ AGRR
Key Communications, Inc.
385 Garrisonville Rd.
Stafford, VA 22554
Ph: (540)720-5584
Fax: (540)720-5687
E-mail: info@glassexpomidwest.com
URL: http://www.agrrmag.com

Bimonthly. Provides information and news for those in the auto glass repair and replacement industry. Features industry movement, forecasts of future trends, and technical advice. Contains advertisements of businesses for sale, employment/help wanted, industry services, products for sale, and used equipment for sale.

5711 ■ Door & Window Manufacturer Magazine
Key Communications, Inc.
385 Garrisonville Rd.
Stafford, VA 22554
Ph: (540)720-5584
Fax: (540)720-5687
E-mail: info@glass.com
URL: http://www.dwmmag.com

11 issues per year. Provides industry information for door and window manufacturers. Contains classified advertising.

5712 ■ GASnews
Glass Art Society
6512 23rd Ave. NW, Ste. 329
Seattle, WA 98117
Ph: (206)382-1305
Fax: (206)382-2630
E-mail: info@glassart.org
URL: http://www.glassart.org

Bi-monthly. Provides a forum for the dissemination of ideas and information as well as a place for regular communication between glass artists around the world. Contains details on classes and workshops, seminars, conferences, events, and exhibitions. Includes other resources such as calls to artists, competitions, exhibitions, galleries, shows and fairs, grants and residencies, job opportunities, and advertising opportunities.

5713 ■ Glass Magazine
National Glass Association
1945 Old Gallows Rd., Ste. 750
Vienna, VA 22182
Fax: (703)442-0630
Fr: (866)342-5642
E-mail: membership@glass.org
URL: http://www.glass.org

Monthly. $34.95/year in the United States, Canada and Mexico; $44.95/year outside the United States, Canada and Mexico. Features editorial direction and informative coverage including market segment surveys, resource guides, reader polls, industry profiles, statistics, and products.

5714 ■ Window & Door
National Glass Association
1945 Old Gallows Rd., Ste. 750
Vienna, VA 22182
Fax: (703)442-0630
Fr: (866)342-5642
E-mail: membership@glass.org
URL: http://www.glass.org

Eleven times a year. $29.95/year for U.S. individuals; $39.95/year individuals outside U.S., Canada, and Mexico. Serves the fenestration industry including manufacturers, distributors, specialty dealers, and others involved in the manufacturing and marketing of window, door, and skylight products.

EMPLOYER DIRECTORIES AND NETWORKING LISTS

5715 ■ GAS Membership Directory and Resource Guide
Glass Art Society
6512 23rd Ave. NW, Ste. 329
Seattle, WA 98117
Ph: (206)382-1305
Fax: (206)382-2630
E-mail: info@glassart.org
URL: http://www.glassart.org

Features GAS members' contact information and ads for manufacturers, suppliers, galleries, publications, and schools. Information listed include: firm name, address, phone, category, specialty, website, and other details as provided by firm. Arrangement: Alphabetical.

5716 ■ Glass Factory Directory of North America and U.S. Factbook
LJV Inc.
PO Box 2267
Hempstead, NY 11551-2267
Ph: (516)481-2188
E-mail: manager@glassfactorydir.com
URL: http://www.glassfactorydir.com

Annual. Lists glass manufacturing locations in Canada, Mexico, and the United States. Provides plant addresses, telephone numbers, fax numbers, contact persons, and a brief product list of the companies. Arranges listings in state and country order.

5717 ■ National Glass Association Directory
National Glass Association
1945 Old Gallows Rd., Ste. 750
Vienna, VA 22182
Ph: (703)442-4890
Fax: (703)442-0630
Fr: (866)342-5642
URL: http://www.glass.org

Features a list of current member companies which includes company name, address, and contact person.

5718 ■ The Sourcebook
Stained Glass Association of America
9313 E 63rd St.
Raytown, MO 64133
Ph: (816)737-2090
Fax: (816)737-2801
Fr: 800-438-9581
URL: http://stainedglass.org

Annual. Features a complete membership directory of the organization. Serves as a general guide to architectural stained glass.

HANDBOOKS AND MANUALS

5719 ■ GANA Glazing Manual (50th Anniversary Edition)
Glass Association of North America
2945 SW Wanamaker Dr., Ste. A
Topeka, KS 66614
Ph: (785)271-0208
Fax: (785)271-0166
URL: http://www.glasswebsite.com/publications/
2008. $35.00 (paper) for members; $70.00 (paper) for non-members. Includes information about primary and fabricated glass products, quality standards, design considerations, general and specific glazing guidelines, and glazing in hazardous locations.

5720 ■ Installation and Safety Glazing
Stained Glass Association of America
9313 E 63rd St.
Raytown, MO 64133
Fr: 800-438-9581
URL: http://www.stainedglass.org
2008. $25.00. 70 pages. Covers installation and safety glazing techniques.

5721 ■ Opportunities in Building Construction Careers
McGraw-Hill
PO Box 182604
Columbus, OH 43218
Fax: (614)759-3749
Fr: 877-833-5524
E-mail: customer.service@mcgraw-hill.com
URL: http://www.mcgraw-hill.com
Michael Sumichrast. 2007. $14.95. 160 pages. Provides information on various fields in the building construction industry. Includes training and education requirements for each career.

EMPLOYMENT AGENCIES AND SEARCH FIRMS

5722 ■ Management Recruiters of Davidson (MR Davidson)
710 Northeast Dr., Ste. 8
Davidson, NC 28036-7424
Ph: (704)896-8890

Fax: (704)896-8933
E-mail: admin@mrdavidson.com
URL: http://www.mrdavidson.com

Specializes in the recruitment and placement of professionals within the window, door, and glass/glazing industries throughout the United States.

ONLINE JOB SOURCES AND SERVICES

5723 ■ Get Glazier Jobs
URL: http://www.getglazierjobs.com

Description: Provides resources for finding and filling glazier positions. Offers job postings worldwide.

5724 ■ Glass Global
URL: http://www.glassglobal.com

Description: Functions as an international e-commerce portal website for the glass industry. Maintains a company directory that gives detailed company information from raw materials suppliers up to the finished product traders. Features a database of job offers and job requests from all areas of the glass industry.

5725 ■ Glass.com
URL: http://www.glass.com

Description: Contains advertisements of businesses for sale, employment/help wanted, industry services, products for sale, and used equipment for sale.

5726 ■ Glassjobsearch.com
URL: http://www.glassjobsearch.com

Description: Provides glass industry job resources. Features job listings as well as resume searches and company profiles for prospective employers.

5727 ■ Glasslinks.com
URL: http://www.glasslinks.com

Description: Provides links and information on jobs, employment, and careers in the glass industry.

5728 ■ GlassOnline.com
URL: http://www.glassonline.com/site

Description: Serves as a glass industry portal featuring news, fairs, conferences, glass magazines, renewable energy magazines, trade opportunities, employment and help wanted listings, forums, tools, and glass publications.

5729 ■ GlassOnWeb.com
URL: http://www.glassonweb.com

Description: Serves as an information portal for the glass industry. Features directories, news and articles, forums, and jobs in the glass business.

5730 ■ Glazier Jobs
URL: http://www.glazierjobs.net

Description: Serves as an online connection for glazier employment candidates and hiring managers. Enables job searching for those who seek employment and job posting for employers.

5731 ■ GlazierJobs.com
URL: http://www.glazierjobs.com

Description: Features a searchable database of job listings for glaziers. Enables job seekers to post their resumes.

5732 ■ IHireBuildingTrades
URL: http://www.ihirebuildingtrades.com

Description: Serves as a job posting board that specializes in matching building jobs and construction candidates.

TRADESHOWS

5733 ■ American Glass Guild Annual Conference
American Glass Guild
21 Highland Cir.
Needham, MA 02494
E-mail: info@americanglassguild.org
URL: http://www.americanglassguild.org

Annual. Features exhibits of artwork, books, glassware, tools, supplies and raw materials, painted and stained art glass panels, and more. Provides an open forum for the exchange of information on stained, leaded, and decorative glass and its creation preservation, restoration, and history. 2012 July 20-22; Pittsburgh, PA.

5734 ■ Deco Seminar and Conference
Society of Glass and Ceramic Decorated Products
PO Box 2489
Zanesville, OH 43702
Ph: (740)588-9882
Fax: (740)588-0245
E-mail: info@sgcd.org
URL: http://www.sgcd.org

Annual. Provides exhibits of dinnerware, glassware, beverage containers, cosmetic containers, tile, giftware, and promotional products.

5735 ■ Glass Art Society Annual Conference
Glass Art Society
6512 23rd Ave. NW, Ste. 329
Seattle, WA 98117
Ph: (206)382-1305
Fax: (206)382-2630
E-mail: info@glassart.org
URL: http://www.glassart.org

Annual. Brings together an international community of glass enthusiasts and artists from every discipline of glass (blowing, hot casting, kiln work, stained glass, flame working, beadmaking, cold work, and others). Gives opportunities for members to network with each other in various capacities: artists connect with gallery owners and others, collectors can meet their favorite artists, technical manufacturers and suppliers show customers the latest innovations.

5736 ■ National Glass Association Glazing Executives Forum
National Glass Association
1945 Old Gallows Rd., Ste. 750
Vienna, VA 22182
Fax: (703)442-0630
Fr: (866)342-5642
URL: http://www.glass.org/gef.html

Annual. Features speakers, peer-to-peer sharing among dealers and contract glaziers, updates on challenging topics impacting the industry, and a networking reception.

OTHER SOURCES

5737 ■ American Glass Guild
21 Highland Cir.
Needham, MA 02494
E-mail: info@americanglassguild.org
URL: http://www.americanglassguild.org

Description: Represents individuals, students, senior advisors, and honorary members interested in decorative glass. Aims to advance knowledge by encouraging education, study, and research of all subjects related to the many disciplines covered by the term decorative glass. Promotes proficiency and skill by practitioners of these disciplines. Maintains a job board for employment opportunities in the industry.

5738 ■ Efficiency First
70 Zoe St., Ste. 201
San Francisco, CA 94107
Ph: (415)449-0551
Fax: (415)449-0559
E-mail: info@efficiencyfirst.org
URL: http://www.efficiencyfirst.org

Description: Advocates for policies that will create the foundation for a sustainable and scalable home retrofit market. Promotes the benefits of efficiency in retrofitting and helps meet industry demand for quality residential energy improvements.

5739 ■ Glass Art Society
6512 23rd Ave. NW, Ste. 329
Seattle, WA 98117
Ph: (206)382-1305
Fax: (206)382-2630
E-mail: info@glassart.org
URL: http://www.glassart.org

Description: Represents artists, educators, students, collectors, gallery and museum personnel, art critics, manufacturers, and all others interested in and involved with the production, technology, and aesthetics of glass. Aims to encourage excellence, to advance education, to promote the appreciation and development of the glass arts, and to support the worldwide community of artists who work with glass. Publishes periodicals and newsletters on glass. Conducts, sponsors, and coordinates workshops and conferences dealing with glass for the benefit of members and friends of the society.

5740 ■ Glass Association of North America
800 SW Jackson St., Ste. 1500
Topeka, KS 66612
Ph: (785)271-0208
Fax: (785)271-0166
URL: http://www.glasswebsite.com

Description: Represents independent glass distributors, contractors, and fabricators covering all flat glass products. Provides members with educational programs, publications, networking opportunities, meetings, and conventions.

5741 ■ Glass Manufacturing Industry Council
600 N Cleveland Ave., Ste. 210
Westerville, OH 43082
Ph: (614)818-9423
Fax: (614)818-9485
E-mail: rwlipetz@gmic.org
URL: http://www.gmic.org

Description: Represents the interests of glass manufacturers, suppliers, customers, and processors who are vital to the glass industry, as well as nonprofit research institutes, universities, and affiliate members. Aims to facilitate, organize, and promote economic growth and sustainability of the glass industry through education and cooperation in the areas of technology, productivity, innovation, and the environment.

5742 ■ National Glass Association
8200 Greensboro Dr., Ste. 302
McLean, VA 22102
Ph: (703)442-4890
Fax: (703)827-0557
Fr: (866)342-5642
E-mail: membership@glass.org
URL: http://www.glass.org

Description: Represents professionals in the architectural and automotive glass industry. Promotes quality workmanship, ethics, and safety in the architectural, automotive, and window and door glass industries. Serves as a clearinghouse for industry information, a catalyst for education and training matters, and a voice on behalf of members.

SOURCES OF HELP-WANTED ADS

5743 ■ ACM Transactions on Graphics (TOG)
Association for Computing Machinery
PO Box 30777
New York, NY 10087
Ph: (212)626-0500
Fax: (212)944-1318
Fr: 800-342-6626
URL: http://tog.acm.org/

Quarterly. $215.00/year for nonmembers; $172.00/year for nonmembers, online; $258.00/year for nonmembers, online & print. Computer graphics journal.

5744 ■ Computer Graphics World
PennWell Corp.
98 Spit Brook Rd.
Nashua, NH 03062-5737
Ph: (603)891-0123
Fax: (603)891-9294
Fr: 800-225-0556
URL: http://www.cgw.com

Monthly. $68.00/year for individuals; $90.00/year for Canada; $105.00/year for other countries; $126.00/year for two years; $178.00/year for Canada, 2 years; $205.00/year for other countries, 2 years; $12.00/year for single issue. Publication reporting on the use of modeling, animation, and multimedia in the areas of science and engineering, art and entertainment, and presentation and training.

5745 ■ Creative Business
101 Tremont St., Ste. 300
Boston, MA 02108
Ph: (617)451-0041
Fax: (617)338-6570
E-mail: mail@creativebusiness.com
URL: http://www.creativebusiness.com/newsletter.lasso

Description: Nine issues/year. $149/year for electronic subscription. Provides business information for freelance graphic designers and studio principals.

5746 ■ Design Perspectives
Industrial Designers Society of America
45195 Business Ct., Ste. 250
Dulles, VA 20166-6717
Ph: (703)707-6000
Fax: (703)787-8501
E-mail: donnap@idsa.org
URL: http://www.idsa.org

Description: Ten issues/year. The largest newsletter examining the news and trends of industrial design. Recurring features include: new and cutting-edge products, news of people and events in industrial design, resource section, reports of chapter and national activities of IDSA, and a calendar of events.

5747 ■ The Eagle
Fitzpatrick Management Inc.
1522 Lilac Rd.
Charlotte, NC 28209
Ph: (704)334-2047
Fax: (704)334-0220
E-mail: robertf765@aol.com
URL: http://members.whattheythink.com/home/theeagle.cfm

Description: Three issues/year. Serves as a publication about issues pertaining to dealer/manufacturer relations in the graphic arts industry. Recurring features include interviews, reports of meetings, and the analysis and interpretation of topical issues in North America and internationally.

5748 ■ Graphic Communicator
Graphic Communication Conference of the International Brotherhood of Teamsters
25 Louisiana Ave. NW
Washington, DC 20001
Ph: (202)624-6800
URL: http://www.gciu.org/

$12.00/year for U.S. and Canada; $15.00/year for other countries. Trade newspaper of the Graphic Communications International Union.

5749 ■ Graphics Update
Printing Association of Florida Inc.
6275 Hazeltine National Dr.
Orlando, FL 32822
Ph: (407)240-8009
Fax: (407)240-8333
Fr: 800-331-0461
E-mail: george@flprint.org
URL: http://www.pafgraf.org

Description: Monthly. Concerned with developments within the field of graphic arts. Covers aspects of the industry with an emphasis on Florida, including news of exhibitions, statistics, new technologies and products, and events affecting the ancillary industries. Recurring features include letters to the editor, reports of meetings, news of educational opportunities, seminars, notices of publications available, news of members, and a calendar of events.

5750 ■ I.D. Magazine
F+W Media Inc.
4700 E Galbraith Rd.
Cincinnati, OH 45236
Ph: (513)531-2690
Fax: (513)531-0798
Fr: 800-289-0963
URL: http://www.fwmagazines.com/category/id

$30.00/year for individuals; $45.00/year for Canada; $60.00/year for other countries. Magazine covering art, business and culture of design.

5751 ■ IEEE Computer Graphics and Applications
IEEE Computer Society
10662 Los Vaqueros Cir.
PO Box 3014
Los Alamitos, CA 90720-1314

Ph: (714)821-8380
Fax: (714)821-4010
Fr: 800-272-6657
E-mail: cga-ma@computer.org
URL: http://www.computer.org/portal/web/cga

Bimonthly. $1,020.00/year for individuals, online; $1,065.00/year for individuals, print; $1,330.00/year for individuals, print and online. Magazine addressing the interests and needs of professional designers and users of computer graphics hardware, software, and systems.

5752 ■ Jobline News
Graphic Artists Guild
32 Broadway, Ste. 1114
New York, NY 10004
Ph: (212)791-3400
Fax: (212)791-0333
E-mail: jobline@gag.org
URL: http://www.graphicartistsguild.org

Description: Weekly. Lists jobs for freelance and staff artists in areas such as graphic design, illustration, and art education. Lists jobs from across the country; quantity and locales vary weekly.

5753 ■ Journal of Mathematics and the Arts
Taylor & Francis Group Journals
325 Chestnut St., Ste. 800
Philadelphia, PA 19106-2608
Ph: (215)625-8900
Fax: (215)625-2940
Fr: 800-354-1420
URL: http://www.tandf.co.uk/journals/titles/17513472.asp

$418.00/year for institutions, print and online; $376.00/year for institutions, online only; $91.00/year for individuals, print. Peer-reviewed journal focusing on connections between mathematics and the arts.

5754 ■ SEGDesign
Society for Environmental Graphic Design
1000 Vermont Ave. NW, Ste. 400
Washington, DC 20005
Ph: (202)638-5555
Fax: (202)638-0891
URL: http://www.segd.org

Quarterly. $200.00/year for individuals, in U.S.; $275.00/year for elsewhere. Publication that covers environmental graphics, exhibit and industrial design, architecture, interiors, landscape architecture, and communication arts.

5755 ■ TAGA Newsletter
TAGA (Technical Association of the Graphic Arts)
200 Deer Run Rd.
Sewickley, PA 15143
Ph: (412)741-6860
Fax: (412)741-2311
Fr: 800-910-4283
E-mail: taga@piagatf.org
URL: http://www.printing.org/taga

Description: Quarterly. Disseminates information in

the graphic arts industry to members. Recurring features include interviews, news of research, reports of meetings, news of educational opportunities, and standards updates.

5756 ■ *Trace*
American Institute of Graphic Arts
164 5th Ave.
New York, NY 10010
Ph: (212)807-1990
Fax: (212)807-1799
Fr: 800-548-1634

Triennial. $13.00/year for individuals, quantity available: 1. Journal of design and visual culture.

EMPLOYER DIRECTORIES AND NETWORKING LISTS

5757 ■ *Discovering Careers for Your Future—Art*
Facts On File Inc.
132 W 31st St., 17th Fl.
New York, NY 10001
Ph: (212)967-8800
Fax: 800-678-3633
Fr: 800-322-8755
URL: http://factsonfile.infobasepublishing.com

Latest edition 2nd, 2008. $21.95 for individuals. Covers: Artists, cartoonists, graphic designers, illustrators, and photographers; links career education to curriculum, helping children investigate the subjects they are interested in, and the careers those subjects might lead to.

5758 ■ *Printworld Directory of Contemporary Prints and Prices*
Printworld International Inc.
937 Jefferson Way
PO Box 1957
West Chester, PA 19380
Ph: (610)431-6654
Fax: (610)431-6653
Fr: 800-788-9101
URL: http://www.printworlddirectory.com

Irregular, Latest edition 13th; April 2010. $359.00 for individuals; $259.00 for individuals. Publication includes: Biographical data on 5,000 international artists in contemporary printmaking; thousands of galleries who handle prints and hundreds of print publishers, and 600,000 print/price listings.

5759 ■ *Society for Environmental Graphic Design-Messages*
Society for Environmental Graphic Design
1000 Vermont Ave., NW. Ste. 400
Washington, DC 20005
Ph: (202)638-5555
Fax: (202)478-2286
E-mail: segd@segd.org
URL: http://www.segd.org/publications/
messages.html

Description: Monthly. Reports on Society program news, member services, resources, and product news.

5760 ■ *Who's Who in SGIA*
Screenprinting and Graphic Imaging Association International
10015 Main St.
Fairfax, VA 22031-3489
Ph: (703)385-1335
Fax: (703)273-0456
Fr: 888-385-3588
URL: http://www.sgia.org

Annual, August. Covers: About 3,800 screen printers and graphic imaging companies, suppliers of screen printing equipment and graphic imaging materials, and investors in the Screen Printing Technical Foundation; international coverage. Entries include: Company name, address, phone, fax, e-mail, name of contact, products or services. Arrangement: Clas-

sified by type of business, then geographical. Indexes: Alphabetical by company, within state or country.

5761 ■ *The Workbook*
Scott & Daughters Publishing Inc.
6762 Lexington Ave.
Los Angeles, CA 90038
Ph: (323)856-0008
Fax: (323)856-4368
Fr: 800-547-2688
URL: http://www.workbook.com

Annual, Latest edition 2011. $60.00 for individuals; $30.00 for individuals; $35.00 for individuals. Covers: 55,000 advertising agencies, art directors, photographers, freelance illustrators and designers, artists' representatives, interactive designers, pre-press services, and other graphic arts services in the U.S. Entries include: Company or individual name, address, phone, specialty. National in scope. Arrangement: Classified by product or service.

HANDBOOKS AND MANUALS

5762 ■ *100 Habits of Successful Graphic Designers: Insider Secrets on Working Smart and Staying Creative*
Rockport Publishers
100 Cummings Center, Ste. 406-L
Beverly, MA 01915
Ph: (978)282-9590
Fax: (978)283-2742
URL: http://www.rockpub.com

Sarah Dougher and Josh Berger. 2005. $18.75. 192 pages. Designers from the graphic design, fashion, architecture, typography, and industrial design fields address topics ranging from deadlines, inspiration, competition, rules, respect, education, and criticism.

5763 ■ *2010 Artists and Graphic Designers Market*
Writers Digest Books
4700 E Galbraith Rd.
Cincinnati, OH 45236
Ph: (513)531-2690
Fax: (513)531-0798
Fr: 800-289-0963
URL: http://www.writersdigestshop.com/product/
2010-artists-graphic-designers-market

Mary Cox and Michael Schweer. 2010. $4.99. 576 pages.

5764 ■ *All Access: The Making of Thirty Extraordinary Graphic Designers*
Rockport Publishers
100 Cummings Center, Ste. 406-L
Beverly, MA 01915
Ph: (978)282-9590
Fax: (978)283-2742
E-mail: e-info@rockpub.com
URL: http://www.rockpub.com

Stefan G. Bucher. 2006. $25.00. 192 pages. Features the work of top graphic designers along with profiles of 20 newcomers.

5765 ■ *Becoming a Graphic Designer*
John Wiley and Sons, Inc.
1 Wiley Dr.
Somerset, NJ 08875-1272
Fax: (732)302-2300
Fr: 800-225-5945
E-mail: custserv@wiley.com
URL: http://as.wiley.com/WileyCDA/WileyTitle/
productCd-0470575565.html

Steven Heller and Teresa Fernandes. Third edition, 2005. $35.00 (paper). 368 pages.

5766 ■ *Career Opportunities in the Visual Arts*
Facts On File Inc.
132 W 31st St., 17th Fl.
New York, NY 10001

Fax: 800-678-3633
Fr: 800-322-8755
E-mail: custserv@factsonfile.com
URL: http://factsonfile.infobasepublishing.com

2006. $49.50. Covers over 65 profiles such as art teacher, book designer, financial officer, framer, gallery director, graphic designer, medical illustrator, storyboard artists. Includes comprehensive descriptions of certification, education, special skills, and trainings required.

5767 ■ *Careers for Color Connoisseurs and Other Visual Types*
The McGraw-Hill Companies
PO Box 182604
Columbus, OH 43272
Fax: (614)759-3749
Fr: 877-883-5524
E-mail: customer.service@mcgraw-hill.com
URL: http://www.mhprofessional.com/
product.php?isbn=0071465197

Jan Goldberg. Second edition, 2005. $19.95 (paper). 176 pages.

5768 ■ *Careers for Crafty People and Other Dexterous Types*
The McGraw-Hill Companies
PO Box 182604
Columbus, OH 43272
Fax: (614)759-3749
Fr: 877-883-5524
E-mail: customer.service@mcgraw-hill.com
URL: http://www.mhprofessional.com/
product.php?isbn=0071487263

Mark Rowh. Third edition, 2006. $13.95 (paper). 160 pages.

5769 ■ *The Education of a Graphic Designer*
Allworth Press
307 W 36th St., 11th Fl.
New York, NY 10018
Ph: (212)643-6816
Fax: (212)643-6819
URL: http://www.allworth.com

Steven Heller, editor. Second edition, 2005. $29.95 (paper). 352 pages. Designers discuss how they acquired knowledge of design and then succeeded in applying this academic training to practical solutions in their careers.

5770 ■ *Ferguson Career Coach: Managing Your Career in the Art Industry*
Facts On File
132 W 31st St., 17th Fl.
New York, NY 10001
Fax: 800-678-3633
Fr: 800-322-8755
E-mail: custserv@factsonfile.com
URL: http://factsonfile.infobasepublishing.com

Shelly Field. 2008. $39.95 (hardcover). 304 pages. Contains tips for students who dream of a career as a graphic artist or an art gallery curator.

5771 ■ *Fresh Dialogue 6: Friendly Fire*
Princeton Architectural Press
37 E 7th St.
New York, NY 10003
Ph: (212)995-9620
Fax: (212)995-9454
Fr: 800-759-0190
E-mail: sales@papress.com
URL: http://www.papress.com

American Institute of Graphic Arts Staff. 2006. $16.95. 112 pages.

5772 ■ *How to Survive and Prosper as an Artist: Selling Yourself Without Selling Your Soul*
Holt Paperbacks
175 Fifth Ave.
New York, NY 10010
Ph: (646)307-5095
Fax: (212)633-0748

Fr: 800-672-2054
URL: http://us.macmillan.com

Caroll Michels. 6 edition, 2009. $21.99. 400 pages. Includes index and bibliographical references.

5773 ■ *Opportunities in Arts and Crafts Careers*
The McGraw-Hill Companies
PO Box 182604
Columbus, OH 43272
Fax: (614)759-3749
Fr: 877-883-5524
E-mail: customer.service@mcgraw-hill.com
URL: http://www.mhprofessional.com/
product.php?isbn=0071448497

Elizabeth Gardner. 2005. $13.95 (paper). 211 pages.

5774 ■ *Opportunities in Visual Arts Careers*
The McGraw-Hill Companies
PO Box 182604
Columbus, OH 43272
Fax: (614)759-3749
Fr: 877-883-5524
E-mail: customer.service@mcgraw-hill.com
URL: http://www.mhprofessional.com/
product.php?isbn=0071545298

Mark Salmon. 2008. $14.95 (paper). 160 pages. Points the way to a career in the visual arts, examining opportunities for designers, painters, sculptors, illustrators, animators, photographers, art therapists, educators, and others. Offers a view of the pros and cons of working for an art or design company or on your own.

5775 ■ *Taking the Leap: Building a Career as a Visual Artist*
Chronicle Books LLC
680 Second St.
San Francisco, CA 94107
Ph: (415)537-4200
Fax: (415)537-4460
Fr: 800-722-6657
E-mail: frontdesk@chroniclebooks.com
URL: http://www.chroniclebooks.com

Cay Lang. 2006. $19.95. 256 pages.

EMPLOYMENT AGENCIES AND SEARCH FIRMS

5776 ■ Artisan Creative
1830 Stoner Ave., No. 6
Los Angeles, CA 90025
Ph: (310)312-2062
Fax: (310)312-0670
E-mail: lainfo@artisancreative.com
URL: http://www.artisancreative.com

Description: Serves as a network of designers, developers, account managers and production people providing companies with temporary staffing, full-time recruitment and project management solutions. Provides clients with the top creative resources to complete creative projects. Provides creative talent with opportunities to work for a variety of clients, in a number of roles, at locations around the country.

5777 ■ Artisan for Hire, Inc.
216 S Jefferson, Ste. 202
Chicago, IL 60661
Ph: (312)382-0200
Fr: 800-216-0600
E-mail: chicago@artisantalent.com
URL: http://www.artisantalent.com

Description: Provides listings for jobs within the creative industry.

5778 ■ Brattle Temps
50 Congress St., Ste. 935
Boston, MA 02109-4008
Ph: (617)523-4600
Fax: (617)523-3939
E-mail: temps@brattletemps.com

Personnel consulting firm specializes in providing temporary consultants. Skill areas available include: computer operators, secretaries, editors, librarians, graphic artists, and marketing professionals. Industries served: universities, publishing, engineering, manufacturing, and government agencies.

5779 ■ Caprio & Associates Inc.
1415 W 22nd St., Tower Level
Oak Brook, IL 60523
Ph: (630)705-9101
Fax: (630)705-9102
E-mail: jerry@caprioassociates.com
URL: http://www.caprioassociates.com

Executive search firm.

5780 ■ Cook Associates Inc.
212 W Kinzie St.
Chicago, IL 60610
Ph: (312)329-0900
Fax: (312)329-1528
E-mail: info@cookassociates.com
URL: http://www.cookassociates.com

Management and executive recruiting specialists offering a commitment to clients to find the best candidates and to find those candidates as efficiently as possible. Approach provides a flexible and effective structure that serves the special needs of both large and small companies. Serves the following industries: industrial, equipment manufacturer, food processing, graphic arts, chemical process, retailing, mechanical products, healthcare services, financial and professional services, legal, consumer products, construction and engineering, packaging, pulp and paper.

5781 ■ Creative Talent Source
10 S. Riverside Plz., Ste. 1800
Chicago, IL 60606
Ph: (312)238-9004
Fax: (866)536-4719
Fr: 888-843-4864
E-mail: info@creativetalentsource.com
URL: http://creativetalentsource.com

Description: Provides professionals for design, writing and creative project management whether for print, web or multimedia. Specializes in freelance and full time placement of Chicago-area creative talent.

5782 ■ FILTER, LLC
1505 Fifth Ave., Ste. 600
Seattle, WA 98101
Ph: (206)682-6005
Fax: (206)682-5830
Fr: 800-336-0809
URL: http://www.filterdigital.com

Serves as creative resources company that provides talent in web, marketing, and creative professions. Represents virtually every discipline: designers, copywriters, web architects, icon artists, illustrators, animators, and other specialized artistic and technological talents.

5783 ■ Graphic Arts Employment Specialists, Inc.
409 Pacific Coast Hwy., Ste. 455
Redondo Beach, CA 90277
Fax: (310)937-3760
Fr: 888-499-9722
E-mail: info@gaes.com
URL: http://www.gaes.com

Employment agency specializing in the publishing and packaging industries.

5784 ■ LandaJob Advertising Staffing Specialists
222 W Gregory Blvd., Ste. 304
Kansas City, MO 64114
Ph: (816)523-1881
Fax: (816)523-1876
Fr: 800-931-8806
E-mail: adstaff@landajobnow.com
URL: http://www.landajobnow.com

Personnel consultants and recruiters for advertising, marketing, and communications positions. Industries served: advertising, communications, marketing, graphic arts, printing and publishing.

5785 ■ Lloyd Staffing
445 Broadhollow Rd., Ste. 119
Melville, NY 11747
Ph: (631)777-7600
Fax: (631)777-7626
Fr: 888-292-6678
E-mail: info@lloydstaffing.com
URL: http://www.lloydstaffing.com

Personnel agency and search firm.

5786 ■ Printemps
18 Avery Pl.
Westport, CT 06880
Ph: (203)226-6869
Fax: (203)226-1594
E-mail: printemps7@aol.com

Specializes in providing temporary support for graphic design, document management and the electronic printing industry. Provides permanent placement for professionals and production personnel. Consults with printers and in-house print shops for greater production efficiency. Handles personnel management and policy programs as well. Industries served: printing, advertising, manufacturing, insurance, banking, and government agencies.

5787 ■ Semper, LLC
607 Boylston St., 3rd Fl.
Boston, MA 02116
Fax: 888-836-9703
Fr: 800-954-4993
E-mail: dhresumes1@semperllc.com
URL: http://www.semperllc.com

Description: Serves as a placement firm in the graphic arts and printing industry. Specializes in the print, copy and digital industries. Offers several staffing options such as flexible, permanent, flex-to-hire and direct. Offers outplacement service that provides professional career management assistance and counseling to employees who are facing a career change.

5788 ■ TECHEAD
111 N 17th St.
Richmond, VA 23219
Ph: (804)782-6971
Fax: (804)782-2033
Fr: 877-TEC-HEAD
E-mail: info@techead.com
URL: http://www.techead.com

Description: Offers creative and IT staffing services for both job seekers and employers. Provides graphics support and desktop publishing services to local clients. Provides creative talent and information technology staffing services, ADOBE product software training, and creative web development solutions to clients.

ONLINE JOB SOURCES AND SERVICES

5789 ■ ArtJob Online
E-mail: artjob@westaf.org
URL: http://www.artjob.org

Description: Contains up-to-date national and international listings of arts employment and related opportunities in the arts: full- and part-time employment, internships, grants, public art projects, and residencies. User can search by region, art discipline, type of organization. Fee: Subscribers pay $25 for 3 months, $40 for six months and $75 for one year.

5790 ■ Creative Hotlist
E-mail: contact@creativehotlist.com
URL: http://www.creativehotlist.com

Description: Career site for professionals in the web design and graphic design fields. Enables individuals and companies to find resources for any aspect of the creative marketplace including job openings, creative services, artists, designers, programmers, printers, service bureaus, schools and clubs.

5791 ■ GetGigs.com
URL: http://www.getgigs.com

Description: Seeks to provide an on-line experience for creative types, performing artists, and musicians around the world by integrating internet technologies into a one-stop information resource. Also functions as a creative directory and talent network.

5792 ■ Graphic Artists Guild
32 Broadway, Ste. 1114
New York, NY 10004
Ph: (212)791-3400
Fax: (212)791-0333
E-mail: membership@gag.org
URL: http://www.graphicartistsguild.org

Description: JOBLine News section of Guild Resources page contains weekly e-mail newsletter of job listings. Fee: Must subscribe to e-mail newsletter non-member six-month rates start at $80. Visitors may download a free sample.

5793 ■ GraphicArtistDesigner.com
URL: http://www.graphicartistdesigner.com

Description: Connects business professionals with the information and professional contacts needed to advance a career in graphic design. Provides access to books, magazines, articles and continuing education.

5794 ■ PrintJobs.com
E-mail: printjobs@roadrunner.com
URL: http://www.printjobs.com

Description: Aims to find suitable graphic arts jobs for qualified candidates. Over a hundred jobs are maintained and updated on the site. Fee: Must be paid by employers using the site; no registration charge for job hunters.

5795 ■ You the Designer
URL: http://www.youthedesigner.com

Description: Serves as an online career resource that contains a graphic design blog, graphic design tips and graphic design job openings.

TRADESHOWS

5796 ■ Graph Expo and Converting Expo
Graphic Arts Show Co. GASC
1899 Preston White Dr.
Reston, VA 20191-5468
Ph: (703)264-7200
Fax: (703)620-9187
E-mail: info@gasc.org
URL: http://www.gasc.org

Annual. Primary Exhibits: Graphic art equipment, supplies, and services. Printing, publishing, and converting equipment. Dates and Locations: 2012 Oct 07-10; Chicago, IL; McCormick Place; 2013 Sep 06-11; Chicago, IL; McCormick Place.

5797 ■ Graphic Arts/Awards Exhibition
Association of Graphic Communications
330 Seventh Ave., 9th Fl.
New York, NY 10001-5010
Ph: (212)279-2100
Fax: (212)279-5381
E-mail: cmg@agcomm.org
URL: http://www.agcomm.org

Annual. Primary Exhibits: A network for industry information and idea exchange; a provider for graphic arts education and training; a vehicle for industry promotion and marketing; an advocate on legislative and environmental issues and a source for bottom-line savings for the benefit of its New York/New Jersey membership.

5798 ■ Graphics of the Americas
Printing Association of Florida, Inc.
6275 Hazeltine National Dr.
Orlando, FL 32822
Ph: (407)240-8009
Fax: (407)240-8333
Fr: 800-749-4855
E-mail: agaither@pafgraf.org
URL: http://www.pafgraf.org

Annual. Primary Exhibits: Graphic arts and specialty printing equipment, supplies, and services. Dates and Locations: 2012 Mar 01-03; Miami Beach, FL; Miami Beach Convention Center.

5799 ■ MediaXchange
Newspaper Association of America
4401 Wilson Boulevard, Ste. 900
Arlington, VA 22203-1867
Ph: (571)366-1000
Fax: (571)366-1195
E-mail: sales@nna.org
URL: http://www.naa.org

Annual. Primary Exhibits: Newspaper publishing graphic arts systems and equipment and electronic publishing, ranging from computerized systems to newspaper presses to post press systems. Dates and Locations: 2012 Apr 02-05; Washington, DC.

5800 ■ National Federation of Press Women Conference
National Federation of Press Women
PO Box 5556
Arlington, VA 22205
Fax: (703)237-9808
Fr: 800-780-2715
E-mail: presswomen@aol.com
URL: http://www.nfpw.org

Annual. Features speakers as well as other activities, workshops, resources, and networking opportunities.

5801 ■ Society for News Design Annual Workshop & Exhibition
Society for News Design
424 E Central Blvd., Ste. 406
Orlando, FL 32801
Ph: (407)420-7748
Fax: (407)420-7697
E-mail: snd@snd.org
URL: http://www.snd.org

Annual. Gathers visual journalists from around the world for workshops and general sessions. 2012 October 11-13; Cleveland, OH; The Plain Dealer.

OTHER SOURCES

5802 ■ Advertising Production Club of New York (APC)
Euro RSCG Life, 7th Fl.
200 Madison Ave.
New York, NY 10016
Ph: (212)251-7295
Fax: (212)726-5057
E-mail: admin@apc-ny.org
URL: http://www.apc-ny.org

Description: Production and traffic department personnel from advertising agencies, corporate or retail advertising departments, and publishing companies; college level graphic arts educators. Meetings include educational programs on graphic arts procedures and plant tours. Maintains employment service for members.

5803 ■ American Artists Professional League (AAPL)
47 5th Ave.
New York, NY 10003
Ph: (212)645-1345
Fax: (212)792-2275
E-mail: aaplinc@gmail.com
URL: http://
www.americanartistsprofessionalleague.org

Description: Advances the cause of fine arts in America through the promotion of high standards of beauty, integrity and craftsmanship in painting, sculpture and the graphic arts.

5804 ■ American Institute of Graphic Arts (AIGA)
164 5th Ave.
New York, NY 10010-5901
Ph: (212)807-1990
Fax: (212)807-1799
E-mail: grefe@aiga.org
URL: http://www.aiga.org

Description: Graphic designers, art directors, illustrators and packaging designers. Sponsors exhibits and projects in the public interest. Sponsors traveling exhibitions. Operates gallery. Maintains library of design books and periodicals; offers slide archives.

5805 ■ Art Directors Club (ADC)
106 W 29th St.
New York, NY 10001
Ph: (212)643-1440
Fax: (212)643-4266
E-mail: info@adcglobal.org
URL: http://www.adcglobal.org

Description: Art directors of advertising magazines and agencies, visual information specialists, and graphic designers; associate members are artists, cinematographers, photographers, copywriters, educators, journalists, and critics. Promotes and stimulates interest in the practice of art direction. Sponsors Annual Exhibition of Advertising, Editorial and Television Art and Design; International Traveling Exhibition. Provides educational, professional, and entertainment programs; on-premise art exhibitions; portfolio review program. Conducts panels for students and faculty.

5806 ■ Design Management Institute (DMI)
101 Tremont St., Ste. 300
Boston, MA 02108
Ph: (617)338-6380
Fax: (617)338-6570
E-mail: dmistaff@dmi.org
URL: http://www.dmi.org

Description: In-house design groups and consultant design firms; individuals involved in the management of designers with in-house corporate design groups or consultant design firms. Aims to share management techniques as applied to design groups, and to facilitate better understanding by business management of the role design can play in achieving business goals. Design disciplines included are: architecture, advertising, communications, exhibit design, graphics, interior design, packaging and product design. Develops and distributes design management education materials. Sponsors seminars for design professionals. Identifies critical areas of design management study; conducts surveys and research on corporate design management. Maintains design management archive. Operates Center for Research, Center for Education, and Center for Design and Management Resources.

5807 ■ Gravure Education Foundation (GEF)
PO Box 25617
Rochester, NY 14625
Ph: (201)523-6042
Fax: (201)523-6048
E-mail: bcarlson@gaa.org
URL: http://www.gaa.org/gravure-education-foundation

Description: Purpose: Aims to establish gravure curricula with graphic arts educational facilities at all educational levels; provides financial assistance to students; develops new resources for conducting educational programs; encourages postgraduate projects and research within the graphic arts; provides career orientation at the high school level; provides for internships throughout the gravure industry. Seeks to serve as a catalyst within the framework of established institutions and to provide encouragement to enterprising individuals.

5808 ■ International Association of Printing House Craftsmen (IAPHC)
PO Box 2549
Maple Grove, MN 55311-7549
Ph: (763)560-1620
Fax: (763)560-1350
Fr: 800-466-4274
E-mail: headquarters@iaphc.org
URL: http://www.iaphc.org

Description: Individuals world-wide employed or interested in any facet of the graphic arts. Conducts field trips; maintains speakers' bureau; sponsors educational programs. Sponsors International Printing Week and International Gallery of Superb Printing.

5809 ■ International Graphic Arts Education Association (IGAEA)
1899 Preston White Dr.
Reston, VA 20191-4367
Ph: (703)758-0595
E-mail: igaea@npes.org
URL: http://www.igaea.org

Description: Graphic arts and printing teachers. Develops an integrated and comprehensive system of graphic arts education in schools and colleges of the U.S. Assists organizations in arranging lectures or other programs relating to graphic arts. Sponsors annual Graphic Communications Week; Visual Communication Journal; conducts research programs.

5810 ■ National Federation of Press Women
PO Box 5556
Arlington, VA 22205
Fax: (703)237-9808
Fr: 800-780-2715
E-mail: presswomen@aol.com
URL: http://www.nfpw.org

Description: Serves as a group of professional women and men pursuing careers across the communications spectrum.

5811 ■ Organization of Women Architects and Design Professionals
PO Box 10078
Berkeley, CA 94709
E-mail: info@owa-usa.org
URL: http://owa-usa.org

Description: Comprised of architects, interior designers, landscape architects, planners, lighting designers, graphic designers, photographers, artists, writers, educators and students. Strives to improve the professional standing of women in architecture and design-related fields. Advocates young women and students entering design related fields through mentoring, education, and employment opportunities.

5812 ■ Photo Imaging Education Association (PIEA)
3000 Picture Pl.
Jackson, MI 49201
Ph: (517)788-8100
Fax: (517)788-8371
E-mail: nshaver@pmai.org
URL: http://www.pieapma.org

Description: Represents photo imaging education practitioners and students. Builds a network where educators and students can create resources, solve problems and discuss issues relating to photo industry. Inspires members to be successful and to become better teachers of photo imaging.

5813 ■ Society of American Graphic Artists (SAGA)
32 Union Sq., Rm. 1214
New York, NY 10003
E-mail: sagaprints@verizon.net
URL: http://sagaprints.org

Description: Workers in the print media (etching, lithography, engraving, woodcut, wood engraving); also offers associate membership. Sponsors exhibitions and traveling shows.

5814 ■ Society for News Design
424 E Central Blvd., Ste. 406
Orlando, FL 32801
Ph: (407)420-7748
Fax: (407)420-7697
E-mail: snd@snd.org
URL: http://www.snd.org

Description: Comprised of editors, designers, graphic artists, publishers, illustrators, art directors, photographers, advertising artists, website designers, students and faculty. Encourages high standards of journalism through design. Serves as a forum and resource for all those interested in news design.

5815 ■ Technical Association of the Graphic Arts (TAGA)
200 Deer Run Rd.
Sewickley, PA 15143
Ph: (412)259-1706
Fax: (412)259-1765
E-mail: jmeyers@printing.org
URL: http://www.printing.org/taga

Description: Professional society of individuals interested in or engaged in research or technical control of graphic arts processes or related industries. Promotes advanced technical study and research in the graphic arts.

5816 ■ Type Directors Club (TDC)
347 W 36th St., Ste. 603
New York, NY 10018
Ph: (212)633-8943
Fax: (212)633-8944
E-mail: director@tdc.org
URL: http://tdc.org

Description: Serves as a professional society of typographic designers, type directors, and teachers of typography; sustaining members are individuals with interests in typographic education. Seeks to stimulate research and disseminate information. Provides speakers, classes and offers presentations on history and new developments in typography.

5817 ■ Typophiles
15 Gramercy Park S, No. 6C
New York, NY 10003
E-mail: info@typophiles.org
URL: http://www.typophiles.org

Description: Represents designers, printers, book collectors, artists, calligraphers, private press owners, wood engravers, librarians and others interested in graphic arts. Promotes the love and appreciation of fine graphic design and printing. Conducts quarterly meeting-luncheons and maintains publications.

Hazardous Waste Management Specialists

SOURCES OF HELP-WANTED ADS

5818 ■ BioCycle
The JG Press Inc.
63 S 7th St.
Emmaus, PA 18049
Ph: (610)967-4135
URL: http://www.jgpress.com/biocycle.htm

Monthly. $49.00/year for individuals; $105.00/year for other countries; $181.00/year for out of country, 2 years. Magazine focusing on management of city and industrial wastes by recycling and composting.

5819 ■ Drinking Water & Backflow Prevention
IAPMO
9878 Burke Pond Ct.
Burke, VA 22015
Ph: (703)934-0115
Fax: (703)934-0119
Fr: 888-367-3927
E-mail: curtis@iapmo.org
URL: http://www.iapmodwbp.org
Description: Monthly. $45. Presents articles directed toward individuals, companies, organizations, agencies, and municipalities with an interest in drinking water protection and backflow prevention. Contains information on safety standards, water system protection, training programs, cross-connection control, and all issues related to preventing the contamination of potable drinking water supplies with backflow prevention devices. Recurring features include case studies, letters to the editor, news of research, columns titled Test Your Investigative Skills and Backflow Prevention Device Repairs, and reports of meetings. Also carries news of educational opportunities, job listings, notices of publications available, and a calendar of events.

5820 ■ EHS Today
Penton Media Inc.
249 W 17th St.
New York, NY 10011
Ph: (212)204-4200
URL: http://ehstoday.com/

Monthly. Free to qualified subscribers. Monthly publication for safety professionals featuring information to meet OSHA and EPA compliance requirements, improve management of safety, industrial hygiene and environmental programs and find products and services to protect employees and property.

5821 ■ Industrial Hygiene News
Rimbach Publishing Inc.
8650 Babcock Blvd.
Pittsburgh, PA 15237
Ph: (412)364-5366
Fax: (412)369-9720
Fr: 800-245-3182
URL: http://www.rimbach.com

Bimonthly. Free to qualified subscribers. Magazine covering industrial hygiene, occupational health, and safety.

5822 ■ Onsite Installer
Cole Publishing Inc.
PO Box 220
1720 Maple Lake Dam Rd.
Three Lakes, WI 54562
Ph: (715)546-3346
Fax: (715)546-3786
Fr: 800-257-7222
E-mail: info@onsiteinstaller.com
URL: http://www.onsiteinstaller.com/

Monthly. $80.00/year for other countries; free to members; $150.00/year for other countries, 2 years. Magazine that offers information for professionals who design and install septic systems and other onsite wastewater treatment systems serving single-family homes, small businesses, and small communities.

5823 ■ Operations Forum
Water Environment Federation
601 Wythe St.
Alexandria, VA 22314-1994
Ph: (703)684-2400
Fax: (703)684-2492
Fr: 800-666-0206
URL: http://www.wef.org

Monthly. $79.00/year for nonmembers. Magazine covering operation/maintenance of WWTPs and wastewater collections systems.

5824 ■ Pollution Engineering
BNP Media
2401 W Big Beaver Rd., Ste. 700
Troy, MI 48084-3333
Ph: (847)763-9534
Fax: (847)763-9538
E-mail: pe@halldata.com
URL: http://www.pollutionengineering.com/

Magazine focusing on pollution control, air, water, solid waste, and toxic/hazardous waste.

5825 ■ Pollution Equipment News
Rimbach Publishing Inc.
8650 Babcock Blvd.
Pittsburgh, PA 15237
Ph: (412)364-5366
Fax: (412)369-9720
Fr: 800-245-3182
URL: http://www.rimbach.com/RimPub/PEN/PEN.htm

Bimonthly. Free to qualified subscribers. Pollution control equipment and products magazine (tabloid).

5826 ■ Public Works
Hanley Wood L.L.C.
1 Thomas Cir. NW, Ste. 600
Washington, DC 20005-5803
Ph: (202)452-0800
Fax: (202)785-1974

Fr: 877-275-8647
URL: http://www.pwmag.com

$60.00/year for individuals; $75.00/year for Canada; $90.00/year for other countries. Trade magazine covering the public works industry nationwide for city, county, and state.

5827 ■ Stormwater
Forester Media, Inc.
2946 De La Vina
Santa Barbara, CA 93105
Ph: (805)682-1300
Fax: (805)682-0200
URL: http://www.stormh2o.com

$79.00/year for individuals; $95.00/year for Canada; $160.00/year for other countries. Journal devoted to surface water quality professionals.

5828 ■ Waste & Recycling News
Crain Communications Inc.
1155 Gratiot Ave.
Detroit, MI 48207-2997
Ph: (313)446-6000
Fr: 800-678-9595
URL: http://www.wasterecyclingnews.com

Biweekly. Tabloid newspaper published for environmental managers. Features report on the generation and handling of solid and hazardous waste and the management of wastewater and air pollution. Provides classified advertising that includes professional recruiters, help wanted, requests for proposals, new and used equipment, containers, safety supplies, equipment leasing, balers, landfill products and services, recycling and MRF equipment, shredders, business opportunities and computer and software services.

5829 ■ Water Environment Research
Water Environment Federation
601 Wythe St.
Alexandria, VA 22314-1994
Ph: (703)684-2400
Fax: (703)684-2492
Fr: 800-666-0206
URL: http://www.wef.org/Publications/page_
   detail.aspx?id=796

Monthly. $125.00/year for individuals, WEF Member, print plus online; $350.00/year for individuals, print plus online; $850.00/year for institutions, print plus online; $200.00/year for other countries, WEF Member, print plus online; $350.00/year for other countries, print plus online; $905.00/year for institutions, other countries, print plus online; $100.00/year for members, print only; $324.00/year for individuals, print only; $770.00/year for institutions, print only; $125.00/year for other countries, members, print only. Technical journal covering municipal and industrial water pollution control, water quality, and hazardous wastes.

5830 ■ Water & Wastes Digest
Scranton Gillette Communications Inc.
3030 W Salt Creek Ln., Ste. 201
Arlington Heights, IL 60005-5025

Ph: (847)391-1000
Fax: (847)390-0408
URL: http://www.wwdmag.com

Monthly. Magazine (tabloid) featuring product news for decision makers in the municipal and industrial water and water pollution control industries.

EMPLOYER DIRECTORIES AND NETWORKING LISTS

5831 ■ Hazardous Waste Consultant—Directory of Commercial Hazardous Waste Management Facilities Issue
Elsevier Science
PO Box 945
New York, NY 10159-0945
Ph: (212)989-5800
Fax: (212)633-3680
Fr: 888-615-4500
URL: http://www.info.sciencedirect.com

Semiannual. Publication includes: List of 170 licensed commercial facilities that treat and/or dispose of hazardous waste in North America. Entries include: Facility name, address, phone, contact name, type of waste handled, methods of on-site treatment and/or disposal, Environmental Protection Agency permit status and identification number, restrictions, description of other services. Arrangement: Geographical. Indexes: Organization name.

5832 ■ Who's Who in Environmental Engineering
American Academy of Environmental Engineers
130 Holiday Ct., Ste. 100
Annapolis, MD 21401
Ph: (410)266-3311
Fax: (410)266-7653
URL: http://www.aaee.net/Website/WhosWho.htm

Annual, Latest edition 2011. $75.00 for individuals. Covers: About 2,400 licensed professional environmental engineers that have been certified by examination in one or more of seven specialties: air pollution control, general environmental engineering, industrial hygiene, hazardous waste management, radiation protection, solid waste management, water supply and wastewater. Entries include: Name, affiliation, address, phone, area of specialization, biographical data. Arrangement: Alphabetical, geographical, area of specialization.

EMPLOYMENT AGENCIES AND SEARCH FIRMS

5833 ■ The Energists
10260 Westheimer Blvd., Ste. 300
Houston, TX 77042
Ph: (713)781-6881
Fax: (713)781-2998
E-mail: search@energists.com
URL: http://www.energists.com

Executive search firm.

5834 ■ Search Consultants International, Inc.
701 N Post Oak Rd., Ste. 610
Houston, TX 77024
Ph: (713)622-9188
E-mail: info@searchconsultants.com
URL: http://www.searchconsultants.com

Management executive search firm.

ONLINE JOB SOURCES AND SERVICES

5835 ■ Bright Green Talent - Green Jobs
URL: http://www.brightgreentalent.com/green-jobs
Description: Serves as online tool that offers green jobs listing and career advice to candidates interested and engaged in environmental career.

5836 ■ Diversity Environmental Jobs
URL: http://www.diversityenvironmentaljobs.com
Description: Serves as a niche job board that provides diverse environmental career opportunities.

5837 ■ Environmental Jobs
URL: http://environmental.jobs4.org
Description: Offers a searchable database of environmental job opportunities available throughout the United States.

OTHER SOURCES

5838 ■ Air and Waste Management Association (A&WMA)
1 Gateway Ctr., 3rd Fl.
420 Ft. Duquesne Blvd.
Pittsburgh, PA 15222-1435
Ph: (412)232-3444
Fax: (412)232-3450
Fr: 800-270-3444
E-mail: info@awma.org
URL: http://www.awma.org

Description: Serves as environmental, educational, and technical organization. **Purpose:** Seeks to provide a neutral forum for the exchange of technical information on a wide variety of environmental topics.

5839 ■ American Academy of Environmental Engineers (AAEE)
130 Holiday Ct., Ste. 100
Annapolis, MD 21401
Ph: (410)266-3311
Fax: (410)266-7653
E-mail: info@aaee.net
URL: http://www.aaee.net

Description: Environmentally oriented registered professional engineers certified by examination as Diplomates of the Academy. Seeks to improve the standards of environmental engineering. Certifies those with special knowledge of environmental engineering. Furnishes lists of those certified to the public. Maintains speakers' bureau. Recognizes areas of specialization: Air Pollution Control; General Environmental; Hazardous Waste Management; Industrial Hygiene; Radiation Protection; Solid Waste Management; Water Supply and Wastewater. Requires written and oral examinations for certification. Works with other professional organizations on

environmentally oriented activities. Identifies potential employment candidates through Talent Search Service.

5840 ■ Environmental Industry Associations (EIA)
4301 Connecticut Ave. NW, Ste. 300
Washington, DC 20008-2304
Ph: (202)244-4700
Fax: (202)966-4824
Fr: 800-424-2869
E-mail: membership@envasns.org
URL: http://www.environmentalistseveryday.org

Description: Compiles statistics; conducts research and educational programs.

5841 ■ Spill Control Association of America (SCAA)
2105 Laurel Bush Rd., Ste. 200
Bel Air, MD 21015
Ph: (443)640-1085
Fax: (443)640-1086
E-mail: info@scaa-spill.org
URL: http://www.scaa-spill.org

Description: Third party contractors; manufacturers or suppliers of pollution control and containment equipment; individuals in private or governmental capacities involved with spill clean-up and containment operations; associate companies. Aims to provide information on the oil and hazardous material emergency response and remediation industry's practices, trends, and achievements; to establish liaison with local, state and federal government agencies responsible for laws and regulations regarding pollution caused by oil and hazardous materials; to cooperate in the development of industry programs and efforts so that pollutants are properly controlled and removed from land and water. Provides certification for hazardous material technicians. Maintains Spill Control Institute, Technical Services Division; collects and disseminates educational and technical information. Operates speakers' bureau; conducts research. Maintains placement service.

5842 ■ Water Environment Federation (WEF)
601 Wythe St.
Alexandria, VA 22314-1994
Ph: (703)684-2400
Fax: (703)684-2492
Fr: 800-666-0206
E-mail: jeger@wef.org
URL: http://www.wef.org

Description: Technical societies representing chemists, biologists, ecologists, geologists, operators, educational and research personnel, industrial wastewater engineers, consultant engineers, municipal officials, equipment manufacturers, and university professors and students dedicated to the enhancement and preservation of water quality and resources. Seeks to advance fundamental and practical knowledge concerning the nature, collection, treatment, and disposal of domestic and industrial wastewaters, and the design, construction, operation, and management of facilities for these purposes. Disseminates technical information; and promotes good public relations and regulations that improve water quality and the status of individuals working in this field. Conducts educational and research programs.

Sources of Help-Wanted Ads

5843 ■ *Health*
Scientific Research Publishing
PO Box 54821
Irvine, CA 92619-4821
E-mail: health@scirp.org
URL: http://www.scirp.org/journal/health/

Monthly. $948.00/year for individuals. Peer-reviewed journal publishing articles on the latest advancements in human health.

5844 ■ *Health Planning Today*
American Health Planning Association
7245 Arlington Blvd., Ste. 300
Falls Church, VA 22042
Ph: (703)573-3103
Fax: (703)573-3103
E-mail: info@ahpanet.org
URL: http://www.ahpanet.org

Quarterly. Features articles and essays relevant to health planning and policy professionals.

5845 ■ *HFM Magazine*
Healthcare Financial Management Association
3 Westbrook Corporate Ctr., Ste. 600
Westchester, IL 60154
Ph: (708)531-9600
Fax: (708)531-0032
Fr: 800-252-4362
URL: http://www.hfma.org

Monthly. $250/year for individuals; $151/year for institutions; $240/year for non-US subscribers. Magazine whose primary audience is senior and mid-level healthcare financial managers including CFOs, VPs of finance, controllers, revenue cycle directors, patient financial services managers, business office managers, and others responsible for healthcare financial management.

5846 ■ *Journal of Health Politics, Policy and Law*
Duke University Press
905 W Main St., Ste. 18B
Durham, NC 27701
Ph: (919)687-3600
Fax: (919)688-4574
Fr: 888-651-0122
E-mail: subscriptions@dukeupress.edu
URL: http://www.dukeupress.edu/Catalog/
  ViewProduct.php?productid=45615

Description: Bimonthly. Focuses on the initiation, formulation and implementation of health policy and analyzes the relations between government and health. Tracks the latest news; job listings; fellowships and internships; education, training, and professional opportunities; conferences and meetings; calls for papers; grants awarded; grants available; organization news; and publications in the fields of health politics, policy and law.

5847 ■ *Public Health Dispatch*
National Association of County and City Health Officials
1100 17th St. NW, Second Fl.
Washington, DC 20036
Ph: (202)783-5550
Fax: (202)783-1583
E-mail: info@naccho.org
URL: http://www.naccho.org

Monthly. Free for members; $4.95 for non-members. Contains news, resources and information about community health, environmental health, public health infrastructure and systems and public health preparedness. Includes information about funding and grants, award opportunities, careers, the national identity for local public health and upcoming events.

Placement and Job Referral Services

5848 ■ Hutton Group, Inc.
1855 Bridgepointe Cir., Ste. 23
Vero Beach, FL 32967
Ph: (772)770-1787
Fax: (772)365-7766
E-mail: hutton@huttongrouphc.com
URL: http://www.huttongrouphc.com/positions.html

Experienced healthcare professionals. Locates professionals and positions quickly and confidentially by thoroughly examining a client's and candidate's needs, analyzing competitive business environments, and continually instituting new search methods. Provides healthcare job recruitment and placement service.

5849 ■ Public Consulting Group
101 N First Ave., Ste. 1850
Phoenix, AZ 85003
Ph: (602)257-8024
Fax: (602)257-8025
Fr: 800-391-5193
URL: http://www.publicconsultinggroup.com

Specializes in providing solutions and customer services to clients in education, health, human consumer direct services and IT services. Helps health agencies increase program revenue, cut costs and improve compliance with state and federal regulations.

Employer Directories and Networking Lists

5850 ■ *National Managed Care Leadership Directory*
HealthQuest
1101 Standiford Ave., Ste. C-3
Modesto, CA 95350
Ph: (209)577-4888

Fax: (209)577-3557
E-mail: mcare@mcol.com
URL: http://www.managedcarestore.com/yhlthqst/
  hqlead.htm

Annual. 450 pages. May be used for networking, recruitment, research and sales prospecting. Categorizes each position by standard job functions. Contains approximately 6,950 executive listings from 850 companies.

Handbooks and Manuals

5851 ■ *Essential Readings in Health Policy and Law*
Jones & Bartlett Learning
5 Wall St.
Burlington, MA 01803
Ph: (978)443-5000
Fax: (978)443-8000
Fr: 800-832-0034
E-mail: info@jblearning.com
URL: http://www.jblearning.com/catalog/
  9780763738518/

Joel B. Teitelbaum. 2009. $84.95 (paper). 454 pages. Covers public health, topics in health care quality, intersection of policy and law with medicine and ethics and offers several resources on the topic of health system reform. Features perspectives of individual authors, policymakers, and judges that span the spectrum of political and social thought. Includes practical articles describing the methods and potential pitfalls of policy analysis as well as examples of administrative regulations, informal government memoranda and budget proposals that serve as important instruments in a policymaker's toolbox.

5852 ■ *Health Policy Analysis: An Interdisciplinary Approach*
Jones & Bartlett Learning
5 Wall St.
Burlington, MA 01803
Ph: (978)443-5000
Fax: (978)443-8000
Fr: 800-832-0034
E-mail: info@jblearning.com
URL: http://www.jblearning.com/catalog/
  9780763744427/

Curtis P. McLaughlin. 2008. $93.95 (paper). 438 pages. Provides analysis on current U.S. health policy and proposes various alternatives for developing future health policy by considering the viewpoints of economics, political science, management, communications, technology and public health.

5853 ■ *Health Policy: Crisis and Reform in the U.S. Health Care Delivery System*
Jones & Bartlett Learning
5 Wall St.
Burlington, MA 01803
Ph: (978)443-5000
Fax: (978)443-8000

Fr: 800-832-0034
E-mail: info@jblearning.com
URL: http://www.jblearning.com/catalog/
9780763746575/

Charlene Harrington, Carroll L. Estes . 2008. $92.95 (paper). 464 pages. Focuses on the health policy and financing issues that health professionals and nurses need to know. Provides an overview of the health policy and political process as it relates to the health status of the U.S., the organization and issues of the healthcare system, and healthcare economics.

5854 █ Health Policy and Politics: A Nurse's Guide

Jones & Bartlett Learning
5 Wall St.
Burlington, MA 01803
Ph: (978)443-5000
Fax: (978)443-8000
Fr: 800-832-0034
E-mail: info@jblearning.com
URL: http://www.jblearning.com/catalog/
9781449665098/

Jeri Milstead. 2008. $86.95 (hardcover). 236 pages. Provides information on the relationship between health policy and politics as they relate to the field of nursing.

5855 █ Introduction to U.S. Health Policy: The Organization, Financing, and Delivery of Health Care in America

The Johns Hopkins University Press
2715 N Charles St.
Baltimore, MA 21218-4363
Ph: (410)516-6900
Fax: (410)516-6968
URL: http://www.press.jhu.edu/index.html

Donald A. Barr. 2011. $75 (paper). 376 pages. Provides an overview of the U.S. health system and the dilemmas that policy makers currently face. Introduces the various organizations and institutions that make the U.S. health care system work or fail to work. Identifies historical, social, political and economic forces that shape the system and create policy dilemmas.

5856 █ Public Health: Career Choices That Make a Difference

Jones & Bartlett Learning
5 Wall St.
Burlington, MA 01803
Ph: (978)443-5000
Fax: (978)443-8000
Fr: 800-832-0034
E-mail: info@jblearning.com
URL: http://www.jblearning.com/catalog/
9780763737900/

Bernard J. Turnock. 2006. $72.95 (paper). 275 pages. Offers information for individuals considering a career in public health. Complements texts and courses on public health used by graduate and undergraduate programs. Provides an introduction to career possibilities for individuals looking for a career in the health sector.

5857 █ Understanding Health Policy

McGraw-Hill Companies
7500 Chavenelle Rd.
Dubuque, IA 52002
Fax: (614)759-3749
Fr: 877-833-5524
E-mail: pbg.ecommerce_custserv@mcgraw-hill.com
URL: http://www.mhprofessional.com/
product.php?cat=116&isbn=0071496068

Thomas S. Bodenheimer, Kevin Grumbach. 2008. $45.95 (paper). 232 pages. Features principles, descriptions and examples of health policy issues. Explores the issues in the world of healthcare and addresses how these issues affect an individual from the structure and organization of the industry.

EMPLOYMENT AGENCIES AND SEARCH FIRMS

5858 █ Ahern Search Partners

3982 Powell Rd., Ste. 205
Powell, OH 43065
Ph: (614)436-4126
Fax: (614)436-4125
E-mail: mollie@ahernsearch.com
URL: http://www.ahernsearch.com

Executive search firm. Concentrates on the healthcare market.

5859 █ Breitner Transcription Services, Inc.

1017 Turnpike St., Ste. 22A
Canton, MA 02021
Ph: (781)828-6411
Fax: (781)828-6431
Fr: 800-331-7004
E-mail: info@breitner.com
URL: http://www.breitner.com

Executive search firm focused on the healthcare industry.

ONLINE JOB SOURCES AND SERVICES

5860 █ HealthcareSource Job Board

URL: http://jobs.healthcaresource.com

Description: Healthcare human resources professionals. Provides employers and job seekers with resources for all areas of the healthcare field.

5861 █ HealthEconomics.com

URL: http://www.healtheconomics.com

Description: Health outcomes professionals. Lists internet resources focused on health outcomes and health care value. Provides a world-wide list of resources on outcomes research, health economics, pharmacoeconomics, managed care, value in medicine, health-related quality of life, performance assessment, and quality of care.

5862 █ HealthNewsDigest.com

E-mail: contact@healthnewsdigest.com
URL: http://healthnewsdigest.com/news

Description: Electronic news network. Covers breaking news and features on health, science and the environment. Lists jobs from all areas of the healthcare arena.

5863 █ MedHealthJobs.com

URL: http://medhealthjobs.com

Description: Covers online healthcare career resource and job search tools. Includes non-clinical jobs in the healthcare field.

5864 █ MedicalWorkers.com

URL: http://www.medicalworkers.com

Description: Provides a forum where employers and job seekers in the healthcare field can find each other.

5865 █ WellnessJobs.com

URL: http://www.wellnessjobs.com

Description: Features employment listings across the United States. Includes review of salary information, free resume posting and healthcare recruiters.

TRADESHOWS

5866 █ Annual State Health Policy Conference

National Academy for State Health Policy
10 Free St., 2nd Fl
Portland, ME 04101
Ph: (208)874-6524

Fax: (207)874-6527
E-mail: info@nashp.org
URL: http://www.nashp.org

Annual. Brings together state policymakers to learn about promising new programs and best practices and gain new insights on how to tackle the public's healthcare needs.

5867 █ National Association of County and City Health Officials Conference

National Association of County and City Health Officials
1100 17th St. NW, 7th Fl.
Washington, DC 20036
Ph: (202)783-5550
Fax: (202)783-1583
E-mail: info@naccho.org
URL: http://www.naccho.org

Annual. Offers learning and networking opportunities geared toward the needs of local public health professionals.

5868 █ National Forum on Quality Improvement in Health Care

Institute for Healthcare Improvement
20 University Rd., 7th Fl.
Cambridge, MA 02138
Ph: (617)301-4800
Fax: (617)301-4848
Fr: (866)787-0831
URL: http://www.ihi.org

Annual. Serves as a meeting place for people committed to the mission of improving health care. Features four keynote presentations, more than 100 workshops, a full resource exhibition hall, the National Forum bookstore, quality improvement storyboards and opportunities for networking.

5869 █ National Health Policy Conference

AcademyHealth
1150 17th St. NW, Ste. 600
Washington, DC 20036
Ph: (202)292-6700
Fax: (202)292-6800
URL: http://www.academyhealth.org

Annual. Discusses health care issues confronting policymakers and provides a health policy scan of the year ahead.

OTHER SOURCES

5870 █ AcademyHealth

1150 17th St. NW, Ste. 600
Washington, DC 20036
Ph: (202)292-6700
Fax: (202)292-6800
URL: http://www.academyhealth.org

Description: Health services researchers, policy analysts, and practitioners. Promotes interaction across the health research and policy arenas by bringing together a broad spectrum of players to share their perspectives, learn from each other, and strengthen their working relationships. Conducts programs that serve the interests of the research community, health policy leaders, and business and government decision-makers.

5871 █ Alliance for Health Reform

1444 Eye St. NW, Ste. 910
Washington, DC 20005
Ph: (202)789-2300
Fax: (202)789-2233
E-mail: info@allhealth.org
URL: http://www.allhealth.org

Description: Pursues equality in health coverage at a reasonable cost. Lists internships and job opportunities for individuals sharing the same interest with the alliance. Provides an unbiased source of information so that opinion leaders can understand the roots of the nation's health care problems.

5872 ■ America's Health Insurance Plans Center for Policy and Research

601 Pennsylvania Ave. NW, South Bldg., Ste. 500
Washington, DC 20004
Ph: (202)778-3200
Fax: (202)331-7487
E-mail: research@ahip.org
URL: http://www.ahipresearch.org

Description: Works to advance ideas, research and policy solutions to help Americans build a 21st Century health system. Strives to stimulate dialogue and develop a workable health policy agenda. Offers in-depth research on the interrelated issues of health care quality, cost and access and insurance markets.

5873 ■ Center for Health Improvement

1330 21st St., Ste. 100
Sacramento, CA 95811
Ph: (916)930-9200
Fax: (916)930-9010
E-mail: kshore@chipolicy.org
URL: http://centerforhealthimprovement.org

Description: Aims to improve population health by encouraging healthy behaviors. Analyzes evidence-based research to help public, private and nonprofit organizations strengthen their capacity to improve the quality and value of health care and enhance public health at the community level.

5874 ■ Center for Public Health and Health Policy

99 Ash St., 2nd Fl., MC 7160
East Hartford, CT 06108
Ph: (860)282-8525
Fax: (860)282-8514
E-mail: publichealth@uconn.edu
URL: http://publichealth.uconn.edu/aboutus.php

Description: Seeks to enable collaboration across University campuses and to encourage partnerships with regional and state programs. Provides resources and establishes doctoral training programs that support initiatives designed to expand outreach opportunities in selected areas of public health. Expands University partnerships with the State Department of Public Health and local health agencies throughout Connecticut to enhance public health practice and support workforce development.

5875 ■ Center for Studying Health System Change

1100 1st St. SW, 12th Fl.
Washington, DC 20002-4221
Ph: (202)484-5261
Fax: (202)863-1763
E-mail: hscinfo@hschange.org
URL: http://www.hschange.com

Description: Strives to inform policy makers and private decision makers about how local and national changes in the financing and delivery of health care affect people. Provides employment opportunities for people who wish to conduct research about healthcare.

5876 ■ Community Health International (CHI)

59 Windsor Rd.
Brookline, MA 02445
Ph: (617)739-2638
E-mail: contact@communityhealthinternational.org
URL: http://www.communityhealthinternational.org

Description: Aims to support the provision of health care to communities affected by conflict, natural disasters and epidemics. Improves the health and well being of communities emerging from crises by providing primary health care programs, access to safe, clean water, preventative health education and programs for traumatized individuals and communities.

5877 ■ Delaware Health Care Commission

410 Federal St., Ste. 7
Dover, DE 19901
Ph: (302)739-2730
Fax: (302)739-6927
E-mail: paula.roy@state.de.us
URL: http://dhcc.delaware.gov

Description: Strives to develop recommendations that represent the best healthcare policy for most Delawareans. Conducts pilot projects to test methods for catalyzing private-sector activities that will help the state meet its health care needs.

5878 ■ Global Health

United States Department of Health and Human Services
200 Independence Ave. SW, Rm. 639H
Washington, DC 20201
Ph: (202)690-6174
Fax: (202)690-7127
Fr: 877-696-6775
E-mail: globalhealth@hhs.gov
URL: http://www.globalhealth.gov

Description: Represents the United States Department of Health and Human Services to other governments, other Federal Departments and agencies, international organizations and the private sector on international and refugee health issues. Provides policy guidance and coordination on refugee health policy issues, in collaboration with the U.S. Public Health Service (PHS) Operating Divisions, the Office of Refugee Resettlement in the Administration for Children and Families, the Department of State and others. Develops U.S. policy and strategy positions related to health issues.

5879 ■ Global Health Council

1111 19th St. NW, Ste. 1120
Washington, DC 20036
Ph: (202)833-5900
Fax: (202)833-0075
E-mail: information@globalhealth.org
URL: http://www.globalhealth.org

Description: Represents health-care professionals and organizations that include NGOs, foundations, corporations, government agencies and academic institutions. Works to save lives by improving health throughout the world. Ensures that all who strive for improvement and equity in global health have the necessary information and resources. Supports improved health and development legislation.

5880 ■ Institute for Health Policy Solutions

1444 Eye St. NW, Ste. 900
Washington, DC 20005
Ph: (202)789-1491
Fax: (202)789-1879
E-mail: pshrestha@ihps.org
URL: http://www.ihps.org

Description: Develops creative and workable solutions to health system problems. Addresses a variety of health care coverage and associated cost issues, with the overarching goal of achieving coverage by and for all.

5881 ■ Institute for Safe Medication Practices

200 Lakeside Dr., Ste. 200
Horsham, PA 19044-2321
Ph: (215)947-7797
Fax: (215)914-1492
URL: http://www.ismp.org

Description: Helps healthcare practitioners keep patients safe by improving the medication use process. Serves as a resource for medication safety information. Collaborates on a continuing basis with a wide variety of partners, including healthcare practitioners, legislative and regulatory bodies, healthcare institutions, consumers, healthcare professional organizations, regulatory and accrediting agencies, employer and insurer groups and the pharmaceutical industry.

5882 ■ IntraHealth International

6340 Quadrangle Dr., Ste. 200
Chapel Hill, NC 27517
Ph: (919)313-9100
Fax: (919)313-9108
E-mail: intrahealth@intrahealth.org
URL: http://www.intrahealth.org

Description: Empowers health workers to better serve communities in need around the world. Fosters solutions to health care challenges by improving health worker performance, strengthening health systems, harnessing technology and leveraging partnerships.

5883 ■ National Academy for State Health Policy

10 Free St., 2nd Fl.
Portland, ME 04101
Ph: (207)874-6524
Fax: (207)874-6527
E-mail: info@nashp.org
URL: http://www.nashp.org

Description: Independent academy of state health policy makers. Works together to identify emerging issues and develop policy solutions. Improves and strives to achieve excellence in state health policy and practice.

5884 ■ National Association of County and City Health Officials

1100 17th St. NW, Second Fl.
Washington, DC 20036
Ph: (202)783-5550
Fax: (202)783-1583
E-mail: info@naccho.org
URL: http://www.naccho.org

Description: Represents local health departments. Supports efforts that protect and improve the health of all people and all communities by promoting national policy, developing resources and programs, seeking health equity and supporting effective local public health practice and systems. Supports community education about public policy measures beyond reducing specific diseases, such as those that eliminate inequality and prevent individuals from becoming disadvantaged.

5885 ■ National Center for Policy Analysis

12770 Coit Rd., Ste. 800
Dallas, TX 75251-1339
Ph: (972)386-6272
Fax: (972)386-0924
E-mail: publications@ncpa.org
URL: http://www.ncpa.org

Description: Serves as a public policy research organization that develops and promotes private alternatives to government regulation and control. Discusses policy topics that include reforms in health care, retirement, economic growth, energy and the environment.

5886 ■ National Committee for Quality Assurance

1100 13th St. NW, Ste. 1000
Washington, DC 20005
Ph: (202)955-3500
Fax: (202)955-3599
Fr: 888-275-7585
E-mail: customersupport@ncqa.org
URL: http://www.ncqa.org

Description: Seeks to improve the quality of health care. Works in coalition with other involved organizations to advance policies that will improve the quality and efficiency of the health care system.

5887 ■ National Human Services Assembly

1101 14th St. NW, Ste. 600
Washington, DC 20005
Ph: (202)347-2080
Fax: (202)393-4517
E-mail: pcollyer@nassembly.org
URL: http://www.nationalassembly.org

Description: Represents non-profits in the fields of health, human and community development and human services. Engages leaders of the nonprofit health and human service sector in collective efforts to advance the effectiveness of health and human services in the United States.

5888 ■ Project HOPE
255 Carter Hall Ln.
Millwood, VA 22646
Fax: 800-544-4673
E-mail: hope@projecthope.org
URL: http://www.projecthope.org

Description: Works to develop and permanently institute long-term solutions to pressing health problems. Seeks to address new health threats.

5889 ■ PublicServiceCareers.org
1029 Vermont Ave. NW, Ste. 1100
Washington, DC 20005
Ph: (202)628-8965
URL: http://www.publicservicecareers.org

Description: Serves as a source of professional job opportunities in the new public sector, which includes government, nonprofits, NGO's, consulting, contracting and academia.

5890 ■ UCLA Center for Health Policy Research
10960 Wilshire Blvd., Ste. 1550
Los Angeles, CA 90024
Ph: (310)794-0909
Fax: (310)794-2686
E-mail: chpr@ucla.edu
URL: http://www.healthpolicy.ucla.edu

Description: Works to improve the public's health by advancing health policy through research, public service, community partnership and education.

5891 ■ U.S. Department of Health and Human Services
200 Independence Ave. SW
Washington, DC 20201
Ph: (202)619-0257
Fr: 877-696-6775
URL: http://www.hhs.gov

Description: Provides detailed instruction for finding job opportunities within the U.S. Federal Government, especially in the health policy/healthcare field.

5892 ■ URAC
1220 L St. NW, Ste. 400
Washington, DC 20005
Ph: (202)216-9010

Fax: (202)216-9006
URL: http://www.urac.org

Description: Promotes continuous improvement in the quality and efficiency of health care management through processes of accreditation and education. Offers benchmarking programs and services that keep pace with the rapid changes in the health care system. Ensures that all stakeholders are represented in establishing meaningful quality measures for the entire health care industry.

5893 ■ Urban Institute's Health Policy Center
2100 M St. NW
Washington, DC 20037
Ph: (202)833-7200
E-mail: uihealthpolicy@urban.org
URL: http://www.urban.org/center/hpc/index.cfm

Description: Provides extensive research and analysis of key health issues including: private insurance, the uninsured, Medicaid, Medicare and SCHIP, disability and long-term care, vulnerable populations and health care reform.

SOURCES OF HELP-WANTED ADS

5894 ■ AABB Weekly Report
American Association of Blood Banks
8101 Glenbrook Rd.
Bethesda, MD 20814-2749
Ph: (301)907-6977
Fax: (301)907-6895
Fr: 800-458-9388
E-mail: aabb@aabb.org
URL: http://www.aabb.org

Description: 4 issues/year. Reports on developments in the area of blood banking and transfusion medicine. Covers scientific, regulatory, legislative, and legal information. Recurring features include news summaries and notices of employment positions.

5895 ■ AAOHN News
American Association of Occupational Health Nurses Inc.
7794 Grow Dr.
Pensacola, FL 32514
Ph: (850)474-6963
Fax: (850)484-8762
Fr: 800-241-8014
E-mail: aaohn@dancyamc.com
URL: http://www.aaohn.org/membership/corporate-partnerships.html

Description: Quarterly. Covers Association events as well as trends and legislation affecting occupational and environmental health nursing. Recurring features include news of research, a calendar of events, reports of meetings, news of educational opportunities, job listings, notices of publications available, resources for career-building, briefs on governmental issues concerning occupational and environment health, and a President's column.

5896 ■ Advisor for Medical and Professional Staff Services
Medical Staff Solutions
32 Wood St.
Nashua, NH 03064
Ph: (603)886-0444
Fax: (810)277-0578
E-mail: info@medicalstaffsolutions.net
URL: http://www.medicalstaffsolutions.net

Description: Monthly. Offers news and advice for medical office staff. Recurring features include interviews, notices of publications available.

5897 ■ American Academy of Medical Administrators - Executive
American Academy of Medical Administrators
701 Lee St., Ste. 600
Des Plaines, IL 60016-4516
Ph: (847)759-8601
Fax: (847)759-8602
E-mail: info@aameda.org
URL: http://www.aameda.org

Description: Bimonthly. Covers membership activities. Contains article abstracts and book reviews.

5898 ■ American Dental Hygienists' Association Access
American Dental Hygienists' Association
444 N Michigan Ave., Ste. 3400
Chicago, IL 60611
Ph: (312)440-8900
Fr: 800-243-ADHA
URL: http://www.adha.org/publications/index.html

$48.00/year for individuals; $85.00/year for two years; $120.00/year for individuals, for 3 years. Magazine covering current dental hygiene topics, regulatory and legislative developments, and association news.

5899 ■ CAP Today
College of American Pathologists
325 Waukegan Rd.
Northfield, IL 60093-2750
Ph: (847)832-7000
Fax: (847)832-8000
Fr: 800-323-4040
URL: http://www.cap.org

Monthly. $110.00/year for individuals; $30.00/year for U.S. and Canada; $135.00/year for individuals, Canada; $135.00/year for other countries; $40.00/year for other countries, single copy. Magazine covering advances in pathology tests and equipment, clinical lab management and operations trends, and related regulatory and legislative changes.

5900 ■ Catholic Health World
Healing Ministry of Catholic Health Care
4455 Woodson Rd.
St. Louis, MO 63134
Ph: (314)427-2500
Fax: (314)427-0029
URL: http://www.chausa.org/pages/publications/catholic_health_wor

Semimonthly. $40.00/year for members; $48.00/year for nonmembers; $48.00/year for other countries. Tabloid containing national and regional news stories, human interest items, healthcare legislation articles, and photos of interest to administrators of U.S. Catholic hospitals, medical centers, and longterm care facilities.

5901 ■ CME Supplement to Emergency Medicine Clinics of North America
Elsevier Science Inc.
360 Park Ave. S
New York, NY 10010-1710
Ph: (212)989-5800
Fax: (212)633-3990
Fr: 888-437-4636
URL: http://www.elsevier.com/wps/find/journaldescription.cws_home

$209.00/year for individuals. Journal covering emergency medicine clinics.

5902 ■ Diversity
Career Recruitment Media
2 LAN Dr., Ste. 100
Westford, MA 01886
Ph: (978)692-5092
Fax: (978)692-4174
URL: http://www.diversityalliedhealth.com/

Magazine focus on multicultural career and educational development magazine for allied health students and professionals.

5903 ■ Ethnicity and Health
Routledge Journals
270 Madison Ave.
New York, NY 10016-0601
Ph: (212)216-7800
Fax: (212)563-2269
URL: http://www.tandf.co.uk/journals/titles/13557858.asp

Bimonthly. $1,127.00/year for institutions, print + online; $1,014.00/year for institutions, online only; $390.00/year for individuals, print only. Journal covering ethnicity and health.

5904 ■ Group Practice Journal
American Medical Group Association
1 Prince St.
Alexandria, VA 22314-3318
Ph: (703)838-0033
Fax: (703)548-1890
E-mail: srozga@amga.org
URL: http://www.amga.org/Publications/GPJ/index_gpj.asp

$116.00/year for individuals; $218.00/year for two years; $222.00/year for other countries; $344.00/year for other countries, 2 years. Magazine covering the business of medicine.

5905 ■ Health Care Registration
Aspen Publishers Inc.
76 Ninth Ave., 7th Fl.
New York, NY 10011
Ph: (212)771-0600
Fax: (301)644-3550
Fr: 800-234-1660
URL: http://www.aspenpublishers.com

Description: Monthly. 844 pages. $285. Provides information and tips for health care administrators on how to run their departments more effectively. Topics include patient relations, collections, admissions, employee management, productivity, and others.

5906 ■ Health Facilities Management
Health Forum L.L.C.
155 N Wacker Dr., Ste. 400
Chicago, IL 60606
Ph: (312)893-6800
Fax: (312)422-4500
Fr: 800-821-2039
URL: http://www.hfmmagazine.com

Monthly. Free. Magazine covering health care.

5907 ■ Health & Place
Mosby Inc.
11830 Westline Industrial Dr.
St. Louis, MO 63146-3326
Ph: (314)872-8370
Fax: (314)432-1380
Fr: 800-325-4177
URL: http://www.elsevier.com/wps/find/
    journaldescription.cws_home

$806.00/year for institutions, all countries except Europe, Japan and Iran; $142.00/year for individuals, all countries except Europe, Japan and Iran. Journal publishing articles for health care professionals.

5908 ■ Health Planning Today
American Health Planning Association
7245 Arlington Blvd., Ste. 300
Falls Church, VA 22042
Ph: (703)573-3103
Fax: (703)573-3103
E-mail: info@ahpanet.org
URL: http://www.ahpanet.org

Quarterly. Features articles and essays relevant to health planning and policy professionals.

5909 ■ Health Policy, Economics and Management
Elsevier Science Inc.
360 Park Ave. S
New York, NY 10010-1710
Ph: (212)989-5800
Fax: (212)633-3990
Fr: 888-437-4636
URL: http://www.elsevier.com/wps/find/
    journaldescription.cws_home

$441.00/year for individuals, for all countries except Europe, Japan and Iran; $441.00/year for individuals, European countries and Iran; $58,100.00/year for individuals, Japan; $447,400.00/year for institutions, Japan; $3,726.00/year for institutions, other countries; $3,359.00/year for institutions, European countries and Iran. Journal covering the economic, social and political aspects of health care and its organization includes hospital management, health care marketing, hospital automation, and the assessment of new technology for the health care industry.

5910 ■ Health Progress
Healing Ministry of Catholic Health Care
4455 Woodson Rd.
St. Louis, MO 63134
Ph: (314)427-2500
Fax: (314)427-0029
URL: http://www.chausa.org/pages/publications/
    health_progress/cur

Bimonthly. $50.00/year for members, CHA; $61.00/year for other countries; $55.00/year for individuals, ministry partners; $10.00/year for nonmembers, single copy; for free, to members, single copy; $3.00/year for nonmembers, special section reprints; for free, to members, special section reprints. Magazine for administrative-level and other managerial personnel in Catholic healthcare and related organizations. Featured are articles on management concepts, legislative and regulatory trends, and theological, sociological, ethical, legal, and technical issues.

5911 ■ Healthcare Purchasing News
Nelson Publishing Inc.
2500 Tamiami Trl. N
Nokomis, FL 34275
Ph: (941)966-9521
Fax: (941)966-2590
E-mail: krussell@hpnonline.com
URL: http://www.hpnonline.com

Monthly. $72.00/year for individuals; $110.00/year for Canada; $130.00/year for other countries. Magazine for healthcare material management, central services, operating room and infection control professionals, and others involved in supply chain issues with hospitals and outpatient settings.

5912 ■ HIMSS News
Healthcare Information and Management Systems Society
33 W Monroe St., Ste. 1700
Chicago, IL 60603-5616
Ph: (312)664-4467
Fax: (312)664-6143
E-mail: himss@himss.org
URL: http://www.himss.org/ASP/
    PublicationsHome.asp

Description: Monthly. Tracks developments in the health care information and management systems field. Provides latest management trends in information systems, management engineering, and telecommunications.

5913 ■ Hospital Outlook
Federation of American Hospitals
750 9th St., NW Ste. 600
Washington, DC 20001
Ph: (202)624-1500
Fax: (202)737-6462
E-mail: info@fah.org
URL: http://www.fah.org

Description: Bimonthly. Monitors health legislation, regulatory and reimbursement matters and developments of interest to the investor-owned hospital industry.

5914 ■ Hospitals & Health Networks
Health Forum L.L.C.
155 N Wacker Dr., Ste. 400
Chicago, IL 60606
Ph: (312)893-6800
Fax: (312)422-4500
Fr: 800-821-2039
URL: http://www.hhnmag.com

Weekly. Free. Publication covering the health care industry.

5915 ■ The IHS Primary Care Provider
Indian Health Service
The Reyes Bldg.
801 Thompson Ave., Ste. 400
Rockville, MD 20852-1627
Ph: (301)443-1011
URL: http://www.ihs.gov/provider

Monthly. Journal for health care professionals, physicians, nurses, pharmacists, dentists, and dietitians.

5916 ■ The International Electronic Journal of Health Education
American Alliance for Health, Physical Education, Recreation & Dance
1900 Association Dr.
Reston, VA 20191-1598
Ph: (703)476-3400
Fax: (703)476-9527
Fr: 800-213-7193
URL: http://www.aahperd.org/aahe/publications/iejhe/

Annual. Free, health education professionals and students. Journal promoting health through education and other systematic strategies.

5917 ■ International Journal of Healthcare Information Systems and Informatics
IGI Global
701 E Chocolate Ave.
Hershey, PA 17033
Ph: (717)533-8845
Fax: (717)533-8661
Fr: (866)342-6657
URL: http://www.igi-global.com/Bookstore/
    TitleDetails.aspx?TitleI

Quarterly. $595.00/year for institutions, print only; $860.00/year for institutions, print & online; $595.00/year for institutions, online only; $210.00/year for individuals, print only. Peer-reviewed journal covering advance health care and clinical practices and research.

5918 ■ JONA's Healthcare Law, Ethics, and Regulation
Lippincott Williams & Wilkins
351 W Camden St.
Baltimore, MD 21201
Ph: (410)528-4000
Fr: 800-638-3030
URL: http://journals.lww.com/jonalaw/pages/
    default.aspx

Quarterly. $62.99/year for individuals; $100.01/year for institutions; $36.16/year for individuals, in-training; $114.60/year for other countries; $171.57/year for institutions, other countries. Peer-reviewed journal covering the legal, ethical and regulatory issues facing nursing care management.

5919 ■ Journal of the American Society of Podiatric Medical Assistants
American Society of Podiatric Medical Assistants
1616 N 78th Ct.
Elmwood Park, IL 60707
Fr: 888-882-7762
URL: http://www.aspma.org

Quarterly. Included in membership. Professional journal covering issues in podiatry.

5920 ■ Journal of Clinical Ethics
University Publishing Group Inc.
219 W Washington St.
Hagerstown, MD 21740
Ph: (240)420-0036
Fax: (240)420-0037
Fr: 800-654-8188
URL: http://www.organizationalethics.com

Semiannual. $175.00/year for institutions; $160.00/year for individuals, online; $200.00/year for individuals, print and online. Magazine covering business and healthcare policy.

5921 ■ Journal of Health Administration Education
Association of University Programs in Health Administration
2000 N 14th St., Ste. 780
Arlington, VA 22201-2543
Ph: (703)894-0940
Fax: (703)894-0941
URL: http://www.aupha.org/i4a/pages/
    index.cfm?pageid=3321#top

Quarterly. $100.00/year for individuals; $130.00/year for other countries. Peer-reviewed journal covering health administration education.

5922 ■ Journal of Health and Life Sciences Law
American Health Lawyers Association
1620 Eye St. NW, 6th Fl.
Washington, DC 20006-4010
Ph: (202)833-1100
Fax: (202)833-1105
URL: http://www.healthlawyers.org

Quarterly. $149.00/year for individuals. Professional journal covering healthcare issues and cases and their impact on the health care arena.

5923 ■ Journal of Health Management
Sage Publications Inc.
2455 Teller Rd.
Thousand Oaks, CA 91320-2218
Ph: (805)499-9774
Fax: (805)583-2665
Fr: 800-818-7243
URL: http://www.sagepub.com/
    journalsProdAdv.nav?prodId=Journal200

$416.00/year for institutions, print & e-access; $374.00/year for institutions, e-access; $408.00/year for institutions, print only; $107.00/year for individuals, print only; $112.00/year for institutions, single print; $35.00/year for individuals, single print. Journal focusing on health management and policy.

5924 ■ Journal for Healthcare Quality

National Association for Healthcare Quality
4700 W Lake Ave.
Glenview, IL 60025
Ph: (847)375-4720
Fax: (847)375-6320
Fr: 800-966-9392
E-mail: jhq@nahq.org
URL: http://www.wiley.com/bw/journal.asp?ref=1062-2551

Bimonthly. $193.00/year for individuals, print and on-line; $252.00/year for institutions, print and online. Professional publication that explores safe, cost-effective, quality healthcare.

5925 ■ Journal of Hospital Medicine

John Wiley & Sons Inc.
111 River St.
Hoboken, NJ 07030-5773
Ph: (201)748-6000
Fax: (201)748-6088
Fr: 800-825-7550
URL: http://onlinelibrary.wiley.com/journal/10.1002/(ISSN)1553-56

$827.00/year for U.S., Canada, and Mexico, print only; $827.00/year for institutions, other countries, print only. Journal on hospital medicine.

5926 ■ Journal of Nursing Care Quality

Lippincott Williams & Wilkins
351 W Camden St.
Baltimore, MD 21201
Ph: (410)528-4000
Fr: 800-638-3030
URL: http://journals.lww.com/jncqjournal/pages/default.aspx

Quarterly. $104.99/year for individuals; $356.00/year for institutions; $74.49/year for individuals, in-training; $199.73/year for other countries; $496.73/year for institutions, other countries. Peer-reviewed journal providing practicing nurses and those who play leadership roles in nursing care quality programs the latest on the utilization of quality principles and concepts in the practice setting.

5927 ■ Journal of Nursing Scholarship

John Wiley & Sons Inc.
350 Main St., Commerce Pl.
Malden, MA 02148-5089
Ph: (781)388-8200
Fax: (781)388-8210
URL: http://www.wiley.com/bw/journal.asp?ref=1527-6546&site=1

Quarterly. $63.00/year for individuals, print & online; $263.00/year for institutions, print & online; $228.00/year for institutions, print, online; $73.00/year for individuals, print & online; $191.00/year for institutions, other countries, print & online; $243.00/year for institutions, print & online; $49.00/year for individuals, print & online. Peer-reviewed journal covering nursing.

5928 ■ Magnetic Resonance Imaging Clinics

Mosby Inc.
11830 Westline Industrial Dr.
St. Louis, MO 63146-3326
Ph: (314)872-8370
Fax: (314)432-1380
Fr: 800-325-4177
URL: http://www.mri.theclinics.com

Quarterly. $448.00/year for other countries; $628.00/year for institutions, other countries; $228.00/year for students, other countries; $309.00/year for individuals; $501.00/year for institutions; $158.00/year for students; $628.00/year for institutions, Canada; $228.00/year for students, Canada; $345.00/year for Canada. Journal publishing articles and research on the latest trends in magnetic resonance imagining clinics and patient management.

5929 ■ Medical Care

Lippincott Williams & Wilkins
351 W Camden St.
Baltimore, MD 21201

Ph: (410)528-4000
Fr: 800-638-3030
E-mail: medicalcare@comcast.net
URL: http://journals.lww.com/lww-medicalcare/pages/default.aspx

Monthly. $493.00/year for individuals; $1,102.00/year for institutions; $240.00/year for individuals, in-training; $645.50/year for other countries; $1,327.50/year for institutions, other countries; $256.50/year for other countries, in-training. Peer-reviewed journal focusing on all aspects of the administration and delivery of healthcare.

5930 ■ Medical Records Briefing

HCPro Inc.
200 Hoods Ln.
Marblehead, MA 01945
Ph: 877-727-1728
Fax: (781)639-7857
Fr: 800-650-6787
E-mail: customerservice@hcpro.com
URL: http://www.hcmarketplace.com/prod-140/Medical-Records-Briefing.html

Description: Monthly. $249/year. Provides news and advice of interest to medical records professionals, including reimbursement, coding, legalities, regulations, and reviews. Recurring features include interviews, book reviews, and columns titled Computer Chronicle, Focus on JCAHO, Benchmarking Report, In Brief, and This Month's Idea. Subscription includes bimonthly "A Minute for the Medical Staff."

5931 ■ MEEN Imaging Technology News

Reilly Communications Group
16 E Schaumburg Rd.
Schaumburg, IL 60194-3551
Ph: (847)882-6336
Fax: (847)882-0631
URL: http://www.itnonline.net

Trade magazine (tabloid) serving users and buyers of medical imaging technologies and services.

5932 ■ Minnesota Medicine

Minnesota Medical Association
1300 Godward St. NE, Ste. 2500
Minneapolis, MN 55413
Ph: (612)378-1875
Fax: (612)378-3875
Fr: 800-342-5662
URL: http://www.minnesotamedicine.com/

Monthly. $45.00/year for individuals; $81.00/year for two years; $80.00/year for other countries; $144.00/year for other countries, 2 years. Magazine on medical, socioeconomic, public health, medical-legal, and biomedical ethics issues of interest to physicians.

5933 ■ Modern Healthcare

Crain Communications Inc.
360 N Michigan Ave.
Chicago, IL 60601
Ph: (312)649-5200
E-mail: subs@crain.com
URL: http://www.modernhealthcare.com

Weekly. $164.00/year for individuals; $255.00/year for Canada; $218.00/year for other countries. Weekly business news magazine for healthcare management.

5934 ■ Neuroimaging Clinics of North America

Mosby Inc.
11830 Westline Industrial Dr.
St. Louis, MO 63146-3326
Ph: (314)872-8370
Fax: (314)432-1380
Fr: 800-325-4177
URL: http://www.neuroimaging.theclinics.com

Quarterly. $546.00/year for institutions, international; $461.00/year for individuals, international; $226.00/year for students, international; $436.00/year for institutions, U.S.; $158.00/year for students, U.S.; $363.00/year for individuals, Canada; $226.00/year for students, Canada; $546.00/year for institutions,

Canada. Journal publishing articles on newest advances in neuroimaging and patient treatment options.

5935 ■ Nursing Administration Quarterly

Lippincott Williams & Wilkins
351 W Camden St.
Baltimore, MD 21201
Ph: (410)528-4000
Fr: 800-638-3030
URL: http://www.lww.com/product/?0363-9568

Quarterly. $119.49/year for individuals; $394.00/year for institutions; $74.49/year for individuals, in-training; $208.73/year for other countries; $541.73/year for institutions, other countries. Peer-reviewed journal providing nursing administrators with information on the effective management of nursing services in all health care settings.

5936 ■ Nursing Economics

Jannetti Publications Inc.
East Holly Ave., Box 56
Pitman, NJ 08071-0056
Ph: (856)256-2300
E-mail: nejrnl@ajj.com
URL: http://www.nursingeconomics.net/cgi-bin/WebObjects/NECJourna

Bimonthly. $72.00/year for individuals; $120.00/year for two years; $89.00/year for institutions; $150.00/year for institutions, 2 years; $120.00/year for institutions, other countries; $180.00/year for other countries, 2 years; $210.00/year for institutions, other countries, 2 years. Business magazine for nursing administrators.

5937 ■ Nutrition Business Journal

Penton Media Inc.
249 W 17th St.
New York, NY 10011
Ph: (212)204-4200
E-mail: info@nutritionbusiness.com
URL: http://www.nutritionbusiness.com/

Monthly. Journal catering to nutrition, natural products and alternative health care industries. Publishes information regarding business activities, market size/growth, trends, and opportunities, with a particular emphasis on the nutrition industry.

5938 ■ Patient Education and Counseling

Mosby Inc.
11830 Westline Industrial Dr.
St. Louis, MO 63146-3326
Ph: (314)872-8370
Fax: (314)432-1380
Fr: 800-325-4177
URL: http://www.elsevier.com/wps/find/journaldescription.cws_home

Monthly. $284.00/year for individuals, all countries except Europe, Japan and Iran; $2,648.00/year for institutions, all countries except Europe, Japan and Iran; $314,200.00/year for institutions; $33,700.00/year for individuals. Journal publishing articles on patient education and health promotion researchers, managers, physicians, nurses and other health care provider.

5939 ■ Patient Safety & Quality Healthcare

Lionheart Publishing Inc.
506 Roswell St., Ste. 220
Marietta, GA 30060-4101
Ph: (770)431-0867
Fax: (770)432-6969
Fr: 888-303-5639
URL: http://www.psqh.com

Monthly. $27.00/year for individuals; $47.00/year for Canada and Mexico; $67.00/year for other countries; $8.00/year for single issue. Publication that provides information about patient safety and quality health-care for patients, doctors, hospital administrators, and others in the healthcare industry.

5940 ■ Public Health Forum
Elsevier Science Inc.
360 Park Ave. S
New York, NY 10010-1710
Ph: (212)989-5800
Fax: (212)633-3990
Fr: 888-437-4636
URL: http://www.elsevier.com/wps/find/
journaldescription.cws_home

$35.00/year for institutions, European countries and Iran; $5,200.00/year for institutions, Japan; $49.00/year for institutions, other countries; $31.00/year for students, other countries; $3,400.00/year for students, Japan; $26.00/year for students, European countries and Iran. Journal focused on research methods, and program evaluation in the field of public health.

5941 ■ Public Health Jobs Worldwide
Carlyle Corp.
PO Box 6729
Charlottesville, VA 22906-6729
Ph: (434)985-4924
URL: http://www.jobspublichealth.com

Weekly. Electronic newspaper with current public health job openings in the United States and worldwide.

5942 ■ Public Health Law & Policy Journal
University of Hawaii
1859 E-W Rd., No. 106
Honolulu, HI 96822-2322
Ph: (808)956-9424
Fax: (808)956-5983
E-mail: phlo@hawaii.edu
URL: http://www.hawaii.edu/phlo/phlpj/

Free, online. Open access academic journal covering worldwide public health issues.

5943 ■ Public Health, Social Medicine and Epidemiology
Elsevier Science Inc.
360 Park Ave. S
New York, NY 10010-1710
Ph: (212)989-5800
Fax: (212)633-3990
Fr: 888-437-4636
URL: http://www.elsevier.com/wps/find/
journaldescription.cws_home

Semimonthly. $8,824.00/year for institutions, other countries; $1,048,500.00/year for institutions, Japan; $7,949.00/year for institutions, European countries and Iran. Journal covering public health and social medicine, and includes health planning and education, epidemiology and prevention of communicable disease, public health aspects of risk populations.

5944 ■ PublicHealthJobs.net
Association of Schools of Public Health
1900 M St., NW, Ste. 710
Washington, DC 20036
Ph: (202)296-1099
Fax: (202)296-1252
E-mail: publichealthjobs@asph.org
URL: http://www.publichealthjobs.net

Online service that provides links to epidemiology job postings in the private sector, not-for-profit sector, and the federal government.

5945 ■ Quality Management in Health Care
Lippincott Williams & Wilkins
351 W Camden St.
Baltimore, MD 21201
Ph: (410)528-4000
Fr: 800-638-3030
URL: http://www.lww.com/product/?1063-8628

Quarterly. $115.99/year for individuals; $351.00/year for institutions; $63.49/year for individuals, in-training; $208.73/year for other countries; $524.73/year for institutions, other countries. Peer-reviewed journal providing a forum to explore the theoretical, technical, and strategic elements of total quality management in health care.

5946 ■ Trustee
Health Forum L.L.C.
155 N Wacker Dr., Ste. 400
Chicago, IL 60606
Ph: (312)893-6800
Fax: (312)422-4500
Fr: 800-821-2039
URL: http://www.trusteemag.com

Monthly. $52.00/year for individuals; $120.00/year for Canada; $200.00/year for other countries; $10.00/year for single issue, domestic; $16.00/year for single issue, other countries. Magazine for hospital and health care system governing board members containing information about events and issues affecting the health care industry.

PLACEMENT AND JOB REFERRAL SERVICES

5947 ■ Hutton Group, Inc.
1855 Bridgepointe Cir., Ste. 23
Vero Beach, FL 32967
Ph: (772)770-1787
Fax: (772)365-7766
E-mail: hutton@huttongrouphc.com
URL: http://www.huttongrouphc.com/positions.html

Experienced healthcare professionals. Locates professionals and positions quickly and confidentially by thoroughly examining a client's and candidate's needs, analyzing competitive business environments, and continually instituting new search methods. Provides healthcare job recruitment and placement service.

EMPLOYER DIRECTORIES AND NETWORKING LISTS

5948 ■ Crain's List—Chicago's Largest Hospitals
Crain Communications Inc.
360 N Michigan Ave.
Chicago, IL 60601
Ph: (312)649-5200
URL: http://www.chicagobusiness.com/section/lists

Published November, 2010. $25.00 for individuals; $45.00 for individuals. Covers: 25 hospitals in Chicago area ranked by net patient revenues. Entries include: Name, address, phone number, fax, web address, corporate e-mail, hospital administrator, network affiliation, 2009 net patient revenue, percentage change from 2008, 2009 net profits, percentage change from 2008, inpatient days, available beds, daily occupancy rate, number of hospital employees as of December 31, 2009, fiscal year end, Chairman, President, CEO, Chief Financial Officer, Human Resources Manager, Media Relations/Public Relations Director, and Hospital Administrator.

5949 ■ Directory of Healthcare Recruiters
Pam Pohly Associates
2707 Woodrow, Ste. 100
Hays, KS 67601
URL: http://www.pohly.com

2011. $39.95. Provides complete listings of over 1,000 medical recruiters and healthcare executive firms with company descriptions, contact person, web site addresses, e-mail addresses, phone and fax numbers.

5950 ■ Directory of Hospital Personnel
Grey House Publishing
4919 Rte. 22
PO Box 56
Amenia, NY 12501
Ph: (518)789-8700
Fax: (518)789-0556
Fr: 800-562-2139
URL: http://www.greyhouse.com/hospital_
personnel.htm

Annual, Latest edition 2011. $325.00 for individuals. Covers: 200,000 executives at 6,000 U.S. Hospitals. Entries include: Name of hospital, address, phone, number of beds, type and JCAHO status of hospital, names and titles of key department heads and staff, medical and nursing school affiliations; number of residents, interns, and nursing students. Arrangement: Geographical. Indexes: Hospital name, personnel, hospital size.

5951 ■ Directory of Personnel Responsible for Radiological Health Programs
Conference of Radiation Control Program Directors Inc.
1030 Burlington Ln., Ste. 4B
Frankfort, KY 40601
Ph: (502)227-4543
Fax: (502)227-7862
URL: http://www.crcpd.org

Annual, Latest edition 2010. $55.00 for individuals. Covers: About 350 individuals who conduct radiological health program activities in federal, state, and local government agencies; members of the conferences. Entries include: For directors—Name and title, name of agency address, phone; office hours listed with state heading. For members—name, address, phone, affiliation, department, and title. Arrangement: Directors are by level of agency and geographical. Indexes: Personal name, agency, state.

5952 ■ Health Care Careers Directory
American Medical Association
515 N State St.
Chicago, IL 60654
Fr: 800-621-8335
E-mail: dorothy-grant@ama-assn.org
URL: http://www.ama-assn.org

Annual, Latest edition 2010-2011. $30.00 for individuals. Covers: More than 8,600 health career educational programs in over 82 health occupations at 2,700 sponsoring institutions. Entries include: Occupational descriptions, employment characteristics, and information on education programs, such as length, curriculum, and prerequisites. Arrangement: Classified by occupation, then geographical. Indexes: Institution name, program name.

5953 ■ Hospital Blue Book
Billian Publishing Inc. and Trans World Publishing Inc.
2100 River Edge Pky.
Atlanta, GA 30328
Ph: (770)955-5656
Fax: (770)952-0669
Fr: 800-800-5668
E-mail: blu-book@billian.com
URL: http://www.billianshealthdata.com/Products/
bluebook.html

Annual, Latest edition 2010. $575.00 for individuals; $575.00 for individuals. Covers: More than 6,500 hospitals; some listings also appear in a separate southern edition of this publication. Entries include: Name of hospital, accreditation, mailing address, phone, fax, number of beds, type of facility (nonprofit, general, state, etc.); list of administrative personnel and chiefs of medical services, with specific titles. Arrangement: Geographical.

5954 ■ Medical and Health Information Directory
Gale
PO Box 6904
Florence, KY 41022-6904
Fr: 800-354-9706
URL: http://www.gale.cengage.com

Annual, Latest edition April 2011. $1190.00 for individuals; $501.00 for individuals. Covers: In volume 1, more than 33,000 medical and health oriented associations, organizations, institutions, and government agencies, including health maintenance organizations (HMOs), preferred provider organizations (PPOs), insurance companies, pharmaceutical companies, research centers, and medical and allied health schools. In Volume 2, over 20,000 medical book publishers; medical periodicals, directories, audiovisual producers and services, medical libraries and information centers, electronic resources, and health-related internet search engines. In Volume 3, more than 40,500 clinics, treatment centers, care programs, and counseling/diagnostic services for 34 subject areas. Entries include: Institution, service, or firm name, address, phone, fax, email and URL; many include names of key personnel and, when pertinent, descriptive annotation. Volume 3 was formerly listed separately as Health Services Directory. Arrangement: Classified by organization activity, service, etc. Indexes: Each volume has a complete alphabetical name and keyword index.

5955 ■ *Vault Guide to the Top Health Care Employers*

Vault.com Inc.
150 W 22nd St., 5th Fl.
New York, NY 10011
Ph: (212)366-4212
Fax: (212)366-6117
Fr: 888-562-8285
URL: http://www.vault.com/store/book_
    preview.jsp?product_id=37972

Latest edition May, 2005. $19.95 for individuals; $19.95 for members. Covers: Health care employers. Entries include: Name, address, phone, fax, website, branch office location, and major departments. Also include company overviews, recent company news, information on the hiring process, key competitors, and employment contact. Arrangement: Alphabetical by company name.

HANDBOOKS AND MANUALS

5956 ■ *Career Opportunities in Health Care (Career Opportunities)*

Facts On File Inc.
132 W 31st St., 17th Fl.
New York, NY 10001-2006
Fax: 800-678-3633
Fr: 800-322-8755
E-mail: custserv@factsonfile.com
URL: http://www.infobasepublishing.com

Shelly Field. 2007. Third Edition. $49.50. 304 pages. Part of the Career Opportunities Series.

5957 ■ *Exploring Health Careers*

Delmar Cengage Learning
5 Maxwell Dr.
Clifton Park, NY 12065
Fr: 800-648-7450
URL: http://www.delmarlearning.com/about/
    contact.aspx

Maureen McCutcheon, Mary Phillips. 2006. $98.95. Provides an overview of the many career opportunities available within the health care field. Covers career descriptions, including educational requirements, salary information, skills and procedures performed within the various careers and more.

5958 ■ *Great Jobs for Business Majors*

The McGraw-Hill Companies
PO Box 182604
Columbus, OH 43272
Fax: (614)759-3749
Fr: 877-883-5524
E-mail: customer.service@mcgraw-hill.com
URL: http://www.mhprofessional.com/
    product.php?isbn=0071544836

Stephen Lambert. Third edition, 2008. $16.95 (paper). 240 pages.

5959 ■ *Introduction to the Health Professions*

Jones & Bartlett Learning, LLC
PO Box 417289
Boston, MA 02241-7289
Ph: (978)443-5000
Fax: (978)443-8000

Fr: 800-832-0034
E-mail: info@jblearning.com
URL: http://www.jblearning.com

Peggy S. Stanfield, Y. H. Hui and Nanna Cross. 2012. $93.95. 502 pages. Sixth edition. Provides current coverage of all major health professions. Outlines health-related careers, a review of the U.S. healthcare delivery system, managed care, and impact of new technology on healthcare services.

5960 ■ *Opportunities in Health and Medical Careers*

The McGraw-Hill Companies
PO Box 182604
Columbus, OH 43272
Fax: (614)759-3749
Fr: 877-883-5524
E-mail: customer.service@mcgraw-hill.com
URL: http://www.mhprofessional.com/
    product.php?isbn=0071437274

I. Donald Snook, Jr. and Leo D'Orazio. 2004. $14.95 (paper). 157 pages. Covers the full range of medical and health occupations. Illustrated.

5961 ■ *Opportunities in Hospital Administration Careers*

The McGraw-Hill Companies
PO Box 182604
Columbus, OH 43272
Fax: (614)759-3749
Fr: 877-883-5524
E-mail: customer.service@mcgraw-hill.com
URL: http://www.mhprofessional.com/
    product.php?isbn=0071467688

I. Donald Snook. 2006. $13.95. 160 pages. Discusses opportunities for administrators in a variety of management settings: hospital, department, clinic, group practice, HMO, mental health, and extended care facilities.

5962 ■ *Plunkett's Health Care Industry Almanac 2012*

Plunkett Research, Ltd.
PO Drawer 541737
Houston, TX 77254-1737
Ph: (713)932-0000
Fax: (713)932-7080
E-mail: customersupport@plunkettresearch.com
URL: http://www.plunkettresearch.com

Jack W. Plunkett. 2011. $299.99. 717 pages. Features in-depth profiles of leading companies, associations and professional societies in the healthcare field. Covers major issues and trends, market forecasts and industry statistics.

5963 ■ *Resumes for Health and Medical Careers*

The McGraw-Hill Companies
PO Box 182604
Columbus, OH 43272
Fax: (614)759-3749
Fr: 877-883-5524
E-mail: customer.service@mcgraw-hill.com
URL: http://www.mhprofessional.com/
    product.php?isbn=0071545352

Third edition, 2008. $12.95 (paper). 144 pages.

5964 ■ *Tyler's Guide: The Healthcare Executive's Job Search*

American College of Healthcare Executives
One N Franklin St., Ste. 1700
Chicago, IL 60606-3529
Ph: (312)424-2800
Fax: (312)424-0023
E-mail: ache@ache.org
URL: http://www.ache.org

J. Larry Tyler. 2011. $65.00 (softbound). 312 pages. Tackles current practices and trends that will advance readers towards competitive employment marketplace.

EMPLOYMENT AGENCIES AND SEARCH FIRMS

5965 ■ Aegis Group Search Consultants LLC

41451 W 11 Mile Rd.
Novi, MI 48375-1855
Ph: (248)344-1450
Fax: (248)347-2231
E-mail: resume@aegis-group.com
URL: http://www.aegis-group.com

Executive search and consultant firm. Focuses on the medical industry.

5966 ■ Ahern Search Partners

3982 Powell Rd., Ste. 205
Powell, OH 43065
Ph: (614)436-4126
Fax: (614)436-4125
E-mail: mollie@ahernsearch.com
URL: http://www.ahernsearch.com

Executive search firm. Concentrates on the healthcare market.

5967 ■ Alan Darling Consulting

374 Dover Rd.
South Newfane, VT 05351-7901
Ph: (802)348-6365
Fax: (802)348-7826
URL: http://www.alandarling.com

Executive search firm focused on the healthcare industry.

5968 ■ Allen Adell Executive Search and Consulting

7853 Gunn Hwy., No. 260
Tampa, FL 33626-1611
Ph: (813)920-8900
E-mail: info@allenadell.com
URL: http://www.allenadell.com

Functions as a retained executive search and human capital consulting firm that specializes in recruiting potential candidates for senior, mid-managerial and high-performing individual positions in the healthcare industry. Conducts talent assessment, competitive compensation surveys and objective and comprehensive exit interviews.

5969 ■ Alliance Search Management Inc.

594 Sawdust Rd., Ste. 194
The Woodlands, TX 77380
Ph: (281)419-5111
E-mail: kathy@alliancesearch.com
URL: http://www.alliancesearch.com

Employment agency.

5970 ■ Anderson & Associates

112 S Tryon St., Ste. 700
Charlotte, NC 28284
Ph: (704)347-0090
Fax: (704)347-0064
E-mail: info@andersonexecsearch.com
URL: http://www.andersonexecsearch.com

Executive search firm. Branch in Cumming, Georgia.

5971 ■ Aster Search Group

555 Madison Ave.
New York, NY 10022
Ph: (212)888-6182
E-mail: ecohen@astersearch.com
URL: http://www.astersearch.com

Executive search firm focused on the healthcare industry.

5972 ■ Barro Global Search Inc.

The Tower, Ste. 1600
10940 Wilshire Blvd.
Los Angeles, CA 90024
Ph: (310)443-4277

Fax: (310)441-5305
E-mail: drbarro@winwithoutcompeting.com
URL: http://www.barroglobal.com

Executive search firm focused on healthcare and hospitals.

5973 ■ The Bauman Group
1514 Redwood Dr.
Los Altos, CA 94022
Ph: (650)941-0800
Fax: (650)941-1729
E-mail: info@thebaumangroup.com
URL: http://www.thebaumangroup.com

Executive search firm.

5974 ■ Boone-Scaturro Associates Inc.
8831 S Somerset Ln.
Alpharetta, GA 30004
Ph: (770)740-9737
Fax: (770)475-5055
Fr: 800-749-1884
E-mail: mes@boone-scaturro.com
URL: http://www.boone-scaturro.com

Executive search firm focused on the healthcare industry.

5975 ■ Bowen & Briggs Inc.
646 Turner Ave.
Drexel Hill, PA 19026
Ph: (610)284-6631
Fax: (610)284-6651
Fr: 877-853-9611
E-mail: solutions@bowenbriggs.com
URL: http://www.bowenbriggs.com

Specializes in executive search, coaching and consulting for children's healthcare.

5976 ■ Breitner Transcription Services, Inc.
1017 Turnpike St., Ste. 22A
Canton, MA 02021
Ph: (781)828-6411
Fax: (781)828-6431
Fr: 800-331-7004
E-mail: info@breitner.com
URL: http://www.breitner.com

Executive search firm focused on the healthcare industry.

5977 ■ Calland & Company
2296 Henderson Mill Rd. NE, Ste. 222
Atlanta, GA 30345
Ph: (770)270-9100
Fax: (770)270-9300
E-mail: bob@callandcompany.com
URL: http://www.callandcompany.com

Executive search firm focused on senior management and healthcare.

5978 ■ Capodice & Associates
Midtown Plaza
1243 S Tamiami Trail
Sarasota, FL 34239
Ph: (941)906-1990
Fax: (941)906-1991
E-mail: peter@capodice.com
URL: http://www.capodice.com

Executive search firm. Branch in Carlisle, MA.

5979 ■ Carson Kolb Healthcare Group Inc.
27201 Puerta Real, Ste. 420
Mission Viejo, CA 92691
Fax: (949)272-1483
Fr: 800-606-9439
E-mail: info@carsonkolb.com
URL: http://www.carsonkolb.com

Executive search firm focused on the healthcare industry.

5980 ■ Cejka Search
4 CityPlace Dr., Ste. 300
St. Louis, MO 63141

Fr: 800-678-7858
E-mail: info@cejkasearch.com
URL: http://www.cejkasearch.com

Executive search firm for the healthcare industry. Branch in Norcross, GA.

5981 ■ Celia D. Crossley & Associates Ltd.
3011 Bethel Rd., Ste. 201
Columbus, OH 43220
Ph: (614)538-2808
Fax: (614)442-8886
E-mail: info@crosworks.com
URL: http://www.crosworks.com

Firm specializes in career planning and development, executive and organizational career coaching, assessment, key employee selection and team integration. Also offers career transition services, including in-placement, outplacement, and career coaching. Serves government, nonprofit, health-care, higher education and service industries.

5982 ■ Charles Aris, Inc.
300 N Greene St., Ste. 1800
Greensboro, NC 27401
Ph: (336)378-1818
Fax: (336)378-0129
E-mail: info@charlesaris.com
URL: http://www.charlesaris.com

Provides executive search and placement services in the areas of consumer packaged goods, retail, strategy/business development, global life sciences, healthcare, chemicals, textiles/apparel, private equity, and business services.

5983 ■ CNR Search & Services
30752 Via Conquista
San Juan Capistrano, CA 92675
Ph: (949)488-0065
Fax: (775)851-4514
E-mail: cnrkenmiller@juno.com
URL: http://www.cnrsearch.com

Provides staffing services of permanent and temporary employees. Works primarily on a retained basis. Contingency on a limited basis. Services include human resources consulting, mergers and acquisitions in high technology firms. Industries served: computer; information services; insurance, pharmaceutical and health care. Provides staffing services of permanent and temporary employees. Works primarily on a retained basis. Contingency on a limited basis. Services include human resources consulting, mergers and acquisitions in high technology firms. Industries served: computer; information services; insurance, pharmaceutical and health care.

5984 ■ Compass Group Ltd.
Birmingham Place Bldg.
401 S Old Woodward, Ste. 310
Birmingham, MI 48009-6613
Ph: (248)540-9110
Fax: (248)647-8288
URL: http://www.compassgroup.com

Executive search firm. Second location in Oak Brook, IL.

5985 ■ Conyngham Partners LLC
PO Box 94
Ridgewood, NJ 07451
Ph: (201)652-3444
E-mail: info@conynghampartners.com
URL: http://www.conynghampartners.com

Executive search firm.

5986 ■ Cook Associates Inc.
212 W Kinzie St.
Chicago, IL 60610
Ph: (312)329-0900
Fax: (312)329-1528
E-mail: info@cookassociates.com
URL: http://www.cookassociates.com

Management and executive recruiting specialists offering a commitment to clients to find the best candidates and to find those candidates as efficiently

as possible. Approach provides a flexible and effective structure that serves the special needs of both large and small companies. Serves the following industries: industrial, equipment manufacturer, food processing, graphic arts, chemical process, retailing, mechanical products, healthcare services, financial and professional services, legal, consumer products, construction and engineering, packaging, pulp and paper.

5987 ■ CSI Executive Search LLC
9600 Great Hills Trl., Ste. 150W
Austin, TX 78759
Ph: (512)301-1119
Fax: (512)301-5559
Fr: 877-329-1828
E-mail: info@csi-executivesearch.com
URL: http://www.csi-executivesearch.com

Executive search firm that specializes in the following arenas: accounting, engineering, healthcare, information technology, and legal. Utilizes behavioral, performance, retention variable, social intelligence, and cultural assessments to ensure the best candidate/client fit. Works on a retained, retingency, and contingency search basis.

5988 ■ D'Antoni Partners Inc.
122 W John Carpenter Fwy., Ste. 525
Irving, TX 75039
Ph: (972)719-4400
Fax: (972)719-4401
E-mail: richard@dantonipartners.com
URL: http://www.dantonipartners.com

Executive search firm.

5989 ■ Daudlin, De Beaupre & Company Inc.
18530 Mack Ave., No. 315
Grosse Pointe Farms, MI 48236
Ph: (313)885-1235
E-mail: ptd@daudlindebeaupre.com
URL: http://www.daudlindebeaupre.com

Executive search firm focused on the healthcare industry.

5990 ■ Diversified Health Resources Inc.
875 N Michigan Ave., Ste. 3250
Chicago, IL 60611-1901
Ph: (312)266-0466
Fax: (312)266-0715

Offers healthcare consulting for hospitals, nursing homes including homes for the aged, and other health related facilities and companies. Specializes in planning and marketing. Also conducts executive searches for top level healthcare administrative positions. Serves private industries as well as government agencies.

5991 ■ Eton Partners
1185 Springdale Rd.
Atlanta, GA 30306
Ph: (404)348-3576
E-mail: ebirchfield@etonpartners.com
URL: http://etonpartners.com

Executive search firm.

5992 ■ Executive Dimensions
5820 Main St., Ste. 403
Williamsville, NY 14221
Ph: (716)632-9034
Fax: (716)632-2889
E-mail: execsearch@executivedimensions.com
URL: http://www.executivedimensions.com

Executive search firm.

5993 ■ Flannery & Associates, LLC
N27 W23953 Paul Rd., Ste. 204
Pewaukee, WI 53072
Ph: (262)523-1206
Fax: (262)523-1873
E-mail: peter@flannerysearch.com
URL: http://flannerysearch.com

Executive search firm.

5994 ■ Foley Proctor Yoskowitz LLC
1 Cattano Ave.
Morristown, NJ 07960
Ph: (973)605-1000
Fax: (973)605-1020
Fr: 800-238-1123
E-mail: resumes@fpysearch.com
URL: http://www.fpysearch.com

Executive search firm for the healthcare industry. Second location in New York, NY.

5995 ■ The Ford Group Inc.
295 E Swedesford Rd., No. 282
Wayne, PA 19087
Ph: (610)316-6226
E-mail: info@thefordgroup.com
URL: http://www.thefordgroup.com

Executive search firm.

5996 ■ Gans, Gans and Associates
7445 Quail Meadow Rd.
Plant City, FL 33565-3314
Ph: (813)986-4441
Fax: (813)986-4775
E-mail: simone@gansgans.com
URL: http://www.gansgans.com

A human resources firm that specializes in executive search, human resources, management consulting, diversity consulting, and resume assessment. Takes a personal approach in the development of tailored programs that consider the corporate culture, history, and objectives of client. Industries served: consulting, financial services, legal, insurance, engineering, healthcare, manufacturing, utilities, and the public sector.

5997 ■ International Healthcare Recruiters Inc.
9840 SW 4th St.
Plantation, FL 33324
Ph: (954)848-5330
Fax: (954)530-0618
E-mail: info@internationalhr.net
URL: http://www.internationalhr.net

Description: Specializes in career-track positions for mid- and senior-level nurse managers, supervisors and administrators, as well as clinical nurse specialists and educators.

5998 ■ JPM International
26034 Acero
Mission Viejo, CA 92691
Ph: (949)699-4300
Fax: (949)699-4333
Fr: 800-685-7856
E-mail: qtek37@yahoo.com
URL: http://www.jpmintl.com/pages/qss.html

Executive search firm and employment agency.

5999 ■ Karen Dexter & Associates Inc.
2012 Chestnut Ave. N, Ste. 29
Wilmette, IL 60091-1512
Ph: (847)853-9500
Fax: (847)256-7108

Training and development consultant offering interpersonal skills training and one on one performance counseling for employees of large organizations. Industries served: advertising, banking and finance, consumer products, entertainment, food and beverage, healthcare, legal profession, manufacturing, government agencies, publishing and broadcasting.

6000 ■ Lee Calhoon & Company Inc.
1621 Birchrun Rd.
PO Box 201
Birchrunville, PA 19421
Ph: (610)469-9000
Fax: (610)469-0398
Fr: 800-469-0896
E-mail: info@leecalhoon.com
URL: http://www.leecalhoon.com

Executive search firm.

6001 ■ McCormack & Farrow Co.
949 S Coast Dr., Ste. 620
Costa Mesa, CA 92626
Ph: (714)549-7222
Fax: (714)549-7227
E-mail: resumes@mfsearch.com
URL: http://www.mfsearch.com

General practice retained search in most industries. Special emphasis on high-technology, start-up and emerging companies, manufacturing, healthcare, financial services, nonprofit and privately owned businesses.

6002 ■ Minority Executive Search Inc.
3060 Monticello Blvd.
PO Box 18063
Cleveland, OH 44118
Ph: (216)932-2022
Fax: (216)932-7988
E-mail: info@minorityexecsearch.com
URL: http://www.minorityexecsearch.com

Firm specializes in finding executives for the consumer, financial, military, automotive, medical, legal, and telecommunications industries.

6003 ■ Noyes & Associates Ltd.
5179 NE Sullivan Rd.
Bainbridge Island, WA 98110
Ph: (206)780-8142
Fax: (206)780-8144
E-mail: info@noyesconsult.com
URL: http://www.noyesconsult.com

Provides nationwide consulting services to health care clients. Major services include management education course and skill assessment survey; departmental performance reviews; and temporary and permanent management/executive search.

6004 ■ Pate Resources Group Inc.
505 Orleans St., Ste. 300
Beaumont, TX 77701
Ph: (409)833-4514
Fax: (409)833-4646
Fr: 800-669-4514
E-mail: opportunities@pateresourcesgroup.com
URL: http://www.pateresourcesgroup.com

Offers executive search and recruiting services to professionals who include physicians, healthcare administrators, engineers, accounting and financial disciplines, legal, outplacement, sales and marketing. Industries served: healthcare, petrochemicals, accounting, utility, legal, and municipalities.

6005 ■ Paul Bodner & Associates Inc.
9217 Tudor Park Pl.
Las Vegas, NV 89145
Ph: (702)528-0780
E-mail: paul@paulbodnerassociates.com
URL: http://www.paulbodnerassociates.com/
  index.html

Executive search firm. Second branch in Denver, CO.

6006 ■ Roberson & Co.
10751 Parfet St.
Broomfield, CO 80021
Ph: (303)410-6510
E-mail: roberson@recruiterpro.com
URL: http://www.recruiterpro.com

Professional and executive recruiting firm working the national and international marketplace. Specializes in accounting, finance, data processing and information services, health care, environmental and mining, engineering, manufacturing, human resources, and sales and marketing.

6007 ■ Robert Howe and Associates
3331 Bolero Dr.
Atlanta, GA 30341
Ph: (770)270-1211

Provides consulting services in the area of executive search and recruitment. Industries served: healthcare, hospitality, chemical, metals, electronics, construction, and food processing.

6008 ■ Skott/Edwards Consultants
7 Royal Dr.
Brick, NJ 08723
Ph: (732)920-1883
Fax: (732)477-1541
E-mail: search@skottedwards.com
URL: http://www.skottedwards.com

Firm specializes in providing executive search services to clients in the health care, biotechnology, medical device and pharmaceutical industries. Offers are strategic organizational development advice, corporate governance, employee appraisal and related services.

6009 ■ Theken Associates Inc.
Ridge Rd.
PO Box 307
Randolph, VT 05060
Ph: (802)728-5811
Fax: (802)728-5996

Executive search firm for nursing administrators. Consulting services include emphasis on organizational development in the healthcare field and interim leadership in patient care services across the continuum.

6010 ■ Tyler & Co.
375 N Ridge Rd., Ste. 400
Atlanta, GA 30350-3299
Ph: (770)396-3939
Fax: (770)396-6693
Fr: 800-989-6789
E-mail: art@tylerandco.com
URL: http://www.tylerandco.com

Retained executive search for the healthcare, food, market research, manufacturing and insurance industries.

6011 ■ Vine and Associates
225 W Broadway., Ste. 120
Glendale, CA 91204
Ph: (818)550-9802
Fax: (818)550-9806
E-mail: info@vineassociates.com
URL: http://www.vineassociates.com

Engaged in executive search and management consulting for healthcare in both the United States and overseas. In addition, the company develops feasibility and strategic planning for its clients who is primarily engaged in staffing, joint ventures and operations of institutions connected with the health industry.

6012 ■ Weatherby Locums
6451 N Federal Hwy., Ste. 800
Fort Lauderdale, FL 33308
Ph: (954)343-3050
Fax: (866)588-0085
Fr: (866)906-1637
E-mail: jobs@weatherbylocums.com
URL: http://www.weatherbylocums.com

Executive search firm for physicians. Branch office in Fairfax, VA.

ONLINE JOB SOURCES AND SERVICES

6013 ■ Bristol Associates, Inc.
5757 W Century Blvd., Ste. 855
Los Angeles, CA 90045
Ph: (310)670-0525
Fax: (310)670-4075
E-mail: bfarber@bristolassoc.com
URL: http://www.bristolassoc.com

Description: Executive search firm specializing in direct marketing, hospitality and food industries. Applicants can post their resumes online for recruiters' viewing and search current job databank. Also contains job tools and resources.

6014 ■ ExploreHealthCareers.org
E-mail: feedback@explorehealthcareers.org
URL: http://explorehealthcareers.org/en/home

Description: Provides employment information in health professions. Includes links to health-related education/training programs, financial aid resources, specialized learning opportunities, and current issues in health care.

6015 ■ Health Care Job Store
395 South End Ave., Ste. 15-D
New York, NY 10280
Ph: (561)630-5201
E-mail: jobs@healthcarejobstore.com
URL: http://www.healthcarejobstore.com

Description: Job sites include every job title in the healthcare industry, every healthcare industry and every geographic location in the U.S.

6016 ■ HealthcareCrossing.com
URL: http://www.healthcarecrossing.com

Description: Provides a collection of health care jobs, hospitals and medical jobs, nursing jobs and healthcare employment. Includes a variety of employers in the health care business.

6017 ■ HealthCareerWeb.com
URL: http://www.healthcareerweb.com

Description: Advertises jobs for healthcare professionals. Main files include: Jobs, Employers, Resumes, Jobwire. Relocation tools and career guidance resources available.

6018 ■ HealthcareSource Job Board
URL: http://jobs.healthcaresource.com

Description: Healthcare human resources professionals. Provides employers and job seekers with resources for all areas of the healthcare field.

6019 ■ HEALTHeCAREERS Network
Fr: 888-884-8242
E-mail: info@healthecareers.com
URL: http://www.healthecareers.com

Description: Career search site for jobs in all health care specialties; educational resources; visa and licensing information for relocation; interesting articles; relocation tools; links to professional organizations and general resources.

6020 ■ HealthNewsDigest.com
E-mail: contact@healthnewsdigest.com
URL: http://healthnewsdigest.com/news

Description: Electronic news network. Covers breaking news and features on health, science and the environment. Lists jobs from all areas of the healthcare arena.

6021 ■ Hospital Jobs OnLine
E-mail: support@hospitaljobsonline.com
URL: http://www.hospitaljobsonline.com

Description: Serves as a niche healthcare job board designed exclusively for hospitals, healthcare companies, and healthcare job seekers.

6022 ■ iHireHealthCareAdministration
URL: http://www.ihirehealthcareadministration.com

Description: Provides job listings and services to facilitate job searches in the field of health care administration.

6023 ■ JobsInLTC.com
URL: http://www.jobsinltc.com

Description: Serves as a job board for long-term care jobs for nursing home administrators, assisted living staff, directors of nursing, MDS coordinators, and other related fields.

6024 ■ MedHealthJobs.com
URL: http://medhealthjobs.com

Description: Covers online healthcare career resource and job search tools. Includes non-clinical jobs in the healthcare field.

6025 ■ MedicalHealthServicesManager.com
URL: http://www.medicalhealthservicesmanager.com

Description: Covers career opportunities and training information for aspiring medical health managers. Offers links, job listings, resumes and more.

6026 ■ Medzilla.com
URL: http://www.medzilla.com

Description: General medical website which matches employers and job hunters to their ideal employees and jobs through search capabilities. Main files include: Post Jobs, Search Resumes, Post Resumes, Search Jobs, Head Hunters, Articles, Salary Survey.

6027 ■ ProHealthJobs.com
Ph: (484)443-8545
Fax: (484)443-8549
E-mail: info@prohealthjobs.com
URL: http://prohealthjobs.com/jobboard

Description: Career resources site for the medical and health care field. Lists professional opportunities, product information, continuing education and open positions.

TRADESHOWS

6028 ■ American Academy of Medical Administrators Annual Conference and Convocation
American Academy of Medical Administrators
701 Lee St., Ste. 600
Des Plaines, IL 60016
Ph: (847)759-8601
Fax: (847)759-8602
E-mail: info@aameda.org
URL: http://www.aameda.org

Annual. Primary Exhibits: Equipment, supplies, and services related to healthcare. Dates and Locations: 2012 Nov 13-16; San Antonio, TX.

6029 ■ Medical Dental Hospital Business Associates Annual Convention
Medical Dental Hospital Business Associates
350 Poplar Ave.
Elmhurst, IL 60126
Ph: (630)941-8100
Fax: (630)359-4274
E-mail: info@mdhba.org
URL: http://www.mdhba.org

Annual. Primary Exhibits: Exhibits relating to medical, dental, and hospital services. Dates and Locations: 2012 Oct 11-12; Las Vegas, NV; New York, New York.

6030 ■ NADONA's Conference
National Association Directors of Nursing Administration
Reed Hartman Tower
11353 Reed Hartman Hwy., Ste. 210
Cincinnati, OH 45241
Ph: (513)791-3679
Fax: (513)791-3699
Fr: 800-222-0539
URL: http://www.nadona.org

Annual. Discusses new topics in the field and features exhibits of new technology, products, and services. 2012 July 21-25; Nashville, TN; Gaylord Opryland Resort.

OTHER SOURCES

6031 ■ Alliance for Health Reform
1444 Eye St. NW, Ste. 910
Washington, DC 20005
Ph: (202)789-2300

Fax: (202)789-2233
E-mail: info@allhealth.org
URL: http://www.allhealth.org

Description: Pursues equality in health coverage at a reasonable cost. Lists internships and job opportunities for individuals sharing the same interest with the alliance. Provides an unbiased source of information so that opinion leaders can understand the roots of the nation's health care problems.

6032 ■ American Academy of Medical Administrators (AAMA)
701 Lee St., Ste. 600
Des Plaines, IL 60016-4516
Ph: (847)759-8601
Fax: (847)759-8602
E-mail: info@aameda.org
URL: http://www.aameda.org

Description: Serves healthcare management at all levels, within all types of healthcare organizations by providing solid solutions, unique connections, resources and professional recognition that healthcare professionals need to navigate today's complex healthcare environment and stay competitive. Has 7 specialty groups: American College of Cardiovascular Administrators; American College of Oncology Administrators; American College of Contingency Planners; Federal Sector; Small or Rural Healthcare; American College of Managed Care Administrators; and American College of Healthcare Information Administrators.

6033 ■ American Academy of Medical Administrators Research and Educational Foundation (AAMA)
701 Lee St., Ste. 600
Des Plaines, IL 60016
Ph: (847)759-8601
Fax: (847)759-8602
E-mail: renee@aameda.org
URL: http://www.aameda.org/AboutAAMA/ aboutfoundation.html

Description: Individuals with health care backgrounds. Conducts research in the health care field and seminars geared toward professional development. Maintains placement services.

6034 ■ American College Health Association (ACHA)
891 Elkridge Landing Rd., Ste. 100
Linthicum, MD 21090
Ph: (410)859-1500
Fax: (410)859-1510
E-mail: contact@acha.org
URL: http://www.acha.org

Description: Provides an organization in which institutions of higher education and interested individuals may work together to promote health in its broadest aspects for students and all other members of the college community. Offers continuing education programs for health professionals. Maintains placement listings for physicians and other personnel seeking positions in college health. Compiles statistics. Conducts seminars and training programs.

6035 ■ American College of Health Care Administrators (ACHCA)
1321 Duke St., Ste. 400
Alexandria, VA 22314
Ph: (202)536-5120
Fax: (866)874-1585
E-mail: mgrachek@achca.org
URL: http://www.achca.org

Description: Persons actively engaged in the administration of long-term care facilities, such as nursing homes, retirement communities, assisted living facilities, and sub-acute care programs. Administers professional certification programs for assisted living, sub-acute and nursing home administrators. Works to elevate the standards in the field and to develop and promote a code of ethics and standards of education and training. Seeks to inform allied professions and the public that good administration of long-term care facilities calls for special formal academic training and experience. Encourages research in all aspects of geriatrics, the chronically ill, and administration. Maintains placement service. Holds special education programs; facilitates networking among administrators.

6036 ■ American College of Healthcare Executives (ACHE)

1 N Franklin St., Ste. 1700
Chicago, IL 60606
Ph: (312)424-2800
Fax: (312)424-0023
E-mail: ache@ache.org
URL: http://www.ache.org

Description: Healthcare executives. Conducts credentialing and educational programs and an annual Congress on Healthcare Management. Conducts groundbreaking research and career development and public policy programs. Publishing division, Health Administration Press, publishes books and journals on health services management and textbooks for use in college and university courses. Works to improve the health status of society by advancing healthcare leadership management excellence.

6037 ■ American College of Medical Quality (ACMQ)

5272 River Rd., Ste. 630
Bethesda, MD 20816
Ph: (301)718-6516
Fax: (301)656-0989
Fr: 800-924-2149
E-mail: krumholz.alan@mayo.edu
URL: http://www.acmq.org

Description: Physicians, affiliates, and institutions. Seeks to educate and set standards of competence in the field of quality improvement and management. Offers a core curriculum in quality. Maintains speakers' bureau.

6038 ■ American Correctional Health Services Association (ACHSA)

3990 Bullard Rd.
Monticello, GA 31064
Fax: (866)365-3838
Fr: (855)825-5559
E-mail: admin@achsa.org
URL: http://www.achsa.org

Description: Represents individuals interested in improving the quality of correctional health services. Aims to promote the provision of health services to incarcerated persons consistent in quality and quantity with acceptable health care practices. Promotes and encourages continuing education and provides technical and professional guidance for correctional health care personnel. Establishes a forum for the sharing and discussion of correctional health care issues. Conducts conferences on correctional health care management, nursing, mental health, juvenile corrections, dentistry and related subjects. Maintains placement service.

6039 ■ American Health Care Association (AHCA)

1201 L St. NW
Washington, DC 20005
Ph: (202)842-4444
Fax: (202)842-3860
E-mail: hr@ahca.org
URL: http://www.ahcancal.org/Pages/Default.aspx

Description: Federation of state associations of long-term health care facilities. Promotes standards for professionals in long-term health care delivery and quality care for patients and residents in a safe environment. Focuses on issues of availability, quality, affordability, and fair payment. Operates as liaison with governmental agencies, Congress, and professional associations. Compiles statistics.

6040 ■ American for the Healthcare Environmental (ASHES)

American Hospital Association (AHA)
155 N Wacker Dr., Ste. 400
Chicago, IL 60606

Ph: (312)422-3860
Fax: (312)422-4578
E-mail: ahe@ahe.org
URL: http://www.ahe.org

Description: Managers and directors of hospital environmental services, laundry and linen services, as well as housekeeping departments and waste management (non-hazardous and hazardous), in government or university settings. Provides a forum for discussion among members of common challenges, professional development, and career advancement. Maintains liaison between members and governmental and standards setting bodies. Certified Healthcare Environmental Services Professional (CHESP) available through education and Examination.

6041 ■ American Hospital Association (AHA)

155 N Wacker Dr.
Chicago, IL 60606
Ph: (312)422-3000
Fax: (312)422-4796
E-mail: rich@aha.org
URL: http://www.aha.org

Description: Represents health care provider organizations. Seeks to advance the health of individuals and communities. Leads, represents, and serves health care provider organizations that are accountable to the community and committed to health improvement.

6042 ■ American Public Health Association (APHA)

800 I St. NW
Washington, DC 20001
Ph: (202)777-2742
Fax: (202)777-2534
E-mail: comments@apha.org
URL: http://www.apha.org

Description: Professional organization of physicians, nurses, educators, academicians, environmentalists, epidemiologists, new professionals, social workers, health administrators, optometrists, podiatrists, pharmacists, dentists, nutritionists, health planners, other community and mental health specialists, and interested consumers. Seeks to protect and promote personal, mental, and environmental health. Services include: promulgation of standards; establishment of uniform practices and procedures; development of the etiology of communicable diseases; research in public health; exploration of medical care programs and their relationships to public health. Sponsors job placement service.

6043 ■ American Society of Ophthalmic Administrators (ASOA)

4000 Legato Rd., Ste. 700
Fairfax, VA 22033
Ph: (703)788-5777
Fax: (703)547-8827
Fr: 800-451-1339
E-mail: asoa@asoa.org
URL: http://www.asoa.org

Description: Serves as a division of the American Society of Cataract and Refractive Surgery. Represents persons involved with the administration of an ophthalmic office or clinic. Facilitates the exchange of ideas and information in order to improve management practices and working conditions.

6044 ■ Association for the Advancement of Medical Instrumentation (AAMI)

4301 N Fairfax Dr., Ste. 301
Arlington, VA 22203-1633
Ph: (703)525-4890
Fax: (703)276-0793
Fr: 800-332-2264
E-mail: mlogan@aami.org
URL: http://www.aami.org

Description: Clinical engineers, biomedical equipment technicians, physicians, hospital administrators, consultants, engineers, manufacturers of medical devices, nurses, researchers and others interested in medical instrumentation. Works to improve the qual-

ity of medical care through the application, development, and management of technology. Maintains placement service. Offers certification programs for biomedical equipment technicians and clinical engineers. Produces numerous standards and recommended practices on medical devices and procedures. Offers educational programs.

6045 ■ Association of Healthcare Internal Auditors (AHIA)

10200 W 44th Ave., Ste. 304
Wheat Ridge, CO 80033
Ph: (303)327-7546
Fax: (303)422-8894
Fr: 888-ASK-AHIA
E-mail: ahia@ahia.org
URL: http://www.ahia.org

Description: Health care internal auditors and other interested individuals. Promotes cost containment and increased productivity in health care institutions through internal auditing. Serves as a forum for the exchange of experience, ideas, and information among members; provides continuing professional education courses and informs members of developments in health care internal auditing. Offers employment clearinghouse services.

6046 ■ Food and Drug Law Institute (FDLI)

1155 15th St. NW, Ste. 800
Washington, DC 20005
Ph: (202)371-1420
Fax: (202)371-0649
Fr: 800-956-6293
E-mail: comments@fdli.org
URL: http://www.fdli.org

Description: Provides forum regarding laws, regulations and policies related to drugs, medical devices, and other health care technologies.

6047 ■ International Executive Housekeepers Association (IEHA)

1001 Eastwind Dr., Ste. 301
Westerville, OH 43081-3361
Ph: (614)895-7166
Fax: (614)895-1248
Fr: 800-200-6342
E-mail: excel@ieha.org
URL: http://www.ieha.org

Description: Persons engaged in facility housekeeping management in hospitals, hotels and motels, schools and industrial establishments. Established educational standards. Sponsors certificate and collegiate degree programs. Holds annual International Housekeepers Week celebration.

6048 ■ Medical Group Management Association (MGMA)

104 Inverness Terr. E
Englewood, CO 80112-5306
Ph: (303)799-1111
Fr: 877-275-6462
E-mail: support@mgma.com
URL: http://www.mgma.com

Description: Represents professionals involved in the management of medical group practices and administration of other ambulatory healthcare facilities. Provides products and services that includes education, benchmarking, surveys, national advocacy and networking opportunities for members.

6049 ■ National Association Directors of Nursing Administration

Reed Hartman Tower
11353 Reed Hartman Hwy., Ste. 210
Cincinnati, OH 45241
Ph: (513)791-3679
Fax: (513)791-3699
Fr: 800-222-0539
URL: http://www.nadona.org

Description: Represents the interests of nurses and administrators in long term care. Promotes ethical principles and practices within the long term care continuum. Advocates for the benefit of directors of nursing, assistant directors of nursing, and registered nurses in long term care. Supports and promotes quality of care for individuals who are receiving long-term care.

6050 ■ National Association of Health Services Executives (NAHSE)

1050 Connecticut Ave. NW, 10th Fl.
Washington, DC 20036
Ph: (202)772-1030
Fax: (202)772-1072
E-mail: nahsehq@nahse.org
URL: http://netforum.avectra.com/eweb/
DynamicPage.aspx?Site=NAHSE&WebCode=HomePage

Description: Black health care executive managers, planners, educators, advocates, providers, organizers, researchers, and consumers participating in academic ventures, educational forums, seminars, workshops, systems design, legislation, and other activities. Conducts National Work-Study Program and sponsors educational programs.

6051 ■ National Association for Healthcare Quality (NAHQ)

4700 W Lake Ave.
Glenview, IL 60025
Ph: (847)375-4720
Fax: (847)375-6320
Fr: 800-966-9392
E-mail: info@nahq.org
URL: http://www.nahq.org

Description: Healthcare professionals in quality assessment and improvement, utilization and risk management, case management, infection control, managed care, nursing, and medical records. Objectives are: to encourage, develop, and provide continuing education for all persons involved in health care quality; to give the patient primary consideration in all actions affecting his or her health and welfare; to promote the sharing of knowledge and encourage a high degree of professional ethics in health care quality. Offers accredited certification in the field of healthcare quality, utilization, and risk management. Facilitates communication and cooperation among members, medical staff, and health care government agencies. Conducts educational seminars and conferences.

6052 ■ National Health Council (NHC)

1730 M St. NW, Ste. 500
Washington, DC 20036
Ph: (202)785-3910
Fax: (202)785-5923
E-mail: info@nhcouncil.org
URL: http://www.nationalhealthcouncil.org

Description: National association of voluntary and professional societies in the health field; national organizations and business groups with strong health interests. Seeks to improve the health of patients, particularly those with chronic diseases, through conferences, publications, policy briefings and special projects. Distributes printed material on health careers and related subjects. Promotes standardization of financial reporting for voluntary health groups.

6053 ■ National Rural Health Association (NRHA)

Administrative Office
521 E 63rd St.
Kansas City, MO 64110-3329
Ph: (816)756-3140
Fax: (816)756-3144
E-mail: mail@nrharural.org
URL: http://www.ruralhealthweb.org

Description: Administrators, physicians, nurses, physician assistants, health planners, academicians, and others interested or involved in rural health care. Creates a better understanding of health care problems unique to rural areas; utilizes a collective approach in finding positive solutions; articulates and represents the health care needs of rural America; supplies current information to rural health care providers; serves as a liaison between rural health care programs throughout the country. Offers continuing education credits for medical, dental, nursing, and management courses.

6054 ■ National Society of Certified Healthcare Business Consultants (NSCHBC)

12100 Sunset Hills Rd., Ste. 130
Reston, VA 20190
Ph: (703)234-4099
Fax: (703)435-4390
E-mail: info@nschbc.org
URL: http://www.nschbc.org/index.cfm

Description: Advances the profession of healthcare business consultants through education, certification and professional interaction. Provides education and training to assist members in fulfilling the requirements of certification.

6055 ■ Radiology Business Management Association (RBMA)

10300 Eaton Pl., Ste. 460
Fairfax, VA 22030
Ph: (703)621-3355
Fax: (703)621-3356
Fr: 888-224-7262
E-mail: info@rbma.org
URL: http://www.rbma.org

Description: Provides education, resources and solutions to manage the business of radiology. Offers an online course in radiology coding.

6056 ■ Society for Radiation Oncology Administrators (SROA)

5272 River Rd., Ste. 630
Bethesda, MD 20816
Ph: (301)718-6510
Fax: (301)656-0989
Fr: (866)458-7762
E-mail: sroa@paimgmt.com
URL: http://www.sroa.org

Description: Individuals with managerial responsibilities in radiation oncology at the executive, divisional, or departmental level, and whose functions include personnel, budget, and development of operational procedures and guidelines for therapeutic radiology departments. Strives to improve the administration of the business and nonmedical management aspects of therapeutic radiology, to promote the field of therapeutic radiology administration, to provide a forum for communication among members, and to disseminate information among members. Maintains speakers' bureau; offers placement service.

SOURCES OF HELP-WANTED ADS

6057 ■ *Air Conditioning, Heating and Refrigeration News*
BNP Media
2401 W Big Beaver Rd., Ste. 700
Troy, MI 48084-3333
Ph: (847)763-9534
Fax: (847)763-9538
URL: http://www.achrnews.com/

$59.00/year for individuals, print; $91.00/year for two years, print; $118.00/year for individuals, 3 years; print; $69.00/year for individuals, print and digital; $111.00/year for two years, print and digital; $148.00/year for individuals, 3 years; print and digital. Tabloid for HVAC and commercial refrigeration contractors, wholesalers, manufacturers, engineers, and owners/managers.

6058 ■ *ASHRAE Journal*
American Society of Heating, Refrigerating and Air-Conditioning Engineers Inc.
1791 Tullie Cir. NE
Atlanta, GA 30329
Ph: (404)636-8400
Fax: (404)321-5478
Fr: 800-527-4723
URL: http://www.ashrae.org/publications/page/540

Monthly. $177.00/year for institutions, nonmembers; $197.00/year for institutions, Canada, nonmembers; $267.00/year for institutions, other countries, non-members; for Included in membership. Magazine for the heating, refrigeration, and air conditioning trade.

6059 ■ *Contractor Magazine*
Penton Media Inc.
330 N Wabash Ave., Ste. 2300
Chicago, IL 60611
Ph: (312)840-8498
Fax: (312)595-0295
URL: http://contractormag.com/

Monthly. Free, USA/Canada; $110.00/year for other countries; $189.00/year for other countries, 2 years. Industry news and management how-to magazine for heating, plumbing, piping, fire sprinkler, and other mechanical specialties contracting firms.

6060 ■ *Heating/Piping/Air Conditioning Engineering (HPAC)*
Penton Media Inc.
249 W 17th St.
New York, NY 10011
Ph: (212)204-4200
E-mail: hpac@penton.com
URL: http://hpac.com/

Monthly. Business magazine serving the growing mechanical engineered systems market in the areas of building construction, renovation, and retrofit.

6061 ■ *Industrial Heating*
Business News Publishing Co.
2401 W Big Beaver Rd., Ste. 700
Troy, MI 48084-3333
Ph: (248)362-3700
URL: http://www.industrialheating.com/
Monthly. Magazine.

6062 ■ *MCAA Reporter*
Mechanical Contractors Association of America Inc.
1385 Piccard Dr.
Rockville, MD 20850
Ph: (301)869-5800
Fax: (301)990-9690
Fr: 800-556-3653
E-mail: abreedlove@mcaa.org
URL: http://www.mcaa.org/reporter/

Description: Bimonthly. Covers labor issues and government affairs as they affect mechanical contractors in the plumbing, pipefitting, air conditioning, refrigeration, fire protection, and high-purity piping industries. Recurring features include reports on the activities of the Association and notices of pertinent seminars and meetings.

6063 ■ *Snips Magazine*
Snips Magazine
2401 W Big Beaver Rd., Ste. 700
Troy, MI 48084-3333
Ph: (248)362-3700
Fax: (248)362-0317
URL: http://www.snipsmag.com/

Monthly. Free. Magazine for the sheet metal, warm-air heating, ventilating and air conditioning industry. Provides helpful hints for contractors.

6064 ■ *World Journal of Mechanics*
Scientific Research Publishing
PO Box 54821
Irvine, CA 92619-4821
E-mail: wjm@scirp.org
URL: http://www.scirp.org/journal/wjm/

Quarterly. $156.00/year for individuals. Peer-reviewed journal publishing articles in the general field of mechanics.

EMPLOYER DIRECTORIES AND NETWORKING LISTS

6065 ■ *ABC Today—Associated Builders and Contractors National Membership Directory Issue*
Associated Builders and Contractors Inc.
4250 N Fairfax Dr., 9th Fl.
Arlington, VA 22203-1607
Ph: (703)812-2000
Fax: (703)812-8235
URL: http://www.abc.org

Annual, December. $150.00. Publication includes:

List of approximately 19,000 member construction contractors and suppliers.

6066 ■ *Air Conditioning Contractors of America—Membership Directory*
Air Conditioning Contractors of America
2800 Shirlington Rd., Ste. 300
Arlington, VA 22206
Ph: (703)575-4477
Fax: (703)575-4449
Fr: 888-290-2220
URL: http://www.acca.org

Annual, summer. Covers: Member air conditioning and heating contractors, manufacturers, vocational technical schools. Entries include: Company name, address, phone, fax, names and titles of key personnel, description of fields, and types of work performed. Arrangement: Geographical. Indexes: Alphabetical.

6067 ■ *Air Conditioning, Heating & Refrigeration News—Directory Issue*
BNP Media
2401 W Big Beaver Rd., Ste. 700
Troy, MI 48084-3333
Ph: (847)763-9534
Fax: (847)763-9538
E-mail: directories@bnpmedia.com
URL: http://www.achrnews.com

Annual, Latest edition 2011. Publication includes: Lists of about 2,086 manufacturers, 4,383 wholesalers and factory outlets, 1,667 HVACR products, exporters specializing in the industry; related trade organizations; manufacturers representatives, consultants, services; videos and software.

6068 ■ *ENR—Top 400 Construction Contractors Issue*
McGraw-Hill Inc.
PO Box 182604
Columbus, OH 43218
Ph: (614)430-4000
Fax: (614)759-3749
Fr: 877-833-5524
URL: http://enr.construction.com/toplists/Contractors/001-100.asp

Annual, Latest edition 2011. $35.00 for individuals. Publication includes: List of 400 United States contractors receiving largest dollar volume of contracts in preceding calendar year. Separate lists of 50 largest design/construct management firms; 50 largest program and construction managers; 25 building contractors; 25 heavy contractors.

6069 ■ *Michigan Plumbing and Mechanical Contractors Association—Membership Directory*
Michigan Plumbing and Mechanical Contractors Association
400 N Walnut St.
Lansing, MI 48933
Ph: (517)484-5500

Fax: (517)484-5225
E-mail: info@mpmca.org
URL: http://www.mpmca.org

Annual, Latest edition 2010. Covers: Member firms, industry and auxiliary associations, legislative and regulatory agencies in the plumbing and heating industry of Michigan. Entries include: Organization name, address, phone, names and titles of key personnel. Arrangement: Separate sections for members, industry associations, legislative and regulatory, and auxiliaries; members are geographical. Indexes: Company name (members), president name (members).

6070 ■ *North American Heating, Refrigeration & Airconditioning Wholesaler Association—Membership Directory*
Heating, Airconditioning, & Refrigeration Distributors International (HARDI)
3455 Mill Run Dr., Ste. 820
Columbus, OH 43026
Ph: (614)345-4328
Fax: (614)345-9161
Fr: 888-253-2128
URL: http://www.hardinet.org/aws/HARDI/pt/sp/directory

Annual, spring. Covers: about 2,000 wholesalers and distributors. Entries include: Company name, address, phone and names of executives. Arrangement: Alphabetical.

Employment Agencies and Search Firms

6071 ■ Magna Search
7946 Sunburst Terr.
Lake Worth, FL 33467
Ph: (561)967-3211
Fax: (561)967-3369
E-mail: magnas@i-2000.com
URL: http://www.magnasearch.com

Serves as an executive search and recruiting firm specializing in the HVAC, controls, and energy management industries nationwide.

Online Job Sources and Services

6072 ■ ConstructionJobs.com
URL: http://www.constructionjobs.com/index_eng.cfm

Description: Serves as an employment job board and resume database built exclusively for the construction, design, and building industries. Provides targeted candidate searches by geographic region, specific industries, job titles, education, and experience.

6073 ■ Great Green Careers
URL: http://www.greatgreencareers.com

Description: Serves as online resource that connects employers and job seekers in the green jobs industries.

6074 ■ HVAC-Industry.com
URL: http://www.hvac-industry.com

Description: Provides job opportunities and products to the heating ventilation and air conditioning industry.

Tradeshows

6075 ■ AHR Expo - International Air-Conditioning, Heating, Refrigerating Exposition
International Exposition Co., Inc.
15 Franklin St.
Westport, CT 06880
Ph: (203)221-9232

Fax: (203)221-9260
E-mail: info@chemshow.com
URL: http://www.chemshow.com

Annual. Primary Exhibits: Industrial, commercial, and residential heating, refrigeration, air conditioning, and ventilation equipment and components. Dates and Locations: 2012 Jan 23-25; Chicago, IL; McCormick Place North & South; 2013 Jan 28-30; Dallas, TX; 2014 Jan 21-23; New York, NY ; 2015 Jan 26-28; Chicago, IL; 2016 Jan 25-27; Orlando, FL.

6076 ■ Massachusetts Association of Plumbing/Heating/Cooling Contractors Convention and Tradeshow
Massachusetts Association of Plumbing/Heating/Cooling Contractors
400 Washington St., Ste. 401
Braintree, MA 02184-4767
Ph: (781)843-3800
Fax: (781)843-1178
Fr: 800-542-7422
E-mail: phcc.ma@verizon.net
URL: http://www.phccma.org

Annual. Primary Exhibits: Plumbing, heating and cooling equipment, supplies, and services. Dates and Locations: 2012 Mar 10.

6077 ■ North American Heating and Air Conditioning Wholesalers Association
North American Heating and Air Conditioning Wholesalers Association
1389 Dublin Rd.
Columbus, OH 43215-1084
Ph: (614)488-1835
Fax: (614)488-0482
Fr: 888-253-2128
E-mail: HARDImail@HARDInet.org

Annual. Primary Exhibits: Heating and air conditioning equipment, supplies, and services.

6078 ■ Plumbing-Heating-Cooling Contractors Association Annual Convention
Plumbing-Heating-Cooling Contractors Association
PO Box 6808
Falls Church, VA 22046
Ph: (703)237-8100
Fax: (703)237-7442
Fr: 800-533-7694
E-mail: naphcc@naphcc.org
URL: http://www.phccweb.org

Annual. Primary Exhibits: Exhibits relating to plumbing and heating.

6079 ■ Refrigeration Service Engineers Society Educational Conference
Refrigeration Service Engineers Society
1666 Rand Rd.
Des Plaines, IL 60016
Ph: (847)297-6464
Fax: (847)297-5038
Fr: 800-297-5660
URL: http://www.rses.org

Annual. Primary Exhibits: Equipment, supplies, and services for refrigeration, air-conditioning and heating installation, service, sales, and maintenance.

Other Sources

6080 ■ Air Conditioning Contractors of America (ACCA)
2800 Shirlington Rd., Ste. 300
Arlington, VA 22206
Ph: (703)575-4477
Fax: (703)575-4449
E-mail: info@acca.org
URL: http://www.acca.org

Description: Contractors involved in installation and service of heating, air conditioning, and refrigeration systems. Associate members are utilities, manufacturers, wholesalers, and other market-oriented businesses. Monitors utility competition and operat-

ing practices of HVAC manufacturers and wholesalers. Provides consulting services, technical training, and instructor certification program; offers management seminars. Operates annual educational institute.

6081 ■ Associated Builders and Contractors (ABC)
4250 N Fairfax Dr., 9th Fl.
Arlington, VA 22203-1607
Ph: (703)812-2000
Fax: (703)812-8201
E-mail: gotquestions@abc.org
URL: http://www.abc.org

Description: Construction contractors, subcontractors, suppliers and associates. Aims to foster and perpetuate the principles of rewarding construction workers and management on the basis of merit. Sponsors management education programs and craft training; also sponsors apprenticeship and skill training programs. Disseminates technological and labor relations information.

6082 ■ Associated Specialty Contractors (ASC)
3 Bethesda Metro Ctr., Ste. 1100
Bethesda, MD 20814
E-mail: dgw@necanet.org
URL: http://www.assoc-spec-con.org

Description: Works to promote efficient management and productivity. Coordinates the work of specialized branches of the industry in management information, research, public information, government relations and construction relations. Serves as a liaison among specialty trade associations in the areas of public relations, government relations, and with other organizations. Seeks to avoid unnecessary duplication of effort and expense or conflicting programs among affiliates. Identifies areas of interest and problems shared by members, and develops positions and approaches on such problems.

6083 ■ Mechanical Contractors Association of America (MCAA)
1385 Piccard Dr.
Rockville, MD 20850-4340
Ph: (301)869-5800
Fax: (301)990-9690
E-mail: mcaainfo@mcaa.org
URL: http://www.mcaa.org

Description: Represents firms involved in heating, air conditioning, refrigeration, plumbing, piping, and mechanical service. Provides educational materials and programs to help members attain the highest level of managerial and technical expertise.

6084 ■ National Association of Home Builders (NAHB)
1201 15th St. NW
Washington, DC 20005
Ph: (202)266-8200
Fax: (202)266-8400
Fr: 800-368-5242
E-mail: jhoward@nahb.com
URL: http://www.nahb.org

Description: Single and multifamily home builders, commercial builders, and others associated with the building industry. Lobbies on behalf of the housing industry and conducts public affairs activities to increase public understanding of housing and the economy. Collects and disseminates data on current developments in home building and home builders' plans through its Economics Department and nationwide Metropolitan Housing Forecast. Maintains NAHB Research Center, which functions as the research arm of the home building industry. Sponsors seminars and workshops on construction, mortgage credit, labor relations, cost reduction, land use, remodeling, and business management. Compiles statistics; offers charitable program, spokesman training, and placement service; maintains speakers' bureau, and Hall of Fame. Subsidiaries include the National Council of the Housing Industry. Maintains over 50 committees in many areas of construction; operates

National Commercial Builders Council, National Council of the Multifamily Housing Industry, National Remodelers Council, and National Sales and Marketing Council.

6085 ■ National Association of Women in Construction (NAWIC)
327 S Adams St.
Fort Worth, TX 76104
Ph: (817)877-5551
Fax: (817)877-0324
Fr: 800-552-3506
E-mail: nawic@nawic.org
URL: http://www.nawic.org

Description: Seeks to enhance the success of women in the construction industry.

6086 ■ Plumbing-Heating-Cooling Contractors Association (PHCC)
PO Box 6808
Falls Church, VA 22046
Ph: (703)237-8100
Fax: (703)237-7442
Fr: 800-533-7694
E-mail: naphcc@naphcc.org
URL: http://www.phccweb.org

Description: Federation of state and local associations of plumbing, heating, and cooling contractors. Seeks to advance sanitation, encourage sanitary laws, and generally improve the plumbing, heating, ventilating, and air conditioning industries. Conducts apprenticeship training programs, workshops, seminars, political action committee, educational and research programs.

6087 ■ Refrigeration Service Engineers Society (RSES)
1666 Rand Rd.
Des Plaines, IL 60016-3552
Ph: (847)297-6464
Fr: 800-297-5660
E-mail: bruceirma@aol.com
URL: http://www.rses.org

Description: Persons engaged in refrigeration, air-conditioning and heating installation, service, sales and maintenance. Conducts training courses and certification testing. Maintains a hall of fame and a speakers' bureau.

Sources of Help-Wanted Ads

6088 ■ *American Nineteenth Century History*
Routledge Journals
270 Madison Ave.
New York, NY 10016-0601
Ph: (212)216-7800
Fax: (212)563-2269
URL: http://www.tandf.co.uk/journals/titles/
14664658.asp

$396.00/year for institutions, print + online; $356.00/year for institutions, online only; $116.00/year for individuals, print only. Peer-reviewed journal covering topics of the history of the United States during the nineteenth century.

6089 ■ *American Studies Association Newsletter*
American Studies Association
1120 19th St. NW, Ste. 301
Washington, DC 20036
Ph: (202)467-4783
Fax: (202)467-4786
E-mail: asastaff@theasa.net
URL: http://www.theasa.net/

Description: Quarterly. Has a circulation of approximately 6,000. Promotes the interdisciplinary study of American culture. Presents news of research, publications, and conferences. Also includes information on grants, employment opportunities, and Association activities.

6090 ■ *Annotation*
National Historical Publications and Records Commission
700 Pennsylvania Ave. NW, Rm. 106
Washington, DC 20408-0001
Ph: (202)357-5010
Fax: (202)357-5914
E-mail: nhprc@nara.gov
URL: http://www.archives.gov/nhprc/annotation

Description: Quarterly. Contains information of interest to National Historical Publications and Records Commission members. Recurring features include columns titled From the Editor, and The Executive Director's Column.

6091 ■ *Classical Antiquity*
University of California Press/Journals
2120 Berkeley Way
Berkeley, CA 94704-1012
Ph: (510)642-4247
Fax: (510)643-7127
URL: http://www.ucpressjournals.com/
journal.asp?j=ca

Semiannual. $52.00/year for individuals, print only; $201.00/year for institutions, print & electronic; $28.00/year for students, print only; $161.00/year for institutions, electronic only; $27.00/year for single issue, individual/student/retired; $109.00/year for single issue, institutions. Peer-reviewed scholarly journal

covering interdisciplinary research and issues in Classics-Greek and Roman literature, history, art, philosophy, archaeology, and philology.

6092 ■ *Common-place*
American Antiquarian Society
185 Salisbury St.
Worcester, MA 01609-1634
Ph: (508)755-5221
Fax: (508)753-3311
URL: http://www.common-place.org/

Quarterly. Journal on early American history and culture.

6093 ■ *Dispatch*
American Association for State & Local History
1717 Church St.
Nashville, TN 37203-2991
Ph: (615)320-3203
Fax: (615)327-9013
E-mail: membership@aaslh.org
URL: http://www.aaslh.org/pdispatch.htm

Description: Monthly. Offers general information about state and local historical societies and the study of state and local history in the U.S. and Canada. Informs members of new training programs, seminars, and exhibits in the field. Recurring features include information on grant opportunities, updates on legislation, Association activities, and historical society personnel, interviews, job listings, and notices of publications available.

6094 ■ *The Historian*
John Wiley & Sons Inc.
350 Main St., Commerce Pl.
Malden, MA 02148-5089
Ph: (781)388-8200
Fax: (781)388-8210
E-mail: historian@cas.usf.edu
URL: http://www.wiley.com/bw/journal.asp?ref=0018-2370&site=1

Quarterly. $52.00/year for individuals, print & online; $202.00/year for institutions, print & online; $175.00/year for institutions, U.S. print or online; $46.00/year for individuals, print & online; $68.00/year for individuals, print & online; $170.00/year for institutions, other countries, print & online; $147.00/year for institutions, other countries, print or online. Journal focusing on contemporary and relevant historical scholarship.

6095 ■ *History News*
American Association for State and Local History
1717 Church St.
Nashville, TN 37203-2991
Ph: (615)320-3203
Fax: (615)327-9013
URL: http://www.aaslh.org/historynews.htm

Quarterly. Magazine for employees of historic sites, museums, and public history agencies. Coverage includes museum education programs and techniques for working with volunteers.

6096 ■ *Journal of the American Institute for Conservation*
American Institute for Conservation of Historic & Artistic Works
1156 15th St. NW, Ste. 320
Washington, DC 20005-1714
Ph: (202)452-9545
Fax: (202)452-9328
URL: http://cool.conservation-us.org/coolaic/jaic

$100.00/year for U.S.; $130.00/year for other countries. Peer-reviewed journal covering field of conservation and preservation of historic and cultural works.

6097 ■ *Journal of America's Military Past*
Council on America's Military Past
PO Box 4209
Charlottesville, VA 22905
E-mail: nereyn@earthlink.net
URL: http://www.campjamp.org/The%20Journal.htm

Quarterly. Included in membership. Journal covering military history in the U.S., including famous battles, military personnel, and the bases where they served.

6098 ■ *Mid-Atlantic Archivist*
Mid-Atlantic Regional Archives Conference
PO Box 1773
Carlisle, PA 17013
Ph: (717)713-9973
Fax: (717)245-1439
E-mail: administrator@marac.info
URL: http://www.marac.info

Description: Quarterly. $35 per year. Contains news and information for and about members of the Conference. Seeks exchange of information between colleagues, improvement of competence among archivists, and encourages professional involvement of persons actively engaged in the preservation and use of historical research materials. Recurring features include letters to the editor, news of members, book reviews, a calendar of events, and columns titled Preservation News, Reference Shelf, Session Abstracts, Software News, and Employment Opportunities.

6099 ■ *The Minnesota History Interpreter*
Minnesota Historical Society
345 W Kellogg Blvd.
St. Paul, MN 55102-1906
Ph: (651)259-3000
Fax: (651)282-2374
Fr: 800-657-3773
URL: http://www.mnhs.org/about/publications/
interpreter.html

Description: Six issues/year. Promotes the preservation of Minnesota history. Explores statewide Historical Society activities, providing news of exhibits, programs, seminars, conferences, and research findings. Recurring features include news of meetings, Heritage Preservation Commission News, news of members, job listings, book reviews, individual/

organization profiles, and "how to" articles on topics such as museum work.

6100 ■ *Preservation*
National Trust for Historic Preservation
1785 Massachusetts Ave. NW
Washington, DC 20036-2117
Ph: (202)588-6000
Fax: (202)588-6038
Fr: 800-944-6847
URL: http://www.preservationnation.org/
Bimonthly. $20.00/year for members, individual; $30.00/year for members, family; $50.00/year for members, contributing; $100.00/year for members, sustaining; $250.00/year for members, preservation council steward; $1,000.00/year for members, preservation council heritage society. Magazine featuring historic preservation.

6101 ■ *Presidential Studies Quarterly*
John Wiley & Sons Inc.
350 Main St., Commerce Pl.
Malden, MA 02148-5089
Ph: (781)388-8200
Fax: (781)388-8210
URL: http://www.wiley.com/bw/journal.asp?ref=0360-4918&site=1
Quarterly. $466.00/year for institutions, print & online; $405.00/year for institutions, print, online; $302.00/year for institutions, other countries, print & online; $262.00/year for institutions, other countries, print, online. Publication covering political science and history.

6102 ■ *Southern Association for Women Historians Newsletter*
Southern Association for Women Historians
c/o Shannon Frystak
Dept. of History
409 Stroud Hall
East Stroudsburg University of Pennsylvania
East Stroudsburg, PA 18301-2999
E-mail: h-sawh-request@h-net.msu.edu
URL: http://www.h-net.org/~sawh
Description: Three issues/year. Informs members of the Association's activities aimed at advancing the professional development of women historians and historians of women. Carries minutes of the annual meeting, announcements of awards and prizes available for work published in a variety of areas, and calls for papers at various conferences. Recurring features include notices of publications available, job listings, and member updates.

6103 ■ *The Southwestern Archivist*
Society of Southwest Archivists
PO Box 301311
Austin, TX 78703-0022
URL: http://southwestarchivists.org
Description: Quarterly. Supports the aims of the Society, which include: "to provide a means for effective cooperation among people concerned with the documentation of human experience," and "to promote the adoption of sound principles and standards for the preservation and administration of records." Recurring features include news of research, news of members, and a calendar of events.

6104 ■ *White House Studies*
Nova Science Publishers Inc.
400 Oser Ave., Ste. 1600
Hauppauge, NY 11788-3667
Ph: (631)231-7269
Fax: (631)231-8175
URL: http://www.novapublishers.com/catalog/product_info.php?cPath
Quarterly. $400.00/year for individuals. Publication covering political science and history.

6105 ■ *World History Connected*
University of Illinois Press
1325 S Oak St.
Champaign, IL 61820-6903
Ph: (217)333-0950
Fax: (217)244-8082
E-mail: worldhistoryconnected@wsu.edu
URL: http://worldhistoryconnected.press.uiuc.edu
Journal covering a variety of global history topics for teachers and students.

EMPLOYER DIRECTORIES AND NETWORKING LISTS

6106 ■ *Discovering Careers for Your Future—History*
Facts On File Inc.
132 W 31st St., 17th Fl.
New York, NY 10001
Ph: (212)967-8800
Fax: 800-678-3633
Fr: 800-322-8755
URL: http://factsonfile.infobasepublishing.com
$21.95 for individuals; $19.75 for libraries. Covers: Archeologists, genealogists, historians, museum curators, and sociologists; links career education to curriculum, helping children investigate the subjects they are interested in, and the careers those subjects might lead to.

6107 ■ *Grants, Fellowships, and Prizes of Interest to Historians*
American Historical Association
400 A St. SE
Washington, DC 20003-3889
Ph: (202)544-2422
Fax: (202)544-8307
E-mail: grantguide@theaha.org
URL: http://www.historians.org
Annual, latest edition 2006. for members. Covers: Over 450 sources of funding (scholarships, fellowships, internships, awards, and book and essay prizes) in the United States and abroad for graduate students, postdoctoral researchers, and institutions in the humanities. Entries include: Name of source, institution name or contact, address, phone, eligibility and proposal requirements, award or stipend amount, location requirements for research, application deadlines. Arrangement: Alphabetical in three categories: support for individual research and teaching; grants for groups and organizations for research and education; and book, article, essay, and manuscript prizes.

6108 ■ *Newsletter—Society for Historical Archaeology Membership Directory Issue*
Society for Historical Archaeology
9707 Key West Ave., Ste. 100
Rockville, MD 20850
Ph: (301)990-2454
Fax: (301)990-9771
URL: http://www.sha.org
Quarterly, Latest edition 2011. Publication includes: List of about 2,100 member archaeologists, historians, anthropologists, and ethnohistorians, and other individuals and institutions having an interest in historical archeology or allied fields. Entries include: Name, address. Arrangement: Alphabetical.

6109 ■ *Top Careers for History Graduates*
Facts On File Inc.
132 W 31st St., 17th Fl.
New York, NY 10001
Ph: (212)967-8800
Fax: 800-678-3633
Fr: 800-322-8755
URL: http://factsonfile.infobasepublishing.com
Published 2004. $14.95 for individuals. Covers: The information needed to transform a history degree into a satisfying job, exploring everything from reasons to major in history to what types of jobs are available and how much they pay.

HANDBOOKS AND MANUALS

6110 ■ *Careers for History Buffs & Others Who Learn from the Past*
The McGraw-Hill Companies
PO Box 182604
Columbus, OH 43272
Fax: (614)759-3749
Fr: 877-883-5524
E-mail: customer.service@mcgraw-hill.com
URL: http://www.mhprofessional.com
Blythe Camenson. Third edition, 2008. $14.95 (paper). 176 pages.

6111 ■ *Great Jobs for History Majors*
The McGraw-Hill Companies
PO Box 182604
Columbus, OH 43272
Fax: (614)759-3749
Fr: 877-883-5524
E-mail: customer.service@mcgraw-hill.com
URL: http://www.mhprofessional.com
Julie DeGalan and Stephen Lambert. 2007. $16.95 (paper). 192 pages.

6112 ■ *Opportunities in Social Science Careers*
The McGraw-Hill Companies
PO Box 182604
Columbus, OH 43272
Fax: (614)759-3749
Fr: 877-883-5524
E-mail: customer.service@mcgraw-hill.com
URL: http://www.mcgraw-hill.com
Rosanne J. Marek. 2004. $13.95. 160 Pages. VGM Opportunities Series.

ONLINE JOB SOURCES AND SERVICES

6113 ■ *eCulturalResources*
URL: http://www.eculturalresources.com
Description: Provides sources of news, jobs, announcements, consultant listings, and resources for the cultural resource industry.

6114 ■ *HistorianJobs.org*
URL: http://historianjobs.org
Description: Features historian jobs and employment opportunities across the country. Allows users to search for jobs in specific areas/regions.

TRADESHOWS

6115 ■ *American Association for State and Local History Annual Meeting*
American Association for State and Local History
1717 Church St.
Nashville, TN 37203-2991
Ph: (615)320-3203
Fax: (615)327-9013
E-mail: membership@aaslh.org
URL: http://www.aaslh.org
Annual. Primary Exhibits: Products and services directed toward the museum and history field, including: publications, fund-raising devices, software, exhibit design, historic preservation, historic research and technical information.

6116 ■ *American Historical Association Annual Meeting*
American Historical Association
400 A St. S.E.
Washington, DC 20003-3889
Ph: (202)544-2422
Fax: (202)544-8307
E-mail: info@historians.org
URL: http://www.historians.org
Annual. Primary Exhibits: Books and journals from

commercial publishers and university presses. Dates and Locations: 2013 Jan 03-06; New Orleans, LA.

6117 ■ American Society for Ethnohistory Conference
American Society for Ethnohistory
c/o R. David Edmunds, Pres.
University of Texas at Dallas
2601 N Floyd Rd.
Richardson, TX 75080
URL: http://ethnohistory.org

Annual. Primary Exhibits: Exhibits relating to the cultural history of ethnic groups worldwide.

6118 ■ Congress of the International Society for Human Ethology
International Society for Human Ethology
PO Box 418
Nyack, NY 10960
Ph: (207)581-2044
Fax: (207)581-6128
URL: http://www.ishe.org

Biennial. Primary Exhibits: Books, journals, and equipment for observational research. Dates and Locations: 2012 Aug 13-17; Vienna, Austria; University of Vienna.

6119 ■ Oral History Association Conference
Oral History Association
Dickinson College
PO Box 1773
Carlisle, PA 17013
Ph: (717)245-1036
Fax: (717)245-1046
E-mail: oha@dickinson.edu
URL: http://www.oralhistory.org

Annual. Primary Exhibits: Equipment, supplies, and services related to recording, transcribing, and preserving conversations constituting oral history.

6120 ■ Organization of American Historians Annual Meeting
Organization of American Historians
112 N. Bryan Ave.
PO Box 5457
Bloomington, IN 47408-5457
Ph: (812)855-7311
Fax: (812)855-0696
E-mail: help@oah.org
URL: http://www.oah.org

Annual. Primary Exhibits: Equipment, supplies, and services of interest to historians, including textbooks and computer software. Dates and Locations: 2012 Apr 19-22; Milwaukee, WI.

6121 ■ Society of Architectural Historians Annual Meeting
Society of Architectural Historians
1365 N Astor St.
Chicago, IL 60610-2144
Ph: (312)573-1365
Fax: (312)573-1141
E-mail: info@sah.org
URL: http://sah.org

Annual. Features a preservation colloquium, workshops for historians, roundtable discussions, reunions, evening lectures and receptions, and an extensive array of local and regional tours.

6122 ■ Southern Historical Association Meeting
Southern Historical Association
220 LeConte Hall
Athens, GA 30602-1602
Ph: (706)542-2053
Fax: (706)542-2455
E-mail: osfa@uga.edu
URL: http://www.uga.edu

Annual. Primary Exhibits: Publications.

OTHER SOURCES

6123 ■ African Studies Association (ASA)
Rutgers University, Livingston Campus
54 Joyce Kilmer Ave.
Piscataway, NJ 08854-8045
Ph: (848)445-8173
Fax: (732)445-1366
E-mail: karen.jenkins@africanstudies.org
URL: http://www.africanstudies.org

Description: Persons specializing in teaching, writing, or research on Africa including political scientists, historians, geographers, anthropologists, economists, librarians, linguists, and government officials; persons who are studying African subjects; institutional members are universities, libraries, government agencies, and others interested in receiving information about Africa. Seeks to foster communication and to stimulate research among scholars on Africa. Sponsors placement service; conducts panels and discussion groups; presents exhibits and films.

6124 ■ American Association for State and Local History (AASLH)
1717 Church St.
Nashville, TN 37203-2921
Ph: (615)320-3203
Fax: (615)327-9013
E-mail: membership@aaslh.org
URL: http://www.aaslh.org

Description: Works to preserve and promote history. Ensures the highest-quality expressions of state and local history in publications, exhibitions, and public programs through its diverse services. Represents more than 6,200 individual and institutional members.

6125 ■ American Catholic Historical Association (ACHA)
Catholic University of America
Mullen Library, Rm. 320
Washington, DC 20064
Ph: (202)319-5079
Fax: (202)319-5079
E-mail: acha@achahistory.org
URL: http://research.cua.edu/acha

Description: Professional society of historians, educators, students, and others interested in the history of the Catholic Church in the United States and abroad and in the promotion of historical scholarship among Catholics. Has sponsored the publication of the papers of John Carroll, first Bishop and Archbishop of Baltimore, MD.

6126 ■ American Historical Association (AHA)
400 A St. SE
Washington, DC 20003-3889
Ph: (202)544-2422
Fax: (202)544-8307
E-mail: info@historians.org
URL: http://www.historians.org

Description: Professional historians, educators, and others interested in promoting historical studies and collecting and preserving historical manuscripts. Conducts research and educational programs.

6127 ■ American Institute for Conservation of Historic and Artistic Works (AIC)
1156 15th St., Ste. 320
Washington, DC 20005-1714
Ph: (202)452-9545
Fax: (202)452-9328
E-mail: info@conservation-us.org
URL: http://www.conservation-us.org

Description: Professionals, scientists, administrators, and educators in the field of art conservation; interested individuals. Advances the practice and promotes the importance of the preservation of cultural property. Coordinates the exchange of knowledge, research, and publications. Establishes and upholds professional standards. Publishes conservation literature. Compiles statistics. Repre-

sents membership to allied professional associations and advocates on conservation-related issues. Solicits and dispenses money exclusively for charitable, scientific, and educational objectives.

6128 ■ American Society for Eighteenth-Century Studies (ASECS)
Wake Forest University
PO Box 7867
Winston-Salem, NC 27109
Ph: (336)727-4694
Fax: (336)727-4697
E-mail: asecs@wfu.edu
URL: http://asecs.press.jhu.edu

Description: Scholars and others interested in the cultural history of the 18th century. Encourages and advances study and research in this area; promotes the interchange of information and ideas among scholars from different disciplines (such as librarianship and bibliography) who are interested in the 18th century. Co-sponsors seven fellowship programs; sponsors Graduate Student Caucus.

6129 ■ Flag Research Center (FRC)
PO Box 580
Winchester, MA 01890-0880
Ph: (781)729-9410
Fax: (781)721-4817
E-mail: flags@flagresearchcenter.com
URL: http://www.FlagResearchCenter.com

Description: Professional and amateur vexillologists (flag historians) seeking to coordinate flag research activities and promote vexillology as a historical discipline and hobby and to increase knowledge of and appreciation for flags of all kinds. Provides data and gives lectures on flag history, etiquette, design, symbolism, and uses. Operates speakers' bureau; offers children's services and placement service; compiles statistics. Plans to establish museum.

6130 ■ International Studies Association (ISA)
University of Arizona
324 Social Sciences Bldg.
Tucson, AZ 85721
Ph: (520)621-7715
Fax: (520)621-5780
E-mail: isa@isanet.org
URL: http://www.isanet.org

Description: Social scientists and other scholars from a wide variety of disciplines who are specialists in international affairs and cross-cultural studies; academicians; government officials; officials in international organizations; business executives; students. Promotes research, improved teaching, and the orderly growth of knowledge in the field of international studies; emphasizes a multidisciplinary approach to problems. Conducts conventions, workshops and discussion groups.

6131 ■ National Coalition for History (NCH)
400 A St. SE
Washington, DC 20003
Ph: (202)544-2422
E-mail: lwhite@historycoalition.org
URL: http://historycoalition.org

Description: Archival and historical organizations such as: American Historical Association; Organization of American Historians; Phi Alpha Theta; Society of American Archivists; Western History Association. Serves as central advocacy office and information clearinghouse for history/archival related topics affecting government agencies, legislative aides, and professional history and archival associations; develops network of constituent contacts in districts and states; testifies before congressional committees; monitors employment opportunities.

6132 ■ National Council on Public History (NCPH)
327 Cavanaugh Hall - IUPUI
425 University Blvd.
Indianapolis, IN 46202
Ph: (317)274-2716

Fax: (317)278-5230
E-mail: ncph@iupui.edu
URL: http://www.ncph.org

Description: Aims to encourage a broader interest in professional history and to stimulate national interest in public history by promoting its use at all levels of society. (Public history deals with nonacademic history. History is brought to the public rather than the classroom through museum work, public displays, and federal, local, and corporate historians.) Serves as an information clearinghouse; sponsors training programs, local and regional colloquia, projects, and panels. Offers advice to departments of history, historical associations, and others seeking information on public history, professional standards, opportunities, and internships. Conducts surveys and analyses.

6133 ■ Natural History Network

PO Box 11363
Prescott, AZ 86304
Ph: (928)350-2219
E-mail: tfleischner@prescott.edu
URL: http://www.naturalhistorynetwork.org

Description: Promotes the importance of natural history and natural history education in the development of healthy people, vibrant human communities and integrated learning institutions. Facilitates the discussion and dissemination of ideas and techniques pertaining to natural history studies. Serves as a resource of information for the study, practice and teaching of natural history.

6134 ■ Organization of American Historians (OAH)

112 N Bryan Ave.
Bloomington, IN 47408-4141
Ph: (812)855-7311
Fax: (812)855-0696
E-mail: questions@oah.org
URL: http://www.oah.org

Description: Professional historians, including college faculty members, secondary school teachers, graduate students, and other individuals in related fields; institutional subscribers are college, university, high school and public libraries, and historical agencies. Promotes historical research and study. Sponsors 12 prize programs for historical writing; maintains speakers' bureau. Conducts educational programs.

6135 ■ Society of Architectural Historians

1365 N Astor St.
Chicago, IL 60610-2144
Ph: (312)573-1365
Fax: (312)573-1141
E-mail: info@sah.org
URL: http://sah.org

Description: Architectural historians, architects, preservationists, students, professionals in allied fields and the interested public. Advances the knowledge and understanding of the history of architecture, design, landscape and urbanism worldwide. Offers an on-site tours, lectures, discussions, and other events geared toward appreciation and understanding of architectural history.

6136 ■ United States Capitol Historical Society (USCHS)

200 Maryland Ave., Ste. 400 NE
Washington, DC 20002
Ph: (202)543-8919
Fax: (202)544-8244
Fr: 800-887-9318
E-mail: uschs@uschs.org
URL: http://www.uschs.org

Description: Preserves and communicates the history and heritage of the U.S. Capital, its institutions, and the individuals who have served in Congress. Activities include educational programs, popular and scholarly symposia and publications, enhancement of the Capitol's collection of art and artifacts, and research in the U.S. Capitol and the U.S. Congress.

SOURCES OF HELP-WANTED ADS

6137 ■ Addiction Professional
Vendome Group L.L.C.
6 E 32nd St.
New York, NY 10016
Ph: (212)812-8420
E-mail: addiction_professional@halldata.com
URL: http://www.addictionpro.com/ME2/default.asp

Bimonthly. $67.00/year for individuals. Magazine that publishes innovations and trends in the clinical care of persons with substance use and dependence disorders.

6138 ■ ADVANCE for Nurse Practitioners
Merion Publications Inc.
2900 Horizon Dr.
PO Box 61556
King of Prussia, PA 19406-0956
Ph: (610)278-1400
Fr: 800-355-5627
URL: http://nurse-practitioners-and-physician-assistants.advancew

Monthly. Free to qualified subscribers. For practicing nurse practitioner students with senior status.

6139 ■ American Dental Hygienists'
Association Access
American Dental Hygienists' Association
444 N Michigan Ave., Ste. 3400
Chicago, IL 60611
Ph: (312)440-8900
Fr: 800-243-ADHA
URL: http://www.adha.org/publications/index.html

$48.00/year for individuals; $85.00/year for two years; $120.00/year for individuals, for 3 years. Magazine covering current dental hygiene topics, regulatory and legislative developments, and association news.

6140 ■ American Journal of Nursing
American Journal of Nursing
c/o Lippincott, Williams & Wilkins
2 Commerce Sq., 2001 Market St.
Philadelphia, PA 19103
Ph: (215)521-8300
Fax: (215)521-8902
URL: http://www.nursingcenter.com

Monthly. $51.00/year for individuals; $425.00/year for institutions; $129.00/year for other countries; $465.00/year for institutions, other countries. Peer-reviewed journal promoting excellence in nursing and health care.

6141 ■ The American Nurse
American Nurses Association
8515 Georgia Ave., Ste. 400
Silver Spring, MD 20910
Ph: (301)628-5000
Fax: (301)628-5001

Fr: 800-274-4262
E-mail: adsales@ana.org
URL: http://nursingworld.org/tan/

Monthly. $20.00/year for individuals, practicing nurses; $10.00/year for students. Newspaper (tabloid) for the nursing profession.

6142 ■ Bountiful Health
JNE Publishing, Inc.
PO Box 5647
Huntsville, AL 35814
Ph: (256)837-3035
Fr: 800-313-7751
URL: http://www.jnepublishing.com/bountifulhealth.php?page=public

Magazine focusing on complementary and alternative medicine, exercise, vitamins and supplements, healthy eating, and green living.

6143 ■ Cancer Nursing
Lippincott Williams & Wilkins
530 Walnut St.
Philadelphia, PA 19106-3619
Ph: (215)521-8300
Fax: (215)521-8902
Fr: 800-638-3030
E-mail: editor@gator.net
URL: http://journals.lww.com/cancernursingonline/pages/default.as

Bimonthly. $109.99/year for individuals; $378.00/year for institutions; $63.99/year for individuals, in-training; $203.22/year for other countries; $518.22/year for institutions, other countries. Medical journal covering problems arising in the care and support of cancer patients.

6144 ■ Diversity
Career Recruitment Media
2 LAN Dr., Ste. 100
Westford, MA 01886
Ph: (978)692-5092
Fax: (978)692-4174
URL: http://www.diversityalliedhealth.com/

Magazine focus on multicultural career and educational development magazine for allied health students and professionals.

6145 ■ Environmental Pollution
Elsevier Science Inc.
360 Park Ave. S
New York, NY 10010-1710
Ph: (212)989-5800
Fax: (212)633-3990
Fr: 888-437-4636
E-mail: environmentalpollution@mindspring.com
URL: http://www.elsevier.com/wps/find/journaldescription.cws_home

Monthly. $5,698.00/year for institutions, other countries, for all countries except Europe, Japan and Iran; $162.00/year for other countries, for all countries except Europe, Japan and Iran; $5,091.00/year for institutions, European and Iran; $676,600.00/year for

institutions; $143.00/year for individuals, European and Iran; $18,700.00/year for individuals. Journal covering issues relevant to chemical pollutants in air, soil and water.

6146 ■ Ethnicity and Health
Routledge Journals
270 Madison Ave.
New York, NY 10016-0601
Ph: (212)216-7800
Fax: (212)563-2269
URL: http://www.tandf.co.uk/journals/titles/13557858.asp

Bimonthly. $1,127.00/year for institutions, print + online; $1,014.00/year for institutions, online only; $390.00/year for individuals, print only. Journal covering ethnicity and health.

6147 ■ Geriatric Nursing
Mosby Inc.
10801 Executive Center Dr., Ste. 509
Little Rock, AR 72211
Ph: (501)223-5165
Fax: (501)223-0519
URL: http://journals.elsevierhealth.com/periodicals/ymgn

Bimonthly. $80.00/year for individuals; $141.00/year for individuals, Canada; $141.00/year for individuals, Mexico; $141.00/year for individuals, international. Magazine for nurses in geriatric and gerontologic nursing practice, the primary professional providers of care for the aging. Provides news on issues affecting elders and clinical information on techniques and procedures.

6148 ■ Health & Place
Mosby Inc.
11830 Westline Industrial Dr.
St. Louis, MO 63146-3326
Ph: (314)872-8370
Fax: (314)432-1380
Fr: 800-325-4177
URL: http://www.elsevier.com/wps/find/journaldescription.cws_home

$806.00/year for institutions, all countries except Europe, Japan and Iran; $142.00/year for individuals, all countries except Europe, Japan and Iran. Journal publishing articles for health care professionals.

6149 ■ Health Policy, Economics and
Management
Elsevier Science Inc.
360 Park Ave. S
New York, NY 10010-1710
Ph: (212)989-5800
Fax: (212)633-3990
Fr: 888-437-4636
URL: http://www.elsevier.com/wps/find/journaldescription.cws_home

$441.00/year for individuals, for all countries except Europe, Japan and Iran; $441.00/year for individuals, European countries and Iran; $58,100.00/year for individuals, Japan; $447,400.00/year for institutions, Japan; $3,726.00/year for institutions, other countries; $3,359.00/year for institutions, European countries and Iran. Journal covering the economic, social and political aspects of health care and its organization includes hospital management, health care marketing, hospital automation, and the assessment of new technology for the health care industry.

6150 ■ Home Healthcare Nurse
Lippincott Williams & Wilkins
530 Walnut St.
Philadelphia, PA 19106-3619
Ph: (215)521-8300
Fax: (215)521-8902
Fr: 800-638-3030
URL: http://journals.lww.com/
homehealthcarenurseonline/pages/defa

$62.14/year for individuals; $324.00/year for institutions; $156.11/year for other countries; $481.11/year for institutions, other countries; $40.99/year for individuals, in-training. Magazine for the practicing professional nurse working in the home health, community health, and public health areas.

6151 ■ HomeCare Magazine
Penton Media
249 W 17th St.
New York, NY 10011-5390
Ph: (212)204-4200
URL: http://homecaremag.com/

Monthly. Free, in US; $135.00/year for Canada; $150.00/year for two years, Canada; $250.00/year for other countries; $250.00/year for two years, other countries. Magazine serving home medical equipment suppliers, including independent and chain centers specializing in home care, pharmacies or chain drug stores with home care products, and joint-ventured hospital home health care businesses. Contains industry news and new product launches and marketing strategies.

6152 ■ Hospitals & Health Networks
Health Forum L.L.C.
155 N Wacker Dr., Ste. 400
Chicago, IL 60606
Ph: (312)893-6800
Fax: (312)422-4500
Fr: 800-821-2039
URL: http://www.hhnmag.com

Weekly. Free. Publication covering the health care industry.

6153 ■ The IHS Primary Care Provider
Indian Health Service
The Reyes Bldg.
801 Thompson Ave., Ste. 400
Rockville, MD 20852-1627
Ph: (301)443-1011
URL: http://www.ihs.gov/provider

Monthly. Journal for health care professionals, physicians, nurses, pharmacists, dentists, and dietitians.

6154 ■ The International Electronic Journal of Health Education
American Alliance for Health, Physical Education, Recreation & Dance
1900 Association Dr.
Reston, VA 20191-1598
Ph: (703)476-3400
Fax: (703)476-9527
Fr: 800-213-7193
URL: http://www.aahperd.org/aahe/publications/iejhe/

Annual. Free, health education professionals and students. Journal promoting health through education and other systematic strategies.

6155 ■ JONA's Healthcare Law, Ethics, and Regulation
Lippincott Williams & Wilkins
351 W Camden St.
Baltimore, MD 21201
Ph: (410)528-4000

Fr: 800-638-3030
URL: http://journals.lww.com/jonalaw/pages/default.aspx

Quarterly. $62.99/year for individuals; $100.01/year for institutions; $36.16/year for individuals, in-training; $114.60/year for other countries; $171.57/year for institutions, other countries. Peer-reviewed journal covering the legal, ethical and regulatory issues facing nursing care management.

6156 ■ Journal of the American College of Nutrition
American College of Nutrition
300 S Duncan Ave., Ste. 225
Clearwater, FL 33755
Ph: (727)446-6086
Fax: (727)446-6202
URL: http://www.jacn.org

Bimonthly. $45.00/year for members; $85.00/year for other countries, members; $90.00/year for nonmembers; $130.00/year for other countries; $235.00/year for institutions; $275.00/year for institutions, other countries. Journal on nutrition.

6157 ■ Journal of the American Society of Podiatric Medical Assistants
American Society of Podiatric Medical Assistants
1616 N 78th Ct.
Elmwood Park, IL 60707
Fr: 888-882-7762
URL: http://www.aspma.org

Quarterly. Included in membership. Professional journal covering issues in podiatry.

6158 ■ Journal of Clinical Ethics
University Publishing Group Inc.
219 W Washington St.
Hagerstown, MD 21740
Ph: (240)420-0036
Fax: (240)420-0037
Fr: 800-654-8188
URL: http://www.organizationalethics.com

Semiannual. $175.00/year for institutions; $160.00/year for individuals, online; $200.00/year for individuals, print and online. Magazine covering business and healthcare policy.

6159 ■ Journal of Gerontological Nursing
SLACK Incorporated
6900 Grove Rd.
Thorofare, NJ 08086-9447
Ph: (856)848-1000
Fax: (856)848-6091
E-mail: jgn@slackinc.com
URL: http://www.slackjournals.com/jgn

Monthly. $95.00/year for individuals; $190.00/year for two years; $315.00/year for institutions; $630.00/year for institutions, two years; $29.00/year for single issue. Gerontological nursing journal.

6160 ■ Journal of Health and Life Sciences Law
American Health Lawyers Association
1620 Eye St. NW, 6th Fl.
Washington, DC 20006-4010
Ph: (202)833-1100
Fax: (202)833-1105
URL: http://www.healthlawyers.org

Quarterly. $149.00/year for individuals. Professional journal covering healthcare issues and cases and their impact on the health care arena.

6161 ■ Journal of Nursing Care Quality
Lippincott Williams & Wilkins
351 W Camden St.
Baltimore, MD 21201
Ph: (410)528-4000
Fr: 800-638-3030
URL: http://journals.lww.com/jncqjournal/pages/default.aspx

Quarterly. $104.99/year for individuals; $356.00/year for institutions; $74.49/year for individuals, in-training; $199.73/year for other countries; $496.73/year for

institutions, other countries. Peer-reviewed journal providing practicing nurses and those who play leadership roles in nursing care quality programs the latest on the utilization of quality principles and concepts in the practice setting.

6162 ■ Journal of Nursing Scholarship
John Wiley & Sons Inc.
350 Main St., Commerce Pl.
Malden, MA 02148-5089
Ph: (781)388-8200
Fax: (781)388-8210
URL: http://www.wiley.com/bw/journal.asp?ref=1527-6546&site=1

Quarterly. $63.00/year for individuals, print & online; $263.00/year for institutions, print & online; $228.00/year for institutions, print, online; $73.00/year for individuals, print & online; $191.00/year for institutions, other countries, print & online; $243.00/year for institutions, print & online; $49.00/year for individuals, print & online. Peer-reviewed journal covering nursing.

6163 ■ McKnight's Long-Term Care News
McKnight's Long-Term Care News
1 Northfield Plz., Ste. 521
Northfield, IL 60093-1216
Ph: (847)784-8706
Fax: (847)784-9346
Fr: 800-558-1703
URL: http://www.mcknightsonline.com/home

$60.00/year for individuals; $108.00/year for two years; $75.00/year for Canada; $135.00/year for Canada, two years; $75.00/year for other countries; $135.00/year for other countries, two years. Professional magazine.

6164 ■ Medical Care
Lippincott Williams & Wilkins
351 W Camden St.
Baltimore, MD 21201
Ph: (410)528-4000
Fr: 800-638-3030
E-mail: medicalcare@comcast.net
URL: http://journals.lww.com/lww-medicalcare/pages/default.aspx

Monthly. $493.00/year for individuals; $1,102.00/year for institutions; $240.00/year for individuals, in-training; $645.50/year for other countries; $1,327.50/year for institutions, other countries; $256.50/year for other countries, in-training. Peer-reviewed journal focusing on all aspects of the administration and delivery of healthcare.

6165 ■ Modern Healthcare
Crain Communications Inc.
360 N Michigan Ave.
Chicago, IL 60601
Ph: (312)649-5200
E-mail: subs@crain.com
URL: http://www.modernhealthcare.com

Weekly. $164.00/year for individuals; $255.00/year for Canada; $218.00/year for other countries. Weekly business news magazine for healthcare management.

6166 ■ Nursing Administration Quarterly
Lippincott Williams & Wilkins
351 W Camden St.
Baltimore, MD 21201
Ph: (410)528-4000
Fr: 800-638-3030
URL: http://www.lww.com/product/?0363-9568

Quarterly. $119.49/year for individuals; $394.00/year for institutions; $74.49/year for individuals, in-training; $208.73/year for other countries; $541.73/year for institutions, other countries. Peer-reviewed journal providing nursing administrators with information on the effective management of nursing services in all health care settings.

6167 ■ Nursing Outlook
Mosby Inc.
10801 Executive Center Dr., Ste. 509
Little Rock, AR 72211
Ph: (501)223-5165
Fax: (501)223-0519
URL: http://journals.elsevierhealth.com/periodicals/ymno

Bimonthly. $133.00/year for Canada; $84.00/year for individuals; $133.00/year for individuals, Mexico; $133.00/year for other countries. Official journal of the American Academy of Nursing, reporting on trends and issues in nursing.

6168 ■ Nutrition Business Journal
Penton Media Inc.
249 W 17th St.
New York, NY 10011
Ph: (212)204-4200
E-mail: info@nutritionbusiness.com
URL: http://www.nutritionbusiness.com/

Monthly. Journal catering to nutrition, natural products and alternative health care industries. Publishes information regarding business activities, market size/growth, trends, and opportunities, with a particular emphasis on the nutrition industry.

6169 ■ Patient Education and Counseling
Mosby Inc.
11830 Westline Industrial Dr.
St. Louis, MO 63146-3326
Ph: (314)872-8370
Fax: (314)432-1380
Fr: 800-325-4177
URL: http://www.elsevier.com/wps/find/journaldescription.cws_home

Monthly. $284.00/year for individuals, all countries except Europe, Japan and Iran; $2,648.00/year for institutions, all countries except Europe, Japan and Iran; $314,200.00/year for institutions; $33,700.00/year for individuals. Journal publishing articles on patient education and health promotion researchers, managers, physicians, nurses and other health care provider.

6170 ■ Physical & Occupational Therapy in Geriatrics
Informa Healthcare
52 Vanderbilt Ave., 7th Fl.
New York, NY 10017-3846
Ph: (212)520-2777
URL: http://informahealthcare.com/pog

Quarterly. $520.00/year for institutions; $920.00/year for institutions; $685.00/year for institutions. Journal for allied health professionals focusing on current practice and emerging issues in the health care of and rehabilitation of the older client.

6171 ■ Provider
American Health Care Association
1201 L St. NW
Washington, DC 20005
Ph: (202)842-4444
Fax: (202)842-3860
E-mail: sales@ahca.org
URL: http://www.providermagazine.com

Monthly. $48.00/year for U.S.; $61.00/year for Canada and Mexico; $85.00/year for other countries; free to qualified subscribers. Provider Magazine.

6172 ■ Public Health Forum
Elsevier Science Inc.
360 Park Ave. S
New York, NY 10010-1710
Ph: (212)989-5800
Fax: (212)633-3990
Fr: 888-437-4636
URL: http://www.elsevier.com/wps/find/journaldescription.cws_home

$35.00/year for institutions, European countries and Iran; $5,200.00/year for institutions, Japan; $49.00/year for institutions, other countries; $31.00/year for students, other countries; $3,400.00/year for stu-

dents, Japan; $26.00/year for students, European countries and Iran. Journal focused on research methods, and program evaluation in the field of public health.

6173 ■ Public Health Law & Policy Journal
University of Hawaii
1859 E-W Rd., No. 106
Honolulu, HI 96822-2322
Ph: (808)956-9424
Fax: (808)956-5983
E-mail: phlo@hawaii.edu
URL: http://www.hawaii.edu/phlo/phlpj/

Free, online. Open access academic journal covering worldwide public health issues.

6174 ■ Public Health, Social Medicine and Epidemiology
Elsevier Science Inc.
360 Park Ave. S
New York, NY 10010-1710
Ph: (212)989-5800
Fax: (212)633-3990
Fr: 888-437-4636
URL: http://www.elsevier.com/wps/find/journaldescription.cws_home

Semimonthly. $8,824.00/year for institutions, other countries; $1,048,500.00/year for institutions, Japan; $7,949.00/year for institutions, European countries and Iran. Journal covering public health and social medicine, and includes health planning and education, epidemiology and prevention of communicable disease, public health aspects of risk populations.

6175 ■ Quality Management in Health Care
Lippincott Williams & Wilkins
351 W Camden St.
Baltimore, MD 21201
Ph: (410)528-4000
Fr: 800-638-3030
URL: http://www.lww.com/product/?1063-8628

Quarterly. $115.99/year for individuals; $351.00/year for institutions; $63.49/year for individuals, in-training; $208.73/year for other countries; $524.73/year for institutions, other countries. Peer-reviewed journal providing a forum to explore the theoretical, technical, and strategic elements of total quality management in health care.

6176 ■ Rehabilitation Nursing
Rehabilitation Nursing
4700 W Lake Ave.
Glenview, IL 60025
Ph: (847)375-4710
Fax: (847)375-6481
Fr: 800-229-7530
E-mail: info@rehabnurse.org
URL: http://awebsource.com/clients/arn/ws_resource/public_index.p

Bimonthly. $120.00/year for individuals, regular; $150.00/year for individuals, premium; $195.00/year for other countries, regular; $240.00/year for other countries, premium; $175.00/year for institutions, regular (USA); $220.00/year for institutions, premium (USA); $195.00/year for institutions, regular (international); $240.00/year for institutions, premium (international). Magazine focusing on rehabilitation nursing involving clinical practice, research, education, and administration.

6177 ■ Supporting Innovations in Gerontological Nursing
National Gerontological Nursing Association
3493 Lansdowne Dr., Ste. 2
Lexington, KY 40517
Ph: (859)977-7453
Fax: (859)271-0607
Fr: 800-723-0560
E-mail: info@ngna.org
URL: http://www.ngna.org

Bimonthly. Provides updates on NGNA's activities as well as other information of interest to gerontological nurses. Features job opportunities in the field.

EMPLOYER DIRECTORIES AND NETWORKING LISTS

6178 ■ Careers in Focus—Geriatric Care
Facts On File Inc.
132 W 31st St., 17th Fl.
New York, NY 10001
Ph: (212)967-8800
Fax: 800-678-3633
Fr: 800-322-8755
URL: http://www.infobasepublishing.com

Latest edition 3rd; Published December, 2010. $32.95 for individuals. Covers: An overview of geriatric care, followed by a selection of jobs profiled in detail, including the nature of the job, earnings, prospects for employment, what kind of training and skills it requires, and sources for further information.

6179 ■ Medical and Health Information Directory
Gale
PO Box 6904
Florence, KY 41022-6904
Fr: 800-354-9706
URL: http://www.gale.cengage.com

Annual, Latest edition April 2011. $1190.00 for individuals; $501.00 for individuals. Covers: In volume 1, more than 33,000 medical and health oriented associations, organizations, institutions, and government agencies, including health maintenance organizations (HMOs), preferred provider organizations (PPOs), insurance companies, pharmaceutical companies, research centers, and medical and allied health schools. In Volume 2, over 20,000 medical book publishers; medical periodicals, directories, audiovisual producers and services, medical libraries and information centers, electronic resources, and health-related internet search engines. In Volume 3, more than 40,500 clinics, treatment centers, care programs, and counseling/diagnostic services for 34 subject areas. Entries include: Institution, service, or firm name, address, phone, fax, email and URL; many include names of key personnel and, when pertinent, descriptive annotation. Volume 3 was formerly listed separately as Health Services Directory. Arrangement: Classified by organization activity, service, etc. Indexes: Each volume has a complete alphabetical name and keyword index.

HANDBOOKS AND MANUALS

6180 ■ Being a Nursing Assistant
Prentice Hall PTR
1 Lake St.
Upper Saddle River, NJ 07458
Ph: (201)236-7000
Fax: (317)428-3343
Fr: 800-922-0579
URL: http://www.pearsonhighered.com

Francie Wolgin. Ninth edition, 2005. $76.13 (paper). 800 pages.

6181 ■ Careers in Health Care
The McGraw-Hill Companies
PO Box 182604
Columbus, OH 43272
Fax: (614)759-3749
Fr: 877-883-5524
E-mail: customer.service@mcgraw-hill.com
URL: http://www.mhprofessional.com/product.php?isbn=0071466533

Barbara M. Swanson. Fifth edition, 2005. $19.95 (paper). 192 pages. Describes job duties, work settings, salaries, licensing and certification requirements, educational preparation, and future outlook. Gives ideas on how to secure a job.

6182 ■ Core Curriculum for the Licensed Practical/Vocational Hospice and Palliative Nurse
Kendall/Hunt Publishing Company
4050 Westmark Dr.
Dubuque, IA 52004

Ph: (563)589-1000
Fax: (563)589-1046
Fr: 800-228-0810
E-mail: orders@kendallhunt.com
URL: http://www.kendallhunt.com

Hospice & Palliative Nurses Association. 2010. $60.00. 250 pages.

6183 ■ Home Health Aide Training Manual and Handbook

iUniverse, Inc.
1663 Liberty Dr.
Bloomington, IN 47403
Fax: (812)355-4085
Fr: 800-288-4677
URL: http://www.iuniverse.com

Emmanuel C. Anene. 2009. $12.95 (softcover). 108 pages. Serves as a teaching and training tool for home health aides. Includes information on federal and state rules and regulations that a home health aide must be familiar with.

6184 ■ Nursing Today: Transition and Trends

W. B. Saunders Co.
6277 Sea Harbor Dr.
Orlando, FL 32887
Ph: (407)345-2000
Fr: 800-545-2522
URL: http://www.elsevier.com

JoAnn Zerwekh and Jo C. Claborn, editors. Sixth edition, 2009. $52.95 (paper). 640 pages.

6185 ■ Opportunities in Health and Medical Careers

The McGraw-Hill Companies
PO Box 182604
Columbus, OH 43272
Fax: (614)759-3749
Fr: 877-883-5524
E-mail: customer.service@mcgraw-hill.com
URL: http://www.mhprofessional.com/product.php?isbn=0071437274

I. Donald Snook, Jr. and Leo D'Orazio. 2004. $14.95 (paper). 157 pages. Covers the full range of medical and health occupations. Illustrated.

6186 ■ Resumes for Health and Medical Careers

The McGraw-Hill Companies
PO Box 182604
Columbus, OH 43272
Fax: (614)759-3749
Fr: 877-883-5524
E-mail: customer.service@mcgraw-hill.com
URL: http://www.mhprofessional.com/product.php?isbn=0071545352

Third edition, 2008. $12.95 (paper). 144 pages.

EMPLOYMENT AGENCIES AND SEARCH FIRMS

6187 ■ Boone-Scaturro Associates Inc.

8831 S Somerset Ln.
Alpharetta, GA 30004
Ph: (770)740-9737
Fax: (770)475-5055
Fr: 800-749-1884
E-mail: mes@boone-scaturro.com
URL: http://www.boone-scaturro.com

Executive search firm focused on the healthcare industry.

6188 ■ Professional Placement Associates, Inc.

287 Bowman Ave.
Purchase, NY 10577-2517
Ph: (914)251-1000
Fax: (914)251-1055
E-mail: careers@ppasearch.com
URL: http://www.ppasearch.com

Executive search firm specializing in the health and medical field.

ONLINE JOB SOURCES AND SERVICES

6189 ■ CertifiedHomeHealthAide.net

URL: http://www.certifiedhomehealthaide.net

Description: Lists job openings for home health aid professionals. Includes job and resume posting and other services.

6190 ■ HealthCareerWeb.com

URL: http://www.healthcareerweb.com

Description: Advertises jobs for healthcare professionals. Main files include: Jobs, Employers, Resumes, Jobwire. Relocation tools and career guidance resources available.

6191 ■ HEALTHeCAREERS Network

Fr: 888-884-8242
E-mail: info@healthecareers.com
URL: http://www.healthecareers.com

Description: Career search site for jobs in all health care specialties; educational resources; visa and licensing information for relocation; interesting articles; relocation tools; links to professional organizations and general resources.

6192 ■ Monster Healthcare

URL: http://healthcare.monster.com

Description: Delivers nationwide access to healthcare recruiting. Employers can post job listings or ads. Job seekers can post and code resumes, and search over 150,000 healthcare job listings, healthcare career advice columns, career resources information, and member employer profiles and services.

6193 ■ ProHealthJobs.com

Ph: (484)443-8545
Fax: (484)443-8549
E-mail: info@prohealthjobs.com
URL: http://prohealthjobs.com/jobboard

Description: Career resources site for the medical and health care field. Lists professional opportunities, product information, continuing education and open positions.

TRADESHOWS

6194 ■ NAHC's Annual Meeting and Home Care and Hospice Expo

National Association for Home Care
228 7th St. S.E.
Washington, DC 20003
Ph: (202)547-7424
Fax: (202)547-3540
URL: http://www.nahc.org

Annual. Primary Exhibits: General home health products, emergency response systems, computers, uniforms, publications, surgical and medical supplies, pharmaceuticals, durable and home medical equipment. Dates and Locations: 2012 Oct 20-24; Orlando, FL.

OTHER SOURCES

6195 ■ American Assembly for Men in Nursing (AAMN)

PO Box 130220
Birmingham, AL 35213
Ph: (205)956-0146
Fax: (205)956-0149
E-mail: aamn@aamn.org
URL: http://aamn.org

Description: Registered nurses. Works to: help eliminate prejudice in nursing; interest men in the nursing profession; provide opportunities for the discussion of common problems; encourage education and promote further professional growth; advise and assist in areas of professional inequity; help develop sensitivities to various social needs; promote the principles and practices of positive health care. Acts as a clearinghouse for information on men in nursing. Conducts educational programs. Promotes education and research about men's health issues.

6196 ■ American Geriatrics Society

40 Fulton St., 18th Fl.
New York, NY 10118
Ph: (212)308-1414
Fax: (212)832-8646
E-mail: info.amger@americangeriatrics.org
URL: http://www.americangeriatrics.org

Description: Represents health professionals. Focuses on improving the health, independence and quality of life of older people. Provides leadership to healthcare professionals, policy makers, and the public by implementing and advocating for programs in patient care, research, professional and public education, and public policy.

6197 ■ American Health Care Association (AHCA)

1201 L St. NW
Washington, DC 20005
Ph: (202)842-4444
Fax: (202)842-3860
E-mail: hr@ahca.org
URL: http://www.ahcancal.org/Pages/Default.aspx

Description: Federation of state associations of long-term health care facilities. Promotes standards for professionals in long-term health care delivery and quality care for patients and residents in a safe environment. Focuses on issues of availability, quality, affordability, and fair payment. Operates as liaison with governmental agencies, Congress, and professional associations. Compiles statistics.

6198 ■ American Public Health Association (APHA)

800 I St. NW
Washington, DC 20001
Ph: (202)777-2742
Fax: (202)777-2534
E-mail: comments@apha.org
URL: http://www.apha.org

Description: Professional organization of physicians, nurses, educators, academicians, environmentalists, epidemiologists, new professionals, social workers, health administrators, optometrists, podiatrists, pharmacists, dentists, nutritionists, health planners, other community and mental health specialists, and interested consumers. Seeks to protect and promote personal, mental, and environmental health. Services include: promulgation of standards; establishment of uniform practices and procedures; development of the etiology of communicable diseases; research in public health; exploration of medical care programs and their relationships to public health. Sponsors job placement service.

6199 ■ National Association of Professional Geriatric Care Managers (NAPGCM)

3275 W Ina Rd., Ste. 130
Tucson, AZ 85741-2198
Ph: (520)881-8008
Fax: (520)325-7925
E-mail: kboothroyd@napgcm.org
URL: http://www.caremanager.org

Description: Promotes quality products and care for elderly citizens. Provides referral service and distributes information to individuals interested in geriatric care management. Maintains referral network.

6200 ■ National Gerontological Nursing Association

3493 Landowne Dr., Ste. 2
Lexington, KY 40517
Ph: (859)977-7453
Fax: (859)271--060

Fr: 800-723-0560
E-mail: info@ngna.org
URL: http://www.ngna.org

Description: Dedicated to the clinical care of older adults across diverse care settings. Represents the interests of clinicians, educators, and researchers with vastly different educational preparation, clinical roles, and interests in practice issues.

6201 ■ National League for Nursing (NLN)
61 Broadway, 33rd Fl.
New York, NY 10006
Ph: (212)363-5555
Fax: (212)812-0391
Fr: 800-669-1656
E-mail: generalinfo@nln.org
URL: http://www.nln.org

Description: Champions the pursuit of quality nursing education. A professional association of nursing faculty, education agencies, health care agencies, allied/public agencies, and public members whose mission is to advance quality nursing education that prepares the nursing workforce to meet the needs of diverse populations in an ever-changing health care environment. Serves as the primary source of information about every type of nursing education program, from the LVN and LPN to the EdD and PhD. There are 20 affiliated constituent leagues that provide a local forum for members. The National League for Nursing Accrediting Commission is an independent corporate affiliate of the NLN, responsible for providing accreditation services to all levels of nursing education.

6202 ■ National Rural Health Association (NRHA)
Administrative Office
521 E 63rd St.
Kansas City, MO 64110-3329
Ph: (816)756-3140
Fax: (816)756-3144
E-mail: mail@nrharural.org
URL: http://www.ruralhealthweb.org

Description: Administrators, physicians, nurses, physician assistants, health planners, academicians, and others interested or involved in rural health care. Creates a better understanding of health care problems unique to rural areas; utilizes a collective approach in finding positive solutions; articulates and represents the health care needs of rural America; supplies current information to rural health care providers; serves as a liaison between rural health care programs throughout the country. Offers continuing education credits for medical, dental, nursing, and management courses.

6203 ■ Visiting Nurse Associations of America (VNAA)
900 19th St. NW, Ste. 200
Washington, DC 20006
Ph: (202)384-1420
Fax: (202)384-1444
Fr: 888-866-8773
E-mail: vnaa@vnaa.org
URL: http://www.vnaa.org

Description: Home health care agencies. Develops competitive strength among community-based non-profit visiting nurse organizations; works to strengthen business resources and economic programs through contracting, marketing, governmental affairs and publications.

Hotel Managers and Assistants

SOURCES OF HELP-WANTED ADS

6204 ■ Hotel F & B Executive
Hotel Forums L.L.C.
613 Kane St.
West Dundee, IL 60118
Ph: (847)551-9956
URL: http://www.hotelfandb.com

Bimonthly. $49.00/year for individuals; $15.00/year for students; $59.00/year for institutions. Magazine that addresses the needs of the hospitality F&B markets, which include hotels, resorts, cruise lines and conference, and convention & meeting centers.

6205 ■ Hotel & Motel Management
Questex Media Group
275 Grove St., 2-130
Newton, MA 02466
Ph: (617)219-8300
Fax: (617)219-8310
Fr: 888-552-4346
URL: http://www.hospitalityworldnetwork.com/hotel-management

$58.85/year for individuals; $81.40/year for Canada and Mexico; $143.00/year for other countries; $75.00/year for individuals, additional airmail shipping; free to qualified subscribers. Magazine (tabloid) covering the global lodging industry.

6206 ■ HOTELS
Marketing & Technology Group
1415 N Dayton St.
Chicago, IL 60622
Ph: (312)274-2200
Fax: (312)266-3363
URL: http://www.hotelsmag.com/

Monthly. Free. Magazine covering management and operations as well as foodservice and design in the hospitality industry.

6207 ■ Lodging Hospitality
Penton Media Inc.
249 W 17th St.
New York, NY 10011
Ph: (212)204-4200
URL: http://lhonline.com/

Free to qualified subscribers. Magazine serving managers of independent, franchise, chain-owned, and referral groups in the hospitality industry.

EMPLOYER DIRECTORIES AND NETWORKING LISTS

6208 ■ Career Opportunities in Casinos and Casino Hotels
Facts On File Inc.
132 W 31st St., 17th Fl.
New York, NY 10001
Ph: (212)967-8800
Fax: 800-678-3633
Fr: 800-322-8755
URL: http://factsonfile.infobasepublishing.com/

Irregular, Latest edition 2nd; Published May, 2009. $49.50 for individuals. Publication includes: A directory of casinos and cruise lines, gaming conferences and expos, seminars, workshops, and industry Web sites. Principal content of publication is 100 occupations in 10 employment sections on careers in gaming, administration, management, security, entertainment, hotel management, and food and beverage service in the casino industry.

6209 ■ Official Hotel Guide
Northstar Travel Media L.L.C.
100 Lighting Way, 2nd Fl.
Secaucus, NJ 07094
Ph: (201)902-2000
Fax: (201)902-2045
URL: http://www.northstartravelmedia.com/

Annual. Covers: in four volumes, 29,000 hotels, motels, and resorts worldwide. Volume 1 covers most of the U.S. Volume 2 covers the rest of the U.S. and the Western Hemisphere; Volume 3 covers Europe, the Middle East, Asia, and Africa. Volume 4 specialty travel guide includes listings of golf resorts and tennis resorts; health spas, dude ranches, bed and breakfasts, and casino & hotels in the United States; also includes lists of hotels in the Caribbean with golf, tennis, casinos, and all-inclusive. Entries include: Hotel/motel/resort name, address, phone, fax, CRS's, number of rooms or units, rates, brief description of facilities, ratings, codes indicating credit cards accepted, email and website addresses, and travel agent's commission, if any. Arrangement: Geographical.

6210 ■ Red Roof Directory
Red Roof
2071 N Bechtle Ave.
Springfield, OH 45504-1583
Fr: 800-733-7663
URL: http://www.redroof.com

Covers: Listings of 345 inns in 36 states.

6211 ■ Vault Guide to the Top Hospitality & Tourism Industry Employers
Vault.com Inc.
150 W 22nd St., 5th Fl.
New York, NY 10011
Ph: (212)366-4212
Fax: (212)366-6117
Fr: 888-562-8285
URL: http://www.vault.com/store/book_preview.jsp?product_id=38815

Latest edition May, 2008. $19.95 for individuals. Covers: Hospitality and tourism industry employers. Entries include: Name, address, phone, fax, website, and branch office location. Also include company overviews, recent company news, information on the hiring process, key competitors, and employment contact. Arrangement: Alphabetical by company name.

HANDBOOKS AND MANUALS

6212 ■ Careers in Travel, Tourism, and Hospitality
The McGraw-Hill Companies
PO Box 182604
Columbus, OH 43272
Fax: (614)759-3749
Fr: 877-883-5524
E-mail: customer.service@mcgraw-hill.com
URL: http://www.mhprofessional.com

Marjorie Eberts, Linda Brothers, and Ann Gisler. Second edition, 2005. $15.95 (paper). 224 pages.

6213 ■ Jobs for Travel Lovers: Opportunities at Home and Abroad
Impact Publications
9104 Manassas Dr., Ste. N
Manassas Park, VA 20111-5211
Ph: (703)361-7300
Fax: (703)335-9486
URL: http://www.impactpublications.com

2006. $19.95. 320 pages. Covers job search strategies, with hundreds of jobs in business, government, and education, including the travel and hospital industry, non-profit organizations, international organizations, education institutions, and consulting. Includes opportunities involving airlines and cruise lines, international jobs, travel agencies and tour operators, internships and volunteering, hotels and resorts, military and merchant marine, teaching abroad, travel writing, and short-term work experiences. Provides names, addresses, telephone/fax numbers, e-mails, and websites for contacting potential employers.

6214 ■ Opportunities in Hotel and Motel Management Careers
The McGraw-Hill Companies
PO Box 182604
Columbus, OH 43272
Fax: (614)759-3749
Fr: 877-883-5524
E-mail: customer.service@mcgraw-hill.com
URL: http://www.mhprofessional.com/product.php?isbn=0071388362

Shepard Henkin. 2000. $12.95 (paper). 160 pages.

6215 ■ Purchasing for Chefs: A Concise Guide
John Wiley & Sons, Inc.
111 River St.
Hoboken, NJ 07030
Ph: (201)748-6000
Fax: (201)748-6088
E-mail: info@wiley.com
URL: http://as.wiley.com/WileyCDA/Section/index.html

Andrew H. Feinstein and John M. Stefanelli. 2010. $51.95. 256 pages. Guide details purchasing principles to chefs and hospitality managers for obtaining goods and services for their business.

6216 ■ *So You Want to Be an Innkeeper*

Chronicle Books LLC
680 Second St.
San Francisco, CA 94107
Ph: (415)537-4200
Fax: (415)537-4460
Fr: 800-759-0190
E-mail: frontdesk@chroniclebooks.com
URL: http://www.chroniclebooks.com

Jo Ann M. Bell, Susan Brown, Mary Davies, and Pat Hardy, et al. Fourth edition, 2004. $16.95 (paper). 336 pages.

EMPLOYMENT AGENCIES AND SEARCH FIRMS

6217 ■ The Alfus Group Inc.

353 Lexington Ave.
New York, NY 10016
Ph: (212)599-1000
Fax: (212)599-1523
E-mail: mail@thealfusgroup.com
URL: http://www.thealfusgroup.com

Executive search firm. Specializes in the hospitality industry.

6218 ■ Boutique Search Firm

1173 Rodeo Dr.
Los Angeles, CA 90035
Ph: (310)552-2221
Fax: (310)552-2224
URL: http://www.boutiquesearchfirm.com

Serves as a recruiting firm specializing in hospitality management. Offers jobs in luxury hotels and resorts worldwide.

6219 ■ Bowman & Associates

1660 S Amphlett Blvd., Ste. 245
San Mateo, CA 94402
Ph: (650)573-0188
Fax: (650)573-8209
E-mail: contact@bowmansearch.com
URL: http://www.bowmansearch.com

Executive search firm specializes in the hospitality industry. Also specializes: food service, asset management, lodging, real estate development, e-commerce, gaming, travel, theme parks.

6220 ■ ChaseAmerica Inc.

300 Park Ave.
New York, NY 10022
Ph: (215)338-1952
Fr: 800-491-4980
E-mail: info@chaseamericainc.com
URL: http://www.chaseamericainc.com

Executive search firm.

6221 ■ The Elliot Group LLC

505 White Plains Rd., Ste. 228
Tarrytown, NY 10591
Ph: (914)631-4904
Fax: (914)631-6481
URL: http://www.theelliotgroup.com

Executive search firm. Six locations throughout the United States.

6222 ■ Gecko Hospitality

718 Ogden Ave., Ste. 202
Downers Grove, IL 60515
Ph: (630)390-1000
Fax: (630)598-0753
URL: http://www.geckohospitality.com

Serves as a hospitality recruiter specializing in placing candidates in hospitality jobs as well as securing qualified hospitality professionals for its clients.

Provides a database of hospitality jobs, restaurant jobs, hotel jobs, and casino jobs.

6223 ■ Global Hospitality

3579 E Foothill Blvd., Ste. 229
Pasadena, CA 91107
Ph: (626)836-1222
Fax: (626)836-1223
E-mail: mail@globalhospitality.com
URL: http://www.globalhospitality.com

Executive search firm that specializes in identifying, evaluating, and placing leadership and management talent in the hospitality industry.

6224 ■ Harper Associates

31000 NW Hwy., Ste. 240
Farmington Hills, MI 48334
Ph: (248)932-1170
Fax: (248)932-1214
E-mail: info@harperjobs.com
URL: http://www.harperjobs.com

Executive search firm and employment agency.

6225 ■ Hospitality International

236 5th Ave., Ste. 907
New York, NY 10001
Ph: (212)696-1661
Fax: (212)696-1669
E-mail: jar@hospitalityinternational.com
URL: http://www.hospitalityinternational.com

Executive search firm. Branch office in New York, NY.

6226 ■ Hospitality Marketing & Recruiting

PO Box 970023
Boca Raton, FL 33497
Ph: (561)289-1873
Fax: (561)852-6447
E-mail: rstevens@hospitalityjobsbyhmr.com
URL: http://www.hospitalityjobsbyhmr.com

Description: Provides executive search and placement services of management level hospitality personnel for hotels, country clubs, cruise ships, attractions and restaurants.

6227 ■ Hospitality Pro Search

12134 Attlee Dr.
Houston, TX 77077
Ph: (281)584-0601
Fax: (832)230-5504
E-mail: gary@hprosearch.com
URL: http://www.hprosearch.com

Serves as an executive search firm for the hospitality industry. Specializes in worldwide management placements for restaurants, hotels and resorts, entertainment venues, and private clubs.

6228 ■ Hospitality Recruiters

10706 Cortland Ridge Ln.
Cypress, TX 77433
Fax: 877-684-3106
Fr: 877-735-1133
E-mail: career@hospitalityrecruiters.com
URL: http://www.hospitalityrecruiters.com

Description: Specializes in the placement of managers within the restaurant and hotel industries.

6229 ■ HospitalityStaff.com

3195 Tamiami Trail, Ste. 204
Port Charlotte, FL 33952
Ph: (941)743-8540
Fax: (941)743-9684
Fr: 800-987-1555
URL: http://www.hospitalitystaff.com

Serves as a placement agency, specializing in the supply of temporary and permanent staff to the hospitality industry.

6230 ■ The IMC Group of Companies Ltd.

120 White Plains Rd., Ste. 405
Tarrytown, NY 10591
Ph: (914)468-7050

Fax: (914)468-7051
E-mail: herbert.regehly@the-imc.com
URL: http://www.the-imc.com

International executive recruiting and management consulting company providing leading-edge services for the hospitality, leisure, entertainment, gaming and new media industries throughout the United States, Europe, Africa, Asia Pacific and Latin America.

6231 ■ J.D. Hersey and Associates

8 E Poplar Ave.
Columbus, OH 43215
Ph: (614)228-4022
Fax: (614)228-4085
URL: http://www.jdhersey.com

Executive search firm for permanent and contingency placements.

6232 ■ Prospection Group

PO Box 1999
Santa Monica, CA 90406
Ph: (310)398-3795
URL: http://www.prospectiongroup.com

Executive search firm for the hospitality industry. Searches for hospitality executives ranging from the level of general management to private chefs.

6233 ■ Robert Howe and Associates

3331 Bolero Dr.
Atlanta, GA 30341
Ph: (770)270-1211

Provides consulting services in the area of executive search and recruitment. Industries served: healthcare, hospitality, chemical, metals, electronics, construction, and food processing.

6234 ■ Robert W. Dingman Company Inc.

650 Hampshire Rd., No. 116
Westlake Village, CA 91361
Ph: (805)778-1777
Fax: (805)778-9288
E-mail: info@dingman.com
URL: http://www.dingman.com

Executive search firm with a second office in Black Forest, CO.

6235 ■ Travel People Personnel

1199 Park Ave., Ste. 3E
New York, NY 10128-1762
Ph: (212)348-6942
Fax: (212)348-6958
E-mail: sue@travelpeople.com
URL: http://www.travelpeople.com

Provides temporary and regular placement services to travel related companies. Industries served: travel and hospitality.

ONLINE JOB SOURCES AND SERVICES

6236 ■ Bristol Associates, Inc.

5757 W Century Blvd., Ste. 855
Los Angeles, CA 90045
Ph: (310)670-0525
Fax: (310)670-4075
E-mail: bfarber@bristolassoc.com
URL: http://www.bristolassoc.com

Description: Executive search firm specializing in direct marketing, hospitality and food industries. Applicants can post their resumes online for recruiters' viewing and search current job databank. Also contains job tools and resources.

6237 ■ FoodServicesCrossing.com

URL: http://www.foodservicescrossing.com

Description: Features job listings for the food services industry.

6238 ■ HCareers.com

E-mail: hospitalitydivision@hcareers.com
URL: http://www.hcareers.com

Description: Connects employers and candidates within the hospitality industry. Enables candidates to search for jobs within a specific industry or location.

6239 ■ Hospitality Jobs Online
URL: http://www.hospitalityonline.com

Description: Enables hospitality industry job seekers to find career information, information about employers and tips and techniques to help them succeed. Provides daily updates of hotel jobs, resort jobs, restaurant jobs and club jobs nationwide.

6240 ■ Hotel Jobs Network
E-mail: info@hoteljobsnetwork.com
URL: http://www.hoteljobsnetwork.com/home

Online job site for the hospitality industry.

6241 ■ Hotel Online
E-mail: contactus@hotel-online.com
URL: http://www.hotel-online.com

Description: Provides news, trends, discussion forums, employment opportunities, and classified advertising for the hospitality industry.

6242 ■ HotelJobs.com
URL: http://www.hoteljobs.com

Description: Provides job postings and resume database for hotel, casino and cruise ship professionals and recruiters.

TRADESHOWS

6243 ■ Americas Lodging Investment Summit
Burba Hotel Network
2900 Bristol St., Ste. D101
Costa Mesa, CA 92626
Ph: (714)540-9300
URL: http://www.burba.com

Annual. Features an array of seminars, workshops and presentations about timely issues facing the hotel investment community. Brings together experts and investors to discuss trends and to identify new opportunities.

6244 ■ Annual Hotel, Motel, and Restaurant Supply Show of the Southeast
Leisure Time Unlimited, Inc.
708 Main St.
PO Box 332
Myrtle Beach, SC 29577
Ph: (843)448-9483
Fax: (843)626-1513
Fr: 800-261-5591
E-mail: ltushows@sc.rr.com
URL: http://www.leisuretimeunlimited.com/

Annual. Primary Exhibits: Carpeting, furniture, coffee makers, produce companies, wine and beer and food companies, and services to motels, hotels, and restaurants. Dates and Locations: 2012 Jan 24-26; Myrtle Beach, SC; Myrtle Beach Convention Center.

6245 ■ Hospitality Design
VNU Expositions
14685 Avion Pkwy., Ste. 400
Chantilly, VA 20151
Ph: (703)488-2700
Fax: (703)488-2725
Fr: 800-765-7615
URL: http://www.vnuexpo.com

Annual. Primary Exhibits: Hospitality industry equipment, supplies, and services.

6246 ■ IH/M & RS - International Hotel/Motel & Restaurant Show
George Little Management, LLC (New York, New York)
1133 Westchester Ave., Ste. N136
White Plains, NY 10606

Ph: (914)421-3200
Fr: 800-272-SHOW
E-mail: cathy_steel@glmshows.com
URL: http://www.glmshows.com

Annual. Primary Exhibits: Products and services for lodging and food serving properties, including: technology, uniforms, linens and bedding, tabletop accessories, guest amenities and services, food and beverages, cleaning maintenance, food service equipment and supplies, franchising information, finance and management furnishings and fixtures, fitness equipment, and leisure and entertainment services.

6247 ■ West Ex: The Rocky Mountain Regional Hospitality Exposition
Colorado Restaurant Association
430 E. 7th Ave.
Denver, CO 80203
Ph: (303)830-2972
Fax: (303)830-2973
Fr: 800-522-2972
E-mail: info@coloradorestaurant.com
URL: http://www.coloradorestaurant.com

Annual. Primary Exhibits: Food service and lodging products, equipment, and services.

6248 ■ Western Food Service & Hospitality Expo Los Angeles
California Restaurant Association
621 Capitol Mall, Ste. 2000
Sacramento, CA 95814
Ph: (916)447-5793
Fax: (916)447-6182
Fr: 800-765-4842
E-mail: membership@calrest.org
URL: http://www.calrest.org

Primary Exhibits: Food, equipment, supplies, and services for food service and lodging industries.

OTHER SOURCES

6249 ■ American Hotel and Lodging Association (AH&LA)
1201 New York Ave. NW, No. 600
Washington, DC 20005-3931
Ph: (202)289-3100
Fax: (202)289-3199
E-mail: informationcenter@ahla.com
URL: http://www.ahla.com

Description: Represents state lodging associations throughout the United States with some 13,000 property members worldwide, representing more than 1.7 million guest rooms. Provides its members with assistance in operations, education and communications and lobbies on Capitol Hill to provide a business climate in which the industry can continue to prosper. Individual state associations provide representation at the state level and offer many additional cost-saving benefits.

6250 ■ Association for Convention Operations Management (ACOM)
191 Clarksville Rd.
Princeton Junction, NJ 08550
Ph: (609)799-3712
Fax: (609)799-7032
E-mail: info@acomonline.org
URL: http://www.acomonline.org

Description: Convention service directors and managers of hotels, convention centers, and convention bureaus. Works to increase the effectiveness, productivity and quality of meetings, conventions and exhibitions. Works to establish high ethical standards, improve professional management techniques and increase awareness of client, employer and provider needs. Maintains speakers' bureau, resource center, and placement services; compiles statistics. Conducts research and educational programs.

6251 ■ Association for International Practical Training (AIPT)
10400 Little Patuxent Pkwy., Ste. 250
Columbia, MD 21044-3519
Ph: (410)997-2200
Fax: (410)992-3924
E-mail: aipt@aipt.org
URL: http://www.aipt.org

Description: Providers worldwide of on-the-job training programs for students and professionals seeking international career development and life-changing experiences. Arranges workplace exchanges in hundreds of professional fields, bringing employers and trainees together from around the world. Client list ranges from small farming communities to Fortune 500 companies.

6252 ■ Club Managers Association of America (CMAA)
1733 King St.
Alexandria, VA 22314
Ph: (703)739-9500
Fax: (703)739-0124
E-mail: cmaa@cmaa.org
URL: http://www.cmaa.org

Description: Professional managers and assistant managers of private golf, yacht, athletic, city, country, luncheon, university, and military clubs. Encourages education and advancement of members and promotes efficient and successful club operations. Provides reprints of articles on club management. Supports courses in club management. Compiles statistics; maintains management referral service.

6253 ■ International Council on Hotel, Restaurant, and Institutional Education (CHRIE)
2810 N Parham Rd., Ste. 230
Richmond, VA 23294
Ph: (804)346-4800
Fax: (804)346-5009
E-mail: kmccarty@chrie.org
URL: http://www.chrie.org

Description: Schools and colleges offering specialized education and training in hospitals, recreation, tourism and hotel, restaurant, and institutional administration; individuals, executives, and students. Provides networking opportunities and professional development.

6254 ■ International Executive Housekeepers Association (IEHA)
1001 Eastwind Dr., Ste. 301
Westerville, OH 43081-3361
Ph: (614)895-7166
Fax: (614)895-1248
Fr: 800-200-6342
E-mail: excel@ieha.org
URL: http://www.ieha.org

Description: Persons engaged in facility housekeeping management in hospitals, hotels and motels, schools and industrial establishments. Established educational standards. Sponsors certificate and collegiate degree programs. Holds annual International Housekeepers Week celebration.

6255 ■ National Association of Black Hotel Owners, Operators and Developers (NABHOOD)
3520 W Broward Blvd., Ste. 119
Fort Lauderdale, FL 33312
Ph: (954)797-7102
Fax: (954)337-2877
E-mail: horizons@gate.net
URL: http://nabhood.net

Description: Enhances the stability and growth of the lodging industry. Aims to increase the number of African-Americans owning, developing, managing and operating hotels. Strives to create vendor opportunities and executive level jobs for minorities.

SOURCES OF HELP-WANTED ADS

6256 ■ EAP Digest
Performance Resource Press Inc.
1270 Rankin Dr., Ste. F
Troy, MI 48083-2843
Ph: (248)588-7733
Fax: (248)588-6633
Fr: 800-453-7733
URL: http://store.prponline.net/index.php/ea-providers/eaprovider

Quarterly. $36.00/year for individuals; $60.00/year for two years; $72.00/year for individuals, 3years. Magazine covering planning, development, and administration of employee assistance programs.

6257 ■ Human Service Newsbytes
National Human Services Assembly
1101 14th St. NW, Ste. 600
Washington, DC 20005
Ph: (202)347-2080
Fax: (202)393-4517
E-mail: irv@nassembly.org
URL: http://www.nationalassembly.org/News/Newsbytes.aspx

Biweekly. Provides information on the nonprofit and human services sector.

6258 ■ Journal of Career Development
Sage Publications Inc.
2455 Teller Rd.
Thousand Oaks, CA 91320-2218
Ph: (805)499-9774
Fax: (805)583-2665
Fr: 800-818-7243
URL: http://www.sagepub.com/journalsProdDesc.nav?prodId=Journal20

Quarterly. $719.00/year for institutions, current volume print and online; $654.00/year for institutions, print and e-access; $589.00/year for institutions, e-access; $641.00/year for institutions, print only; $118.00/year for individuals, single print; $23.00/year for individuals, single print. Journal for professionals in counseling, psychology, education, student personnel, human resources, and business management.

6259 ■ The Lutheran
Augsburg Fortress, Publishers
PO Box 1209
Minneapolis, MN 55440
Ph: (612)330-3300
Fax: (612)330-3455
E-mail: lutheran@thelutheran.org
URL: http://www.thelutheran.org

Monthly. $17.95/year for individuals; $30.95/year for two years; $40.95/year for individuals, three years. Magazine of the Evangelical Lutheran Church in America.

6260 ■ The NonProfit Times
NPT Publishing Group Inc.
201 Littleton Rd., 2nd Fl.
Morris Plains, NJ 07950
Ph: (973)401-0202
Fax: (973)401-0404
E-mail: ednchief@nptimes.com
URL: http://www.nptimes.com/

$49.95/year for individuals, print; $19.95/year for individuals, digital only; $59.95/year for individuals, digital & print. Trade journal serving nonprofit organizations.

EMPLOYER DIRECTORIES AND NETWORKING LISTS

6261 ■ Directory of Catholic Charities USA Directories
Catholic Charities USA
66 Canal Center Pl., Ste. 600
Alexandria, VA 22314-1583
Ph: (703)549-1390
Fax: (703)549-1656
URL: http://www.catholiccharitiesusa.org

Annual. $25.00 for individuals. Covers: Nearly 1,200 Catholic community and social service agencies. Listings include diocesan agencies, state Catholic conferences. Entries include: Organization name, address, name and title of director, phone, fax. Arrangement: Geographical by state, then classified by diocese.

6262 ■ Public Human Services Directory
American Public Human Services Association
1133 19th St., NW, Ste. 400
Washington, DC 20036-3631
Ph: (202)682-0100
Fax: (202)289-6555
URL: http://www.aphsa.org

Annual, Latest edition 2009. $225.00 for individuals; $200.00 for members; $350.00 for institutions. Covers: Federal, state, territorial, county, and major municipal public human service agencies. Entries include: Agency name, address, phone, fax, e-mail address, web site address, names of key personnel, program area. Arrangement: Geographical.

HANDBOOKS AND MANUALS

6263 ■ Careers for Good Samaritans and Other Humanitarian Types
The McGraw-Hill Companies
PO Box 182604
Columbus, OH 43272
Fax: (614)759-3749
Fr: 877-883-5524
E-mail: customer.service@mcgraw-hill.com
URL: http://www.mhprofessional.com

Marjorie Eberts and Margaret Gisler. Third edition, 2006. $16.95 (paper). 160 pages. Contains hundreds of ideas for turning good work into paid work. Inventories opportunities in service organizations like the Red Cross, Goodwill, and the Salvation Army; religious groups, VISTA, the Peace Corps, and UNICEF; and agencies at all levels of the government. Part of Careers for You series.

6264 ■ Careers in Health Care
The McGraw-Hill Companies
PO Box 182604
Columbus, OH 43272
Fax: (614)759-3749
Fr: 877-883-5524
E-mail: customer.service@mcgraw-hill.com
URL: http://www.mhprofessional.com/product.php?isbn=0071466533

Barbara M. Swanson. Fifth edition, 2005. $19.95 (paper). 192 pages. Describes job duties, work settings, salaries, licensing and certification requirements, educational preparation, and future outlook. Gives ideas on how to secure a job.

6265 ■ Great Jobs for Liberal Arts Majors
The McGraw-Hill Companies
PO Box 182604
Columbus, OH 43272
Fax: (614)759-3749
Fr: 877-883-5524
E-mail: customer.service@mcgraw-hill.com
URL: http://www.mhprofessional.com/product.php?isbn=0071482148

Blythe Camenson. Second edition, 2007. $16.95 (paper). 192 pages.

6266 ■ A Guidebook to Human Service Professions: Helping College Students Explore Opportunities in the Human Services Field
Charles C Thomas Publisher, Ltd.
PO Box 19265
Springfield, IL 62794-9265
Ph: (217)789-8980
Fax: (217)789-9130
Fr: 800-258-8980
E-mail: books@ccthomas.com
URL: http://www.ccthomas.com

William G. Emener, Michael A. Richard and John J. Bosworth. 2009. $44.95 (paper). 286 pages. Provides guidelines on human service profession. Offers an insightful look at the rewards of pursuing a career as a human service professional.

EMPLOYMENT AGENCIES AND SEARCH FIRMS

6267 ■ Gatti & Associates
266 Main St., Ste. 21
Medfield, MA 02052

Ph: (508)359-4153
Fax: (508)359-5902
E-mail: info@gattihr.com
URL: http://www.gattihr.com

Executive search firm specializing exclusively in the search and placement of Human Resources professionals.

Online Job Sources and Services

6268 ■ HSCareers.com
E-mail: info@hscareers.com
URL: http://www.hscareers.com

Description: Offers employment and human services niche site to assist human service professionals.

6269 ■ Social Work Job Search
E-mail: support@socialworkjobsearch.com
URL: http://www.socialworkjobsearch.com/socialworkjobsearch.cgi

Description: Provides a database of jobs for social workers, counselors, mental health providers, social services professionals, school social workers and counselors, therapists, case managers, and all other helping professionals.

6270 ■ SocialServiceNetwork.com
URL: http://socialservicenetwork.com

Description: Provides a database of social work positions. Includes various listings of social work jobs, social services jobs, human services jobs, mental health jobs, counseling jobs, and more.

Other Sources

6271 ■ American Public Health Association (APHA)
800 I St. NW
Washington, DC 20001
Ph: (202)777-2742
Fax: (202)777-2534
E-mail: comments@apha.org
URL: http://www.apha.org

Description: Professional organization of physicians, nurses, educators, academicians, environmentalists, epidemiologists, new professionals, social workers, health administrators, optometrists, podiatrists, pharmacists, dentists, nutritionists, health planners, other community and mental health specialists, and interested consumers. Seeks to protect and promote personal, mental, and environmental health. Services include: promulgation of standards; establishment of uniform practices and procedures; development of the etiology of communicable diseases; research in public health; exploration of medical care programs and their relationships to public health. Sponsors job placement service.

6272 ■ Association on Higher Education and Disability (AHEAD)
107 Commerce Center Dr., Ste. 204
Huntersville, NC 28078
Ph: (704)947-7779

Fax: (704)948-7779
E-mail: ahead@ahead.org
URL: http://www.ahead.org

Description: Individuals interested in promoting the equal rights and opportunities of disabled postsecondary students, staff, faculty, and graduates. Provides an exchange of communication for those professionally involved with disabled students; collects, evaluates, and disseminates information; encourages and supports legislation for the benefit of disabled students. Conducts surveys on issues pertinent to college students with disabilities; offers resource referral system and employment exchange for positions in disability student services. Conducts research programs; compiles statistics.

6273 ■ Child Life Council (CLC)
11821 Parklawn Dr., Ste. 310
Rockville, MD 20852-2539
Ph: (301)881-7090
Fax: (301)881-7092
Fr: 800-252-4515
E-mail: clcadmin@childlife.org
URL: http://www.childlife.org

Description: Professional organization representing child life personnel, patient activities specialists, and students in the field. Promotes psychological well-being and optimum development of children, adolescents, and their families in health care settings. Works to minimize the stress and anxiety of illness and hospitalization. Addresses professional issues such as program standards, competencies, and core curriculum. Provides resources and conducts research and educational programs. Offers a Job Bank Service listing employment openings.

6274 ■ Child Welfare League of America (CWLA)
1726 M St. NW, Ste. 500
Washington, DC 20036-4522
Ph: (202)688-4200
Fax: (202)833-1689
E-mail: register@cwla.org
URL: http://www.cwla.org

Description: Works to improve care and services for abused, dependent, or neglected children, youth, and their families. Provides training and consultation; conducts research; maintains information service and develops standards for child welfare practice.

6275 ■ Council for Health and Human Service Ministries of the United Church of Christ (CHHSM)
700 Prospect Ave.
Cleveland, OH 44115
Ph: (216)736-2260
Fax: (216)736-2251
Fr: (866)822-8224
E-mail: sickberb@chhsm.org
URL: http://www.chhsm.org

Description: Health and human service institutions related to the United Church of Christ. Seeks to study, plan, and implement a program in health and human services; assist members in developing and providing quality services and in financing institutional and non-institutional health and human service ministries; stimulate awareness of and support for these programs; inform the UCC of policies that affect the needs, problems, and conditions of patients; cooper-

ate with interdenominational agencies and others in the field. Maintains placement service and hall of fame. Compiles statistics; provides specialized education programs.

6276 ■ National Association of Benefits and Work Incentive Specialists (NABWIS)
12009 Shallot St.
Orlando, FL 32837
Ph: (407)859-7767
Fax: (407)240-6592
E-mail: nabwis@gmail.com
URL: http://www.ilr.cornell.edu/edi/nabwis

Description: Represents professionals providing assistance to individuals who receive disability benefits. Ensures that people with disabilities have access to relevant information that will support their choices regarding work and increased economic self-sufficiency. Facilitates a national listserv and news group.

6277 ■ National Organization for Human Services (NOHS)
5341 Old Hwy. 5, Ste. 206, No. 214
Woodstock, GA 30188
Ph: (770)924-8899
Fax: (678)494-5076
E-mail: admin@nationalhumanservices.org
URL: http://www.nationalhumanservices.org

Description: Human service professionals, faculty, and students. Fosters excellence in teaching, research and curriculum planning in the human service area. Encourages and supports the development of local, state, and national human services organizations. Aids faculty and professional members in their career development. Provides a medium for cooperation and communication among members. Maintains registry of qualified consultants in human service education. Conducts professional development workshop. Operates speakers' bureau.

6278 ■ Nonprofit Leadership Alliance (NLA)
1100 Walnut St., Ste. 1900
Kansas City, MO 64106
Ph: (816)561-6415
Fax: (816)531-3527
Fr: 800-343-6466
E-mail: michael.cruz@humanics.org
URL: http://www.humanics.org

Description: Individuals, corporations, and foundations supporting NLA work in preparing young people for professional leadership in youth and human service agencies. Provides leadership for co-curricular program on over 55 campuses of colleges that feature specialized professional courses that lead to B.A., B.S., or M.A. degrees and prepare graduates to serve professionally with groups such as Boy Scouts of America, Boys and Girls Clubs of America, American Red Cross, Big Brothers/Big Sisters of America, Camp Fire USA, Girl Scouts of the U.S.A., YMCA of the USA, and Girls, Inc., Habitat for Humanity International, National Urban League, Voices for America's Children, Volunteers of America and National 4-H Council. Sponsors field trips, workshops, and special courses; offers counseling, loan assistance, and career placement services to students; also operates graduate programs. Conducts research, compiles statistics.

SOURCES OF HELP-WANTED ADS

6279 ■ *Journal of Cosmetics, Dermatological Sciences and Applications*
Scientific Research Publishing
PO Box 54821
Irvine, CA 92619-4821
URL: http://www.scirp.org/journal/jcdsa/

Peer-reviewed journal covering the basic sciences, engineering aspects and applied technology of cosmetics, toiletries, perfumery and related fields.

HANDBOOKS AND MANUALS

6280 ■ *Careers for Fashion Plates and Other Trendsetters*
The McGraw-Hill Companies
PO Box 182604
Columbus, OH 43272
Fax: (614)759-3749
Fr: 877-883-5524
E-mail: customer.service@mcgraw-hill.com
URL: http://www.mhprofessional.com/product.php?isbn=0071642005

Lucia Mauro. 2008. $14.95 (paper). 176 pages. Describes career opportunities in fashion, entertainment, retail, and promotion, with advice from fashion professionals.

ONLINE JOB SOURCES AND SERVICES

6281 ■ **ByFerial**
URL: http://www.imageconsultantstraining.com

Description: Offers training seminars and news articles for image consulting.

6282 ■ **The ImageMaker, Inc.**
E-mail: imagemaker@bellsouth.net
URL: http://www.imagemaker1.com

Description: Provides educational materials for image consulting.

6283 ■ **The Rothschild Image**
E-mail: info@rothschildimage.com
URL: http://www.rothschildimage.com

Description: Offers training workshops and seminars for image consulting.

OTHER SOURCES

6284 ■ **Association of Image Consultants International (AICI)**
100 E Grand Ave., Ste. 330
Des Moines, IA 50309
Ph: (515)282-5500
Fax: (515)243-2049
E-mail: info@aici.org
URL: http://www.aici.org

Description: Personal color, style, wardrobe, and image planning consultants. Promotes quality service for clients; aids in establishing working relations between retail stores and consultants; assists community colleges in offering accredited image consulting programs; maintains standards of professionalism for members in the image consulting industry. Provides continuing education and training; maintains speakers' bureau.

6285 ■ **Body Beautiful**
1343 Lucile Ave.
Los Angeles, CA 90026
Ph: (323)708-9855
Fr: 800-510-5528
E-mail: info@bodybeautiful.net
URL: http://www.bodybeautifulonline.com/index.php

Description: Provides an online newsletter. Offers training and a support network after training is complete.

6286 ■ **Conselle Institute of Image Management**
7052 University Station
Provo, UT 84602
Ph: (801)224-1207
Fax: (801)226-6122
E-mail: judith@conselle.com
URL: http://www.conselle.com/index.php

Description: Offers workshops and training in image management.

6287 ■ **Gillian Armour Image Consulting**
323 Geary St., Ste. 808
San Francisco, CA 94102
Ph: (415)230-0015
Fr: 800-591-2353
E-mail: gillian@gillianarmour.com
URL: http://www.gillianarmour.com

Description: Offers seminars and educational materials for image consulting certification.

6288 ■ **Impression Strategies Institute**
921 Botetourt Gardens
Norfolk, VA 23507
Ph: (757)627-6669
Fax: (757)627-4044
Fr: 877-245-5015
E-mail: sandy@theimagearchitect.com
URL: http://www.impressionstrategiesinstitute.com/about.html

Description: Offers training seminars and education materials in image consulting.

6289 ■ **New York Image Consultant**
351 E 84th St., Apt. 11A
New York, NY 10028
Ph: (212)879-5790
E-mail: contact@newyorkimageconsultant.com
URL: http://www.newyorkimageconsultant.com

Description: Provides tips for getting started in image consulting. Interested persons may also sign up for classes regarding the different aspects of image consulting, or apply for an internship with the agency.

Immigration Specialists

Sources of Help-Wanted Ads

6290 ■ *Immigration Daily*
American Immigration LLC
PO Box 1830
New York, NY 10156
Ph: (212)545-0818
Fax: (212)545-0869
E-mail: editor@ilw.com
URL: http://www.ilw.com/immigrationdaily

Description: Daily. Serves as the news resource for immigration professionals.

6291 ■ *RefugeeWorks Employment Quarterly*
Lutheran Immigration and Refugee Service
700 Light St.
Baltimore, MD 21230
Ph: (410)230-2886
Fax: (410)230-2859
E-mail: information@refugeeworks.org
URL: http://www.refugeeworks.org

Quarterly. Focuses on various issues impacting former refugees in the world of employment.

Placement and Job Referral Services

6292 ■ Special Counsel
10151 Deerwood Park Blvd., Bldg. 200, Ste. 400
Jacksonville, FL 32202
Fr: 800-737-3436
E-mail: info@specialcounsel.com
URL: http://www.specialcounsel.com

Provides legal workforce solutions across the legal spectrum. Assists clients in managing everyday workload or resources, specific cases or business transactions. Provides qualified legal professionals with benefits such as competitive pay, holidays, insurance and bonuses.

Handbooks and Manuals

6293 ■ *Essentials of Immigration Law*
American Immigration Lawyers Association
PO Box 753
Waldorf, MD 20604-0753
Ph: (301)374-9000
Fax: (301)843-0159
Fr: 800-982-2839
E-mail: pubs@aila.org
URL: http://www.ailapubs.org/esofimlaw.html

Richard A. Boswell. 2006. $74 (paper). 280 pages. Provides the foundation necessary for an understanding of immigration from the passage of the first immigration-related statute to the current state of affairs of laws and amendments. Provides the foundation every attorney, law student and law office staff member needs to build understanding of U.S. immigration laws.

6294 ■ *Immigration Employment Compliance Handbook*
Thomson West
610 Opperman Dr.
Eagan, MN 55123
Ph: (651)687-7000
Fr: 800-937-8529
URL: http://store.westlaw.com

Austin T. Fragomen Jr., Careen Shannon, Daniel Montalvo. 2011. $718. Provides employer sanctions, eligibility procedures and antidiscrimination developments.

6295 ■ *Immigration Law for Paralegals*
Carolina Academic Press
700 Kent St.
Durham, NC 27701
Ph: (919)489-7486
Fax: (919)493-5668
E-mail: web@cap-press.com
URL: http://www.cap-press.com/books/isbn/9781594608179/Immigration+Law+for+Paralegals

Maria Isabel Casablanca, Gloria Roa Bodin. 2010. $58 (paper). 364 pages. Provides guidelines on U.S. immigration, citizenship and visa procedures for instructing and training students or anyone interested in career as an immigration paralegal or legal assistant. Features interviewing, gathering information, case management and document preparation techniques; analysis of temporary and permanent employment visas; analysis of family-based petitions, political asylum and naturalization; as well as samples of completed applications, a glossary of terms and appendices.

6296 ■ *Immigration Procedures Handbook*
Thomson West
610 Opperman Dr.
Eagan, MN 55123
Ph: (651)687-7000
URL: http://store.westlaw.com

Austin T. Fragomen Jr., Careen Shannon, Daniel Montalvo. 2011. $828 (paper). Contains explanations on present specific types of petitions and applications under present immigration laws. Includes analysis of the law to assist in determining the method of proceeding with a case. Covers changes that affect immigration practice and procedure.

6297 ■ *Immigration Trial Handbook*
Thomson West
610 Opperman Dr.
Eagan, MN 55123
Ph: (651)687-7000
URL: http://store.westlaw.com

Maria Baldini-Potermin, Anna Marie Gallagher. 2011. $263 (paper). Discusses the procedures, techniques, and strategies for representing non-citizens in removal proceedings at the administrative level. Contains practice tips, checklists, cautions concerning pitfalls to avoid and citations to statutes, regulations, case authorities, practice rules and agency memoranda. Features coverage of trial practice under the executive office for immigration review's immigration court practice manual.

6298 ■ *Kurzban's Immigration Law Sourcebook*
American Immigration Lawyers Association
9 Jay Gould Ct.
Waldorf, MD 20602
Ph: (301)374-9000
Fax: (301)843-0159
Fr: 800-982-2839
E-mail: pubs@aila.org
URL: http://www.ailapubs.org/kurimlawsour1.html

Ira J. Kurzban. 2010. $399 (paper). 1872 pages. Provides guides and resources on immigration law with explanations. Features subject-matter index, table of cases and multiple tables of authorities to help find answers on immigration issues.

6299 ■ *Working With Refugee and Immigrant Children: Issues of Culture, Law and Development*
Lutheran Immigration and Refugee Service
Children's Services Unit
700 Light St., 2nd Fl.
Baltimore, MD 21230
Ph: (410)230-2757
E-mail: childrenservices@lirs.org
URL: http://www.lirs.org/What/children/manual.htm

$20. Serves as a resource tool for lawyers, social workers and advocates. Combines information about migration issues, child welfare and child development to bridge the gap between these disciplines.

Online Job Sources and Services

6300 ■ Asylum Law
E-mail: info@probono.net
URL: http://www.probono.net/asylum

Description: Supports lawyers who are providing pro bono assistance to individuals seeking asylum in the United States. Contains online support and resources for participating lawyers including news, a calendar of trainings and events, online listings of new cases for volunteers and an online library of training manuals, briefs and practice materials.

6301 ■ GetImmigrationAttorneyJobs.com
URL: http://www.getimmigrationattorneyjobs.com

Description: Provides online job searches for immigration law professionals. Gives free weekly job listings via email.

6302 ■ Immigration Advocates Network
URL: http://www.immigrationadvocates.org

Description: Provides an online resource and communication site to enhance and unify the work of the nation's immigrants' rights organizations.

6303 ■ Immigration Assistant
URL: http://www.immigration-usa.com

Description: Computer program that combines U.S. immigration law reference materials, learning tools and all the immigration forms that an immigrant might need.

6304 ■ Immigration.com
URL: http://www.immigration.com

Description: Supports the immigrant community by providing information and resources. Provides extensive visa information, legal services, and general legal advice to high technology and other businesses, and negotiates and drafts high-tech contracts. Provides links to resources that immigrants and other individuals can use to start a life in the United States.

6305 ■ LawCrossing.com
URL: http://www.lawcrossing.com

Description: Offers a collection of active legal jobs. Monitors the hiring needs of legal employers including law firms, corporations, government offices and public interest organizations in the United States.

TRADESHOWS

6306 ■ American Immigration Lawyers Association Conference
American Immigration Lawyers Association
1331 G St. NW, Ste. 300
Washington, DC 20005
Ph: (202)507-7600
Fax: (202)783-7853
URL: http://www.aila.org

Annual. Offers educational sessions, workshops for practitioners who practice before the immigration courts, and open forums. 2013 June 26-29; San Francisco, CA; 2014 June 18-21; Boston, MA.

6307 ■ Annual Immigration Law & Policy Conference
Migration Policy Institute
1400 16th St. NW, Ste. 300
Washington, DC 20036
Ph: (202)266-1940
Fax: (202)266-1900
E-mail: events@migrationpolicy.org
URL: http://www.migrationpolicy.org

Annual. Features law and policy analysis and discussion on immigration issues. Features panelists from government, academics and immigration advocates and experts.

6308 ■ CLINIC Annual Convening
Catholic Legal Immigration Network
415 Michigan Ave. NE, Ste. 200
Washington, DC 20017
Ph: (202)635-2556
Fax: (202)635-2649
E-mail: national@cliniclegal.org
URL: http://cliniclegal.org/taxonomy/term/61

Annual. Offers workshops and networking opportunities. Conducts training for staff and attorneys that serve low income and indigent immigrants.

6309 ■ Massachusetts Continuing Legal Education Annual Immigration Law Conference
Massachusetts Continuing Legal Education
Ten Winter Pl.
Boston, MA 02108-4751

Ph: (617)482-2205
Fax: (617)482-9498
Fr: 800-966-6253
URL: http://www.mcle.org

Annual. Addresses the current issues in immigration law and practice.

OTHER SOURCES

6310 ■ Advocates for Human Rights
330 2nd Ave. S, Ste. 800
Minneapolis, MN 55401
Ph: (612)341-3302
Fax: (612)341-2971
E-mail: hrights@advrights.org
URL: http://www.theadvocatesforhumanrights.org

Description: Seeks to promote and protect the human rights of asylum seekers, refugees and immigrants. Provides access to free legal services in many immigration cases annually. Offers educational materials related to immigrant rights and immigration policy.

6311 ■ American Civil Liberties Union
125 Broad St.
New York, NY 10004
Ph: (212)549-2666
E-mail: media@aclu.org
URL: http://www.aclu.org/immigrants-rights

Description: Strives to guarantee the fundamental rights and civil liberties of every person in the United States. Protects the most vulnerable members of the society, especially the immigrants "who have been the targets of discrimination, government abuse and divisive and inhumane immigration policies."

6312 ■ Asian Pacific American Legal Center of Southern California
1145 Wilshire Blvd., 2nd Fl.
Los Angeles, CA 90017
Ph: (213)977-7500
Fax: (213)977-7595
E-mail: info@apalc.org
URL: http://www.apalc.org

Description: Serves as an organization that combines traditional legal services with civil rights advocacy. Provides direct legal services and education especially to those who speak little or no English. Provides Asian language hotlines and other modes of assistance. Provides individual immigration and citizenship assistance, educates the public on immigration issues and advocates for fair immigration laws and policies.

6313 ■ Catholic Legal Immigration Network
415 Michigan Ave. NE, Ste. 200
Washington, DC 20017
Ph: (202)635-2556
Fax: (202)635-2649
E-mail: national@cliniclegal.org
URL: http://cliniclegal.org

Description: Catholic charities, Catholic diocesan programs and religious orders. Enhances delivery of legal services to indigent and low-income immigrants through diocesan immigration programs. Meets the legal immigration needs of archdioceses, dioceses and congregations through various supporting activities and its own direct representation of the foreign-born religious.

6314 ■ Federation for American Immigration Reform
25 Massachusetts Ave. NW, Ste. 300
Washington, DC 20001
Ph: (202)328-7004
Fax: (202)387-3447

Fr: 877-627-3247
E-mail: imehlman@fairus.org
URL: http://www.fairus.org

Description: Seeks to improve border security, stop illegal immigration and promote immigration levels consistent with the national interest.

6315 ■ Immigration Equality
40 Exchange Pl., 17th Fl.
New York, NY 10005
Ph: (212)714-2904
Fax: (212)714-2973
URL: http://www.immigrationequality.org

Description: Provides information and support to advocates, attorneys, politicians and those who are threatened by persecution or the discriminatory impact of the law. Works to end discrimination in U.S. immigration law, reduce the negative impact of that law on the lives of lesbian, gay, bisexual, transgender and HIV-positive people and help obtain asylum for those persecuted in their home country based on their sexual orientation, transgender identity or HIV-status. Offers education, outreach, advocacy and the maintenance of a nationwide network of resources.

6316 ■ Immigration and Visas International
21 Clyde Rd., Ste. 201
Somerset, NJ 08873
Ph: (732)873-9600
Fax: (732)873-9787
URL: http://www.immigrationandvisas.com

Description: Represents immigration attorneys, lawyers and consultants who deal primarily with immigration and visa matters. Specializes in immigration services.

6317 ■ Lutheran Immigration and Refugee Service
700 Light St.
Baltimore, MD 21230
Ph: (410)230-2700
Fax: (410)230-2890
E-mail: lirs@lirs.org
URL: http://www.lirs.org

Description: Works to resettle refugees, protect foreign-born children, advocate for fair treatment of asylum seekers and pursue alternatives for those in immigration detention. Advocates to ensure that America's doors remain open to newcomers.

6318 ■ National Immigration Project
14 Beacon St., Ste. 602
Boston, MA 02108
Ph: (617)227-9727
Fax: (617)227-5495
E-mail: dan@nationalimmigrationproject.org
URL: http://www.nationalimmigrationproject.org

Description: Lawyers, law students, and legal workers. Educates and organizes for progressive immigration law. Works in defense of the civil liberties of the foreign born. Conducts immigration law skills seminars.

6319 ■ United States Committee for Refugees and Immigrants
2231 Crystal Dr., Ste. 350
Arlington, VA 22202-3794
Ph: (703)310-1130
Fax: (703)769-4241
E-mail: uscri@uscridc.org
URL: http://www.refugees.org

Description: Addresses the needs and rights of persons in forced or voluntary migration worldwide by advancing fair and humane public policy, facilitating and providing direct professional services and promoting the full participation of migrants in community life.

SOURCES OF HELP-WANTED ADS

6320 ■ AIE Perspectives Newsmagazine
American Institute of Engineers
4630 Appian Way, Ste. 206
El Sobrante, CA 94803-1875
Ph: (510)758-6240
Fax: (510)758-6240
URL: http://www.members-aie.org

Monthly. Professional magazine covering engineering.

6321 ■ Engineering
Scientific Research Publishing
PO Box 54821
Irvine, CA 92619-4821
E-mail: eng@scirp.org
URL: http://www.scirp.org/journal/eng/

Monthly. $708.00/year for individuals. Peer-reviewed journal publishing articles on the latest advancements in engineering.

6322 ■ Engineering Conferences International Symposium Series
Berkeley Electronic Press
2809 Telegraph Ave., Ste. 202
Berkeley, CA 94705-1167
Ph: (510)665-1200
Fax: (510)665-1201
URL: http://services.bepress.com/eci/

Journal focusing on advance engineering science.

6323 ■ The Engineering Economist
Institute of Industrial Engineers
3577 Parkway Ln., Ste. 200
Norcross, GA 30092
Ph: (770)449-0460
Fax: (770)441-3295
Fr: 800-494-0460
E-mail: advertising@iienet.org
URL: http://www.iienet2.org

Description: Quarterly. Discusses news of the Institute. Recurring features include a column titled In-Coming Director's Message. Discusses engineering economics. Articles featured have an academic slant with an emphasis on research.

6324 ■ ENR: Engineering News-Record
McGraw-Hill Inc.
PO Box 182604
Columbus, OH 43218
Ph: (614)430-4000
Fax: (614)759-3749
Fr: 877-833-5524
URL: http://enr.construction.com/Default.asp

Weekly. $49.00/year for individuals, print; $89.00/year for Canada, print; $125.00/year for other countries, print. Magazine focusing on engineering and construction.

6325 ■ Graduating Engineer & Computer Careers
Career Recruitment Media
2 LAN Dr., Ste. 100
Westford, MA 01886
Ph: (978)692-5092
Fax: (978)692-4174
URL: http://www.graduatingengineer.com

Quarterly. $16.95/year for individuals. Magazine focusing on employment, education, and career development for entry-level engineers and computer scientists.

6326 ■ High Technology Careers Magazine
HTC
4701 Patrick Henry Dr., No. 1901
Santa Clara, CA 95054
Fax: (408)567-0242
URL: http://www.hightechcareers.com

Bimonthly. $29.00/year; $35.00/year for Canada; $85.00/year for out of country. Magazine (tabloid) containing employment opportunity information for the engineering and technical community.

6327 ■ IIE Solutions
Institute of Industrial Engineers
3577 Pky. Ln., Ste. 200
Norcross, GA 30092
Ph: (770)449-0460
Fax: (770)441-3295
Fr: 800-494-0460
E-mail: advertising@iienet.org
URL: http://www.iienet2.org/Default.aspx

Monthly. Magazine covering industrial engineering, facilities design, systems integration, production control, material handling, quality, productivity, management, and other industrial engineering topics.

6328 ■ InterJournal
New England Complex Systems Institute
283 Main St., Ste. 319
Cambridge, MA 02142
Ph: (617)547-4100
Fax: (617)661-7711
URL: http://www.interjournal.org/

Journal covering the fields of science and engineering.

6329 ■ Journal of Engineering Education
American Society for Engineering Education
1818 N St. NW, Ste. 600
Washington, DC 20036-2479
Ph: (202)331-3500
Fax: (202)265-8504
URL: http://www.jee.org

Quarterly. $100.00/year for libraries, online; $160.00/year for other countries, library; $150.00/year for U.S., Canada, and Mexico, library; $160.00/year for other countries, library. Peer-reviewed journal covering scholarly research in engineering education.

6330 ■ Journal of Women and Minorities in Science and Engineering
Begell House Inc.
50 Cross Hwy.
Redding, CT 06896
Ph: (203)938-1300
Fax: (203)938-1304
URL: http://www.begellhouse.com/journals/00551c876cc2f027

$248.00/year for institutions. Peer-reviewed journal featuring innovative ideas and programs for classroom teachers, scientific studies, and formulation of concepts related to the education, recruitment, and retention of under-represented groups in science and engineering.

6331 ■ Managing Automation
Thomas Publishing Co.
5 Penn Plz.
New York, NY 10001
Ph: (212)695-0500
Fax: (212)290-7362
E-mail: contact@thomaspublishing.com
URL: http://www.managingautomation.com/maonline/

Monthly. $60.00/year for individuals; $75.00/year for Canada and Mexico; $125.00/year for other countries. Managing Automation covers advanced manufacturing technology including automation, integrated manufacturing, enterprise applications, and IT and e-business for the manufacturing enterprise.

6332 ■ NSBE Magazine
NSBE Publications
205 Daingerfield Rd.
Alexandria, VA 22314
Ph: (703)549-2207
Fax: (703)683-5312
URL: http://www.nsbe.org/News-Media/Magazines/About-NSBE-Magazine

$20.00/year for individuals; $35.00/year for other countries; $15.00/year for students. Journal providing information on engineering careers, self-development, and cultural issues for recent graduates with technical majors.

6333 ■ PE
National Society of Professional Engineers
1420 King St.
Alexandria, VA 22314
Ph: (703)684-2800
Fax: (703)684-4875
URL: http://www.nspe.org/PEmagazine/index.html

Monthly. Magazine (tabloid) covering professional, legislative, and techology issues for an engineering audience.

6334 ■ Plant Engineering
CFE Media LLC
1111 W 22nd St., Ste. 250
Oak Brook, IL 60523
Ph: (630)571-4070

Fax: (630)214-4504
URL: http://www.plantengineering.com/

Monthly. Free. Magazine focusing on engineering support and maintenance in industry.

6335 ■ SPE Technical Journals
Society of Petroleum Engineers (SPE)
830 S. Greenville Ave.
Allen, TX 75002
Ph: (972)952-9393
Fax: (972)952-9435
Fr: 800-456-6863

$80.00/year for members, print or online. Journal devoted to engineers and scientists.

6336 ■ Structure Magazine
American Council of Engineering Companies
1015 15th St. NW, 8th Fl.
Washington, DC 20005-2605
Ph: (202)347-7474
Fax: (202)898-0068
URL: http://www.structuremag.org

Annual. $65.00/year for nonmembers, for U.S residents; $35.00/year for students; $90.00/year for Canada; $125.00/year for other countries. Magazine focused on providing tips, tools, techniques, and innovative concepts for structural engineers.

6337 ■ SWE, Magazine of the Society of Women Engineers
Society of Women Engineers
120 S La Salle St., Ste. 1515
Chicago, IL 60603
Ph: (312)596-5223
Fr: 877-793-4636
URL: http://societyofwomenengineers.swe.org/
index.php

Quarterly. $30.00/year for nonmembers. Magazine for engineering students and for women and men working in the engineering and technology fields. Covers career guidance, continuing development and topical issues.

6338 ■ WEPANEWS
Women in Engineering Programs & Advocates Network
1901 E Asbury Ave., Ste. 220
Denver, CO 80208
Ph: (303)871-4643
Fax: (303)871-4628
E-mail: dmatt@wepan.org
URL: http://www.wepan.org

Description: 2/year. Seeks to provide greater access for women to careers in engineering. Includes news of graduate, undergraduate, freshmen, pre-college, and re-entry engineering programs for women. Recurring features include job listings, faculty, grant, and conference news, international engineering program news, action group news, notices of publications available, and a column titled Kudos.

6339 ■ Wire & Cable Technology International
Initial Publications Inc.
3869 Darrow Rd., Ste. 109
Stow, OH 44224
Ph: (330)686-9544
Fax: (330)686-9563
E-mail: info@wiretech.com
URL: http://www.wiretech.com/

Bimonthly. Magazine for manufacturers of ferrous, nonferrous, bare, and insulated wire.

6340 ■ Woman Engineer
Equal Opportunity Publications, Inc.
445 Broadhollow Rd., Ste. 425
Melville, NY 11747
Ph: (631)421-9421
Fax: (631)421-1352
E-mail: info@eop.com
URL: http://www.eop.com

Annual. Magazine that is offered at no charge to qualified female engineering, computer-science, and information-technology students and professionals seeking to find employment and advancement in their careers.

PLACEMENT AND JOB REFERRAL SERVICES

6341 ■ Aerotek Automotive
Aerotek, Inc.
7301 Parkway Dr.
Hanover, MD 21076
Ph: (410)694-5100
Fr: 800-237-6835
URL: http://automotive.aerotek.com

Description: Provides technical, professional and industrial recruiting and staffing services within the automotive field.

EMPLOYER DIRECTORIES AND NETWORKING LISTS

6342 ■ American Men and Women of Science
Gale
PO Box 6904
Florence, KY 41022-6904
Fr: 800-354-9706
URL: http://www.gale.cengage.com

Biennial, even years; New edition expected 29th, June 2011. $1,368.00 for individuals. Covers: Over 135,000 U.S. and Canadian scientists active in the physical, biological, mathematical, computer science, and engineering fields; includes references to previous edition for deceased scientists and nonrespondents. Entries include: Name, address, education, personal and career data, memberships, honors and awards, research interest. Arrangement: Alphabetical. Indexes: Discipline (in separate volume).

6343 ■ Careers in Focus—Engineering
Facts On File Inc.
132 W 31st St., 17th Fl.
New York, NY 10001
Ph: (212)967-8800
Fax: 800-678-3633
Fr: 800-322-8755
URL: http://www.infobasepublishing.com

Latest edition 3rd; Published July, 2007. $32.95 for individuals. Covers: An overview of engineering, followed by a selection of jobs profiled in detail, including the nature of the job, earnings, prospects for employment, what kind of training and skills it requires, and sources for further information.

6344 ■ Directory of Contract Staffing Firms
C.E. Publications Inc.
PO Box 3006
Bothell, WA 98041-3006
Ph: (425)806-5200
Fax: (425)806-5585
URL: http://www.cjhunter.com/dcsf/overview.html

Annual. Covers: Nearly 1,300 contract firms actively engaged in the employment of engineering, IT/IS, and technical personnel for 'temporary' contract assignments throughout the world. Entries include: Company name, address, phone, name of contact, email, web address. Arrangement: Alphabetical. Indexes: Geographical.

6345 ■ Forming & Fabricating Industry Directory
FMA Communications, Inc.
833 Featherstone Rd.
Rockford, IL 61107-6302
Ph: (815)399-8700

Fax: (815)381-1370
E-mail: info@thefabricator.com
URL: http://www.thefabricator.com/directory

Online searchable guide of metal forming and fabricating suppliers. Contains company listings by category.

HANDBOOKS AND MANUALS

6346 ■ Engineering, Mechanics, and Architecture
Ferguson Publishing
132 W 31st St., 17th Fl.
New York, NY 10001
Fax: 800-678-3633
Fr: 800-322-8755
E-mail: custserv@factsonfile.com
URL: http://www.infobasepublishing.com

Kelly Wiles. 2010. $39.95. 160 pages (hardcover). Serves as a guide for readers interested in switching jobs. Contains useful advice, career tips, interviews and self-asessment questions.

6347 ■ Engineering, Mechanics, and Architecture
Ferguson Publishing
132 W 31st St., 17th Fl.
New York, NY 10001
Fax: 800-678-3633
Fr: 800-322-8755
E-mail: custserv@factsonfile.com
URL: http://www.infobasepublishing.com

Kelly Wiles. 2010. $39.95. 160 pages (hardcover). Serves as a guide for readers interested in switching jobs. Contains useful advice, career tips, interviews and self-asessment questions.

6348 ■ Expert Resumes for Engineers
JIST Publishing
875 Montreal Way
St. Paul, MN 55102
Fr: 800-648-5478
E-mail: educate@emcp.com
URL: http://www.jist.com

Louise M. Kursmark and Wendy S. Enelow. 2009. $16.95 (softcover). 272 pages. Features a collection of written resume samples for all types of engineers including civil, mechanical, industrial, electrical, electronics, computer, and more. Contains tips and strategies for writing engineering resumes and finding the best jobs.

6349 ■ Great Jobs for Engineering Majors
The McGraw-Hill Companies
PO Box 182604
Columbus, OH 43272
Fax: (614)759-3749
Fr: 877-883-5524
E-mail: customer.service@mcgraw-hill.com
URL: http://www.mhprofessional.com/
product.php?isbn=0071641963

Geraldine O. Garner. Second edition, 2008. $16.95. 192 pages. Covers all the career options open to students majoring in engineering.

6350 ■ Resumes for Scientific and Technical Careers
The McGraw-Hill Companies
PO Box 182604
Columbus, OH 43272
Fax: (614)759-3749
Fr: 877-883-5524
E-mail: customer.service@mcgraw-hill.com
URL: http://www.mhprofessional.com/
product.php?isbn=0071482199

Third edition, 2007. $12.95 (paper). 144 pages. Provides resume advice for individuals interested in working in scientific and technical careers. Includes sample resumes and cover letters.

EMPLOYMENT AGENCIES AND SEARCH FIRMS

6351 ■ The Aspire Group
711 Boylston St.
Boston, MA 02116-2616
Fax: (617)500-7284
Fr: 800-487-2967
URL: http://www.bmanet.com/Aspire/index.html
Employment agency.

6352 ■ ATR Engineering
1230 Oakmead Pkwy.
Sunnyvale, CA 94085
Ph: (408)328-8000
Fax: (408)328-8001
Fr: 877-412-1100
E-mail: corporate@atr1.com
URL: http://www.atr-engineering.com

Description: Serves as an executive search firm specializing in the placement of engineering professionals in contract, contract-to-hire and full-time basis across all disciplines including design engineering, manufacturing engineering, hardware engineering, design engineering, electrical engineering and mechanical engineering.

6353 ■ Auguston and Associates Inc.
1010 S Ocean Blvd., Ste. 601
Pompano Beach, FL 33062
Ph: (954)943-0503
Fax: (954)784-1660
E-mail: g.auguston@augustonandassociates.com
URL: http://www.augustonandassociates.com/
Executive search firm focused on medical devices.

6354 ■ Bell Oaks Co.
115 Perimeter Center Pl., Ste. 400
Atlanta, GA 30346
Ph: (678)287-2000
Fax: (678)287-2002
E-mail: info@belloaks.com
URL: http://www.belloaks.com
Personnel service firm.

6355 ■ Career Advocates International
1539 Ave. A
Katy, TX 77493
Ph: (281)395-9848
Fax: (281)574-3949
URL: http://www.careeradvocates.org

Provides permanent placement and temporary staffing for executive and staff level positions. Specializes in multiple niches including: sales and marketing, accounting and financial services, banking, communications, human resources, chemicals, oil and gas, medical and dental, legal, information technology, energy, technology, engineering, manufacturing, construction, and light industrial.

6356 ■ Centennial, Inc.
8044 Montgomery Rd., Ste. 260
Cincinnati, OH 45236
Ph: (513)366-3760
Fax: (513)366-3761
E-mail: info@centennialinc.com
URL: http://www.centennialinc.com

Serves as an executive search firm specializing in the areas of executive and general management, accounting and finance, human resources, information technology, manufacturing, engineering, marketing and advertising, not-for-profit, sales and business development, and supply chain and logistics. Performs executive coaching as well as career coaching for clients.

6357 ■ CEO Resources Inc.
PO Box 2883
Framingham, MA 01703-2883
Ph: (508)877-2775

Fax: (508)877-8433
E-mail: info@ceoresourcesinc.com
URL: http://ceoresourcesinc.com
Executive search firm.

6358 ■ C.H. Cowles Associates
93 W Alyssa Canyon Pl.
PO Box 89291
Tucson, AZ 85755
Ph: (520)297-1014
Fax: (520)297-7608
E-mail: desertkiwanis@aol.com

Firm provides services in industrial engineering and industrial management including long-range planning, facilities planning, work improvement, profit improvement, executive search, quality assurance, manufacturing engineering and staff reorganization, site search and site planning.

6359 ■ Cizek Associates Inc.
2415 E Camelback Rd., Ste. 700
Phoenix, AZ 85016
Ph: (602)553-1066
Fax: (602)553-1166
E-mail: phx@cizekassociates.com
URL: http://www.cizekassociates.com
Executive search firm. Also maintains offices in Chicago and San Francisco.

6360 ■ Dinte Resources Inc.
8300 Greensboro Dr., Ste. 750
McLean, VA 22102
Ph: (703)448-3300
Fax: (703)448-0215
E-mail: pdinte@dinte.com
URL: http://www.dinte.com
Executive search firm.

6361 ■ Electronic Careers
21355 Pacific Coast Hwy., Ste. 100
Malibu, CA 90265
Ph: (310)317-6113
E-mail: e-careers@electroniccareers.com
URL: http://www.electroniccareers.com
Executive search firm.

6362 ■ Elite Resources Group
1239 Stetson Ln.
Sevierville, TN 37876
Ph: (865)774-8228
Fax: (865)774-8229
URL: http://www.elite-rg.com
Executive search firm.

6363 ■ Engineer One, Inc.
PO Box 23037
Knoxville, TN 37933
Fax: (865)691-0110
E-mail: engineerone@engineerone.com
URL: http://www.engineerone.com

Engineering employment service specializing in engineering and management in the chemical process, power utilities, manufacturing, mechanical, electrical, and electronic industries. Maintains an Information Technology Division that works nationwide across all industries. Also provides systems analysis consulting services specializing in VAX based systems.

6364 ■ Executive Recruiters Agency
PO Box 21810
Little Rock, AR 72211
Ph: (501)224-7000
Fax: (501)224-8534
E-mail: jobs@execrecruit.com
URL: http://www.execrecruit.com
Personnel service firm.

6365 ■ Executive Resource Group Inc.
1330 Cedar Point, No. 201
Amelia, OH 45102
Ph: (513)947-1447

Fax: (513)752-3026
URL: http://www.executiveresource.net
Executive search firm.

6366 ■ Fisher Personnel Management Services
2351 N Filbert Rd.
Exeter, CA 93221
Ph: (559)594-5774
Fax: (559)594-5777
E-mail: hookme@fisheads.net
URL: http://www.fisheads.net
Executive search firm.

6367 ■ Global Employment Solutions
10375 Park Meadows Dr., Ste. 375
Littleton, CO 80124
Ph: (303)216-9500
Fax: (303)216-9533
URL: http://www.gesnetwork.com
Employment agency.

6368 ■ International Staffing Consultants
31655 2nd Ave.
Laguna Beach, CA 92651
Ph: (949)255-5857
Fax: (949)767-5959
E-mail: iscinc@iscworld.com
URL: http://www.iscworld.com
Employment agency. Provides placement on regular or temporary basis. Affiliate office in London.

6369 ■ Mfg/Search, Inc.
205 W Jefferson Blvd., Ste. 601
South Bend, IN 46601
Ph: (574)282-2547
Fax: (574)232-0982
E-mail: hmueller@mfgsearch.com
URL: http://www.mfgsearch.com
Executive search firm. Offices in GA, IL, MI, NY.

6370 ■ Palladian International, LLC
105-A Lew Dewitt Blvd., Ste. 197
Waynesboro, VA 22980
Fr: (866)766-8447
E-mail: palladian@palladianinternational.com
URL: http://palladianinternational.com

Acts as an executive recruiting firm that specializes in manufacturing and engineering, distribution and logistics, and former military officers. Offers free guides in resume writing, interview preparation, and resume benchmarking surveys.

6371 ■ SPECTRA Associates
PO Box 688
Stevensville, MT 59870
Ph: (406)369-1188
E-mail: engineering@spectra-assoc.com
URL: http://www.spectra-assoc.com

Description: Serves as an executive search firm specializing in recruitment for engineering markets including companies involved with manufacturing, production and engineering.

ONLINE JOB SOURCES AND SERVICES

6372 ■ AECWorkForce.com
E-mail: jclarke@zweigwhite.com
URL: http://aecworkforce.com

Description: Serves as job board for professionals and employers in architecture, engineering and construction.

6373 ■ Design Engineer Jobzone
URL: http://designengineerjobzone.com/site/2791/about.htm

Description: Database of job openings for design engineers. Lists the latest jobs from top companies in the field.

6374 ■ Engineering Classifieds
URL: http://www.engineeringclassifieds.com

Description: Serves as a career site for engineering professionals. Provides services including job search agents, resume creation and posting.

6375 ■ EngineerJobs.com
URL: http://www.engineerjobs.com

Description: Provides job opportunities for engineering professionals in the following disciplines: aerospace, agricultural, biomedical, chemical, civil, electrical, environmental, industrial, manufacturing, marine, materials, mechanical, mining, nuclear, petroleum, process, project, quality, sales, software, solar, systems, and structural.

6376 ■ Engineer.net
URL: http://www.engineer.net

Description: Provides engineering employment tools such as job search, job posting, and engineering resumes.

6377 ■ IndustrialEngineerCareers.com
URL: http://www.industrialengineercareers.com

Description: Covers information about industrial engineering employment and career opportunities. Lists job openings according to job type, city and state.

6378 ■ IndustrialEngineer.com
URL: http://www.industrialengineer.com

Description: Provides industrial engineering job listings and products to industrial engineers.

6379 ■ Spherion
2050 Spectrum Blvd.
Fort Lauderdale, FL 33309
Ph: (954)308-7600
Fr: 800-774-3746
E-mail: help@spherion.com
URL: http://www.spherion.com

Description: Recruitment firm specializing in accounting and finance, sales and marketing, interim executives, technology, engineering, retail and human resources.

6380 ■ ThinkEnergyGroup.com
E-mail: resumes@thinkjobs.com
URL: http://www.thinkenergygroup.com

Description: Serves as a job board for professionals looking for positions in engineering, power plant, energy, and technical fields. Contains advice and tips on interviews, job searching, resume writing, hiring, and management. Provides choices of work location, pay rates in the field of expertise and contract, temp-to-hire, and direct hiring options.

TRADESHOWS

6381 ■ American Society for Engineering Education Annual Conference and Exposition
American Society for Engineering Education
1818 N. St. N.W., Ste. 600
Washington, DC 20036-2479
Ph: (202)331-3500
Fax: (202)265-8504
E-mail: conferences@asee.org
URL: http://www.asee.org

Annual. Primary Exhibits: Publications, engineering supplies and equipment, computers, software, and research companies all products and services related to engineering education. Dates and Locations: 2012 Jun 10-13; San Antonio, TX.

OTHER SOURCES

6382 ■ American Association of Engineering Societies (AAES)
1801 Alexander Bell Dr.
Reston, VA 20191

Ph: (202)296-2237
Fax: (202)296-1151
Fr: 888-400-2237
E-mail: dbateson@aaes.org
URL: http://www.aaes.org

Description: Coordinates the efforts of the member societies in the provision of reliable and objective information to the general public concerning issues which affect the engineering profession and the field of engineering as a whole; collects, analyzes, documents, and disseminates data which will inform the general public of the relationship between engineering and the national welfare; provides a forum for the engineering societies to exchange and discuss their views on matters of common interest; and represents the U.S. engineering community abroad through representation in WFEO and UPADI.

6383 ■ American Engineering Association (AEA)
533 Waterside Blvd.
Monroe Township, NJ 08831
Ph: (201)664-6954
E-mail: aea@aea.org
URL: http://www.aea.org

Description: Members consist of Engineers and engineering professionals. Purpose to advance the engineering profession and U.S. engineering capabilities. Issues of concern include age discrimination, immigration laws, displacement of U.S. Engineers by foreign workers, trade agreements, off shoring of U.S. Engineering and manufacturing jobs, loss of U.S. manufacturing and engineering capability, and recruitment of foreign students. Testifies before Congress. Holds local Chapter meetings.

6384 ■ American Indian Science and Engineering Society (AISES)
PO Box 9828
Albuquerque, NM 87119-9828
Ph: (505)765-1052
Fax: (505)765-5608
E-mail: info@aises.org
URL: http://www.aises.org

Description: Represents American Indian and non-Indian students and professionals in science, technology, and engineering fields; corporations representing energy, mining, aerospace, electronic, and computer fields. Seeks to motivate and encourage students to pursue undergraduate and graduate studies in science, engineering, and technology. Sponsors science fairs in grade schools, teacher training workshops, summer math/science sessions for 8th-12th graders, professional chapters, and student chapters in colleges. Offers scholarships. Adult members serve as role models, advisers, and mentors for students. Operates placement service.

6385 ■ American Supplier Institute (ASI)
30200 Telegraph Rd., Ste. 100
Bingham Farms, MI 48025
Ph: (734)464-1395
Fax: (734)464-1399
Fr: 800-462-4500
E-mail: asi@asiusa.com
URL: http://www.amsup.com

Description: Seeks to encourage change in U.S. industry through development and implementation of advanced manufacturing and engineering technologies such as Taguchi Methods, Quality Function Deployment, Statistical Process Control, and Total Quality Management. Offers educational courses, training seminars, and workshops to improve quality, reduce cost, and enhance competitive position of U.S. products. Maintains international network of affiliates for developing training specialists and technologies curriculum. Provides training services to government supplier companies.

6386 ■ Association for Facilities Engineering
12801 Worldgate Dr., Ste. 500
Herndon, VA 20170
Ph: (571)203-7171

Fax: (571)766-2142
E-mail: info@afe.org
URL: http://www.afe.org

Description: Represents professionals involved in plant engineering/facilities management. Provides education, certification, technical information, and other relevant resources to plant and facility engineering, operations, and maintenance professionals worldwide.

6387 ■ Association for Finishing Processes (AFP)
Society for Manufacturing Engineers
1 SME Dr.
Dearborn, MI 48121
Ph: (313)425-3000
Fax: (313)425-3400
Fr: 800-733-4763
E-mail: service@sme.org
URL: http://www.sme.org/cgi-bin/communities.pl?/communities/afp/afphome.htm&&&SME

Description: Promotes the technology, process, and management aspects of the cleaning and coating of metal or plastic manufactured products and trade organizations concerned with the dissemination of knowledge related to industrial finishing. Conducts clinics and expositions. Offers professional certification. Maintains placement service with free listings for members.

6388 ■ Association for International Practical Training (AIPT)
10400 Little Patuxent Pkwy., Ste. 250
Columbia, MD 21044-3519
Ph: (410)997-2200
Fax: (410)992-3924
E-mail: aipt@aipt.org
URL: http://www.aipt.org

Description: Providers worldwide of on-the-job training programs for students and professionals seeking international career development and life-changing experiences. Arranges workplace exchanges in hundreds of professional fields, bringing employers and trainees together from around the world. Client list ranges from small farming communities to Fortune 500 companies.

6389 ■ Engineering Society of Detroit (ESD)
20700 Civic Center Dr., Ste. 450
Southfield, MI 48076
Ph: (248)353-0735
Fax: (248)353-0736
E-mail: esd@esd.org
URL: http://ww2.esd.org/home.htm

Description: Engineers from all disciplines; scientists and technologists. Conducts technical programs and engineering refresher courses; sponsors conferences and expositions. Maintains speakers' bureau; offers placement services; although based in Detroit, MI, society membership is international.

6390 ■ Institute of Industrial Engineers (IIE)
3577 Parkway Ln., Ste. 200
Norcross, GA 30092
Ph: (770)449-0460
Fax: (770)441-3295
Fr: 800-494-0460
E-mail: dgreene@iienet.org
URL: http://www.iienet2.org/Default.aspx

Description: Serves as professional society of industrial engineers. Concerned with the design, improvement, and installation of integrated systems of people, materials, equipment, and energy. Draws upon specialized knowledge and skill in the mathematical, physical, and social sciences together with the principles and methods of engineering analysis and design, to specify, predict, and evaluate the results obtained from such systems. Maintains technical societies and divisions.

6391 ■ Intelligent Transportation Society of America
1100 17th St. NW, Ste. 1200
Washington, DC 20036

Ph: (202)484-4847
Fr: 800-374-8472
E-mail: info@itsa.org
URL: http://www.itsa.org

Description: Includes private corporations, public agencies, and academic institutions involved in the research, development, and design of intelligent transportation systems technologies that enhance safety, increase mobility, and sustain the environment.

6392 ■ Korean-American Scientists and Engineers Association (KSEA)
1952 Gallows Rd., Ste. 300
Vienna, VA 22182
Ph: (703)748-1221
Fax: (703)748-1331
E-mail: sejong@ksea.org
URL: http://www.ksea.org

Description: Represents scientists and engineers holding single or advanced degrees. Promotes friendship and mutuality among Korean and American scientists and engineers; contributes to Korea's scientific, technological, industrial, and economic developments; strengthens the scientific, technological, and cultural bonds between Korea and the U.S. Sponsors symposium. Maintains speakers' bureau, placement service, and biographical archives. Compiles statistics.

6393 ■ National Action Council for Minorities in Engineering (NACME)
440 Hamilton Ave., Ste. 302
White Plains, NY 10601-1813
Ph: (914)539-4010
Fax: (914)539-4032
E-mail: info@nacme.org
URL: http://www.nacme.org

Description: Leads the national effort to increase access to careers in engineering and other science-based disciplines. Conducts research and public

policy analysis, develops and operates national demonstration programs at precollege and university levels, and disseminates information through publications, conferences and electronic media. Serves as a privately funded source of scholarships for minority students in engineering.

6394 ■ National Society of Professional Engineers (NSPE)
1420 King St.
Alexandria, VA 22314-2794
Ph: (703)684-2800
Fax: (703)836-4875
Fr: 888-285-6773
E-mail: memserv@nspe.org
URL: http://www.nspe.org

Description: Represents professional engineers and engineers-in-training in all fields registered in accordance with the laws of states or territories of the U.S. or provinces of Canada; qualified graduate engineers, student members, and registered land surveyors. Is concerned with social, professional, ethical, and economic considerations of engineering as a profession; encompasses programs in public relations, employment practices, ethical considerations, education, and career guidance. Monitors legislative and regulatory actions of interest to the engineering profession.

6395 ■ Society of Hispanic Professional Engineers (SHPE)
13181 Crossroads Pkwy. N, Ste. 450
City of Industry, CA 91746-3496
Ph: (323)725-3970
Fax: (323)725-0316
E-mail: shpenational@shpe.org
URL: http://oneshpe.shpe.org/wps/portal/national

Description: Represents engineers, student engineers, and scientists. Aims to increase the number of Hispanic engineers by providing motivation and sup-

port to students. Sponsors competitions and educational programs. Maintains placement service and speakers' bureau; compiles statistics.

6396 ■ Society of Women Engineers (SWE)
203 N La Salle St., Ste. 1675
Chicago, IL 60601
Ph: (312)596-5223
Fax: (312)596-5252
Fr: 877-SWE-INFO
E-mail: hq@swe.org
URL: http://societyofwomenengineers.swe.org

Description: Educational and service organization representing both students and professional women in engineering and technical fields.

6397 ■ SOLE - The International Society of Logistics (SOLE)
8100 Professional Pl., Ste. 111
Hyattsville, MD 20785-2229
Ph: (301)459-8446
Fax: (301)459-1522
E-mail: solehq@erols.com
URL: http://www.sole.org

Description: Represents corporate and individual management and technical practitioners in the field of logistics, including scientists, engineers, educators, managers, and other specialists in commerce, aerospace, and other industries, government, and the military. (Logistics is the art and science of management engineering and technical activities concerned with requirements, and designing, supplying, and maintaining resources to support objectives, plans, and operations.) Covers every logistics specialty, including reliability, maintainability, systems and equipment maintenance, maintenance support equipment, human factors, training and training equipment, spare parts, overhaul and repair, handbooks, field site activation and operation, field engineering, facilities, packaging, supply chain management, materials handling, and transportation. Sponsors on-line job referral service; conducts specialized education programs.

SOURCES OF HELP-WANTED ADS

6398 ■ Academy of Management Journal
Academy of Management
235 Elm Rd.
PO Box 3020
Briarcliff Manor, NY 10510-8020
Ph: (914)923-2607
Fax: (914)923-2615
URL: http://journals.aomonline.org/amj/
Bimonthly. Professional journal covering management.

6399 ■ Academy of Management Learning & Education
Academy of Management
235 Elm Rd.
PO Box 3020
Briarcliff Manor, NY 10510-8020
Ph: (914)923-2607
Fax: (914)923-2615
URL: http://journals.aomonline.org/amle
Quarterly. $85.00/year for individuals, print; $130.00/year for individuals, print & online; $125.00/year for libraries, print; $170.00/year for libraries, print and online; $105.00/year for other countries, print; $150.00/year for other countries, print & online; $195.00/year for other countries, print, corporate library; $235.00/year for other countries, print & online, corporate library. Journal covering management issues for professionals.

6400 ■ Business Performance Management
Penton Media Inc.
249 W 17th St.
New York, NY 10011
Ph: (212)204-4200
URL: http://www.bpmmag.net/
Free to qualified subscribers. Magazine for business managers. Covers organizing, automating, and analyzing of business methodologies and processes.

6401 ■ CXO
IDG Communications Inc.
3 Speen St.
Framingham, MA 01701
Ph: (508)875-5000
URL: http://www.idg.com/www/IDGProducts.nsf/0/022796185EED5984852
Monthly. Magazine providing technology information for chief officers and managers.

6402 ■ D & O Advisor
American Lawyer Media L.P.
120 Broadway, 5th Fl.
New York, NY 10271
Ph: (212)457-9400
Fax: (646)417-7705
Fr: 800-603-6571
URL: http://www.alm.com

Quarterly. Magazine that offers advice and perspective on corporate oversight responsibilities for directors and officers.

6403 ■ E Journal of Organizational Learning and Leadership
WeLEAD Inc.
PO Box 202
Litchfield, OH 44253
Fr: 877-778-5494
URL: http://www.leadingtoday.org/weleadinlearning/
Semiannual. Free. Online academic journal about organizational leadership.

6404 ■ Event Management
Cognizant Communications Corp.
3 Hartsdale Rd.
Elmsford, NY 10523-3701
Ph: (914)592-7720
Fax: (914)592-8981
URL: http://www.cognizantcommunication.com/journal-titles/event-
Quarterly. $445.00/year for institutions, online only; $525.00/year for institutions, online & hard copy; $52.00/year for individuals, professional; $50.00/year for members, online & hard copy; $65.00/year for single issue. Peer-reviewed journal covering research and analytic needs of a rapidly growing profession focused on events.

6405 ■ Executive Legal Adviser
Incisive Media
120 Broadway, 5th Fl.
New York, NY 10271
Ph: (212)457-9400
Fax: (646)417-7705
URL: http://www.executivelegaladviser.com
Bimonthly. Free to qualified subscribers. Magazine that offers legal advice for corporate executives.

6406 ■ Fleet Maintenance
Cygnus Business Media Inc.
3 Huntington Quadrangle, Ste. 301 N
Melville, NY 11747
Ph: (631)845-2700
Fax: (631)845-7109
Fr: 800-308-6397
URL: http://www.fleetmag.com
Business tabloid magazine offering a chapterized curriculum of technical, regulatory and managerial information designed to help maintenance managers, directors and supervisors better perform their jobs and reduce their overall cost-per-mile.

6407 ■ Forrester
Forrester Research Inc.
400 Technology Sq.
Cambridge, MA 02139
Ph: (617)613-5730
Fr: (866)367-7378
URL: http://www.forrester.com/mag

Free. Journal that aims to provide ideas and advice that is relevant to today's CEOs.

6408 ■ Industrial Distribution
Reed Business Information
360 Park Ave. S
New York, NY 10010-1710
Ph: (646)746-6400
URL: http://www.inddist.com
Monthly. $121.00/year for individuals; $145.00/year for Canada; $140.00/year for individuals, for Mexico; $280.00/year for other countries. Magazine covering industrial supplies marketing, management, sales, telecommunications, computers, inventory, and warehouse management.

6409 ■ International Journal of Business Research
International Academy of Business and Economics
PO Box 2536
Ceres, CA 95307
Ph: (702)560-0653
Fax: (702)508-9166
URL: http://www.iabe.eu/domains/iabeX/journal.aspx?journalid=12
Peer-reviewed journal publishing theoretical, conceptual, and applied research on topics related to research, practice and teaching in all areas of business, management, and marketing.

6410 ■ Journal of Academic Leadership
Academic Leadership
600 Park St.
Rarick Hall 219
Hays, KS 67601-4099
Ph: (785)628-4547
URL: http://www.academicleadership.org/
Journal focusing on the leadership issues in the academic world.

6411 ■ Journal of Business and Psychology
Springer-Verlag New York Inc.
233 Spring St.
New York, NY 10013-1578
Ph: (212)460-1500
Fax: (212)460-1575
Fr: 800-777-4643
URL: http://www.springer.com/psychology/community+%26+environment
$904.00/year for institutions, print or online; $1,085.00/year for institutions, print & enchanced access. Journal covering all aspects of psychology that apply to the business segment. Includes topics such as personnel selection and training, organizational assessment and development, risk management and loss control, marketing and consumer behavior research.

6412 ■ Journal of International Business Strategy
International Academy of Business and Economics
PO Box 2536
Ceres, CA 95307

Ph: (702)560-0653
Fax: (702)508-9166
URL: http://www.iabe.eu/domains/iabeX/
journal.aspx?journalid=7

Peer-reviewed journal publishing theoretical, conceptual, and applied research on topics related to strategy in international business.

6413 ■ Management Research
M.E. Sharpe Inc.
80 Business Pk. Dr.
Armonk, NY 10504
Ph: (914)273-1800
Fax: (914)273-2106
Fr: 800-541-6563
URL: http://www.mesharpe.com/mall/
results1.asp?ACR=JMR

$75.00/year for individuals; $399.00/year for institutions; $87.00/year for other countries; $441.00/year for institutions, other countries. International journal dedicated to advancing the understanding of management in private and public sector organizations through empirical investigation and theoretical analysis. Attempts to promote an international dialogue between researchers, improve the understanding of the nature of management in different settings, and achieve a reasonable transfer of research results to management practice in several contexts. Receptive to research across a broad range of management topics such as human resource management, organizational behavior, organizational theory, and strategic management. While not regional in nature, articles dealing with Iberoamerican issues are particularly welcomed.

6414 ■ Organization Management Journal
Eastern Academy of Management
c/o Vicki Fairbanks Taylor, VP
John I. Grove College of Business
45 Keefer Way
Mechanicsburg, PA 17011
Ph: (518)762-4651
Fax: (518)736-1716
E-mail: omj@palgrave.com
URL: http://www1.wnec.edu/omj

Free to qualified subscribers. Refereed, online journal focusing on organization management issues.

6415 ■ Public Performance and Management Review
M.E. Sharpe Inc.
80 Business Pk. Dr.
Armonk, NY 10504
Ph: (914)273-1800
Fax: (914)273-2106
Fr: 800-541-6563
URL: http://www.mesharpe.com/mall/
results1.asp?ACR=pmr

Quarterly. $95.00/year for individuals; $528.00/year for institutions; $111.00/year for other countries; $560.00/year for institutions, other countries. Journal addressing a broad range of factors influencing the performance of public and nonprofit organizations and agencies. Aims to facilitate the development of innovative techniques and encourage a wider application of those already established; stimulate research and critical thinking about the relationship between public and private management theories; present integrated analyses of theories, concepts, strategies and techniques dealing with productivity, measurement and related questions of performance improvement; and provide a forum for practitioner-academic exchange. Continuing themes include managing for productivity, measuring and evaluating performance, improving budget strategies, managing human resources, building partnerships, and applying new technologies.

6416 ■ Supply Chain Management Review
Reed Business Information
360 Park Ave. S
New York, NY 10010-1710
Ph: (646)746-6400
URL: http://www.scmr.com

$199.00/year for individuals; $199.00/year for Canada; $337.00/year for other countries. Publication covering business and management.

EMPLOYMENT AGENCIES AND SEARCH FIRMS

6417 ■ APA Search Inc.
1 Byram Brook Pl., Ste. 104
Armonk, NY 10504
Ph: (914)273-6000
Fax: (914)273-8025
E-mail: info@apasearch.com
URL: http://www.apasearch.com

Employment agency specializing in the automotive, retail, and hardware industries.

6418 ■ Boyden
275 Madison Ave., Ste. 1500
New York, NY 10016
Ph: (212)949-9400
Fax: (212)949-5905
E-mail: newyork@boyden.com
URL: http://www.boyden.com

Executive search firm.

6419 ■ Boyle Ogata Bregman
17461 Derian Ave., Ste. 202
Irvine, CA 92614
Ph: (949)474-3365
E-mail: info@bobsearch.com
URL: http://www.bobsearch.com

Executive search firm.

6420 ■ Career Advocates International
1539 Ave. A
Katy, TX 77493
Ph: (281)395-9848
Fax: (281)574-3949
URL: http://www.careeradvocates.org

Provides permanent placement and temporary staffing for executive and staff level positions. Specializes in multiple niches including: sales and marketing, accounting and financial services, banking, communications, human resources, chemicals, oil and gas, medical and dental, legal, information technology, energy, technology, engineering, manufacturing, construction, and light industrial.

6421 ■ Cochran, Cochran & Yale LLC
955 E Henrietta Rd.
Rochester, NY 14623
Ph: (585)424-6060
E-mail: roch@ccy.com
URL: http://www.ccy.com

Executive search firm. Branches in Denver, CO and Williamsville, NY.

6422 ■ Conboy Sur Morice & Associates
15 Churchville Rd., No. 170
Bel Air, MD 21014-3837
E-mail: wks@csma-cons.com
URL: http://www.conboysur.com

Executive search firm.

6423 ■ Dieck Executive Search
30 Rough Lee Ct.
Madison, WI 53705
Ph: (608)238-1000
E-mail: dan@dieckexecutivesearch.com
URL: http://dieckexecutivesearch.com

Executive search firm focused on pulp, paper and the packaging industries.

6424 ■ The Ferneborg Group
1700 S El Camino Real, Ste. 375
San Mateo, CA 94402
Ph: (650)577-0100

Fax: (650)577-0122
E-mail: mailbox@execsearch.com
URL: http://www.execsearch.com

Executive search firm.

6425 ■ FPC of Savannah
145 Bull St.
Savannah, GA 31401
Ph: (912)233-4556
Fax: (912)223-8633
E-mail: info@fpcsav.com
URL: http://www.fpcnational.com/savannah

Executive search firm.

6426 ■ K.S. Frary & Associates
16 Schooner Ridge
Marblehead, MA 01945
Ph: (781)631-2464
Fax: (781)631-2465
E-mail: ksfrary@comcast.net
URL: http://www.ksfrary.com

Executive search firm.

6427 ■ Miller Personnel Consultants Inc.
931 E 86th St., Ste. 103
Indianapolis, IN 46240
Ph: (317)251-5938
Fax: (317)251-5762
Fr: 800-851-5938
E-mail: markmiller@netdirect.net
URL: http://www.millerpersonnel.com

Executive search firm.

6428 ■ Palladian International, LLC
105-A Lew Dewitt Blvd., Ste. 197
Waynesboro, VA 22980
Fr: (866)766-8447
E-mail: palladian@palladianinternational.com
URL: http://palladianinternational.com

Acts as an executive recruiting firm that specializes in manufacturing and engineering, distribution and logistics, and former military officers. Offers free guides in resume writing, interview preparation, and resume benchmarking surveys.

6429 ■ Recruiting Services Group Inc.
3107 E Corporate Edge Dr.
Germantown, TN 38138
Ph: (901)367-0778
Fax: (901)367-0868
E-mail: info@rsghunt.com
URL: http://www.rsghunt.com

Executive search firm.

6430 ■ RGT Associates Inc.
2 Greenleaf Woods Dr., Ste. 101
PO Box 1032
Portsmouth, NH 03802
Ph: (603)431-9500
Fax: (603)431-6984
E-mail: inquires@rgtassociatesinc.com
URL: http://rgtassociatesinc.com/rgt

Executive search firm.

6431 ■ Ronald Dukes Associates LLC
20 N Wacker, Ste. 2010
Chicago, IL 60606
Ph: (312)357-2895
Fax: (312)357-2897
E-mail: ron@rdukesassociates.com
URL: http://www.rdukesassociates.com

Executive search firm focused on the industrial and automotive industries.

6432 ■ Russ Hadick & Associates Inc.
77 W Elmwood Dr., Ste 100
Dayton, OH 45459
Ph: (937)439-7700
Fax: (937)439-7705
URL: http://www.rharecruiters.com

Executive search firm.

6433 ■ Southern Recruiters & Consultants Inc.
PO Box 2745
Aiken, SC 29802
Ph: (803)648-7834
Fax: (803)642-2770
E-mail: recruiters@southernrecruiters.com
URL: http://www.southernrecruiters.com

Executive search firm.

6434 ■ Stiles Associates LLC
276 Newport Rd., Ste. 208
New London, NH 03257
Ph: (603)526-6566

Fr: 800-322-5185
E-mail: tberio@leanexecs.com
URL: http://www.leanexecs.com

Executive search firm.

6435 ■ William J. Christopher Associates Inc.
307 N Walnut St.
West Chester, PA 19380
Ph: (610)696-4397
Fax: (610)692-5177
E-mail: wjc@wjca.com
URL: http://www.wjca.com

Executive search firm.

TRADESHOWS

6436 ■ International Thermal Spray Conference and Exposition
ASM International
9639 Kinsman Rd.
Materials Park, OH 44073-0002
Ph: (440)338-5151
E-mail: customerservice@asminternational.org
URL: http://www.asminternational.org

Annual. Primary Exhibits: Thermal spray and welding equipment, supplies, and services.

Sources of Help-Wanted Ads

Sources of Help-Wanted Ads

6437 ■ American City and County
Penton Media Inc.
9800 Metcalf Ave.
Overland Park, KS 66212
Ph: (913)341-1300
Fax: (913)967-1898
URL: http://americancityandcounty.com

Monthly. Municipal and county administration magazine.

6438 ■ American Industrial Hygiene Association Journal
American Industrial Hygiene Association
2700 Prosperity Ave., Ste. 250
Fairfax, VA 22031
Ph: (703)849-8888
Fax: (703)207-3561
URL: http://www.aiha.org/Pages/default.aspx

Bimonthly. Journal providing a forum for peer-reviewed articles in the field of industrial hygiene.

6439 ■ Cal-OSHA Reporter
Providence Publications
PO Box 2610
Granite Bay, CA 95746
Ph: (916)774-4000
Fax: (916)780-0600
E-mail: newsdesk@cal-osha.com
URL: http://www.cal-osha.com/

Description: 48/year. Reports on laws, regulations, court cases, and other issues of interest to occupational safety and health professionals. Recurring features include a calendar of events, reports of meetings, news of educational opportunities, job listings, and notices of publications available. Reviews all Cal-OSHA cases.

6440 ■ Industrial Hygiene News
Rimbach Publishing Inc.
8650 Babcock Blvd.
Pittsburgh, PA 15237
Ph: (412)364-5366
Fax: (412)369-9720
Fr: 800-245-3182
URL: http://www.rimbach.com

Bimonthly. Free to qualified subscribers. Magazine covering industrial hygiene, occupational health, and safety.

6441 ■ Journal of Occupational and Environmental Medicine
Lippincott Williams & Wilkins
530 Walnut St.
Philadelphia, PA 19106-3619
Ph: (215)521-8300
Fax: (215)521-8902
Fr: 800-638-3030
URL: http://www.lww.com/product/?1076-2752

Monthly. $422.00/year for individuals; $758.00/year for institutions; $615.00/year for other countries; $998.00/year for institutions, other countries; $394.00/year for other countries, in-training; $265.00/year for individuals, in-training. Occupational and environmental medicine journal.

6442 ■ Occupational Health & Safety
1105 Media, Inc.
14901 Quorum Dr., Ste. 425
Dallas, TX 75254
Ph: (972)687-6700
Fax: (972)687-6799
URL: http://ohsonline.com/Home.aspx

Monthly. $99.00/year for individuals. Magazine covering federal and state regulation of occupational health and safety.

6443 ■ Pharmaceutical Technology
Advanstar Communications
485 Rte. 1 S
Bldg. F, 1st Fl.
Iselin, NJ 08830
Ph: (732)596-0276
Fax: (732)596-0003
URL: http://pharmtech.findpharma.com/

Monthly. $185.00/year for individuals; $331.00/year for two years; $263.00/year for individuals, Canada and Mexico; $458.00/year for two years, Canada and Mexico; $55.00/year for individuals, back issue; $85.00/year for two years, Canada/international, back issue. Magazine on applied technology for pharmaceutical firms.

Employer Directories and Networking Lists

6444 ■ American Industrial Hygiene Association—Directory
American Industrial Hygiene Association
2700 Prosperity Ave., Ste. 250
Fairfax, VA 22031
Ph: (703)849-8888
Fax: (703)207-3561
URL: http://www.aiha.org

Annual, September. Covers: Approximately 12,000 members concerned with the study and control of environmental factors affecting people at work. Entries include: Name, address, phone, affiliation. Arrangement: Alphabetical. Indexes: Employer, geographical.

6445 ■ Carroll's State Directory
Carroll Publishing
4701 Sangamore Rd., Ste. S-155
Bethesda, MD 20816
Ph: (301)263-9800
Fax: (301)263-9801
Fr: 800-336-4240
URL: http://www.carrollpub.com/stateprint.asp

3x/yr. $425.00 for individuals. Covers: About 70,000 state government officials in all branches of government; officers, committees and members of state legislatures; managers of boards and authorities. Entries include: Name, address, phone, fax, title. Arrangement: Geographical; separate sections for state offices and legislatures. Indexes: Personal name (with phone and e-mail address), organizational, keyword.

6446 ■ Federal Staff Directory
CQ Press
2300 North St. NW, Ste. 800
Washington, DC 20037
Ph: (202)729-1900
Fax: 800-380-3810
Fr: (866)427-7737
URL: http://www.cqpress.com/product/Federal-Staff-Directory-Winte

Latest edition Winter 2010. $348.00 for individuals. Covers: Approximately 45,000 persons in federal government offices and independent agencies, with biographies of 2,600 key executives; includes officials at policy level in agencies of the Office of the President, Cabinet-level departments, independent and regulatory agencies, military commands, federal information centers, and libraries, and United States attorneys, marshals, and ambassadors. Entries include: Name, title, location (indicating building, address, and/or room), phone, fax, e-mail address, website, symbols indicating whether position is a presidential appointment and whether senate approval is required. Arrangement: Classified by department/agency. Indexes: Office locator page; extensive subject/keyword; individual name.

Handbooks and Manuals

6447 ■ Start Your Own Home Inspection Service
The McGraw-Hill Companies
PO Box 182604
Columbus, OH 43272
Fax: (614)759-3749
Fr: 877-883-5524
E-mail: customer.service@mcgraw-hill.com
URL: http://www.mcgraw-hill.com

2007. $15.95. Illustrated. 120 pages. Entrepreneur Magazine's Start Up Series.

Employment Agencies and Search Firms

6448 ■ Conselium
14850 Montfort Dr., Ste. 106
Dallas, TX 75254
Ph: (972)934-8444
E-mail: maurice@conselium.com
URL: http://www.conselium.com

Executive search firm with a core expertise in corporate compliance, audit and information technology security.

6449 ■ Food Management Search
235 State St., Ste. 326
Springfield, MA 01103
Ph: (413)732-2666
Fax: (413)732-6466
E-mail: recruiters@foodmanagementsearch.com
URL: http://foodmanagementsearch.com/index.cfm

Specializes in contingency recruiting projects exclusively in the food manufacturing and food service industries. Provides positions covering food production/manufacturing, supply chain, food service, sales and marketing.

6450 ■ Wellington Executive Search
3162 Johnson Ferry Rd., Ste. 260
Marietta, GA 30062
Ph: (770)645-5799
Fax: (678)278-0928
E-mail: jobs@wellingtonsearch.com
URL: http://www.wellingtonsearch.com

Serves as an executive search firm covering sales representative, research and development, food scientists, and purchasing managers.

ONLINE JOB SOURCES AND SERVICES

6451 ■ ComplianceCrossing.com
URL: http://www.compliancecrossing.com

Description: Features a comprehensive collection of compliance job openings. Includes listings from Fortune 500 and Fortune 1,000 companies.

TRADESHOWS

6452 ■ Annual Ethics & Compliance Conference
Ethics and Compliance Officer Association
411 Waverley Oaks Rd., Ste. 324
Waltham, MA 02452
Ph: (781)647-9333
Fax: (781)647-9399
URL: http://www.theecoa.org/iMIS15/ECOAPublic

Annual. Addresses the latest issues and provides opportunities for the exchange of ideas and practical, proven methods for implementing and maintaining successful ethics, compliance and business conduct programs. 2012 October 2-25; St. Louis, MO.

6453 ■ National Safety Council Congress and Expo
National Safety Council
1121 Spring Lake Dr.
Itasca, IL 60143-3201
Ph: (630)285-1121
Fax: (630)285-1315
Fr: 800-621-7615
E-mail: info@nsc.org
URL: http://www.nsc.org

Annual. Primary Exhibits: Safety- and health-related products and services, including protective clothing, footwear, consulting services, breathing apparatuses, educational materials, films and related equipment, supplies, and services.

OTHER SOURCES

6454 ■ American Public Health Association (APHA)
800 I St. NW
Washington, DC 20001
Ph: (202)777-2742
Fax: (202)777-2534
E-mail: comments@apha.org
URL: http://www.apha.org

Description: Professional organization of physicians, nurses, educators, academicians, environmentalists, epidemiologists, new professionals, social workers, health administrators, optometrists, podiatrists, pharmacists, dentists, nutritionists, health planners, other community and mental health specialists, and interested consumers. Seeks to protect and promote personal, mental, and environmental health. Services include: promulgation of standards; establishment of uniform practices and procedures; development of the etiology of communicable diseases; research in public health; exploration of medical care programs and their relationships to public health. Sponsors job placement service.

6455 ■ American Society of Safety Engineers (ASSE)
1800 E Oakton St.
Des Plaines, IL 60018
Ph: (847)699-2929
Fax: (847)768-3434
E-mail: customerservice@asse.org
URL: http://www.asse.org

Description: Professional society of safety engineers, safety directors, and others concerned with accident prevention, environmental protection and safety and health programs. Sponsors National Safety Month and conducts research and educational

programs. Develops/publishes ANSI safety-related standards and other technical literature. Compiles statistics; maintains job placement service.

6456 ■ Ethics and Compliance Officer Association
411 Waverley Oaks Rd., Ste. 324
Waltham, MA 02452
Ph: (781)647-9333
Fax: (781)647-9399
URL: http://www.theecoa.org

Description: Comprised of ethics and compliance practitioners. Provides resources to ethics and compliance professionals worldwide. Offers members with access to a network of ethics and compliance professionals. Serves as a global forum for the exchange of ideas and strategies.

6457 ■ National Environmental Health Association (NEHA)
720 S Colorado Blvd., Ste. 1000-N
Denver, CO 80246-1926
Ph: (303)756-9090
Fax: (303)691-9490
Fr: (866)956-2258
E-mail: staff@neha.org
URL: http://www.neha.org

Description: Represents all professionals in environmental health and protection, including Registered Sanitarians, Registered Environmental Health Specialists, Registered Environmental Technicians, Certified Environmental Health Technicians, Registered Hazardous Substances Professionals and Registered Hazardous Substances Specialists. Advances the environmental health and protection profession for the purpose of providing a healthful environment for all. Provides educational materials, publications, credentials and meetings to members and non-member professionals who strive to improve the environment.

6458 ■ United States Pharmacopeia
12601 Twinbrook Pkwy.
Rockville, MD 20852
Ph: (301)881-0666
Fr: 800-227-8772
E-mail: professionalaffairs@usp.org
URL: http://www.usp.org

Description: Acts as the non-governmental, official public standards-setting authority of prescription and over-the-counter medicines and other healthcare products manufactured or sold in the United States. Strives to improve the health of people around the world through public standards and related programs that help ensure the quality, safety, and benefit of medicines and foods.

6459 ■ Better
The Johns Hopkins University Press
2715 N Charles St.
Baltimore, MD 21218-4319
Ph: (410)516-6900
Fax: (410)516-6968
URL: http://www.press.jhu.edu/journals/better_
evidence_based_educ

$29.50/year for individuals, print and electronic;
$80.00/year for institutions, print and electronic.
Magazine for educators and policy makers interested
in evidence-based education reform.

6460 ■ Creative Education
Scientific Research Publishing
PO Box 54821
Irvine, CA 92619-4821
E-mail: ce@scirp.org
URL: http://www.scirp.org/journal/ce/

$195.00/year for individuals. Peer-reviewed journal
publishing articles on the latest advancements in
creative education.

**6461 ■ International Journal of Critical
Pedagogy**
University of North Carolina at Greensboro
1400 Spring Garden St.
Greensboro, NC 27412
Ph: (336)334-5000
URL: http://libjournal.uncg.edu/ojs/index.php/ijcp/
index

Peer-reviewed journal publishing innovative understandings and applications of critical pedagogy.

**6462 ■ Journal of Diversity in Higher
Education**
American Psychological Association
750 1st St. NE
Washington, DC 20002-4242
Ph: (202)336-5500
Fax: (202)336-5549
Fr: 800-374-2721
URL: http://www.apa.org/pubs/journals/dhe/
index.aspx

Quarterly. $65.00/year for members; $89.00/year for
other countries, members; $415.00/year for institu-
tions; $464.00/year for institutions, other countries;
$65.00/year for students; $105.00/year for nonmembers; $134.00/year for other countries, nonmembers.
Journal publishing research findings, theory and
promising practices in higher education.

**6463 ■ Journal of Intelligent Learning
Systems and Applications**
Scientific Research Publishing
PO Box 54821
Irvine, CA 92619-4821
URL: http://www.scirp.org/journal/jilsa/

Peer-reviewed journal covering all aspects of intelligent learning systems and applications.

**6464 ■ Accelerating Student and Staff
Learning**
Corwin Press, Inc.
2455 Teller Rd.
Thousand Oaks, CA 91320
Ph: (805)499-9734
Fax: (805)499-5323
Fr: 800-233-9936
E-mail: order@corwin.com
URL: http://www.corwin.com

Kay Psencik. 2009. $36.95 (paperback); $80.95
(hardcover). 192 pages. Engages teachers in collaborative curriculum design and professional
development.

**6465 ■ Aligning Your Curriculum to the
Common Core State Standards**
Corwin Press
2455 Teller Rd.
Thousand Oaks, CA 91320
Ph: (805)499-9734
Fax: (805)499-5323
Fr: 800-233-9936
E-mail: order@corwin.com
URL: http://www.corwin.com

Joe Crawford. 2011. $39.95 (paper). 248 pages.
Explains how to facilitate learning for all students
while taking advantage of the new culture, technology, and norms of the current learning environment.
Includes charts, graphs and access to internet-based
software for mapping the common core state standards to curriculum, instruction and assessment.

**6466 ■ Assessment Clear and Simple: A
Practical Guide for Institutions,
Departments, and General Education**
Jossey-Bass
c/o John Wiley & Sons, Inc.
111 River St.
Hoboken, NJ 07030
Ph: (201)748-6000
Fax: (201)748-6088
E-mail: info@wiley.com
URL: http://www.josseybass.com

Barbara E. Walvoord. 2010. $30.00 (paperback). 144
pages. 2nd edition. Provides step-by-step guide for
the assessment process. Explores the areas of planning, budgeting, and the changes in curriculum, pedagogy and programming. Emphasizes and shows how
to move from data to actions to improve student
learning.

**6467 ■ Concept-Based Curriculum and
Instruction for the Thinking Classroom
(Multimedia Kit)**
Corwin Press, Inc.
2455 Teller Rd.
Thousand Oaks, CA 91320

Ph: (805)499-9734
Fax: (805)499-5323
Fr: 800-233-9936
E-mail: order@corwin.com
URL: http://www.corwin.com

H. Lynn Erickson. 2009. $360.00. Includes a CD-
ROM and 102-minute DVD. Demonstrates how a
concept-based instructional approach can deepen
students' intellectual abilities and transform the
classroom experience for both teachers and learners.

6468 ■ Creating the Curriculum
Routledge
711 3rd Ave., 8th Fl.
New York, NY 10017
Ph: (212)216-7800
Fax: (212)563-2269
URL: http://www.routledge.com

Dominic Wyse, Vivienne Marie Baumfield, David
Egan, Louise Hayward, Moira Hulme, Ian Menter,
Carmel Gallagher and Kay Livingston. 2012. $39.95
(paper); $155.00 (hardback). Discovers strategies
and new approaches that make an effective and
meaningful curriculum.

**6469 ■ Creating Standards-Based Integrated
Curriculum**
Corwin Press, Inc.
2455 Teller Rd.
Thousand Oaks, CA 91320
Ph: (805)499-9734
Fax: (805)499-5323
Fr: 800-233-9936
E-mail: order@corwin.com
URL: http://www.corwin.com

Susan M. Drake. 2012. $36.95 (paper). 208 pages.
Provides a new approach to standards-based curriculum, instruction and assessment.

6470 ■ Creativity in the Primary Curriculum
Routledge
711 3rd Ave., 8th Fl.
New York, NY 10017
Ph: (212)216-7800
Fax: (212)563-2269
URL: http://www.routledge.com

Russell Jones and Dominic Wyse. 2012. Second
Edition. $35.95 (paper); $128.00 (hardback). 224
pages. Offers guidelines and advice on the planning
and implementation of effective creative primary
teaching.

**6471 ■ Cultures of Curriculum, Second
Edition**
Routledge
711 3rd Ave., 8th Fl.
New York, NY 10017
Ph: (212)216-7800
Fax: (212)563-2269
URL: http://www.routledge.com

Pamela Bolotin Joseph. 2010. $45.95 (paper);
$145.00 (hardcover). 304 pages. Fosters awareness,

examination, and deliberation about the approaches to curriculum and practice.

6472 ■ The Curriculum Bridge: From Standards to Actual Classroom Practice
Corwin Press
2455 Teller Rd.
Thousand Oaks, CA 91320
Ph: (805)499-9734
Fax: (805)499-5323
Fr: 800-233-9936
E-mail: order@corwin.com
URL: http://www.corwin.com

Pearl G. Solomon. 2009. $36.95 (paper). 248 pages. Lays out what a classroom teacher or curriculum developer needs in order to create an effective curriculum that can be adapted into actual classroom instruction. Serves as an educator's tool for making informed and significant decisions in order to promote standards-based instruction, improve student outcomes and create a suitable environment for learning.

6473 ■ Curriculum Development in the Postmodern Era
Routledge
711 3rd Ave., 8th Fl.
New York, NY 10017
Ph: (212)216-7800
Fax: (212)563-2269
URL: http://www.routledge.com

Patrick Slattery. 2012. Third Edition. $49.95 (paper); $150.00 (hardback). Introduces and analyzes contemporary concepts of curriculum that emerged from the reconceptualization of curriculum studies in the 1970s and 1980s. Serves as reference guide for educators and educational leaders, curriculum development specialist, researchers and policy advocators of higher learning, doctoral students in all disciplines, trainers and those who are interested in improving the dynamics of learning.

6474 ■ Curriculum and Instruction
SAGE Publications, Inc.
2455 Teller Rd.
Thousand Oaks, CA 91320
Ph: (805)499-0721
Fax: 800-583-2665
Fr: 800-818-7243
E-mail: info@sagepub.com
URL: http://www.sagepub.com

A. Jonathan Eakle. 2012. $85.00 (hardcover). 400 pages. Explores multiple curriculum and instruction issues including alternative curriculum, curriculum control, standardized curricula, subject- versus student-centered curricula, and textbooks.

6475 ■ Curriculum Leadership: Strategies for Development and Implementation
SAGE Publications, Inc.
2455 Teller Rd.
Thousand Oaks, CA 91320
Ph: (805)499-0721
Fax: 800-583-2665
Fr: 800-818-7243
E-mail: info@sagepub.com
URL: http://www.sagepub.com

Allan A. Glatthorn, Floyd A. Boschee, Bruce M. Whitehead, and Bonni F. Boschee. 2011. $110.00 (hardcover). 552 pages. Provides educational leaders, teachers, and administrators with innovative programs, learning experiences, and creative, up-to-date curriculum strategies and ideas.

6476 ■ The Curriculum Manager's Handbook
CreateSpace
7290 B. Investment Dr.
Charleston, SC 29418
E-mail: info@createspace.com
URL: http://www.createspace.com

Guy W. Wallace. 2011. $30.00 (paper). 274 pages. Defines the responsibilities as well as performance and competency skills required for a curriculum manager.

6477 ■ Curriculum, Syllabus Design and Equity
Routledge
711 3rd Ave., 8th Fl.
New York, NY 10017
Ph: (212)216-7800
Fax: (212)563-2269
URL: http://www.routledge.com

Allan Luke, Annette Woods and Katie Weir. 2012. $44.95 (paper); $135.00 (hardback). 208 pages. Advances a unified, principled approach to the design of syllabus documents that aims for high quality/high equity educational outcomes and enhances teacher professionalism. Serves as guide for teachers, teacher educators, and curriculum policy workers who are engaged in curriculum writing and implementation.

6478 ■ Deciding What to Teach and Test
Corwin Press, Inc.
2455 Teller Rd.
Thousand Oaks, CA 91320
Ph: (805)499-9734
Fax: (805)499-5323
Fr: 800-233-9936
E-mail: order@corwin.com
URL: http://www.corwin.com

Fenwick W. English. 2010. $27.95 (paperback). 168 pages. Addresses the fundamentals of curriculum design in the context of a standards-based environment. Includes insights on providing effective curriculum leadership, increasing student success, and closing the achievement gap.

6479 ■ Designing Effective Instruction
John Wiley & Sons, Inc.
111 River St.
Hoboken, NJ 07030-5774
Ph: (201)748-6000
Fax: (201)748-6088
E-mail: info@wiley.com
URL: http://as.wiley.com

Gary R. Morrison, Steven M. Ross, Jerrold E. Kemp, Howard Kalman. 2010. $142.95 (paper). 491 pages. Equips educators with practical skills for successful instructional design.

6480 ■ An Educational Leader's Guide to Curriculum Mapping
Corwin
2455 Teller Rd.
Thousand Oaks, CA 91320
Ph: (805)499-9734
Fax: (805)499-5323
Fr: 800-233-9936
E-mail: order@corwin.com
URL: http://www.corwin.com

Janet A. Hale and Richard F. Dunlap, Jr. 2010. $36.95 (paper). 200 pages. Provides an overview of key concepts and processes of curriculum mapping. Presents leadership strategies for successful implementation of curriculum mapping.

6481 ■ Encyclopedia of Curriculum Studies
SAGE Publications, Inc.
2455 Teller Rd.
Thousand Oaks, CA 91320
Ph: (805)499-0721
Fax: 800-583-2665
Fr: 800-818-7243
E-mail: info@sagepub.com
URL: http://www.sagepub.com

Craig Kridel. 2010. $370.00 (hardcover). 1,064 pages. Describes the conventions, ways, and accepted research and writing practices in the field of curriculum studies.

6482 ■ From Mandate to Achievement: 5 Steps to a Curriculum System That Works!
Corwin Press, Inc.
2455 Teller Rd.
Thousand Oaks, CA 91320
Ph: (805)499-9734
Fax: (805)499-5323

Fr: 800-233-9936
E-mail: order@corwin.com
URL: http://www.corwin.com

Elaine Makas. 2009. $38.95 (paperback); $85.95 (hardcover). 248 pages. Guides principals, district administrators, curriculum facilitators and teachers in establishing a consistent and accurate curriculum process that increases academic achievement and drives continuous school improvement.

6483 ■ Getting Serious About the System
Corwin Press, Inc.
2455 Teller Rd.
Thousand Oaks, CA 91320
Ph: (805)499-9734
Fax: (805)499-5323
Fr: 800-233-9936
E-mail: order@corwin.com
URL: http://www.corwin.com

D'Ette Cowan, Stacey Joyner and Shirley Beckwith. 2012. $31.95 (paperback). 120 pages. Provides teachers, administrators and leaders with a comprehensive resource in aligning curriculum, instruction and assessment. Presents a step-by-step, research-based approach to district and school transformation.

6484 ■ Habits of Mind Across the Curriculum: Practical and Creative Strategies for Teachers
ASCD
1703 N Beauregard St.
Alexandria, VA 22311-1714
Ph: (703)578-9600
Fax: (703)575-5400
Fr: 800-933-2723
URL: http://www.ascd.org

Arthur L. Costa and Bena Kallick. 2009. $26.95. 236 pages. Presents a collective wisdom and experience of educators who have successfully implemented the habits of mind in their curriculum, instruction, and assessments.

6485 ■ How to Build an Instructional Coaching Program for Maximum Capacity
Corwin Press
2455 Teller Rd.
Thousand Oaks, CA 91320
Ph: (805)499-9734
Fax: (805)499-5323
Fr: 800-233-9936
E-mail: order@corwin.com
URL: http://www.corwin.com

Nina Jones Morel, Carla Staton Cushman. 2012. $36.95 (paper). 208 pages. Serves as a resource for school and district leaders to develop and sustain an effective coaching program. Provides a practical framework for starting and sustaining a viable instructional coaching program.

6486 ■ How to Integrate the Curricula
Corwin Press, Inc.
2455 Teller Rd.
Thousand Oaks, CA 91320
Ph: (805)499-9734
Fax: (805)499-5323
Fr: 800-233-9936
E-mail: order@corwin.com
URL: http://www.corwin.com

Robin J. Fogarty and Brian M. Pete. 2009. $31.95 (paper); $72.95 (hardcover). 152 pages. Supports educators as they integrate concepts, skills, and attitudes and immerse students in content through self-selected, personally relevant learning experiences.

6487 ■ Idea-Based Learning
Stylus Publishing, LLC
22883 Quicksilver Dr.
Sterling, VA 20166-2012
Ph: (703)661-1504
Fax: (703)661-1547
E-mail: stylusinfo@styluspub.com
URL: http://www.styluspub.com

Edmund J. Hansen. 2011. $75.00 (hardback); $24.95

(paperback). Serves as guide in developing college instruction that has clear purpose, is well integrated into the curriculum, and improves student learning.

6488 ■ Improving Standards-Based Learning

Corwin Press, Inc.
2455 Teller Rd.
Thousand Oaks, CA 91320
Ph: (805)499-9734
Fax: (805)499-5323
Fr: 800-233-9936
E-mail: order@corwin.com
URL: http://www.corwin.com

Judy F. Carr and Doug Harris. 2009. $36.95 (paperback); $80.95 (hardcover). 200 pages. Provides tools and processes for developing a curriculum that can generate substantive improvement in teaching and learning.

6489 ■ Instructional Design for Action Learning

AMACOM Publishing
1601 Broadway
New York, NY 10019-7420
Fax: (518)891-2372
Fr: 800-250-5308
E-mail: pubs_cust_serv@amanet.org
URL: http://www.amacombooks.org

Geri McArdle. 2010. $34.95 (paper). Serves as a guide to developing learner-based training that works. Includes action learning techniques for training design and presentation.

6490 ■ The Instructional Leadership Toolbox: A Handbook for Improving Practice

Corwin Press
2455 Teller Rd.
Thousand Oaks, CA 91320
Ph: (805)499-9734
Fax: (805)499-5323
Fr: 800-233-9936
E-mail: order@corwin.com
URL: http://www.corwin.com

Sandra Lee Gupton. 2009. $36.95 (paper); $82.95 (hardcover). 216 pages. Establishes practical ways for leaders to reflect on and improve their practice. Provides a blueprint that demonstrates how school leaders can focus on student learning, while using tools and building teams to increase student achievement.

6491 ■ Internationalizing the Curriculum in Higher Education

Jossey-Bass
c/o John Wiley & Sons, Inc.
111 River St.
Hoboken, NJ 07030-5774
Ph: (201)748-6000
Fax: (201)748-6088
E-mail: info@wiley.com
URL: http://www.josseybass.com

Carolin Kreber. 2009. $29.00 (paper). 128 pages. Explores different concepts of internationalization in higher education. Describes the nine cases of internationalization initiatives at the curricular level.

6492 ■ Leading Curriculum Improvement

Rowman & Littlefield Education
c/o Rowman & Littlefield Publishing Group
4501 Forbes Blvd., Ste. 200
Lanham, MD 20706
Ph: (301)459-3366
Fax: (301)429-5748
E-mail: customercare@rowman.com
URL: http://rowman.com

Marilyn Tallerico. 2011. $40.00 (hardback); $19.95 (paper). 136 pages. Offers guidance and curriculum leadership fundamentals to teacher leaders, instructional coordinators, central office personnel for facilitating curriculum improvement at the building level.

6493 ■ The Learner-Centered Curriculum: Design and Implementation

Jossey-Bass
c/o John Wiley & Sons, Inc.
111 River St.
Hoboken, NJ 07030-5774
Ph: (201)748-6000
Fax: (201)748-6088
E-mail: info@wiley.com
URL: http://www.josseybass.com

Roxanne Cullen, Michael Harris, Reinhold R. Hill and Maryellen Weimer. 2012. $40.00 (hardcover). 272 pages. Offers both design specifications for a learner-centered approach to curriculum as well as practical recommendations for implementation and assessment.

6494 ■ The Principal's Guide to Curriculum Leadership

Corwin
2455 Teller Rd.
Thousand Oaks, CA 91320
Ph: (805)499-9734
Fax: (805)499-5323
Fr: 800-233-9936
E-mail: order@corwin.com
URL: http://www.corwin.com

Richard D. Sorenson, Lloyd Milton Goldsmith, Zulma Y. Mendez, and Karen Taylor Maxwell. 2011. $41.95 (paper). 320 pages. Provides practical guidance for principal and other school administrators in initiating curriculum development and change. Features discussion questions, case studies, activities, specialized curriculum models, resources, and references.

6495 ■ Shaping the College Curriculum: Academic Plans in Context

Jossey-Bass
c/o John Wiley & Sons, Inc.
111 River St.
Hoboken, NJ 07030-5774
Ph: (201)748-6000
Fax: (201)748-6088
E-mail: info@wiley.com
URL: http://www.josseybass.com

Lisa R. Lattuca and Joan S. Stark. 2nd edition. 2009. $50.00 (hardcover). 400 pages. Focuses on research-based educational practices relevant to curriculum development in higher education.

6496 ■ Staff Development Guide for the Parallel Curriculum

Corwin Press, Inc.
2455 Teller Rd.
Thousand Oaks, CA 91320
Ph: (805)499-9734
Fax: (805)499-5323
Fr: 800-233-9936
E-mail: order@corwin.com
URL: http://www.corwin.com

Cindy A. Strickland and Kathy Tuchman Glass. 2009. $36.95 (paperback); $80.95 (hardcover). 192 pages. Contributes to the professional training that results in enhanced teacher expertise and a multidimensional, high-quality curriculum that challenges the learners.

6497 ■ Strategic Curriculum Change

Routledge
711 3rd Ave., 8th Fl.
New York, NY 10017
Ph: (212)216-7800
Fax: (212)563-2269
URL: http://www.routledge.com

Paul Blackmore and Camille B. Kandiko. 2012. $44.95 (paperback); $155.00 (hardback). 224 pages. Presents a theorized and contextualized approach to the study of the curriculum and focuses on the necessary research on the curriculum in higher education.

6498 ■ Teaching for Intellectual and Emotional Learning (TIEL): A Model for Creating Powerful Curriculum

Rowman & Littlefield Education
c/o Rowman & Littlefield Publishing Group
4501 Forbes Blvd., Ste. 200
Lanham, MD 20706

Ph: (301)459-3366
Fax: (301)429-5748
E-mail: customercare@rowman.com
URL: http://rowman.com

Christy Folsom. 2009. $90.00 (hardback); $36.95 (paperback). 310 pages. Educates teachers in developing standards-based curriculum that includes social-emotional learning.

6499 ■ Using Power Standards to Build an Aligned Curriculum

Corwin Press, Inc.
2455 Teller Rd.
Thousand Oaks, CA 91320
Ph: (805)499-9734
Fax: (805)499-5323
Fr: 800-233-9936
E-mail: order@corwin.com
URL: http://www.corwin.com

Joe Crawford. 2011. $36.95 (paper). 216 pages. Assists administrators and teachers in developing a useful, aligned curriculum that can effectively support student achievement and assessment.

ONLINE JOB SOURCES AND SERVICES

6500 ■ Curriculum Development Jobs

URL: http://www.curriculumdevelopmentjobs.org

Description: Serves as a niche job board for curriculum development professionals. Offers employment opportunities and candidate recruiting.

6501 ■ Get Curriculum Development Jobs

URL: http://www.getcurriculumdevelopmentjobs.com

Description: Serves as a one-stop resource for finding and filling curriculum development positions. Offers free curriculum development job postings and career opportunities.

6502 ■ Instructional Design Central

URL: http://www.instructionaldesigncentral.com

Description: Provides instructional design related information, career and learning opportunities, and other resources to instructional design professionals, educators, and students.

OTHER SOURCES

6503 ■ American Association for Teaching and Curriculum

c/o Lynne Bailey
528 S Samuel St.
Charles Town, WV 25414
E-mail: lmbailey22@yahoo.com
URL: http://www.aatchome.org

Description: Promotes the scholarly study of teaching and curriculum through its annual conferences, peer-reviewed journal, and the interaction of its members.

6504 ■ National Council on Measurement in Education

2424 American Ln.
Madison, WI 53704
Ph: (608)443-2487
Fax: (608)443-2474
URL: http://ncme.org

Description: Consists of individuals involved in assessment, evaluation, testing and other aspects of educational measurement. Helps members involved in the construction and the use of standardized tests.

Sources of Help-Wanted Ads

6505 ■ *ASCnet Quarterly*
Applied Systems Client Network
801 Douglas Ave., Ste. 205
Altamonte Springs, FL 32714
Ph: (407)869-0404
Fax: (407)869-0418
Fr: 800-605-1045
URL: http://www.ascnet.org/AM/
Template.cfm?Section=About

Quarterly. $24.00/year for individuals. Professional magazine covering technical information, association news, and industry information for insurance professionals.

6506 ■ *Best's Review*
A.M. Best Company, Inc.
Ambest Rd.
Oldwick, NJ 08858
Ph: (908)439-2200
URL: http://www.ambest.com/sales/
newsoverview.asp#br

Monthly. $50.00/year for individuals. Magazine covering issues and trends for the management personnel of life/health insurers, the agents, and brokers who market their products.

6507 ■ *Business Insurance*
Crain Communications Inc.
1155 Gratiot Ave.
Detroit, MI 48207-2997
Ph: (313)446-6000
URL: http://www.businessinsurance.com

Weekly. $399.00/year for individuals, print; $149.00/year for individuals, print & digital; $69.00/year for individuals, digital edition. International newsweekly reporting on corporate risk and employee benefit management news.

6508 ■ *Claims*
Claims
15112 64th Ave. W
Edmonds, WA 98026
Ph: (425)745-6394
URL: http://www.propertycasualty360.com/Claims-Magazine

Monthly. $72.00/year for individuals; $93.00/year for Canada; $131.00/year for other countries. Magazine for the property-casualty insurance claims industry.

6509 ■ *National Underwriter Property and Casualty/Risk and Benefits Management*
National Underwriter Co.
5081 Olympic Blvd.
PO Box 14367
Erlanger, KY 41018
Ph: (859)692-2100
Fax: (859)692-2175
Fr: 800-543-0874
URL: http://www.propertycasualty360.com/National-Underwriter-Prop

Weekly. $94.00/year for individuals, 2nd class; $133.00/year for Canada, air mail; $178.00/year for U.S. and Canada, air mail; $211.00/year for other countries, air mail. Newsweekly for agents, brokers, executives, and managers in risk and benefit insurance.

6510 ■ *The Standard*
Standard Publishing Corp.
155 Federal St., 13th Fl.
Boston, MA 02110
Ph: (617)457-0600
Fax: (617)457-0608
E-mail: stnd@earthlink.net
URL: http://www.spcpub.com

Weekly (Fri.). $95.00/year for individuals, U.S.; $165.00/year for two years. Trade newspaper covering insurance events, legislation, regulatory hearings, and court sessions for independent insurance agents in New England.

6511 ■ *Today's Insurance Professionals*
National Association of Insurance Women (International)
9343 E 95th Ct. S
Tulsa, OK 74133
Ph: (918)294-3700
Fax: (918)294-3711
Fr: 800-766-6249
URL: http://www.naiw.org/?page=todays_mag_full

Quarterly. $15.00/year for individuals; $5.00/year for single issue. Magazine on insurance and professional development topics for men and women in the risk and insurance field.

Employer Directories and Networking Lists

6512 ■ *Best's Insurance Reports*
A.M. Best Co.
Ambest Rd.
Oldwick, NJ 08858
Ph: (908)439-2200
URL: http://www.ambest.com

Annual, Latest edition 2011. Published in three editions—Life-health insurance, covering about 1,750 companies, property-casualty insurance, covering over 3,200 companies; and international, covering more than 1,200 insurers. Each edition lists state insurance commissioners and related companies and agencies (mutual funds, worker compensation funds, underwriting agencies, etc.). Entries include: For each company—Company name, address, phone; history; states in which licensed; names of officers and directors; financial data; financial analysis and Best's rating. Arrangement: Alphabetical.

6513 ■ *Business Insurance—Agent/Broker Profiles Issue*
Business Insurance
360 N Michigan Ave.
Chicago, IL 60601-3806
Ph: (312)649-5200
Fax: (312)280-3174
Fr: 888-446-1422
URL: http://www.businessinsurance.com

Annual, Latest edition 2008. Publication includes: List of top 10 insurance agents/brokers worldwide specializing in commercial insurance. Entries include: Firm name, address, phone, fax, branch office locations, year established, names of subsidiaries, gross revenues, premium volume, number of employees, principal officers, percent of revenue generated by commercial retail brokerage, acquisitions. Arrangement: Alphabetical by company. Indexes: Geographical.

6514 ■ *Directory of Insurance Wholesalers*
Crain Communications, Inc.
1155 Gratiot Ave.
Detroit, MI 48207-2997
Ph: (313)446-6000
URL: http://www.businessinsurance.com/section/
directories

Latest edition 2011. $439.00 for individuals; $499.00 for other countries. List of underwriting managers, managing general agents and wholesale brokers. Entries include: Contact information.

6515 ■ *Insurance Phone Book*
Briefings Media Group
2807 N Parham Rd., Ste. 200
Richmond, VA 23294
Ph: (570)567-1982
Fr: 800-791-8699
URL: http://www.douglaspublications.com

Annual, latest edition 2009-2010. $195.00; $389.00. Covers: About 3,700 life, accident and health, worker's compensation, auto, fire and casualty, marine, surety, and other insurance companies; 2,300 executive contacts from presidents and CEOs to claims and customer service managers. Entries include: Company name, address, phone, fax, toll-free number, type of insurance provided. Arrangement: Alphabetical.

6516 ■ *Kirschner's Insurance Directories*
National Underwriter Co.
5081 Olympic Blvd.
PO Box 14367
Erlanger, KY 41018
Ph: (859)692-2100
Fax: (859)692-2175
Fr: 800-543-0874
URL: http://www.nationalunderwriter.com

Annual, Latest edition 2007. Covers: Insurance agents and agencies in all 50 states and the District of Columbia. Published in 24 separate editions for Southern California, Northern California, Pacific

Northwest (AK, ID, HI, OR, WA, MT), Michigan, Illinois, New England states (CT, ME, MA, RI, VT), Ohio, Rocky Mountain states (AZ, CO, NV, NM, UT, WY), South Central states (GA, AL, MS), Indiana, Texas, Kentucky/Tennessee, East Central states (VA, WV, NC, SC), South Central West states (AR, OK, LA), Wisconsin, Central states (KS, MO, NE), North Central states (IA, MN, ND, SD), Mid-Atlantic states (DE, MD, NJ, DC), Pennsylvania, Florida. Entries include: For companies—Name, address, key personnel (with addresses and phone numbers). Arrangement: Separate alphabetical sections for insurance companies, wholesalers, field agents, and agencies. Indexes: Type of insurance.

6517 ■ *Vault Guide to the Top Insurance Employers*

Vault.com Inc.
150 W 22nd St., 5th Fl.
New York, NY 10011
Ph: (212)366-4212
Fax: (212)366-6117
Fr: 888-562-8285
URL: http://www.vault.com

Latest edition June, 2006. $19.95 for individuals; $19.95 for members. Covers: Insurance companies in United States. Entries include: Company name, contact person, address, zip code, phone and fax numbers, statistics, hiring process and email. Arrangement: Alphabetical by company name.

6518 ■ *Women in Insurance and Financial Services—Membership Directory*

Women in Insurance and Financial Services
6748 Wauconda Dr.
Larkspur, CO 80118
Ph: (303)681-9777
Fr: (866)264-9437
URL: http://www.w-wifs.org

Covers: list of contact information of WIFS' members who are devoted to helping women succeed in both insurance and financial services.

6519 ■ *Yearbook*

American Association of Managing General Agents
150 S Warner Rd., Ste. 156
King of Prussia, PA 19406
Ph: (610)225-1999
Fax: (610)225-1996
URL: http://www.aamga.org

Annual, Latest edition 2006. Covers: 250 managing general agents of insurance companies and their more than 500 branch offices; coverage includes Canada. Entries include: Name, address, names and titles of principal and contact, insurance companies represented. Arrangement: Geographical.

HANDBOOKS AND MANUALS

6520 ■ *Opportunities in Insurance Careers*

The McGraw-Hill Companies
PO Box 182604
Columbus, OH 43272
Fax: (614)759-3749
Fr: 877-883-5524
E-mail: customer.service@mcgraw-hill.com
URL: http://www.mhprofessional.com/
    product.php?isbn=0071482075

Robert M. Schrayer. Revised, 2007. $14.95 (paper). 160 pages. A guide to planning for and seeking opportunities in the field. Contains bibliography and illustrations.

EMPLOYMENT AGENCIES AND SEARCH FIRMS

6521 ■ Burkholder Group Inc.

985 Pico Pt.
Colorado Springs, CO 80906
Ph: (719)867-1222

Fax: (719)623-0033
E-mail: info@burkholdergroup.com
URL: http://www.burkholdergroup.com

Executive search firm focused on the insurance industry.

6522 ■ Insperity, Inc.

19001 Crescent Springs Dr.
Kingwood, TX 77339-3802
Ph: (281)358-8986
Fr: 800-237-3170
E-mail: douglas.sharp@insperity.com
URL: http://www.insperity.com

Description: Serves as a full-service human resources department for small and medium-sized businesses throughout the United States. Provides client companies with benefits and services such as employment administration, government compliance, recruiting and selection, performance management, benefits management, employer liability management, training and development, and business services.

6523 ■ International Insurance Consultants Inc.

1191 E Newport Center Dr., Ste. 206
Deerfield Beach, FL 33442
Ph: (954)421-0122
Fax: (954)449-0497
E-mail: info@insurancerecruitersusa.com
URL: http://www.insurancerecruitersusa.com

Offers executive search to the insurance industry. Clients include insurance companies, brokers, consultants and investment banks. Industries served: insurance and financial services industries.

6524 ■ International Insurance Personnel, Inc.

300 W Wieuca Rd., Bldg. 2, Ste. 101
Atlanta, GA 30342
Ph: (404)255-9710
Fax: (404)255-9864
E-mail: iipjulie@bellsouth.net
URL: http://realpages.com/sites/intlinspersonnel/
    index.html

Employment agency specializing in the area of insurance.

6525 ■ J. R. Peterman Associates, Inc.

PO Box 3083
Stowe, VT 05672
Ph: (802)253-6304
Fax: (802)253-6314
E-mail: peterman@jrpeterman.com
URL: http://www.jrpeterman.com

Description: Recruit professionals in permanent and contract positions for the life and health insurance industry and employee benefits consulting.

6526 ■ Questor Consultants, Inc.

2515 N Broad St.
Colmar, PA 18915
Ph: (215)997-9262
Fax: (215)997-9226
E-mail: sbevivino@questorconsultants.com
URL: http://www.questorconsultants.com

Executive search firm specializing in the insurance and legal fields.

6527 ■ Quirk-Corporon and Associates Inc.

1229 N Jackson St., Ste. 205
Milwaukee, WI 53202-2655
Ph: (414)224-9399
Fax: (414)224-9472
E-mail: quirkrecruiters@sbcglobal.net
URL: http://www.quirkinsrecruiters.com

Employment agency specializing in all disciplines of the insurance and financial industries; insurance recruiters, is a contingency and retained recruiting and consulting firm specializing in the placement of permanent candidates; provides talented professional and technical employees, locally and nationally, who are skilled in property or casualty, life or health,

employee benefits and managed care; provides a highly respected dimension of counseling skill to both clients and candidates in all areas of staffing and employee relations.

6528 ■ ReadWaering Associates

PO Box 290755
Nashville, TN 37229
Ph: (615)415-3462
Fr: 800-489-3602
E-mail: pam@readwaering.com
URL: http://www.readwaering.com

Specializes in insurance and healthcare recruiting.

6529 ■ SHS of Cherry Hill

207 Barclay Pavilion W
Cherry Hill, NJ 08034
Ph: (856)216-9030
Fax: (856)216-7784
E-mail: shs@shsofcherryhill.com
URL: http://www.shsofcherryhill.com

Personnel recruiters operating in the disciplines of accounting, sales, insurance, engineering, and administration. Industries served: insurance, distribution, manufacturing, and service.

6530 ■ Tyler & Co.

375 N Ridge Rd., Ste. 400
Atlanta, GA 30350-3299
Ph: (770)396-3939
Fax: (770)396-6693
Fr: 800-989-6789
E-mail: art@tylerandco.com
URL: http://www.tylerandco.com

Retained executive search for the healthcare, food, market research, manufacturing and insurance industries.

ONLINE JOB SOURCES AND SERVICES

6531 ■ Great Insurance Jobs

URL: http://www.greatinsurancejobs.com

Description: Contains varied insurance positions. Job seekers may browse employee profiles, post resumes, and read descriptions of hundreds of recently-posted insurance jobs.

6532 ■ InsuranceAgencyCareers.com

URL: http://www.insuranceagencycareers.com

Description: Online job search provides employment opportunities in the insurance industry.

6533 ■ InsuranceIndustryCentral.com

URL: http://www.insuranceindustrycentral.com

Description: Features insurance jobs and products to the insurance community.

6534 ■ InsuranceJobs.com

E-mail: info@insurancejobs.com
URL: http://www.insurancejobs.com

Description: Offers employment and careers in the insurance industry.

6535 ■ National Insurance Recruiters Association

URL: http://www.insurancerecruiters.com

Description: Contains lists of recruiters (listed by department and line of business) and available insurance positions.

6536 ■ Premier Careers, Inc.

913 Dogwood Dr.
Fayetteville, TN 37334
Ph: (931)227-8496
E-mail: jim@premiercareers.com
URL: http://www.premiercareers.com

Description: Contains a database with information on candidates searching for jobs in the property and casualty insurance industry and with national sales organizations. Houses resumes and letters of reference. Candidate searches may be run by industry, geography, job title, years of experience, compensation, education, and/or accreditation. Also offers resume writing and interviewing tips to job hunters.

6537 ■ UltimateInsuranceJobs.com

URL: http://www.ultimateinsurancejobs.com/index.asp

Description: Provides insurance job listings, recruiter directory, and resources. Offers job seekers the opportunity to post and edit their resumes, and employers the opportunity to search through insurance resumes.

TRADESHOWS

6538 ■ Annual NAIW Convention - National Association of Insurance Women International

National Association of Insurance Women International
9343 E. 95th Ct. S.
Tulsa, OK 74133
Ph: (918)294-3700
Fax: (918)294-3711
Fr: 800-766-6249
E-mail: joinnaiw@naiw.org
URL: http://www.naiw.org

Annual. Primary Exhibits: Equipment, supplies, and services for insurance industry professionals. Dates and Locations: 2012 Jun 06-09; Dallas, TX; Omni Hotel Downtown.

6539 ■ Independent Insurance Agents of Indiana Annual Convention

Independent Insurance Agents of Indiana
3435 W. 96th St.
Indianapolis, IN 46268
Ph: (317)824-3780
Fax: (317)824-3786
Fr: 800-438-4424
E-mail: bigiinfo@bigi.org
URL: http://www.iiaba.net

Annual. Primary Exhibits: Small business supplies, automation equipment, solutions, insurance service, coverage providers and carriers.

6540 ■ Insurance Accounting and Systems Association Conference

Insurance Accounting and Systems Association
PO Box 51340
Durham, NC 27717-1340
Ph: (919)489-0991
URL: http://www.iasa.org

Annual. Primary Exhibits: Insurance equipment, supplies, and services. Dates and Locations: 2012 Jun 03-06; San Diego, CA; San Diego Convention Center.

6541 ■ Massachusetts Association of Insurance Agents Convention

Massachusetts Association of Insurance Agents
91 Cedar St.
Milford, MA 01757
Ph: (508)634-2900
Fax: (508)634-2929
Fr: 800-972-9312
E-mail: info@massagent.com
URL: http://www.massagent.com

Annual. Primary Exhibits: Computers and related services, office equipment, financial consultation services, managerial services, car rental, restoration, premium finance companies.

6542 ■ Professional Independent Insurance Agents of Illinois Annual Convention

Professional Independent Insurance Agents of Illinois
4360 Wabash Ave.
Springfield, IL 62711
Ph: (217)793-6660
Fax: (217)793-6744

Fr: 800-628-6436
E-mail: info@piiai.org
URL: http://www.iiaofillinois.org

Annual. Primary Exhibits: Insurance-related products, including computers and office supplies, restoration services and cell phones. Dates and Locations: 2012 Oct 03-05; Springfield, IL; Crowne Plaza; 2013 Oct 09-11; East Peoria, IL; Embassy Suites.

6543 ■ Risk and Insurance Management Society Annual Conference and Exhibition

Risk and Insurance Management Society
1065 Avenue of the Americas., 13th Fl.
New York, NY 10018
Ph: (212)286-9292
URL: http://www.rims.org

Annual. Primary Exhibits: Insurance industry related equipment, supplies, and services. Dates and Locations: 2012 Apr 15-19; Philadelphia, PA; Pennsylvania Convention Center.

6544 ■ Society of Insurance Trainers and Educators Conference

Society of Insurance Trainers and Educators
1821 University Ave. W., Ste. S256
St. Paul, MN 55104
Ph: (651)999-5354
Fax: (651)917-1835
E-mail: ed@insurancetrainers.org
URL: http://www.insurancetrainers.org

Annual. Primary Exhibits: Insurance education equipment, supplies, and services.

OTHER SOURCES

6545 ■ American Association of Insurance Management Consultants (AAIMCo)

Texas Insurance Consulting
8980 Lakes at 610 Dr., Ste. 100
Houston, TX 77054
Ph: (713)664-6424
E-mail: thomas.braniff@aaimco.com
URL: http://www.aaimco.com

Description: Consists of individuals who devote a substantial portion of their services to insurance consulting, risk management activities, legal representation relating to insurance issues; as well as education and professional development training, employment consulting, and other technical and management advice to the insurance industry. Advises and assists the insurance industry and seeks to achieve professional recognition for insurance management consultants. Mediates the exchange of ideas; sets standards of service and performance; maintains a code of ethics; offers a referral service and a series of educational conferences and seminars. Operates speakers' bureau; offers placement services; compiles statistics.

6546 ■ American Council of Life Insurers (ACLI)

101 Constitution Ave. NW, Ste. 700
Washington, DC 20001-2133
Ph: (202)624-2000
Fr: 877-674-4659
E-mail: webadmin@acli.com
URL: http://www.acli.com

Description: Represents the interests of legal reserve life insurance companies in legislative, regulatory and judicial matters at the federal, state and municipal levels of government and at the NAIC. Member companies hold majority of the life insurance in force in the United States.

6547 ■ American Institute for CPCU (AICPCU)

720 Providence Rd., Ste. 100
Malvern, PA 19355-3433
Fax: (610)640-9576
Fr: 800-644-2101
E-mail: customerservice@cpcuiia.org
URL: http://www.aicpcu.org

Description: Purpose: Determines qualifications for professional certification of insurance personnel; conducts examinations and awards designation of Chartered Property Casualty Underwriter (CPCU).

6548 ■ Association of Professional Insurance Women (APIW)

990 Cedarbridge Ave., Ste. B
PMB 210
Brick, NJ 08723-4157
Ph: (973)941-6024
Fax: (732)920-1260
E-mail: scb@thebeaumontgroup.com
URL: http://www.apiw.org

Description: Professional women from the insurance/reinsurance industry. Promotes cooperation and understanding among members; maintains high professional standards in the insurance industry; provides a strong network of professional contacts and educational aid; recognizes the contributions of women to insurance; encourages women to seek employment in the insurance community.

6549 ■ GAMA International

2901 Telestar Ct., Ste. 140
Falls Church, VA 22042-1205
Fax: (703)770-8182
Fr: 800-345-2687
E-mail: gamamail@gamaweb.com
URL: http://www.gamaweb.com

Description: Provides world-class education and training resources for individuals, companies and organizations involved with the recruitment and development of field managers, representatives and staff in the life insurance and financial services industry; advocates of the value-added role of field management and representatives in the ethical distribution of life insurance and financial products and services industry.

6550 ■ Independent Insurance Agents and Brokers of America (IIABA)

127 S Peyton St.
Alexandria, VA 22314
Fax: (703)683-7556
Fr: 800-221-7917
E-mail: info@iiaba.org
URL: http://www.iiaba.net

Description: Sales agencies handling property, fire, casualty, and surety insurance. Organizes technical and sales courses for new and established agents. Sponsors Independent Insurance Agent Junior Classic Golf Tournament.

6551 ■ Insurance Information Institute (III)

110 William St.
New York, NY 10038
Ph: (212)346-5500
E-mail: members@iii.org
URL: http://www.iii.org

Description: Property and casualty insurance companies. Provides information and educational services to mass media, educational institutions, trade associations, businesses, government agencies, and the public.

6552 ■ LOMA

2300 Windy Ridge Pkwy., Ste. 600
Atlanta, GA 30339-8443
Ph: (770)951-1770
Fax: (770)984-0441
Fr: 800-275-5662
E-mail: askloma@loma.org
URL: http://www.loma.org

Description: Life and health insurance companies and financial services in the U.S. and Canada; and overseas in 45 countries; affiliate members are firms that provide professional support to member companies. Provides research, information, training, and educational activities in areas of operations and systems, human resources, financial planning and employee development. Administers FLMI Insurance Education Program, which awards FLMI (Fellow, Life

Management Institute) designation to those who complete the ten-examination program.

6553 ■ National Alliance of General Agents (NAGA)
Tri-State General Insurance Agency
PO Box 4072
Salisbury, MD 21803
Fax: (410)219-7880
Fr: 800-556-7894
E-mail: edickerson@tsgia.com
URL: http://www.nagains.org

Description: Represents the interests of professional managing general agents and wholesale brokers. Promotes and supports improvements in the business of insurance for the benefit of the insuring public. Cooperates with other segments of the insurance industry. Fosters better understanding of the excess and surplus lines brokerage systems. Aims to perpetuate the Independent Agency System.

6554 ■ National Association of Health Underwriters (NAHU)
2000 N 14th St., Ste. 450
Arlington, VA 22201
Ph: (703)276-0220
Fax: (703)841-7797
E-mail: info@nahu.org
URL: http://www.nahu.org

Description: Insurance agents and brokers engaged in the promotion, sale, and administration of disability income and health insurance. Sponsors advanced health insurance underwriting and research seminars. Testifies before federal and state committees on pending health insurance legislation. Sponsors Leading Producers Roundtable Awards for leading salesmen. Maintains a speakers' bureau and a political action committee.

6555 ■ National Association of Insurance Women International (NAIW)
9343 E 95th Ct. S
Tulsa, OK 74133
Ph: (918)294-3700

Fax: (918)294-3711
Fr: 800-766-6249
E-mail: joinnaiw@naiw.org
URL: http://www.naiw.org

Description: Insurance industry professionals. Promotes continuing education and networking for the professional advancement of its members. Offers education programs, meetings, services, and leadership opportunities. Provides a forum to learn about other disciplines in the insurance industry.

6556 ■ National Association of Professional Allstate Agents (NAPAA)
PO Box 7666
Gulfport, MS 39506
Fr: 877-627-2248
E-mail: hq@napaausa.org
URL: http://www.napaausa.org

Description: Monitors legislative and legal issues pertinent to Allstate agents and their clients. Fosters the independence and entrepreneurial spirit of its members. Provides a forum where members can exchange ideas and give advice.

6557 ■ National Association of Professional Insurance Agents (PIA)
400 N Washington St.
Alexandria, VA 22314
Ph: (703)836-9340
Fax: (703)836-1279
E-mail: web@pianet.org
URL: http://www.pianet.com

Description: Represents independent agents in all 50 states, Puerto Rico and the District of Columbia. Represents members' interests in government and industry; provides educational programs; compiles statistics; conducts research programs; develops products/services unique to independent agencies; provides information and networking opportunities.

6558 ■ Nationwide Insurance Independent Contractors Association (NIICA)
2001 Jefferson Davis Hwy., Ste. 104
Arlington, VA 22202-3617

Ph: (703)416-4422
Fax: (703)416-0014
E-mail: info@niica.org
URL: http://www.niica.org

Description: Represents active and retired agents of the Nationwide Insurance Company. Promotes professionalism and ethical practice among its members. Encourages increased competence through continuous study and professional industry courses. Researches and recommends legislative programs to provide fair treatment to insurance consumers and independent contractors. Fosters and encourages fellowship among agents and their families.

6559 ■ Professional Insurance Marketing Association
35 E Wacker Dr., Ste. 850
Chicago, IL 60601-2101
Ph: (817)569-7462
Fax: (312)644-8557
E-mail: pima@pima-assn.org
URL: http://www.pima-assn.org

Description: Comprised of agents, brokers, third-party administrators, insurance underwriting companies and business partners involved in the direct marketing of insurance products. Serves as a forum for leaders in the insurance direct marketing industry to craft strategic relationships, develop business opportunities and expertise.

6560 ■ Society of Financial Service Professionals (SFSP)
19 Campus Blvd., Ste. 100
Newtown Square, PA 19073-3239
Ph: (610)526-2500
Fax: (610)527-1499
Fr: 800-392-6900
E-mail: info@financialpro.org
URL: http://www.financialpro.org

Description: Represents the interests of financial advisers. Fosters the development of professional responsibility. Assists clients to achieve personal and business-related financial goals. Offers educational programs, online professional resources and networking opportunities.

SOURCES OF HELP-WANTED ADS

6561 ■ Design Cost Data
DC & D Technologies Inc.
PO Box 948
Valrico, FL 33595-0948
Ph: (813)662-6830
Fax: (813)662-6793
Fr: 800-533-5680
URL: http://www.dcd.com

Bimonthly. $94.00/year for individuals, silver; $157.00/year for two years, silver; $149.00/year for individuals, gold; $239.00/year for two years, gold. Publication providing real cost data case studies of various types completed around the country for design and building professionals.

6562 ■ Dwell
Echo Media
900 Cir. 75 Pky., Ste. 1600
Atlanta, GA 30339-6014
Ph: (770)955-3535
Fax: (770)955-3599
URL: http://www.echo-media.com

Magazine covering articles on interior design, including innovative design and architecture.

6563 ■ InStyle Home
Time Inc.
1271 Avenue of the Americas
New York, NY 10020
Ph: (212)522-1212
URL: http://www.instyle.com/instyle/

Monthly. $19.50/year for individuals. Interior design magazine for the fashion-conscious.

6564 ■ Interior Design
Reed Business Information
360 Park Ave. S
New York, NY 10010-1710
Ph: (646)746-6400
URL: http://www.interiordesign.net/

$59.95/year for individuals; $87.00/year for Canada; $187.00/year for other countries. Interior designing and furnishings magazine.

6565 ■ Journal of Interior Design Education and Research
Interior Design Educators Council
9100 Purdue Rd., Ste. 200
Indianapolis, IN 46268
Ph: (317)328-4437
Fax: (317)280-8527
URL: http://www.idec.org/news/jid.php

Annual. Journal covering research, educational, historical, and critical aspects of interior design and allied fields.

6566 ■ Kitchen and Bath Business
Nielsen Business Media
770 Broadway
New York, NY 10003-9595
E-mail: kbb@mediabrains.com
URL: http://www.kitchen-bath.com/kbb/index.jsp

Monthly. $10.00/year for individuals, cover; $79.00/year for individuals, domestic; $94.00/year for Canada and Mexico; $139.00/year for other countries. Trade magazine on kitchen and bath remodeling and construction.

6567 ■ Kitchen and Bath Design News
Cygnus Business Media Inc.
3 Huntington Quadrangle, Ste. 301 N
Melville, NY 11747
Ph: (631)845-2700
Fax: (631)845-7109
Fr: 800-308-6397
URL: http://www.cygnusb2b.com/
   PropertyPub.cfm?PropertyID=78

Monthly. Trade journal.

6568 ■ LDB Interior Textiles
E.W. Williams Publications Co.
2125 Center Ave., Ste. 305
Fort Lee, NJ 07024-5898
Ph: (201)592-7007
Fax: (201)592-7171
URL: http://www.ldbinteriortextiles.com

Monthly. $72.00/year for individuals; $125.00/year for Canada; $150.00/year for elsewhere, airmail; $100.00/year for two years; $7.00/year for single issue; $12.00/year for single issue, Canada; $18.00/year for single issue, elsewhere. Magazine for buyers of home fashions, including bed, bath and table linens, hard and soft window treatments, home fragrances, decorative pillows and home accessories, accent rugs, and decorative fabrics.

6569 ■ Portfolio
Interior Design Society
164 S Main St., Fl. 8
High Point, NC 27260
Ph: (336)884-4437
Fax: (336)885-3291
Fr: 888-884-4469
E-mail: info@interiordesignsociety.org
URL: http://www.interiordesignsociety.org

Description: Quarterly. Reports on society activities and news of the interior design industry.

6570 ■ Qualified Remodeler Magazine
Cygnus Business Media
1233 Janesville Ave.
Fort Atkinson, WI 53538
Ph: (920)563-6388
Fax: (920)563-1702
Fr: 800-547-7377
URL: http://www.qualifiedremodeler.com

Monthly. Magazine for remodeling contractor/distributors.

6571 ■ Remodeling
Hanley-Wood L.L.C.
1 Thomas Cir. NW, Ste. 600
Washington, DC 20005-5803
Ph: (202)452-0800
Fax: (202)785-1974
E-mail: rm@omeda.com
URL: http://www.remodeling.hw.net

$25.00/year for individuals; $40.00/year for individuals, Canadian residents; $192.00/year for individuals, international residents. Trade magazine for the professional remodeling industry.

6572 ■ Visual Merchandising and Store Design
ST Media Group International Inc.
11262 Cornell Park Dr.
Cincinnati, OH 45242
Ph: (513)421-2050
Fax: (513)421-5144
Fr: 800-421-1321
URL: http://www.stmediagroup.com/
   index.php3?d=pubs&p=vm

Monthly. $42.00/year for individuals, U.S.; $66.00/year for individuals, 2 years, U.S.; $62.00/year for individuals, Canada (surface); $100.00/year for individuals, 2 years, Canada (surface); $65.00/year for individuals, Mexico/Foreign (surface); $105.00/year for individuals, 2 years, Mexico/Foreign (surface); $100.00/year for individuals, Mexico, 1st Class; $175.00/year for individuals, 2 years, Mexico 1st Class; $115.00/year for individuals, Central/South America; $205.00/year for individuals, 2 years, Central/South America. The leading magazine of the retail design industry covering the latest trends in retail design, store planning, and merchandise presentation.

6573 ■ Walls, Windows, and Floors
Hachette Filipacchi Media U.S. Inc.
1633 Broadway
New York, NY 10019-6708
Ph: (212)767-6000
URL: http://www.pointclickhome.com

Special interest home and garden magazine focusing on decorating the home.

EMPLOYER DIRECTORIES AND NETWORKING LISTS

6574 ■ Almanac of Architecture and Design
Greenway Consulting
25 Technology Pkwy. S, Ste. 101
Norcross, GA 30092-2952
Ph: (678)879-0929
Fax: (678)879-0930
URL: http://www.greenway.us

Annual, Latest edition 9th, 2008. $49.50 for individuals. Publication includes: Lists of professional organizations, degree programs, and leading firms in architecture and design. Principal content of publication is a collection of information regarding architecture and design.

6575 ■ *ENR—Top 500 Design Firms Issue*
McGraw-Hill Inc.
PO Box 182604
Columbus, OH 43218
Ph: (614)430-4000
Fax: (614)759-3749
Fr: 877-833-5524
URL: http://enr.construction.com/toplists/
sourcebooks/2010/design

Annual, latest edition 2010. $82.00 for individuals. Publication includes: List of 500 leading architectural, engineering, and specialty design firms selected on basis of annual billings. Entries include: Company name, headquarters location, type of firm, current and prior year rank in billings, types of services, countries in which operated in preceding year. Arrangement: Ranked by billings.

Handbooks and Manuals

6576 ■ *Careers for Color Connoisseurs and Other Visual Types*
The McGraw-Hill Companies
PO Box 182604
Columbus, OH 43272
Fax: (614)759-3749
Fr: 877-883-5524
E-mail: customer.service@mcgraw-hill.com
URL: http://www.mhprofessional.com/
product.php?isbn=0071465197

Jan Goldberg. Second edition, 2005. $19.95 (paper). 176 pages.

6577 ■ *The Creative Business Guide to Running a Graphic Design Business*
W. W. Norton & Company, Incorporated
500 Fifth Ave.
New York, NY 10110-0017
Ph: (212)354-5500
Fax: (212)869-0856
Fr: 800-233-4830
URL: http://books.wwnorton.com/books/
detail.aspx?ID=9939

Cameron Foote. 2009. $35.00. 416 pages.

6578 ■ *Opportunities in Interior Design and Decorating Careers*
The McGraw-Hill Companies
PO Box 182604
Columbus, OH 43272
Fax: (614)759-3749
Fr: 877-883-5524
E-mail: customer.service@mcgraw-hill.com
URL: http://www.mhprofessional.com

David Stearns. Third edition, 2008. $14.95 (paper). 160 pages. Covers opportunities and job search techniques in interior design. Addresses working for a design house, contract work, and starting a business. Illustrated.

6579 ■ *Portfolios for Interior Designers*
John Wiley & Sons, Inc.
111 River St.
Hoboken, NJ 07030-5774
Ph: (201)748-6000
Fax: (201)748-6088
E-mail: info@wiley.com
URL: http://www.wiley.com

Maureen Mitton. 2010. $55.00. 224 pages. Serves as guide to portfolio development for interior designers. Delivers step-by-step instruction on properly and effectively displaying their work in fashion. Includes graphic design concepts necessary for portfolio development, specific information for designing digital portfolios, useful tips on using popular graphics software applications, and samples of cover letters and resumes.

6580 ■ *Professional Interior Design: A Career Guide*
iUniverse, Inc.
1663 Liberty Dr.
Bloomington, IN 47403
Ph: (402)323-7800
Fax: (812)355-4085
Fr: 800-288-4677
URL: http://www.iuniverse.com/

Jason Znoy, ASID Illinois Association. May 2004. $9.95 (paper). 64 pages.

6581 ■ *Residential Interior Design: A Guide to Planning Spaces*
John Wiley & Sons, Inc.
111 River St.
Hoboken, NJ 07030
Ph: (201)748-6000
Fax: (201)748-6088
E-mail: info@wiley.com
URL: http://as.wiley.com/WileyCDA/Section/
index.html

Maureen Mitton and Courtney Nystuen. 2011. $54.95. 304 pages. Fundamental skills for designers working in any type of home or decorative style, focusing on planning, human factors, code and building systems, storage and exterior spaces.

6582 ■ *Starting Your Career as an Interior Designer*
Allworth Press
307 W 36th St., 11th Fl.
New York, NY 10018
Ph: (212)643-6816
Fax: (212)643-6819
URL: http://www.allworth.com

Robert K. Hale and Thomas L. Williams. 2009. $24.95 (paper). 240 pages. Contains tools and strategies to successfully launch and grow a professional design business in the competitive world of interior design. Includes case studies and personal anecdotes.

Employment Agencies and Search Firms

6583 ■ Claremont-Branan, Inc.
1298 Rockbridge Rd., Ste. B
Stone Mountain, GA 30087
Fr: 800-875-1292
URL: http://cbisearch.com

Employment agency. Executive search firm.

6584 ■ Interior Talent
1430 Lake Baldwin Ln., Ste. A
Orlando, FL 32814
Ph: (407)228-1938
Fax: (407)228-1935
Fr: 800-915-3012
URL: http://www.interiortalent.com

Description: Recruiters for architecture and design professionals worldwide.

6585 ■ Randolph Associates, Inc.
950 Massachusetts Ave., Ste. 105
Cambridge, MA 02139-3174
Ph: (617)441-8777
Fax: (617)441-8778
E-mail: jobs@greatjobs.com
URL: http://www.greatjobs.com

Employment agency. Provides regular or temporary placement of staff.

6586 ■ RitaSue Siegel Resources, Inc.
PO Box 845
New York, NY 10150
Ph: (917)725-1603
E-mail: contact@ritasue.com
URL: http://www.ritasue.com

Executive search firm specializing in industrial and product design.

Online Job Sources and Services

6587 ■ InteriorDesignJobs.com
URL: http://interiordesignjobs.sellisp.com/Default.asp

Description: Provides sources of employment information for professionals in the interior design industry.

Tradeshows

6588 ■ Annual Home Decorating and Remodeling Show
Show Pros International, LLC.
PO Box 230669
Las Vegas, NV 89123-0012
Fr: 800-343-8344
E-mail: spvandy@cox.net
URL: http://www.showprosintl.com/

Annual. Primary Exhibits: Home products.

6589 ■ Chicago Design Show
Merchandise Mart Properties Inc.
222 Merchandise Mart, Ste. 470
Chicago, IL 60654
Fr: 800-677-6278
URL: http://www.merchandisemart.com

Annual. Primary Exhibits: Contemporary design in furniture, fashion, food.

6590 ■ Coverings
National Trade Productions, Inc.
313 S. Patrick St.
Alexandria, VA 22314
Fax: (703)836-4486
Fr: 800-687-7469
E-mail: ntpinfo@ntpshow.com
URL: http://www.ntpshow.com

Annual. Primary Exhibits: Residential and commercial covering industries: flooring, ceramic tile, natural stone and related products and services. Also hardwood flooring, laminate flooring, resilient flooring and related adhesives, grouts, sealants, tools and allied products. Dates and Locations: 2012 Apr 17-20; Orlando, FL.

6591 ■ Old House/New House Home Show
Kennedy Productions, Inc.
1208 Lisle Pl.
Lisle, IL 60532-2262
Ph: (630)515-1160
Fax: (630)515-1165
E-mail: kp@core.com
URL: http://www.kennedyproductions.com

Semiannual. Primary Exhibits: Products and services for home remodeling, improvement, enhancement, decorating, landscaping and more. Hundreds of ideas to improve and beautify every home. Dates and Locations: 2012 Feb 10-12; St. Charles, IL; Pheasant Run Resort.

6592 ■ Surfaces
World Floor Covering Association
2211 E Howell Ave.
Anaheim, CA 92806
Ph: (714)978-6440
Fax: (714)978-6066
Fr: 800-624-6880
E-mail: wfca@wfca.org
URL: http://www.wfca.org

Annual. Primary Exhibits: Floor covering equipment, supplies, and services. Dates and Locations: 2012 Jan 24-26; Las Vegas, NV; Mandalay Bay Convention Center.

Other Sources

6593 ■ Council of Educational Facility Planners International (CEFPI)
9180 E Desert Cove Dr., Ste. 104
Scottsdale, AZ 85260-6231

Ph: (480)391-0840
Fax: (480)391-0940
E-mail: michelle@cefpi.org
URL: http://www.cefpi.org

Description: Individuals and firms who are responsible for planning, designing, creating, maintaining, and equipping the physical environment of education. Sponsors an exchange of information, professional experiences, best practices research results, and other investigative techniques concerning educational facility planning. Activities include publication and review of current and emerging practices in educational facility planning; identification and execution of needed research; development of professional training programs; strengthening of planning services on various levels of government and in institutions of higher learning; leadership in the development of higher standards for facility design and the physical environment of education. Operates speakers' bureau; sponsors placement service; compiles statistics.

6594 ■ Interior Design Society (IDS)
164 S Main St., Fl. 8
High Point, NC 27260
Ph: (336)884-4437
Fax: (336)885-3291
Fr: 888-884-4469
E-mail: info@interiordesignsociety.org
URL: http://www.interiordesignsociety.org

Description: Represents independent designers and decorators, retail designers and sales people, design-oriented firms, and manufacturers. Grants accreditation and recognition to qualified residential interior designers and retail home furnishing stores. Conducts educational seminars in design, sales training, and marketing. Offers products and publications for designers and a correspondence course for home furnishing sales people.

6595 ■ Interior Redesign Industry Specialists (IRIS)
1100-H Brandywine Blvd.
Zanesville, OH 43701-7303
Ph: (740)450-1330
Fax: (740)452-2552
E-mail: iris@irisorganization.org
URL: http://www.irisorganization.org

Description: Represents the interests of professional redesigners and stagers. Seeks to establish and maintain high industry standards. Promotes public awareness and expands the fields of redesign and staging.

6596 ■ International Design Guild (IDG)
670 Commercial St.
Manchester, NH 03101
Fr: 800-205-4345
E-mail: info@design-guild.com
URL: http://www.design-guild.com

Description: Brings together interior designers to share and gain insight for business development and networking. Provides members with customizable marketing, merchandising, educational and operational tools. Aims to help members operate their businesses more profitably.

6597 ■ International Interior Design Association (IIDA)
222 Merchandise Mart, Ste. 567
Chicago, IL 60654
Ph: (312)467-1950
Fax: (312)467-0779
Fr: 888-799-4432
E-mail: iidahq@iida.org
URL: http://www.iida.org

Description: Represents professional interior designers, including designers of commercial, healthcare, hospitality, government, retail, residential facilities;

educators; researchers; representatives of allied manufacturing sources. Conducts research, student programs and continuing education programs for members. Has developed a code of ethics for the professional design membership.

6598 ■ Organization of Women Architects and Design Professionals
PO Box 10078
Berkeley, CA 94709
E-mail: info@owa-usa.org
URL: http://owa-usa.org

Description: Comprised of architects, interior designers, landscape architects, planners, lighting designers, graphic designers, photographers, artists, writers, educators and students. Strives to improve the professional standing of women in architecture and design-related fields. Advocates young women and students entering design related fields through mentoring, education, and employment opportunities.

6599 ■ Retail Design Institute (ISP)
25 N Broadway
Tarrytown, NY 10591-3221
Fax: (914)332-1541
Fr: 800-379-9912
E-mail: info@ispo.org
URL: http://www.retaildesigninstitute.org

Description: Persons active in store planning and design; visual merchandisers, students and educators; contractors and suppliers to the industry; dedicated to the professional growth of members while providing service to the public through improvement of the retail environment. Provides forum for debate and discussion by store design experts, retailers and public figures. Makes available speakers for store planning and design courses at the college level; develops programs for store planning courses. Sponsors student design competitions and annual international store design competition with awards in 10 categories. Maintains placement service.

Jewelers

SOURCES OF HELP-WANTED ADS

6600 ■ Couture International Jeweler
Nielsen Business Media
770 Broadway
New York, NY 10003-9595
URL: http://www.nielsenbusinessmedia.com/c_
Couture-Int-Jeweler.ht

Quarterly. $60.00/year for U.S.; $105.00/year for other countries. Trade magazine covering the jewelry and retail industry.

6601 ■ Diamond Intelligence Briefs
Nielsen Business Media
770 Broadway
New York, NY 10003-9595
URL: http://www.diamondintelligence.com/template/
default.aspx?Pa

Trade publication for the diamond and jewelry industry.

6602 ■ Jewelers' Circular-Keystone
Reed Exhibitions
383 Main Ave.
Norwalk, CT 06851
Ph: (203)840-4800
Fax: (203)840-5805
URL: http://www.jckonline.com/

Monthly. $19.95/year for individuals; $64.95/year for Canada; $144.95/year for other countries. Retail jewelers trade magazine.

6603 ■ National Jeweler
Nielsen Business Media
770 Broadway
New York, NY 10003-9595
URL: http://www.nationaljewelernetwork.com/njn/
index.jsp

Semimonthly. $10.00/year for single issue, cover; $89.00/year for U.S.; $104.00/year for Canada; $330.00/year for other countries, airmail only. Jewelry industry magazine.

6604 ■ New York Diamonds
Reed Business Information (New York, New York)
360 Park Ave. S
New York, NY 10010
Ph: (646)746-6400
Fax: (646)746-7431
Fr: 800-446-6551
URL: http://www.reedbusiness.com/
index.asp?groupID=39&industryid=

Bimonthly. Publication covering the jewelry trade.

6605 ■ Watch & Jewelry Review
Golden Bell Press
2403 Champa St.
Denver, CO 80205
Ph: (303)296-1600

Fax: (303)295-2159
URL: http://www.goldenbellpress.com/Pages/
front.html

$19.50/year for individuals; $35.00/year for two years; $60.00/year for other countries; $115.00/year for two years, other countries. Magazine on watches and clocks.

EMPLOYER DIRECTORIES AND NETWORKING LISTS

6606 ■ Jewelers Board of Trade—Confidential Reference Book
Jewelers Board of Trade
95 Jefferson Blvd.
Warwick, RI 02888
Ph: (401)467-0055
Fax: (401)467-6070
URL: http://www.jewelersboard.com

Semiannual, March and September. $60.00 for individuals. Covers: About 30,000 jewelry manufacturers, importers, distributors, and retailers. Entries include: Company name, address, phone, whether a wholesaler, retailer, or manufacturer, credit rating. Arrangement: Geographical.

6607 ■ National Association of Jewelry Appraisers—Membership Directory
National Association of Jewelry Appraisers Inc.
PO Box 18
Rego Park, NY 11374-0018
Ph: (718)896-1536
Fax: (718)997-9057
URL: http://www.najaappraisers.com

Annual, April. Covers: Nearly 750 members. Entries include: Name, address, phone, business affiliation, area of specialization. Arrangement: Alphabetical, with separate geographical listing. Indexes: Specialty.

EMPLOYMENT AGENCIES AND SEARCH FIRMS

6608 ■ Premier Placements
9713 Herons Cove
Indianapolis, IN 46280
Fr: 800-474-8047
URL: http://www.jewelryjobs.com

Executive search firm that specializes in the jewelry industry. Provides professional opportunities for jewelers.

ONLINE JOB SOURCES AND SERVICES

6609 ■ Jobs4Gems.com
URL: http://jobs4gems.com
Description: Serves as a web location for employ-

ment opportunities in the jewelry industry. Includes services that allow job seekers to work with professionals in the jewelry industry and gain employment at the top jewelry companies.

6610 ■ US-Jewelers.com
URL: http://www.us-jewelers.com

Description: Offers temporary and permanent jewelry job listings and employment opportunities across the United States.

TRADESHOWS

6611 ■ Atlanta Jewelry Show
Southern Jewelry Travelers Association
4 Executive Pk. Dr. N.E., Ste. 1202
Atlanta, GA 30329-2235
Ph: (404)634-3434
Fax: (404)634-4663
Fr: 800-241-0399
E-mail: info@atlantajewelryshow.com
URL: http://www.atlantajewelryshow.com/

Semiannual, and August. Primary Exhibits: Fine jewelry, diamonds, pearls, gemstones, watches, jewelry boxes, safes, store fixtures, and jewelry computer programming. Dates and Locations: 2012 Feb 25-27; Atlanta, GA; Cobb Galleria Centre ; 2012 Aug 11-13; Atlanta, GA; Cobb Galleria Centre.

6612 ■ Gem Fair
American Gem Trade Association
3030 LBJ Freeway, Ste. 840
Dallas, TX 75234
Ph: (214)742-4367
Fax: (214)742-7334
Fr: 800-972-1162
E-mail: info@agta.org
URL: http://www.agta.org

Annual. Primary Exhibits: Suppliers of natural colored gemstones; retail jewelers and jewelry manufacturers. Dates and Locations: 2012 Jan 31 - Feb 05; Tucson, AZ; Tucson Convention Center.

6613 ■ JCK Las Vegas
Reed Exhibitions North American Headquarters
383 Main Ave.
Norwalk, CT 06851
Ph: (203)840-4800
Fax: (203)840-5805
E-mail: inquiry@reedexpo.com
URL: http://www.reedexpo.com

Annual. Primary Exhibits: Trade event only for high end jewelry manufacturers, related products and services. Dates and Locations: 2012 Jun 01-04; Las Vegas, NV; Mandalay Bay and Convention Center.

6614 ■ Jewelers International Showcase
Jewelers International Showcase, Inc.
6421 Congress Ave., Ste. 105
Boca Raton, FL 33487

Ph: (561)998-0209
URL: http://www.jisshow.com

3/year. Primary Exhibits: Fine jewelry, fashion jewelry, and related products and services to jewelry trade members.

6615 ■ Mid-America Jewelry Show

Mid-America Jewelers Association
1100-H Brandywine Blvd.
Zanesville, OH 43701-7303
Ph: (740)450-1318
Fax: (740)452-2552
Fr: 800-652-6257
E-mail: info@midamericajewelers.org
URL: http://www.midamericajewelers.org/

Annual. Primary Exhibits: Fine jewelry, display units, security systems, gems, diamonds, and other accessories and equipment for the retail jeweler. Dates and Locations: 2012 Aug 17-19.

Other Sources

6616 ■ American Watchmakers-Clockmakers Institute (AWCI)

701 Enterprise Dr.
Harrison, OH 45030
Ph: (513)367-9800
Fax: (513)367-1414
Fr: (866)367-2924
E-mail: jlubic@awci.com
URL: http://www.awci.com

Description: Jewelers, watchmakers, clockmakers, watch and clock engineers, scientists, repairmen, and others in the watch, clock, and jewelry industry. Examines and certifies master watchmakers and clockmakers. Maintains a museum displaying horological items, and the National Watch Mark Identification Bureau. Conducts home study course in clock repairing and bench courses for watchmakers in most major U.S. cities. Disseminates career information to vocational counselors in the form of brochures and filmstrips.

6617 ■ Gemological Institute of America (GIA)

The Robert Mouawad Campus
5345 Armada Dr.
Carlsbad, CA 92008
Ph: (760)603-4000
Fr: 800-421-7250
E-mail: marketing@gia.edu
URL: http://www.gia.edu

Description: Works to ensure the public trust in gems and jewelry by upholding the highest standards of integrity, academics, science, and professionalism through research, education, gemological laboratory services, and instrument development; alumni are sustaining members. Conducts home study programs, resident courses, online classes and traveling seminars in identification and quality analysis of diamonds and other gemstones and pearls, and in jewelry making and repair, jewelry designing, and jewelry sales. Manufactures and sells gem testing, diamond grading equipment and audiovisual gemstone presentations through subsidiaries. Maintains gem testing and research laboratories in Carlsbad, CA and New York City. Offers job placement service; organizes gemological study tours. Awards diplomas and operates speakers' bureau.

6618 ■ Jewelers of America (JA)

52 Vanderbilt Ave., 19th Fl.
New York, NY 10017-3827
Ph: (646)658-0246
Fax: (646)658-0256
Fr: 800-223-0673
E-mail: info@jewelers.org
URL: http://www.jewelers.org

Description: Retailers of jewelry, watches, silver, and allied merchandise. Conducts surveys and compiles statistics. Conducts educational programs. Provides information to consumers.

6619 ■ Manufacturing Jewelers and Suppliers of America (MJSA)

57 John L. Dietsch Sq.
Attleboro Falls, MA 02763
Ph: (401)274-3840

Fax: (401)274-0265
Fr: 800-444-6572
E-mail: info@mjsa.org
URL: http://www.mjsa.org

Description: Represents American manufacturers and suppliers within the jewelry industry. Seeks to foster long-term stability and prosperity of the jewelry industry. Provides leadership in government affairs and industry education.

6620 ■ National Association of Jewelry Appraisers (NAJA)

PO Box 18
Rego Park, NY 11374-0018
Ph: (718)896-1536
Fax: (718)997-9057
E-mail: office@najaappraisers.com
URL: http://www.najaappraisers.com

Description: Gem and jewelry appraisers, jewelers, importers, brokers, manufacturers, gemological students, and others professionally interested in jewelry appraisal. Seeks to recognize and make available to the public the services of highly qualified, experienced, independent, and reliable jewelry appraisers. Conducts seminars on jewelry appraisal techniques, methods, and pricing for members and the public. Supports legislation to establish minimum standards of competency and licensing of jewelry appraisers; maintains code of professional ethics. Operates appraiser referral program; sponsors ongoing public relations campaign. Offers equipment discounts, new appraisal forms, travel discounts, insurance, and professional aids for members only. Compiles statistics.

6621 ■ Women's Jewelry Association (WJA)

52 Vanderbilt Ave., 19th Fl.
New York, NY 10017-3827
Ph: (212)687-2722
Fax: (646)355-0219
E-mail: info@womensjewelry.org
URL: http://wjamarion.memberlodge.com

Description: Represents those involved in jewelry design, manufacture, retail, and advertising. Aims to: enhance the status of women in the jewelry industry; make known the contribution of women to the industry; provide a network for women involved with fine jewelry. Maintains hall of fame.

SOURCES OF HELP-WANTED ADS

6622 ▪ *About Campus*
John Wiley & Sons Inc.
111 River St.
Hoboken, NJ 07030-5773
Ph: (201)748-6000
Fax: (201)748-6088
Fr: 800-825-7550
URL: http://onlinelibrary.wiley.com/journal/10.1002/
(ISSN)1536-06

Bimonthly. $207.00/year for institutions, print only;
$267.00/year for institutions, Canada and Mexico,
print only; $318.00/year for institutions, other coun-
tries, print only; $60.00/year for U.S., Canada, and
Mexico, print only; $96.00/year for other countries,
print only. Journal focused on the critical issues faced
by both student affairs and academic affairs staff as
they work on helping students learn.

6623 ▪ *American Academic*
American Federation of Teachers
555 New Jersey Ave. NW
Washington, DC 20001
Ph: (202)879-4400
URL: http://www.aft.org/pubs-reports/american_
academic/index.htm

Higher education policy journal.

6624 ▪ *The American Biology Teacher*
National Association of Biology Teachers
1313 Dolley Madison Blvd., Ste. 402
McLean, VA 22101
Ph: (703)264-9696
Fax: (703)264-7778
Fr: 800-406-0775
URL: http://www.nabt.org/websites/institution/
index.php?p=26

$9.00/year for members; $24.00/year for nonmembers; $24.00/year for institutions. Peer-reviewed
journal featuring articles on biology, science, and
education for elementary, high school and college
level biology teachers. Includes audio-visual, book,
computer, and research reviews.

6625 ▪ *Annals of Medicine*
Informa Healthcare
52 Vanderbilt Ave., 7th Fl.
New York, NY 10017-3846
Ph: (212)520-2777
URL: http://informahealthcare.com/ann

$595.00/year for institutions; $980.00/year for institutions; $780.00/year for institutions. Journal covering
health science and medical education.

**6626 ▪ *Assessment & Evaluation in Higher
Education***
Routledge Journals
270 Madison Ave.
New York, NY 10016-0601

Ph: (212)216-7800
Fax: (212)563-2269
URL: http://www.tandf.co.uk/journals/titles/
02602938.asp

Bimonthly. $1,316.00/year for institutions, online only;
$2,547.00/year for institutions, print + online;
$1,462.00/year for individuals, print + online;
$2,292.00/year for institutions, online only; $578.00/
year for individuals, print only; $314.00/year for
individuals, print only. Peer-reviewed journal focusing
on publishing papers and reports on all aspects of
assessment and evaluation within higher education.

6627 ▪ *Better*
The Johns Hopkins University Press
2715 N Charles St.
Baltimore, MD 21218-4319
Ph: (410)516-6900
Fax: (410)516-6968
URL: http://www.press.jhu.edu/journals/better_
evidence_based_educ

$29.50/year for individuals, print and electronic;
$80.00/year for institutions, print and electronic.
Magazine for educators and policy makers interested
in evidence-based education reform.

**6628 ▪ *Brookings Papers on Education
Policy***
Brookings Institution Press
1775 Massachusetts Ave. NW
Washington, DC 20036
Ph: (202)797-6000
URL: http://www.brookings.edu/press/Journals/2007/
brookingspapers

$36.00/year for individuals. Journal dealing with all
aspects of American education.

6629 ▪ *Creative Education*
Scientific Research Publishing
PO Box 54821
Irvine, CA 92619-4821
E-mail: ce@scirp.org
URL: http://www.scirp.org/journal/ce/

$195.00/year for individuals. Peer-reviewed journal
publishing articles on the latest advancements in
creative education.

6630 ▪ *Current Jobs in Education*
Foster Opportunities, Inc.
1834 Olmstead Dr.
Falls Church, VA 22043
Ph: (703)506-4400
Fr: 888-870-3069
E-mail: admin@graduatejobs.com
URL: http://www.graduatejobs.com/education.htm

Monthly. $49.50/year. Provides teaching and adminis-
trative job vacancies in educational settings.

6631 ▪ *Education & Treatment of Children*
West Virginia University Press
139 Stansbury Hall
PO Box 6295
Morgantown, WV 26506

Ph: (304)293-8400
Fax: (304)293-6585
URL: http://www.educationandtreatmentofchildren.net

Quarterly. $85.00/year for institutions; $45.00/year for
individuals; $100.00/year for institutions, elsewhere;
$60.00/year for individuals, elsewhere. Periodical
featuring information concerning the development of
services for children and youth. Includes reports written for educators and other child care and mental
health providers focused on teaching, training, and
treatment effectiveness.

6632 ▪ *Education Week*
Editorial Projects in Education Inc.
6935 Arlington Rd., Ste. 100
Bethesda, MD 20814-5287
Ph: (301)280-3100
Fax: (301)280-3200
Fr: 800-346-1834
E-mail: ew@epe.org
URL: http://www.edweek.org/ew

$90.00/year for individuals, print plus online. Profes-
sional newspaper for elementary and secondary
school educators.

6633 ▪ *Educational Research and Evaluation*
Routledge Journals
270 Madison Ave.
New York, NY 10016-0601
Ph: (212)216-7800
Fax: (212)563-2269
URL: http://www.tandf.co.uk/journals/titles/
13803611.asp

Bimonthly. $428.00/year for institutions, print + on-
line; $385.00/year for institutions, online only;
$165.00/year for individuals, print only; $731.00/year
for institutions, print + online; $658.00/year for institu-
tions, online only; $275.00/year for individuals, print
only. Peer-reviewed journal on theory and practice.

6634 ▪ *Educational Researcher*
American Educational Research Association
1430 K St. NW, Ste. 1200
Washington, DC 20005
Ph: (202)238-3200
Fax: (202)238-3250
URL: http://www.aera.net/publications/?id=317

Monthly. $48.00/year for individuals, plus foreign mail-
ing charges; $150.00/year for institutions, plus foreign
mailing charges. Educational research journal.

6635 ▪ *Environmental Education Research*
Routledge Journals
270 Madison Ave.
New York, NY 10016-0601
Ph: (212)216-7800
Fax: (212)563-2269
URL: http://www.tandf.co.uk/journals/titles/
13504622.asp

Bimonthly. $1,373.00/year for institutions, print + on-
line; $1,236.00/year for institutions, online only;

$364.00/year for individuals, print only. Journal covering all aspects of environmental education.

6636 ■ *Essays in Education*
University of South Carolina
471 University Pky.
Aiken, SC 29801
Ph: (803)648-6851
URL: http://www.usca.edu/essays/

Monthly. Journal covering issues that impact and influence education.

6637 ■ *Hematology*
American Society of Hematology
2021 L St. NW, Ste. 900
Washington, DC 20036
Ph: (202)776-0544
Fax: (202)776-0545
URL: http://asheducationbook.hematologylibrary.org

Annual. $75.00/year for members; $125.00/year for nonmembers. Journal providing continuing medical education for physicians.

6638 ■ *Interdisciplinary Journal of Teaching and Learning*
Southern University at Baton Rouge
PO Box 9942
Baton Rouge, LA 70813
Ph: (225)711-4500
Fax: (225)771-4400
URL: http://www.subr.edu/CollegeofEducation/
COE%20ONLINE%20Journa

Online academic journal that publishes research and scholarly articles in the field of education and learning.

6639 ■ *The International Electronic Journal of Health Education*
American Alliance for Health, Physical Education, Recreation & Dance
1900 Association Dr.
Reston, VA 20191-1598
Ph: (703)476-3400
Fax: (703)476-9527
Fr: 800-213-7193
URL: http://www.aahperd.org/aahe/publications/iejhe/

Annual. Free, health education professionals and students. Journal promoting health through education and other systematic strategies.

6640 ■ *International Journal of Critical Pedagogy*
University of North Carolina at Greensboro
1400 Spring Garden St.
Greensboro, NC 27412
Ph: (336)334-5000
URL: http://libjournal.uncg.edu/ojs/index.php/ijcp/
index

Peer-reviewed journal publishing innovative understandings and applications of critical pedagogy.

6641 ■ *International Journal of Early Years Education*
Routledge Journals
270 Madison Ave.
New York, NY 10016-0601
Ph: (212)216-7800
Fax: (212)563-2269
URL: http://www.tandf.co.uk/journals/titles/
09669760.asp

$705.00/year for institutions, online only; $783.00/year for institutions, print + online; $271.00/year for individuals, print only. Journal focusing on education world-wide.

6642 ■ *International Journal of Inclusive Education*
Routledge Journals
270 Madison Ave.
New York, NY 10016-0601
Ph: (212)216-7800
Fax: (212)563-2269
URL: http://www.tandf.co.uk/journals/titles/
13603116.asp

$589.00/year for individuals, print only; $1,135.00/year for institutions, online only; $1,261.00/year for individuals, print + online; $355.00/year for individuals, print only; $694.00/year for institutions, online only; $771.00/year for institutions, print + online. Journal providing information on the nature of schools, universities and technical colleges for the educators and educational policy-makers.

6643 ■ *International Journal of Leadership in Education*
Routledge
711 3 Ave., 8 Fl.
New York, NY 10016
Ph: (212)216-7800
Fax: (212)563-2269
Fr: 800-634-7064
E-mail: ijle@txstate.edu
URL: http://www.tandf.co.uk/journals/tf/
13603124.html

Quarterly. $240.00/year for individuals, print only; $612.00/year for institutions, online only; $680.00/year for institutions, print and online; $408.00/year for institutions, print and online; $367.00/year for institutions, online only; $142.00/year for individuals, print only. Journal dealing with leadership in education.

6644 ■ *International Journal of Progressive Education*
International Journal of Progressive Education
c/o Alex Jean-Charles, PhD, Asst. Mng. Ed.
320 Fitzelle Hall, Ravine Pky.
Oneonta, NY 13820
URL: http://www.inased.org/ijpe.htm

$35.00/year for members; $45.00/year for individuals; $140.00/year for institutions, library; $35.00/year for students; $25.00/year for single issue; $50.00/year for students, other countries. Peer-reviewed online journal that aims to create an open and continuing dialogue about current educational issues and future conceptions of educational theory.

6645 ■ *International Journal of Whole Schooling*
Whole Schooling Press
Wayne State University
217 Education
Detroit, MI 48202
URL: http://www.wholeschooling.net/Journal_of_
Whole_Schooling/IJW

Free. International, refereed academic journal dedicated to exploring ways to improve learning and schooling for all children.

6646 ■ *Journal of Academic Leadership*
Academic Leadership
600 Park St.
Rarick Hall 219
Hays, KS 67601-4099
Ph: (785)628-4547
URL: http://www.academicleadership.org/

Journal focusing on the leadership issues in the academic world.

6647 ■ *Journal of Cases in Educational Leadership*
Sage Publications Inc.
2455 Teller Rd.
Thousand Oaks, CA 91320-2218
Ph: (805)499-9774
Fax: (805)583-2665
Fr: 800-818-7243
URL: http://jel.sagepub.com

Quarterly. $411.00/year for institutions, e-access; $94.00/year for individuals, e-access. Journal covering cases appropriate for use in programs that prepare educational leaders.

6648 ■ *Journal of Curriculum and Supervision*
Association for Supervision and Curriculum Development
1703 N Beauregard St.
Alexandria, VA 22311-1714

Ph: (703)578-9600
Fax: (703)575-5400
Fr: 800-933-2723
URL: http://www.ascd.org/publications/jcs/fall2002/
On_Community.a

Scholarly journal focusing on curriculum and supervision.

6649 ■ *Journal of Direct Instruction*
Association for Direct Instruction
PO Box 10252
Eugene, OR 97440
Ph: (541)485-1293
Fax: (541)868-1397
Fr: 800-995-2464
URL: http://www.adihome.org/
index.php?option=com_content&view=art

Quarterly. Included in membership. Journal covering education.

6650 ■ *Journal of Language, Identity, and Education*
Routledge Journals
270 Madison Ave.
New York, NY 10016-0601
Ph: (212)216-7800
Fax: (212)563-2269
URL: http://www.tandf.co.uk/journals/titles/
15348458.asp

$316.00/year for institutions, print + online; $284.00/year for institutions, online; $43.00/year for individuals, print + online; $527.00/year for institutions, print + online; $474.00/year for institutions, online; $71.00/year for individuals, print + online; $421.00/year for institutions, print + online; $379.00/year for institutions, online; $57.00/year for individuals, print + online. Scholarly, interdisciplinary journal covering issues in language, identity and education worldwide for academics, educators and policy specialists in a variety of disciplines, and others.

6651 ■ *Journal of Latinos and Education*
Routledge Journals
270 Madison Ave.
New York, NY 10016-0601
Ph: (212)216-7800
Fax: (212)563-2269
URL: http://www.tandf.co.uk/journals/titles/
15348431.asp

Quarterly. $286.00/year for institutions, print + online; $257.00/year for institutions, online; $38.00/year for individuals, print + online; $480.00/year for institutions, print + online; $432.00/year for institutions, online; $63.00/year for individuals, print + online; $331.00/year for institutions, print + online; $343.00/year for institutions, online; $51.00/year for individuals, print + online. Scholarly, multidisciplinary journal covering educational issues that impact Latinos for researchers, teaching professionals, academics, scholars, institutions, and others.

6652 ■ *Journal of Learning Disabilities*
Sage Publications Inc.
2455 Teller Rd.
Thousand Oaks, CA 91320-2218
Ph: (805)499-9774
Fax: (805)583-2665
Fr: 800-818-7243
URL: http://www.sagepub.com/
journalsProdDesc.nav?ct_p=boardsII

Bimonthly. $77.00/year for individuals, print & e-access; $260.00/year for institutions, print & e-access; $255.00/year for institutions, print only; $234.00/year for institutions, e-access. Special education journal.

6653 ■ *Journal of STEM Education*
Auburn University
9088 Haley Ctr.
Auburn, AL 36849
Ph: (334)844-9088
Fax: (334)844-9027
URL: http://ojs.jstem.org/index.php?journal=JSTEM

Semiannual. Journal for educators in Science, Technology, Engineering, and Mathematics (STEM) education.

6654 ■ Leadership and Policy in Schools
Routledge Journals
270 Madison Ave.
New York, NY 10016-0601
Ph: (212)216-7800
Fax: (212)563-2269
URL: http://www.tandf.co.uk/journals/titles/
    15700763.asp

Quarterly. $567.00/year for institutions, print and online; $260.00/year for individuals, print only; $510.00/year for institutions, online only. Journal providing information about leadership and policy in primary and secondary education.

6655 ■ Learning
Education Center Inc.
3515 W Market St., Ste. 200
PO Box 9753
Greensboro, NC 27429-0753
Ph: 877-696-0825
Fax: 888-883-7454
Fr: 800-334-0298
URL: http://www.theeducationcenter.com/tec/afc/
    learning/go.do

Quarterly. $4.95/year for single issue; $14.95/year for U.S. Definitive guide to products and services for K-6 grade teachers in the classroom.

6656 ■ Music Educators Journal
MENC: The National Association for Music Education
1806 Robert Fulton Dr.
Reston, VA 20191
Ph: (703)860-4000
Fax: (703)860-1531
Fr: 800-336-3768
URL: http://www.menc.org/resources/view/menc-
    journals

$165.00/year for institutions, print & E-access; $149.00/year for institutions, E-access; $162.00/year for institutions, print only. Journal covering all levels of music education. Published on alternate months with Teaching Music.

6657 ■ NJEA Review
New Jersey Education Association
180 W State St.
PO Box 1211
Trenton, NJ 08607-1211
Ph: (609)599-4561
Fax: (609)392-6321
E-mail: njeareview@njea.org
URL: http://www.njea.org/page.aspx?z=1094&pz=8

Monthly. $250.00/year for nonmembers. Educational journal for public school employees.

6658 ■ Oxford Review of Education
Routledge Journals
270 Madison Ave.
New York, NY 10016-0601
Ph: (212)216-7800
Fax: (212)563-2269
URL: http://www.tandf.co.uk/journals/titles/
    03054985.asp

$709.00/year for institutions, print + online; $1,224.00/year for institutions, print + online; $249.00/year for individuals, print only; $454.00/year for individuals, print only. Journal covering advance study of education.

6659 ■ The Physics Teacher
American Association of Physics Teachers
1 Physics Ellipse
College Park, MD 20740-3845
Ph: (301)209-3311
Fax: (301)209-0845
URL: http://tpt.aapt.org

; $434.00/year for nonmembers, domestic; $469.00/

year for nonmembers, international. Scientific education magazine.

6660 ■ School and Community
Missouri State Teachers Association
407 S Sixth St.
PO Box 458
Columbia, MO 65205
Ph: (573)442-3127
Fax: (573)443-5079
Fr: 800-392-0532
URL: http://www.msta.org/resources/publications/snc/

Quarterly. Education magazine.

6661 ■ School Effectiveness and School Improvement
Routledge
711 3 Ave., 8 Fl.
New York, NY 10016
Ph: (212)216-7800
Fax: (212)563-2269
Fr: 800-634-7064
URL: http://www.tandf.co.uk/journals/titles/
    09243453.asp

Quarterly. $387.00/year for institutions, print and online; $348.00/year for institutions, online only; $186.00/year for individuals, print only; $660.00/year for institutions, print and online; $594.00/year for institutions, online only; $312.00/year for individuals, print only. Journal focusing on educational progress of all students.

6662 ■ The Science Teacher
National Science Teachers Association
1840 Wilson Blvd.
Arlington, VA 22201-3000
Ph: (703)243-7100
Fax: (703)243-7177
URL: http://www.nsta.org/highschool/

Peer-reviewed journal for secondary science teachers.

6663 ■ Strategies
American Alliance for Health, Physical Education, Recreation & Dance
1900 Association Dr.
Reston, VA 20191-1598
Ph: (703)476-3400
Fax: (703)476-9527
Fr: 800-213-7193
E-mail: strategies@aahperd.org
URL: http://www.aahperd.org/naspe/publications/
    journals/strategie

Bimonthly. $130.00/year for U.S. and Canada, institutions, schools & libraries; print & online; $50.00/year for U.S. and Canada, add $5 GST; $62.00/year for other countries, schools & libraries, print & online; $130.00/year for institutions, other countries, schools & libraries, online; $142.00/year for institutions, other countries, schools & libraries, print; $162.00/year for institutions, other countries, schools & libraries, print & online. Peer-reviewed journal providing practical, hands-on information to physical educators and coaches.

6664 ■ Teacher Magazine
Editorial Projects in Education Inc.
6935 Arlington Rd., Ste. 100
Bethesda, MD 20814-5287
Ph: (301)280-3100
Fax: (301)280-3200
Fr: 800-346-1834
URL: http://www.teachermagazine.org/tm/index.html

$90.00/year for individuals. Professional magazine for elementary and secondary school teachers.

6665 ■ Teaching Children Mathematics
National Council of Teachers of Mathematics
1906 Association Dr.
Reston, VA 20191-1502
Ph: (703)620-9840
Fax: (703)476-2970

Fr: 800-235-7566
URL: http://www.nctm.org/publications/tcm.aspx

for Included in membership. Peer-reviewed journal covering mathematics content and methods for pre-service and in-service teachers of grades pre-kindergarten through 6th.

6666 ■ Teaching Exceptional Children
Council for Exceptional Children
2900 Crystal Dr., Ste. 1000
Arlington, VA 22202
Ph: (703)620-3660
Fax: (703)264-9494
Fr: 888-232-7733
URL: http://www.cec.sped.org/Content/
    NavigationMenu/Publications2

$90.00/year for individuals, print; $152.00/year for two years, print; $101.00/year for Canada, print; $169.00/year for two years, Canada; $197.00/year for institutions, print; $332.00/year for two years, print; $208.00/year for institutions, Canada, print; $236.00/year for institutions, other countries, print; $399.00/year for two years, institutional (print); $225.00/year for institutions, Canada, print and online. Peer-reviewed journal exploring practical methods for teaching students who have exceptionalities and those who are gifted and talented.

6667 ■ Teaching/K-8
Teaching/K-8
40 Richards Ave.
Norwalk, CT 06854
Ph: (203)855-2650
Fr: 800-249-9363
URL: http://www.essentiallearningproducts.com

$16.00/year for individuals; $4.50/year for single issue. Magazine for elementary teachers.

6668 ■ Teaching and Learning in Nursing
Elsevier Science Inc.
360 Park Ave. S
New York, NY 10010-1710
Ph: (212)989-5800
Fax: (212)633-3990
Fr: 888-437-4636
URL: http://www.elsevier.com/wps/find/
    journaldescription.cws_home

Quarterly. $232.00/year for institutions, other countries; $134.00/year for other countries; $160.00/year for institutions; $91.00/year for individuals. Journal devoted to associate degree nursing education and practice.

6669 ■ Tech Directions
Prakken Publications Inc.
832 Phoenix Dr.
Ann Arbor, MI 48108
Ph: (734)975-2800
Fax: (734)975-2787
Fr: 800-530-9673
E-mail: tdedit@techdirections.com
URL: http://www.techdirections.com

Monthly. $30.00/year for individuals, U.S.; $47.00/year for institutions; $50.00/year for other countries; $100.00/year for individuals, domestic. Magazine covering issues, programs, and projects in industrial education, technology education, trade and industry, and vocational-technical career education. Articles are geared for teacher and administrator use and reference from elementary school through postsecondary levels.

6670 ■ Theory and Research in Education
Sage Publications Inc.
2455 Teller Rd.
Thousand Oaks, CA 91320-2218
Ph: (805)499-9774
Fax: (805)583-2665
Fr: 800-818-7243
URL: http://www.sagepub.com/
    journalsProdDesc.nav?prodId=Journal20

$546.00/year for institutions, print and e-access; $491.00/year for institutions, e-access; $535.00/year for institutions, print; $85.00/year for individuals, print; $196.00/year for single issue, institutional; $37.00/year for single issue, individual. Interdisciplinary journal covering normative and theoretical issues concerning education including multi-faceted philosophical analysis of moral, social, political and epistemological problems and issues arising from educational practice.

EMPLOYER DIRECTORIES AND NETWORKING LISTS

6671 ■ Boarding Schools Directory
The Association of Boarding Schools
9 SW Pack Sq., Ste. 201
Asheville, NC 28801-3526
Ph: (828)258-5354
Fax: (828)258-6428
URL: http://www.schools.com

Annual, Latest edition 2007-2008. for U.S. and Canada. Covers: Boarding schools that are members of the Association of Boarding Schools. Entries include: School name, address, phone, e-mail and url's, grades for which boarding students are accepted, enrollment, brief description. Arrangement: Classified by type of school. Indexes: Geographical; program; Alphabetical.

6672 ■ Career Ideas for Teens in Education and Training
Facts On File Inc.
132 W 31st St., 17th Fl.
New York, NY 10001
Ph: (212)967-8800
Fax: 800-678-3633
Fr: 800-322-8755
URL: http://factsonfile.infobasepublishing.com

Published 2005. $40.00 for individuals. Covers: A multitude of career possibilities based on a teenager's specific interests and skills and links his/her talents to a wide variety of actual professions.

6673 ■ Christian Schools International—Directory
Christian Schools International
3350 E Paris Ave. SE
Grand Rapids, MI 49512-2907
Ph: (616)957-1070
Fax: (616)957-5022
Fr: 800-635-8288
URL: http://www.store.csionline.org/index.php?main_page=index&cPath=

Annual, Latest edition 2007-2008. $15.00 for members. Covers: Nearly 450 Reformed Christian elementary and secondary schools; related associations; societies without schools. Entries include: For schools—School name, address, phone; name, title, and address of officers; names of faculty members. Arrangement: Geographical.

6674 ■ Directory of Public School Systems in the U.S.
American Association for Employment in Education
3040 Riverside Dr., Ste. 117
Columbus, OH 43221
Ph: (614)485-1111
Fax: (360)244-7802
E-mail: office@aaee.org
URL: http://www.aaee.org/

Annual, Winter; latest edition 2004-2005 edition. $55.00 for members; $80.00 for nonmembers. Covers: About 14,000 public school systems in the United States and their administrative personnel. Entries include: System name, address, phone, website address, name and title of personnel administrator, levels taught and approx. Student population. Arrangement: Geographical by state.

6675 ■ Educators Resource Directory
Grey House Publishing
4919 Rte. 22
PO Box 56
Amenia, NY 12501
Ph: (518)789-8700
Fax: (518)789-0556
Fr: 800-562-2139
E-mail: books@greyhouse.com
URL: http://www.greyhouse.com/education.htm

Annual, latest edition 2011-2012. $145.00 for individuals. Covers: Publishing opportunities, state by state information on enrollment, funding and grant resources, associations and conferences, teaching jobs abroad all geared toward elementary and secondary school professionals. Also covers online databases, textbook publishers, school suppliers, plus state and federal agencies. Entries include: Contact name, address, phone, fax, description, publications. A unique compilation of over 6,500 educational resources and over 130 tables and charts of education statistics and rankings. Arrangement: By subject categories. Indexes: Entry, geographical, publisher, web sites.

6676 ■ Ganley's Catholic Schools in America—Elementary/Secondary/College & University
Fisher Publishing Co.
PO Box 5729
Sun City West, AZ 85376
Ph: (623)328-8326
URL: http://www.ganleyscatholicschools.com

Annual, summer; Latest edition 38th, 2010. $67.00 for individuals. Covers: over 8,400 Catholic K-12 Schools. Arrangement: Geographical by state, then alphabetical by Diocese name.

6677 ■ Handbook of Private Schools
Porter Sargent Publishers Inc.
11 Beacon St., Ste. 1400
Boston, MA 02108-3099
Ph: (617)523-1670
Fax: (617)523-1021
Fr: 800-342-7470
URL: http://www.portersargent.com

Annual, latest edition 92nd, 2011-2012. $99.00 for individuals. Covers: More than 1,700 elementary and secondary boarding and day schools in the United States. Entries include: School name, address, phone, fax, E-mail, URL, type of school (boarding or day), sex and age range, names and titles of administrators, grades offered, academic orientation, curriculum, new admissions yearly, tests required for admission, enrollment and faculty, graduate record, number of alumni, tuition and scholarship figures, summer session, plant evaluation and endowment, date of establishment, calendar, association membership, description of school's offerings and history, test score averages, uniform requirements, geographical, and demographic date. Arrangement: Geographical. Indexes: Alphabetical by school name, cross indexed by state, region, grade range, sexes accepted, school features and enrollment.

6678 ■ Independent Schools Association of the Southwest—Membership List
Independent Schools Association of the Southwest
Energy Sq., 505 N Big Spring St., Ste. 406
Midland, TX 79701
Ph: (432)684-9550
Fax: (432)684-9401
Fr: 800-688-5007
URL: http://www.isasw.org

Annual, August. Covers: Over 84 schools located in Arizona, Kansas, Louisiana, Mexico, New Mexico, Oklahoma, and Texas enrolling over 38,000 students. Entries include: School name, address, phone, chief administrative officer, structure, and enrollment. Arrangement: Geographical. Indexes: Alphabetical.

6679 ■ MDR's School Directories
Market Data Retrieval
6 Armstrong Rd., Ste. 301
Shelton, CT 06484-4722
Ph: (203)926-4800
Fax: (203)926-1826
Fr: 800-333-8802
URL: http://www.schooldata.com/mdrdir.asp

Annual, Latest edition 2008-2009. Covers: Over 90,000 public, 8,000 Catholic, and 15,000 other private schools (grades K-12) in the United States; over 15,000 school district offices, and 76,000 school librarians; and 27,000 media specialists, 33,000 technology coordinators. Includes names of over 165,000 school district administrators and staff members in county and state education administration. Entries include: District name and address; telephone and fax number; number of schools; number of teachers in the district; district enrollment; special Ed students; limited-English proficient students; minority percentage by race, college bound students; expenditures per student for instructional materials; poverty level; title 1 dollars; site-based management; district open/close dates; construction indicator; technologies and quantities; district-level administrators, *new superintendents shaded*; school name and address—new public shaded; telephone and fax number; principal new principal shaded; librarian, media specialist and technology coordinator; grade span; special programs and school type; student enrollment; technologies and quantities (instructional computer brand noting predominant brand); Multi-Media Computers; Internet connection or access; Tech Sophistication Index. Arrangement: Geographical. Indexes: District County; District Personnel; Principal; New Public Schools and Key Personnel; District and School Telephone; District URLs.

6680 ■ National Directory for Employment in Education
American Association for Employment in Education
3040 Riverside Dr., Ste. 117
Columbus, OH 43221
Ph: (614)485-1111
Fax: (360)244-7802
URL: http://www.aaee.org/

Annual, winter; latest edition 2008-2009. $20.00 for nonmembers; $10.00 for members. Covers: about 600 placement offices maintained by teacher-training institutions and 300 school district personnel officers and/or superintendents responsible for hiring professional staff. Entries include: Institution name, address, phone, contact name, email address, and website. Arrangement: Geographical. Indexes: Personal name, subject-field of teacher training, institutions which provide vacancy bulletins and placement services to non-enrolled students.

6681 ■ Patterson's American Education
Educational Directories Inc.
1025 W Wise Rd., Ste. 101
PO Box 68097
Schaumburg, IL 60168-0097
Ph: (847)891-1250
Fax: (847)891-0945
Fr: 800-357-6183
URL: http://www.ediusa.com

Annual, Latest edition 2012, vol. 108. $97.00 for individuals. Covers: Over 11,000 school districts in the United States; more than 34,000 public, private, and Catholic high schools, middle schools, and junior high schools; Approximately 300 parochial superintendents; 400 state department of education personnel. Entries include: For school districts and schools—District and superintendent Name, address, phone, fax, grade ranges, enrollment, school names, addresses, phone numbers, grade ranges, enrollment, names of principals. For postsecondary schools—School name, address, phone number, URL, e-mail, names of administrator or director of admissions. For private and Catholic high schools—name, address, phone, fax, enrollment, grades offered, name of principal. Postsecondary institutions are covered in 'Patterson's Schools Classified'. Arrangement: Geographical by state, then alphabetical by city.

6682 ■ Patterson's Elementary Education
Educational Directories Inc.
1025 W Wise Rd., Ste. 101
PO Box 68097
Schaumburg, IL 60168-0097

Ph: (847)891-1250
Fax: (847)891-0945
Fr: 800-357-6183
URL: http://www.ediusa.com

Annual, Latest edition 2012. $97.00 for individuals. Covers: Over 12,000 school districts; more than 78,000 public, private, and Catholic elementary and middle schools; and 400 state department of education personnel. Entries include: County name, city, population, public school district name, enrollment, grade range; superintendent Name, address, phone, fax, names of public schools, address, phone, fax, principal's name, enrollment; private and Catholic school listings include school name, enrollment, grade ranges, principal's name, address, phone, fax. Arrangement: Geographical by state, then alphabetical by city.

6683 ■ Private Independent Schools
Bunting and Lyon Inc.
615 Broad Swamp Rd.
Cheshire, CT 06410
Ph: (203)668-1897
Fax: (203)269-8908
URL: http://www.buntingandlyon.com

Annual, Latest edition 2010. $115.00 for individuals. Covers: 1,200 English-speaking elementary and secondary private schools and summer programs in North America and abroad. Entries include: School name, address, phone, fax, e-mail, website, enrollment, tuition and other fees, financial aid information, administrator's name and educational background, director of admission, regional accreditation, description of programs, curriculum, activities, learning differences grid. Arrangement: Geographical. Indexes: School name; geographical. Summer programs, general classification grid, learning differences reference grid.

6684 ■ Requirements for Certification of Teachers, Counselors, Librarians, Administrators for Elementary and Secondary Schools
University of Chicago Press
Journals Division
1427 E 60th St.
Chicago, IL 60637-2954
Ph: (773)702-7636
Fax: (773)702-9756
URL: http://www.press.uchicago.edu

Annual, Latest edition 74th. $53.00. Publication includes: List of state and local departments of education. Entries include: Office name, address, phone. Principal content of publication is summaries of each state's teaching and administrative certification requirements. Arrangement: Geographical.

HANDBOOKS AND MANUALS

6685 ■ Best Careers for Teachers: Making the Most of Your Teaching Degree
LearningExpress, LLC
2 Rector St., 26th Fl.
New York, NY 10006
Fr: 800-295-9556
E-mail: customerservice@learningexpressllc.com
URL: http://www.learningexpressllc.com

LearningExpress Editors. 2010. $16.95 (paper). 208 pages. Serves as a guide for current, former and aspiring teachers towards ways to leverage their teaching education and experiences and find and establish a more rewarding career.

6686 ■ Ferguson Career Coach: Managing Your Career in Education
Facts On File
132 W 31st St., 17th Fl.
New York, NY 10001
Fax: 800-678-3633
Fr: 800-322-8755
E-mail: custserv@factsonfile.com
URL: http://factsonfile.infobasepublishing.com

Shelly Field. 2008. $39.95 (hardcover). 272 pages. Contains tips on achieving career success in the field of education. Provides students with advice on making contacts, interviewing, and career strategies.

6687 ■ Get That Teaching Job!
Continuum International Publishing Group
80 Maiden Ln., Ste. 704
New York, NY 10038
Ph: (212)953-5858
Fax: (212)953-5944
E-mail: info@continuum-books.com
URL: http://www.continuumbooks.com

Paul K. Ainsworth. 2012. $27.95 (paperback). 184 pages. Serves as job search guide for primary and secondary school teachers. Features role-specific advice on developing an application letter and preparing for the interview. Includes list of interview questions and curriculum vitae templates.

6688 ■ Great Jobs for Music Majors
The McGraw-Hill Companies
PO Box 182604
Columbus, OH 43272
Fax: (614)759-3749
Fr: 877-883-5524
E-mail: customer.service@mcgraw-hill.com
URL: http://www.mhprofessional.com/
 product.php?isbn=0071454616

Jan Goldberg. Second edition, 2004. $15.95 (paper). 180 pages.

6689 ■ The Inside Secrets of Finding a Teaching Job
Jist Works
875 Montreal Way
St. Paul, MN 55102
Fr: 800-648-5478
E-mail: info@jist.com
URL: http://www.jist.com

Jack Warner and Clyde Bryan. Third edition, 2006. $12.95. 208 pages. Tips from educators on finding an entry-level teaching position.

6690 ■ Job Hunting in Education: An Insider's Guide to Success
ScracrowEducation
4501 Forbes Blvd., Ste. 200
Lanham, MD 20706-4310
Ph: (301)459-3366
Fax: (301)429-5748
URL: http://www.rowmaneducation.com

Herbert F. Pandiscio. May 2004. $44.95 (paper). 192 pages.

6691 ■ Learning Green: Careers in Education
Crabtree Publishing
350 5th Ave., 59th Fl.
New York, NY 10118
Ph: (212)496-5040
Fax: 800-355-7166
Fr: 800-387-7650
URL: http://www.crabtreebooks.com

Suzy Gazlay. 2010. $31.93. 64 pages (hardcover). Features careers in education that address conservation and environmentalism.

6692 ■ Opportunities in Teaching Careers
The McGraw-Hill Companies
PO Box 182604
Columbus, OH 43272
Fax: (614)759-3749
Fr: 877-883-5524
E-mail: customer.service@mcgraw-hill.com
URL: http://www.mhprofessional.com/
 product.php?isbn=0071438173

Janet Fine. 2005. $13.95 (paper). 160 pages. Discusses licensing and accreditation programs, sources of placement information, job-seeking correspondence, selection procedures, and paths to advancement. Also covers professional associations,

non-traditional teaching opportunities, and jobs abroad.

6693 ■ The Teaching Career
Teachers College Press, Teachers College, Columbia University
1234 Amsterdam Ave.
New York, NY 10027
Ph: (212)678-3929
Fax: (212)678-4149
E-mail: tcpress@tc.columbia.edu
URL: http://www.teacherscollegepress.com

John I. Goodlad, Timothy J. McMannon. February 2004. $24.95 (paper). Illustrated. 240 pages. The Series in School Reform.

6694 ■ Why Choose a Career in Teaching?
The Graduate Group
PO Box 370351
West Hartford, CT 06137-0351
Ph: (860)233-2330
Fax: (860)233-2330
E-mail: graduategroup@hotmail.com
URL: http://www.graduategroup.com

James Abbott. April 2004. $30.00 (paper). Book explores traditional and non-traditional routes to becoming an elementary or secondary teacher.

ONLINE JOB SOURCES AND SERVICES

6695 ■ ABCTeachingJobs.com
URL: http://www.abcteachingjobs.com

Description: Serves as a source of teacher job postings and recruitment. Offers jobs for K-12 teachers and administrators.

6696 ■ Elementary School Teacher Jobs
URL: http://www.elementaryschoolteacherjobs.org

Description: Features a searchable database of job postings for elementary school teachers.

6697 ■ Elementary Teacher Jobs
URL: http://www.elementaryteacherjobs.us

Description: Serves as a resource of employment opportunities for elementary teachers.

6698 ■ GreatTeacher.net
URL: http://greatteacher.net

Description: Provides resources and information about the field of education and teaching. Also features a job board.

6699 ■ MyTeachingJobSearch.com
URL: http://www.myteachingjobsearch.com

Description: Provides teaching and teacher jobs at public and private schools and school districts across the United States.

6700 ■ School-Jobs.net
URL: http://www.school-jobs.net/jobs

Description: Matches teachers, administrators, support staff, and other school employees to related jobs across the country. Features jobs by salary, location, and area of expertise.

6701 ■ SchoolSpring.com
E-mail: contact@schoolspring.com
URL: http://www.schoolspring.com

Description: Serves as an employment source for educators. Offers teaching jobs and other education job listings including complete archiving of all necessary documents and certifications, as well as access to all education jobs in a specific area.

6702 ■ WantToTeach.com
URL: http://www.wanttoteach.com

Description: Serves as an education website to search for administrative, instructional and support openings throughout the United States. Features job openings and job fairs and allows access to various education resources.

TRADESHOWS

6703 ■ Association for Childhood Education International Annual International Conference & Exhibition
Association for Childhood Education International
17904 Georgia Ave., Ste. 215
Olney, MD 20832
Ph: (301)570-2111
Fax: (301)570-2212
Fr: 800-423-3563
E-mail: headquarters@acei.org
URL: http://www.acei.org

Annual. Primary Exhibits: Commercial and educational exhibits of interest to teachers, teacher educators, college students, daycare personnel and other care givers.

6704 ■ National Art Education Association National Convention
National Art Education Association
1806 Robert Fulton Dr., Ste. 300
Reston, VA 20191
Ph: (703)860-8000
Fax: (703)860-2960
Fr: 800-299-8321
E-mail: info@arteducators.org
URL: http://www.naea-reston.org

Annual. Primary Exhibits: Art materials; art-related books and magazines; art career education information; arts and crafts supplies. Dates and Locations: 2012 Mar 01-04; New York, NY; 2013 Mar 07-10; Fort Worth, TX.

6705 ■ National Association for Bilingual Education Conference
National Association for Bilingual Education
8701 Georgia Ave., Ste. 611
Silver Spring, MD 20910
Ph: (240)450-3700
Fax: (240)450-3799
E-mail: nabe@nabe.org
URL: http://www.nabe.org

Annual. Features speakers, sessions, product exhibits, and job fair.

6706 ■ National Association for the Education of Young Children Annual Conference
National Association for the Education of Young Children
1313 L St. NW, Ste. 500
Washington, DC 20005
Ph: (202)232-8777
Fax: (202)328-1846
Fr: 800-424-2460
URL: http://www.naeyc.org

Annual. Primary Exhibits: Educational materials and equipment designed for children ages birth through eight years old. Dates and Locations: 2012 Nov 07-10; Atlanta, GA.

OTHER SOURCES

6707 ■ American Alliance for Health, Physical Education, Recreation and Dance (AAHPERD)
1900 Association Dr.
Reston, VA 20191-1598
Ph: (703)476-3400
Fax: (703)476-9527
Fr: 800-213-7193
E-mail: membership@aahperd.org
URL: http://www.aahperd.org

Description: Students and educators in physical education, dance, health, athletics, safety education, recreation, and outdoor education. Works to improve

its fields of education at all levels through such services as consultation, periodicals and special publications, leadership development, determination of standards, and research. Sponsors placement service.

6708 ■ American Association of Christian Schools (AACS)
602 Belvoir Ave.
East Ridge, TN 37412
Ph: (423)629-4280
Fax: (423)622-7461
E-mail: info@aacs.org
URL: http://www.aacs.org

Description: Maintains teacher/administrator certification program and placement service. Participates in school accreditation program. Sponsors National Academic Tournament. Maintains American Christian Honor Society. Compiles statistics; maintains speakers' bureau and placement service.

6709 ■ American Association for Health Education (AAHE)
1900 Association Dr.
Reston, VA 20191-1599
Ph: (703)476-3400
Fax: (703)476-9527
Fr: 800-213-7193
E-mail: aahe@aahperd.org
URL: http://www.aahperd.org/aahe

Description: Professionals who have responsibility for health education in schools, colleges, communities, hospitals and clinics, and industries. Aims to advance the health education through program activities and federal legislation; encourage close working relationships between all health education and health service organizations; achieve good health and well-being for all Americans automatically, without conscious thought and endeavor. Member of the American Alliance for Health, Physical Education, Recreation and Dance.

6710 ■ American Association of Teachers of French (AATF)
Southern Illinois University
Mail Code 4510
Carbondale, IL 62901
Ph: (618)453-5731
Fax: (618)453-5733
E-mail: aatf@frenchteachers.org
URL: http://www.frenchteachers.org

Description: Teachers of French in public and private elementary and secondary schools, colleges and universities. Sponsors National French Week each November to take French out of the classroom and into the schools and community. Conducts National French Contest in elementary and secondary schools and awards prizes at all levels. Maintains Materials Center with promotional and pedagogical materials; National French Honor Society (high school), Placement Bureau, summer scholarships.

6711 ■ American Association of Teachers of German (AATG)
112 Haddontowne Ct., No. 104
Cherry Hill, NJ 08034-3668
Ph: (856)795-5553
Fax: (856)795-9398
E-mail: headquarters@aatg.org
URL: http://www.aatg.org

Description: Represents teachers of German at all levels; individuals interested in German language and culture. Offers in-service teacher-training workshops, materials, student honor society, national German examination and stipends/scholarships.

6712 ■ American Association of Teachers of Spanish and Portuguese (AATSP)
900 Ladd Rd.
Walled Lake, MI 48390
Ph: (248)960-2180
Fax: (248)960-9570
E-mail: aatspoffice@aatsp.org
URL: http://www.aatsp.org

Description: Teachers of Spanish and Portuguese languages and literatures and others interested in Hispanic culture. Operates placement bureau and maintains pen pal registry. Sponsors honor society, Sociedad Honoraria Hispanica and National Spanish Examinations for secondary school students.

6713 ■ American Federation of Teachers (AFT)
555 New Jersey Ave. NW
Washington, DC 20001
Ph: (202)879-4400
E-mail: online@aft.org
URL: http://www.aft.org

Description: Affiliated with the AFL-CIO. Works with teachers and other educational employees at the state and local level in organizing, collective bargaining, research, educational issues, and public relations. Conducts research in areas such as educational reform, teacher certification, and national assessments and standards. Represents members' concerns through legislative action; offers technical assistance. Serves professionals with concerns similar to those of teachers, including state employees, healthcare workers, and paraprofessionals.

6714 ■ American Montessori Society (AMS)
281 Park Ave. S
New York, NY 10010-6102
Ph: (212)358-1250
Fax: (212)358-1256
E-mail: ams@amshq.org
URL: http://www.amshq.org

Description: School affiliates and teacher training affiliates; heads of schools, teachers, parents, non-Montessori educators, and other interested individuals dedicated to stimulating the use of the Montessori teaching approach and promoting better education for all children. Seeks to meet demands of growing interest in the Montessori approach to early learning. Assists in establishing schools; supplies information and limited services to member schools in other countries. Maintains school consultation and accreditation service; provides information service; assists research and gathers statistical data; offers placement service. Maintains Montessori and related materials exhibit.

6715 ■ Association of Christian Schools International (ACSI)
PO Box 65130
Colorado Springs, CO 80962-5130
Fax: (719)531-0631
Fr: 800-367-0798
E-mail: acsi_email@acsi.org
URL: http://www.acsi.org

Description: Seeks to enable Christian educators and schools worldwide to effectively prepare students for life.

6716 ■ Association for Direct Instruction (ADI)
PO Box 10252
Eugene, OR 97440
Ph: (541)485-1293
Fax: (541)868-1397
Fr: 800-995-2464
E-mail: brywick@adihome.org
URL: http://www.adihome.org

Description: Public school regular and special education teachers and university instructors. Encourages, promotes, and engages in research aimed at improving educational methods. Promotes dissemination of developmental information and skills that facilitate the education of adults and children. Administers a preschool for developmentally delayed children. Offers educational training workshops for instructors. Maintains speaker's bureau and placement service.

6717 ■ Council for Supervision and Leadership (ITEEA-CSL)
International Technology and Engineering Educators Association
Maryland Dept. of Education
200 W Baltimore St.
Baltimore, MD 21201

Ph: (410)767-0177
Fax: (410)333-2099
E-mail: lrhine@msde.state.md.us
URL: http://itea-cs.org

Description: Technology education supervisors from the U.S. Office of Education; local school department chairpersons; state departments of education, local school districts, territories, provinces, and foreign countries. Improves instruction and supervision of programs in technology education. Conducts research; compiles statistics. Sponsors competitions. Maintains speakers' bureau.

6718 ■ Friends Council on Education (FCE)
1507 Cherry St.
Philadelphia, PA 19102
Ph: (215)241-7245
Fax: (215)241-7299
E-mail: info@friendscouncil.org
URL: http://www.friendscouncil.org

Description: Representatives appointed by Friends Yearly Meetings; heads of Quaker secondary and elementary schools and colleges; members-at-large. Acts as a clearinghouse for information on Quaker schools and colleges. Holds meetings and conferences on education and provides in-service training for teachers, administrators and trustees in Friends schools.

6719 ■ Green Parent Association
2601 Westhall Ln.
Maitland, FL 32751
Ph: (407)493-1372
E-mail: joy@greenparentassociation.org
URL: http://www.greenparentassociation.org

Description: Strives to empower families, teachers and businesses to live greener lifestyles through education and awareness. Seeks to share information about clean, healthy living that benefits families and the communities in which they live. Aims to inspire parents to continue to improve their children's lives through the food that they eat and the world in which they live.

6720 ■ The International Educator (TIE)
PO Box 513
Cummaquid, MA 02637
Ph: (508)790-1990
Fax: (508)790-1922
Fr: 877-375-6668
E-mail: tie@tieonline.com
URL: http://www.tieonline.com

Description: Facilitates the placement of teachers and administrators in American, British, and international schools. Seeks to create a network that provides for professional development opportunities and improved financial security of members. Offers advice and information on international school news, recent educational developments, job placement, and investment, consumer, and professional development opportunities. Makes available insurance and travel benefits. Operates International Schools Internship Program.

6721 ■ International Reading Association (IRA)
PO Box 8139
Newark, DE 19714-8139
Ph: (302)731-1600
Fax: (302)731-1057
Fr: 800-336-7323
E-mail: pubinfo@reading.org
URL: http://www.reading.org

Description: Represents teachers, reading specialists, consultants, administrators, supervisors, researchers, psychologists, librarians, and parents interested in promoting literacy. Seeks to improve the quality of reading instruction and promote literacy worldwide. Disseminates information pertaining to research on reading, including information on adult literacy, early childhood and literacy development, international education, literature for children and adolescents, and teacher education and professional

development. Maintains over 40 special interest groups and over 70 committees.

6722 ■ Jewish Education Service of North America (JESNA)
318 W 39th St., 5th Fl.
New York, NY 10018
Ph: (212)284-6950
Fax: (212)284-6951
E-mail: info@jesna.org
URL: http://www.jesna.org

Description: Widely recognized leader in the areas of research and program evaluation, organizational change and innovative program design and dissemination. Operates the Mandell J. Berman Jewish Heritage Center for Research and Evaluation. Supports the Covenant Foundation, a joint venture with the Crown Family, which makes awards and grants for creativity in Jewish education.

6723 ■ Jewish Educators Assembly (JEA)
PO Box 413
Cedarhurst, NY 11516
Ph: (516)569-2537
Fax: (516)295-9039
E-mail: jewisheducators@jewisheducators.org
URL: http://www.jewisheducators.org

Description: Educational and supervisory personnel serving Jewish educational institutions. Seeks to: advance the development of Jewish education in the congregation on all levels in consonance with the philosophy of the Conservative Movement; cooperate with the United Synagogue of America Commission on Jewish Education as the policy-making body of the educational enterprise; join in cooperative effort with other Jewish educational institutions and organizations; establish and maintain professional standards for Jewish educators; serve as a forum for the exchange of ideas; promote the values of Jewish education as a basis for the creative continuity of the Jewish people. Maintains placement service and speaker's bureau.

6724 ■ NAFSA: Association of International Educators (NAFSA)
1307 New York Ave. NW, 8th Fl.
Washington, DC 20005-4701
Ph: (202)737-3699
Fax: (202)737-3657
E-mail: inbox@nafsa.org
URL: http://www.nafsa.org

Description: Individuals, organizations, and institutions dealing with international educational exchange, including foreign student advisers, overseas educational advisers, credentials and admissions officers, administrators and teachers of English as a second language, community support personnel, study-abroad administrators, and embassy cultural or educational personnel. Promotes self-regulation standards and responsibilities in international educational exchange; offers professional development opportunities primarily through publications, workshops, grants, and regional and national conferences. Advocates for increased awareness and support of international education and exchange on campuses, in government, and in communities. Offers services including: a job registry for employers and professionals involved with international education; a consultant referral service. Sponsors joint liaison activities with a variety of other educational and government organizations to conduct a census of foreign student enrollment in the U.S.; conducts workshops about specific subjects and countries.

6725 ■ National Alliance of Black School Educators (NABSE)
310 Pennsylvania Ave. SE
Washington, DC 20003
Ph: (202)608-6310
Fax: (202)608-6319
Fr: 800-221-2654
E-mail: info@nabse.org
URL: http://www.nabse.org

Description: Black educators from all levels; others

indirectly involved in the education of black youth. Promotes awareness, professional expertise, and commitment among black educators. Goals are to: eliminate and rectify the results of racism in education; work with state, local, and national leaders to raise the academic achievement level of all black students; increase members' involvement in legislative activities; facilitate the introduction of a curriculum that more completely embraces black America; improve the ability of black educators to promote problem resolution; create a meaningful and effective network of strength, talent, and professional support. Sponsors workshops, commission meetings, and special projects. Encourages research, especially as it relates to blacks, and the presentation of papers during national conferences. Plans to establish a National Black Educators Data Bank and offer placement service.

6726 ■ National Art Education Association (NAEA)
1806 Robert Fulton Dr., Ste. 300
Reston, VA 20191
Ph: (703)860-8000
Fax: (703)860-2960
Fr: 800-299-8321
E-mail: info@arteducators.org
URL: http://www.arteducators.org

Description: Teachers of art at elementary, middle, secondary, and college levels; colleges, libraries, museums, and other educational institutions. Studies problems of teaching art; encourages research and experimentation. Serves as a clearinghouse for information on art education programs, materials, and methods of instruction. Sponsors special institutes. Cooperates with other national organizations for the furtherance of creative art experiences for youth.

6727 ■ National Association for Bilingual Education
8701 Georgia Ave., Ste. 611
Silver Spring, MD 20910
Ph: (240)450-3700
Fax: (240)450-3799
E-mail: nabe@nabe.org
URL: http://www.nabe.org

Description: Comprised of bilingual and English language learner (ELL) teachers, parents, paraprofessionals, administrators, professors, advocates, researchers, and policy makers. Promotes English proficiency and respect for cultural and linguistic diversity. Creates and supports policies, programs, research, pedagogy, and professional development to achieve bilingualism and biliteracy.

6728 ■ National Association of Blind Teachers (NABT)
2200 Wilson Blvd., Ste. 650
Arlington, VA 22201
Ph: (202)467-5081
Fax: (703)465-5085
Fr: 800-424-8666
E-mail: info@acb.org
URL: http://www.acb.org

Description: Public school teachers, teachers of the visually impaired, college and university professors, and teachers in residential schools for the blind. Promotes employment and professional goals of blind persons entering the teaching profession or those established in their respective teaching fields. Serves as a vehicle for the dissemination of information and the exchange of ideas addressing special problems of members.

6729 ■ National Association of Catholic School Teachers (NACST)
1700 Sansom St., Ste. 903
Philadelphia, PA 19103
Fr: 800-99N-ACST
E-mail: nacst.nacst@verizon.net
URL: http://www.nacst.com

Description: Catholic school teachers. Aims to unify, advise, and assist Catholic school teachers in matters of collective bargaining. Promotes the welfare and rights of Catholic schools and teachers; determines needs of Catholic schools and teachers. Monitors legislation, trends, and statistics concerning Catholic education; promotes legislation favorable to nonpublic schools and Catholic school teachers; offers legal advice and addresses issues such as unemployment compensation; assists teachers in organizing and negotiating contracts. Maintains speakers' bureau.

6730 ■ National Association for the Education of Young Children (NAEYC)
PO Box 97156
Washington, DC 20090-7156
Ph: (202)232-8777
Fax: (202)328-1846
Fr: 800-424-2460
E-mail: naeyc@naeyc.org
URL: http://www.naeyc.org

Description: Teachers and directors of preschool and primary schools, kindergartens, child care centers, and early other learning programs for young childhood; early childhood education and child development educators, trainers, and researchers and other professionals dedicated to young children's healthy development.

6731 ■ National Association of Episcopal Schools (NAES)
815 2nd Ave., Ste. 819
New York, NY 10017-4594
Ph: (212)716-6134
Fax: (212)286-9366
Fr: 800-334-7626
E-mail: info@episcopalschools.org
URL: http://www.episcopalschools.org

Description: Represents Episcopal day and boarding schools and preschools. Promotes the educational ministry of the Episcopal Church. Provides publications, consultation services and conference focusing on Episcopal identity of schools, worship, religious education, spirituality, leadership development and governance for heads/directors, administrators, chaplains and teachers of religion, trustees, rectors and other church and school leaders.

6732 ■ National Association of Independent Schools (NAIS)
1620 L St. NW, Ste. 1100
Washington, DC 20036-5695
Ph: (202)973-9700
Fax: (202)973-9790
Fr: 800-793-6701
E-mail: bassett@nais.org
URL: http://www.nais.org

Description: Independent elementary and secondary school members; regional associations of independent schools and related associations. Provides curricular and administrative research and services. Conducts educational programs; compiles statistics.

6733 ■ National Association for Research in Science Teaching (NARST)
12100 Sunset Hills Rd., Ste. 130
Reston, VA 20190-3221
Ph: (703)234-4138
Fax: (703)435-4390
E-mail: info@narst.org
URL: http://www.narst.org

Description: Science teachers, supervisors, and science educators specializing in research and teacher education. Promotes and coordinates science education research and interprets and reports the results.

6734 ■ National Association for Sport and Physical Education (NASPE)
1900 Association Dr.
Reston, VA 20191-1598
Ph: (703)476-3410
Fax: (703)476-8316
Fr: 800-213-7193
E-mail: naspe@aahperd.org
URL: http://www.naspeinfo.org

Description: Men and women professionally involved with physical activity and sports. Seeks to improve the total sport and physical activity experience in America. Conducts research and education programs in such areas as sport psychology, curriculum development, kinesiology, history, philosophy, sport sociology, and the biological and behavioral basis of human activity. Develops and distributes public information materials which explain the value of physical education programs. Supports councils involved in organizing and supporting elementary, secondary, and college physical education and sport programs; administers the National Council of Athletic Training in conjunction with the National Association for Girls and Women in Sport; serves the professional interests of coaches, trainers, and officials. Maintains hall of fame, placement service, and media resource center for public information and professional preparation. Member benefits include group insurance and discounts.

6735 ■ National Communication Association (NCA)
1765 N St. NW
Washington, DC 20036
Ph: (202)464-4622
Fax: (202)464-4600
E-mail: nkidd@natcom.org
URL: http://www.natcom.org

Description: Elementary, secondary, college, and university teachers, speech clinicians, media specialists, communication consultants, students, theater directors, and other interested persons; libraries and other institutions. Works to promote study, criticism, research, teaching, and application of the artistic, humanistic, and scientific principles of communication, particularly speech communication. Sponsors the publication of scholarly volumes in speech. Conducts international debate tours in the U.S. and abroad. Maintains placement service.

6736 ■ National Community Education Association (NCEA)
3929 Old Lee Hwy., No. 91-A
Fairfax, VA 22030-2401
Ph: (703)359-8973
Fax: (703)359-0972
E-mail: ncea@ncea.com
URL: http://www.ncea.com

Description: Community school directors, principals, superintendents, professors, teachers, students, and laypeople. Promotes and establishes community schools as an integral part of the educational plan of every community. Emphasizes community and parent involvement in the schools, lifelong learning, and enrichment of K-12 and adult education. Serves as a clearinghouse for the exchange of ideas and information, and the sharing of efforts. Offers leadership training.

6737 ■ National Council for Accreditation of Teacher Education (NCATE)
2010 Massachusetts Ave. NW, Ste. 500
Washington, DC 20036
Ph: (202)466-7496

Fax: (202)296-6620
E-mail: ncate@ncate.org
URL: http://www.ncate.org

Description: Representatives from constituent colleges and universities, state departments of education, school boards, teacher, and other professional groups. Voluntary accrediting body devoted exclusively to: evaluation and accreditation of institutions for preparation of elementary and secondary school teachers; preparation of school service personnel, including school principals, supervisors, superintendents, school psychologists, instructional technologists, and other specialists for school-oriented positions.

6738 ■ National Council for Geographic Education (NCGE)
1145 17th St. NW, Rm. 7620
Washington, DC 20036
Ph: (202)857-7695
Fax: (202)618-6249
E-mail: ncge@ncge.org
URL: http://www.ncge.org

Description: Teachers of geography and social studies in elementary and secondary schools, colleges and universities; geographers in governmental agencies and private businesses. Encourages the training of teachers in geographic concepts, practices, teaching methods and techniques; works to develop effective geographic educational programs in schools and colleges and with adult groups; stimulates the production and use of accurate and understandable geographic teaching aids and materials.

6739 ■ National Council of Teachers of Mathematics (NCTM)
1906 Association Dr.
Reston, VA 20191-1502
Ph: (703)620-9840
Fax: (703)476-2970
Fr: 800-235-7566
E-mail: nctm@nctm.org
URL: http://www.nctm.org

Description: Aims to improve teaching and learning of mathematics.

6740 ■ *Overseas Employment Opportunities for Educators: Department of Defense Dependents Schools*
DIANE Publishing Co.
PO Box 617
Darby, PA 19023-0617
Fr: 800-782-3833
URL: http://www.dianepublishing.net

Barry Leonard, editor. $20.00. 52 pages. An introduction to teachings positions in the Dept. of Defense Dependents Schools (DoDDS), a worldwide school system, operated by the DoD in 14 countries.

6741 ■ U.S.-China Education Foundation (USCEF)
4140 Oceanside Blvd., Ste. 159, No. 112
Oceanside, CA 92056-6005
E-mail: info@sage-usa.net
URL: http://www.sage-usa.net

Description: Aims to promote the learning of the Chinese languages (including Mandarin, Cantonese, and minority languages such as Mongolian) by Americans, and the learning of English by Chinese. Conducts short-term travel-study program to prepare Americans and Chinese for stays of four, six, or eight months or one to four years in China or the U.S., respectively. Operates teacher placement service and speakers' bureau. A project of The Society for the Development of Global Education (S.A.G.E. Inc.).